THE
NEUROLOGIC
EXAMINATION

To study the phenomena of disease without books is to sail an uncharted sea, while to study books without patients is not to go to sea at all.

—*Sir William Osler*

The charm of neurology, above all other branches of practical medicine, lies in the way it forces us into daily contact with principles. A knowledge of the structure and functions of the nervous system is necessary to explain the simplest phenomena of disease, and this can be only attained by thinking scientifically.

—*Sir Henry Head*

THE NEUROLOGIC EXAMINATION

*Incorporating the Fundamentals of
Neuroanatomy and Neurophysiology*

THIRD EDITION

By RUSSELL N. DeJONG, M.D.

*Professor and Chairman of the Department of Neurology,
University of Michigan Medical School*

With 395 Illustrations

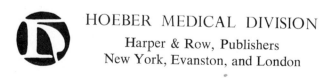

HOEBER MEDICAL DIVISION
Harper & Row, Publishers
New York, Evanston, and London

THE NEUROLOGIC EXAMINATION
THIRD EDITION

Library of Congress catalog card number: 67-17597

*To the three people who have taught me what I know
of Neurology and Medicine:*

To Dr. Carl Dudley Camp, *my Mentor in Clinical Neurology*

To Dr. Elizabeth Caroline Crosby, *my Teacher in Neuroanatomy*

To the memory of my father, Dr. Conrad DeJong, *my Preceptor
in the Art and Practice of Medicine*

CONTENTS

I am deeply grateful for the helpful suggestions and criticisms of the many friends and colleagues who have assisted in the preparation of this book. I wish to express special appreciation to Dr. Elizabeth C. Crosby, who read many sections of the manuscript, advised me throughout the writing of the book, and gave me immeasurable assistance; to Dr. Lois A. Gillilan, who acted as assistant, secretary, and artist for a portion of the book; to Dr. Eugene S. McCartney, who read sections of the manuscript and gave much-needed help from an editorial standpoint; to Dr. Edmond L. Cooper, who read and criticized the portions dealing with neuro-ophthalmology; and to Miss Sue Biethan, who carefully checked all of the references. Individual credit is given to the authors and publishers who allowed me to reproduce illustrations from their books and articles, for which I wish to express my indebtedness at this time. Particular gratitude is due, however, to Miss Janet E. McLaughlin and Mrs. Elizabeth S. Eder, who made most of the original drawings herein contained; to Mr. Charles R. Burd and his assistants, Mrs. M. Rita Eriksen, Mrs. Eloise Duffy Bell, and Mr. Robert P. Logan, who took the original photographs which make an important part of the book; and to Mr. George J. Smith, who made the microphotographs. Dr. Robert Wartenberg was generous in lending not only illustrations from his articles, but also a large collection of valuable reprints of foreign articles. Finally, I wish to thank my secretaries, Mrs. Gertrude B. Null and Mrs. Virginia B. Gross, for their helpful assistance; to acknowledge the aid and cooperation given by my publisher; and to express my appreciation for the assistance rendered by my wife, without whose encouragement, patience, helpful editorial advice, and wise and critical judgment, the manuscript would never have reached completion.

RUSSELL N. DEJONG, M.D.

Ann Arbor, Michigan

PART ONE

The Neurologic Examination

CHAPTER 1

INTRODUCTION

THE IMPORTANCE of the neurologic examination in the diagnosis of diseases of the nervous system cannot be overemphasized. In no other branch of medicine is it possible to build up a clinical picture so exact with reference to localization and pathologic anatomy as in clinical neurology. In order to do this, however, one must have not only diagnostic acumen, but also a thorough knowledge of the underlying anatomy and physiology of the voluntary and involuntary (autonomic) nervous systems and of the changes in them that result from pathologic processes. This knowledge must be augmented by a comprehension of the ontogeny and phylogeny of the nervous system, neuropathology, normal psychology, psychiatry, psychopathology, pharmacology, and the effects of drugs on the normal and diseased nervous systems. Too frequently these subjects are studied individually in the medical curriculum and are separated from one another by long periods of time, but in the examination of the patient they must be synthesized and correlated.

The nervous system is an essential part of the living organism, and neurologic diagnosis is a correlation of data in the study of the human nervous system in health and disease—a synthesis of all the details obtained from the history and the examination. Nervous tissue, it has been said, makes up about 2 per cent of the human body, yet it is supplied to all portions of the body. Should all the rest of the body tissues be dissolved away, there would remain an immense network of fibers, in addition to the brain, brain stem, and spinal cord. This network is the great receptor, effector, and correlating mechanism of the body. It acts in response to stimuli, acclimates the individual to his environment, and aids in defense against pathologic changes. In order to understand man, one must first understand the nervous system. Since the nervous system governs the mind and mental operations, one cannot study psychology without a knowledge of it. Since the nervous system regulates and controls all the bodily functions, one cannot study disease of any organ or system of the body without a comprehension of neural function. Since the nervous system relates man to his environment and to others, one cannot study psychiatry or social pathology without first understanding nervous integration. We are not interested,

3

however, in studying the nervous system alone, but in studying man equipped with a nervous system. We are not interested primarily in disease, but in the patient, the man who is diseased. We do not study disease first and man later, but man first and disease later. We must insist that more important than the precise diagnosis of the case is its formulation in terms of the relationship of the individual to his disease and the relationship of the patient to his associates and to his environment. If we bear this in mind, we can most effectively aid our patient, treat his illnesses, restore him to health, re-establish his personal equilibrium, and aid him to regain his place in the social group.

The problem of the neurologic diagnosis is often considered to be a difficult one by the physician who does not specialize in clinical neurology. Most parts of the nervous system are inaccessible to direct examination, and its intricate organization and integrated functions are difficult to comprehend on superficial observation. Many practitioners are of the opinion that all neurologic matters belong to the realm of the specialist, and, consequently, they make little attempt at the diagnosis of nervous disease. This impression is far from correct, for many neurologic disorders come within the everyday experience of most practitioners, who should know how to examine the nervous system and utilize the data collected. Furthermore, as will be stressed in Chapter 3, many systemic diseases may show evidences of nervous dysfunction as their first manifestations. Medical diagnosis cannot be made without some knowledge of neurologic diagnosis. There are certain rare conditions and diagnostic problems, it is true, that require long experience in the field of diseases of the nervous system for adequate appraisal, but the majority of the more common neurologic entities could and should be diagnosed and treated by the physician in general practice. It is hoped that this book will help the practitioner and the student to understand nervous function as a whole, and to appreciate the fact that not all neurologic questions are complex and esoteric, but that an understanding of certain fundamentals is necessary.

It should be emphasized, however, that there are certain complexities of nervous dysfunction that must be comprehended for critical evaluation of signs and symptoms. For instance, in pathologic neurophysiology one finds manifestations of destruction, release, irritation, and partial assumption of function by healthy tissues. Symptoms and signs of *destruction* result from a transient or a permanent loss of function due to disease of a part; these are similar to the manifestations of disease that may be found in other systems of the body. If a nerve is injured, its continuity is interrupted and it no longer carries sensory and motor impulses or participates in trophic function and reflex action; as a consequence there is paralysis (loss of power), with anesthesia and areflexia in its distribution. If an area in the cerebral cortex is destroyed, certain functions are lost, and paresis, hypesthesia, blindness, or intellectual loss may follow. The symptoms of *release* are somewhat more difficult to comprehend. Certain portions of the nervous system have a function of inhibition. When these areas are destroyed, there is an exaggeration of response owing to the loss of this inhibitory function and the release of intact centers from higher control. Such a phenomenon occurs in the presence of a lesion of the pyramidal system, an inhibitory mechanism, which is followed by increase in tone, increase in reflexes, and the presence of certain pathologic reflexes. These are *positive* rather than *negative* signs of disturbed function.

Positive signs are apparent in a different manner in the presence of *irritation,* or excitation, of a part of the nervous system. Here there is increased activity as a result of response to stimulation. The most characteristic examples of this are the pain and muscle spasm that follow disease of a peripheral nerve, and the so-called jacksonian convulsions in which signs of increased motor activity appear on one side of the body with irritation of the contralateral motor cortex.

In addition to these manifestations of destruction, release, and irritation, there may be *partial assumption of function by healthy tissues* to compensate for impairment or loss of function due to disease in another part. The destruction of one area may be followed by disruption of the nervous connections to neighboring or distant areas. There is, however, a certain amount of overlapping and duplication of function in the nervous system, and an intact center, nerve, or muscle may assume some of the physiologic activity of a diseased part. Furthermore, certain areas may be supplied with an overabundance of cells, so that a lesion in these sites, unless it is extensive, may be followed by a minimum of signs or symptoms. In other parts of the nervous system, in the "silent areas" of the brain, for instance, large lesions may exist without signs or symptoms, owing to a minimum of physiologic activity of the part, duplication of function, or compensatory activity elsewhere. For these many reasons neurologic diagnosis may present its pitfalls.

The neurologic examination requires skill, intelligence, and patience. It requires accurate and trained observation, together with, in most instances, the help and cooperation of the patient. It must be carried out in an orderly manner if it is to be complete, and time and attention are necessary if the details are to be elicited. Each clinician eventually works out his own method, based on his personal experiences, but the student should make it an invariable rule to follow a fixed and systematic routine in every examination, at least until he is very familiar with the subject. This is more essential in neurology than in any other field of medicine, for the multiplicity of signs and variations in interpretation may prove confusing. The specific order that is followed in the examination is not as important as the persistence with which one adheres to this order. The procedure herein outlined starts with the neurologic history and the physical and mental appraisals. In dealing with the neurologic examination per se, the sensory system is taken up first, because of the need for the patient's alertness in the sensory evaluation. Next the cranial nerves are investigated in sequence, followed by the motor system with all of its ramifications, including coordination, station, and gait. Since the reflexes depend upon the integrity of both the motor and sensory functions, they are examined after the motor system. Then the autonomic nervous system, peripheral nerve and spinal cord localization, and cerebral localization are considered individually. Finally the investigation of special conditions (coma, hysteria, etc.) and the examination of the cerebrospinal fluid are undertaken.

It may, however, be necessary on occasion to vary the sequence of the tests or to modify them according to the state of the patient and the nature of his illness. Under certain circumstances, as in chorea and Parkinson's disease, it may be possible to make a diagnosis at a glance, but no neurologic examination—and this is especially true for the student—can be considered to be satisfactory unless it is complete. There should be no attempt to arrive at conclusions before the examination is finished. If the investigation is necessarily long and the patient's interest flags, or if he fails to understand the significance of and the need for cooperating in diagnostic procedures whose purpose is not apparent or which seem to be unrelated to his presenting complaints, it may be well to explain the tests or their results to him, or to use other means to stimulate his interest and cooperation. On the other hand, if fatigue and lack of attention interfere with the results, it may be advisable to change the order of the examination or to complete it at a later date. Uniformity of procedure, however, greatly facilitates subsequent analysis of case records.

The chief causes for incorrect diagnoses are *insufficient examination, inaccurate observations,* and, less commonly, *false conclusions from correct and sufficient facts.* More errors result from the omission of a part of the examination than from the misinterpretation of findings. It is important to bear in mind, however, that slight deviations from the normal may be as significant as more pronounced changes, and absence of certain signs may be as significant as their presence. On occasion slight clues may be obtained merely by watching the patient dress or undress himself, tie his shoe laces, look about the room, or walk into the examining room. Abnormalities in carrying out these actions may point to disorders which might be missed in the more formal examination. The patient's attitude, facial expression, mode of reaction to questions, motor activity, and speech should all be noted.

Interpretation and judgment are also of extreme importance for evaluation and appraisal, and the ability to interpret neurologic signs can be gained only by carrying out repeated thorough and detailed examinations, and by keen and accurate observation. In the interpretation of a reflex, for instance, or in the appraisal of tone or of changes in sensation, differences of opinion may be evident. The only way in which the observer may become sure of his judgment is by experience, so that he may be certain of the normal and of any variation from it. It must be borne in mind, however, that the personal equation may enter into any situation, and that conclusions may vary. The important factor is not a seemingly quantitative evaluation of the findings, but an interpretation or appraisal of the situation as a whole.

The use of a printed outline or form with a check-list for recording the essentials of both the history and the neurologic examination is advocated by some authorities and in some clinics. With such an outline various items can be underlined, circled, or checked as being either positive or negative, and numerical designations can be used to record such factors as the degree of activity of the reflexes or an approximate quantitation of motor strength. Such forms may serve as teaching exercises for the novice or student and as time-saving devices for the clinician, but they cannot replace a careful narrative description of the results of the examination.

Neurologic diagnosis is a deductive process and is reached by a synthesis of all the details from the history and the examination. The physician must observe the findings, correlate and interpret them, and record them systematically. It may not be possible, however, to make a conclusive diagnosis until laboratory studies have been carried out or therapeutic tests have been tried; changes in the clinical state and either development of new signs and symptoms or disappearance of manifestations may alter the impression. The first step of the neurologic evaluation should be to *determine whether an organic lesion of the nervous system exists*; it may be a *focal lesion* with injury to all tissues within it regardless of their structures or functions, a *diffuse disease* with incomplete involvement in which some nerve cells and fibers suffer more than others, or a *systemic affection* in which only anatomically and functionally related systems of cells or fibers are involved. Secondly, an attempt should be made to *localize the lesion* with reference to cell structures, nerve fibers, or tracts involved. The symptoms and signs may be *primary* ones, correlated directly with focal structural disease or local disorders of function, or *secondary* (indirect) manifestations, due to release from inhibition normally exerted by the injured parts or the result of disordered reactions or disintegration of function of the physiologic mechanisms of the part injured. Then *the nature and etiology of the lesion* should be decided by interpreting symptoms and signs in terms of disordered function. When this information is available, *study can be made of the symptomatology of the disease process as a whole—the morbid phenomena, the pathologic anatomy and physiology.* Finally, diagnosis having been made by distinguishing the pathologic process and differentiating it from similar processes, *treatment, prognosis,* and, in certain instances, *epidemiology and prophylaxis* may be determined. It does not matter whether the disease process is secondary to disturbances of development, infection, toxic factors, trauma, neoplasia, vascular change, degeneration, or the aging process; in all the essentials of diagnosis are the same.

No other branch of medicine lends itself so well to the correlation of signs and symptoms with diseased structure as does neurology, but it is only by means of a systematic examination and an accurate appraisal that one can elicit and properly interpret his findings. Some individuals have a keen intuitive diagnostic sense and can reach correct conclusions by shorter routes, but in most instances the recognition of disease states can be accomplished only through a scientific discipline based on repeated practical examinations. Diagnosis alone, however, should not be considered the ultimate objective of the examination, but diagnostic investigations make up the first step toward treatment and toward attempts to help the patient.

Quantitative evaluation of neurologic abnormalities may be used for the accurate determination of a patient's clinical status, the study of the natural history of disease, and the measurement of response to either medical or surgical treatment. Such quantitative testing can be carried out for the appraisal of certain types of sensory and motor deficits, abnormal movements, reflex responses, and other functions and disturbances of function. It often, however, requires extensive instrumentation, and in the past has been carried out mainly for experimental purposes. There has recently been a renewed interest in such testing, principally for the evaluation of response to various therapeutic regimes. References to such testing are given in chapters where they are applicable.

CHAPTER 2

THE NEUROLOGIC HISTORY

A GOOD CLINICAL HISTORY often holds the key to diagnosis. This is true in the medical history, surgical history, and psychiatric history. It is especially true in the neurologic history, where a carefully obtained, properly analyzed, detailed account of the patient's symptoms, past and present, may lead to an accurate discernment of the nature and location of the disease process. A skillfully taken history, with a careful analysis and interpretation of the chief complaints and of the course of the illness, will very frequently indicate the probable diagnosis, even before physical, neurologic, and laboratory examinations are carried out. In many instances the physician can learn more from what the patient says and how he says it than from any other avenue of inquiry. Every neurologic examination must be preceded by an accurate anamnesis, if it is possible to obtain one. Many errors in diagnosis may be due to incomplete or inaccurate histories.

The principal objective of the history is, of course, to acquire pertinent clinical data that will lead to a correct analysis of the patient's illness. Herein one elicits the *symptoms,* the subjective manifestations of disease as related by the patient, in contrast to the *signs,* the objective manifestations, which are revealed in the physical, the neurologic, and the laboratory examinations. Many dysfunctions of the nervous system are largely subjective, without visible or outward signs of disease, and we can learn of their nature and course only by description. The information obtained in the history is not only essential to the diagnosis of the disease from which the patient is suffering, but also valuable in the proper understanding of the patient as an individual and of his relationship to himself, to his disease, and to others. The data elicited become a permanent record which may be referred to from time to time during the progress of the illness.

POINTS IN TAKING THE HISTORY

The taking of the history is no simple task. It may require greater skill and experience than are necessary to carry out a detailed examination. Time, diplomacy, kindness, patience, reserve, and a manner which conveys interest, understanding, and sympathy are all essential. The history is obtained most satisfactorily if the physician presents a friendly and courteous attitude, centers all his attention on the patient, appears anxious to help, words his questions tactfully, and asks them in a conversational tone. The mode of questioning may vary with the age and educational and cultural background of the patient. The physician should meet the patient on a common ground of language and vocabulary, and resort to the vernacular if necessary. The history is best taken in privacy, with the patient comfortable and at ease. An appearance of haste should be avoided. The method of questioning may vary from patient to patient, but the use of a regular order for recording the details is of value both in insuring completeness and in facilitating future reference. One should never attempt, however, to elicit a history by following a stereotyped form or by repeating a memorized list of questions to each of which a specific answer is expected. No mechanical measures can take the place of a careful consideration of the patient's complaints. The reliability of the information obtained may depend largely upon the intuition of the physician and his ability to analyze and interpret the symptoms and to appraise the thoughts and personality of the patient. By following these precepts a favorable patient-physician relationship may be developed; the physician may acquire empathy for the patient and enter into his feelings or experiences, and rapport may be established, based on the confidence of the patient in the physician.

The history should be recorded clearly and concisely, in a logical, well-organized manner. It can never be sufficiently complete, and no symptom may be left unanalyzed. Each statement must be considered in its relationship to the whole. It is important, however, to stress the outstanding manifestations and keep irrelevancies at a minimum; the essential factual material must be separated from the extraneous matter. Diagnosis involves the careful sifting of evidence, and the art of selecting and emphasizing the pertinent data may make it possible to arrive at a correct conclusion in a seemingly complicated case. It may be of value to record negative as well as positive statements, so that later examiners may know that the historian inquired into and did not overlook certain aspects of the disease.

The essentials of the history should be obtained from the patient himself, if at all possible. He must be encouraged to give a detailed account of his illness in his own words. The observer should intervene as little as possible, and only to exclude obviously irrelevant material, to obtain amplification on statements which seem to be vague or incomplete, or to lead the story into directions in which useful information may be obtained. Rarely, however, is the patient's spontaneous narrative complete enough to be of value in diagnosis. It is the exceptional patient who recalls all the particulars of his illness and repeats them in an accurate, chronologic order without confusing symptoms and his interpretation of symptoms. Furthermore, if his mind is focused on a particular manifestation, he may fail to mention others of equal importance. Consequently, it is usually necessary to augment the patient's account by means of suitable leading questions, and often to interrogate him in detail regarding specific factors, many of which he may not relate to his present condition, but the presence or absence of which may be of significance. The importance of an accurate and detailed record of events in patients with compensation and medicolegal problems cannot be overemphasized. The patient should be allowed to use his own words, and any suggestion of symptoms or diagnoses should be avoided. The latter must be borne in mind especially in obtaining histories from overly suggestible and psychoneurotic patients. It may be necessary, however, to attempt to determine the precise meaning which the patient attaches to the words he employs, as ambiguity of language may make it difficult for the physician to interpret the exact significance of the symptoms described.

Special consideration may have to be used in taking the history of certain types of individuals. The timid, inarticulate, or worried patient may have to be helped by means of sympathetic questions or reassuring comments. The garrulous person may have to be stopped from losing himself in a mass of irrelevant detail. The evasive or undependable patient may have to be questioned more searchingly. The fearful, antagonistic, or paranoid patient may have to be questioned guardedly lest one arouse his fears or suspicions. The person with multiple or vague complaints may have to be held down to specificities. The elated patient may minimize or neglect his symptoms; the depressed or anxious patient may exaggerate them, and the excitable or neurasthenic person may be overconcerned about them and describe them at length. Apprehension may impair logic. One must remember that the range of individual variations is wide, and this must be taken into account in appraising symptoms. What is pain to the sensitive, nervous, or exhausted patient may be but a minor discomfort to another. A blasé attitude or seeming indifference may indicate a pathologic euphoria in one individual, but it may be a defense reaction in another. One person may take offense at questions which another would consider commonplace. Even in a single individual such factors as fatigue, pain, emotional conflicts, or diurnal fluctuations in mood or temperament may cause a wide range of variation in response to questions.

During the taking of the history the examiner has an unequaled opportunity to study the patient—his manner, attitude, behavior, and emotional reactions. The tone of voice, the bearing, the expression of the eyes, the swift play of facial muscles, the appearance of weeping or smiling, or the presence of pallor, blushing, sweating, patches of erythema on the neck, furrowing of the brows, drawing of the lips, clenching of the teeth, dilatation of the pupils, or rigidity of the muscles may give information of great importance. Gesticulations, restlessness, delay, hesitancy, and the relation of demeanor and emotional responses to descriptions of symptoms or to details in the family or marital history should all be noted and recorded. These and his mode of response to the questions that are asked of him are of immeasurable value in the estimate of his character, personality, and emotional state. The manner of presenting his story may also give information with reference to the intelligence, powers of observation, attention, and memory of the patient. The examiner must, of course, be careful not to make a mental diagnosis of the patient's illness immediately upon meeting him, for some individuals are quick to sense and resent a physician's preconceived ideas about his symptoms. On the other hand, the patient's preconceived ideas should not alter the physician's interpretation of his symptoms, past or present.

The patient's story may not at all times be correct or complete. He may not possess full or detailed information regarding his illness; he may be misinterpreting his symptoms or giving someone else's interpretation of them; he may be wishfully altering or withholding information or may even be deliberately prevaricating for some purpose; he may be a phlegmatic, insensitive individual who does not comprehend the significance of his symptoms; he may be a garrulous person who cannot give a relevant or coherent story; he may have multiple or vague complaints which cannot be readily articulated. Infants or young children or comatose or confused patients obviously may be unable to give any history, and those who are in pain or distress, have difficulty with speech or expression, are of low intelligence, or are unable to speak the examiner's language may not be able to give a satisfactory history for themselves. Consequently, it may be necessary on many occasions to corroborate or supplement the history given by the patient with one given by an observer, relative, or friend, or even to obtain the entire history from someone else. Members of the family may also be able to give important information about changes in behavior, memory, hearing, vision, speech, or coordination of which the patient may not be aware. Under most circumstances it is necessary to question both the patient and others in order to obtain a complete account of the illness. Data from earlier examinations and previous medical records should also be abstracted and added to the history.

The importance of the clinical history cannot be overemphasized. History taking is an art; it can be learned partly through reading and study, but it is completely acquired only through experience and repeated trials. The ability to elicit a satisfactory anamnesis is one of the prime requisites to neurologic diagnosis.

GENERAL OUTLINE OF THE HISTORY

The neurologic history, as is true of all clinical histories, usually starts with certain *statistical data*. These include the patient's name, sex, age, date and place of birth, residence, marital status, occupation, religion, race, nationality and handedness. Then one records the patient's *major, or presenting, complaint*. This is followed by a detailed description of the symptoms and course of the *present illness,* including a chronologic account of its development. The *past medical history* is then outlined. Herein are listed the following: a record of serious illnesses, operations, and injuries; a history of the birth and early development; a detailed account of symptoms referable to the various organs and systems of the body; the marital history; the occupational history; a record of habits and contacts; a personality inventory with history of adjustment to family, school, marriage, work, and community. The *family history* concludes the anamnesis.

THE PRESENTING COMPLAINT AND THE PRESENT ILLNESS

It is important to have the patient relate the *presenting complaint* or complaints in detail, because these are the symptoms for which help is being sought, and relief from them is the objective of treatment. The patient should give his complaints in his own words and as completely as possible, and the examiner should record them as given and not in terms which he believes to be more descriptive scientifically. The physician, however, must clearly understand what the patient means by the terms that he uses; for instance, the expression "kidney trouble" may be used to indicate urinary incontinence, or "dizziness" to signify giddiness, unsteadiness, or confusion.

In obtaining the history of the *present illness,* each symptom is described and expanded, and the historian should draw out the chronologic occurrence of each manifestation, with the character, exact date and mode of onset, apparent precipitating or etiologic factors, duration, treatment, and progression or regression of each symptom. Statements are obtained regarding the stationary, remittent, intermittent, progressive, or regressive character of the illness, including circumstances which alleviate or increase the complaint, and seasonal, diurnal, and nocturnal variations. In trauma, for instance, and cerebrovascular accidents, there is an abrupt onset followed by gradual improvement which either terminates in complete recovery or is followed by incomplete resolution. In tumors and chronic, progressive degenerative diseases there is a gradual onset of symptoms; in certain neoplasms, however, hemorrhage may cause sudden onset or exacerbation. In cerebral arteriosclerosis there are repeated small episodes with resulting gradual progression of symptoms, but there may be temporary improvement between episodes. In multiple sclerosis there may be remissions alternating with exacerbations, but with a progressive increase in the severity of the manifestations; stationary, intermittent, and progressive varieties of multiple sclerosis are also encountered. In infections there is a relatively sudden, but not precipitous, onset, followed by gradual improvement and either complete or incomplete recovery.

In many conditions symptoms may appear some time before striking physical signs of disease are evident, and before laboratory tests are useful in detecting disordered physiology. It is important to know when the patient last considered himself to be well, when he had to stop work, and when he was forced to take to his bed. A history of previous manifestations of the present symptoms, past evidences of disease which might in any way be related to the present disorder, and any physical illness, activity, trauma, emotional conflict, etc., which had any temporal relationship to the onset of symptoms or to remissions or exacerbations should be elicited, even though the physician may not believe an etiologic relationship exists. One must attempt to determine how disabling the illness is and what crystallized the patient's decision to undergo the examination just when he did. The social, environmental, and economic factors, including the patient's reaction to his illness and the reactions to his family and his employer, may be of significance. Of equal importance is information regarding previous examinations and diagnoses and the patient's reaction to them, as well as his response to prior therapeutic regimens.

To illustrate the need for specific and detailed questioning, the *convulsive disorder,* one of the commoner manifestations of disease seen in the neurologic clinic, may be taken as an example. The patient himself may feel that it is sufficient merely to state that he has "attacks," but inasmuch as convulsive seizures may be manifestations of such varying classes of nervous system and systemic diseases as inflammations, toxemias, degenerations, neoplasms, and metabolic disorders, it is extremely important to question the patient in detail, and to question observers. The patient himself may be unconscious during the spell and may not be aware of its characteristics, he may withhold or alter information, or the relatives may withhold information from the patient.

In the first place, the *presenting complaint* may vary in individuals. One patient may say that he has "epilepsy," another may complain of "convulsions," another of "fits," "spells," "fainting attacks," "lapses," "seizures," or "falling spells." Some of these may be accurate so far as the patient knows, whereas others may be euphemisms to hide the true nature of the disorder.

Once the examiner has received the information that the patient is suffering from a convulsive disorder, he must obtain an *adequate, detailed description of the manifestations of the individual attack in the order of occurrence.* This is necessary for adequate diagnosis and interpretation, for differentiation between organic and hysterical attacks, for localization in the event of focal brain disease, and for information relative to possible therapeutic measures. First, one questions the patient regarding *precipitating factors* and the *aura,* or premonition of the attacks. "Have you any warning that an attack is imminent? If so, what are its nature and duration?" The aura may not be of localizing value. It may be described as a sensation of apprehension or anxiety, a queer feeling in the stomach, a pain in the stomach, a headache, or an increased frequency of small attacks. The aura, however, is often of localizing value, especially if it consists of auditory hallucinations or tinnitus, vertigo, visual illusions or hallucinations, an unusual odor or taste, or a recurring thought or memory. Of great localizing value are such manifestations as stuttering, asphasia, and numbness, tingling, or motor phenomena in one part of the body. In the presence of the latter one should elicit the area of onset, mode of extension, severity, and duration. In addition to asking the patient whether he himself is aware of such an approaching attack, he is asked whether observers can predict one, since they often become aware of an impending attack by noting flushing, pallor, sweating, staring, interruption of speech, confusion of thinking and speech, unusual sucking or swallowing movements, or sucking of the lips.

After information is obtained with reference to the aura, an adequate *description of the attack itself* is obtained. During the seizure the patient may be either flaccid or rigid, and either akinetic or hyperkinetic; movements may be either focal or generalized. Any localization of motor manifestations, either tonic or clonic, such as a turning of the eyes, the head, the eyes and head, or the entire body to one side, either at the beginning or during the attack, may be of significance. The patient is asked whether he consistently falls to one side during attacks, or whether one arm, leg, hand, foot, or one side of the face moves before the other, and the nature of the movements and their duration and sequence. It is important to know whether the movements are bizarre and purposeless, or coordinated and purposeful, and directed toward persons or objects; fighting, kicking, and resistance to examination may suggest a nonorganic basis for the attacks, although such features may also be present in organic attacks. The automatisms of psychomotor seizures are often seemingly purposeful. One should inquire whether there is either amnesia or loss of consciousness during attacks, how deep the loss of consciousness is, whether it comes on suddenly or gradually, and how long it lasts. The presence of a cry at the onset of the attack or during it, flushing, cyanosis or pallor, incontinence of urine or feces, and frothing at the mouth may give relevant information, as may injury to the body during the attack, biting of the tongue, and chewing of the lips.

The *postconvulsion manifestations* are next investigated. The patient is asked whether he regains consciousness immediately and, if he does, how he feels, and whether he notices fatigue, sleepiness, confusion, or muscular soreness. He is asked whether there is weakness of any part of the body, such as the face, arm, or leg, and how long this weakness lasts; whether there is any unusual feeling in any part of the body, such as numbness, deadness, or tingling; whether there are nausea and vomiting or localized headache; whether speech is disturbed, and whether there is partial or complete amnesia for the attack. If there is any difference in behavior after an attack, its nature and duration should be noted.

After an adequate description of the individual attack has been obtained, one inquires about the *chronology of the disorder*. It is important to know the age of the patient at the time of his first attack; the frequency of seizures and variations in their character; the relationship to rest, activity, sleep, emotional stress, irritability, presence of other people, and meals; the time of occurrence during the day or month. The birth history and the presence of convulsions immediately following birth or in infancy may be important, as may information about breath-holding attacks, dizzy or fainting spells, twitching of the muscles, brief periods of staring or confusion, temper tantrums, automatisms or episodic bizarre behavior, or recurring bouts of headache or abdominal pain. A detailed history should be obtained of any injury or illness preceding the onset of the attacks, especially trauma to the head, or a possible encephalitis or meningitis. The relationship to toxins and infections must always be borne in mind. Of importance, likewise, is information regarding previous diagnoses and the patient's reaction to them, and the response of the disorder to various therapeutic endeavors.

The convulsive attack is but one illustration of the diseases encountered in neurologic practice. An equally detailed description is obtained of every symptom and illness. In *headaches,* for instance, an accurate picture of the symptom may be of great help in diagnosis. A headache is a pain, and, consequently, is entirely subjective. One should determine whether the pain is localized or general, regional or diffuse, unilateral or bilateral, or bandlike. If it is localized, it is well to inquire whether it is frontal, occipital, temporal, or vertical, and whether there is localized tenderness. The character is also important—whether it is dull, aching, steady, throbbing, boring, burning, griping, sharp, lancinating, constricting, intermittent, continuous, or paroxysmal. One may have difficulty in evaluating its intensity, but may obtain indirect information by determining whether it is incapacitating and interferes with work or sleep, or can be endured, and whether it increases or lessens with activity or inactivity. The incidence, mode of onset, duration, frequency, periodicity of occurrence, time interval during the day or month, seasonal appearance, and the relationship to food, movement, exercise, position, coughing, mental effort, use of the eyes, emotional stress and strain, changes in mood, rest, and sleep are of importance, as are the mode of cessation and the response to special therapeutic measures. Finally, the presence of various associated phenomena such as nausea or vomiting, scotomas, diplopia, blurring vision, hemianopia, hyperacusis, hyperosmia, photophobia, tenderness, syncope, vertigo, aphasia, drowsiness, convulsions, or fever may be of diagnostic significance. Similar information is obtained in every instance of *pain* or *disturbance of sensation* such as numbness, paresthesias, itching, tingling, burning, or girdle phenomena. One inquires about the location and distribution, including depth from the surface, radiation, extent of diffusion, and paths of reference; the mode of onset; the character; the severity; the relation to rest, position, motion, and sleep; the incidence, duration, and frequency or periodicity; aggravating factors; localized tenderness; muscle rigidity and spasm; associated symptoms, and finally, the method of alleviation.

In the narration of the present illness the patient may have disregarded certain data which have a direct bearing on the present symptoms. Therefore it is very important to record all pertinent facts, especially those dealing with disease of the nervous system. In addition to convulsions, headaches, pains, and paresthesias, the following should be stressed:

Motor Disturbances: If there is a history of paralysis, paresis, atrophy, or ataxia, one determines the time and mode of onset, location, severity, type, and progression or improvement. If there have been hyperkinetic manifestations, one ascertains their type or nature, location, onset, duration, amplitude, frequency, and exciting factors. Inquiry should also be made regarding weakness, fatigue, stiffness and abnormalities of tone, clumsiness, stumbling, staggering, and disturbances of equilibrium.

Vertigo: Vertigo, giddiness, and lightheadedness, and subjective and objective vertigo should be differentiated. If these are present, it is important to determine their nature, mode of onset, duration, frequency, severity, direction, and relationship to posture or change of position, and to inquire about the presence and laterality of associated symptoms such as staggering or falling. In organic vertigo there is usually a sense of rotation, either of the individual or of the environment, and this may be accompanied by nausea, vomiting, tinnitus, deafness, perspiration, and prostration.

Visual Disturbances: Dimness or blurring of vision, scotomas, diplopia, transient blindness, hemianopic defects in the visual fields, and formed or unformed visual hallucinations may be significant.

Auditory Disturbances: Tinnitus, deafness, and auditory hallucinations indicate cochlear nerve involvement; with abnormalities of vestibular function there may be vertigo, unsteadiness, and disturbances of equilibrium.

Other Cranial Nerve Manifestations: These may include dysfunction of smell, taste, salivation, and lacrimation; numbness or paralysis of the face; dysarthria; dysphagia for liquids or solids; and regurgitation.

Disturbances of Speech or Expression: Abnormalities of speech, writing, and drawing, and of comprehension of spoken or written words should be noted.

Disturbances in Sleep Rhythm or State of Consciousness: A history of drowsiness, hypersomnia, attacks of uncontrollable sleep, insomnia, inversion of the sleep cycle, stupor, delirium, or coma may give diagnostic information.

Visceral Symptoms: Dysfunction of the autonomic nervous system may be indicated by changes in thirst, appetite, and elimination. Other important visceral symptoms include vomiting, which may or may not be projectile or accompanied by nausea; diarrhea and constipation; urinary symptoms including retention, frequency, urgency, dysuria, precipitancy, and incontinence; changes in potency or libido; sweating, flushing, and vasomotor disturbances.

Mental Symptoms: It is important to determine whether there is a history of delirium, confusion, personality change, memory difficulties, anxieties, nervous tensions, alcoholism, delinquency or misdemeanors, and "nervous breakdown."

If any of the above has been present, one should obtain exact data on the onset, nature, frequency, description, duration, progression or improvement, and degree of incapacity. It may be necessary to interrogate the patient in detail regarding symptoms and systems which apparently are not related to the present disorder. If there is a history of trauma to the head, one should inquire regarding loss of consciousness and its duration, confusion, disorientation, convulsions, amnesia, bleeding from the nose or ears, cerebrospinal fluid rhinorrhea, headaches, memory loss, and personality change. In all cases in which trauma plays a part the details of the accident must always be recorded, along with independent information from observers if it is possible to obtain it. One should get independent testimony in all instances in which industrial hazards or toxins or conduct disorders play a part and in those cases with possible forensic or medicolegal aspects.

THE PAST MEDICAL HISTORY

A history or an examination that is directed exclusively toward the nervous system is incomplete. It may seem irrelevant at times to follow the history of the present illness with a detailed medical history. The nervous system, however, is but one part of the body, and neurologic manifestations or complications are frequently the first clinical evidences of serious systemic disease. In pernicious anemia and other blood dyscrasias, diabetes, syphilis, subacute bacterial endocarditis, hypertension, arteriosclerosis, tuberculosis, acute infections, metabolic disorders, undulant fever, and toxemias, and even in neoplasms in distant portions of the body, nervous system manifestations may be evident before one observes other signs or symptoms of the disease. Furthermore, the nervous system, through the central control of visceral function and through its autonomic division, is important in the regulation of heart rate, blood pressure, respiration, gastrointestinal function, and bladder control. Visceral dysfunction, either organic or psychogenic, may be of nervous system origin. For these many reasons, the medical history should be detailed and complete.

First, the *general health* prior to the onset of the present illness is recorded, then a history of the *past illnesses, operations,* and *accidents* or *injuries* is obtained, with the date and nature of each, period of incapacitation, and sequelae. Information should be obtained about prior illnesses of all types and all hospitalizations, but often it is necessary to be somewhat skeptical in accepting previous diagnoses and to inquire instead about the symptoms and manifestations of the disease. In recording operations and injuries one should list the type of anesthetic used, the complications, and the end results. The patient is also questioned about his susceptibility to disease and his reaction to illnesses, operations, and injuries.

The history of the patient's *birth and early development* includes the following: the health of the mother during pregnancy, including vomiting, hypertension, eclampsia, and viral illnesses such as rubella; the possibility of Rh incompatability in the parents; their age at the time of the patient's birth; the duration of gestation; any abnormalities of labor and delivery, such as prolonged labor, instrumental delivery, or precipitate birth; the type of anesthesia used for delivery; birth trauma; postnatal cyanosis, icterus, paralysis, or convulsions; birth weight; difficulty with respirations or with feeding after birth; health during infancy, with mode of feeding and gain of weight; age of weaning, dentition, holding head erect, sitting alone, standing, walking, talking, and development of toilet habits; the presence of delirium, "spasms," or convulsions with febrile states; handedness and possible shift of handedness; learning ability; mental characteristics, such as brightness and good nature, irritability, nervousness, peevishness, dullness, or timidity; habits and so-called neuropathic traits, such as enuresis, thumb sucking, somnambulism, nail biting, temper tantrums, night terrors, childhood fears, tics, stammering, and masturbation. Not only is the somatic developmental history important, but one must also study the social development, including progress at school and a record of the adjustment of the individual to others and to his environment.

In relating his past illnesses the patient may list only the serious or outstanding ones, and may fail to mention individual symptoms that may be of diagnostic significance. As a consequence, detailed questioning is important in the diagnosis both of systemic and of psychosomatic illnesses. *Symptoms referable to the various organs and systems* may be investigated by making inquiries about the following specific manifestations and details:

The Eyes: Visual difficulty, the wearing of glasses, the time of the last refraction, changes in vision following refraction, diplopia, blurring, transient blindness, hemianopic defects, scotomas, pain, asthenopia, swelling, discharge, and inflammation.

The Ears: Hearing, tinnitus, deafness, pain, discharge, paracenteses, and vertigo.

The Nose: Head colds, discharge, allergic rhinitis, atrophic rhinitis, sinus disease, epistaxis, symptoms of obstruction, and olfaction.

The Mouth and Throat: Head colds, tonsillitis, sore throats, quinsy, difficulty in swallowing or talking, hoarseness, sore mouth or gums, the condition of the teeth, care of the teeth, roentgenographic examination of the teeth, and abnormalities of the tongue.

The Cardiorespiratory System: Colds, bronchitis, asthma, dyspnea, orthopnea, cough, sputum, hemoptysis, pleural pain, night sweats, cardiac pain or irregularity, tachycardia, palpitation, edema, history of blood-pressure changes, and history of exposure to tuberculosis or inhalants.

The Gastrointestinal System: Habits of eating, changes in appetite or thirst, normal weight and changes in weight, nausea, vomiting, hematemesis, eructations, heart burn, pain and its location and character and relationship to meals, jaundice, flatulence, distension, bowel function and habits, the use of cathartics, rectal incontinence with or without cathartics, character of stools, melena, hemorrhoids, fissures, and fistulas. A complete dietary history may give valuable information.

The Genitourinary System: Hematuria, pyuria, frequency, nocturia, enuresis, dysuria, urgency, precipitate micturition, incontinence, retention, and pain. An inquiry should also be made into the history of signs or symptoms of veneral diseases. A few frank questions should be asked of both sexes about childhood and adult sexual activity and adjustment, noting the mental attitude toward the sexual act and possible abnormalities of sexual function such as change in libido, impotence, frigidity, dyspareunia, nymphomania, autoerotic practices, and perversions. It is important to remember that some individuals will respond candidly and others will be offended by questioning on this subject, and the questions must be worded accordingly.

The Catamenial History: Age at the menarche and at the menopause and reactions thereto, the regularity of the menstrual cycle, recent changes in the menstrual cycle, the length of each period, amount of flow, dysmenorrhea, intermenstrual pain or bleeding, discharge, pruritus, and date of last period. If the patient has gone through the menopause, either physiologic or artificial, or if she is approaching it, one should inquire about hot flushes and other vasomotor and nervous symptoms.

The Orthopedic History: Injuries, growth disturbances, swelling of the joints, pain or redness, limitation of motion, and leg and back pains.

The Skin: Eruptions, urticaria, bruises, color changes, scaling, sweat disturbances, and pruritus.

The Allergic History: Hay fever, allergic rhinitis, sneezing, urticaria, asthma, bronchitis, food intolerance, idiosyncracies to foods and drugs, previous sera and vaccines, pollen and dust sensitivity, and physical allergy.

The *marital history* should include the duration of marriage; the health of the partner and children; the number of times the patient has been married; the reasons for and circumstances leading to change in marital status; the number of children living and dead, with the cause of death; the number of miscarriages, with their causes and the duration of pregnancy at the time of the miscarriages. Other important data deal with the adjustment to the marriage; the personality of the mate; conflicts, compatibility, fidelity, and objective of marriage; the use of, reason for, and type of contraceptive procedures.

The *occupational history* should give information about both present and past occupations, with special reference to contact with toxins, heavy metals, fumes, silica, unhygienic routines, and industrial hazards. Other significant factors include information on the duration, type, and nature of the employment; hours of labor; environment; physical and mental strain; work record, with history of promotions and data regarding future outlook. If there has been frequent change of employment or a poor work history with absenteeism and a dissatisfied attitude toward employment, the reasons should be elicited. If the patient is no longer working, one should determine when and why he stopped.

A *history of habits and contacts* outside of working hours is obtained, with special reference to the use of alcohol, tobacco and drugs, coffee and tea, etc., or the reasons for abstinence. Previous residences, especially in the tropics or in areas where certain diseases are endemic, may be of importance. One should also record a history of the routine of the day with information on the amount of and habits of sleep, regularity and habits of meals, diversions and avocations, exercise, energy output, and ease of fatigue.

A *personality inventory* of the patient is also included, especially in instances in which there have been changes in the individual's reactions as a result of the disease process. The mental characteristics during infancy and childhood about which one should have information have been mentioned, but the reactions, adjustment, and predominant emotional tendencies during puberty and adolescence and in adult life are of equal importance. One should determine whether the patient has been sensitive, shy, seclusive, shut-in, and given to daydreaming; sociable, gregarious, outgoing, friendly, and affectionate; submissive or aggressive; dependent or independent; good-natured and pleasant, with a ready sense of humor; moody, irritable, impulsive, suspicious, or jealous; rigid, stubborn, and obstinate; serious, persevering, and ambitious, or wavering, with ideas of inferiority. It is essential to learn how he has conformed to the mores and to social customs and legal restrictions. His attitude toward his body and his health are also pertinent—whether he is generally unconcerned about appearances or dress, or careful and meticulous; whether he is indifferent toward minor ills and pains, or is hypochrondriacal in his attitude. One should ascertain whether he exhibits an excessive reaction to troubles and interests with wakefulness, anorexia, diarrhea, and exhaustion, and determine his attitude toward his present symptoms and his insight into and judgment regarding his illness.

The *social, economic, and adjustment factors* are of extreme importance: the patient's educational attainment and age at and reason for stopping school, with information about school records, repeated grades, truancy, and incorrigibility; the patient's place in the family—first child, last child, only child, etc.; his age at the time of the death of his parents, and his reactions to illness, separation, divorce, or death of relatives; the patient's employment and his reaction and adjustment to it; the financial and economic situation; the home situation—whether he lives in a house, apartment, tenement, rooming house, boardinghouse, or house trailer, or is a nomad; the number of rooms in the house and the number of people living in them; the presence of outsiders and "in-laws" in the home; separation or estrangement from parents or other relatives; likes and dislikes; hobbies and interests; social relationships; hopes and fears and goal ideal; capacity to enjoy life and profit by experience; crimes, misdemeanors, and prison sentences; religious affiliations and moral life; special successes and difficulties. Forensic or medicolegal factors in the illness must always be borne in mind, especially if the symptoms are felt to be related to employment or injury. The possibility of later claims for compensation must be considered, even though the patient and his family may deny that any litigation is pending. In the postwar period a military history is elicited. Adjustment to military service and experiences, wounds and illnesses, promotions, and reason for rejection or discharge should be stressed.

THE FAMILY HISTORY

Inasmuch as many neurologic conditions are of genetic or familial incidence, the family history should be obtained in detail. One records not only the age and cause of death of the parents and siblings, but also data with reference to their physical and mental health during life. More important than the fact that a parent died of pneumonia may be the knowledge that he died of pneumonia while in a hospital for the treatment of mental diseases. One should determine the general health of the family and whether members of it are short- or long-lived. Information should be obtained regarding both the direct and the collateral lines, and the possibility of consanguinity should be taken into consideration. In the neurologic history one is especially interested in inherited, familial, and congenital nervous and mental disorders and tendencies, including epilepsy, migraine, feeble-mindedness, organic or functional nervous or mental disorders, alcoholism, eccentricities, suicide, and criminal or other sociopathic tendencies. In certain neurologic disorders, such as Huntington's chorea, there is a single manner of inheritance which has been well documented; in others, such as the spinocerebellar ataxias and the myopathies, there are variable modes of inheritance; in others, such as dystrophica myotonica, individual members of the family may exhibit only certain aspects of the disease; in still others, such as certain of the inborn errors of metabolism, an inherited tendency is suspected but has not been proved. In some of the birth defects and chromosomal abnormalities extrinsic factors may have altered the germ plasm or interfered with embryonic development. Recent developments in genetics stress the need for a careful and detailed family history. In addition to information about disorders related to the nervous system one should always include in the family history data about syphilis, cancer, tuberculosis, diabetes, cardiovascular disease, hypertension, and allergic disease. It is also important to obtain some history of the cultural and economic background of the family, with information as regards race, nativity, length of time in this country, religion, social and economic level, and the temperament and character of the parents and siblings.

CHAPTER 3

THE PHYSICAL EXAMINATION

THE NERVOUS SYSTEM must be regarded as but one part of the body, and the clinical examination of it should be preceded, in every instance, first by a physical examination and constitutional evaluation of the patient, and then by a mental appraisal. These are important preliminaries, and they must never be minimized or overlooked. An examination directed exclusively toward the functions of the nervous system is incomplete.

Neurology is closely linked to internal medicine. Serious nervous system manifestations and complications not only may accompany systemic disease, but may even be the first evidences of such disease. This may be true in the case of the anemias and other blood dyscrasias, vascular disease, heart disease, diabetes, syphilis, acute infections, tuberculosis, toxemias, neoplasms, metabolic disorders, and many other conditions. Furthermore, the patient with neurologic symptoms of either organic or psychogenic origin may also have symptoms referable to other organs and systems. These may result from central or autonomic nervous system effects on visceral function or they may be so-called psychosomatic manifestations. There is a close relationship between neurologic disease and psychosomatic disorders. As a consequence, all somatic complaints must be adequately appraised, and one cannot arrive at a diagnosis of disease of the nervous system without an adequate knowledge of the general physical status of the patient. The physical examination need not be so detailed or so painstaking as that made in an attempt to diagnose some obscure somatic ailment, but it must be complete enough to bring to the fore any outstanding deviation, and no important physical sign should be overlooked. It is not within the scope of this book to dwell on the details of the physical examination and on physical diagnosis, but certain features will be stressed. The examination is most satisfactory and complete if an orderly routine is followed.

GENERAL OBSERVATIONS

The *general appearance* of the patient may yield important information. One looks for manifestations of acute or chronic illness, and special note should be made of signs of fever, pain, or distress; evidence of loss of weight, emaciation, or cachexia; the appearance of physical strength or weakness; the relative position of the trunk, head, and extremities; the posture and attitude in standing, walking, sitting, or lying; the general motor behavior, and any irregular or unusual attitudes, outstanding mannerisms, bizarre activities, restlessness, or increase or decrease in motor activity. The detailed examination of the posture, gait, muscle tone and atrophy, and of hyperkinetic phenomena is discussed in "The Motor System" (Part IV), and the complete evaluation of the state of consciousness and the mental and emotional reactions in Chapter 4 and "Examination in States of Disordered Consciousness" (Chapter 55), but any outstanding motor manisfestations and abnormalities in the behavior, attitude, and emotional reactions of the patient are noticed and recorded at the outset. One should make mention of the degree of cooperation, the appearance of apathy or lethargy and of fatigue, the presence of alertness or nervous tension, and the promptness or delay of responses.

The *physique and habitus* are taken into consideration, and the examiner observes the body build, the state of nutrition, the degree of development of the musculature, the body contour, the relative size of the shoulders and breasts and of the waist and hips, the inclination of the thighs, and the carrying angle of the arms. In the presence of obesity, the amount, texture, and distribution of the subcutaneous fat are significant. The relationship between the morphologic, physiologic, and psychologic factors in the individual, and the correlation between constitution and temperament and body build and disease are well known. Some knowledge and recognition of the various constitutional types and of constitutional medicine are valuable in neurologic diagnosis, although anthropometric measurements and the determination of the various indices need not be considered to be a part of the routine examination. The above factors, together with the hair distribution and the extent of development of the primary and secondary sexual characteristics, are also pertinent in the appraisal of the degree of physical maturity in the preadolescent, adolescent, and postadolescent subjects, and in the diagnosis of the endocrinopathies and disorders of the hypothalamus. Individual variations in the rate of physical development must, of course, be borne in mind, but observations of extremes and of wide deviations from the normal may be significant. This same individual variation must also be borne in mind in the evaluation of senility and the involutional processes. It is always well to note whether a patient "looks his age" or whether he appears to be older or younger than his stated age. Premature physical senility may connote early involution of the nervous system, although this is not necessarily the case. Premature graying of the hair may be familial in occurrence and of no clinical significance, but it is frequently observed in pernicious anemia and multiple sclerosis, and it may occur in hypothalamic disorders.

Note should be made of any outstanding *abnormalities in development or structure* such as giantism, dwarfism, gross deformities, amputations, contractures, unusual conformations, or disproportion between parts of the body. Diseases of the nervous system are found in association with such skeletal and developmental anomalies as syndactyly, polydactyly, and arachnodactyly. Other developmental changes to be recorded include asymmetries; cranial abnormalities; deformities of the teeth, tongue, lips, palate, or uvula; abnormalities of the eyes or the ears: deformities of the face or jaw; disproportion of the extremities; genital anomalies, and spina bifida. The presence of gross tumor masses, signs of pregnancy, and injuries, scars, and bruises should also be mentioned.

Specific deformities constitute important criteria in the diagnosis of nervous system lesions. In spastic hemiparesis there is flexion of the upper extremity with flexion and adduction at the shoulder, flexion at the elbow and wrist, and flexion and adduction of the fingers; in the lower extremity there is extension at the hip, knee, and ankle, with an equinus deformity of the foot. In paraplegia in flexion there is a drawing up of both lower extremities. In Parkinson's disease and the related syndromes there is flexion of the neck, trunk, elbows, wrists, and knees, with stooping, rigidity, masking, slowness of movement, and tremors. A somewhat similar flexion of the neck and spine may be seen in spondylitis rhizomelica, hypertrophic spondylitis, and camptocormia. In the myopathies there may be lordosis, protrusion of the abdomen, waddling of gait, and hypertrophy of the calves. In amyotrophic lateral sclerosis and progressive spinal muscular atrophy there are atrophy of the muscles of the hands and shoulder girdles, deformities of the hands, and weakness of gait. In peripheral neuropathies involving the upper extremities there may be a wrist drop, or a claw or simian hand; somewhat similar deformities may be seen in Dupuytren's contracture or in deforming arthritis. A foot drop of the lower extremity may be a manifestation of poliomyelitis or of a peripheral neuritis; this should be differentiated from the equinus deformity of a spastic paresis, the cavus foot of Friedreich's ataxia, congenital clubfoot, and changes that may be due to trauma or arthritis. The deformities that result from changes in muscle power, tone, and volume are discussed further in "The Motor System" (Part IV). As a part of the physical examination, however, one should appraise those secondary to trauma, arthritic or periarthritic inflammations with consequent ankylosis, bursitis or periostitis, muscular or tendinous strain or infiltration, disturbances of development, habitual postures, and occupational factors, and attempt to differentiate them from deformities of neurogenic origin.

THE FACIES

An evaluation of the facies, or of the facial expression, may aid in neurologic diagnosis. Gross abnormalities in the configuration of the face are found in such conditions as acromegaly, cretinism, myxedema, hyperthyroidism, and mongolism. One may note outstanding manifestations, such as color changes, flushing, sweating, tears, pupillary dilatation, tremors, muscular tension, or manifestations of anxiety, fear, or depression. The facies may suggest intelligence or stupidity, restlessness or lethargy, emotional lability or apathy, apprehension or resignation, depression or elation. The facial expression may be alert and mobile, attentive and pleasant, placid and cheerful, or it may be vacant, stolid, sulky, scowling, perplexed, distressed, distrustful, or fearful. In some neurologic disorders there are characteristic changes in facial expression or configuration. Among them are the fixed (or masked) face of parkinsonism, the immobile face with precipitate laughter or crying seen in pseudobulbar palsy, the grimacing of athetosis and dystonia, the ptosis and weakness of the facial muscles of myasthenia gravis, and the localized atrophy seen in some of the muscular atrophies and dystrophies.

THE PHYSICAL EXAMINATION

Although the details of the physical examination will not be presented, certain points will be stressed inasmuch as they may have particular significance in neurologic disease.

The *temperature, pulse, respiratory rate and rhythm,* and *blood pressure* are recorded, and it is also well to record the *height* and *weight,* especially if they are outside the normal range. These observations are followed by a systemic examination.

The Skin and Mucous Membranes: The appearance, consistency, texture, elasticity, tension, looseness or tightness, color, temperature, oiliness, and moisture or dryness of the skin are noted, as well as the color, moisture or dryness, and abnormalities of the mucous membrances. Aberrations of pigmentation, such as those seen in albinism, leucoderma, vitiligo, Addison's disease, pernicious anemia, argyria, icterus, and cyanosis may be significant. Redness or pallor, evidences of anemia or hyperemia, edema, outstanding eruptions, acne or furuncles, unusual markings, vasomotor changes, urticaria, dermatographia, scleroderma, ichthyotic change, striae, keloid formation, atrophy or hypertrophy, scars, bruises, herpetiform eruptions, trophic changes, indolent ulcers, decubiti, and tattoo marks should be noted. The degree of moisture or perspiration may be neurologically pertinent, and any localized or generalized increase or decrease in perspiration should be recorded.

Changes in the skin may be of diagnostic significance in the endocrinopathies, diseases of the hypothalamus, imbalance of the autonomic nervous system, and certain diseases of the central or peripheral nervous systems. In encephalitis and postencephalitic states the skin may be greasy and seborrheic. In herpes zoster there is a vesicular eruption in the distribution of the involved dorsal root ganglia. Hemangiomas of the spinal cord may be accompanied by skin nevi in the same metamere. Symmetrically placed, painless, recurring, poorly healing lesions of the skin of the extremities may be found in syringomyelia (Morvan's disease). In lesions of the peripheral nerves, tabes dorsalis, and transverse myelitis there may be trophic changes in the skin, indolent ulcers, and decubiti. In Raynaud's and Buerger's diseases there may be symmetrical gangrene. In neurodermatoangiomyositis there may be cutaneous manifestations, often with localized scleroderma. In the neurocutaneous syndromes, or congenital ectodermatoses with associated nervous system involvement, cutaneous changes may accompany disease of the nervous system: in tuberous sclerosis, or epiloia (Bourneville's disease), there are sebaceous adenomas suggesting acne rosacea (Fig. 1) together with localized areas of pigmentation and hyperplasia of the skin; in Recklinghausen's disease, or multiple neurofibromatosis, there are *café-au-lait* spots, pigmentary changes, and pedunculated polyps (Fig. 2); congenital nevi or "port wine marks," usually in the distribution of the trigeminal nerve, may accompany homolateral cortical cerebral angiomas or telangiectases (encephalotrigeminal angiomatosis). Skin changes may also be of diagnostic consequence in the avitaminoses: in deficiency in vitamin A there may be atrophy of the sweat and sebaceous glands and hyperkeratinization of the epithelium; in pellagra and niacin deficiencies the skin may be red and edematous, changing to a dull bronze or a deep brown; in thiamin deficiency there may be edema and trophic changes in the extremities; a deficiency of ascorbic acid may be accompanied by petechiae and ecchymoses.

The Hair and Nails: The texture, amount, distribution, color, and character of the hair, and baldness or premature graying are noted. Hair texture and distribution are important in the evaluation of the endocrinopathies, the degree of physical maturity, and the androgynic index. The nails should be examined, and attention is paid to the texture and smoothness; abnormalities such as fissuring, roughness, brittleness, cyanosis, and splitting; evidence of nail biting.

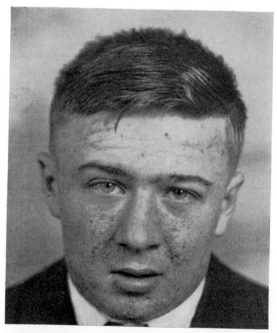

FIG. 1. A patient with tuberous sclerosis (Bourneville's disease); characteristic distribution of sebaceous adenomas.

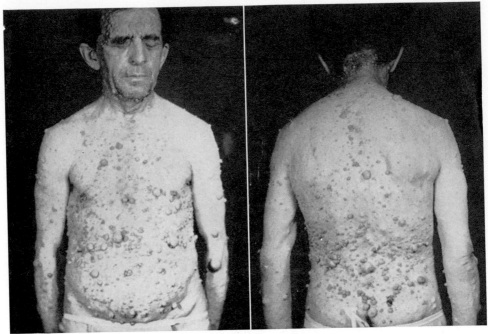

FIG. 2.   A patient with multiple neurofibromatosis (Recklinghausen's disease).

The Extremities: The appearance, temperature, moistness, and color of the extremities should be observed, and the character of the blood vessels determined by palpation. One looks for color change with change of position, pallor, redness, cyanosis, and edema. Any variation from the normal in the size or shape of the hands or fingers and the feet or toes, as well as deformities, joint changes, contractures, pain on motion, limitation of movement, localized tenderness, wasting, clubbed fingers, varicosities, and ulcerations may be significant. The consistency of the skin and muscles is noted, and it may be wise to measure the corresponding parts. The peripheral nerves, muscles, and tendons should be palpated, and tenderness, abnormalities of size and consistency, and signs of infiltration may be apparent.

The significance of changes in the skin, hair, nails, and extremities is discussed in more detail in "The Autonomic Nervous System" (Part VI).

The Eyes: The detailed examination of the eyes from the neurologic point of view, including ophthalmoscopy, is a part of the examination of the cranial nerves. Structural changes in the eyes and their adnexa should, however, be included in the physical examination. One looks for abnormalities of the cornea, conjunctiva, sclera, iris, lens, and eyelids. The width of the palpebral fissures, edema or discoloration of the eyeballs or lids, proptosis, chemosis, exophthalmos or enophthalmos, lid lag, lacrimation, and the presence of a Kayser-Fleischer ring should be noted.

The Ears and Nose: Significant findings in the examination of the ears include abnormalities in contour, stigmas, tophi, foreign bodies, wax, and discharge. The size and shape of the nose and the presence of deformities, discharge, edema, obstruction, deviation of the septum, and hypertrophy of the turbinates may give pertinent information.

The Mouth: In the inspection of the *lips* one notes the color, pallor or cyanosis, ulcerations, fissures, and herpetiform eruptions. The *teeth* should be examined for their appearance and condition, abnormalities in dentition, stigmas, extractions, caries, and oral hygiene. The notched incisors described by Hutchinson are said to be pathognomonic of congenital syphilis. Significant changes in the *gums* include hypertrophy, pyorrhea alveolaris, redness, bleeding, and lead line. The color of the *tongue* is important, as well as fissuring, atrophy or hypertrophy of the papillae, coating or lack of coating, mucous patches, and scars. Abnormalities of the tongue, gums, or lips are diagnostic signs in various disease processes involving the nervous system. In pernicious anemia the tongue is smooth and translucent with atrophy of the fungiform and filiform papillae and associated redness and lack of coating. In pellagra and niacin deficiency the tongue is smooth, and there are desquamation and atrophy of the papillae; in the acute stages it is scarlet-red and swollen, but in the chronic or mild deficiency states the papillae are mushroomed, and the tongue is not so deeply red. In thiamin deficiency the tongue is smooth, shiny, atrophic, and reddened. In riboflavin deficiency the papillae are flattened, and the tongue may be a purplish or magenta hue. Riboflavin deficiency may also result in cheilosis with fissuring of the lips at the angles of the mouth. Ascorbic acid deficiency may cause hypertrophy of the gums; a similar hypertrophy is sometimes the result of sensitivity to diphenylhydantoin sodium (Dilantin) (Fig. 3).

The Throat and Neck: Abnormalities of the throat include redness, inflammation, exudation, hypertrophy of the tonsils, and edema of the palate and the pharyngeal wall. In the inspection of the *neck,* adenopathy, thyroid enlargement, abnormal pulsations, and abnormality of contour are looked for. The character of the *voice* and any abnormality of the breath may be significant. A *laryngeal examination* should be carried out if there are any suggestions of changes in structure or function.

The Respiratory System and Thorax: Special stress should be placed upon the examination of the respiratory and the cardiovascular systems. In the examination of the former, the respiratory rate and rhythm and the depth and character of respirations are noted. Pain on breathing, dyspnea, orthopnea, or shortness of breath on slight activity may be significant. Abnormalities of respiration such as Cheyne-Stokes', Biot's, and Kussmaul's breathing may be seen in comatose states and other neurologic disorders. Either hyperpnea or periods of apnea may occur in increased intracranial pressure and in disturbances of the hypothalamus. The thorax is examined by inspection, auscultation, palpation, and percussion. The symmetry, amount of expansion on both sides, size and shape, and abnormal pulsations of the thorax are noted, as well as the character of the breath sounds and any abnormalities of conduction and fremitus. The frequent association of cerebral complications with pulmonary disease, including cerebral metastasis from lung abscesses and neoplasms, makes this portion of the investigation essential. In the examination of the

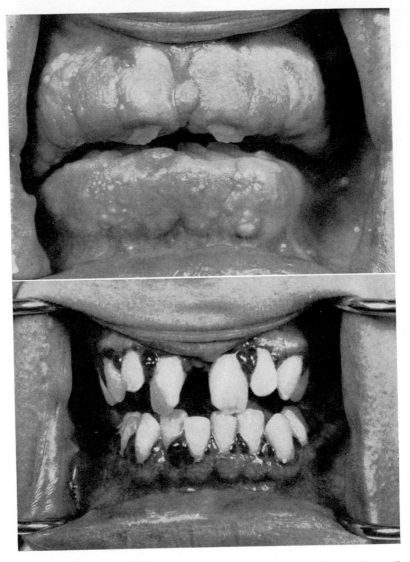

Fig. 3. Marked gingival hypertrophy following diphenylhydantoin sodium (Dilantin) therapy, before and after surgical resection of hyperplastic tissue.

thorax one should also inspect the breasts and search for lymphadenopathy in the axillae.

The Cardiovascular System: The examination of the cardiovascular system is equally important because of the frequent occurrence of cerebral and other neurologic complications and manifestations with hypertension, arteriosclerosis, acute and subacute bacterial endocarditis, and aortitis. The character of the peripheral blood vessels, especially the radial, brachial, and temporal arteries, and, under many circumstances, the dorsalis pedis and posterior tibial arteries, is significant. It must be stated, however, that peripheral or even retinal arteriosclerosis may not always mean that cerebral arteriosclerosis is present, nor is peripheral or retinal arterio-sclerosis necessarily present in individuals who have cerebral arteriosclerosis. These do, however, occur together with enough frequency to be noteworthy. The blood pressure, both systolic and diastolic, is recorded on every patient, and it is well to determine the blood pressure in both arms, and with the patient upright, seated, and lying down. The pulse rate and character are extremely important, especially if increased intracranial pressure is suspected. In the examination of the heart, the point of maximum impulse is determined by inspection and palpation, and the heart size by percussion. The rate, rhythmicity, character, and tone of the heart sounds are recorded, as are murmurs, bruits, and other abnormal sounds. Special procedures to be used in patients with suspected cerebrovascular disease are outlined below.

The Abdomen and Genitalia: In examining the abdomen one should observe the development and symmetry and look for spasm, rigidity, tenderness, pain, ab-normal masses, enlarged viscera, abnormal pulsations or respiratory movements, and the presence of fluid or herniae. Enlargement of the liver or the spleen is inves-tigated by palpation and percussion, and palpability, motility, or displacement of the kidneys noted. The external genitalia are inspected for abnormalities of develop-ment, cryptorchidism, tumor masses, scars, ulcers, discharge, phimosis, varicocele and hydrocele, and evidences of inguinal lymphadenopathy. Often it is necessary to carry out rectal and pelvic examinations, and even sigmoidoscopic investigations; these are indicated under many circumstances, but especially if there are symptoms or signs of rectal or vesical disease which may be due to either organic involvement of these structures or neurogenic dysfunction, or if malignant tumors of the rectum, pelvis, prostate, or internal genitalia are suspected. Cystometry and colonmetrog-raphy are discussed in "The Autonomic Nervous System" (Part VI).

EXAMINATION OF THE HEAD, NECK, AND SPINE

A special examination of the head, neck, and spine should be a part of every physical examination in patients with nervous system disease.

The Head: By *inspection* one observes the posture, shape, symmetry, and size of the head, and any apparent abnormalities or irregularities such as deformities or developmental anomalies, hydrocephaly, macrocephaly, microcephaly, oxycephaly, asymmetries or abnormalities of contour, disproportion between the facial and the cerebral portions, acromegaly, tumefactions or tumor masses, enlarged frontal bossae, rachitic deformities, depressions, scars, and signs of recent trauma. It is informative to measure the skull, especially in infants. Exostoses may indicate an underlying meningioma; dilated veins, telangiectatic areas, or "port wine" angiomas on the scalp or face may overlie a cerebral hemangioma, especially when such nevi are present in the distribution of the trigeminal nerve; scars of previous accidents or operations or trephine openings may be significant. Next, by *palpation,* one searches for areas of tenderness, scars, deformities, old fractures, depressions, trephine openings, or residuals of craniotomies. The size or patency of the fontanelles is important in infants. Separation of the sutures is sometimes present in increased intracranial pressure in children, as is bulging of the fontanelles. If there is an operative or decompression defect, any bulging or tumefaction should be noted. Either tenderness or distension of certain extracranial arteries is of importance in the diagnosis of certain types of headache and of temporal arteritis. The *percussion* note should be observed. In tumors and subdural hematomas there may be a difference on the two sides. The tympanitic percussion note found in hydrocephalus and increased intracranial pressure in infants and children is spoken of as Macewen's sign, or as the "cracked pot" resonance. Percussion is often more helpful than palpation in outlining areas of tenderness. *Auscultation* also yields information. *Bruits* are sometimes heard over angiomas, aneurysms, arteriovenous fistulas, neoplasms that compress large arteries, and in the presence of atherosclerotic plaques that partially occlude cerebral or carotid arteries. They may also be present in the absence of disease. One should listen for them over the head, the eyeballs, and the carotid arteries. A bruit heard over the eye in an arteriovenous aneurysm may disappear on carotid compression. Murmurs may be transmitted from the heart or large vessels; systolic murmurs heard over the entire cranium in children are not always of pathologic significance. *Transillumination* is often of value in the diagnosis of hydrocephalus and hydranencephaly.

The Neck: Deformities, tenderness, and rigidity of the neck, and tilting or other abnormalities of posture, asymmetries, changes in contour, and pain on movement are noted. Normally the neck can be flexed so that the chin can be placed upon the chest, and it can be rotated from side to side without difficulty. In meningeal irritation there may be nuchal rigidity, retraction of the head, and opisthotonos. Torticollis, or wryneck, is characterized by a retraction or turning of the head and neck toward one side (Chapter 16). The neck may also be tilted with some ocular palsies, and its movement is restricted with cervical spondylitis. In the Klippel-Feil syndrome and platybasia the neck is short and broad, movement is limited, and the hairline if often low. Gross abnormalities in the position of the head or neck in hysteria and rigidity with flexion deformities of the neck in cervical arthritis may simulate the changes of neurologic disease. The pulsations of the carotid arteries should be noted and bruits listened for.

The Spine: Inspection, palpation, and percussion are also used in the examination of the spine. *Inspection* may reveal the presence of abnormalities, deformities, or disturbances of posture or development. The motility (or limitation of movement) of the spinal muscles, active flexion and extension, lateral movement, rigidity, asymmetries, kyphosis, lordosis, and scoliosis should be recorded. *Palpation* may aid in the diagnosis of structural abnormalities, and it is valuable in demonstrating arthropathies and localized tenderness and pain. One should also palpate the contiguous muscles and note their function and any apparent rigidity or spasm. *Percussion* of the individual spinous processes may further demonstrate the presence of localized pain or tenderness.

In Pott's disease and neoplasms of the spine there may be a marked kyphosis; in the dystrophies, an increase in the lumbar lordosis; in poliomyelitis, syringomyelia, or Friedreich's ataxia, a scoliosis. In hypertrophic spondylitis and spondylitis rhizomelica there may be deformities, pain, tenderness, and rigidity. Localized rigidity with a slight list or scoliosis and absence of the normal lordosis are frequent symptoms of spinal irritation, sciatica, and ruptured intervertebral disks. Spinal rigidity and associated signs of meningeal irritation are described in Chapter 40 and manifestations of specific nerve root irritation in Chapters 45 and 46. Signs suggestive of spina bifida or meningocele, such as dimpling of the skin, unusual hair growths, or palpable abnormalities should be taken into consideration. In all conditions where bony abnormalities of the skull or spine are suspected, the physical examination is followed by roentgen examination.

EXAMINATION OF PATIENTS WITH CEREBROVASCULAR DISEASE

Modification of the above methods of examination as well as certain special procedures are indicated in patients with symptoms suggesting the presence of atheromatous involvement, intermittent insufficiency, or partial or complete occlusion of either the extracerebral or intracerebral circulation. These methods are as follows: *Palpation* of the carotid pulse may give important information about the patency of this artery or interruption of blood flow through it in certain cases. By careful palpation either low in the neck or just below the mandible, one may be able to distinguish between pulsations in the common and the internal carotid arteries; diminished, unequal, or absent pulsations may indicate either partial or complete obstruction. Some observers feel that palpation of the internal carotid artery by placing a finger in the anesthetized pharynx and against the postero-lateral pharyngeal wall is more valuable than palpation in the neck. *Auscultation* may reveal the presence of bruits or murmurs over a partially occluded carotid artery; with complete occlusion of one carotid artery, a bruit may be heard on the opposite side. Either *compression* of the carotid artery or *stimulation* of the carotid sinus may also give important information, especially if they are monitored with electroencephalographic, electrocardiographic, and blood pressure recordings. Many physicians, however, are reluctant to use these technics because of fear of producing contralateral numbness or weakness, syncope, cardiac arrest, or seizures. *Ophthalmodynamometry,* or the measurement of the pressure in the central artery of the retina, is one of the most delicate tests of carotid artery stenosis or occlusion. Most authorities feel that both the diastolic and systolic pressures should be recorded. There is a wide range of normal variation and the exact pressure measurement may not be significant, but inequality of the pressures on the two sides is of definite diagnostic value.

Other and more specialized technics may also be carried out. The time taken for intravenously injected fluorescein to appear in the retinal vessels may be compared on the two sides; there will be a delay on the side of a stenosed or occluded carotid artery. Abrupt tilting of a patient from a horizontal to an upright position may cause a sudden drop in the blood supply to the brain on the side where there is impairment of cerebral circulation; this may be accompanied by electroencephalographic changes, a decrease in the retinal artery pressures, and, at times, a transient hemiparesis or syncope. Angiography may give the most specific and localizing information about the site, type, and extent of extracerebral and intracerebral vascular disease. In most instances indirect or retrograde angiography should be carried out to give information about the subclavian and innominate arteries and the origins of the carotid and vertebral arteries as well as the branches of these latter vessels. Recently developed technics for the measurement of carotid artery and cerebral blood flow by the use of radioactive isotopes of various types and electromagnetic devices are still in the experimental stages and cannot as yet be used as routine diagnostic procedures.

LABORATORY PROCEDURES

To complete the physical study of the patient, various laboratory examinations and related diagnostic procedures are carried out. Many of these are routine measures and should be done in every case; others are special tests which, under certain circumstances, may be essential to the diagnosis or to the complete evaluation of the patient; still others are procedures that are largely experimental but that may in time afford valuable diagnostic information. Some of the more important diagnostic tests are as follows:

The Urine: The routine urinalysis includes checking the color, specific gravity, and reaction; chemical tests for glucose, albumin, and acetone bodies; microscopic examination for the presence of erythrocytes, casts, and micro-organisms. Special studies may give additional information. Tests for excretion of bromides, barbiturates, or phenothiazine drugs, or of lead, arsenic or other poisons may aid in the diagnosis of toxic states and coma; porphyrin bodies are found in the urine of patients with hematoporphyria, and phenylpyruvic acid is found in a specific type of mental deficiency; abnormalities of creatine and creatinine excretion as well as increased levels of certain enzymes are found in the myopathies; aminoaciduria and increased urinary excretion of copper appear in Wilson's disease, and abnormalities of amino acid excretion have also been reported in other metabolic disorders and certain types of mental retardation; increased amounts of catecholamines and products of their metabolism are found in the urines of patients with pheochromocytoma; Bence-Jones's protein is found in cases of multiple myeloma; in diabetes insipidus the specific gravity of the urine and the measured fluid intake and urinary output are important; urea clearance and urine concentration tests may be essential to the diagnosis of renal disease; important abnormalities in electrolyte and nitrogen excretion may be found in patients with spinal cord and cerebral lesions as well as in those with systemic disease; in the myelitides, bacteriologic studies, cultures, and chemical examinations of the urine are often indicated.

The Blood: An erythrocyte and leukocyte count of the blood, with a differential study and hemoglobin determination, should be carried out on every patient, and often additional hematologic studies are necessary. The color index and the mean corpuscular volume may aid in the diagnosis of pernicious anemia; a study of the reticulocytes and of immature erythrocytes is indicated in every case of anemia; studies of the white cells and of the platelets are often necessary diagnostic procedures; basophilic stippling is important in the diagnosis of plumbism and other toxic states; an increased number of eosinophils is found in periarteritis nodosa, trichinosis, and allergic conditions, and eosinophil counts give information in adrenocortical insufficiency; specific changes in the blood cells are found in disseminated lupus erythematosus; a detailed study of the blood is essential in malaria. A sternal puncture or bone marrow biopsy may give additional information in the blood dyscrasias and in multiple myeloma.

One of the serologic tests for syphilis should be done on every neurologic patient. In the past most laboratories have used one of the standard complement fixation (Wassermann or Kolmer) or flocculation (Kahn, Kline, or Hinton) tests, but the one that is used most extensively at the present time is the VDRL (Venereal Disease Research Laboratory) test, which is a rapid, highly sensitive, slide test employing cardiolipin antigen. When indicated, one of the tests for the detection of antibody to treponemata may be used, such as the Treponema pallidum immobilization (TPI), agglutination, or complement fixation tests, the fluorescent treponemal antibody determination, or the Reiter complement fixation test. An erythrocyte sedimentation rate gives information in certain infectious states. Blood cultures and agglutination tests are valuable in the presence of infections, especially septicemia, meningitis, and undulant fever. If the latter condition is suspected, the opsonocytophagic index may also be determined. In hemophilia, purpura, and related conditions the clotting, bleeding, and prothrombin times should be determined, in addition to the platelet count.

Among the blood chemical studies are included the determinations of glucose content, nonprotein nitrogen, blood urea nitrogen, uric acid, carbon dioxide combining power, pH, calcium, phosphorus, sodium, potassium, magnesium, bicarbonate, chlorides, cholesterol, bilirubin, serum proteins and protein factors (including electrophoresis), blood ammonia, and various steroids. An abnormal content of many enzymes may be found in neurologic disorders; these include ceruloplasmin, aldolase, and the phosphatases, transaminases, and dehydrogenases. The bromide, barbiturate, lead, and alcohol content of the blood may also be measured. The rate of disappearance of Congo red from the blood gives information important in the diagnosis of amyloidosis. In certain cerebral disorders one finds elevated serum sodium, plasma chlorides, and blood nitrogenous bodies, with potassium depletion; this is associated with decreased urinary excretion of sodium and chlorides. In spinal cord lesions, on the other hand, there may be catabolism of body protein with urinary excretion of large amounts of nitrogenous bodies; spinal cord lesions may also have associated endocrine changes with gynecomastia, testicular atrophy, and altered excretion of 17-ketosteroids.

Other Laboratory Procedures: Additional laboratory and diagnostic tests often add to the diagnosis. A basal metabolic rate and other calorimetric studies may be indicated, although recent data show that the determination of the protein-bound iodine concentration of the blood plasma and the radioactive iodine uptake give more specific information about thyroid function. Kidney and liver function tests are often necessary for the total evaluation of the patient. Skin tests may aid in the diagnosis of tuberculosis, undulant fever, trichinosis, coccidioidomycosis, histoplasmosis, and many other infectious processes. Special skin tests are also carried out as part of a survey of allergies. Chemical tests and spectrographic studies of the hair, skin, and nails may be valuable in the diagnosis of poisoning by lead, arsenic, mercury, or other heavy metals. A gastric analysis, done especially for the determination of the presence of free hydrochloride acid, as well as a Schilling test to measure the absorption of cobalt-labelled radioactive vitamin B_{12}, may be necessary for the diagnosis of pernicious anemia. An electrocardiographic examination is often essential; in some patients with periodic coma or convulsions it may be of value to stimulate the region of the carotid sinus during the test. The Kepler water test is important in Addison's disease, and the cold pressor tests in hypertension. The phentolamine hydrochloride (Regitine) and piperoxan hydrochloride (Benodaine)tests are used in the diagnosis of pheochromocytoma. Biologic tests for pregnancy are sometimes indicated. Determination of the estrogen and androgen excretion, the pituitary follicle-stimulating hormone, and the 17-ketosteroids are of aid in the diagnosis of certain endocrinopathies. In testing for adrenocortical insufficiency one observes the alteration in the number of circulating eosinophils and the change in the urinary 17-ketosteroids and 17-hydroxycorticoids following the administration of corticotropin (ACTH). Detailed bacteriologic investigations, including sensitivity studies, are important in both the diagnosis and treatment of various infectious disorders. Chromosome studies give important information in many metabolic and other disorders.

The glucose tolerance, insulin tolerance, and related tests are used in the diagnosis of diabetes mellitus and also that of hyperinsulinism and hypoglycemic reaction states. In diagnosing the latter, the routine study carried out by obtaining a fasting blood specimen with hourly specimens after the oral administration of glucose may not give the desired information, and the low point of the curve may not be determined. It is preferable to obtain a fasting specimen, followed by the administration of glucose, and then specimens at one hour, two hours, and then half-hourly until five hours. Furthermore, the glucose tolerance curve is influenced by the patient's previous diet, and in suspected hypoglycemia a more diagnostic curve is obtained if the patient is placed on a high carbohydrate diet for three or four days in preparation for the test.

Expanding interest in cerebral chemistry, neurochemistry, neuropharmacology, and in endocrine changes in systemic and neurologic disease has brought forth many additional laboratory procedures that are of value in diagnosis, but many of these are still in experimental stages and are not carried out routinely. Studies of cerebral blood flow, oxygen consumption, arteriovenous oxygen difference, and enzyme chemistry, for instance, give valuable information, but cannot be used regularly. This applies also to the chemical and other alterations in the blood, brain, spinal cord, and cerebrospinal fluid that have been found in experimental studies in multiple sclerosis, the convulsive disorders, the psychoses, and many other conditions. Further development of these research methods will doubtless bring forth important diagnostic tests. That investigative technics may develop into diagnostic procedures is shown in the increasing use of radioactive isotopes in the diagnosis and localization in cerebral lesions.

Pathologic Examination: These may include biopsy examinations of tumor masses or lymph nodes, especially in the diagnosis of malignant neoplasms and tumors of lymphoid tissues. In muscular diseases of various types, such as the myositides, trichinosis, periarteritis nodosa, and the myopathies, muscle biopsy examinations may give pertinent information. Pathologic examinations are also carried out for the diagnosis of inflammatory lesions, identification of parasites, and recognition of amyloid infiltration and other specific changes in nerve structure.

Rectal biopsy is of value in the diagnosis of amyloidosis and of the leuko-dystrophies and neurolipidoses. Cerebral biopsy has been employed for the purpose of distinguishing various types of cerebral degeneration that can be differentiated only by histologic study, as well as in the diagnosis of neoplasms. It has become a more valuable procedure since the introduction of histochemical techniques and enzyme studies.

Roentgen Examinations: Roentgen studies of the skull and spine are indicated in most diseases of the nervous system. Often special or detailed examinations of these regions are carried out. Specific procedures such as pneumoencephalography, ventriculography, myelography, and arteriography are often essential to the diagnosis of neurologic disorders. These are not discussed in detail in this volume, but current references are listed below and some further discussion may be found in Chapter 60. In many instances it is also important to secure roentgen examinations of the chest, gastrointestinal tract, urinary system, long bones, and other parts of the body.

Spinal Puncture and Examination of the Cerebrospinal Fluid: These arc discussed in detail in Part X.

Ancillary Studies: Various ancillary diagnostic technics, such as brain scanning after the injection of radioactive isotopes and ultrasonic scanning (echoence-phalography), have become important in the diagnosis and localization of intra-cranial lesions. These are referred to in Chapter 54.

Electroencephalography and Electromyography: The electroencephalogram has become an extremely useful addition to the neurologist's armamentarium. It is espe-cially valuable in the diagnosis of the convulsive disorders and in the localization and differentiation of various intracranial lesions, such as neoplasms, abscesses, and hematomas. Characteristic changes in the electroencephalogram also appear in trauma, infections, interruption of cerebral blood supply, coma and anesthesia, alter-ations in the body chemistry, and certain psychiatric conditions. The electroenceph-alogram is often essential to the complete neurologic examination, but inasmuch as the subject is a complex one, to be discussed in great detail if it is to be dealt with adequately, it will not be considered further in the present volume, but current references are listed. Electromyography is discussed more in detail in Chapter 33.

REFERENCES

ALTMAN, P. L. Blood and Other Body Fluids. Washington, D.C., Federation of Societies for Experimental Biology, 1961.

BAGCHI, B. K. "Electroencephalographic Localization of Intracranial Tumors," in KAHN, E. A., BASSETT, R. C., SCHNEIDER, R. C. and CROSBY, E. C., Correlative Neurosurgery. Springfield, Ill., Charles C Thomas, 1955.

BLACKWOOD, W., and CUMINGS, J. N.   Diagnostic cortical biopsy. *Lancet* 2:23, 1959.

BODIAN, M., and LAKE, B. D.   The rectal approach to neuropathology. *Brit. J. Surg.* 50:702, 1963.

BULL, J. E. D.   "Diagnostic Neuroradiology," in FEILING, A. (ed.), Modern Trends in Neurology. New York, Paul B. Hoeber, Inc., 1951.

COHN, R.   Clinical Electroencephalography. New York, McGraw-Hill Book Company, Inc., 1949.

CUMINGS, J. N., and KREMER, M.   Biochemical Aspects of Neurological Disorders. Springfield, Ill., Charles C Thomas, 1959.

DAVIDOFF, L. M., and DYKE, C. G.   The Normal Encephalogram (ed. 3). Philadelphia, Lea & Febiger, 1955.

DAVIDOFF, L. M., and EPSTEIN, B. S.   The Abnormal Pneumoencephalogram (ed. 2). Philadelphia, Lea & Febiger, 1950.

DICHIRO, G.   An Atlas of Detailed Normal Pneumoencephalographic Anatomy. Springfield, Ill., Charles C Thomas, 1961.

ECKER, A., and RIEMENSCHNEIDER, P. H.   Angiographic Localization of Intracranial Masses. Springfield, Ill., Charles C Thomas, 1955.

EPSTEIN, B. S., and DAVIDOFF, L. M.   An Atlas of Skull Roentenograms. Philadelphia, Lea & Febiger, 1953.

ETTER, L. E.   Atlas of Roentgen Anatomy of the Skull. Springfield, Ill., Charles C Thomas, 1955.

GIBBS, F. A., and GIBBS, E. L.   Atlas of Electroencephalography (ed. 3). Cambridge, Mass., Addison-Wesley Press, Inc., 1953.

HADLEY, L. A.   The Spine. Springfield, Ill., Charles C Thomas, 1956.

HILL, D., and PARR, G.   Electroencephalography: A Symposium on Its Various Aspects. New York, The Macmillan Company, 1963.

JASPER, H.   "Electroencephalography," in PENFIELD, W., and JASPER, H. Epilepsy and the Functional Anatomy of the Human Brain. Boston, Little, Brown & Company, 1954.

LASSEN, N. A., and INGVAR, D. H.   Regional cerebral blood flow measurement in man. *Arch. Neurol.* 9:615, 1963.

LIMA, P. A.   Cerebral Angiography. London, Oxford University Press, 1950.

MAC KENZIE, I.   The intracranial bruit. *Brain* 78:350, 1955.

MC DOWELL, F., and EJRUP, B.   Arterial bruits in cerebrovascular disease. *Neurology* 16:1127, 1966.

MENKES, J. H., RICHARDSON, F., and VERPLANCK, S.   Program for the detection of metabolic diseases. *Arch. Neurol.* 6:462, 1962.

MOORE, G. E.   Diagnosis and Localization of Brain Tumors: A Clinical and Experimental Study Employing Fluorescent and Radioactive Tracer Methods. Springfield, Ill., Charles C Thomas, 1953.

O'LEARY, J. L., and LANDAU, W. M.   "Electroencephalography and Electromyography," in BAKER, A. B. (ed.), Clinical Neurology (ed. 2). New York, Hoeber Medical Division, Harper & Row, 1962, vol. 1, pp. 121–276.

ORLEY, A.   Neuroradiology. Springfield, Ill., Charles C Thomas, 1949.

PENDERGRASS, E. P., SCHAEFFER, J. P., and HODES, P. J.   The Head and Neck in Roentgen Diagnosis (ed. 2). Springfield, Ill., Charles C Thomas, 1956.

PETERSON, H. O.   "Neuroroentgenography," in BAKER, A. B. (ed.), Clinical Neurology (ed. 2). New York, Hoeber Medical Divisoin, Harper & Row, 1962, vol. 1, pp. 101–211.

ROBERTSON, E. G. Pneumoencephalography. Springfield, Ill., Charles C Thomas, 1957.

SCHWAB, R. E. Electroencephalography in Clinical Practice. Philadelphia, W. B. Saunders Company, 1951.

SCHWARTZ, C. W., and COLLINS, L. C. The Skull and Brain Roentgenologically Considered. Springfield, Ill., Charles C Thomas, 1951.

SHAPIRO, R., Myelography. Chicago, Year Book Medical Publishers, 1962.

SHAPIRO, R., and JANZEN, A. H. The Normal Skull: A Roentgen Study. New York, Paul B. Hoeber, Inc., 1960.

STRAUSS, H., OSTOW, M., and GREENSTEIN, L. Diagnostic Electroencephalography. New York, Grune & Stratton, Inc., 1952.

TAVERAS, J. M., and WOOD, E. H. Diagnostic Neuroradiology. Baltimore, Williams & Wilkins Company, 1964.

THOMAS, M. H., and PETROHELOS, M. A. Diagnostic significance of retinal artery pressure in internal carotid involvement. *Amer. J. Ophth.* 36:335, 1953.

TODD, J. C., STANFORD, A. H., and WELLS, B. B. Clinical Diagnosis by Laboratory Methods (ed. 12). Philadelphia, W. B. Saunders Company, 1954.

WILLIAMS, D. "Clinical Electroencephalography," in FEILING, A. (ed.), Modern Trends in Neurology. New York, Hoeber Medical Division, Harper & Row, 1951.

WILSON, M. The Anatomical Foundation of Neuroradiology of the Brain. Boston, Little, Brown & Company, 1963.

WOOD, E. J., JR. An Atlas of Myelography. Washington, D.C., Registry Press, 1948.

CHAPTER 4

THE MENTAL
EXAMINATION

THERE ARE a number of reasons why a mental evaluation is an extremely important part of the neurologic examination, or, indeed, of every physical examination. No appraisal of the neurologic status is complete without a mental examination. We must know something about the patient's personality, background, intellectual status, and emotional reactions in order to understand him as an individual, to interpret his illness and the origin and progress of his symptoms, and to provide him with that type of care best suited to him. A good psychiatric history and a knowledge both of his premorbid personality and of the changes in his personality that the disease process has wrought are important in the appraisal of the patient and his adjustment in adolescent and adult life, in understanding why he reacts the way he does, and in comprehending why his illness has taken a specific course. The reliability of the history and of the responses to diagnostic procedures depends upon the patient's intelligence, memory, ability to express himself, emotional reactions, and state of consciousness.

The mental examination is also important in the differential diagnosis of neurologic disorders, and is often of aid in distinguishing between organic disease, psychotic states, hysteria, and malingering. Changes in the intellectual status and emotional reactions occur in many diseases of the nervous system—in toxic states, infections, neoplasms, vascular abnormalities, organic deliriums, posttraumatic syndromes, organic psychoses, and degenerative processes. In disease of the hypothalamus there may be changes in the emotions and affective tone. Cortical lesions are often accompanied by abnormalities of memory, judgment, and intelligence, and it may be necessary to differentiate between native impairment of intelligence and intellectual deterioration. In diffuse disease of the cerebrum there may be marked psychic aberrations and disturbances of consciousness, with disorientation and abnormalities of thought content. In general paresis, toxic encephalopathies, frontal lobe tumors, senile and presenile degenerations, and many other conditions there are pathognomonic mental syndromes. In psychosomatic disorders there are changes in function of the autonomic nervous system. In other neurologic disorders, such as epilepsy, migraine, multiple sclerosis, and Parkinson's disease, a specific personality type has been described, and the presence of such personality deviations may aid in diagnosis.

Neurology and psychiatry are interdependent, and a mental history and appraisal are important parts of a complete neurologic examination, just as a neurologic appraisal is essential to a complete psychiatric examination. Every neurologist must have an adequate knowledge of psychiatry and a comprehension of psychodynamics, and every psychiatrist must understand the fundamentals of neurology. Internal medicine is likewise dependent upon neurology and psychiatry, and both neurologic and psychiatric appraisals are essential in a complete physical examination and in the diagnosis of systemic disease. Recent interest in constitutional medicine and in psychosomatic medicine has stressed the relationship between constitutional factors, specific personality patterns, and certain disease syndromes and entities.

The neurologic history may contribute invaluable information to the mental appraisal of the patient. The developmental history, personality inventory, and social and economic review may give data regarding the patient's emotional reactions, personality pattern, and adjustment to his environment. Furthermore, the careful observation of the patient during the narration of the history may aid in evaluating his emotional status, memory, intelligence, powers of observation, character, and personality.

It is not the purpose of this text to outline the procedure for the complete psychiatric examination, for such an examination is time-consuming and cannot be carried out in detail on every neurologic patient. Certain manifestations must, however, be taken into consideration, and for this the following outline may be used.

STATE OF CONSCIOUSNESS

By the state, or level, of consciousness is meant the individual's awareness and the responsiveness of his mind to himself, to his environment, and to the impressions made by the senses. A patient may be conscious, alert, accessible, and attentive; drowsy or lethargic; apathetic with delayed responses; in a clouded or dreamy state; confused; delirious; semicomatose, stuporous, or comatose. In clouding of consciousness not only the reception of impressions but also their identification and interpretation are impaired, and responses are delayed. The detailed appraisal of sensorium, orientation, personal identification, and comprehension will be presented later in the mental examination. The diagnosis of the semicomatose or comatose patient is also described in detail in "The Examination in States of Disordered Consciousness" (Chapter 55).

APPEARANCE AND GENERAL BEHAVIOR

In observing the appearance, attitude, and general behavior of the patient, one includes not only the physical appearance of illness, pain, and tension, as mentioned in the discussion of "The Physical Examination" (Chapter 3), but also his attitude, conduct, and reactions. One notices whether the patient looks strong, sick, or weak. He may be tidy, neat, clean, and of good appearance; slovenly, careless, and unkempt; cooperative and helpful; indifferent, irritable, hostile, resentful, and resistive; calm, quiet, reserved, adaptable, frank, social, friendly, and natural, free, and alert in his reactions; shy, anxious, perplexed, tense, agitated, fearful, suspicious, introspective, brooding, dull, "queer," inhibited, negativistic, or withdrawn. One observes the patient's manner, speech, and posture, and looks for abnormalities of facial expression or motor activity, especially restlessness or stereotypy of movements, gestures and grimaces, bizarre mannerisms, and posturing. Eccentricities of dress and gait should be recorded, as well as habits of eating, sleeping, and elimination.

One notes whether the patient shows interest in the interview and seems to be able to grasp the situation and to be in touch with his surroundings, or whether he is distractible, confused, absorbed, and preoccupied, with flagging of attention. It is valuable to observe the adaptability and manner of the patient both when he is and when he is not aware of being watched. The patient's attitude toward the physician and toward the examination is important, as are his insight into or his understanding of the general nature, cause, and implications of his illness, and his attitude toward his family and other patients. Finally, one takes into consideration the patient's ability to establish rapport with the physician, based upon the confidence of the patient in the physician. The physician's emotional reaction toward the patient, or his "empathic index," may also be of diagnostic significance.

STREAM OF MENTAL ACTIVITY

The general stream of mental activity and character of the thinking processes are noted, both in the patient's spontaneous conversation and in his responses to questions and commands. The stream of thought should be clear, logical, relevant, and coherent. Any disorder of thought or abnormality in the tone, form, quantity, quality, rate, coherency, or spontaneity of speech or mental activity is significant—the overproductive, voluble, distractible, accelerated speech with flight of ideas that one sees in manic states; the hesitant, retarded, underproductive, inhibited speech, often with poverty of ideas, mutism, and negativism, that one sees in depressed states; the disordered, irrevelant, incoherent, rambling, circumstantial, repetitive, garrulous speech of organic cerebral deterioration; the sarcastic or bitter speech of the paranoid or psychopath; the concise, compulsive speech with careful choice of words seen in meticulous or obsessive-compulsive individuals; the evidence of evasion or fabrication seen in Korsakoff's psychosis or Ganser's syndrome; the inhibited, incoherent, hesitant speech with blocking that one sees in schizophrenic states. Such manifestations as verbigeration, neologisms, echolalia, palilalia, stereotypy, fragmentation, confabulation, clang associations, alliteration, rhyming, punning, and perseveration are pertinent. It is often valuable to obtain a stenogram, or detailed transcription of the patient's verbal productions, both spontaneous and in response to questioning. Other types of defects in speech, such as the dysarthrias and abnormalities of expression, will be discussed separately in Chapter 19, and "Aphasia, Agnosia, and Apraxia" (Chapter 53).

Coincident with the stream of mental activity, one also observes the type and amount of *general motor activity* and any abnormalities of it—the restlessness, hyperkinesis, and overactivity that one sees in manic states and delirium; the lack of initiative and spontaneity with diminished motor activity seen in depressed states and extrapyramidal syndromes; the bizarre mannerisms of schizophrenic states, and other gestures, eccentricities of movement, and abnormal motor manifestations. Both active and passive movements are noted, along with freedom and spontaneity of motor activity, apparent purposefulness of movements, response to commands, and outstanding abnormalities and paralyses.

EMOTIONAL STATE

The evaluation of the patient's emotional state is an extremely important aspect of the psychiatric appraisal, and one has to take into account both objective and subjective criteria. Somatic manifestations of the affective reactions, or mood, may be apparent in the physical examination—the occurrence of tears, pallor, flushing, tremor, muscular tension, tachycardia, hyperhidrosis, mydriasis, and other evidences of autonomic nervous system imbalance. The prevailing mood of the patient should be noted. He may present a normal emotional display and be calm, quiescent, composed, and complacent. On the other hand he may be cheerful, playful, silly, elated, euphoric, self-satisfied, boastful, grandiose, exalted, ecstatic, or excitable, as is seen in manic states; or anxious, fearful, bewildered, sensitive, discouraged, despondent, despairing, hopeless, distressed, worried, or apprehensive, as occurs in depressed state. In schizophrenia the patient may be cool, distant, aloof, disdainful, suspicious, defensive, perplexed, bewildered, indifferent, withdrawn, apathetic, or dull. There may be emotional lability, irritability or a striking variation in mood with or without apparent external causes. Diurnal or periodic fluctuations should be noted. One should determine not only the patient's current mood, but also his predominant emotional tendencies—whether he is social, friendly, and outgoing, with definite mood swings; shy, seclusive, and withdrawn, or by nature impulsive, irritable, and eccentric. If suicidal ideas are present, these should be recorded.

Especially important is the relationship between emotional expression and thought content and the adequacy of emotional responses to the environmental situation. In schizophrenic states there is often an inappropriate emotional response or there are discrepancies between the patient's ideas and the accompanying mood, with an indifferent or smiling reaction in the presence of ideas which would normally call forth a depressive, anxious, or distressed response, or there may be unmotivated laughter or crying. In hysterical individuals there may be a martyr-like smile in describing severe pain, and the patient may appear to be passive and unconcerned in spite of what are said to be agonizing symptoms. Of course a tendency toward nonchalance or bravado or a defense reaction in the presence of serious disease must be distinguished from true disharmony.

In certain organic diseases of the nervous system one may see variations in the personality and the affective responses. Patients with multiple sclerosis are frequently euphoric with lack of insight and indifference, although they show emotional lability. They seem unconcerned over the seriousness of their disabilities and are always hopeful, with an irrevelance between the prevailing mood and the amount of disability. In frontal lobe neoplasms there is often a silly, facetious behavior, with inappropriate joking and punning; there may be lack of inhibitions with unrestrained behavior and alterations between dullness or apathy, and excitement. Epileptics have been said to have a suspicious, irritable, demanding personality. In cerebral arteriosclerosis and the organic dementias there is a marked emotional lability, and this is seen to an excessive degree in pseudobulbar palsies where there often is precipitate crying or laughing which may appear to be unmotivated or may be brought on by a minimal stimulus.

CONTENT OF THOUGHT

In the review of the patient's mental trend and content of thought, his dominant attitudes and preoccupations are taken into consideration. Delusional ideas, obsessive trends, compulsive manifestations, hallucinatory phenomena, phobias, illusions, misinterpretations, fantasies, visions, feelings of familiarity (*déjà vu*), sensations of unreality or of depersonalization, grandiose or expansive ideas, and peculiar thoughts and experiences should be elicited, not only in psychotic states but also in organic and functional diseases of the nervous system. Anxieties or fears, hypochondriacal mechanisms, somatic delusions, ideas of sin or unworthiness, feelings of self-accusation or self-depreciation, persecutory trends, ideas of unreality or nihilism, sensations of remote control or outside influence, suicidal trends, or other abnormalities of the content of thought may be present. A review of the patient's problems, his story in full, his reason for requesting his examination at the time he has chosen, his attitude toward his illness and toward the physician, his relationship to himself and to others, his feelings toward the law, his thoughts in regard to his past conduct and his present situation, and his plans for the future are important. Special worries, recent deaths or disappointments, financial difficulties, or even small annoyances may be sources of concern. His aim in life and his goal ideal may give relevant information. Also, in this regard, information should be obtained relative to antisocial acts and tendencies, previous crimes and misdemeanors, and the general philosophic outlook of the patient.

Abnormalities of the content of thought are not as characteristic of organic as of functional nervous diseases, but hallucinations are encountered rather frequently in the former. Formed or unformed visual or auditory hallucinations may be encountered in focal brain disease. Visual, auditory, olfactory, or gustatory hallucinations may be experienced during the epileptic aura. Visual and auditory hallucinations may be symptoms of delirium and various toxic states. Olfactory and gustatory hallucinations are encountered in alcoholism, and tactile hallucinations in cocaine poisoning.

SENSORIUM AND INTELLECTUAL RESOURCES

Perhaps the most important part of the mental examination, from the organic neurologic point of view, is the review of the sensorium, mental grasp, and intellectual resources, including orientation, comprehension, insight, memory, judgment, reasoning power, general knowledge and information, and intellectual capacity. Inquiry into this field is essential in order to establish an estimate of the intellectual endowment and resources of the individual, both to appraise his innate abilities and to evaluate the changes that the disease process may have brought about. This is especially true in the organic cerebral disturbances, where a superficial review may reveal no apparent alterations, but a detailed examination may show evidences of severe changes in memory, judgment, reasoning power, and general knowledge. In a brief conversation the patient's stream of thought may appear to be logical and coherent, though slightly circumstantial; his responses may seem adequate and his memory and judgment may appear to be within the normal range. On detailed questioning, however, gross defects in memory, judgment, comprehension, and intelligence may be demonstrated. One must be tactful in this portion of the examination, however, in order to avoid calling the patient's deficiencies to his attention, and one must recall that in many conditions, especially instances of acute sensorial disturbance on a toxic basis, there may be a fluctuation in the degree of impairment, oftentimes with a diurnal or nocturnal variation. Furthermore, in psychic retardation associated with depressions, in confusion, and in aphasic states there may be apparent disturbances of the sensorium and intellectual responses which must be evaluated with care.

Sensorium: The appraisal of the sensorium has in part been mentioned under the review of the "State of Consciousness." A more complete appraisal is carried out at this time, noting orientation, personal identification, attention, comprehension, and grasp of total situations. These may all be impaired in certain focal or diffuse cerebral conditions, namely in brain tumors, vascular and degenerative diseases, senility, toxic and posttraumatic states, and encephalitis and other infections. Delirium and lowering of the state of consciousness may be characterized by clouding of the sensorium, loss of orientation and personal identification, flagging of attention, and lack of comprehension and insight.

Orientation: The patient should be tested for orientation with reference to time, place, and person. He is asked the time of day, the date, the day of the week, the month, the year, the season; the name of the city in which the examination is being carried out, the building, the type of building, the street; the identity of the examiner and of other physicians, nurses, patients, and relatives.

Personal Identification: In testing the personal identification one observes the patient's ability to give relevant data concerning his name, age, residence, the duration of his illness, the length of time he has been in the hospital, and the date and place of birth, and to tell other historical facts about residence, employment, marriage, and family.

Attention: The patient's attention and his ability to maintain it and his interest and capacity to concentrate are worthy of observation. In pathologic states there may be distractibility, flagging or wandering of attention, abstraction, lowering of consciousness, confusion, lethargy, and negativism. In *Bourdon's test* for attention the patient is instructed to strike out or underline certain letters on a printed page, and his speed and accuracy are noted. In other methods of testing the examiner may recite a series of digits and ask the patient to tap his finger every time a specific one is repeated, or read a story and ask the patient to repeat it. In the tachistoscopic examination a group of objects or figures are shown to the patient for a fraction of a second, and he is then asked to recall them; this tests attention and also memory and speed of responses. There may be fluctuation in the attention threshold with flightiness and shifting of powers of observation; there may be absentmindedness and loss of ability to concentrate. Apparent changes in attention may be associated with fatigue, a prolonged reaction time, or a slow, wandering stream of speech.

Comprehension: Comprehension is the ability of the individual to perceive, correctly interpret, and understand the meaning of visual, auditory, and other sensory stimuli, together with his interpretation and *grasp of the total situation*. Comprehension, perception, attention, reasoning power, and volitional functions are all complex factors, and they also contribute to other mental functions, such as memory, judgment, general knowledge, and intelligence, which are mentioned in following paragraphs. Loss of ability to appreciate or interpret certain specific types of sensory stimuli will be discussed in more detail in the section on "Aphasia, Agnosia, and Apraxia" (Chapter 53).

Insight: Comprehension and grasp of the total situation are revealed in a different manner in evaluating the patient's insight, or his understanding of and attitude toward the general nature, cause, and implications of his illness or problems. The patient should demonstrate, either spontaneously or in response to simple questions, this understanding, or lack of it. The most important practical aspects of insight are ability to accept competent professional interpretation and advice regarding treatment, and capability to plan for the future. One should determine whether the patient realizes that he is suffering from physical or mental symptoms, is aware of the presence of difficulties in memory and judgment, and appreciates that he needs treatment, or is indifferent to such symptoms and changes; whether he realizes that the difficulties are within himself, or ascribes them to external causes. If there is an apparent loss of insight, one should decide whether this is a true deficiency, an inappropriate emotional response such as facetiousness or euphoria which masks the insight, or an attempt by the patient to hide his difficulties in order to save embarrassment to himself or his family.

Memory: The term memory is used as a generality to include various factors in the recall of the past experiences. Memory is dependent on specific physiologic and psychologic processes which extend between the perception of a stimulus and its recall or reproduction. The perception itself is dependent upon, among other factors, attention, emotional state, and the content and strength of the stimuli. Recall and reproduction are evidences of the patient's ability to bring the engram to consciousness and to express it verbally. Clinically a differentiation is made between *remote memory, recent memory,* and *registration, retention, and immediate recall.*

Memory should first be tested by asking the patient a few general questions—whether he has noticed loss of memory, either recent or remote; whether he has had difficulty in concentrating, been absent-minded, made mistakes in calculation, or errors in his work. Significant defects in the patient's account of his illness, such as errors and discrepancies in dates and the sequence of events, memory gaps and inconsistencies, and failure to remember important facts or symptoms should be noted. If memory difficulty is present, one should determine whether this is due to an actual loss of memory or to failure to grasp the immediate total situation, and whether it is of recent onset or a manifestation of a native intellectual defect.

In testing *remote memory* one can obtain pertinent information from a review of the chronologic events in the life history—the date and place of birth; present age; places of residence with dates; age at the beginning and stopping of school; grade at which school was stopped; employment history, including wages earned and names of employers; date of marriage and age at the time of marriage; names, dates of birth, and ages of children; history of serious illnesses, with dates. Any discrepancies, such as between date of birth and age, or time of stopping school and age, should be noted. One also tests remote memory by noting the patient's ability to repeat the alphabet, the Lord's prayer, or nursery rhymes or songs. General information, such as the names of the presidents of the United States given in reverse order, dates of the presidents or of important wars, or other significant historical data or facts from the patient's own experiences may be relevant.

To test *recent memory* one may ask the patient his residence (with the street and number), the length of time he has been in the hospital, what he has done in the recent past, or what he has had for his recent meals. He may be asked when he came to the hospital, how he came and with whom, the names of the doctors and nurses, the events of the previous day or of a week ago. Historical data regarding the present illness may also give information in the realm of recent memory. The questions to determine both remote and recent memory may have to be modified to suit the particular situation, and in many instances the review of the patient's complaints, his present illness, and his general background will give the essential information. When testing remote and recent memory by asking the patient questions about his life history and recent experiences, it is assumed that the examiner has the necessary information available or can verify the patient's answers.

Registration, retention, and immediate recall may be tested in a variety of ways. The patient may be given a name, an address, a color, an object, or the time of day, and asked to recall this after three minutes, five minutes, one hour, or one day. The examiner may recite a series of digits at the rate of one per second without rhythmic spacing, and ask the patient to repeat them. An individual of normal intelligence and without memory impairment should be able to repeat seven or even eight digits forward, and should be able to return six digits in reverse order. A normal individual should also be able to repeat a sentence of twenty-eight to thirty syllables without error. One that is commonly used is the Babcock sentence: "One thing a nation must have to become rich and great is a large secure supply of wood." Other tests for retention and immediate recall include giving the patient complicated commands that he is asked to carry out; reciting a series of words that the patient is asked to repeat; reading a short story and asking the patient to give the salient details; having the patient look at a group of objects placed on a table, and then name as many as possible from memory. He may be presented with a series of pairs of words, asked to fix them in his mind, and then respond with one of them every time the examiner mentions the other.

It must be borne in mind, in testing memory, that the ability to retain and recall are not isolated functions but are a part of general cerebral function. In states of lethargy, fatigue, confusion, or lowering of the consciousness there may be impairment of memory; this is, of course, diagnostically significant, but an indication of a general rather than a specific defect. Lack of comprehension or attention will cause defects in memory, especially in registration, retention, and immediate recall, but also in remote memory. In the affective disorders there may be a memory defect, especially in depressed states; the difficulty is in part secondary to lowering of the emotional status and in part due to slowing of intellectual responses. Impairment of memory is one of the outstanding manifestations of intellectual deficiency, and one must be cautious in diagnosing a memory defect in mentally retarded persons.

Defects in memory are especially important in many types of disease of the nervous system. The variety of memory that is lost may have a special clinical significance. Registration, retention, and immediate recall, for instance, may be severely impaired in the organic psychoses, the so-called organic brain syndromes, while the remote memory may seemingly be intact, even remarkably keen. The patient may be able to recall without difficulty dates and events of the distant past, and yet he may have a gross disturbance of recent memory and of retention and immediate recall. A defect in *registration* is found in the acute organic reaction types, such as the toxic deliriums, but also in manic states and in hysteria; the difficulty is largely due to inattention. A defect in *retention* is characteristic of the organic cerebral disturbances in general, namely, the organic psychoses, dementia paralytica, Pick's disease, Alzheimer's disease, senile dementia, and frontal lobe lesions. There may be a defect in *recall* in the various organic cerebral syndromes, in trauma, in the bizarre disturbances such as Korsakoff's psychosis and Ganser's syndrome, in epilepsy, and also in hysteria.

In amnesic states there may be a gap of memory or a loss of memory for a circumscribed period of time or for specific life situations without loss of orientation for the immediate environment. In posttraumatic syndromes and certain epileptic disorders there may be amnesia, both for the period of loss of consciousness and of an anterograde and/or retrograde type. In certain conditions, as in Korsakoff's psychosis, there is a tendency to minimize the difficulty by resorting to evasions or generalities or by filling in the gaps of memory by confabulation or the use of fabricated material. Similar confabulation may also be evident following cerebral trauma and in patients with subarachnoid hemorrhage. In Ganser's syndrome there is loss of orientation with evasion and approximately accurate but consistently inaccurate replies; this is usually of hysterical origin.

Judgment and Reasoning Power: An appraisal of judgment and reasoning power may be made during the process of taking the history and carrying out the mental tests. The history of indifference, change in personality, errors in judgment, loss of restraint, failure to observe the rules of social and ethical conduct, carelessness in habits or dress and personal hygiene, discrepancies in conduct, and sexual promiscuity may give relevant information. The attitude toward social, financial, domestic, and ethical problems is important. One may test judgment by asking the patient how he would conduct himself in certain social situations. Reasoning power is briefly appraised by asking the patient to define or differentiate abstract terms, such as to differentiate between a lie and a mistake, or between misery and poverty, and to detect absurdities. He may be asked to interpret proverbs. One may inquire, for instance, "What is the meaning of 'A rolling stone gathers no moss,' or 'A stitch in time saves nine'?" It is needless to say that the interpretation should never be made by using the same words that appear in the proverb. Other tests of judgment and reasoning power are carried out in the psychometric examination.

General Knowledge and Information: It is often desirable to investigate the patient's ability to reproduce what he has learned at school, and to test his range of general information and his grasp of current events. The examination should, of course, be made with due regard to the nationality, place of birth, educational level, and general experiences of the individual. He may be asked simple questions in the fields of history, geography, and general science: names and political parties of the president, governor, and mayor; names and dates of recent presidents; dates of recent wars; important events taking place in the world; incidents from current newspapers; national holidays and why they are celebrated; names and population of the larger cities of the state or nation; names of the oceans, rivers, or Great Lakes; capitals of foreign countries; differences between a cable and a chain; metals that are attracted by a magnet; uses of electricity. Many other or different questions may be asked if the occasion demands.

Counting and Calculation: Ability to count and calculate may be evaluated by means of simple tests. The patient may be asked to count forward or backward; to count coins; to make change; to carry out simple addition, subtraction, multiplication, and division. He may be asked to subtract successive sevens from one hundred —a test with which deteriorated individuals frequently have difficulty. He may be asked to solve simple problems: "If three apples can be bought for five cents, how many can be bought for a quarter?" "Given a three-pint vessel and a five-pint vessel, how can one measure out seven pints of water?" "If cloth is fifteen cents a yard, how much would seven feet of cloth cost?" "If one's salary is twenty dollars a week and he spends fourteen dollars each week, how long will it take to save three hundred dollars?" "If one is given fifty cents to spend and one buys individual items for ten, nine, and twelve cents, how much change would be left?" These simpler tests should be used on adults only if there is definite evidence of failure to pass the usual "adult level" examinations.

Reading and Writing: The patient's reading and his ability to recall what he has read, and his capacity to write spontaneously, from dictation, and by copying may also be reviewed. These faculties are investigated more completely in appraising the aphasic states.

Intellectual Capacity: An appraisal of the patient's intellectual level, or capacity, may be an extremely important part of the neurologic examination. It may not only be of assistance in the diagnosis of the disease process, but it may also be of aid in judging the patient as a whole, in formulating some plan for therapy, and in determining the prognosis. A rough estimate of the patient's intelligence should be made in every case, but one must take into consideration, of course, his educational and professional level, his past experiences, and his opportunities for intellectual and social development. The vocabulary of the individual and his general choice of words should be noted. The intellectual level of the subject may be judged to a considerable extent by the results of the preceding parts of the examination—such as the appraisal of memory, judgment, general knowledge, and calculation. Some evaluation of the intelligence may be made on the basis of the school achievement record—the highest grade reached, the age at leaving school, and the number of grades failed. The patient who stopped school in the fifth grade at the age of 16 is obviously retarded unless, of course, he missed school because of illness or because of economic or geographic difficulties. One must also note the language factor in judging intelligence, for an individual born in a foreign country or brought up in a foreign-speaking community in this country may have marked difficulty in responding to the testing. On the other hand, the failure to learn the English language may indicate either a subnormal intelligence or a poor adaptability. Halstead has postulated the concept of "biological intelligence" in contrast to psychometric intelligence; he believes that the latter, widely used in educational and clinical investigations, is a poor criterion of operational intelligence, and states that the results of a battery of special examinations give more accurate information regarding the biologically determined, adaptive behavior of the individual and of that aspect of intelligence which is necessary and usable in adjusting to the environment.

In many instances it is extremely valuable to have a quantitative evaluation of the individual's intelligence rating. There are many psychometric tests which are helpful. These may be used to determine the various grades of mental deficiency; to differentiate between educational attainment, acquired knowledge, and native intelligence; to evaluate memory loss and intellectual deterioration; to give corroborative evidence of organic nervous system disease; to differentiate between mental deficiency, intellectual deterioration secondary to some pathologic process, hysterical amnesia, and certain psychotic states; to determine the patient's actual and potential abilities for rehabilitation. They require, however, special technics which fall in the realm of the clinical psychologist. Perhaps the best known of these is the *Binet-Simon test* as modified by Terman, Kuhlmann, and others. In the *Terman* modification of the Stanford-Binet scale, intelligence can be tested from the mental age of 2 through the superior adult level, and printed blanks can be obtained for recording replies to oral questions. The intelligence quotient (I.Q.), an arbitrary statement of intellectual capacity, is obtained by dividing the mental age (M.A.) by the chronologic age (C.A.), providing the latter is not greater than 15 years. In adults 15 years is taken as the chronologic age. The intelligence quotient of the normal or average adult should range between 90 and 110. Readings between 80 and 90 indicate a dull average intelligence, 70 to 80 is considered borderline, and below 70 is considered feeblemindedness. A reading from 50 to 70 indicates a moron classification, 25 to 50, an imbecile rating, and below 25, idiocy. On the other hand, 110 to 120 indicates a superior intellectual level, 120 to 140, very superior, and 140 or more is termed "near genius." The *Wechsler adult intelligence scale* consists of verbal tests (information, comprehension, digit span, arithmetic, similarities, and vocabulary) and performance tests (picture arrangement, picture completion, block design, object assembly, and digit symbol) which are separately and compositely standardized. In the very young the *Kuhlmann* modification of the Binet-Simon test or the *Wechsler intelligence scale for children* may be used, and in those of low intelligence, the Vineland social maturity scale. In certain instances group tests may be given, or abbreviated examinations such as the Kent emergency test. In examining patients who are unable to read or write one may make use of performance tests such as the Pintner-Paterson performance scale, the Kohs block design test, the Porteus maze test, the Goddard form board, the Grace Arthur point scale, the Ferguson form boards, and the Healey picture completion tests.

If it is not necessary or feasible to have a detailed psychometric examination carried out by a psychologist, the clinician evaluates the patient's intelligence by asking a few selected questions from the Binet-Simon or related tests. In this manner memory, calculation, general knowledge, reading, writing, and vocabulary are further tested, and abstract reasoning power, judgment, and comprehension are appraised. One may start with the 10-year level, if the patient is an adult, asking him to repeat six digits or a sentence of twenty-two syllables. He is given a short paragraph to read and is asked to repeat it. He is told to use three words, such as boy, ball, and river, or work, money, and men, in constructing a sentence. He is asked to draw designs from memory. His judgment and comprehension are tested by his response to such questions as: "What ought you to say when someone asks your opinion about a person you don't know very well?" "What ought you to do before undertaking something very important?" "Why should we judge a person more by his actions than by his words?" On the 12-year level he may be asked to repeat five digits backwards, and to define abstract words such as pity, revenge, charity, envy, justice. He should be able to give the similarities between such things as snake, cow, and sparrow; book, teacher, and newspaper; wool, cotton, and leather. His judgment is tested by his ability to interpret fables or proverbs and to detect absurdities. On the 14-year level he is asked to give three differences between a king and a president, and to state the time if the hands of the clock are reversed. He should be able to repeat seven digits forwards. On the average adult level he should be able to repeat six digits backwards; to repeat a sentence of twenty-eight syllables; to give the differences between abstract words such as laziness and idleness, evolution and revolution, poverty and misery, character and reputation. In children and in older individuals with deterioration or low native intelligence the questions asked will have to be from the lower levels of the scale.

Other Psychologic Tests: Many other psychologic tests might be mentioned. These are rarely used as a part of the neurologic examination, but are more important as special modifications of the psychologic or psychiatric evaluation of the patient. Under special circumstances they may add relevant information to the neurologic appraisal, and should be used if indicated. They are usually carried out by the clinical psychologist. Among these ancillary procedures are the various performance tests mentioned on page 49, and some of the Army tests designed for use with illiterates or those with language difficulties. The Babcock and Shipley-Hartford Retreat tests will be discussed below. The personality inventory of Bernreuter, the Minnesota multiphasic personality inventory, and the Cornell selectee index are designed to elicit predominant personality traits. Word-association tests show the patient's ideational content and may give some clue to his emotional status and the psychodynamics of certain disorders. The Rorschach test is especially valuable in demonstrating personality patterns and in the diagnosis of psychotic states, but it may also aid in the evaluation of organic cerebral disease and intracranial pathologic states. Ten inkblots are presented sequentically to the patient, and he is asked to tell what they represent to him. Responses are analyzed in a variety of ways, but the most important criteria are the character of the form perception, the impression of movement, and the shading and color characteristics. The thematic apperception test is a projective test of personality and psychodynamics. The Bender visual-motor gestalt test is especially valuable in the psychoneuroses and the psychoses, but may also be used in organic cerebral disease. Visual-motor organization is determined by judging the patient's ability to copy seriatim ten geometric figures of varying difficulty. Other tests include the Kent-Rosanoff tests for attention, the Goldstein-Scheerer battery of tests, the Hunt-Minnesota test for visual and auditory learning, the Stanford achievement tests for reading and arithmetic, the Haufmann-Kasanin test, sorting tests including the Vigotsky, sentence completion tests, Knox cube test, the Kuder and Cleeton interest inventories, motor performance tests including the Detroit motor speed determination, language evaluations, Robinson deliberation test, Goodenough drawing test, and various aptitude and vocational tests. On many occasions it is desirable to use a battery of psychologic tests for a complete evaluation.

THE MENTAL EXAMINATION IN ORGANIC CEREBRAL DISEASE

As has been stated above, changes in the mental status may occur in focal or in diffuse cerebral disease. There may be lowering or clouding of consciousness, abnormalities in the stream of mental activity and character of the thinking processes, variations in the affective responses and lability of emotions, hallucinatory phenomena and other abnormalities of the content of thought, confusion, disorientation, loss of attention, disorganization in visual perception, and a defect in sustained thinking and in organization of familiar material. The most characteristic changes, however, and those which can best be demonstrated objectively, are those in memory, reasoning power, planning, judgment, and intellectual capacity.

The *deterioration of intellectual processes* that occurs in certain cerebral diseases, senility, toxic and degenerative states, etc., is characterized, early in its course, by loss of certain intellectual functions and preservation of others. As mentioned above, recent memory and retention and immediate recall are lost before remote memory is affected. Old mental habits and rote memory may be retained, while planning and reasoning are affected. Judgment and comprehension may be lost very early. A person's vocabulary tends to remain relatively constant throughout adult life, and even after the onset of cerebral disease the vocabulary may be used as an index of the original level of intellectual attainment. Certain changes may be evident in the psychometric examination, which may show a "patchy" or "scattered" response with failures over a wide range. The Wechsler adult intelligence scale is helpful in determining the presence of intellectual deterioration, especially as distinguished from mental deficiency, in differentiating between psychoses with or without deterioration, and often in differentiating between organic and hysterical mental defects. Vocabulary, information, comprehension, and the ability to carry out object assembly and picture completion tests persist with age and in the presence of organic cerebral disease, whereas there is a loss of arithmetical reasoning, digit retention, appreciation of similarities, and relational thinking as shown in the digit symbol, picture arrangement, and block design tests. The Babcock test for the efficiency of mental functioning demonstrates that in organic cerebral disease the vocabulary remains relatively unaffected, while other performances are impaired. The Shipley-Hartford Retreat test seems to detect in a reasonably accurate manner degrees of intellectual impairment in individuals of normal original intelligence. The scale consists of two parts—a vocabulary test and an abstract thinking test. The degree of disparity between the vocabulary and the abstract (conceptual) thinking levels measures the deterioration, and is expressed as the conceptual quotient (C.Q.), the ratio of the individual's abstract thinking age to that of a normal individual with the same vocabulary score. A conceptual quotient of over 90 can be regarded as normal; one between 80 and 90 as borderline; one between 70 and 80 as doubtful, and one below 70 as pathologic. Two other special technics, the spiral aftereffect and the memory for designs tests, have been shown to be of value in the diagnosis of cortical brain impairment.

Occasionally the Rorschach test is used in the evaluation of organic cerebral disease, intracranial pathology, and posttraumatic states. There is a low number of responses due to paucity of associations, with a prolonged reaction time occasioned by perceptual difficulties, and a high percentage of pure form responses. The response to the entire test is poorly organized and shows perseveration, perplexity, weakened critical capacity, and inability to deal with objective reality. The other so-called projective technics, including the thematic apperception test and the Bender visual-motor gestalt test, as well as the tachistoscopic examination, give important information in organic cerebral disease. The retardation and disorganization of visual perception is demonstrated by loss of ability to copy geometric figures or to reproduce them from memory, and by an increase of from four to ten times the time required to perceive simple forms in the tachistoscopic experiments. Defects in sustained and conceptual thinking and in organization of unfamiliar material are demonstrated in failures in interpretation of proverbs, detection of absurdities, notation of similarities, sorting of forms and colors, and reproduction of patterns. Many of these latter procedures must be analyzed by an experienced psychologist.

The changes that have been mentioned above are the most characteristic of diffuse brain dysfunction or of frontal lobe involvement. In the organic psychoses, dementia paralytica, Alzheimer's disease, Pick's disease, cerebral arteriosclerosis, and senility one sees the changes in intellectual function just described. There is loss of memory and judgment, which may lead to impairment of ability in which the level of function is below that required to carry on social relations and business affairs. The ability to perceive abstract relationships is lost before the simple, well-organized actions; the individual may be able to do ordinary things, but he is incapable of dealing with new problems, even though they may be within the scope or range usually handled by a person of his age and education. Tasks attempted are solved in a roundabout manner; the most difficult to perform are those requiring the subject to break away from old mental habits and adapt to unfamiliar situations. Initiative and decision are lacking. The time and rate of reactions are lengthened; the patient fatigues rapidly. As the condition progresses there is lack of inhibitions, with facetiousness and unrestrained behavior. There may be marked emotional lability. The patient may fail to link immediate impressions with past experiences, and this leads to confusion and disorientation. The above changes may cause the patient to be suspicious of others, and even to have paranoid ideas. Impatience and irritability are common symptoms, and carelessness about personal appearance and dress are often evident. There may be a fluctuating level of awareness with periodic lowering of consciousness and confusion; this latter most often occurs at night. The intravenous administration of amobarbital sodium (Sodium Amytal) has been used as a diagnostic test for the presence of organic brain disease. Patients who show no specific mental abnormality on routine examination may develop patterns of disorientation for time, place, and person, and denial of illness following the administration of this drug.

In conditions in which the pathologic process is limited to the frontal lobes, irritability, confusion, and lack of restraint may be more pronounced. In frontal lobe tumors there is often indifference and apathy, or there may be facetiousness and *witzelsucht*. Toxic states, either due to exogenous toxins such as bromides, barbiturates, or alcohol, or associated with febrile illnesses, may lead to hallucinatory experiences, principally in the visual and auditory spheres, along with confusion and disorientation. In trauma the period of loss of memory may be more extensive than the period of loss of consciousness, and the amnesia often extends in a retrograde direction. With improvement, however, there is a gradual lessening of the amnesic span.

The mental appraisal may constitute the most important part of the neurologic examination in the diagnosis of so-called brain damaged children. Such patients often show marked distractibility, poor attention span, overactivity, aggressiveness, destructive behavior, negativism, failure to respond to reprimand or chastisement, and absence of fear. In addition to these readily apparent abnormalities, specific testing may show perceptual difficulties, disabilities of speech and reading, and poor motor coordination.

A detailed mental evaluation and psychologic examination, often with a battery of tests and the use of both objective and projective technics, may be not only helpful but also essential in neurologic diagnosis. Such procedures are important in both focal and diffuse cerebral disease, and may provide essential data regarding the localization of the disease process as well as in the diagnosis of the underlying disorder.

REFERENCES

BECK, S. J. Rorschach's Test (ed. 3). New York, Grune & Stratton, Inc., 1961.

BENDER, LAURETTA. A Visual Motor Gestalt Test and Its Clinical Use. New York, American Orthopsychiatric Association, 1938.

BURGEMEISTER, B. B. Psychological Techniques in Neurological Diagnosis. New York, Hoeber Medical Division, Harper & Row, 1962.

CHENEY, C. O. Outlines for Psychiatric Examinations. Utica, State Hospital Press, 1934.

FISCHER, J., and GONDA, T. A. Neurologic technique and Rorschach test in detecting brain pathology. A. M. A. Arch. Neurol. & Psychiat. 74:117, 1955.

GARRETT, E. S., PRICE, A. C., and DEABLER, H. L. Diagnostic testing for cortical brain impairment. A. M. A. Arch. Neurol. & Psychiat. 77:223, 1957.

GOLDSTEIN, K. Aftereffects of Brain Injuries in War: Their Evaluation and Treatment. New York, Grune & Stratton, Inc., 1942.

GOODENOUGH, F. L. Mental Testing: Its History, Principles and Applications. New York, Rinehart & Company, 1949.

HALSTEAD, W. C. Brain and Intelligence: A Quantitative Study of the Frontal Lobes. Chicago, University of Chicago Press, 1947.

HARROWER, M. R. (ed.). Recent Advances in Diagnostic Psychological Testing. Springfield, Ill., Charles C Thomas, 1950.

HOEDEMAKER, E. D., and MURRAY, M. E. M. Psychologic tests in the diagnosis of organic brain disease. Neurology 2:144, 1952.

KAMMAN, G. R., and KRAM, C. Value of psychometric examination in medical diagnosis and treatment. J.A.M.A. 158:555, 1955.

KLEIN, R., and MAYER-GROSS, W. The Clinical Examination of Patients with Organic Cerebral Disease. Springfield, Ill., Charles C Thomas, 1957.

KUHLMANN, F. Tests of Mental Development. Minneapolis, Educational Publications, Inc., 1939.

McFIE, J. Psychological testing in clinical neurology, J. Nerv. & Ment. Dis 131:383, 1960.

RAPAPORT, D., GILL, M., and SCHAFER, R. Diagnostic Psychological Testing: The Theory, Statistical Evaluation, and Diagnostic Application of a Battery of Tests. Chicago, Year Book Publishers, Inc., 1946.

SHIPLEY, W. C. A self-administering scale for measuring intellectual impairment and deterioration. J. Psychol. 9:371, 1940.

SPREEN, O., and BENTON, A. L. Comparative studies of some psychological tests for cerebral damage. J. Nerv. & Ment. Dis. 140:323, 1965.

TAYLOR, E. M. Psychological Appraisal of Children with Cerebral Defects. Cambridge, Mass., Harvard University Press, 1959.

TERMAN, L. M., and MERRILL, M. A. Measuring Intelligence: A Guide to the Administration of the New Revised Stanford-Binet Tests of Intelligence. Boston, Houghton Mifflin Co., 1937.

WECHSLER, D. The measurement of Adult Intelligence (ed. 3). Baltimore, Williams & Wilkins Company, 1944.

WECHSLER, D.   "Psychological Diagnosis," in WECHSLER, I. S., Clinical Neurology (ed. 9). Philadelphia, W. B. Saunders Company, 1963.

WECHSLER, H., GROSSER, G. H., and BUSFIELD, B. L., JR. The depression rating scale. *Arch. Gen. Psychiat.* 9:334, 1963.

WILLIAMS, H. L.   "Psychological Testing," in BAKER, A. B. (ed.),   Clinical Neurology (ed. 2). New York, Hoeber Medical Division, Harper & Row, 1962, vol. 1, pp. 389–406.

ZANGWILL, O. L.   Clinical tests of memory impairment.   *Proc. Roy. Soc. Med.* 36:576, 1943.

PART TWO

The Sensory System

THE SENSORY SYSTEM

THE SENSORY SYSTEM places the individual in relationship with his environment. Every sensation depends upon impulses which are excited by adequate stimulation of the receptors, or end organs. These impulses are carried to the cerebrospinal axis by means of afferent, or sensory, nerves, and are then conveyed through fiber tracts to higher centers for conscious recognition. The different types of sensation are classified below. In the present part only the general modalities of sensation are considered; special senses, such as olfaction, vision, gustation, audition, and vestibular sensation, will be discussed with the cranial nerves which mediate them.

Receptors of various types are situated in the skin, subcutaneous tissues, muscles, tendons, periosteum, and visceral structures. They are specific for individual sensibilities. Each responds only to certain stimuli, and each gives rise to impulses which underlie but one variety of sensation. The impulses are carried by individual types of nerve fibers to ganglia which are situated just outside the cerebrospinal axis, and thence into the central nervous system. After a synapse or a series of synapses, the impulses ascend particular fiber tracts and reach the central sensory areas.

Abnormalities of sensation may be characterized by increase, perversion, impairment, or loss of feeling. *Increase in sensation* is usually manifested by *pain*—an unpleasant or disagreeable feeling that results from stimulation, sometimes excessive, of certain sense organs, fibers, or tracts. It may be a result of a stimulus that partially injures the sense organs, and thus may act to make the patient aware of and to protect him from noxious stimuli. The severity of pain depends upon a number of factors: the tissues affected; the duration, extent, and quality of the stimulus; the personality of the individual and his powers of discrimination. Pain may be accompanied by a feeling, or emotional state, as well as by other reactions of a physical nature, so that the entire pain experience is apt to be complex in nature. Oftentimes the patients' description of the symptom is the sole guide to its character and severity. *Perversions of sensation* take the form of *paresthesias, dysesthesias, and phantom sensations.* Some of these are associated with irritation of receptors, fibers, or tracts, whereas others are release phenomena. *Impairment and loss of feeling* result from lessening of the acuity of the sense organs, decrease in the conductivity of the fibers or tracts, or dysfunction of higher centers with consequent decrease in powers of recognition or of perception.

The sensory examination is carried out in an attempt to discover whether areas of absent, decreased, exaggerated, perverted, or delayed sensation are present. One should determine the quality and type of sensation that is affected, the quantity and degree of involvement, and the localization of the change. There may be any of the following: loss, decrease, or increase of one or of all types of sensation; dissociation of sensation with loss of one type but not of others; loss in ability to recognize differences in degrees of sensation; misinterpretations or perversions of sensation; areas of localized tenderness or hyperesthesia. More than one of these may occur simultaneously. The presence of trophic changes, especially painless ulcers and blisters, is also an indication for careful sensory testing.

Before starting the investigation, the examiner should determine whether the patient is aware of subjective changes in sensation or is experiencing spontaneous sensations of an abnormal type. One should ask the patient whether he notices pain, paresthesias, or loss of feeling; whether any part of the body feels numb, dead, hot, or cold; whether he has observed phenomena such as tingling, burning, itching, "pins and needles," pressure, distension, formication, feeling of weight or constriction, girdle sensations, perceptions of absence of portions of the body, or "phantom limb" manifestations. If such abnormalities are present, the examiner should attempt to determine their type and character, intensity, exact distribution, duration, and periodicity, as well as factors that accentuate and decrease them. Subjective pain should be differentiated from tenderness, which is pain on touch or pressure. It should be recalled that pain and numbness may exist together, as they do in the thalamic syndrome and in the neuritides. The manner of description of the pain or sensory disturbance and the associated affective responses, the nature of the terms used, the localization, and the precipitating and relieving factors may aid in differentiating between organic and psychogenic disturbances. Psychogenic pains are often related with inappropriate affect (either excessive emotion or indifference), they are vague in character or location, the patient's reactions to them are not consistent with his disability, and relief may be obtained by nonorganic measures; on the other hand, even potent analgesics may fail to give control of symptoms.

REQUISITES OF A SATISFACTORY SENSORY EXAMINATION

It is advisable, in most instances, to perform the investigation of the sensory system early in the course of the neurologic examination. Although a simple procedure, it must be painstaking and accompanied by critical evaluation. Its results depend largely upon subjective responses, and the full co-operation of the patient is necessary if conclusions are to be accurate. One must record not only the presence or absence of sensation, but slight differences and gradations. Occasionally objective manifestations, such as withdrawal of the part stimulated, wincing, blinking, and changes in countenance, may aid in the delineation of areas of sensory change; pupillary dilatation, acceleration of the pulse, and perspiration may accompany painful stimulation. Keenness of perception and interpretation of stimuli differ in individuals, in various parts of the body, and in the same individual under different circumstances. The examination is most satisfactory if the subject is alert and his mind is keen. Fatigue causes faulty attention and slowing of the reaction time, and the findings are less reliable if the patient has become weary during the examination.

It should be stressed at the outset that the results of the sensory examination may at times seem unreliable and confusing. The process may be a tedious one, and the findings difficult to appraise. Consequently, care must be used in drawing conclusions. It may be necessary to postpone the sensory investigation to a subsequent time if the patient has become fatigued, or to repeat the test on consecutive days if consistent and satisfactory results are to be obtained. In fact, the examination should always be repeated at least once to confirm the findings. This part of the neurologic appraisal, more than any other, requires patience and detailed observation for reliable interpretation.

There are other requisites for a reliable sensory examination. The patient must understand the procedure and be ready and willing to co-operate. Its purpose and method should be explained to him in simple terms, so that he comprehends what is expected of him. He should be able to understand and interpret the questions and commands of the examiner. Patients differ in intelligence and in powers of description. The findings are difficult to evaluate in individuals of low intellectual endowment, with language difficulties, or with a clouded sensorium, but it may be necessary to carry out the examination in spite of these obstacles. Furthermore, the confidence of the patient must be obtained, for a suspicious or a fearful patient never responds satisfactorily. There are times when sensations must be appraised in semi-stuporous, aphasic, or comatose individuals, but in such cases one can only determine whether or not the patient reacts to painful stimuli in various parts of the body.

During the examination the patient should be warm, comfortable, and at ease. Satisfactory results cannot be achieved if he is in pain, shivering, fearful or confused, or distracted by sensations such as noise, hunger, or distention. The best results are obtained when the patient is lying comfortably in bed in a warm, quiet room. The areas under examination should be uncovered, but it is best to expose the various parts of the body as little as possible. If he is experiencing pain or discomfort, or if he has recently been given sedatives or narcotics, the examination should be postponed. It is desirable to have the eyes closed or the areas under examination shielded to eliminate distractions and to avoid misinterpretation of stimuli. Symmetrical areas of the body should be compared whenever possible. Since the presence of hair or of hyperhidrosis may interfere with the accuracy of the tests, it may be wise to shave or dry the part to be examined.

The examiner must remember that the simpler the mode of examination, the more satisfactory the conclusions will be. The subject should be asked to respond by telling the type of stimulus that he perceives, and its location. The examiner must be careful not to suggest responses. Sensory changes that are the result of suggestion are notoriously frequent in psychoneurotic individuals, but nonorganic changes can also be produced by suggestion in subjects who have organic disease. If the patient notices no subjective changes in sensation, the entire body can be tested rapidly, bearing in mind the major sensory nerve and segmental supply to the face, trunk, and extremities. If there are specific sensory symptoms (or motor symptoms such as atrophy, weakness, or ataxia), or if any areas of abnormality are found, the examination should be carried out in detail to determine the quality of sensation that is impaired and to delineate the areas of involvement. The changes demonstrated are marked on the skin with a skin pencil and then transferred to a chart and completely recorded (Fig. 4). If the changes are limited to the extremities or face, special charts of these portions of the body may be used. It is helpful in appraisal if areas of change in different sensory qualities, such as pain, tactile, and temperature, are indicated individually on the chart by horizontal, vertical, and diagonal lines. A notation should also be made on the chart about the patient's co-operation and intelligence as well as an estimate of the reliability of the examination.

TYPES OF SENSATION

Sensations may be classified into various categories. Anatomists differentiate between *somatic* and *visceral* sensations, with *general* and *special* varieties of each. Most of those that can be tested clinically, however, fall into the general somatic group. The terms *epicritic* and *protopathic* sensations were used by Head. By the former he meant the sensibility to stimulations which furnishes the means for making fine discriminations of touch and temperature in order to bring about clear appreciation of the nature of the contact and its localization. By the latter he meant

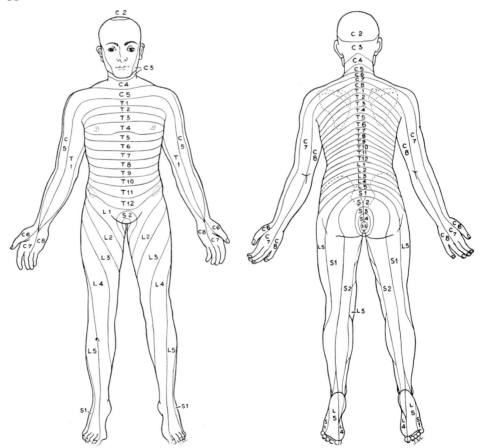

Fig. 4.   Sensory charts showing: *Left,* the anterior aspect of the body; *Right,* the posterior aspect of the body.

the sensibility to strong stimulations of temperature and pain; this is low in degree and poorly localized, and acts as a defensive agent against pathologic changes in the tissues. Others, including Edinger, Ariëns Kappers, and Brock have modified the terms used by Head, and have referred to *vital* and *gnostic* sensations. Included in the former group are such sensibilities as pain, temperature, and pressure, which are utilized in defense. The gnostic sensations are those of a discriminative or informative character, such as joint-position sense, vibration, touch, and two-point, weight, form, and texture discrimination. These terms do have a place in clinical neurology, but a more practical classification is that of Sherrington, who listed *exteroceptive, proprioceptive,* and *interoceptive* sensations, basing his types on the location of the end organs and the types of stimuli that they mediate. To these may be added the group of so-called *combined* sensations, or those which for their recognition require *cerebral function.*

The various sensations discussed below are herein regarded as specific modalities, with underlying anatomic and physiologic differences. Some recent observers, however, question such specificity and express the belief that sensation should be regarded as a pattern or gestalt. These investigators postulate that there is no separate anatomic mechanism in the receptors, nerve fibers, or neural pathways for individual types of sensation, and that different cutaneous sensations arise because variable stimuli affect the same set of end organs or conducting pathways in a different pattern, and not as a result of selective activation of specific receptors or fibers; the intensity and type of stimulus, threshold, discriminatory power, and possible "filtering properties" of cell groups in the sensory system may be important factors in the interpretation of stimuli. Most clinicians, however, feel that specificity of both receptors and conducting pathways cannot be discounted.

REFERENCES

ADRIAN, E. D.   The Basis of Sensation: The Action of the Sense Organs.   London, Christopher's, 1928.

DAVIS, H.   Some principles of sensory receptor action.   *Physiol. Rev.* 41:391, 1961.

HEAD, H.   Studies in Neurology.   London, Oxford University Press, 1920, vols. 1 and 2.

ROSE, J. E., and MOUNTCASTLE, V. B.   "Touch and Kinesthesis," in FIELD, J., MAGOUN, H. W., and HALL, V. E. (eds.), Handbook of Physiology. Washington, D.C., American Physiological Society, 1959, Vol. 1, pp. 387–429.

SCHILLER, F.   The cutaneous sensory modalities: A critique of their "specificity." *A. M. A. Arch. Neurol. & Psychiat.* 75:203, 1956.

SHERRINGTON, C. S.   The Integrative Action of the Nervous System.   New York, Charles Scribner's Sons, 1906.

SINCLAIR, D. C.   Cutaneous sensation and the doctrine of specific energy.   *Brain* 78:584, 1955.

WALL, P. D., and CRONLY-DILLON, J. R.   Pain, itch, and vibration. *Arch. Neurol.* 2:365, 1960.

WEDDELL, G., and MILLER, S.   Cutaneous sensibility.   *Ann. Rev. Physiol.* 24:199, 1962.

WEDDELL, G., TAYLOR, D. A., and WILLIAMS, C. M.   Studies on the innervation of skin. *J. Anat.* 89:317, 1955.

CHAPTER 5

THE EXTEROCEPTIVE SENSATIONS

THE EXTEROCEPTIVE SENSATIONS are those which arise from or originate in sense organs in the skin or mucous membranes and respond to external agents and changes in the environment. They may also be designated the *superficial,* or the *cutaneous and mucous membrane, varieties of sensation.* There are three major types: *pain, temperature* (hot and cold), and *tactile* (light touch).

SUPERFICIAL PAIN SENSATION

Impulses which carry superficial pain sensation arise in nociceptors, or free or branched endings, in the skin and mucous membranes. They travel along un-myelinated or thinly myelinated nerve fibers to the dorsal root ganglia, where the first cell body is situated. The impulses then traverse the lateral division of the dorsal root and enter the fasciculus dorsolateralis of the spinal cord, or Lissauer's tract (Fig. 5). They synapse on the stellate cells (substantia gelatinosa of Rolando) or the dorsal funicular cells (nucleus proprius cornu dorsalis) of the dorsal horn, or both, within one or two segments of their points of entry into the cord, and the neuraxes of the neurons of the next order cross the midline of the cord anterior to the centrol canal and ascend in the lateral spinothalamic tract (Fig. 6). Within this tract the fibers which transmit impulses from the lower portions of the body are lateral to, or nearer to the surface of the cord than, those from higher regions, and are dorsal to those from the upper portion of the body (Fig. 7). Hence the fibers which conduct impulses from the sacral areas lie near the anterior columns in the lumbar region, but in the cervical region, where the lateral spinothalamic tract occupies much of the ventrolateral portion of the cord, they are lateral to the ventral aspect of the pyramidal tracts. Here the fibers which conduct impulses from the sacral areas and lower extremities are dorsolateral; those conducting impulses from the arms are ventrolateral, and those conveying impulses from the cervical region are ventromedial. The cranial nerves which carry superficial pain sensation

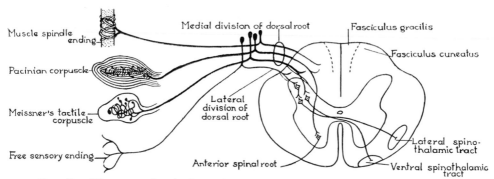

FIG. 5. Diagram of spinal cord and dorsal root showing the peripheral sense organs and the terminations of the impulses from these organs within spinal cord.

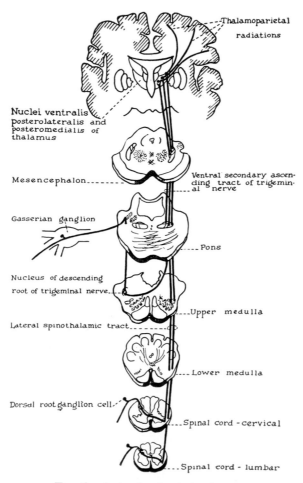

FIG. 6. Lateral spinothalamic tract.

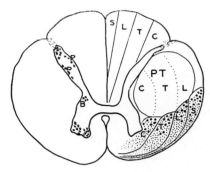

Fig. 7. The cell groups of dorsal horn and arrangement of spinothalamic and other tracts in cervical region of spinal cord. Heavy dots represent fibers concerned with temperature; medium-sized dots, fibers mediating pain; fine dots, fibers carrying tactile impulses. Symbols used: *A, B, P*—ganglion cells in dorsal horn; *C*—fibers from cervical segments of spinal cord; *L*—fibers from lumbar segments of spinal cord; *PT*—pyramidal tract; *S*—fibers from sacral segments of spinal cord; *T*—fibers from thoracic segments of spinal cord. (Walker, A. E.: *Arch. Neurol. & Psychiat.* 43:284, 1940.)

have ganglia corresponding to the dorsal root ganglia and pathways corresponding to the lateral spinothalamic tract. These are discussed in detail for the trigeminal, facial, glossopharyngeal, and vagus nerves.

The lateral spinothalamic tract is situated dorsolateral to the inferior olivary bodies in the medulla, near the periphery. In the pons it is lateral to the medial lemniscus and medial to the middle cerebellar peduncle. Within the mesencephalon it assumes a position dorsal to the medial lemniscus and it is again peripheral, just dorsolateral to the red nucleus. It passes through the colliculi and then, lying medial to the brachium of the inferior colliculus, it enters the diencephalon. Pain impulses carried through the trigeminal nerve ascend in the ventral secondary ascending tract of the trigeminal nerve, which is situated in close proximity to the lateral spinothalamic tract (Chapter 12). These two fasciculi terminate in the nuclei ventralis posterolateralis and posteromedialis of the thalamus. Here the fibers from the lower portion of the body are placed laterally and somewhat rostrally, those from the upper portion of the body are in an intermediate position, and those from the face are placed medially and caudally. The impulses are then transmitted to the most anterior portion of the parietal (somesthetic) cortex, on the posterior lip of the rolandic fissure, for conscious recognition. In the thalamoparietal radiations those fibers which carry sensation from the lower extremities are curved medially to the superior aspect of the surface of the medial longitudinal fissure; those from the upper portion of the body go to the midportion of the surface of the parietal lobe, whereas those from the face terminate laterally on the inferior portion of the postcentral gyrus (Fig. 8).

Pain end organs are found in the skin and mucous membranes of the entire body. They are in close proximity on the tongue, lips, genitalia, and finger tips, and in some of the fossae of the body, and they are farther apart on the upper arms, buttocks, and trunk. One fiber may innervate more than one end organ, but on the other hand each end organ may receive filaments from more than one nerve fiber. Two types of pain are described. *First,* or *fast,* pain is an initial discrete sharpness; it is bright and pricking in character. *Second pain* is slower and more diffuse; it is aching or burning in type and less accurately localized. The faster impulses may adjust the excitability of the synapses in preparation for the arrival of the later ones. The internuncial pool probably reinforces the pain impulses. Within the lateral spinothalamic tract decussation takes place more promptly in the cervical and lumbar areas, which supply the extremities, than in the sacral and thoracic areas. Some impulses may ascend without decussation, and others by means of a series of short synapses, probably in the gray matter. It has been suggested that the direct spinothalamic pathway, as described above, is responsible for that type of pain which is felt immediately, is sharply localized, and lasts only as long as the stimulus lasts, with a spinoreticulothalamic system responsible for more diffuse, less well-localized pain which has an appreciably slower conduction time to consciousness and which persists after withdrawal of the stimulus; these two pathways may run together to the level of the inferior olive, then separate and meet again in the thalamus.

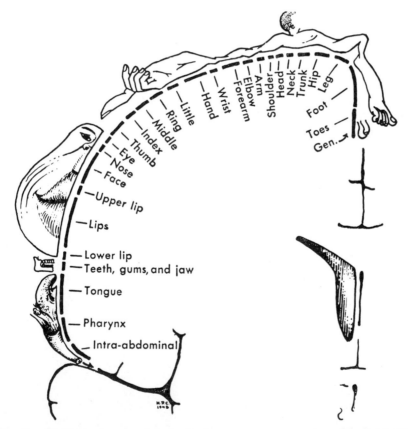

FIG. 8.   Homunculus showing cortical sensory representation. (Penfield, W., and Rasmussen, T.: The Cerebral Cortex of Man. New York, The Macmillan Company, 1950.)

Many methods of testing superficial pain sensation have been described. A large-headed pin may be placed in a small syringe; pressure can be exerted on the skin with the pin point to a degree that will raise the plunger the same distance with each stimulus. A common pin may be inserted throught the end of a wooden tongue blade, which is used as a lever. The intensity of the stimulus can be controlled mechanically by means of the Head spring algesimeter, in which the pressure is recorded by a sliding scale (Fig 9). The simplest method, and one as reliable as any, is to use a common pin. It is best to examine the patient with his eyes closed. He should not be asked, "Do you feel this?" or "Is this sharp?" Alternate stimulations should be made with the head and the point of the pin, and the patient instructed to reply "Sharp" or "Dull." He should also be asked about slight or relative differences in the intensity of the stimulus in different areas. This mode of examination, if carried out in a painstaking manner by an accurate observer, may be more satisfactory than one that involves the use of complicated instruments. Slight changes can sometimes be demonstrated in a co-operative patient by asking him to indicate the alterations in sensation when a nearly vertical pinpoint is stroked or drawn lightly over the skin. A tailor's marking wheel (Fig. 9) aids in the rapid delineation of areas of major change (Wartenberg). If the testing is done too rapidly, however, the area of subjective change may extend beyond the hypalgesic zone. Electrical stimulators and such instruments as the Hardy-Wolff-Goodell thermal dolorimeter are used experimentally in determining pain thresholds, but are not suitable to the routine sensory examination.

The latent time in the response to stimulation is eliminated and the delineation is most accurate if the examination is carried out by proceeding from areas of lesser sensitivity to those of greater sensitivity, rather than the reverse. That is, one should examine from areas of decreased sensation to those of normal sensation; if there is hyperalgesia, one should proceed from the normal to the hyperalgesic area. If the stimuli are applied in too close proximity and if they follow each other too

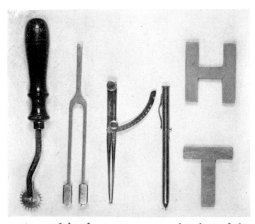

Fig. 9.   Instruments used in the sensory examination: *left to right,* tailor's marking wheel, tuning fork, Weber's compass, spring algesimeter, wooden letters.

quickly, there may be summation of impulses or, on the other hand, if conduction is delayed, the patient's response may refer to a previous stimulation. The terms *algesia* and *algesthesia* are used to indicate pain sensibility. In recording the response to pain stimulation, the terms *alganesthesia* and *analgesia* are used to designate areas insensitive to pain, *hypalgesia* for those having decreased sensitivity, and *hyperalgesia* for those showing increased sensitivity. *Itch* sensation is closely allied to pain; it is perceived by the same nerve endings and is absent following procedures carried out for the relief of pain.

TEMPERATURE SENSATION

There are two types of temperature sensation: *hot* and *cold*. Impulses which carry them may arise in special sensory endings in the skin (corpuscles of Ruffini and end-bulbs of Krause) or in "warm" and "cold" spots. The latter are more superficial and numerous, although the relationship between the density of the temperature sensitive spots varies in different parts of the body. Excess temperature, especially heat, stimulates free nerve endings, causing a sensation of pain. The conduction of temperature impulses from the endings in the skin to the parietal lobe is identical with that for superficial pain sensation. The impulses travel along unmyelinated or thinly myelinated fibers to the dorsal root ganglia, enter the fasciculus dorsolateralis through the lateral division of the dorsal root, synapse on the stellate or dorsal funicular cells or both within one or two segments of entry, decussate anterior to the central canal, and ascend in the lateral spinothalamic tract of the spinal cord (Fig. 6). There is evidence that the paths for pain and temperature are distinct within the tract, the temperature fibers lying dorsally and medially, but the two are so closely associated with so much overlapping that spinal cord injuries will ordinarily affect both of them; dissociation of them may, however, occur with such lesions.

Temperature sensations are tested by the use of test tubes containing cracked ice and hot water, or, better, by the use of cold or warm metal tubes or objects, since glass is a poor conductor. A beam of light, which does not indent the skin and stimulates a restricted area, is valuable in testing heat sensation. For quantitative evaluation one may use a thermophore, which is kept at a constant temperature by means of a rheostat, or an electric thermometer or thermophile. The patient is asked to respond by saying "Hot" or "Cold." For testing cold the stimuli should be from 41° to 50° F. (5° to 10° C.), and for warmth, from 104° to 113° F. (40° to 45° C.). Temperatures much lower or higher than these elicit responses of pain rather than of temperature. In almost every instance the absence of one variety of temperature sensation is accompanied by the absence of the other, but there may be occasional circumstances in which one is involved while the other remains partially intact; the cutaneous distribution of the absence of sensation of heat is usually larger than that of absence of cold. Changes in temperature sensibility are recorded by the terms *thermanesthesia, thermhypesthesia,* and *thermhyperesthesia,* modified by the adjectives *hot* and *cold.*

It may be valuable in investigative work not only to determine whether the patient is able to recognize hot and cold sensations, and what his threshold for these sensations is, but also to test his ability to differentiate between slight variations in temperature, both in the normal and intermediate ranges and in the more extreme degrees of hot and cold. A normal individual should be able to distinguish between stimuli differing from two to five degrees Centigrade in the middle ranges. Greater differences may be necessary in the extreme ranges. In the general examination, however, it is sufficient to determine whether the patient adequately differentiates hot and cold stimuli. Sometimes, following chordotomy or lesions at high levels, the patient perceives either cold or warm stimuli as warm; this is *isothermognosia*.

TACTILE SENSATION

Fibers which carry tactile, or light touch, sensation have their origin in specialized endings in the skin and mucous membrane. Fibers which carry general tactile sensibility, or *thigmesthesia,* have their receptors in the tactile disks of Merkel and around the hair follicles. Impulses travel through myelinated nerves to the dorsal root ganglia, and the axons enter the spinal cord through the medial divisions of the dorsal root and bifurcate into ascending and descending fibers (Fig. 5). These communicate with collaterals and within several segments of their point of entry synapse, and the axons of the neurons of the next order cross to the opposite ventral spinothalmic tract for ascent to the thalamus and thence to consciousness (Fig. 10). Fibers which carry discriminatory and localized tactile sensibility, or *topesthesia,* have as their receptors the corpuscles of Meissner in the hairless portions of the skin; they also enter the dorsal root ganglia through myelinated fibers. The axons enter the spinal cord through the medial division of the dorsal root and enter the ipsilateral fasciculi cuneatus and gracilis of the dorsal funiculus and ascend uncrossed and without synapse to the nuclei cuneatus and gracilis in the lower medulla, where they synapse, decussate as arcuate fibers, and ascend to the thalamus through the medial lemniscus. Tactile impulses carried through the trigeminal nerve ascend in the dorsal secondary ascending tract of the nerve, which is in close proximity to the ventral spinothalamic tract, as well as the ventral secondary ascending tract (Chapter 12). The distribution of the tactile impulses within the nuclei of the thalamus and their radiation to the parietal cortex follows in general that for pain and temperature impulses. Within the thalamus the tactile centers are placed somewhat caudal to those conveying pain, and in the parietal lobe they are posterior to centers for pain. Those fibers which ascend through the ventral spinothalamic tract transmit light touch and light pressure sensations, without accurate localization. The impulses which ascend uncrossed and without synapse in the dorsal funiculus are concerned with highly discriminatory and accurately localized tactile sensibility, including spatial and two-point discrimination. Because there is some overlap and duplication of function, and because of the multisynaptic pathways for general tactile sensation, tactile sensibility is the least apt to be completely abolished with lesions of the spinal cord, and disturbances of it may fail to give localizing information.

Sensations of roughness, tickling, and scraping, although essentially tactile, are

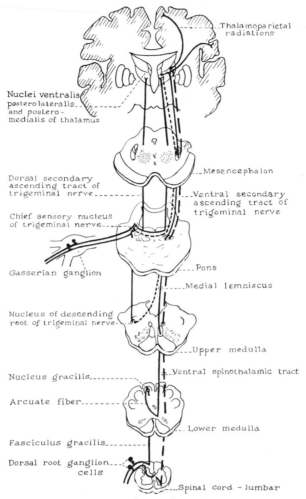

Thalamoparietal radiations

Nuclei ventralis posterolateralis and postero- medialis of thalamus

Mesencephalon

Dorsal secondary ascending tract of trigeminal nerve

Ventral secondary ascending tract of trigeminal nerve

Chief sensory nucleus of trigeminal nerve

Gasserian ganglion

Pons

Medial lemniscus

Nucleus of descending root of trigeminal nerve

Upper medulla

Nucleus gracilis

Ventral spinothalamic tract

Arcuate fiber

Lower medulla

Fasciculus gracilis

Dorsal root ganglion cells

Spinal cord - lumbar

FIG. 10. The tactile pathways.

probably not simple sensations but a combination of sensory qualities regarded as a perception rather than a sensation. Itching has been thought to be more clearly related to pain. "Pins and needles" sensations are probably caused by irritation or interruption of those fibers or tracts that carry tactile sensation. The tingling that follows constriction of a limb has been attributed to stimulation of tactile fibers by asphyxia, whereas the pricking and burning following release of compression have been attributed to stimulation of pain fibers.

Various means are available for evaluating the tactile sensations. *General tactile sensibility* is tested by the use of a light stimulus such as a camel's hair brush, a wisp of cotton, a feather, a piece of paper tissue, or even a very light touch with a finger tip. Touch is tested along with pain by stimulating alternately with the point and head of a pin. Stroking of the hairs is also a delicate means of testing this type of sensation. For detailed or experimental investigations von Frey hairs may be used, but for routine examinations simple methods are adequate, and it is sufficient to determine whether the patient recognizes and roughly localizes light touch stimulations and differentiates intensities. The stimulus should be so light there is no pressure on subcutaneous tissues. Allowance must be made for thicker skin on the palms and soles and the especially sensitive skin in the fossae. The patient is asked to say "Now" or "Yes" when he feels the stimulus and to name or point to the area stimulated. Similar stimuli are used for evaluating *discriminatory tactile sensation,* but this is best tested on the hairless, or glabrous, skin, and motion of the hairs must be avoided. It is also tested by noting the patient's ability to localize the stimuli accurately and by investigating two-point discrimination. Localization is the most accurate on the palmar surfaces of the fingers, especially the thumb and index finger. Two-point discrimination is considered both a delicate tactile modality and a more complex sensation requiring cerebral interpretation; methods of testing it are described in Chapter 8.

The terms *anesthesia, hypesthesia,* and *hyperesthesia* are used to designate changes in tactile sensation, but, unfortunately, these terms also denote changes in all types of sensation. *Thigmanesthesia* denotes loss of light touch. Loss of sensation on stimulation to or movement of the hairs is known as *trichoanesthesia. Topoanesthesia* may be used to indicate loss of tactile localization; *graphanesthesia* is the inability to recognize letters written on the skin. Localization, skin-writing and two-point discrimination are discussed with the cerebral sensory functions. *Pressure sensation* may be regarded as a distinct type of tactile sensation, mediating more gross pressure from the skin. Most pressure impulses, however, arise from subcutaneous structures rather than from the skin, and pressure sense is herein considered to be a variety of proprioceptive rather than of exteroceptive sensation. Two-point discrimination, which in most instances is actually a highly discriminatory tactile modality, is described in Chapter 8.

POINTS IN THE EVALUATION OF EXTEROCEPTIVE SENSATIONS

The *subjective responses of the patient* should be noted in testing all the exteroceptive sensations. *Paresthesias* are usually considered to be abnormal sensations that the patient experiences in the absence of specific stimulation; these include feelings of cold, warmth, numbness, tingling, prickling, crawling, heaviness, compression, and itching. *Dysesthesias* are perverted interpretations of sensation, such as a burning or tingling feeling in response to tactile or painful stimulation. Wartenberg, however, defines these terms in the opposite manner, and states that the word *paresthesia* implies external stimulation. These phenomena, regardless of how the terms are used, should be noted. At times it is also of value to record the response to tickling, scraping, and roughness.

The examiner should carefully interpret and evaluate all changes in sensation reported by the patient. The following are some of the difficulties that may be encountered: The uncooperative patient may be indifferent to the sensory examination or may object to the use of painful stimuli. A child may be fearful of testing, and should be assured at the outset that the examination will be brief and not actually painful. The overly cooperative patient, on the other hand, may make too much of small differences and report changes that are not present. Some areas of the body, such as the antecubital fossae, the supraclavicular fossae, and the neck, are more sensitive than others, and apparent sensory changes in these regions may lead to false interpretation of the examination. The last of a series of identical stimuli may be interpreted as the strongest. Even though pain sensibility is absent, a patient may still be able to identify a sharp stimulus with a pin; occasionally in syringomyelia, with lost pain but preserved tactile sensibility, the patient may recognize the pin point in an analgesic area and give responses that appear to be confusing and inconsistent.

One should observe not only the recognition and discrimination of pain, temperature, and tactile stimulation, but also accuracy in localization, which is important. Responses on the two sides of the body should be compared. Slight gradations and differences in threshold should be recorded. The patient should be asked to name or point to the area stimulated. The terms *allachesthesia, allesthesia,* and *synesthesia* are used when the sensation of touch is experienced at a site remote from the point of stimulation; *allochiria* means the referring of a sensation to the opposite side of the body. Sensation in an affected area may be dulled when it and a normal area, usually the corresponding one on the opposite side of the body, are stimulated simultaneously; this denotes a cutaneous *sensory extinction,* or suppression, in the involved area, even though sensation may appear to be normal at the affected site if it is the only area stimulated. Occasionally a painful stimulus of high intensity in an analgesic area may cause perception of pain in adjacent regions on the same or opposite side of the body, owing to spread of excitatory processes within the segments of the cerebrospinal axis. After a cordotomy the patient may perceive pain on the normal side when the analgesic side is intensely stimulated.

In conditions such as tabes dorsalis there may be a delayed response to painful or other types of stimulation; this is often diagnostically important. In semistuporous or comatose individuals one may test for pain by pricking or pinching the skin, but no accurate delineation of sensory change can be determined; the comparison of the response on the two sides of the body, however, gives valuable information. In testing all types of superficial sensation the best results are obtained by proceeding from the area of lesser sensation to that of greater sensation—that is, by going from the anesthetic to the normal zone, or from the normal to the hyperesthetic. There may be a definite line of demarcation between the areas of normal and abnormal sensation, a gradual change, or at times a zone of hyperesthesia between them.

In delineating and recording alterations in superficial sensations, it is important to differentiate between changes due to lesions of the peripheral nerves, of the nerve roots, and of the cerebrospinal axis. In *peripheral nerve lesions* the areas of anesthesia, hypesthesia, or hyperesthesia correspond to the areas of sensory distribution of specific nerves (Fig. 11). All types of sensation, including the proprioceptive sensations, are altered within the distribution of the affected nerve or nerves. It is necessary to bear in mind, however, that there is an individual variation in the areas supplied by the peripheral nerves, and in one patient the resulting change will differ from that in another, as is shown in the variations in the radial nerve supply (Fig. 12). It is also important to recall that there are areas of algesic overlap, especially for pain and temperature sensations; light touch is less widespread. The demonstrable area of anesthesia in a lesion of a specific nerve is usually smaller than the anatomic distribution of the cutaneous supply of the nerve. Consequently, with careful testing, one may demonstrate first an area of slight hypalgesia, with loss of ability to distinguish slight differences in pain and thermal stimuli; then there is an area of marked hypalgesia and hypesthesia, within which, however, one may identify coarse tactile stimuli; and finally an area of complete anesthesia and analgesia (Fig. 13). Occasionally there is spread of sensory loss beyond the field of an injured nerve. Those nerves supplying the face and body have a certain amount of "crossing" at the midline, more on the body than on the face. Therefore, an organic anesthesia almost always ends before the midline is reached. The sensory and other neurologic changes associated with lesions of specific peripheral nerves are described in Part VII.

It is well established that there is a definite relationship between nerve fiber diameter, sensory modality, rate of conduction of impulses, refractory period, and

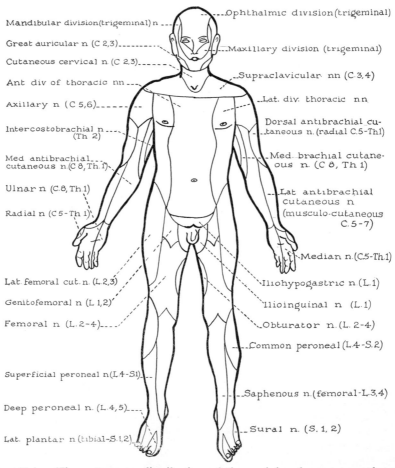

FIG. 11A.   The cutaneous distribution of the peripheral nerves on the anterior aspect of the body.

vulnerability to various types of injury. The greater the diameter of the fibers, the faster the speed of conduction. The largest, or "A," fibers carry motor, proprioceptive, pressure, and discriminatory tactile sensations; they are the most susceptible to pressure and anoxia. The somewhat smaller, or "B," carry general tactile, thermal, and localized, pricking, "first," or fast pain impulses. The smallest, or "C," fibers are mainly unmyelinated and carry less well-localized, burning "second," or slow pain, together with vasomotor impulses. Cocaine, which blocks the conduction of the smaller fibers first, causes loss of sensation in the order of slow pain, cold, warmth, fast pain, touch, and position. Pressure, which blocks the conduction of the larger fibers first, causes loss of sensation in the order of position, vibration, pressure, touch, fast pain, cold, warmth, and slow pain. Aberrations of the skin sensibility caused by mechanical, thermal, radiant, or chemical insults are probably due to liberation in the skin of some substance that reduces the threshold for stimulation of the pain endings.

In *lesions confined to the nerve roots* there are areas of anesthesia, hypesthesia,

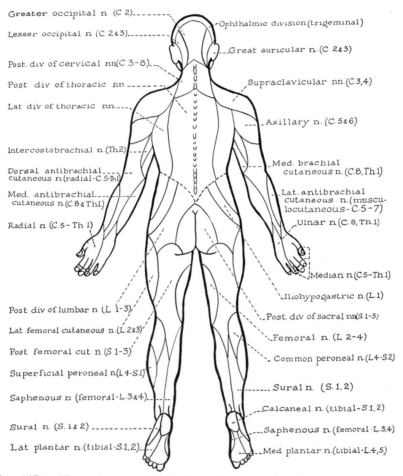

Greater occipital n (C 2)

Lesser occipital n (C 2&3)

Post. div of cervical nn(C 3-8)

Post div of thoracic nn

Lat div of thoracic nn

Intercostobrachial n (Th.2)

Dorsal antibrachial cutaneous n (radial-C.5-Th1)

Med. antibrachial cutaneous n.(C.8 & Th.1)

Radial n (C.5-Th 1)

Ophthalmic division (trigeminal)

Great auricular n. (C 2&3)

Supraclavicular nn.(C.3,4)

Axillary n. (C.5&6)

Med. brachial cutaneous n. (C.8,Th.1)

Lat. antibrachial cutaneous n (musculocutaneous-C.5-7)

Ulnar n (C.8,Th.1)

Median n (C5-Th.1)

Iliohypogastric n (L.1)

Post div of sacral nn(S.1-3)

Femoral n. (L 2-4)

Common peroneal n.(L.4-S.2)

Sural n. (S.1,2)

Calcaneal n. (tibial-S.1,2)

Saphenous n (femoral-L.3,4)

Med plantar n (tibial-L.4,5)

Post div of lumbar n (L 1-3)

Lat femoral cutaneous n.(L.2&3)

Post femoral cut n (S 1-3)

Superficial peroneal n(L.4-S.1)

Saphenous n (femoral-L.3&4)

Sural n. (S.1 & 2)

Lat plantar n.(tibial-S.1,2)

FIG. 11B. The cutaneous distribution of the peripheral nerves on the posterior aspect of the body.

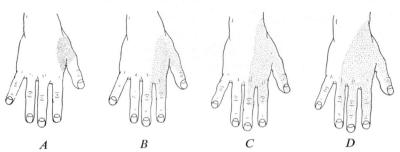

A   *B*   *C*   *D*

FIG. 12. Variations in the cutaneous supply of the radial nerve: *A,* Frequent distribution; *B,* Typical distribution; *C,* Frequent distribution; *D,* Anesthesia beyond the usual limits. (After Tinel.)

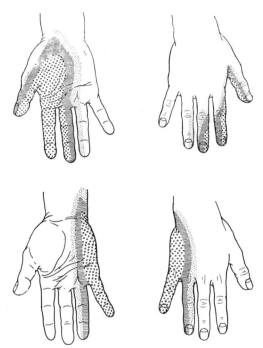

FIG. 13. Transition in sensory changes in: *Top,* median nerves; *Bottom,* ulnar nerves. The smallest area is completely anesthetic; the next area is characterized by pronounced hypesthesia; the largest area is only slightly hypesthetic. (After Tinel.)

analgesia, or hypalgesia which are limited to the segmental distribution of these roots, and all types of sensation are affected. Instead of sensory loss there may be hyperesthesia and radicular, or girdle, pains in this same distribution. The skin areas innervated by specific segments of the cord or their roots or dorsal root ganglia are called *dermatomes.* The distribution of these has been worked out by Head, who based his observations on herpetic lesions and traumatic involvement of the spinal cord and the cauda equina, and later by Sherrington and Foerster, who performed isolated posterior root sections and noted the remaining, or unaltered, sensibility after certain roots were sectioned. Foerster also determined the distribution of the dermatomes by making use of antidromic responses and noting the vasodilation that followed stimulation of the cut end of a dorsal root. There has been some variation in the results. The dermatome innervation of the extremities is somewhat complex, in part due to the migration of the limb buds during evolution. As a result, the fourth and fifth cervical dermatomes approximate the first and second thoracic on the upper chest, and the first and second lumbar are close to the sacral derma-tomes on the inner aspect of the thigh near the genitalia. According to both Head and Foerster there is an overlap of sensory supply by the nerve roots so widespread that it may not be possible to map out an area of sensory loss with a lesion involving only one nerve root, and it may be necessary to have involvement of two or more radicular zones in order to demonstrate an area of anesthesia or analgesia (Fig. 14). Head and Foerster delineated the sensory representation of

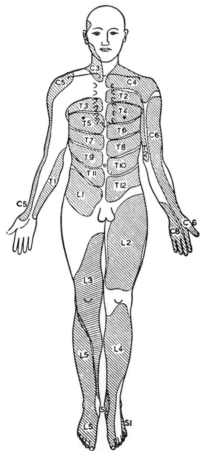

FIG. 14.   Segmental innervation of the body. (Lewis, T.: Pain. New York, copyright, The Macmillan Co., 1942.)

only certain nerve roots in the distal portions of the extremities. Keegan, in a study of a large series of cases of herniated intervertebral disks with the blocking of single nerve roots, has modified the dermatome representation in the extremities. He found little or no overlap, and was able to delineate strips of hypalgesia which extend to the most distal portions of the extremities (Fig 15).

On occasion it may be necessary to differentiate between peripheral nerve and radicular lesions and the more complex type of involvement that is found in lesions of the cervical, brachial, lumbar, or sacral plexuses. A lesion of the upper trunk or of the posterior cord of the brachial plexus, for instance, will result in changes in sensation which differ from those found in segmental or radicular involvement and from those arising from peripheral nerve lesions.

In *lesions of the brain stem and spinal cord,* or *the cerebrospinal axis,* the anesthesia follows the segmental rather than the peripheral distribution (Figs. 14 and 15). One can localize quite accurately the level of involvement if one recalls the following: the first cervical segment has no supply to the skin; the interaural or vortex-mental line forms the border between the areas supplied by the trigeminal nerve and the second cervical segment; the fifth and sixth cervical segments supply the radial side of the arm, forearm, and hand; the eighth cervical and first thoracic, the ulnar side of the forearm and hand; the fourth thoracic, the nipple level; the tenth thoracic, the umbilicus; the twelfth thoracic and first lumbar, the groin; the

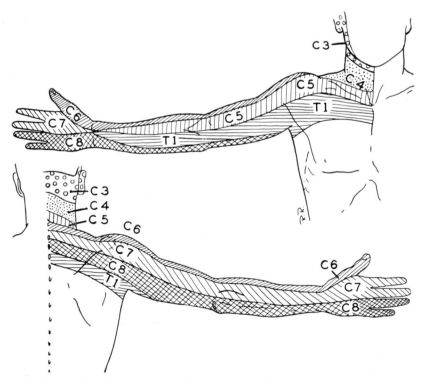

FIG. 15A.   The segmental innervation of the upper extremity.

first three lumbar, the anterior aspect of the thigh; the fourth and fifth lumbar, the anterior and lateral aspects of the leg; the first and second sacral, the little toe, most of the sole of the foot, and the posterior aspect of the thigh and leg; the fourth and fifth sacral segments, the perianal region. In a spinal cord lesion there may be anesthesia of the body below the uppermost level of the lesion as a result of involvement of the ascending pathways. There may be hyperesthesia at the level of the lesion with increased irritability, even though the threshold may be reduced, or there may be a zone of gradual transition (Part VII). The level for pain and temperature sensations is most specific, and it may be difficult to delineate definite changes in tactile sensation. Furthermore, since the pain fibers from the lower portions of the body are lateral, pressure on the cord from one side may affect only the external fibers, and the resulting loss in pain sensation may be far below the level of the lesion. It is important to recall that the segments of the spinal cord and the spinous processes of the vertebrae are not on corresponding levels. In the upper cervical region the spinal cord level is about one segment higher than that of the correspond-

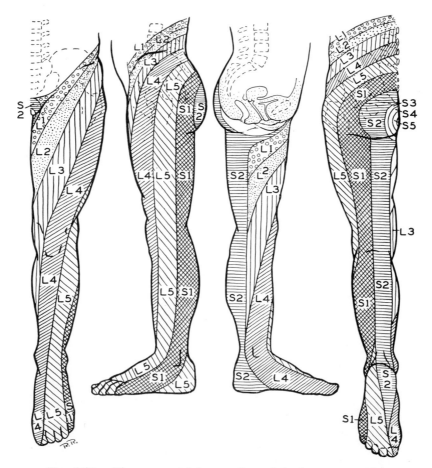

FIG. 15B. The segmental innervation of the lower extremity.

ing spinous process; in the lower cervical and thoracic regions there is a difference of about two segments, while in the lumbar region there is a difference of almost three segments. The spinal cord ends between the bodies of the first and second lumbar vertebrae (Fig. 16). Furthermore, in lesions of the cerebrospinal axis there is often a dissociation of sensation, with loss, for instance, of pain and temperature sensations but little or no impairment of touch, owing to involvement of certain sensory pathways but the sparing of others.

In evaluating responses one must recall that not all portions of the body are equally sensitive, and that there are individual variations in the *sensory reaction threshold*. There is an irregular distribution of receptors in the skin, and the proximity of the sensory endings differs widely in various areas. The tip of the tongue, the lips, the genitalia, and the finger tips are the most sensitive areas, whereas the upper arm, the buttocks, and the trunk are much less sensitive. Calluses over the fingers, the palms, or the feet may impair sensory acuity. Sensations are subjective phenomena, and individuals differ in powers of discrimination, in sensory acuity, and in reaction to pain. It is important to differentiate between a sensation and an individual's reaction to the sensation. Wolff and others have demonstrated that the

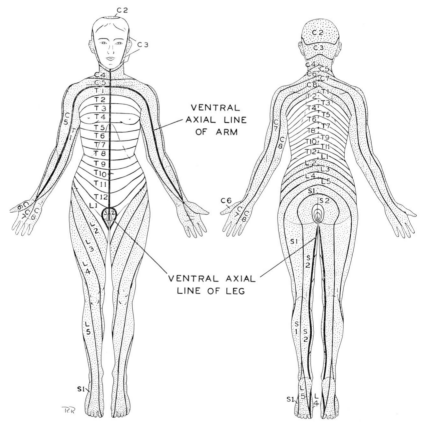

FIG. 15C. The segmental innervation of the entire body. (Keegan, J. J., and Garrett, F. D.: *Anat. Rec.* 102:409, 1948.)

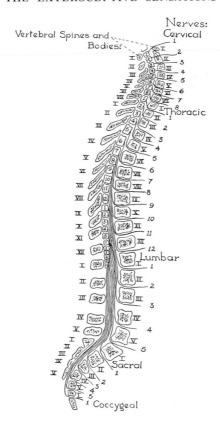

FIG. 16. Relationship of spinal cord segments and spinal nerves to vertebral bodies and spinous processes.

actual *pain perception threshold* is relatively uniform and stable and is independent of age, race, sex, experience, training, emotional state, or fatigue, but the *pain reaction threshold* may vary with any one of these. The same individual may show variations in his reaction to pain from time to time as a result of fatigue, discomfort, alterations in the state of health, or emotional or physical factors. The actual pain threshold may be raised by distraction, concentration, suggestion, damage to the nervous system, local anesthesia, or by the use of analgesic agents, and it may be lowered by nervous system alterations or inflammation of the skin. The threshold may vary according to the site of the stimulus, type of stimulus, strength of stimulus, irritability of the nerves, or the number of nerves involved, and it may be modified by various physical and thermic factors, including changes in the end organs, conducting pathways, and perception centers. There are probably no significant differences in the pain perception thresholds of normal and psychoneurotic individuals, but there is a significant lowering of the pain reaction threshold in the latter; they feel pain no sooner than the normals, but react sooner with a wince or withdrawal. The individual reaction to pain may be tested by the Libman maneuver, in which one compares the patient's response to pain on pressure against the tip of the mastoid with that to pressure against the styloid process, and by similar tests. In all individuals, however, except those rare persons with congenital indifference to pain, overstimulation of a peripheral sensory nerve results in perception of pain.

In *hysterical individuals* there may be changes in sensation which do not correspond to organic nerve distribution and which may be influenced by suggestion. As a consequence, anesthesia extending exactly to the midline or even beyond it, and other changes which do not correspond to peripheral nerve, root, or segmental supply, such as the so-called glove and stocking types of anesthesia, are often indicative of hysterical change. There is absolute loss of all cutaneous sensations. The borders of the anesthetic areas are sharply defined, but they may vary from examination to examination. It may be noted, however, that in spite of marked anesthesia, these individuals can identify objects and can perform skilled movements and fine acts for which cutaneous sensations are indispensable, and they may retain postural sensation even though all other sensations are lost. There may be a midline change for the sense of vibration over the bony areas, such as the skull or sternum, which obviously could not be on an organic basis. Hysterical changes and malingering can often be demonstrated by asking the patient to say "Yes" when he is stimulated and "No" when he is not stimulated, and he will often say "No" every time the pseudoanesthetic area is touched. All so-called hysterical sensory changes should be carefully observed, but it must be remembered that apprehensive patients are often very suggestible, and that a skilled examiner can easily suggest glove and stocking and midline changes to many individuals if he so wishes. The presence or absence of organic anesthesia may be demonstrated by the use of the dermometer and the determination of electrical skin resistance. There is a diminished galvanic skin response and an increase in skin resistance if the nerve pathways are interrupted. It has been said that hysterical individuals often have "hysterogenic" areas of hyperesthesia, especially in the inframammary region, over the ovaries, and over certain joints. Additional methods of examination are described in Chapter 56.

The anatomic differentiation between the conduction of pain and temperature impulses on the one hand, and the conduction of tactile impulses on the other, is valuable in the diagnosis and localization of neurologic disorders and in certain types of therapy. In syringomyelia, for instance, where the primary pathologic change is situated in the vicinity of the central canal of the spinal cord, the decussating pain and temperature fibers are interrupted. The earliest clinical manifestation may be a dissociation of sensation, with loss of pain and temperature modalities in the areas of the body supplied by the involved segments, whereas tactile sensation may not be affected. If the medial portions of the spinothalamic tract are later involved, there may be interference with the conduction of pain and temperature sensations from other parts of the body. In hemisection of the spinal cord of the Brown-Séquard variety pain and temperature sensations are lost on the opposite side of the body below the level of the lesion, whereas tactile sensation shows little if any evidence of change; usually a pyramidal paralysis and a loss of proprioceptive sensations occur on the homolateral side, often with anesthesia in the distribution of the involved segments on the side of the lesion. With transverse lesions of the spinal cord all types of sensation are lost below the level of the lesion, the level for pain and temperature being the most distinct and well demarcated; the level is within one or two segments of the site of the lesion, due to the immediate decussation of the fibers. There may be radicular pain in the distribution of the involved segments.

In cordotomy, a therapeutic procedure for the relief of intractable pain, the ascending lateral spinothalamic pathway is sectioned with resulting contralateral anesthesia starting one to two segments below the level of the operation. Inasmuch as fibers which carry impulses from the upper portion of the body are medial and ventral to those from below, the level of relief depends upon the depth and anterior extent of the section. In order to get a high level of analgesia it is necessary to start at the attachment of the dentate ligament and carry the incision anteriorly and medially to a point just central to the emergence of the anterior roots. Occasionally a bilateral cordotomy is necessary for the relief of unilateral pain. The lateral spinothalamic tract is also near the periphery in the medulla and in the mesencephalon, and it has been sectioned at these sites. It is sectioned in the medulla for the relief of high cervical pain. Here the incision is made at the level of the lower third of the inferior olivary nucleus, just caudal to the lowest filaments of the vagus nerve and the lower end of the fourth ventricle. The descending root of the trigeminal nerve is also sectioned at this site, and analgesia is produced on the ipsilateral side. In the mesencephalon it is possible to section both the spinothalamic tract and the ventral secondary ascending tract of the trigeminal nerve at the level of the posterior margin of the superior colliculus (anterior quadrigeminal body), across the brachium of the inferior colliculus to the base of the superior colliculus. Pain in the distribution of specific nerves or nerve roots may be abolished by section of the nerves or roots or by injection of procaine, alcohol, or phenol into the nerves, roots, or dorsal root ganglia affected or into the subarachnoid space. Posterior cordotomy has been performed for the relief of pain of a phantom limb. Cerebral procedures for the relief of intractable pain are discussed in Chapter 8.

In the neuritides or in conditions where there is irritation of or pressure on the nerve roots, hyperesthesia may be present instead of anesthesia, together with demonstrable tenderness of the involved nerves. The ulnar, the radial, or the common peroneal nerves may often be palpated under the skin, and pressure on them may cause pain. Occasionally, as in the hypertrophic neuritis of Dejerine and Sottas and in leprosy, the hyperplasia of the nerves is palpable under the skin. In the neuritides there may also be pain on brisk passive stretching of the nerves affected. There is increased susceptibility to ischemia in the presence of peripheral nerve and dorsal root lesions, and even in spinal and cerebral lesions, and constriction of a limb will accentuate both subjective and objective sensory changes; this can be used to evaluate both improvement and deterioration of nerve status. On the other hand, pressure and ischemia also cause parethesias in the distribution of normal nerves, probably the result of impairment of conduction of some fibers and irritation of others. In conditions such as trigeminal neuralgia there is irritability of the branches of the nerves as they make their exit from their foramina, with resulting "trigger" or "dolorogenic" zones. Hyperesthesia may precede the development of vesicles in herpes zoster. Hyperesthesia of the hands and the feet, in spite of demonstrable hypesthesia, is a frequent finding in the neuritides. This is especially true of the soles of the feet, which may be almost anesthetic to testing, yet extremely sensitive to all types of stimuli.

Spontaneous, or "central," pain occurs most frequently with lesions of the thalamus. Similar pain, however, has also been described with cortical lesions, brain stem involvement (thrombosis of the posterior inferior cerebellar artery), and affections (usually posttraumatic) of the spinal cord. Either stimulation or section of the spinothalamic may cause a brief, intense, burning pain on the opposite side of the body, and neoplasms of the spinal cord may also cause contralateral pain. Phantom, or spectral, sensations are spontaneous sensations referred to insensitive areas; these may occur with lesions of the spinal cord or cauda equina. A phantom limb, on the other hand, is a sensation of the continued presence of, or of pain, paresthesias, or movement in, an absent portion of the body.

Among the special varieties of sensory changes that may be found in the extremities are the following: *causalgia* is a neuritis characterized by a disagreeable, burning type of pain, often accompanied by trophic changes, and most frequently seen in lesions of the median and sciatic nerves; *acroparesthesia* is a disease characterized by tingling, numbness, burning, and pain of the extremities, chiefly of the tips of the fingers and toes, often accompanied by cyanosis; *meralgia paresthetica* is a painful paresthesia in the area of distribution of the lateral femoral cutaneous nerve; *digitalgia paresthetica* is an isolated neuritis of the dorsal digital nerve of one of the fingers; *gonyalgia paresthetica* is a sensory neuritis of the infrapatellar branch of the saphenous nerve; *cheiralgia paresthetica* is an affection of the superficial branch of the radial nerve.

REFERENCES

BIEMOND, A.   The conduction of pain above the level of the thalamus opticus.   *A. M. A. Arch. Neurol. & Psychiat.* 75:231, 1956.

BISHOP, G. H.   Neural mechanisms of cutaneous sense.   *Physiol. Rev.* 26:77, 1946.

BISHOP, G. H.   The relation between nerve fiber size and sensory modality.   *J. Nerv. & Ment. Dis.* 128:89, 1959.

BOWSHER, D.   Termination of the central pain pathway in man: The conscious appreciation of pain.   *Brain* 80:606, 1957.

CHAPMAN, W. P., and JONES, C. M.   Variations in cutaneous and visceral pain sensitivity in normal subjects.   *J. Clin. Invest.* 23:81, 1944.

ERLANGER, J., and GASSER, H. S.   Electrical Signs of Nervous Activity.   Philadelphia, University of Pennsylvania Press, 1937.

FOERSTER, O.   The dermatomes in man.   *Brain,* 56:1, 1933.

FRAZIER, C. H.   Section of the anterolateral columns of the spinal cord for the relief of pain. A report of six cases.   *Arch. Neurol. & Psychiat.* 4:137, 1920.

GILLIATT, R. W., and WILSON, T. G.   Ischaemic sensory loss in patients with peripheral nerve lesions.   *J. Neurol., Neurosurg. & Psychiat.* 17:104, 1954.

GLUZEK, L. J. B.   Dolorimetry.   *Ohio State M. J.* 40:49, 1944.

HALNAN, C. R. E., and WRIGHT, G. H.   Tactile localization.   *Brain* 83:677, 1960.

HARDY, J. D., WOLFF, H. G., and GOODELL, HELEN.   Pain Sensations and Reactions. Baltimore, The Williams & Wilkins Company, 1952.

HEMPHILL, R. E., HALL, K. R. L., and CROOKES, T. G.   A preliminary report on fatigue and pain tolerance in depressive and psychoneurotic patients.   *J. Ment. Sc.* 98:433, 1952.

JUDOVITCH, BERNARD, and BATES, WILLIAM.   Pain Syndromes: Treatment by Paravertebral Nerve Block.   Philadelphia, F. A. Davis Company, 1949.

KAHN, E. A., and RAND, R. W.   On the anatomy of anterolateral cordotomy.   *J. Neurosurg.* 9:611, 1952.

KEEGAN, J. J., and GARRETT, F. D.   The segmental distribution of the cutaneous nerves in the limbs of man.   *Anat. Rec.* 102:409, 1948.

KIBLER, R. F., and NATHAN, P. W.   A note on warm and cold spots.   *Neurology* 10:784, 1960.

LEWIS, T.   Pain.   New York, The Macmillan Company, 1942.

LIBMAN, E.   Observations on sensitiveness to pain.   *Tr. A. Am. Physicians* 41:305, 1926.

MACBRYDE, C. M.   "Pain," in MACBRYDE, C. M. (ed.),   Signs and Symptoms: Their Clinical Interpretation.   Philadelphia, J. B. Lippincott Company, 1947, pp. 6-13.

MOBERG, E.   Evaluation of sensibility in the hand.   *Surgical Clin. North America* 40:357, 1960.

NATHAN, P. W.   Ischaemic and post-ischaemic numbness and paraesthesia.   *J. Neurol. Neurosurg. & Psychiat.* 21:12, 1958.

NATHAN, P. W., and SCOTT, T. G.   Intrathecal phenol for intractable pain: Safety and dangers of method.   *Lancet* 1:76, 1958.

NOORDENBOS, W.   Pain.   Amsterdam, Elsevier Publishing Company, 1959.

NOTERMANS, S. L. H.   Measurement of the pain threshold determined by electrical stimulation and its clinical application. *Neurology* 16:1071, 1966.

OGILVIE, W. H., and THOMSON, W. A. R. (eds.).   Pain and Its Problems.   London, Eyre & Spottiswoode, 1950.

RENFREW, S., and MELVILLE, I. D.   The somatic sense of space (choraesthesia) and its threshold.   *Brain* 83:93, 1960.

SCHILLING, R. F., and MUSSER, M. J.   Pain reaction thresholds in psychoneurotic patients.   *Am. J. M. Sc.* 215:195, 1948.

SCHWARTZ, H. G., and O'LEARY, J. L.   Section of the spinothalamic tract in the medulla with observations on the pathway for pain.   *Surgery,* 9:183, 1941.

SHERMAN, I. C., and ARIEFF, A. J.   Dissociation between pain and temperature in spinal cord lesions.   *J. Nerv. & Ment. Dis.* 108:285, 1948.

SPILLER, W. G., and MARTIN, E.   The treatment of persistent pain of organic origin in the lower part of the body by division of the anterolateral column of the spinal cord. *J.A.M.A.* 58:1489, 1912.

STOPFORD, J. S. B.   A new conception of the elements of sensation.   *Brain* 45:385, 1922.

SZENTÁGOTHAI, J., and KISS, T.   Projection of dermatomes on the substantia gelatinosa. *Arch. Neurol. & Psychiat.* 62:734, 1949.

TAYLOR, C. W.   Spinothalamic tractotomy for intractable itching.   *J. Neurosurg.* 11: 508, 1954.

WALKER, A. E.   The spinothalamic tract in man.   *Arch. Neurol. & Psychiat.* 43:284, 1940; Relief of pain by mesencephalic tractotomy.   *Ibid.,* 48:865, 1942; Central representation of pain.   *A. Res. Nerv. & Ment. Dis., Proc.* (1942) 23:63, 1943.

WALSHE, F. M. R.   The anatomy and physiology of cutaneous sensibility: A critical review. *Brain* 65:48, 1942.

WARTENBERG, R. Kleine Hilfsmittel der neurologischen Diagnostik. *Nervenarzt* 3: 594, 1930; A pinwheel for neurologic examination. *J.A.M.A.* 109:1294, 1937; A "numeral test" in transverse lesions of the spinal cord. *Am. J. M. Sc.* 198:393, 1939; Digitalgia paresthetica and gonyalgia paresthetica. *Neurology* 4:106, 1954; On neurologic terminology, eponyms, and the Lasègue sign. *Ibid.,* 6:853, 1956.

WEDDELL, G., SINCLAIR, D. C., and FEINDEL, W. H. An anatomic basis for alterations in quality of pain sensibility. *J. Neurophysiol.* 11:99, 1948.

WHITE, J. C., and SWEET, W. H. Pain: Its Mechanisms and Neurosurgical Control. Springfield, Ill., Charles C Thomas, 1955.

WINKELMANN, R. K. Nerve Endings in Normal and Pathologic Skin. Springfield, Ill., Charles C Thomas, 1960.

WOLFF, H. G., and WOLF, S. Pain (ed. 2). Springfield, Ill., Charles C Thomas, 1958.

WYBURN, G. M. The Nervous System: An Outline of the Structures and Function of the Human Nervous System and Sense Organs. London, Academic Press, 1960.

YOUNG, J. H. The revision of the dermatomes. *Australian & New Zealand J. Surg.* 18:171, 1949.

CHAPTER 6

THE PROPRIOCEPTIVE SENSATIONS

THE PROPRIOCEPTIVE SENSATIONS are those which arise from the deeper tissues of the body, principally from the muscles, ligaments, bones, tendons, and joints. *Kinesthesia* is the sense by which muscular motion, weight, and position are perceived. *Bathyesthesia* is deep sensibility, or that from the parts of the body which are below the surface, such as the muscles and the joints. *Myesthesia* is muscle sensation, or the sensibility of impressions coming from the muscles. The above terms are sometimes used as synonyms for proprioceptive sensation, but the latter is somewhat more inclusive and specific varieties of it will be described below.

Most of the impulses which carry proprioceptive sensation ascend in the dorsal funiculus of the spinal cord. The peripheral sense organs are situated in the muscles, tendons, and joints, the important ones being the neuromuscular and neurotendinous spindles, together with pacinian and possibly the Golgi-Mazzoni corpuscles. These respond to pressure, tension, stretching of the muscle fibers, and related stimuli. The impulses travel along heavily myelinated fibers of the "A" type. The first cell body is situated in the dorsal root ganglion. The impulses traverse the medial division of the dosal root (Fig. 5), thence going without synapse into the ipsilateral fasciculi gracilis and cuneatus of the dorsal funiculus, within which they ascend to the nuclei gracilis and cuneatus in the lower medulla, where a synapse occurs. Following a decussation of the arcuate fibers, the impulses ascend in the medial lemniscus to the thalamus (Fig. 17).

Within the dorsal funiculus the fibers carrying the impulses from the lower portions of the body are medial to those from the upper portions, and are pressed farther medially as additional incoming fibers enter the tracts. Fasciculus gracilis (column of Goll) transmits impulses from the sacral, lumbar, and lower thoracic nerves; it is medial to the fasciculus cuneatus (column of Burdach), which conveys impulses from the upper thoracic and cervical regions (Fig. 7). Within the medulla the medial lemniscus is a broad band of fibers situated along the median raphe; the

85

fibers from nucleus gracilis lie in the ventral position, and those from nucleus cuneatus, dorsal. In the pons the tract shifts to a ventromedian position, assuming the form of a flat band; the fibers from nucleus gracilis are in the lateral position, and those from cuneatus, medial. In the mesencephalon the tract is in an oblique position; here the fibers from the nucleus gracilis lie dorsolaterally. In the nucleus ventralis posterolateralis of the thalamus the proprioceptive terminations are caudal to those for pain and general touch, but the distribution is the same as for pain and touch; those from the upper portion of the body (cuneatus) are medial, and those from the lower portion of the body (gracilis) are in the lateral position. The thalamoparietal radiations then go through the posterior limb of the internal capsule, and the impulses are distributed on the cortex; those from the lower portions of the body pass medially, whereas those from the upper areas go laterally. Pro-

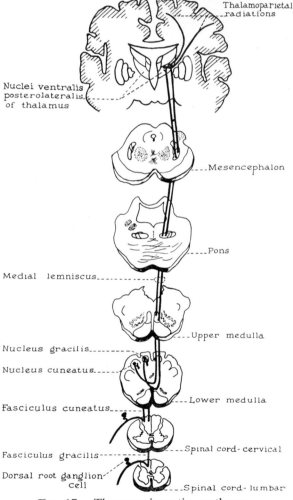

FIG. 17.   The proprioceptive pathway.

prioceptive impulses terminate in the parietal lobe posterior to those which convey touch. Proprioceptive impulses from the head and neck enter the cerebrospinal neuraxis with the cranial nerves. Many terminate on the mesencephalic root of the trigeminal nerve; others accompany motor nerves from the muscles they supply. They are probably carried to the thalamus through the medial lemniscus.

The proprioceptive sensations which can be tested clinically are those of motion and position, vibration, and pressure; considered with proprioceptive sensations but somewhat different in nature, is deep pain.

SENSES OF MOTION AND POSITION

The sense of motion, also known as the *kinetic sense,* or the *sensation of active or passive movement,* consists of an awareness of motion in the various portions of the body. *The sense of position,* or *of posture,* consists of an awareness of the position of the body or its parts in space. Some observers use the term *arthresthesia* to designate the perception of joint movement and position, and *statognosis* to indicate the awareness of posture.

The sensations of motion and position are often tested together. They may be demonstrated by passively moving the digits to note the following: the subject's appreciation of movement and recognition of direction, force, and range of movement; the minimum angle through which the digits have to be moved before one is aware of passive movement; the ability to judge the position of the digits in space. The appreciation of movement depends upon impulses arising as a result of the motion of the joint and of lengthening and shortening of muscles. The normal individual should be able to appreciate movement of one or two degrees at the interphalangeal joints, and even less at more proximal joints. In minimal involvement there is first loss of the sense of position of the digits, then of motion; as the pathologic process becomes more extensive, there may be loss of such recognition for an entire extremitiy, or, at times, for the entire body. In the foot these sensations are lost in the small toes before they disappear in the great toe, and in the hand involvement of the small finger may precede involvement of the ring, middle, or index finger, or thumb. In testing, the completely relaxed digits should be grasped laterally with as little pressure as possible, and passively moved. The examiner's fingers should be applied parallel to the plane of movement to eliminate variations in pressure. The digit being tested should be separated from its mates so that there may be no clues from contact. The patient should be instructed not to attempt active movement of the digit, as such may help him to judge its position. If the senses of motion and position are lost in the digits, one should examine larger portions of the body, such as the leg and the forearm. Reduction in ability to perceive the direction the skin is passively moved may indicate impairment of deep sensibility.

Sensations of motion and position may also be tested by placing the fingers of one of the patient's hands in a certain position while his eyes are closed, then asking him to describe the position or to imitate it with the other hand. The foot may be passively moved while the eyes are closed, and the patient is asked to point to his great toe or his heel. The hands may be held outstretched; with loss of position sense one may waver or droop. One of the outstretched hands may be passively raised or lowered while the eyes are closed, and the patient is asked to place the fellow extremity at the same level. One of the hands may be passively moved while the eyes are closed, and the patient is asked to grasp the thumb or forefinger of that hand with the opposite one. Certain tests for ataxia, such as the finger-to-nose test and the heel-to-knee-to-toe test, are methods for examining the senses of motion and position if they are executed while the eyes are closed. The senses of motion and position are also examined by observation of the station and gait. A patient with significantly disturbed sensations of movement and of position in the lower extremities is not aware of the position of his feet or of the posture of his body. A patient with tabes dorsalis, for instance, can assume a stable, erect posture when standing with his eyes open, but when his eyes are closed he sways and tends to fall, owing to disturbance of the sense of position; he can walk fairly well when his eyes are open, since he is able to see where he is placing his feet, but when his eyes are closed he throws out his feet, staggers, and may fall, because he is not aware of the position of his feet or body. The *Romberg sign* is positive when the patient is able to stand with his feet together while his eyes are open, but sways or falls when they are closed; it is one of the earliest signs of tabes. Sensations of motion and position contribute to the recognition of shape, size, and weight. Their absence may be manifested not only by recognizable changes in sensory acuity, but also by a difficulty in co-ordination known as sensory ataxia and by stereoanesthesia. The methods available for evaluating the senses of motion and position are all relatively crude, however, and there may be definite impairment not adequately brought out by the testing procedures.

SENSE OF VIBRATION, OR PALLESTHESIA

Pallesthesia is the ability to perceive the presence of vibration when an oscillating tuning fork is placed over certain bony prominences. A tuning fork of 128 vibrations per second (C^0), with weighted ends is most frequently used (Fig. 9, p. 66), although some authorities express the belief that a fork of 256 vibrations (C^1) may bring out finer changes in the vibration threshold. Sensation is tested on the great toe, medial and lateral malleoli of the ankle, tibia, anterior superior iliac spine, sacrum, spinous processes of the vertebrae, sternum, clavicle, styloid processes of the radius and ulna, and the finger joints. It is also possible, however, to perceive vibration sense from the skin, or from the bones when relayed from the skin and subcutaneous tissues. It may be tested on the pads of the finger tips. One notes not only the intensity with which the patient perceives the stimulus at those various sites, but also the duration. It should be emphasized, however, that both intensity and duration depend to a great extent upon the force with which the fork is struck and the interval between the time it is set in motion and the time of application. Hence, all observations are relative. There are some recorded statements concerning the duration during which the normal individual perceives vibration at various sites of the body, but there are too many varying factors to make these statements reliable. Quantitative tests for vibration have been described in which an electrically stimulated oscillating rod or vibrating applicator (pallesthesiometer, clinical vibrometer, electronic biothesiometer) is used; this may vary in amplitude of vibration or intensity but generally not in frequency, and thus the threshold of perception of vibratory sensibility can be determined. It is usually possible, however, for an adequate assessment to be made by using the tuning fork alone.

For clinical testing the tuning fork is placed in vibration and held on the great toe or over the lateral or medial malleolus until the patient no longer feels it vibrate in these places. The examiner then notes whether the vibration can still be felt at the wrist or over the sternum or clavicle, or, better still, compares the patient's perception of vibration with his own. Many examiners consider vibration sense to be "normal" when the patient perceives maximum vibration; a much more important criterion, however, is the ability to feel the fork when it has almost stopped vibrating, and relative differences are significant. The threshold for vibratory perception is normally somewhat higher in the lower than in the upper extremities. Loss of vibratory sense is referred to as *pallanesthesia*.

The receptors for vibratory stimuli are probably situated in the skin, subcutaneous tissues, muscles, periosteum, and other deeper structures of the body. Impulses are relayed with the proprioceptive and tactile sensations through the large, fast-conducting, and medium-sized myelinated nerve fibers, and ascend the spinal cord largely with other proprioceptive impulses in the dorsal columns. Many authorities express the belief that vibratory sensation is either a variety of deep cutaneous sensibility or a functional combination or elaboration of the primary senses of touch, rapidly alternating deep pressure, and position, rather than a specific proprioceptive sensory entity, and dependent upon both cutaneous and deep afferent fibers. Bone may act largely as a resonator. For clinical purposes it can well be considered a specific type of sensation, however, changes in which are of definite diagnostic value. Netsky has recently made the statement, based on pathologic study of a group of cases of syringomyelia, that vibratory sensation may be carried up the medial portions of the lateral columns of the spinal cord, rather than the posterior columns. If this is true, it would explain the dissociation occasionally encountered between changes in motion and position and vibration senses.

In patients with diseases of the posterior columns the sense of vibration is lost in the lower extremities much earlier than in the upper, and its loss may be a very early sign in tabes dorsalis. A moderate decrease in the lower extremities or a difference between the lower and the upper extremities may be clinically significant. It is important to recall, however, that with advancing age there is a progressive loss in the ability to recognize vibratory sense, and the sensation may be entirely absent in elderly individuals. The senses of motion and position and vibration do not always parallel each other, and in some clinical conditions one is affected much more and much earlier than the other. Occasionally, in localized spinal cord lesions, a "level" for vibration sense may be found on testing over the spinous processes. This variety of sensation may also be impaired or lost in lesions of the dorsal root ganglia, nerve roots, and peripheral nerves. Such changes may aid in the localization of a ruptured intervertebral disk. In certain of the peripheral neuropathies, especially those associated with pernicious anemia and diabetes mellitus, there may be marked loss of vibration sense in the distal portions of the extremities; there is also impairment in hypothyroidism.

PRESSURE SENSE

Pressure sensation is closely related to tactile sense, but it involves the perception of pressure from the subcutaneous structures rather than light touch from the skin. The peripheral sense organs are the pacinian, or lamellar, and Golgi-Mazzoni corpuscles, which are found in the deeper layers of the skin, connective tissues, subcutaneous tissues, tendon sheaths, muscle aponeuroses, intramuscular septa, and periosteum, and near the tendons and joints. Pressure sense is tested by firm touch upon the skin with the finger or a blunt object, and by pressure on the subcutaneous structures, such as the muscle masses, the tendons, and the nerves themselves, either by the use of a blunt object or by squeezing between the fingers, and one tests both the appreciation and the localization of pressure. For quantitative testing the Head pressure aesthesiometer may be used, or the piesometer, an instrument in which the differentiation in focal pressure is estimated in grams. The term *piesesthesia* means pressure sensibility, and *baresthesia* is sometimes used to signify the sensibility for pressure or weight; this must be differentiated from barognosis (the appreciation, recognition, and differentiation of weight) which is described under the cerebral sensory functions. When strong pressure is applied over the muscle masses, tendons, and nerves, one tests deep pain sensibility.

DEEP PAIN SENSE, OR PRESSURE PAIN

The recognition of pain in the deeper tissues of the body is a proprioceptive sense in that the sense organs stimulated and the origin of the impulse are below the cutaneous level. It is more diffuse and less well localized than superficial pain. The neurons which carry deep pain do not follow the pathway of the other proprioceptive sensations, however, but ascend in the lateral spinothalamic tract with those which carry superficial pain. Deep pain is tested by squeezing the muscles or tendons, by pressure on those nerves which lie close to the surface, or by pressure on the testicles or the eyeballs. Deep pain sense is lost early in tabes, but here its loss is due, not to involvement of the dorsal funiculi, but to the presence of pathologic change in the dorsal root ganglia. Before the loss of deep pain there is a *delayed pain* reaction, for both superficial and deep pain, in which response to a painful stimulation is retarded. *Abadie's sign* is the insensibility of the achilles tendon to pressure. *Biernacki's sign* is the absence of pain on pressure on the ulnar nerve, and *Pitres' sign* is loss of pain on pressure on the testes; these are found in tabes dorsalis. There are increased sensibility and marked tenderness in the muscle masses, tendons, and nerves in the peripheral neuritides (see below), and occasionally there is palpable abnormality of the nerves. Muscle tenderness may also be present in myositis. Tenderness should not be considered an increased acuity for deep pain. *Tinel's sign* is a tingling sensation in the distal end of an extremity on pressure over the site of a divided nerve; it points to beginning regeneration of the nerve.

In addition to the above proprioceptive sensations, which are tested in every neurologic examination, there are other proprioceptive impulses and pathways which are important from both clinical and neurophysiologic points of view. Afferent impulses are carried to the cerebellum through the dorsal and ventral spinocerebellar pathways (Chapter 24). Impulses are carried to the brain stem through the spinotectal and spinoolivary tracts. There are impulses which function in exciting and inhibiting reflexes, in stretch excitation, and in postural and righting reflexes (Part V, "The Reflexes"). Some of the above impulses arise in proprioceptors, others in less well defined end organs. There are no methods for examining these as specific sensory modalities, however, and they may be described as afferent but nonsensory elements. Vestibular sensibility, or balance sense, is a proprioceptive sensation which arises in part from stimulation of the muscles, joints, and tendons, and is carried through pathways in the spinal cord. The principal sensory organs of the vestibular apparatus, however, are the semicircular canals, and vestibular sense may be regarded as one of the special senses, mediated through the cranial nerves (Chapter 14).

REFERENCES

ARING, C. D., and FROHRING, W. O. Apparatus and technique for measurement of vibratory threshold and of vibratory "adaptation" curve. *J. Lab. & Clin. Med.* 28: 204, 1942.

BERGMAN, P. S. Cutaneous vibration perception in neurologic disorders. *Tr. Am. Neurol. A.* 87:170, 1962.

COLLENS, W. S., ZILINSKY, J. D., and BOAS, L. C. Clinical vibrometer: An apparatus to measure vibratory sense quantitatively. *Am. J. Med.* 1:636, 1946.

FOX, J. C., JR., and KLEMPERER, W. W. Vibratory sensibility: A quantitative study of its thresholds in nervous disorder. *Arch. Neurol. & Psychiat.* 48:622, 1942.

GOFF, G. D., ROSNER, B. S., DETRE, T., and KENNARD, D. Vibration perception in normal man and medical patients. *J. Neurol, Neurosurg. & Psychiat.* 28:503, 1965.

GREGG, E. C., JR. Absolute measurement of the vibratory threshold. *A. M. A. Arch. Neurol. & Psychiat.* 66:403, 1951.

HERRICK, C. J. The proprioceptive nervous system. *J. Nerv. & Ment. Dis.* 106:355, 1947.

KEIGHLEY, G. An instrument for measurement of vibration sense in man. *Milbank Mem. Fund. Quart.* 24:36, 1946.

LAIDLAW, R. W., and HAMILTON, M. A. Thresholds of vibratory sensibility as determined by the pallesthesiometer: A study of sixty normal subjects. *Bull. Neurol. Inst. New York* 6:494, 1937.

NETSKY, M. G. Syringomyelia: A clinicopathologic study. *A. M. A. Arch. Neurol. & Psychiat.* 70:741, 1953.

PEARSON, G. H. J. Effect of age on vibratory sensibility. *Arch. Neurol. & Psychiat.* 20:482, 1928.

PLUMB, C. S., and MEIGS, J. W. Human vibration perception: I. Vibration perception at different ages (normal ranges). *Arch. Gen. Psychiat.* 4:611, 1961.

RENFREW, S., and CAVANAGH, D.   The discrimination between pinching and pressing of the skin: The basis of a clinical test.   *Brain* 77:305, 1954.

STEINESS, I.   Vibratory perception in normal subjects.   *Acta med. scand.* 158:315, 1957.

TOOMEY, J. A., KOPECNY, L., and MICKEY, S.   Measurement of sensation: I. Vibratory sensation.   *Arch. Neurol. & Psychiat.* 61:663, 1949.

WISE, B. L.   Disturbances of vibratory sense (pallesthesia) associated with nerve root compression due to herniated nucleus pulposus.   *A. M. A. Arch. Neurol. & Psychiat.* 68:377, 1952.

Yoss, R. E.   Studies of the spinal cord: Part 3.   Pathways for deep pain within the spinal cord and brain.   *Neurology* 3:163, 1953.

CHAPTER 7

THE INTEROCEPTIVE, OR VISCERAL, SENSATIONS

THE INTEROCEPTIVE SENSATIONS are the general visceral sensations, those which arise from the internal organs. The special visceral sensations, such as smell and taste, will be discussed individually. The interoceptive sensations are very important clinically, and the patient may, in his history, give definite information about pain, spasm, or distention in the viscera—a feeling of fullness in the stomach after a meal, gastric discomfiture, spasm of the intestine, a pressure sensation in the chest, a sensation of fullness in the bladder or rectum, a desire for micturition, a sense of engorgement from the genitalia, or pain in the internal organs. Visceral pain is often vaguely localized or diffuse, but is described by the patient as being deep-seated. Certain of the viscera are sensitive to direct stimulation, whereas others are not. Pain endings are found in the parietal pleura over the thoracic wall and the diaphragm, although there are none in the visceral pleura or the lungs. The pericardium is insensitive to pain, but the vessels of the heart are extremely sensitive. The parietal peritoneum is sensitive, especially to distention, but the visceral peritoneum is not. Direct stimulation of the hollow viscera causes no pain, but spasm, inflammation, trauma, pressure, distension, or tension on them may produce severe pain if the stimulus is adequate, possibly the result of involvement of the surrounding tissues.

Afferent fibers are found in the seventh, ninth, and tenth cranial nerves and in the thoracicolumbar and sacral autonomic nerves. They have their cell bodies in the cerebrospinal (dorsal root and associated cranial) ganglia, like the afferent fibers which accompany the somatic nerves, and the impulses enter the central nervous system by way of the posterior roots and ascend to higher centers through the same pathways as those which carry somatic impulses. Although these fibers may be identified within the individual autonomic nerves, after they reach the dorsal root ganglia they are difficult to distinguish from fibers which carry the somatic afferent impulses. There is some controversy regarding the existence of any anatomic or physiologic differentiation between visceral and somatic afferent nerves. The distinction between the two may be entirely on the basis of peripheral distribution rather than associated with fundamental morphologic or functional variation. Many authorities express the belief that there is no good evidence for the existence of afferent axons as a part of the autonomic nervous system. The so-called visceral afferent fibers are probably not actually a part of the autonomic nervous system, although they travel with the outgoing fibers of the different parts of this system. These fibers conduct general visceral afferent but not autonomic afferent impulses.

The afferent impulses from the viscera may reach consciousness by a variety of routes. Some travel in somatic nerves, some with efferent autonomic nerves, and others are found in nerves that are in close proximity to the blood vessels but later join the autonomic nerves. Some synapse soon in the dorsal horn, and the neuraxis of the neuron of the next order crosses to the opposite lateral spinothalamic tract, where the fibers that carry visceral pain lie medial to those that carry superficial pain and temperature sensations, in the secondary visceral ascending tract. Many ascend for a greater distance in the white matter of the dorsolateral fasciculus before synapsing, however, and some may ascend by long intersegmental fibers in the white matter at the border of the dorsal horn, and reach the hypothalamus and thalamus without decussation. Still others may ascend in the ipsilateral spinothalamic tract. As a consequence, localization of visceral pain is not precise, and the threshold may be high. It has been said that the gyrus rectus rather than the parietal cortex may be the end station for visceral afferent sensation.

Visceral pain may on occasion be relieved by sympathectomy or sympathetic ganglionectomy, by means of which afferent neurons that run with the autonomic fibers are sectioned, but other factors may also contribute to the therapeutic result. The relief of the pain of angina pectoris by injection or section of the middle and inferior cervical and upper thoracic sympathetic ganglia may be effected not only by interruption of afferent fibers, but also by interruption of efferent pathways with consequent vasodilatation, chemical alteration, and decrease in spasm. Alleviation of pain in dysmenorrhea and visceral crises by sympathectomy may also be in part the result of relief of spasm. The mitigation of pain in Raynaud's disease by interruption of autonomic pathways is largely due to vasodilatation and increased oxygenation of tissues. The relief of the pain of causalgia by sympathetic block may not be due to interruption of pain fibers in the autonomic nerves but to decrease in vasospasm and interruption of the efferent autonomic system discharges from the hypothalamus, which may be causing direct irritation of the somatic afferent fibers. Visceral pain on the above and other bases is also relieved by posterior root section and by section of the lateral spinothalamic tracts. Because, however, the visceral afferent fibers lie medial in the latter tracts, a cordotomy for the relief of visceral pain must be carried out with a deeper incision than one for the relief of somatic pain. Furthermore, because the afferent impulses from the viscera ascend for a greater distance before decussation, it is necessary to perform a cordotomy at a higher level to control visceral pain than to control pain from somatic structures. Also, because pain impulses from the viscera may be carried in both crossed and un-crossed pathways, a cordotomy done to control visceral pain may have to be bilateral. The pain of causalgia may also be relieved by posterior cordotomy and section of the long intersegmental fibers near the dorsal horn.

In addition to the pain experienced in the viscus itself, which may be vaguely localized and diffuse, but is deep-seated, there may be an associated somatic pain of reflex origin, known as *referred pain*. This is referred to the skin and subcutaneous tissues, and the area in which it is felt may be hyperalgesic to stimulation. It has been stated that this referred pain is experienced in the area of cutaneous distribution of the spinal nerves which correspond to the level of the spinal cord segments that supply the viscus. Head has delineated the zones of pain and hyperalgesia which are found in disease of the various viscera. These are rather poorly localized, however; they vary widely, and the pain is frequently referred to distant areas. Referred pain may arise in the dermatome or skin segment directly over the involved organ, as a result of corresponding segmental innervation, or the pain may be quite distant, as a result of shifting of the viscus during embryologic development. Appendiceal pain is felt directly over the appendix; the pain of angina pectoris may radiate down the left arm, whereas renal pain is referred to the groin and diaphragmatic pain is referred to the shoulder or neck. The phrenic nerve, for instance, which is supplied by fibers from the third, fourth, and fifth cervical nerves, is motor to the diaphragm and is also sensory to it and to the contiguous structures, the extrapleural and extraperitoneal connective tissues in the vicinity of the gall bladder and liver. As a consequence, in irritation of the gall bladder, liver, or central portion of the diaphragm, there may be pain and hyperesthesia not only in the viscus involved, but also on the side of the neck and shoulder in the cutaneous distribution of the third, fourth, and fifth cervical nerves, or in the area supplied by the posterior roots of those nerves whose anterior roots supply the diaphragm.

This referred pain has been said to be produced by the viscerocutaneous reflex (or the peritoneocutaneous reflex if the stimulus results from involvement of the peritoneum rather than the viscus itself) and to be brought about by central spread of the excitatory effects of noxious stimulation. At times there may also be tenderness and spasm of the musculature in the same area; this is a manifestation of the visceromotor, or peritoneomotor, reflex. It may be, however, that the pain and spasm, rather than being true reflex phenomena, may be associated with a central mechanism in the internuncial pool. Both somatic and visceral afferent neurons may carry impulses which converge in and affect a common pool of secondary neurons. Sinclair, Weddell, and Feindel explain referred pain on the basis of branching of the axons which carry pain sensibility, one limb going to the site of irritation, the other to the site to which pain is referred; antidromic impulses are sent from the trigger point to the area of reference. Infiltration of this latter area with local anesthesia may relieve the pain, although residual discomfort may persist; this procedure may give indirect evidence which contributes to the neurologic examination and diagnosis.

The afferent fibers that have been demonstrated in the autonomic nerves may function in visceral reflex action without conveying sensations to consciousness, or the autonomic nervous system may act as an accessory conduction system for painful and other impulses. Abnormal impulses arising from the viscera as a result of spasm or tension are usually due to pressure, inflammation, or trauma. They may be carried through special visceral fibers, or they may be mediated through somatic fibers, secondary to involvement of somatic tissues by the pressure, inflammation, or trauma. Davis and Pollock state that there is no anatomic proof of the existence of autonomic neurons through which afferent impulses are conveyed into the central nervous system, and that the only proved contribution of the autonomic nervous system to pain is in its relationship to referred pain, in the production of which the efferent, not the afferent, fibers are utilized. There is probably no fundamental difference between visceral pain and general somatic pain, except that the latter is better localized. Operations on the sympathetic nervous system do not always afford complete relief from intractable visceral pain, but section of the lateral spinothalamic tracts may relieve such pain if done sufficiently high.

Visceral sensations, regardless of their importance in clinical medicine, cannot be adequately evaluated by the procedures used in the routine neurologic examination. They are poorly localized, and due to their origin within the body, clinical methods for testing them are not available. Some of the sensations tested may be mediated by somatic nerves. There are, however, indirect procedures which may give some information. The use of atropine, for instance, to decrease intestinal spasm or bronchospasm, or of neostigmine to decrease distension, may afford a clue to the underlying mechanism. There are also tests for sensation in specific viscera, such as the appreciation of sensations of distension, pain, heat, and cold in the bladder during the process of the cystometric examination; this subject will be considered more at length in Part VI, "The Autonomic Nervous System."

REFERENCES

DAVIS, L., POLLOCK, L. J., and STONE, T. T.   Visceral pain. *Surg., Gynec. & Obst.* 55:418, 1932.

DORAN, F. S. H., and RATCLIFFE, A. H.   The physiological mechanism of referred shoulder-tip pain. *Brain* 77:425, 1945.

FREEMAN, L. W., SHUMACKER, H. B., JR., and RADIGAN, L. R.   A functional study of afferent fibers in peripheral sympathetic nerves. *Surgery* 28:274, 1950.

HINSEY, J. C.   The anatomical relations of the sympathetic system to visceral sensation. *A Res. Nerv. & Ment. Dis., Proc.* (1934) 15:105, 1935.

LIVINGSTON, W. K.   Pain Mechanisms: A Physiologic Interpretation of Causalgia and Its Related States.   New York, The Macmillan Company, 1943.

POLLOCK, L. J., and DAVIS, L.   Visceral and referred pain.   *A. Res. Nerv. & Ment. Dis., Proc.* (1934) 15:210, 1935.

SINCLAIR, D. C., WEDDELL, G., and FEINDEL, W. H.   Referred pain and associated phenomena.   *Brain* 71:184, 1948.

WHITE, J. C.   Conduction of pain in man: Observations on its afferent pathways within the spinal cord and visceral nerves.   *A. M. A. Arch. Neurol. & Psychiat.* 71:1, 1954.

CHAPTER 8

THE COMBINED SENSATIONS: CEREBRAL SENSORY FUNCTIONS

THE TERM "combined sensation" has been used to describe those varieties of sensation for the recognition of which more than one of the above modalities is utilized. They are not mere combinations of sensation, however, and in most instances a cortical component is necessary for the final perception. This cortical component is a function of the parietal lobes which act to analyze and synthesize the individual varieties of sensation; to correlate, integrate, and elaborate the impulses; to interpret the stimuli; and to call out engrams to aid in discrimination and recognition. The resulting manifestations are perceptual and discriminative functions rather than the simple appreciation of the stimulation of primary sensory endings. The more important of the combined sensory functions are listed below.

Stereognosis is the faculty of perceiving and understanding the form and nature of objects by touch, and of identifying and recognizing them. When this ability is lost, the patient has *astereognosis,* or *tactile agnosia.* Astereognosis can be diagnosed only if cutaneous and proprioceptive sensations are intact, for if these are impaired, the primary impulses cannot reach consciousness for interpretation. Various qualities or steps may be noted in the recognition of objects. First, the *size* is perceived. Then the appreciation of *shape* in *two dimensions* is noted, then *form* in *three dimensions,* and finally, there is *identification* of the object. Size may be tested by the use of objects of the same shape but of different sizes. Shape may be tested by the use of objects of simple shapes, such as a circle, a square, or a triangle, cut out of stiff paper or leather. Form is examined by the use of solid geometric objects, such as a cube, pyramid, or ball. Finally, recognition is evaluated by placing simple objects such as a key, a button, a knife, a pencil, or a safety pin in the hand of the blindfolded patient and asking him to identify them. For more delicate testing the patient may be asked to differentiate coins, to identify letters carved out of wood (Fig. 9), or to count the number on dominoes. Stereognostic sensation, obviously, can be tested only in the hands. If there is weakness of the hands, the examiner may have to manipulate the object as it lies in the patient's fingers. If there is diminution of stereognostic sensation, there may be a delay in identification, or there may be a decrease in the normal exploring movements as the patient manipulates the unknown object.

Barognosis is the recognition of weight, or the ability to differentiate between weights. It is tested by the use of objects of similar size and shape but of different weights, such as a series of leather or wooden balls, or blocks loaded with different weights, which may be appraised by holding them in the hand, either unsupported or resting on a table, but preferably the former. It is essential that the senses of motion and position be intact. Loss of ability to differentiate weights is known as *baragnosis.*

Topesthesia, or *topognosia,* is the ability to localize a tactile sensation. Its loss is known as *topoanesthesia,* or *topagnosia.* Localization is impossible if there is cutaneous anesthesia, but the loss of sense of localization with intact exteroceptive sensibility usually signifies the presence of a cortical lesion.

Graphesthesia is a term used to designate the ability to recognize letters or numbers written on the skin. A pencil or a dull pin is used to write the letters, and the patient is asked to identify them. Loss of this sensation is known as *graphanesthesia.* Ability to identify letters written on the skin is interfered with in peripheral nerve and spinal cord lesions, and impairment of this modality may be a manifestation of slight involvement of cutaneous sensibility. Graphesthesia may be a finely discriminative variety of cutaneous sensation, but its loss in the presence of intact peripheral sensation implies the presence of a cortical lesion.

Recognition of texture may be regarded as a special variety of stereognosis in which the patient is asked to recognize *similarities* and *differences,* but it can probably be considered a specific type of combined sensation. It is tested by asking the subject to differentiate between cotton, silk, and wool, or between wood, glass, and metal.

Two-point, or *spatial, discrimination* is the ability to differentiate between stimulation by one or by two blunt points simultaneously applied. A Weber's compass (Fig. 9) or a calibrated two-point esthesiometer is used, and the patient is stimulated by either a single point or two points. One notes the minimum distance between the two points when felt separately. In carrying out the test the patient's eyes must be closed, and it is best to start with the points relatively far apart, and single and double points should be varied unpredictably; the points are approximated until the patient begins to make errors. The distance varies considerably in different parts of the body. Two points can be differentiated from one at a distance of 1 mm. on the tip of the tongue, at 2–4 mm. on the finger tips, at 4–6 mm. on the dorsum of the fingers, at 8–12 mm. on the palm, and at 20–30 mm. on the dorsum of the hand. Greater distances are necessary for differentiation on the forearm, upper arm, torso, thigh, and leg. The findings on the two sides of the body must always be compared. Two-point discrimination in most instances is a highly discriminatory tactile sensibility, and it is carried through the dorsal funiculi; Head placed it in the epicritic system. Clinically, however, loss of two-point discrimination with preservation of other discriminatory tactile and proprioceptive sensations may indicate a lesion of the parietal lobe.

Sensory extinction, or *inattention,* is the loss of ability to perceive sensation on one side of the body when identical areas on the two sides are stimulated simultaneously. Pin points, cotton, or touch with the finger tip can be used as stimuli. One may also test the patient's ability to recognize double simultaneous stimulation of different segments of the body, on either the same or opposite sides, or to distinguish two cutaneous stimuli separated by a brief time interval.

Recognition of electrical stimulation has been classified by some neurologists as a variety of combined sensation, but probably should not be so considered. *Faradic* stimulation probably affects the tactile endings; *galvanic* current influences the temperature end bulbs, and if sufficiently intense may stimulate the pain organs. *Static electricity and electrical sparks* may also affect the pain endings. The use of electricity in the sensory examination probably has little value.

Autotopagnosia, or *somatotopagnosia,* is the loss of the power to identify or orient the body or the relation of its individual parts—a defect in the body scheme. The patient may have complete loss of personal identification of one limb or of one half of the body. He may drop his hand from the table onto his lap and believe that some other object has fallen, or he may feel an arm next to his body and not be aware that it is his own. Lack of awareness of one half of the body is referred to as *agnosia of the body half.* In the syndrome of *finger agnosia* of Gerstmann there is an inability to recognize, name, and select individual fingers when looking at the hands. This may apply to both the patient's and the examiner's fingers. There is loss of awareness of the position and identity of the parts of the body, with disorientation for right and left, agraphia, and acalculia. *Anosognosia* is defined as the ignorance of the existence of disease and has been used specifically to imply the imperception of hemiplegia, or a feeling of depersonalization toward or loss of perception of paralyzed parts of the body, due either to anesthesia of the paralyzed parts or to amnesia for them. The patient may believe that he is able to use his paretic extremities in a normal manner. The above are all complicated varieties of disturbances of cerebral sensory function, indicating involvement of parietal areas or their connections. Inasmuch, however, as they are actually types of agnosia, their characteristics and significance in localization are discussed in more detail in Chapter 53.

The *parietal cortex* receives, correlates, synthesizes, and elaborates the primary sensory impulses (Chapter 50). It is not concerned with the cruder sensations, such as recognition of pain, temperature, and heavy contact, which are subserved by the thalamus (see below). It is important in the discrimination of the finer or more critical grades of sensation, such as the recognition of intensity, the appreciation of similarities and differences, and the evaluation of the gnostic, or perceiving and recognizing, aspects of sensation. It is also important in localization, in the recognition of spatial relationships and postural sense, in the appreciation of passive movement, and in the recognition of differences in form and weight and of two-dimensional qualities. These elements of sensation are more than simple perceptions, and for their recognition it is necessary to integrate the various stimuli into concrete concepts as well as to call forth engrams. They are diminished or absent in lesions of the parietal lobe as a result of the loss of this synthesis and interpretation. The loss of each of these varieties of combined sensation may be considered a variety of *agnosia,* or the loss of power to recognize the import of sensory stimuli.

It is difficult to diagnose either astereognosis or baragnosis if the peripheral sensations are significantly impaired. Occasionally loss of ability to recognize the form and shape of objects is encountered with lesions of the cervical portion of the spinal cord or medulla, and even autotopagnosia may appear with lesions in these sites. In most of these cases, however, there is severe impairment of proprioceptive sensations and a blunting or deficiency of cutaneous senses. In general, the term *stereoanesthesia* is used when the difficulty results from infracerebral lesions, and the term *astereognosis* is reserved for disturbances that follow interference with cortical synthesis.

Lesions of the parietal cortex are never associated with anesthesia or complete loss of sensation. There may be diminution in the appreciation of the various modalities with raising of the threshold on the opposite side of the body, but both exteroceptive and proprioceptive sensations are perceived. Sensation is often disturbed more in the upper extremity than in the lower extremity, trunk, or face. The distal parts of the extremities are affected more than the proximal portions, with a gradual transition to more normal acuity as one approaches the shoulder and hip. The midline is spared on both the face and trunk. The threshold for pain stimuli is raised very little in cortical lesions, although the pin may feel less sharp than on the normal side; with deeper lesions the threshold is more definitely raised. The qualitative elements of heat and cold are present, but there is loss of discrimination for slight variations in temperature, especially in the intermediate ranges. Light touch sensation is little disturbed, but tactile discrimination and localization may be profoundly affected. There often is severe impairment of postural sense; this may result in sensory ataxia and pseudoathetoid movements. Vibratory sensation is rarely affected. Astereognosis, baragnosis, graphanesthesia, and impairment of two-point discrimination may all be present. The period required for sensory adaptation is prolonged, and occasionally allachesthesia is experienced. Disorders of the body image such as autotopagnosia, anosognosia, and Gerstmann's syndrome occur with localized involvement. Lesions between the thalamus and the cortex, especially those affecting the posterior limb of the internal capsule, cause more severe and extensive sensory loss than isolated cortical lesions, owing to the fact that in this area the fibers are crowded closely together.

Detailed sensory examinations and critical evaluation may be necessary to diagnose lesions of the parietal lobes. Both small and large objects may have to be used in testing for astereognosis; sometimes a delay in answering when objects are placed in the affected hand, with no delay when the other side is examined, may be a clue to minimal involvement. Detailed investigation of tactile localization and discrimination may be essential. *Sensory inattention,* or *extinction,* is often an early and important diagnostic finding in parietal lobe lesions. With involvement of one parietal area, the stimulus on the opposite side of the body will not be perceived, even though sensation on that side may be normal to routine testing. Critchley considers this to be the result of lack of attention or local disregard of the affected body parts, whereas Bender believes that stimulation of the normal parietal lobe suppresses interpretation of impulses by the affected one, producing extinction. Bilateral simultaneous testing for stereognostic sense (placing identical objects in the patient's hands) may yield valuable information. The ability to distinguish two cutaneous stimuli separated by a brief time interval is also impaired with parietal lobe lesions. Double simultaneous stimulation above and below the presumed level of a spinal cord lesion in which there is relative but not absolute sensory loss may aid in demonstrating the level of the lesion. If the upper stimulus only is perceived, the lower is moved more rostrally until the intensity of both is equal; this may indicate the segmental level of the lesion. Bilateral or homolateral double simultaneous stimulation of two different segments of the body (heterologous areas) shows that even in normal subjects one stimulus "dominates" the other, at least for the initial tests. In young children, patients with organic disease of the brain, and the aged this phenomenon is demonstrable still more frequently, and it appears that in general the more rostral area is the dominant one; when the face and hand are stimulated, there is "extinction" of the hand percept (the face-hand test).

All sensory impulses that enter consciousness for interpretation by the parietal cortex must first pass through the *thalamus,* from whence they are redistributed. The thalamus is believed to be the end station in the quantitative appreciation of pain, heat, cold, and heavy contact, and is a primitive receptive center wherein sensory impulses produce a crude, uncritical form of consciousness. A lesion in or near the thalamus may cause loss of various sensations, owing to interruption of the impulses on which they depend. A severe and extensive lesion may cause gross impairment of all forms of sensation on the opposite side of the body, probably as a result of damage to the nucleus ventralis posterolateralis. There is marked loss of appreciation of heavy contact, posture and passive movement, and deep pressure, and the threshold for light touch, pain, and temperature sensations is raised.

In the *thalamic syndrome* of Dejerine and Roussy, which occasionally accompanies a cerebral hemorrhage or a thrombosis, there is a characteristic group of symptoms, the result either of damage which predominates in the nucleus ventralis posterolateralis or of interruption of the pathways from the thalamus to the cortex. There is blunting, or raising of the threshold, of all forms of sensation on the opposite side of the body, without true anesthesia. All stimuli, however, when effective, excite unpleasant sensations, and any stimulus, even the lightest, may evoke a disagreeable, often burning, type of pain response. Extremes of hot and cold and also scraping and tickling sensations excite marked discomfort. This overreaction is termed *hyperpathia,* and the diminution of all varieties of superficial and deep sensibility which is accompanied by subjective intractable pain in the hypesthetic regions is referred to as *anesthesia dolorosa.* In addition to sensory changes, a hemiparesis or hemiplegia and a hemianopia usually occur and, less frequently, hemiataxia, choreoathetosis, and unmotivated emotional responses. Occasionally pleasurable stimulation, such as that produced when a warm hand is applied to the skin on the affected side, may be markedly accentuated. This thalamic overaction is due either to irritation of the thalamus or to release of thalamic function from normal cortical control by damage to higher centers. Every stimulus acting on the thalamus produces an excessive effect on the abnormal half of the body, especially as far as the affective element, the pleasant or unpleasant character in its appreciation, is concerned.

DISORDERS OF SENSORY FUNCTION

To recapitulate briefly, diminution or loss of sensation may occur in the presence of lesions at various levels of the nervous system, as may perversions of sensation, such as pain or paresthesia.

Either diminution or perversion of sensation occurs in the presence of lesions involving the *specific end organs,* or sensory receptors, such as the pain endings and Meissner's corpuscles. These are microscopic structures, and pathologic changes in them are difficult to evaluate. Quantitative studies of the latter, however, have shown that they decrease in number with advancing age, and that their cholinesterase activity is decreased in the distribution of underfunctioning peripheral nerves. The pain that is perceived with irritations of the skin, traumatic denudements, and burns, as well as pruritus and other paresthesias, may result from irritation of these distal structures or the nerve filaments to them, and decreased sensation in callosities and scars may result from involvement of the end organs and smaller filaments. Local infiltration with novocaine or freezing with ethyl chloride will cause anesthesia.

In lesions of the *peripheral nerves* there may be a loss or diminution in all types of sensation, but especially the exteroceptive elements, and this change is in the distribution of the nerve involved. Owing to loss of primary modalities, discriminatory and combined sensations are also impaired. An irritative lesion of a peripheral nerve may also cause abnormal sensation in the form of paresthesias or of pain that is either constant or lancinating in character. The nerves themselves may be hyperalgesic and sensitive, or tender to pressure, and there may be pain on brisk stretching of the affected nerves and increased susceptibility to ischemia. There sometimes is hyperalgesia in the cutaneous distribution of the nerves, even though the sensory threshold is raised. The unmyelinated fibers may be most affected, so the threshold for slow or aching pain is depressed, while the myelinated fibers may suffer less damage, and the threshold for fast or pricking pain is raised. In polyneuritis the distribution of sensory loss is variable, usually involving predominantly the distal segments. There may be what appears to be a glove or stocking distribution, but the margins of this area are poorly demarcated, and usually there is a peripheral blunting of sensation with no sharp border between the normal and hypesthetic areas.

The sensory examination is important in the diagnosis of peripheral nerve injuries and in the evaluation of progress in nerve regeneration. Pain in the distribution of a single nerve or group of nerves can be relieved by section of the nerves involved or injection with procaine or other local anesthetic agents, alcohol, or phenol. Section or injection of a nerve peripheral to the dorsal root ganglion, however, may be followed by regeneration and return of pain.

Disease of the *dorsal root ganglia* (or corresponding ganglia of the cranial nerves) is also associated with sensory changes. In herpes zoster there is severe, lancinating pain in the distribution of the affected ganglia. In tabes dorsalis there is loss of deep pain, a delayed response to superficial painful stimulation, and, sometimes, impairment of superficial pain sensation; there may be transient, spontaneous "lightning" pains, and girdle sensations. In hereditary sensory neuropathy the pathologic lesions are in the dorsal root ganglia; there is severe distal loss of all sensory modalities, along with trophic changes in the extremities.

The *nerve roots* are in reality a part of the peripheral nerve, since they constitute a part of the same neuron. Radicular lesions also are accompanied by diminution or loss of sensation, and by either pain or paresthesias, but the distribution is segmental in type. Irritation of the nerve roots causes pain in a radicular, sometimes girdle, distribution. The pain may be either constant or intermittent, but it is often of a sharp, stabbing, lancinating character. It is increased by movement, coughing, or straining. There may be either hypalgesia or hyperalgesia. Owing to algesic overlap, sensory changes may be difficult to demonstrate if but one root is involved.

Pain of a radicular distribution is relieved by injection or section of the roots. If the nerve root is sectioned between the cerebrospinal axis and the ganglion, as in the rhizotomy or retrogasserian neurectomy done for the relief of pain in tic douloureux, there will be no regeneration of the nerve. Spinal anesthesia, caudal analgesia, or subarachnoid injection of alcohol or phenol also brings about relief of such pain by interrupting the conductivity of the nerve roots.

With lesions of the *cerebrospinal axis,* the *spinal cord* and *brain stem,* there may also be loss or diminution of one or more modalities of sensation, or perversions of sensation in the form of either pain or paresthesias (Part VII). The area of sensory diminution or loss, and the paresthesias as well, may involve the entire body below the level of the lesion, whereas the pain is usually segmental and involves only the dermatomes supplied by centers at the level of the lesion. The sensory loss is usually of the dissociated variety, with impairment of certain modalities and sparing of others. In spite of a raised threshold for pain stimuli, there may be an overreaction to rapidly repeated stimulation. With lesions of the spinal cord there is predominant involvement of pain, temperature, discriminatory, and proprioceptive sensations, whereas with brain stem lesions there may be more loss of tactile sensations. Furthermore, with brain stem lesions there may be ipsilateral sensory changes on the face and contralateral changes on the body. With high cervical cord and medullary lesions there may be more impairment of kinesthetic sensations in the upper than in the lower extremities. As a result of the disturbance of proprioceptive sensations and a raised threshold for cutaneous senses there may be stereoanesthesia, which is difficult to differentiate from astereognosis. Extinction and even autotopagnosia may be present with such lesions. So-called "central" pain is occasionally experienced in patients with pontine, medullary, and spinal cord involvement. *Lhermitte's sign,* which consists of sudden electric-like or painful sensations spreading down the body or into the limbs on flexion of the neck, may be present with either focal lesions of the cervical cord or multiple sclerosis and degenerative processes; this may be secondary to disease of the posterior columns.

The pattern of sensory return with recovering spinal lesions is variable; the impairment may recede downward in a segmental manner, the return may start in the sacral distribution and ascend, or there may be a gradual recovery of function over the entire affected area. Pressure sensation returns first and its recovery is usually the most complete, followed, in turn, by tactile, pain, cold, and heat sensibilities. Intractable pain may be relieved by section of the ascending pathways in the spinal cord, medulla, pons, or mesencephalon.

Lesions of the *thalamus* are followed by diminution of various sensory modalities on the opposite side of the body without loss of sensation. They may be associated with abnormalities of sensation, such as paresthesias and hyperesthesias, or painful hyperpathias (Part VIII). Pain of "central" origin is most often associated with thalamic lesions, although it may occasionally be caused by stimulation of ascending pathways in the cerebrospinal axis or lesions of the cortex. When associated with cerebral lesions it probably is not a "spontaneous" pain, but rather an overreaction to stimuli capable of exciting affective reactions and sensations.

Involvement of the *sensory radiations* in the internal capsule causes variable and sometimes extensive diminution of all types of sensation on the opposite side of the body. The changes are similar to those which follow a thalamic lesion, and it may be difficult to differentiate between the two. Pain, however, is rarely experienced.

Lesions of the *parietal cortex* cause disturbances in the discriminatory sensations. There may be astereognosis, barognosis, and sensory inattention or extinction, as well as autotopagnosia and anosognosia. There is never anesthesia, but there is usually some raising of the threshold for both exteroceptive and proprioceptive sensations of the opposite side of the body (Part VIII). Irritative lesions rarely cause pain, but they frequently result in paresthesias on the opposite side of the body. These paresthesias are especially important clinically when they assume the manifestations of a sensory aura preceding a jacksonian convulsion or constitute sensory jacksonian attacks. The pain of causalgia and of phantom limb, which appears to a certain extent to be upon the basis of a hypersensitive receptive mechanism at the cortical level, has been relieved by interruption of the centripetal sensory pathways leading to consciousness by removal of the cortical sensory representation of the part (gyrectomy or topectomy). Abnormalities of sensation in the form of anesthesias, paresthesias, or pain may be present in the absence of organic etiology and may be of psychogenic origin. In addition to the use of measures mentioned previously, such as nerve and nerve root block and section, cordotomy, and tractotomy, other means have also been used for the relief of intractable pain or the patient's reaction to it; these include prefrontal lobotomy (severing the corticothalamic connections), cingulumotomy, thalamotomy, and stereotactic midbrain surgery. Apparently the patient's awareness of or concern over pain is lessened, even though there may be little or no change in the pain threshold. Universal insensitivity or indifference to pain is a rare condition that is usually congenital. A few cases have been reported in which the absence of pain sensation was a part of a congenital sensory neuropathy or associated with absence of organized nerve endings or of Lissauer's tract and small dorsal root axons, but in others detailed investigations have shown no abnormality. In these latter cases the sensory defect may result from some anatomic, physiologic, or chemical abnormality in the cerebral integration of pathways concerned with pain appreciation, or it may represent a form of sensory agnosia. It must be borne in mind that sensation and motion are interdependent, and that severe motor disabilities may follow impairment of sensory functions. This is especially true with lesions of the parietal cortex, but motor disabilities may also follow section of the posterior nerve roots or peripheral nerves and disease of the posterior columns or other portions of the sensory pathways. On the other hand, motor dysfunction may affect sensory discrimination, and it has been shown that when equal weights are placed in a patient's hands, he may underestimate the weight on the side of a cerebellar lesion or overestimate it on the side of extrapyramidal dysfunction.

REFERENCES

BABINSKI, J. F. F.   Anosognosie.   *Rev. neurol.* 34:365, 1918.

BENDER, M. B.   Disorders in Perception: With Particular Reference to the Phenomena of Extinction and Displacement.   Springfield, Ill., Charles C Thomas, 1952.

BENDER, M. B., FINK, M., and GREEN, M.   Patterns of perception on simultaneous tests of face and hand.   *A. M. A. Arch. Neurol. & Psychiat.* 66:356, 1951.

BENDER, M. B., and JAFFE, R.   Pain of cerebral origin.   *M. Clin. North America* 42:691, 1958.

BING, R.   Cerebellopallidal anisosthenia.   *Neurology* 1:10, 1951.

BOLTON, C. F., WINKELMANN, R. K., and DYCK, P. J.   A quantitative study of Meissner's corpuscles in man.   *Neurology* 16:1, 1966.

BOSHES, B., BROWN, M., and CROUCH, R. L.   Sensory return in partial and recovery spinal lesions.   *Neurology* 2:81, 1952.

CRITCHLEY, M.   The Parietal Lobes.   London, Edward Arnold & Co., 1953.

DICKENS, W. H., WINKELMANN, R. K., and MULDER, D. W.   Cholinesterase demonstration of dermal nerve endings in patients with impaired sensation.   *Neurology* 13:91, 1963.

FALCONER, M. A.   Relief of intractable pain by frontal lobotomy.   *A. Res. Nerv. & Ment. Dis., Proc.* (1947) 27:706, 1948.

FOLTZ, E. L., and WHITE, L. E., JR.   Pain "relief" by frontal cingulumotomy.   *J. Neurosurg.* 19:89, 1962.

FREEMAN, W., and WATTS, J. W.   Pain mechanism and the frontal lobes: A study of prefrontal lobotomy for intractable pain.   *Ann. Int. Med.* 28:747, 1948.

FRENCH, L. A., and JOHNSON, D. R.   Examination of the sensory system in patients after hemispherectomy.   *Neurology* 5:390, 1955.

GARDNER, W. J., KARNOSH, L. J., and McCLURE, C. C., JR.   Function following hemispherectomy for tumour and for infantile hemiplegia.   *Brain* 78:487, 1955.

GERSTMANN, J.   Fingeragnosie: Eine umschreibene Störung der Orientierung am eigenen Körper.   *Wien. klin. Wchnschr.* 37:1010, 1924.

DEGUTIERREZ-MAHONEY, C. G.   The treatment of painful phantom limb by removal of post-central cortex.   *J. Neurosurg.* 1:156, 1944.

HEAD, H.   Sensory disturbances from cerebral lesions.   *Brain* 34:102, 1911.

HENSON, R. A.   On thalamic dysaesthesiae and their suppression by bilateral stimulation.   *Brain* 72:576, 1949.

HOLMES, G.   Disorders of sensation produced by cortical lesions.   *Brain* 50:413, 1927.

MAGEE, K. R. Congenital indifference to pain. *Arch. Neurol.* 9:635, 1963.

MARK, V. H., ERVIN, F. R., and HACKETT, T. P. Clinical aspects of stereotactile thalamotomy in the human: I. The treatment of chronic severe pain. *Arch. Neurol.* 3:351, 1960.

POLLOCK, L. J. *et al.* Relation of recovery of sensation to intraspinal pathways in injuries of the spinal cord. *A. M. A. Arch. Neurol. & Psychiat.* 70:137, 1953.

RIDDOCH, G. The clinical features of central pain. *Lancet* 1:1093 and 1150, 1938.

RILEY, H. A. Discussion of WEINSTEIN, E. A., and WECHSLER, I. S. Dermoid tumor in the foramen magnum with astereognosis and dissociated sensory loss. *Arch. Neurol. & Psychiat.* 44:162, 1940.

SANDIFER, P. H. Anosognosis and disorders of body scheme. *Brain* 69:122, 1946.

SCARFF, J. E. Unilateral prefrontal lobotomy with relief of ipsilateral, contralateral, and bilateral pain. *J. Neurosurg.* 5:288, 1948.

SCHILDER, P., and STENGEL, E. Asymbolia for pain. *Arch. Neurol. & Psychiat.* 25:598 1931.

SHAPIRO, M. F., and FELDMAN, D. S. Double simultaneous stimulation phenomena in spinal cord disease. *Neurology* 2:509, 1952.

SWANSON, A. G., BUCHAN, G. C., and ALVORD, E. C., JR. Absence of Lissauer's tract and small dorsal root axons in familial universal insensitivity to pain. *Trans. Am. Neurol. A.* 88:99, 1963.

WALKER, A. E. Anatomic basis of the thalamic syndrome. *Arch. Neurol. & Psychiat.* 39:1104, 1938.

WINKELMANN, R. K., LAMBERT, E. H., and HAYLES, H. B. Congenital absence of pain. *Arch. Dermat.* 85:325, 1962.

WOOLSEY, C. N. Patterns of sensory representation in the cerebral cortex. *Federation Proc.* 6:437, 1947.

WYCIS, A. T., and SPIEGEL, E. A. Long-range results in the treatment of intractable pain by stereotactic midbrain surgery. *J. Neurosurg.* 19:101, 1962.

PART THREE

The Cranial Nerves

THE CRANIAL NERVES

THE EXAMINATION of the cranial nerves is an exceedingly important part of the neurologic examination, and it should be carried out carefully and in detail. The interpretation of the status of the individual nerves is valuable not only in the localization of disease processes within the central nervous system, but also in the diagnosis of systemic disease. Involvement of one or more of the cranial nerves may have localizing significance in the diagnosis of intracranial lesions; it may indicate the presence of increased intracranial pressure; it may suggest the presence of some diffuse process such as meningitis, vascular disease, toxemia, diabetes, sarcoidosis, or generalized infection; or it may occur when there is a primary pathologic process at some distant site.

The cranial nerves can be examined most thoroughly and most satisfactorily if each is studied individually and if they are examined in consecutive order. In order to comprehend the significance of the signs and symptoms that may result from dysfunction of these structures, it is important to understand their anatomic relationships and functions. In this text the study of the cranial nerves is presented in the following order: first the anatomy and physiology of each is reviewed, then the procedure of the routine examination is outlined, and then some of the disease syndromes in which they may be involved are described.

Diseases of the cranial nerves may be divided into those which involve the peripheral nerve processes or trunks (infranuclear lesions), those which affect the nuclear centers (nuclear lesions), and those which involve the central connections (supranuclear lesions). There are cerebral, or cortical, areas that govern the function of the various motor nerves and wherein the sensory impulses terminate for recognition or interpretation. The peripheral nerves extend from the nuclei to the ultimate distribution of their fibers, and often a part of their course lies within the brain tissue. Although a peripheral nerve may be involved independently of its nucleus, injury to the nucleus is always followed by a degeneration of the nerve. Owing to the proximity of many of the nuclei, especially those in the brain stem, and their proximity to other structures, it is rare to have a single nucleus affected without other involvement. The individual cranial nerves, especially the last ten pairs, are similar in structure and function to the spinal nerves, and react similarly to disease processes. The first two cranial nerves, however, and to a certain extent the eighth nerve, react more as does the brain proper.

CHAPTER 9

THE OLFACTORY NERVE

ANATOMY AND PHYSIOLOGY

THE PERIPHERAL NEURONS of the *olfactory,* or *first cranial, nerves* are bipolar sensory cells, the distal portions of which consist of ciliated processes which penetrate the mucous membrane in the olfactory region of the upper portion of the nasal cavity. These filaments are found on both the lateral and septal surfaces of the nasal mucosa in a relatively small area on the medial wall of the superior nasal concha, the upper part of the septum, and the roof of the nose. They are situated so high in the nasal cavity that by far the greater part of the inspired air which passes through the nostrils fails to reach the olfactory epithelium. Forceful inspiration, or sniffing, may be necessary to create sufficient current to have the air reach the olfactory endings. The central processes, or neuraxes, of these nerves are collected into approximately twenty branches on each side. These, the true olfactory nerves, penetrate the cribriform plate of the ethmoid bone as unmyelinated fibers and synapse in the olfactory bulbs (Fig. 18). As these nerves pass through the cribriform plate, each receives tubular sheaths from the dura and the pia mater, the former being continuous with the periosteum of the nose, the latter adjacent to the neurilemma of the nerve. This communication between the nasal and the intracranial cavities may be a portal of entry of infections to the meninges and the brain.

Within the *olfactory bulbs* the neuraxes of the incoming fibers synapse with the dendrites of the mitral and tufted cells in the *olfactory glomeruli*. The neuraxes of the neurons of the next order, mainly the mitral cells, course posteriorly through the olfactory tract to the tuberculum olfactorium and the olfactory trigone where they divide into the medial and the lateral olfactory striae, or roots. Some fibers decussate in the anterior commissure to join the fibers from the opposite side, and some go to the olfactory trigone and tuberculum olfactorium within the anterior perforated substance. The fibers of the medial olfactory stria terminate on the medial surface of the cerebral hemisphere in the parolfactory area, subcallosal gyrus, and inferior part of the cingulate gyrus. The lateral olfactory stria courses obliquely along the anterolateral margin of the anterior perforated space and under

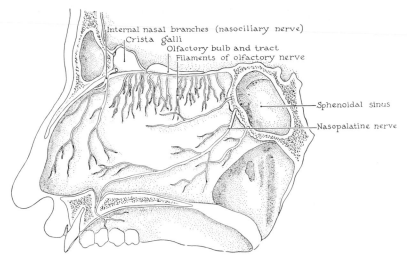

Internal nasal branches (nasociliary nerve)
Crista galli
Olfactory bulb and tract
Filaments of olfactory nerve
Sphenoidal sinus
Nasopalatine nerve

FIG. 18.   Distribution of the olfactory nerves within the nose.

the temporal lobe and terminates in the uncus, anterior portion of the hippocampal gyrus, and amygdaloid nucleus (Fig. 19). The hippocampal gyrus sends impulses to the hippocampus. The hippocampi and amygdaloid nuclei on the two sides are intimately related through the anterior commissure, and these structures in turn send projection fibers to the anterior hypothalamic nuclei, mammillary bodies, tuber cinereum, and habenular nucleus, and thence to the anterior nuclear group of the thalamus, interpeduncular nucleus, dorsal tegmental nucleus, striatum, cingulate gyrus, and mesencephalic reticular formation. Communications with the superior

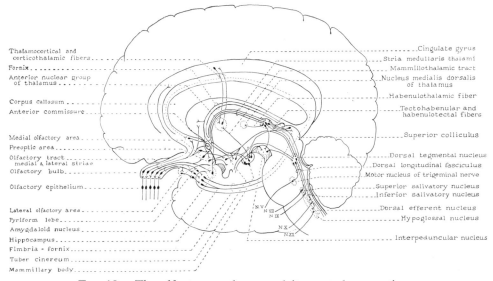

Thalamocortical and corticothalamic fibers
Fornix
Anterior nuclear group of thalamus
Corpus callosum
Anterior commissure
Medial olfactory area
Preoptic area
Olfactory tract medial & lateral striae
Olfactory bulb
Olfactory epithelium
Lateral olfactory area
Pyriform lobe
Amygdaloid nucleus
Hippocampus
Fimbria - fornix
Tuber cinereum
Mammillary body
Cingulate gyrus
Stria medullaris thalami
Mammillothalamic tract
Nucleus medialis dorsalis of thalamus
Habenulothalamic fiber
Tectohabenular and habenulotectal fibers
Superior colliculus
Dorsal tegmental nucleus
Dorsal longitudinal fasciculus
Motor nucleus of trigeminal nerve
Superior salivatory nucleus
Inferior salivatory nucleus
Dorsal efferent nucleus
Hypoglossal nucleus
Interpeduncular nucleus
N V
N VII
N IX
N X
N XII

FIG. 19.   The olfactory pathway and its central connections.

and inferior salivatory nuclei are important in reflex salivation. The olfactory bulbs and tracts are sometimes called the olfactory nerves, but the true nerves are the unmyelinated filaments, whereas the bulbs and tracts are in reality a part of the rhinencephalon of the brain. The olfactory tracts lie in the olfactory sulcus on the orbital surface of the frontal lobes of the brain, and this proximity to the inferior surface of the frontal poles is an anatomic relationship that must always be borne in mind (Fig. 20).

Olfaction is phylogenetically one of the oldest types of sensation. In lower mammals in which the other sensory systems are only partially developed, olfaction is extremely important and the olfactory cortex constitutes a large part of the cerebral hemispheres. In higher primates and in man it is less essential, yet there remains in the brain a complex structure that is of consequence, especially in its relationship with the hypothalamus and with brain stem nuclei. Our knowledge concerning its structure and physiology has been derived largely from comparative neuroanatomy and phylogenetic development. The correlation, however, between the olfactory system, hypothalamus, and autonomic centers is pertinent in the understanding of many visceral functions.

The olfactory nerve is a sensory nerve with but one function, that of smell. Odors have been classified as ethereal, aromatic, balsamic, ambrosial, alliaceous, empyreumatic, caprilic, repulsive, and nauseating, but this classification is a subjective one and has little scientific value. Lesions of the olfactory nerve are characterized by the presence of either *anosmia (anosphrasia),* loss of smell, or *hyposmia,* impairment of olfaction. In true anosmia there is not only loss of ability to perceive or recognize scents, but also flavors, for a large portion of what is interpreted as

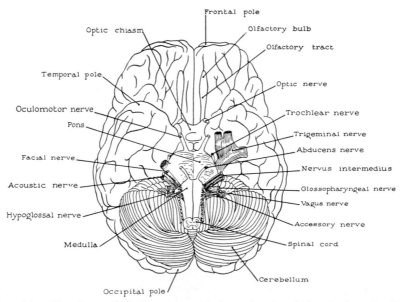

FIG. 20.   The base (inferior, or ventral, surface) of the brain, showing points of emergence of cranial nerves.

taste is perceived through the olfactory system. Salt, sour, sweet, and bitter are the only true tastes; flavor is a synthesis of sensations derived from the olfactory nerves, taste buds, and other sensory end organs within the mouth and pharynx. A patient with involvement of the olfactory system may complain of loss of taste rather than of smell, because of inability to perceive the finer flavors of food, but some anosmic persons can identify and enjoy the flavors of many foods. Patients with unilateral anosmia may not be aware of any disturbance of olfaction. There is said to be a diurnal cycle in olfactory acuity, which is increased before meals and decreased after meals; this may be important in the regulation of appetite and satiety.

CLINICAL EXAMINATION

Smell is tested by the use of nonirritating volatile oils or liquids. Each nostril is examined separately while the other is occluded. One should determine the patient's ability to smell by having him inhale forcibly, or sniff, the test substance through each nostril, and should compare the results from the two sides. Such substances as oil of wintergreen, tar, oil of roses, eucalyptus, oil of cloves, oil of lavender, oil of cinnamon, oil of turpentine, vanilla, anise, almond water, and asafetida have been used for qualitative testing, but probably the most satisfactory test substances are freshly ground coffee, benzaldehyde (bitter almond oil), tar, and oil of lemon. The use of a package of cigarettes or a tube of tooth paste from the patient's bedside table may be of value in carrying out a rough qualitative test. One must avoid substances which, instead of stimulating the olfactory nerve, may stimulate gustatory end organs or the peripheral endings of the trigeminal nerves in the nasal mucosa. Chloroform may stimulate gustatory as well as olfactory endings by imparting a sweet taste; pyridine may give a bitter taste. Peppermint, menthol, and camphor stimulate trigeminal endings and give a feeling of coolness; ammonia, acetic acid, alcohol, and formaldehyde also irritate the trigeminal endings.

Before evaluating loss or decrease of olfactory sensitivity, one must ascertain that the nasal passages are open. Intranasal conditions such as obstructions, allergic rhinitis, atrophic rhinitis, hypertrophic rhinitis, mucoid changes, polypoid formations, and sinusitis may seriously interfere with the sense of smell. It is also important to recall that there may be an individual variation in smell efficiency. One should observe the patient's ability to perceive, identify, and name the test substance. The results on the two sides should always be determined and compared, and any difference noted. In testing infants and hysterical patients, flaring of the alae nasi in response to strong odors may indicate that the sense of smell is intact. Perception of the presence of the odorous substances indicates the continuity of the peripheral nerve and its pathways; identification of the odor reveals intact cortical function as well. Since there is bilateral innervation, lesions central to the decussation of the olfactory pathways never cause loss of smell, and lesions of the olfactory cortex do not produce anosmia. The appreciation of the presence of smell, even without recognition, is sufficient evidence to rule out anosmia.

The above method of testing olfactory sensation is dependent entirely upon the statements of the individual under examination, and is entirely qualitative. Various attempts have been made to devise instruments for the *quantitative measurement* of the sense of smell. Zwaardemaker's olfactometer was an instrument by which the concentration of odorous particles in the inspired air was altered, but the actual amount of air which reached the olfactory epithelium was dependent upon depth of breathing. Elsberg's apparatus forces air containing volatile substances into the nasal cavities during a period of voluntary apnea; by alternate methods the examiner can control both the concentration of odorous substance and the pressure at which it is introduced (Fig. 21). Elsberg proposed methods for determining olfactory threshold, summation, fatigue, and coefficient. These procedures are said to be of value in the differentiation between intracerebral and extracerebral tumors and in the lateralization of frontal lobe lesions, but their complicated nature hardly justifies their inclusion in the routine neurologic examination. Fordyce has described a simple and fairly accurate quantitative test in which he uses graded solutions of phenol in liquid paraffin. Substituting objective for subjective criteria, Adrian, by inserting fine wire electrodes into the olfactory bulbs of laboratory animals, was able to pick up bursts of action potential with each inspiration of scented air, and furthermore noted that different odors stimulated specific portions of the olfactory bulb. This method, however, has no clinical application at the present time.

DISORDERS OF OLFACTORY FUNCTION

The olfactory nerves themselves are rarely the seat of disease, but they are frequently involved in association with disease or injury of the surrounding structures. Loss of smell may occur in a variety of conditions. It may be congenital, associated with senile changes or arteriosclerosis, or present in albinism. Anosmia accompanied by either perversions or loss of taste may be a symptom of pernicious anemia. Trauma to the head with fractures of the cribriform plate of the ethmoid

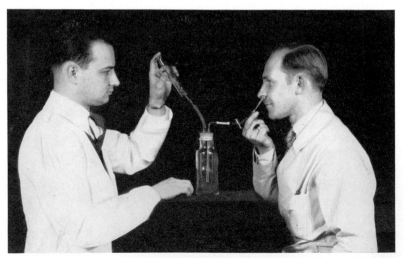

FIG. 21.   Method for carrying out the Elsberg test for olfactory function.

bone and hemorrhage at the base of the frontal lobes may cause loss of smell by tearing, crushing, or pressing on the olfactory filaments; this usually is permanent. Infectious processes involving the meninges at the base of the frontal lobes often cause anosmia, which frequently is a sequel of epidemic meningitis. Impairment of smell occurs in association with frontal lobe abscesses and osteomyelitis of the frontal or ethmoidal regions. A number of toxic substances, including lead and cadmium, cause anosmia. The olfactory nerves may be involved in syphilis, due to either syphilitic meningitis or atrophy of the nerves. Anosmia is common with hydrocephalus. Some decrease in olfactory acuity may accompany aging. Over-stimulation of the sense of smell may cause temporary or permanent loss, as may excessive smoking, amphetamine sulphate, or the prolonged use of cocaine. Partial anosmia may occur with lesions of the trigeminal nerve as a result of trophic changes in the nasal mucosa. Disease of the anterior cerebral artery near its origin in the circle of Willis may produce homolateral loss of smell. Anosmia sometimes occurs, along with other anesthesias, in hysteria; usually in this condition taste is not affected. Hysterical loss of smell may be diagnosed by using irritating substances which stimulate the trigeminal endings, such as ammonia or acetic acid, as well as the volatile oils; in organic anosmia the former will be recognized but not the latter, whereas in hysteria neither will be recognized.

Loss of smell is frequently an early and an important sign in the diagnosis and localization of intracranial neoplasms. This is especially true in meningiomas of the sphenoidal ridge and olfactory groove, gliomas of the frontal lobe, and para-sellar lesions where there is pressure on the olfactory bulbs or tracts. The typical syndrome in the sphenoidal ridge meningiomas consists of unilateral optic atrophy or papilledema and exophthalmos, and ipsilateral anosmia. In meningiomas of the olfactory groove or cribriform plate area there is first unilateral anosmia with retrobulbar neuritis or optic atrophy, progressing to bilateral anosmia. Frontal lobe tumors may also give unilateral anosmia and optic atrophy, and often show the *Foster Kennedy syndrome* with anosmia and optic atrophy on the side of the tumor and papilledema on the opposite side. In parasellar and pituitary lesions bilateral anosmia may be an early manifestation.

Other disorders of smell, aside from hyposmia or anosmia, are occasionally encountered. *Hyperosmia* is an increase in olfactory acuity. It occurs most frequently in hysteria and in certain psychotic states, but it may also be present, along with hyperacusis, in migraine, and it has been described in epidemic encephalitis, in hyperemesis gravidarum, and as an accompaniment of the menstrual period. It is said that hyperosmia may also occur in strychnine poisoning and cystic fibrosis. *Parosmia,* or perversion of smell, and *kakosmia,* or the presence of disagreeable odors, also appear in psychic states and occasionally follow trauma to the head, especially to the uncus region. *Olfactory hallucinations,* which may be present in psychic states or as obsessional phenomena, are more frequently the result of an organic lesion. They indicate the presence of an irritative process in the central olfactory system, and thus are important in neurologic localization; they may occur with neoplasms or vascular lesions. In the so-called *uncinate fit* the seizure is preceded by an aura that consists of a disagreeable olfactory or gustatory hallucination, often described as resembling the odor of burning garbage or decaying animal matter; this may be accompanied, as the patient loses consciousness, by dilatation of the nostrils, smacking of the lips, or chewing or tasting movements. Such attacks occur as the result of an irritative lesion in the uncinate gyrus, hippocampus, amygdala, medial portion of the temporal lobe, or neighboring structures. Olfactory stimulation has both arrested and activated such seizures. The uncinate fit, however, is not in itself a specific variety of seizure, but the olfactory hallucination is one manifestation (often the aura) of the psychomotor or temporal lobe seizure, other elements of which may consist of memory disturbances, automatisms, auditory and visual phenomena, and psychic manifestations (Chapter 55). Neoplasms may or may not be responsible. There is never any evidence of objective loss of smell in these patients.

Disorders of olfactory function may thus be produced by lesions anywhere along the course of the peripheral nerve or its pathways. Respiratory or inflammatory conditions may cause loss of smell due to obstruction of the nasal passages. Involvement of the nasal mucosa or of the cribriform plate area may be followed by a loss of smell as the result of destruction of the peripheral nerve fibers; infectious processes, toxic involvement, etc., may also affect the individual fibers. Intracranial lesions involving the olfactory bulb or tract may cause unilateral or bilateral loss of smell. Lesions of the olfactory radiations or of the olfactory cortex are never followed by loss of smell unless they are bilateral, owing to the decussation of the pathways, but they may produce lowering of olfactory acuity, or, occasionally, "smell agnosia." Irritative lesions in these areas may, however, cause perversions of smell and olfactory hallucinations.

REFERENCES

ADEY, W. R.   "The Sense of Smell," in FIELD, J., MAGOUN, H. W., and HALL, V. E. (eds.)   Hankbook of Physiology. Washington, D. C., American Physiological Society, 1959, Vol. 1, pp. 535–548.

ADRIAN, E. D.   The electrical activity of the mammalian olfactory bulb.   *Electroencephalog. & Clin. Neurophysiol.* 2:377, 1950.

BEDICHECK, R.   The Sense of Smell.   Garden City, New York, Doubleday & Company, 1960.

BRODAL, A.   The hippocampus and the sense of smell: A review.   *Brain* 70:179, 1947.

CLARK, E. C., and DODGE, H. W., JR.   Effect of anosmia on the appreciation of flavor.   *Neurology* 5:671, 1955; Extraolfactory components of flavor. *J.A.M.A.* 159:1721, 1955.

EFRON, R.   The effect of olfactory stimuli in arresting uncinate fits.   *Brain* 79:267, 1956.

ELSBERG, C. A., and LEVY, I.   The sense of smell: I. A new and simple method of quantitative olfactometry.   *Bull. Neurol. Inst. New York* 4:5, 1935.

FORDYCE, I. D.   Olfaction tests.   *Brit. J. Indust. Med.* 18:213, 1961.

GORMAN, W.   Flavor, Taste and the Psychology of Smell.   Springfield, Ill., Charles C Thomas, 1964.

KRISTENSEN, H. K., and ZILSTORFF-PEDERSEN, K.   Quantitative studies on the function of smell.   *Acta oto-laryng.* 43:537, 1953.

KUEHNER, R. L. (ed). Recent advances in odor: Theory, measurement, and control. *Ann. New York Acad. Sc.* 116:357, 1964.

LeGros Clark, W. E., and WARWICK, R. T. T. The pattern of olfactory innervation. *J. Neurol., Neurosurg. & Psychiat.* 9:101, 1946.

McCord, D. P., and WITHERIDGE, W. N. Odors: Physiology and Control. New York, McGraw-Hill Book Company, Inc., 1949.

SEYDELL, E. M. Olfactory disturbances. *J.A.M.A.* 99:627, 1932.

SUMNER, D. On testing the sense of smell. *Lancet* 2:895, 1962; Posttraumatic anosmia. *Brain* 87:107, 1964.

CHAPTER 10

THE OPTIC NERVE

ANATOMY AND PHYSIOLOGY

The *optic nerve* is not a peripheral nerve but is a fiber pathway that unites the retina with the brain. The true peripheral optic nerves are situated in the cellular layers of the retina. The *receptors,* or *end organs* through which visual impulses are mediated, are the *rods and cones* of the retina; these are stimulated by light impulses and synapse with the inner nuclear, or bipolar, layer, the cells of which in turn synapse with those of the ganglion cell layer. The neuraxes of the ganglion cells make up the optic pathways referred to as the optic nerves (Fig. 22). The rods, which are more numerous than the cones, are scattered diffusely throughout the retina, but are absent in the macula. They react to low intensities of illumination and are concerned with peripheral vision, perception of movement, and night sight; they are insensitive to colors. The cones are also scattered diffusely throughout the retina, although they are less numerous. The fovea centralis, the point of clearest vision at the center of the retina, is occupied entirely by cones, which are stimulated by light of a relatively high intensity and are concerned with discrimination of colors and fine details. The macula functions only in "day vision."

The so-called *optic nerve,* which extends from the retina to the optic chiasm, is approximately five centimeters long. The major portion of its course, three and one-half centimeters, is in the orbit, with one and one-half centimeters in the optic foramen and within the skull. The fibers of the optic nerve are usually unmyelinated in the retina and in the nerve head, but they become myelinated as they pass through the lamina cribrosa. The two optic nerves unite at the optic chiasm, which is situated superior to the sella turcica, usually over its posterior two-thirds. The internal carotid arteries are lateral to the chiasm, the anterior cerebral and anterior communicating arteries are in front and above, and the third ventricle and hypothalamus are behind and above. The cerebral dura is continuous over the optic nerve; at the bulb it fuses with Tenon's capsule, and at the optic foramen it is adherent to the periosteum. The pia and arachnoid also continue from the brain and envelop the optic nerve; at termination of the nerve they fuse with the sclera. The

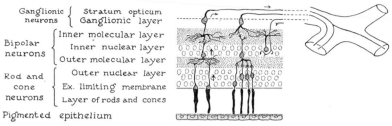

Ganglionic { Stratum opticum
neurons   { Ganglionic layer

Bipolar   { Inner molecular layer
neurons   { Inner nuclear layer
          { Outer molecular layer

Rod and   { Outer nuclear layer
cone   { Ex. limiting membrane
neurons   { Layer of rods and cones

Pigmented epithelium

FIG. 22.   The layers of the retina and their relationship to the optic nerve. (After Cajal.)

subdural and subarachnoid spaces about the optic nerve are continuous with those around the brain. The arachnoid, however, is very thin. The meningeal coverings of the optic nerve are sometimes referred to as the vaginal sheaths. The area between the dura and the pia is called the intervaginal space; it is divided by the arachnoid into a small subdural and a larger subarachnoid space.

The fibers which pass through the optic nerves primarily carry visual impulses, but they also carry impulses which mediate reflex responses to light, accommodation, and other stimuli. Throughout the extent of their entire course, from the retina to the cerebral cortex, the fibers are grouped according to the retinal quadrants from which they arise. The fibers from the lateral, or temporal, half of the retina are also situated in the temporal half of the nerve and pass through the chiasm without crossing; they continue to the ipsilateral reflex centers and visual areas (Fig. 23). The fibers from the medial, or nasal, half of the retina go through the medial portion of the nerve; they decussate at the chiasm, and terminate on the contralateral centers. There are, however, intricacies of the chiasmal crossing. Some of the fibers from the lower nasal retinal quadrant loop forward into the opposite optic nerve for a short distance before turning back again; consequently a lesion of one optic nerve just anterior to the chiasm may cause a defect in the upper temporal field of the opposite eye. Also, some of the upper nasal fibers loop back briefly into the ipsilateral optic tract before decussation. In the chiasm the fibers from the upper retinal quadrants are dorsal and those from the lower quadrants are ventral.

Fibers from the macular portion of the retina, or the fovea centralis, which carry central vision, constitute the *papillomacular bundle*. In the peripheral portions of the optic nerve, near the eye, this is situated laterally and somewhat inferiorly, separating the temporal fibers into dorsal and ventral quadrants. These in turn crowd and somewhat displace the nasal quadrants (Fig. 24). As the nerve approaches the chiasm this bundle approaches the center of the nerve, and the temporal fibers are lateral. The fibers from the medial half of the macula also decussate, whereas those from the lateral half do not. The fibers of the papillomacular bundle are the most vulnerable to toxins and pressure.

Posterior to the optic chiasm the fibers, part of which emanate from the temporal portion of the ipsilateral retina, part from the nasal portion of the opposite retina, traverse the *optic tract*, and the majority of them terminate in the lateral geniculate body. The ratio of crossed to uncrossed fibers in the human optic tract

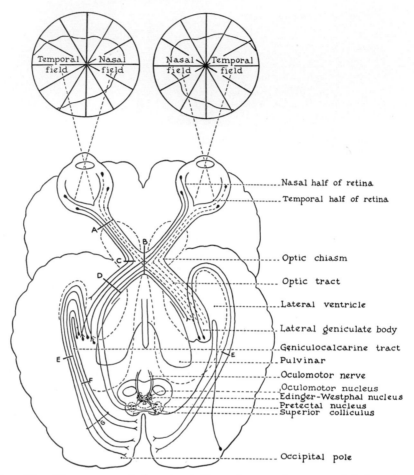

FIG. 23.   The course of the visual fibers from retina to occipital cortex. Letters, *A, B, C, D, E, F, G* show the sites of various lesions which may affect the fields of vision.

is about two to one, which corresponds to the ratio of the area of the temporal field to that of the nasal field. There is a twisting of the fibers in the tract, and those from the macula gradually assume a dorsal and lateral position with a central wedge. The fibers from the upper retinal segments assume a medial and somewhat dorsal position, and those from the inferior quadrants are ventral and somewhat lateral.

Within the *lateral geniculate bodies* there is a definite localization corresponding to the various quadrants of the visual fields and the retinas. Fibers carrying impulses from the upper portion of the retina terminate on the medioventral segment of the geniculate body; those from the lower portion of the retina terminate on the lateroventral segment, and those from the macula occupy an intermediate position in the dorsal, middle, and somewhat caudal portion of the structure. Within the geniculate bodies there is a stratification of fibers, and those from the ipsilateral temporal and contralateral nasal retinal areas probably alternate. Some of the visual fibers may pass

Superior temporal quadrant....

Superior temporal quadrant
     of macula

Inferior temporal quadrant
     of macula

Inferior temporal quadrant....

....Superior nasal quadrant

....Superior nasal quadrant
     of macula

....Inferior nasal quadrant
     of macula

....Inferior nasal quadrant

Left Retina

Left Optic Nerve Just Posterior to the Eye

Left Optic Nerve Approaching Optic Chiasm

Sup. temp. quad. of left retina....

Inf. temp. quad. of left retina....

Macular fibers........

....Sup. nasal quad. of rt. retina

....Inf. nasal quad. of rt. retina

Left Optic Tract Just Posterior to Optic Chiasm

Macular fibers........

Lower half of retinae....

....Upper half of retinae

Left optic tract approaching lateral geniculate body

Macular fibers........

Lower portion of retinae
(temporal half of left, and
nasal half of right)

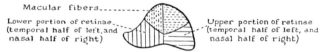

Upper portion of retinae
(temporal half of left, and
nasal half of right)

Left Lateral Geniculate Body

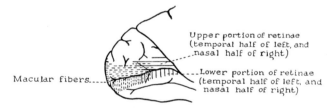

Upper portion of retinae
(temporal half of left, and
nasal half of right)

Lower portion of retinae
(temporal half of left, and
nasal half of right)

Macular fibers....

Region of Left Calcarine Fissure

FIG. 24. Grouping of fibers from retinal quadrants and macular area in optic nerve, optic tract, lateral geniculate body, and occipital cortex.

over or through these structures and terminate in the pulvinar of the thalamus, but the latter connection is not believed to be of importance in vision or in the visual reflexes.

Neurons originating in lateral geniculate bodies pass posteriorly as the *geniculocalcarine pathway,* or the *optic radiations,* and terminate on the striate cortex (area 17) of the occipital lobe (Fig. 25). In the anterior portion of the radiations the fibers subserving peripheral vision are placed medially, and then assume dorsal and ventral positions. The most dorsal, those from the upper retinal quadrants

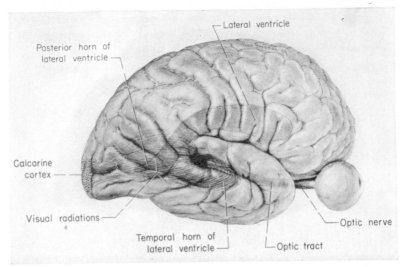

FIG. 25.   Course of the geniculocalcarine fibers. (After Cushing).

and medial portion of the geniculate, pass through the posterior limb of the internal capsule and the depths of the lower part of the parietal and occipital lobes and upper part of the temporal lobe, lateral to the posterior horn of the lateral ventricle, to terminate on the upper lip of the calcarine fissure (cuneus), on the medial surface of the occipital lobe. The most ventral, those from the lower retinal quadrants and the lateral portion of the geniculate, also pass through the posterior limb of the internal capsule and then through the temporal lobe, sweeping forward and lateralward above the inferior horn of the ventricle, and then lateralward, downward, and backward around the inferior horn in a loop described by Meyer and Archambault; they then course through the temporal and occipital lobes to terminate on the lower lip of the calcarine fissure (lingual gyrus). The fibers carrying macular vision come from the middle, dorsal, and caudal portions of the geniculate body; they are first lateral, and then form the intermediate portion of the geniculocalcarine pathway, and pass to the posterior pole of the occipital lobe.

Fibers which carry visual impulses from the peripheral portions of the retina terminate on the anterior third or half of the visual cortex of the occipital lobe in concentric zones, whereas those which carry vision from the fovea centralis, or macular area, terminate on the posterior portion of the occipital cortex. The macula has a wider cortical distribution than the peripheral portion of the retina, and it is represented in a wedge-shaped area, apex anterior, in the striate cortex. It is possible that some of the fibers carrying macular vision cross to the opposite side through the splenium of the corpus callosum and end in the visual cortex on that side, although most recent authorities discount the concept of bilateral macular innervation. The temporal crescents of the binocular visual field are located in the most anterior portions of the visual cortex.

The striate cortex, or area 17 of Brodmann (Chapter 49), is the sensory visual cortex. Surrounding it are areas which function in visual association. Area 18, the parastriate or parareceptive cortex, receives and interprets impulses from area 17. Area 19, the peristriate or perireceptive cortex, has connections with areas 17 and 18 and with other portions of the cortex. It functions in more complex visual recognition and perception, revisualization, visual association, size and shape discrimination, color vision, and spatial orientation.

Fibers carrying impulses which have to do with light and other optic reflexes pass through the optic chiasm in the same order as those which have to do with vision. They may travel in the medial part of the optic tract, and they leave the tract anterior to the lateral geniculate bodies. Those which carry light reflex impulses pass to the pretectal nucleus in the midbrain at the level of the superior colliculi (anterior quadrigeminal bodies), where they synapse, and the neurons of the next order go to the Edinger-Westphal nuclei of the same and the contralateral sides, from which impulses are carried through the oculomotor nerve to the sphincter of the pupil (Fig. 23). Those having to do with somatic visual reflexes, such as movement of the eyes and head in response to visual stimuli, go to the superior colliculus; descending tecto-oculomotor fibers connect with appropriate areas in the nuclei of ocular nerves and impulses going through tectospinal fibers innervate skeletal muscles for response to visual stimuli. For conscious modification of the visual reflex impulses go from the lateral geniculate body to the visual cortex, and thence to the superior colliculus. Fibers also pass from areas 18 and 19 of the occipital cortex through the optic radiations to the superior colliculus. These subserve reflex reactions through connections with the eye muscle nuclei and other structures. The pathway is known as the internal corticotectal tract. There may also be fibers from the occipital cortex to the pulvinar. Fibers which carry impulses having to do with visual-palpebral reflexes go to the facial nuclei.

CLINICAL EXAMINATION: DISORDERS OF FUNCTION

The optic nerve is essentially a sensory nerve, and it carries impulses which have to do with the special sense of vision, or sight. Rays of light pass through the cornea, crystalline lens, and vitreous, and penetrate the retina to reach the rods and cones on its outer surface. From here, by means of fibers of passage, impulses are carried to consciousness for recognition of light, form, and color. The other functions, such as the mediation of afferent impulses for light and visual reflexes, are tested with these reflexes. Its major function is tested by examination of the various modalities of the visual sense, namely, the quantity (acuity) of vision, the range (fields) of vision, and special components of vision, such as color vision and day and night blindness. Finally, the optic nerve is the one cranial nerve that can be examined directly, and no neurologic examination is complete without an inspection of the optic nerve and the retina by means of an ophthalmoscope. The eyes are tested individually, and in examining acuity, fields, and color vision it is important that the patient keep one eye covered while the other is being tested. Before performing the functional examination of the optic nerve, one should look for local ocular changes such as cataract, conjuctival irritation, corneal scarring or opacity, iritis, uveitis, foreign bodies, and glaucoma. The presence of a prosthesis, of photophobia or abnormal intolerance to light, or of an arcus senilis should be recorded. A Kayser-Fleischer ring is found in Wilson's disease (hepatolenticular degeneration); this is a zone of greenish-gold granular pigmentation on the posterior surface of the cornea near the limbus, often best seen with the slit lamp. Recent studies have shown the presence of copper in the Kayser-Fleischer ring. Cataracts may be present in patients with dystrophia myotonica.

VISUAL ACUITY

Visual acuity, or the resolving power of the eye for central or direct vision, is dependent upon the following functions: the sensitivity of the retina to light (intensity threshold), the minimum visible (the smallest area that can be perceived), and the minimum separable, or resolution threshold (the ability to recognize the separateness of two closely approximated points or parallel lines). Visual acuity is tested for both distance and near vision. If glasses are worn, the examination is made with and without correction. In infants acuity can be tested only by noting blinking in response to bright light, pupillary reactions, and following movements. At the age of four months the acuity is said to be 20/400; it gradually increases, but does not reach a normal level until the age of five years.

Distance vision is examined by the use of the *Snellen test charts.* These consist of a series of letters of diminishing size that are placed at a distance of twenty feet, or six meters, from the patient, since at that distance there is relaxation of accommodation and the light rays are nearly parallel. The charts contain letters to be read at distances varying from two hundred to ten feet (Fig. 26). The letters are constructed so that each stroke of the letter subtends an angle of one minute at the nodal point of the eye, and the whole character subtends an angle of five minutes at the usual distance from the eye. Normal vision is present when the subject is able to read at twenty feet, or six meters, the letters designed to be read at that distance, and the acuity is then recorded as 20/20 or 6/6. The eyes are tested separately, and one is covered during the examination. Any defect in vision is recorded fractionally. The figure 20, the distance from the test chart, is used as the numerator, and the distance at which the smallest type read by the patient should be seen by a person with normal vision constitutes the denominator. For example, if the patient is able to read at twenty feet only those letters which should be read at forty feet, he has 20/40 vision. It must be borne in mind, however, that this does not mean that the patient has one half of normal vision, for the fraction is merely a record of his ability to read at twenty feet only those letters which are normally seen at forty feet. It has been found, for instance, that an individual with a Snellen notation for distance of 20/40 has only 16.4 percentage loss of vision, with an 83.6 per cent maintenance of visual efficiency.

Near vision is tested by the use of ordinary printer's types, known as the *Jaeger's test types.* The finest is numbered 1, and the successive numbers indicate coarser types (Fig. 27). Inasmuch as the Jaeger types have never been standardized and since various editions show considerable variation in shape and size, the American Medical Association has printed reading cards composed of optotype block letters for rating visual efficiency at the near point (fourteen inches, or 35.5 centi-

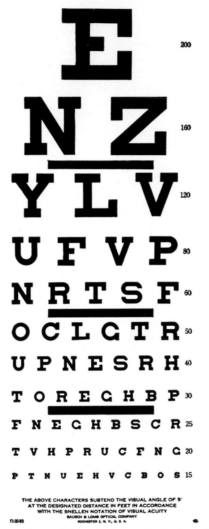

TEST CHART–SNELLEN RATING
DIRECT READING

FIG. 26.   Snellen test chart. (Bausch & Lomb Optical Company.)

meters). The smallest line the patient is able to read is noted, and result is interpreted fractionally, as in the Snellen test, or in percentage of visual efficiency (Fig. 28).

Other test charts are available for use in examining distance and near vision in the bed patient; for a rough approximation of vision the examiner may use ordinary print from a book, and compare the patient's vision with his own. Most physicians are aware of their own visual acuity, and if they have a defect, it is satisfactorily corrected by glasses. If the patient has a marked loss of acuity, the examiner should

READING CARD

15   **J1**

I walked up the street, gazing about, until near the market house I met a boy with bread. I had made many a meal on bread, and asked him where he got it. I then went to the baker's and asked for biscuit such as we had in Boston. I asked for a three penny loaf and was told that they had none such. Not knowing the difference of money and the greater cheapness, I bade him give me three penny worth of any sort. He gave me three great puffy rolls. I was surprised at the quantity but took it, and walked off with a roll under each arm.

20   **J2**

Thus I went up Market Street as far as Fourth Street, passing by the house of Mr. Read, my future wife's father. She, standing at the door, saw me and thought I made a most awkward appearance, as I certainly did. Then I turned and went down Chestnut Street and a part of Walnut Street, and found myself again at the wharf. Being filled with one of my rolls, I gave the other two to a woman and her child.

25   **J3**

By this time the street had many clean and well dressed people in it, all walking the same way. I joined them and was led into the great meeting house of the Quakers. I sat down among them and after looking around a while and hearing nothing said, I fell fast asleep. This was the first house I was in, or slept in, in Philadelphia.

30   **J4**

Looking in the faces of people, I met a young man whose countenance I liked, and asked if he would tell me where a stranger could get lodging. "Here", said he, "is one place that entertains strangers, but it is not a reputable house. If thee wilt walk with me, I will show thee a better." He brought me then to a place in Water Street, where I engaged a room and got dinner.

40   **J7**

While I was eating it several sly questions were asked me, as it seemed to be suspected from my youth and appearance that I might be some runaway. After dinner, my sleepiness returned, and being shown to a bed, I lay down without undressing and slept soundly till six in the evening.

50   **J8**

Our city, though laid out with beautiful regularity, the streets crossing each other at right angles, had the disgrace of allowing those streets to remain long unpaved. The wheels of heavy carriages plowed them into a quagmire.

60   **J10**

I saw the people wading in mud while purchasing their provisions. A strip of ground down the middle of the market was at length paved with brick, so that they had firm footing.

The above letters are Snellen sizes at the designated distance in inches, with Jaeger notations at right.

FIG. 27. Jaeger chart. The numbers indicate the distance in inches at which the letters should be read; the Jaeger notations are at the right. (Bausch & Lomb Optical Company.)

14/14   100%

BELL	WEST	RUST	BLOT	OPEN	PULP	TREE		ECHO	COPY	ENVY	DROP	BULL	SELL	HELP
DEER	FUSS	SLED	OBEY	STUN	POOR	ROSE		FRET	BOLT	FROG	CURE	PART	MOON	OVEN
COLD	HOPE	VOLT	FOOD	NOTE	ROSE	DOOR		DOVE	RULE	CORN	BULB	ROOT	DUEL	YELL

14/21   91.5%

BLUE	REEF	HERO	DEBT	BURN		PROP	DOLL	HERB	LONE	BELT
LENS	BEND	POLE	PURE	PREY		DONE	COLT	REED	POOL	FUEL
GLEN	ROOF	LOVE	DOZY	LEND		COST	BEEF	GULF	ROBE	HOLY

14/24.5   87.5%

HOPE	BEET	EDGE	BOOT		REEL	HOUR	GOLF	HUNT
NEED	TELL	COOL	HORN		BULL	GOLD	BUOY	BERG
CURE	RUDE	LOST	LOUD		GLEE	PUSS	TOOL	DELL

14/28   83.6%

CHEF	FERN	BURN	RUBY	ZERO	SHOP	BONE
DUET	NOTE	TENT	SHOE	YULE	ZONE	CODE
PORT	GULL	SCUD	TREE	VEST	SOUL	LUNG

14/35   76.5%

BLUR	DRUG	NOSE	TUBE	EDDY
CLOD	HOSE	PONY	COVE	BOSS
FELT	LOON	REEF	SHOT	DORY

14/42   69.9%

PLOT	TURN	STEP	SURF	POST
HOOF	SHED	BOND	LUTE	HULL
ROVE	LYRE	LORD	DENT	YELP

14/56   58.5%

CLUB	EVEN	PEER	BUSH
FOOT	TROT	SHOO	LEND
POSE	ROLL	VOTE	NOUN

American Medical Association

Chart to be held 14 inches from eye.
Visual acuity notation in center.
Visual efficiency percentage at right.

FIG. 28. American Medical Association reading card. (Courtesy of American Medical Association.)

determine the distance at which he is able to count fingers, make out gross forms, discern moving objects, or tell light from dark.

It is important to remember that changes in visual acuity may be due either to ocular disease or to disease of the nervous system, and that a large percentage of people have some error of refraction, such as myopia, hyperopia, or astigmatism, which may be present before the onset of more serious or acute eye conditions or neurologic disease. This must be taken into consideration in noting visual acuity, as must corneal opacities and abnormalities of the media or retina. The pinhole test is useful in determining whether poor vision is due to a refractive error or to disease of the eyeball or the visual pathways. Vision which can be improved by looking through a pinhole can usually be improved by glasses. The test is made by requesting the patient to read the chart through a one millimeter pinhole in a disk held before one eye while the other eye is covered. Since the pinhole prevents peripheral rays of light from entering the eye and allows only the central rays to do so, defective vision due to refractive errors will be improved, but poor vision due to organic defects will not. Vision is recorded as above, but with the letters "p.h." suffixed (20/20 p.h.). Hysterical blindness or malingered defects may have to be appraised by special technics (Chapter 56). The term amblyopia is used to designate defects in vision resulting from imperfect sensation of the retina without organic lesions of the eye. *Amaurosis* means blindness of any type, but, more specifically, blindness without apparent lesions of the eye; that caused by disease of the optic nerve or brain.

COLOR VISION; DAY AND NIGHT BLINDNESS

Color blindness, or *achromatopsia,* is an inherited condition present almost exclusively in the male sex but transmitted by the female. It is said to occur in 3 to 4 per cent of males and in 0.3 per cent of females. Disturbances of color vision, however, may also occur in diseases of the choroid, optic nerve, visual pathways, etc., in which there is a disturbance of the visual sense. Loss of color vision may precede loss of general visual acuity or form perception. This is especially evident in the examination of the visual fields, and it has been noted that in diseases of the choroid the field for blue may be lost first, followed by loss for red, and then green, before form perception is lost. Color blindness may be partial or total. There are various means for the testing of color vision. The patient may be asked to match or compare colors of skeins of yarn, the Holmgren test, or, for more accurate testing, the pseudoisochromatic plates of either Ishihara or Hardy, Rand, and Rittler or the Stilling test cards may be used. Tests for color vision are important in the examination of certain industrial workers.

Day blindness, or *hemeralopia,* is a condition in which vision is poor in a bright light, but is better in dim lighting; it may be a fatigue syndrome and it is occasionally found in tobacco and alcohol amblyopia and other conditions causing a central scotoma, and in beginning nuclear cataract formation. It is believed that bright lights fatigue the retina in certain individuals, and since the pupil is contracted by illumination, only central vision is used; when the illumination is less bright, the pupil is dilated, and the individual is also able to use the periphery of the retina.

Night blindness, or *nyctalopia,* is defective vision in feeble illumination or with the approach of dusk, although vision may be normal when there is adequate illumination; this is often a symptom of pigmentary degeneration of the retina, but it is also observed in fatigue or exhaustion states, chronic alcoholism, jaundice, Leber's disease, and debilitating diseases, and it is an early symptom in xerophthalmia. This last condition is the result of a deficiency of vitamin A, and it may be that A avitaminosis frequently manifests itself in night blindness, or in poor adaptation to darkness and to changes in illumination. Many clinicians believe that poor accommodation to changes in intensity of light is one of the earliest signs of a deficiency in vitamin A. There is a special apparatus, the photometer or biphotometer, available for testing of impaired dark adaptation.

The term *hemeralopia* is commonly used for day blindness, and *nyctalopia* for night blindness, but Duke Elder designates day blindness as nyctalopia, and night blindness as hemeralopia.

THE VISUAL FIELDS

The *field of vision* represents the limit of peripheral vision; it is the space within which an object can be seen while the eye remains fixed on some one point. As we fix the eye on an object, a sharp image falls upon the macula, the site of most distinct vision. Simultaneously, however, we are able to observe more or less clearly, with the periphery of the retina, objects lying at some distance from that upon which the eye is fixed. Their images are not so distinct, however, and peripheral objects are more apparent if they are moving.

The examination of the visual fields is as important a part of the neurologic examination as the testing of visual acuity, and it may give more information in the localization of disease within the nervous system. In testing the fields we test the range of vision, determine the position, size and shape of the physiologic blind spot, and search for abnormalities of either central or peripheral vision. The normal visual field has a definite contour. One is able to see laterally a distance of from ninety to one hundred degrees from the fixation point, and medially only about sixty degrees; he can see upward, at the center of vision, fifty to sixty degrees, and downward sixty to seventy-five degrees (Fig. 29). The field of vision is wider in the inferior lateral quadrant than in the superior lateral one. There may be individual variations in the field of vision, dependent to a certain extent upon the facial configuration, the shape of the orbital cavity, the position of the eye in the orbit, and the width of the palpebral fissure. An individual with a projecting brow or a highly bridged nose may have some resulting limitation in the extent of his vision, but such changes are inconsequential in most instances. In binocular vision there is overlapping of the field of one eye by that of the other, with only a narrow crescentic, or sickle-shaped, area at the temporal aspect of the field which is seen by one eye only. This may extend from sixty to ninety degrees on the horizontal meridian. In clinical testing, however, one is usually more concerned with the monocular than the binocular field.

In examining the visual fields the examiner should have adequate cooperation on

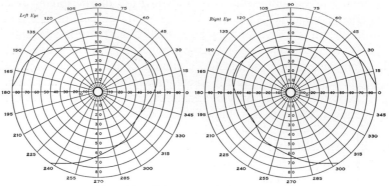

FIG. 29.   The normal visual fields.

the part of the patient. Results are most accurate in an intelligent individual who is alert and interested in the examination. The eye under examination should be fixed on some object, for any wandering of the eye impairs the results. The illumination should be adequate and constant. Fatigue and weakness may lengthen the latent period between the patient's perception of the test object and his recognition of or response to it, and may thus give a false impression of contraction of the fields. Close cooperation, good fixation, adequate illumination, and the absence of fatigue are especially important in measuring the blind spot and in delineating scotomas.

There are three standard methods of testing visual fields, the hand or confrontation method, the perimeter, and the campimeter or tangent screen. Methods of testing the visual fields by flicker fusion, ultraviolet light, and evoked occipital potentials have recently been introduced, as well as a rapid screening test by the tachistoscopic presentation of simple, abstract patterns. These latter procedures, however, are used more for experimental than clinical testing.

In the *confrontation method* the field under investigation is compared with the examiner's, which is used as a standard. The examiner stands, with one eye closed, in front of and two to three feet away from the patient, who also closes one eye and fixes the other on either the examiner's open eye or his nose. The opposite eyes are closed—i.e., if the examiner's left eye is closed, the patient closes his right eye. Each eye is tested individually. A pin with a white or colored head, a cotton-tipped applicator, a pencil, or a finger is used as a test object, and is brought into the field of vision through various meridians of vision (Fig. 30). The test object should be equidistant from the patient and the examiner. The patient is told to respond when he first notices motion, when he perceives whiteness or sees the object, when he can tell the color, and when he can distinguish the form of the object. The patient may also be asked to count fingers (either one or two) in the various quadrants of the visual field. By confrontation any gross defect in the field of vision may be detected, but minor changes and slight irregularities may be overlooked. The advantages of the confrontation method are that it is rapid, that it can be used at the bedside or in the home, and that it can be used on children, persons of low intellectual endowment or in states of lowered consciousness, or aphasic patients. However, it gives

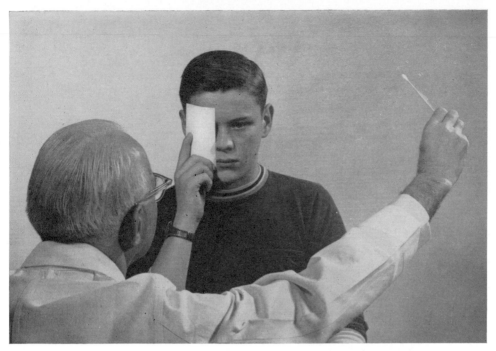

FIG. 30. Confrontation method of testing visual fields.

only approximate results and demonstrates only marked changes, and it is doubtful whether accurate delineation of the blind spot can be made. After testing each eye, *visual extinction,* or *inattention,* is looked for by observing the patient's ability to see identical test objects, or movement of them, when presented simultaneously in the upper and lower temporal quadrants of vision of the two eyes.

At times major defects in the field of vision may be demonstrated in semistuporous or aphasic patients or the fields can be outlined in uncooperative patients, children, and malingerers by bringing in from the side some object that the patient would be interested in having, such as a glass of water or a cigarette, and noting how soon he reaches for it. At the same time there is a turning of the eyes toward the object, an *optically elicited movement.* The presence of such movement indicates that the object is seen, and thus rules out gross field defects in malingering and hysteria. Turning of the head and eyes toward a diffuse light may be present in infants within a few days after birth. In testing aphasic patients and children one may move a flashlight into the field of vision and note when the patient blinks, or one can move the hand rapidly from the side, as if to strike the patient, and notice whether he winces, draws his head back, or blinks. By this means the so-called *blink,* or *menace, reflex* is elicited.

The *perimeter* is an instrument by means of which one tests the field of vision though the arc of a circle concentric with the retina (Fig. 31). It is especially valuable for the accurate delineation of the periphery of the field of vision. The patient is placed before the instrument and is asked to gaze at the fixation point. A

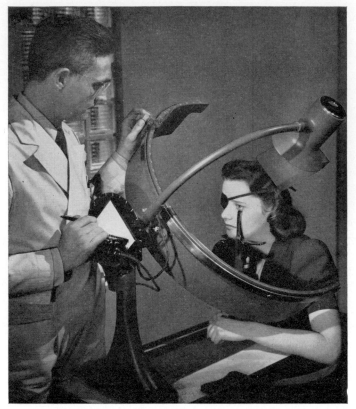

FIG. 31.   A common type of perimeter. (Bausch & Lomb Optical Company.)

test object is brought into the field of vision through multiple meridians. The places where the object is first seen are noted and recorded, and a line is drawn to join these points on the various radii and outline the field of vision. The smaller the test object, the smaller the visual field. The line representing the limits of the field for a given test object and distance is called an isopter. White test objects, varying in size from one to five millimeters, are usually sufficient, but for patients with diminished vision larger ones may be used. Perimetric readings are expressed in fractions, with the numerator the size of the test object and the denominator the distance in millimeters. Thus 3/330 indicates that a three-millimeter object was used at the ordinary perimetric distance of 330 millimeters. Defects in visual fields should be analyzed by plotting at least three isopters with targets of different sizes in order to gain an adequate understanding of the nature and extent of the field loss and to determine whether the defect has abrupt or sloping margins. If the size of a defect in the visual field is the same with all test objects used, it is said to have steep, or abrupt, margins. If, on the other hand, the defect becomes larger with decrease in the size of the test objects, (isopters for smaller stimuli), its margins are said to be gradual, or sloping, in character.

Limits of the visual field vary according to the size and brightness of the test

object, the intensity of illumination, state of adaptation of the eye, and the cooperation of the patient. Colored test objects are sometimes used, and it has been said that
changes in the color fields may precede gross field changes and that altered responses
to color may aid in differentiating between lesions of the retina and of the connecting
pathways. It is probable, however, that reported differences in color fields are not
the result of differing receptor responses, but the fields for all colors are equal if size,
light intensity, and saturation of colors are the same, and the illumination and background are such that the colors are equally perceptible. The perimetric examination is especially valuable because it gives a permanent record. The examination
may be repeated periodically and the fields compared to observe changes accompanying progression or improvement in a lesion. It must be recalled, however, that
a perimetric examination cannot be considered infallible. The cooperation of the
patient and the ability and comprehension of the perimetrist are important criteria.

In the *campimeter,* or *tangent screen,* a flat surface or blackboard is used instead
of the arc of a circle. and the outline of blind spots within the field of vision is
charted, as well as peripheral defects. Since the hemispheric field of vision is
projected upon a tangential plane perpendicular to the line of fixation, only that
portion of the field issuing from the central portions of the retina is studied, and
usually only the central thirty degrees of vision can be charted, but this area can
be evaluated more accurately than with the perimeter. A test object of one to three
millimeters is used, and the patient is seated one to two meters from the screen. The
reading may thus be expressed as 1/2000. A greater distance between the eyes
and the screen furnishes a larger projection of any defect within the field of vision,
and makes possible its earlier detection. The campimeter is especially valuable in
measuring the size of the physiologic blind spot and in demonstrating central
defects. The *Bjerrum screen* is a frequently used type of tangent screen (Fig. 32).
A more detailed method of testing central vision is possible with the *stereocampimeter,* by which each field is examined independently, but with binocular
fixation; this is especially helpful in outlining central scotomas. Instruments for
visual field examination by automation have also been described.

Various *changes in the visual fields* may be demonstrated in neurologic disorders.
Some of the more important of these are listed here.

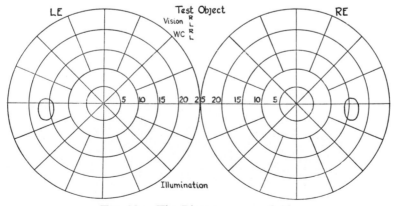

FIG. 32.   The Bjerrum screen field.

Contraction of the visual fields is characterized by a narrowing of the range of vision which may affect one or all parts of the periphery. Contraction may be regular or irregular, concentric or eccentric, temporal or nasal, and upper or lower. Regular, *concentric contraction* is most frequently seen. This is usually an early objective finding in optic atrophy, either primary or secondary, and is characterized by narrowing of the field of vision through all meridians. One also finds concentric contraction of the visual fields in degenerative diseases of the retina, especially in pigmentary degeneration of the retina. Narrowing of the field due to fatigue, poor attention, or inadequate illumination must be ruled out, as must "contraction" due to decreased visual acuity or delayed reaction time. One should be certain to determine whether the patient first responds when he perceives movement or when he distinguishes form.

A specific variety of contraction, the diagnosis of which is often important, is *tubular contraction,* a condition commonly regarded as a stigma of hysteria (Fig. 33). In the normal individual the field of vision widens progressively as the test objects are held farther away from the cornea, but in the hysterical individual this normal widening is not seen, and the entire width of the field is as great at one foot from the cornea as it is at two, five, ten, or fifteen feet. The tubular field is demonstrated either by testing the extent of the gross field at varying distances from a blackboard or screen or by the use of test objects of different sizes at a constant distance. Another type of contraction that is often difficult to evaluate is *spiral contraction,* in which there is a progressive narrowing of the field of vision during the process of testing it. This is also said by some to be a stigma of hysteria, but it is probably more diagnostic of fatigue (Fig. 34). Similar to the spiral field is the *star-shaped field,* in which there is an irregularity of outline. This may be seen in hysteria, fatigue, or poorly concentrated attention. Spiral and tubular fields and ring scotomas with continual fluctuation of the visual threshold for different parts of the field and concomitant phenomena of extinction have been described in cases of head injury.

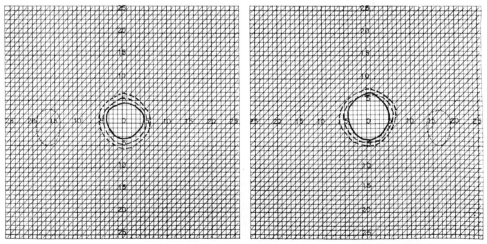

Fig. 33. Tubular contraction of visual fields as shown on tangent screen field. Patient tested at one, two, and three meters from screen.

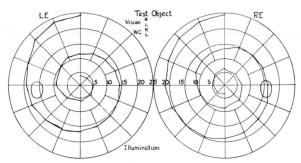

FIG. 34.   Spiral fields in a patient with pronounced fatigability, as shown on the Bjerrum screen field.

Loss of one half of the visual field is termed *hemianopia,* or *hemianopsia.* This may be either *homonymous* or *heteronymous. Homonymous hemianopia* is caused by lesions posterior to the optic chiasm, where there is interruption of the fibers from the temporal half of the ipsilateral retina and of the fibers from the nasal half of the opposite retina. In such lesions there is loss of vision in the nasal field for the ipsilateral eye, and in the temporal field for the opposite eye, and inasmuch as the hemianopia is designated by the field loss and not by the retinal involvement, a lesion posterior to the chiasm on one side always causes hemianopia on the opposite side (Fig. 35).

If the lesion which causes a homonymous hemianopia is situated in the *optic tracts* anterior to the lateral geniculate body, the fibers subserving the light reflex are also involved, and there is loss of pupillary response when a pencil of light is focused on the involved half of the retina (Fig. 23, *D,* p. 120); this is termed *Wernicke's hemianopic phenomenon.* The ipsilateral pupil may also be larger, and if there is optic atrophy, it may be more marked in the ipsilateral eye. In tract lesions, furthermore, the hemianopia is usually incongruous due to the fact that the fibers from the corresponding retinal areas are not evenly mixed or intermingled in the tracts. There may also be incongruity in geniculate lesions owing to stratification of fibers. If the lesion is posterior to the lateral geniculate body, within the *optic radiations,* the light reflex is not lost (Fig. 23, *G*), and the defect is usually congruous, because fibers representing corresponding areas in the two retinas are closely associated. Wounds involving the intermediate portion of the radiations may cause a

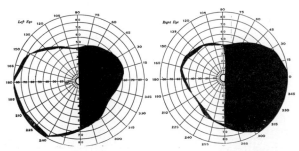

FIG. 35.   Right homonymous hemianopia in patient with tumor of left occipital lobe.

narrow, sector-shaped defect in the horizontal meridian, and with lesions of the anterior portion of the visual cortex there may be sparing of the temporal crescent. In suprageniculate hemianopias there may be no subjective dimness of vision or darkness in the affected portions of the fields, and visual acuity may be normal.

Instead of a complete blindness in the hemianopic fields, other changes may be evident. A partial or irregular defect in one or both of the symmetrical fields may be as significant as loss of the entire field. There may be relative rather than absolute loss of vision, or fluctuation of vision in the affected fields. There may be *extinction,* or suppression of vision toward one side without true loss of vision, or a failure to notice one object when a similar object is held simultaneously in the opposite field. This has also been called visual inattention, but most investigators believe that stimuli originating in a normal field of vision suppress or obscure the image arising simultaneously in an affected field. Extinction may be present rather than hemianopia, or it may appear during the process of development of a hemianopia, and it should always be tested for. Of similar significance are the following: loss of visual discernment, or inability to localize the object seen; impairment of the fusion threshold for intermittent light (as determined by flicker perimetry); hemianopia for color, or hemiachromatopia. In the latter the green field is usually lost first, then red, and finally blue.

It is often not possible to determine, from the field defect alone, the site of the lesion responsible for a homonymous defect. The most frequent location is in the occipital lobe, then the parietal and temporal lobes; tract and geniculate lesions are infrequent. Occipital lobe lesions are most often of vascular origin, whereas parietal and temporal lobe lesions are more commonly neoplastic. A vascular lesion usually has an abrupt onset and the resulting field defect has steep or abrupt margins. The field defects associated with neoplasms are often incomplete, gradual, and progressive in nature, and have gradual or sloping margins; occasionally they are incongruous. An alteration or absence of optokinetic nystagmus toward the hemianopic side is found most often with parietal lobe involvement. With lesions near the tip of the occipital lobe, especially if in the dominant hemisphere, there may be *macular sparing,* or preservation of central vision in the otherwise blind half of the visual field (Fig. 36). Macular sparing was once explained on the basis of bilateral representation of the maculae in the occipital lobes, and it was believed that by means of either radiation of fibers through both optic tracts or crossing of fibers

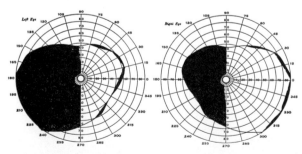

FIG. 36.   Left homonymous hemianopia with macular sparing in patient with tumor of right occipital pole.

through the splenium of the corpus callosum the maculae were represented in the primary visual centers of both hemispheres; this has never been confirmed anatomically. The maculae do have wide distribution, however, both at the occipital pole and anteriorly in the depths of the calcarine fissure. The persistence of central vision with involvement of one occipital lobe can probably be explained by this extensive macular representation, incomplete destruction of the striate cortex by the lesion, overlapping of blood supply, or individual variations. With occipital lesions there is also a constant physiologic shift of fixation, possibly with lower centers taking over a certain amount of visual perception. It may be, therefore, that macular sparing is apparent rather than real, and that the change that appears in the visual fields is a result of instability of fixation and the establishment of an eccentric fixation point, both of which occur with loss of cortical integration and with interruption of corticotectal pathways. In the gradual onset of a hemianopia the macular vision is retained the longest, but it too may disappear.

At times there is loss of one quadrant in the field of vision rather than an entire half; this is termed *quadrantanopia* or *quadrantic hemianopia*. If the loss is in the lower quadrant, there has been involvement of the fibers that radiate through the parietal lobe and terminate on the upper lip of the calcarine fissure; an upper quadrantanopia signifies involvement of fibers that radiate through the temporal lobe and around the lateral ventricle and terminate on the lower lip of the calcarine fissure (Fig. 23, *E* and *F*, Fig. 37).

A unilateral lesion limited to the posterior portion of the occipital lobe may cause a symmetrical hemianopic scotoma. *Calcarine,* or *cortical, blindness* follows bilateral lesions. There may be bilateral homonymous hemianopias, owing to involvement of both optic tracts or radiations or both occipital lobes, or there may be bilateral central scotomas because of lesions of both occipital poles. Cortical blindness may be of vascular, traumatic, neoplastic, or degenerative origin, and occurs with injuries to the posterior part of the brain, thrombosis of the basilar or of both

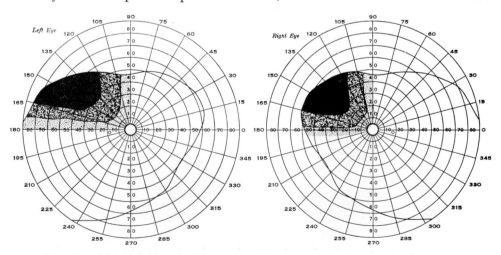

FIG. 37.   Visual fields with sloping borders in a patient with a tumor of the right temporal lobe.

posterior cerebral arteries, severe anoxia or blood loss, air embolism, hemolytic transfusion reactions, and degenerations such as Schilder's disease. Because the pupils may still react to light, cortical blindness is sometimes difficult to differentiate from hysterical blindness, although occasionally there is denial of loss of vision. Lesions of the more anterior portions of the occipital lobes may be accompanied by a disturbance in space perception and loss of absolute localization of objects in the homonymous field without hemianopia, or by such defects as visual agnosia, alexia, loss of visual memory, denial of blindness, and loss of following and reflex movements of the eyes.

In *heteronymous hemianopia* either both nasal or both temporal fields are affected. The bitemporal variety is most common (Fig. 38), and is usually the result of involvement of the optic chiasm (Fig. 23, B), which is situated just above the sella turcica. The most common cause of bitemporal hemianopia is a pituitary adenoma, but other parasellar or suprasellar tumors or cysts such as meningiomas and craniopharyngiomas, as well as gliomas of the optic chiasm, optochiasmatic arachnoiditis, aneurysms, trauma, and hydrocephalus may also cause the syndrome. Interference with the decussating fibers which supply the nasal half of each retina, and therefore carry vision from the temporal fields, is responsible for this change. It is unusual for the fields to be bilaterally symmetrical. Owing to the fact that the fibers from the superior field of vision which travel in the ventral portion of the chiasm are usually first affected, the primary defect of vision appears in the superior quadrant (Fig. 39). There may first be a superior temporal quadrantanopia in one eye, then a temporal field loss, and then contraction or loss of the nasal field. One side usually advances faster than the other. There may be blindness of one eye with a temporal field defect in the other. Occasionally the first manifestation is a central scotoma. Recession with recovery of vision also takes place in sequence, in the reverse order to that of the advancing process.

To get a *binasal hemianopia* there would have to be bilateral lesions which interrupt the continuity of the fibers from the temporal half of each retina without involving the crossing fibers. Binasal hemianopia is very rare, although it is sometimes seen in sclerosis or bilateral aneurysms of the internal carotid arteries. Unilateral nasal hemianopias are seen more frequently (Fig. 23, C).

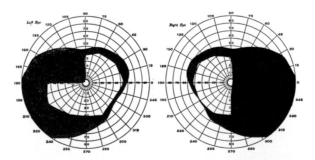

FIG. 38. Bitemporal hemianopia in patient with chromophobe adenoma of pituitary gland; complete hemianopia of the right temporal field, predominant involvement of superior quadrant of left temporal field.

Altitudinal, or *horizontal, hemianopias* occur less frequently. They may be associated with lesions of the sellar region, just below the optic chiasm, pressing on the ventral fibers and causing a superior field loss, or with internal hydrocephalus or third ventricle lesions, pressing on the dorsal aspect of the chiasm and causing an inferior field loss. They may also occur in the presence of bilateral lesions involving either both cuneate lobes or both lingual gyri.

Scotomas are defects, or blind spots, of varying size, shape, and intensity within the field of vision. They are best demonstrated by the use of the tangent screen

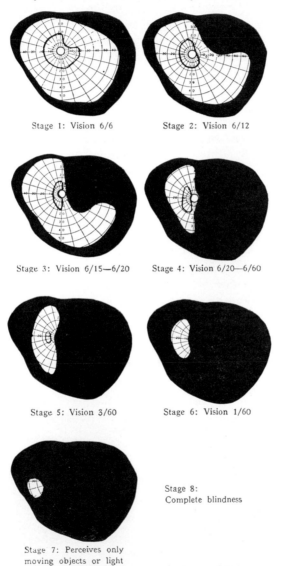

Stage 1: Vision 6/6   Stage 2: Vision 6/12

Stage 3: Vision 6/15—6/20   Stage 4: Vision 6/20—6/60

Stage 5: Vision 3/60   Stage 6: Vision 1/60

Stage 8:
Complete blindness

Stage 7: Perceives only
moving objects or light

Fig. 39.   Progressive loss of vision, beginning in superior temporal quadrant, in patient with pituitary adenoma. (Loder, L. L.: *Univ. Hosp. Bull., Ann Arbor* 6:2, 1940.)

and the stereocampimeter. In every field it should be possible to outline the *physiologic blind spot* (Mariotte's spot), a scotoma corresponding to the papilla, or nerve head, which contains no rods or cones and is therefore blind to all visual impressions. The physiologic blind spot is situated fifteen degrees lateral to and just below the center of fixation. It is elliptic in shape and averages seven to seven and one-half degrees in vertical diameter and five to five and one-half degrees in horizontal diameter, and extends two degrees above and five degrees below the horizontal meridian. If the blind spot is charted on the Bjerrum screen with the patient one meter from the board, and tested with a one-millimeter object, the average measurements are from nine to twelve centimeters in the horizontal diameter and from fifteen to eighteen centimeters in the vertical diameter. Testing at two meters may give more accurate results. The blind spot is enlarged in papilledema and optic neuritis.

Pathologic scotomas, or *blind spots,* may be relative, or indistinct, in which the patient sees form but not color, or in which perception of objects is impaired but not destroyed; or they may be *absolute,* in which the patient sees neither form, color, nor light. Subjectively scotomas may be *positive,* owing to a lesion in or anterior to the retina or choroid, or *negative,* owing to a lesion of the optic nerve, tracts, or radiations. In *positive scotomas* the blind spots are seen by the patient as dark or blind areas; these are usually due to exudate or hemorrhage over the retina or changes in the media, and are not regarded as true scotomas. In *negative scotomas* the blind spots are not perceived by the patient until the visual fields are examined. Scotomas are most frequently central, paracentral, ring, or peripheral in distribution. Scotomas secondary to lesions of the optic disk are usually wedge-shaped due to involvement of one or more bundles of fibers.

A *central scotoma* is characterized by blindness limited to the area of the visual field which corresponds to the macula, or point of fixation, and it results from involvement of the macular area of the retina or of the papillomacular bundle, which is especially susceptible to toxins and pressure (Fig. 40). Such a scotoma is frequently seen in retrobulbar neuritis, toxic amblyopia, and multiple sclerosis. It may entirely abolish central vision. A *paracentral scotoma* is one whose edge passes through the fixation point; it does not cause total loss of central vision. Enlargement

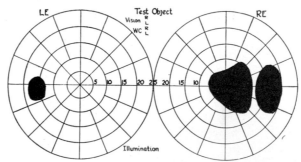

Fig. 40.   Screen fields in a case of retrobulbar neuritis affecting right optic nerve. Central scotoma, together with enlargement of the physiologic blind spot.

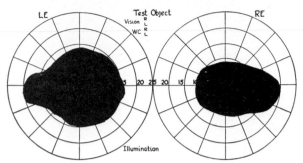

FIG. 41. Screen fields in a case of bilateral optic neuritis. Bilateral ceco-central scotomas.

of the blind spot is referred to as *peripapillary scotoma*. A *cecocentral scotoma* involves both the macular area and the blind spot; it is usually accompanied by loss of all central vision, with preservation of a very small amount of peripheral vision, and is most frequently the result of optic neuritis (Figs. 41 and 42).

Peripheral scotomas may be present anywhere in the field of vision. In *annular,* or *ring, scotomas* there is a scotomatous zone which surrounds the center of the visual field. These may be present with pigmentary degeneration of the retina. In glaucoma there may be arcuate, cuneate, comma-shaped, and partially ring-shaped scotomas. Gliomas of the optic nerve and drüsen, or hyaline bodies, which may be either within or on the surface of the optic nerves, may cause scotomas, contraction of the visual fields, or sector defects. Although scotomas are most often the result of disease of the retinas or optic nerves, they may also be caused by cerebral lesions. Pressure on the intracranial portion of the ophthalmic artery may cause a blind spot within the field of vision, and localized lesions of the posterior portion of one or both occipital lobes may cause homonymous macular, paracentral quadrantic or hemianopic, or bilateral central scotomas. Central scotomas have been reported in hysteria; if present, they are usually bilateral.

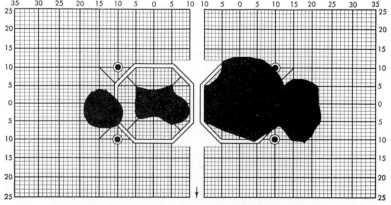

FIG. 42. Stereocampimeter fields in a case of neuromyelitis optica. Central scotoma with enlarged blind spot on the left; cecocentral scotoma on the right.

All the scotomas noted can be demonstrated objectively, but there are also subjective scotomas which cannot be delineated in the field examination, such as the *scintillating scotomas,* or *teichopsias,* of migraine, and the *muscae volitantes* which many normal individuals experience. *Visual hallucinations* and *metamorphopsias,* or distortions of vision, may constitute the aura of a convulsive attack. It should be remembered that scotomas of various types as well as field modifications of all varieties occur in many ocular and intraocular conditions, such as retinitis, chorioretinitis, and glaucoma. These are not related directly to disease of the nervous system.

THE OPHTHALMOSCOPIC EXAMINATION

It can well be repeated that the ophthalmoscopic examination is of extreme importance in the neurologic examination, and no case study is complete without it. This part of the examination is also significant in the diagnosis of many systemic diseases and in the differentiation between neurologic involvement, systemic disease, and various types of ocular pathology.

Although the neurologist is most interested in the appearance of the optic disk, the entire fundus must be examined, and the lens and vitreous should also be appraised. Many varieties of ophthalmoscopes are available, any of which is satisfactory when used by an experienced observer. It is only by *practice* that one learns to evaluate what he sees with the ophthalmoscope, and it is only by performing repeated examinations that one gains the ability to relax his own accommodation, and thus more adequately visualize the fundus of the patient. Every *skillful* ophthalmoscopist should be aware of his own errors of refraction, so that he may correct for these in studying the eyes of his patients.

The ophthalmoscopic part of the neurologic examination should be carried out without the use of mydriatics, if this is at all possible. The pupillary responses and their variations are an important part of the neurologic examination, and every attempt should be made to preserve them. In almost every instance, except when the pupil is miotic, as after morphine administration, it is possible to examine the optic nerve head, the macular area, the surrounding portions of the retina, and the blood vessels without dilating the pupil, especially if the patient is placed in a dark room for a short period of time before the examination is to be made. Sometimes, however, it is necessary to dilate the pupils, especially in examining the periphery of the fundus. This should be done only after the pupillary responses have been carefully noted. It is best to use mydriatics which do not cause cycloplegia and whose action is of short duration.

There are individual variations in the normal fundus. The *retina,* which is transparent and assumes the color of the underlying choroid, varies from a pale orange-red in light-complexioned individuals to a deep red in brunets, and is even darker in Negroes. It is important to remember this variation is coloring, since one's interpretation of the coloring of the optic disk may be influenced by the contrast between the disk and the amount of pigment seen in the retina.

The *optic disk,* or *papilla,* represents the entrance of the optic nerve, and is situated just medial to and slightly above the center of the fundus. It is oval to elliptic in shape, and pale pink in color. The temporal half of the disk is slightly paler than the nasal half. The margins of the disk are usually sharply defined, and are slightly more distinct on the temporal aspect and at times somewhat blurred nasally. Varying amounts of pigmentation are present in the retina near the temporal border of the disk, and at times there is a pigment ring which completely surrounds the disk. The white scleral and dark choroidal rings may sometimes be seen. The outer portions of the disk are elevated slightly above the center, or physiologic cup, and in the depressed central area is seen the cross hatching of the lamina cribosa, where the fibers of the optic nerve pass through the sclera (Fig. 43). Abnormalities of the contour or border of the disk may be caused by many physiologic or non-pathologic conditions: an excess of glial tissue may obscure the outline of the nerve head; myelination of some of the nerve fibers as they pass from the retina into the disk may give the latter an irregular, feathered outline; drüsen, or hyaline bodies, may appear as shiny areas on the surface of the disk.

The central artery and vein emerge from the center of the disk and divide into superior and inferior divisions, whose nasal and temporal branches radiate out to supply the entire retina. The arteries are only seventy-five to one hundred microns in diameter, but the fourteen-diameter magnification provided by the cornea and lens of the patient's eye makes these visible on the ophthalmoscopic examination. The arteries are smaller in caliber than the veins, in a ratio varying from 2:3 to 4:5, and their course is straighter, their color is lighter, and they show a bright reflex stripe along their surfaces. The veins are thicker, more tortuous, of a deep reddish-purple color, and some of them terminate at the border of the disk. The macula lutea is situated at the center of the fundus, about two disk diameters temporally to the disk. Here the choroid is slightly darker or slightly granular, and this area is devoid of large blood vessels. There may be one or more bright spots corresponding to the position of the fovea centralis.

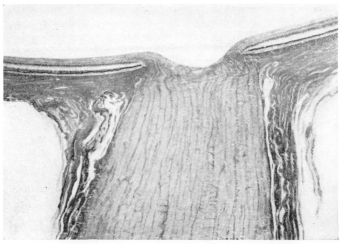

FIG. 43. Section of optic nerve head showing the physiologic cup. (Oatman, E. L.: Diagnostics of the Fundus Oculi. Troy, N. Y., Southworth Company, 1913.)

In examining the fundus, one pays special attention to the optic disks, noting their color, size, and shape. The borders are inspected, as are the physiologic cup and lamina cribrosa. One should also observe the size, shape, and appearance of the vessels, and the appearance of the retina, choroid, and fovea centralis. Hemorrhages, exudates, aberrations in pigmentation, and other variations should be noted and described.

There are many neurologic conditions in which there are important and characteristic abnormalities that are apparent by ophthalmoscopy. Furthermore, the examination of the fundus oculi and the optic disk is a valuable part of the general medical examination and is often of distinct aid in the diagnosis of systemic disease.

In *primary optic atrophy* the disk is paler than normal; it may be an opaque white or a blue-white color (Fig. 44). The disk margins stand out distinctly, the physiologic cup may be increased in size and depth, and the lamina cribrosa is prominent and may extend to the margins of the disk. The capillaries which supply the disk are decreased in number and the larger vessels are diminished in caliber. There may be increased pigment deposits about the margin of the disk. Primary optic atrophy may develop in association with or as the result of many pathologic conditions, some of the more important of which are as follows: as a part of central nervous system syphilis; as a result of retrobulbar neuritis, especially in association with multiple sclerosis, but also that caused by toxic amblyopia, deficiency states, diabetes, and anemia (see below); in Leber's disease, or hereditary optic atrophy;

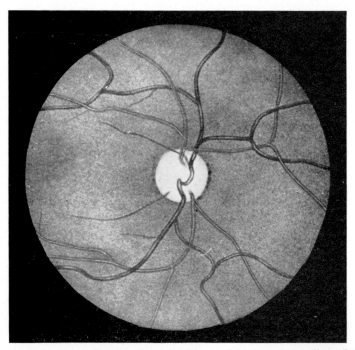

Fig. 44.   Primary optic atrophy in patient with tabes dorsalis. (Oatman, E. L.: Diagnostics of the Fundus Oculi. Troy, N. Y., Southworth Company, 1913.)

secondary to pressure on the optic nerves due to pituitary tumors, craniopharyngiomas, suprasellar aneurysms and tumors, meningiomas, and optochiasmatic arachnoiditis; with orbital tumors, gliomas of the optic nerve, Paget's disease, hydrocephalus, and oxycephalia; as the result of trauma, such as fractures or gunshot wounds with severing of the nerve; by interruption of the blood supply to the nerve. In all of the above conditions there is primary damage to the nerve with resulting degeneration; sometimes the cause of optic atrophy is not determined. If there is marked recession of the disk, the term cavernous, or pseudoglaucomatous, optic atrophy is sometimes used; this variety of atrophy is caused by interruption of blood supply to the nerve, and occurs in vascular disease and pituitary tumors.

In certain conditions, especially multiple sclerosis, there is apt to be increased pallor of the temporal portion of the disk. This may precede atrophy in multiple sclerosis, in retrobulbar neuritis, and in various toxic states. One cannot diagnose multiple sclerosis, however, on the basis of temporal pallor alone, for this may be physiologic. The appearance of temporal pallor with visual loss, especially a central defect (involvement of the papillomacular bundle which runs through the temporal area of the disk), is significant. Leber's disease is a sex-linked, hereditary disease usually affecting males. There is a loss of central vision, due to involvement of the papillomacular bundle, followed by atrophy of the optic nerve and retina.

In *secondary,* or *consecutive, optic atrophy,* which is most frequently a sequel of papilledema and optic neuritis, the appearance may be similar to that noted above, but there are usually residual signs of the previous condition. The disk is often a grayish-white color, and the margins are blurred and the lamina cribrosa may be hidden by connective tissue, glial proliferation, or residuals of previous exudation. Sometimes the term *secondary atrophy* is used for the type that follows neuritis, and consecutive atrophy for that which follows papilledema. In the former there is connective tissue infiltration, with glial proliferation that extends out into the retina; in the latter there may be glial proliferation, but no connective tissue infiltration. Some authorities restrict the use of the term *consecutive atrophy* to that which follows disease of the retina or choroid rather than that which follows neuritis or edema.

It is often difficult to differentiate between primary and secondary optic atrophy, and the two may exist together. In both varieties there is loss of visual acuity, with concentric contraction of the visual fields which may be apparent before visible changes appear in the disk. In secondary atrophy, however, there may also be field changes which are the result of the previous inflammation or edema of the disk or of the intracranial condition responsible for the disturbance of vision.

Papilledema, or *"choked disk,"* is characterized by swelling of the nerve head, usually the result of increased intracranial pressure. The subdural and subarachnoid spaces of the brain are continuous along the course of the optic nerve, and increased pressure within the skull and subarachnoid space is conducted to the nerve. Papilledema is produced mechanically by pressure on the vaginal sheaths of the nerve, which interferes with lymphatic drainage and causes obstruction of venous outflow and rise of intravenous pressure. Consequently, there is swelling of the nerve, with protrusion of the papilla into the globe of the eye (Fig. 45). The first

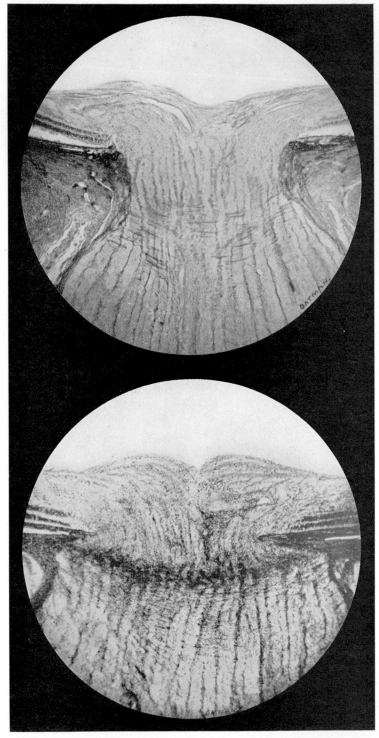

FIG. 45 (*Top*). Section of optic nerve head showing edema.
FIG. 46 (*Bottom*). Section of nerve head showing infiltration. (Oatman, E. L.: Diagnostics of the Fundus Oculi. Troy, N. Y., Southworth Company, 1913.)

visible change is hyperemia of the disk, with a blurring of its margins, primarily evident on the nasal, superior, and inferior borders; this is followed by dilatation of the veins and disappearance of venous pulsations (Fig. 47). Although the increase in intracranial pressure is the most important mechanism in the development of papilledema, swellling of the optic disk is also influenced (either hastened or retarded) by other factors, which include the intraocular tension, the pressure within the central retinal artery and vein, the systemic arterial and venous pressures, the condition of the capillary walls in the optic nerve, the composition of the blood, and the osmotic pressure of the vitreous body and the cerebrospinal fluid.

As the edema increases, the lamina cribrosa becomes obscured, the physiologic cup is obliterated, and the disk itself becomes reddened and elevated. The veins then become increasingly dilated and tortuous, the arteries are contracted, exudate forms over the disk and extends over the retina, and hemorrhages occur in the area surrounding the disk and extend into the retina (Fig. 48). The earlier hemorrhages are linear or flame-shaped and radiate out from the disk; these hemorrhages are present in the nerve cell layer of the retina. Later, large hemorrhagic areas may be seen (Fig. 49). Early in the process there is no interference with the blood supply through the central artery, but later this vessel may also be constricted. The amount of elevation of the disk is recorded in diopters, and the reading is determined by noting the difference in the lens reading in diopters when focusing on the highest portion of the elevated disk and that, in turn, when focusing on an uninvolved portion of the retina. The use of a plus two lens to focus on the disk and a minus one lens to focus on the retina gives a difference of three diopters, or a papilledema of three diopters. Absence of spontaneous pulsations of the retina veins is one of the early signs of papilledema. Occasionally, however, no pulsations can be seen in patients without intracranial hypertension; if such is the case, it should be possible to bring them out by applying light pressure to the globe, thus raising the intraocular pressure above the venous pressure. In early stages of papilledema there may be no significant loss of visual acuity, and the only field change may be an enlargement of the physiologic blind spot. Papilledema may be followed by edema of the retina and may result in optic atrophy.

The presence of papilledema is usually an indication of elevation of the intracranial pressure. It is found most frequently in association with brain tumors and abscesses, but also with meningitis, encephalitis, posttraumatic states, subdural hematoma, subarachnoid hemorrhage, arachnoiditis, benign intracranial hypertension (pseudotumor cerebri), arachnoiditis, thrombosis of the dural sinuses, and hydrocephalus. Other pathologic states in association with which there may also be significant papilledema are as follows: the Guillain-Barré syndrome and other conditions in which there is a marked elevation of the protein content of the cerebrospinal fluid; profound anemia and leukemia; emphysema; hypertension and toxemia; plumbism and hypoparathyroidism; orbital tumors or pressure on the optic nerve in the orbit; gliomas of the optic nerve; decrease of the intraocular pressure; various systemic and metabolic disorders causing alterations of the central nervous system. In the *Foster Kennedy syndrome,* usually the result of a neoplasm in the frontal lobe or in the region of the sphenoidal ridge, there is optic atrophy on the side of the

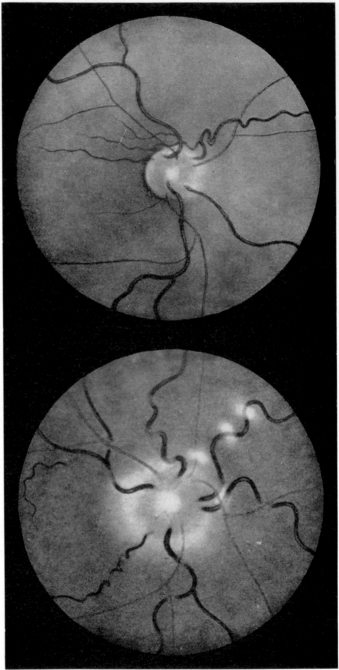

FIG. 47 (*Top*).   Beginning papilledema, showing blurring of nasal portion of optic disks.
FIG. 48 (*Bottom*).   Advanced papilledema in patient with brain tumor. (Oatman, E. L.: Diagnostics of the Fundus Oculi. Troy, N. Y., The Southworth Company, 1913.)

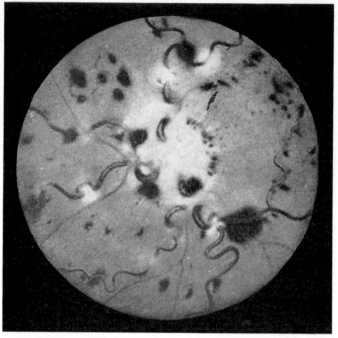

FIG. 49.   Papilledema with hemorrhages in patient with brain tumor. (Oatman, E. L.: Diagnostics of the Fundus Oculi. Troy, N. Y., The Southworth
Company, 1913.)

lesion, probably caused by direct pressure on the optic nerve, with papilledema in
the opposite eye. Papilledema may fail to develop in spite of the presence of increased intracranial pressure if the optic nerves are atrophic, if the nerve heads are
anomalous, as in severe myopia, or if the subarachnoid space around the optic
nerves is sealed off from the intracranial subarachnoid space by the presence of
adhesions.

It may be difficult, on occasion, to differentiate between papilledema and other
conditions in which there is an apparent elevation of the papilla, such as optic neuritis, to be described below, and pseudopapilledema, which is seen in some hyper-
metropic eyes. Here there is blurring of the disk margins, but the surface of the disk
is not raised; there is no dilation of the veins, and no hyperemia or enlargement of
the blind spot. High central branching of the retinal arteries may give an appearance
of elevation of the disk margins. Papilledema must also be differentiated from neuroretinitis, which appears in hypertension and nephritis; from venous engorgement
owing to neoplasms of the orbit, thrombosis of the central retinal vein, cavernous
sinus thrombosis, arteriovenous aneurysm, and intrathoracic venous obstruction;
and from drüsen, or hyaline excrescenses of the papilla, which may sometimes cause
field defects and visual impairment. Photography of the fundus after the intravenous
injection of fluorescein may aid in differentiating between early papilledema and so-
called pseudopapilledema. In true papilledema there is increased capillary permeability of the disk and the surrounding retina, and the fluorescein leaks into the

extravascular tissues, where it remains for several hours. In pseudopapilledema due to hypermetropia, drüsen, and congential anomalies, there is no such leakage.

Optic neuritis resembles papilledema and often is difficult to differentiate from it. Optic neuritis is an inflammation of the optic nerve, and while there may be elevation of the disk, the primary findings are congestion, infiltration, and exudation (Fig. 46). The disk is a deep red or gray with red striations, the margins are blurred, the veins are dilated, and the arteries narrowed. There is extensive exudation over the disk, which often extends onto the retina, and there may be hemorrhages, choroidal changes, and pigment deposits. The retinal vessels are frequently hidden by exudate. The physiologic cup may be lost or the disk be measurably elevated, but the actual edema is not in proportion to the other changes. In contrast to papilledema (where the onset is gradual, there may be little visual loss, and central vision is preserved until late), in optic neuritis there is a marked loss of visual acuity that often comes within a very short period of time, and there is a pronounced loss of the central field, often with a cecocentral scotoma and preservation of only a small amount of the peripheral field (Fig. 41). Neuritis is usually associated with pain in and behind the eye, pain on movement of the eye, and tenderness to pressure, whereas papilledema is painless. Optic neuritis is often unilateral, and papilledema more frequently is bilateral. In papilledema the swelling, engorgement, and hemorrhages are more marked; in optic neuritis there rarely is marked elevation of the disk, but there is more exudation and retinal edema. Optic atrophy is frequently a sequel of optic neuritis.

Optic neuritis may be the first manifestation of neuromyelitis optica, or acute neuroencephalomyelopathy (Fig. 42). The macular fibers and central vision seem to suffer the most, either because the center of the nerve is predominantly involved or because the papillomacular bundle is most susceptible to damage. The process may extend to involve the retina, causing a neuroretinitis. Optic neuritis may be a primary inflammatory condition of the optic nerve, in reality an encephalitis, or it may be secondary to infection elsewhere in the body. Both a *perineuritis* and an *intraneural* neuritis have been described. In the former the involvement is primarily in the sheath of the nerve, the result of extension of an inflammatory process from the meninges, from optochiasmatic arachnoiditis, or from the orbit. An intraneural neuritis may be primary infection, a part of neuromyelitis optica, or may be secondary to sinus disease (especially inflammation of the sphenoidal sinus), or associated with systemic infections such as measles, infectious mononucleosis, and vaccinia. Optic neuritis may also occur in multiple sclerosis, as a manifestation of malnutrition, anemia, and severe vitamin deficiency (especially of thiamin, B_{12}, and the B complex), with diabetes and other metabolic disorders, and following the ingestion of or exposure to certain toxins. Optic neuritis with normal acuity has been reported but is rare; the preservation of vision has been explained by the sparing of the papillomacular bundle.

In *retrobulbar neuritis* there is a marked loss of visual acuity, usually due to a defect in central vision, but no appreciable ophthalmoscopic change. There is involvement of the optic nerve posterior to the globe, and especially of the papillomacular fibers, which are the most vulnerable to toxins and pressure. Although the appearance of the disk is usually normal, there may be either slight edema or temporal pallor. The condition is considered by many to be a clinical entity regardless of the ophthalmoscopic appearance of the disk, but it might be better to term it as a symptom complex. It may be similar to optic neuritis in etiology and pathologic physiology, but the process is sufficiently posterior to the nerve head so that no changes are apparent on ophthalmoscopy. The loss of acuity may vary from a deficiency of vision of from 10 to 20 per cent to complete blindness. There may be central, pericentral, paracentral, or cecocentral scotomas (Fig. 40). The process may either be self-limited or terminate in optic atrophy. Occasionally it occurs bilaterally.

Retrobulbar neuritis is seen most frequently in multiple sclerosis, but it may also occur in neuromyelitis optica, sinus disease, Leber's disease or hereditary optic atrophy, allergic states, and hyperthyroidism; in certain of the conditions listed as causing optic neuritis (systemic infections, anemia, malnutrition, deficiency states, and diabetes); the following exposure to or ingestion of certain toxins, including lead, thallium, carbon disulfide, quinine, tryparsamide, and methyl alcohol. So-called tobacco and alcohol amylopias may be of either toxic or deficiency origin. Pressure on the optic nerve by tumors and trauma may cause a syndrome resembling retrobulbar neuritis, as may certain vascular and circulatory disorders, such as the generalized vascular disease of which temporal arteritis is a part. In many instances the etiology of retrobulbar neuritis is not found, and the process resolves spontaneously. In about 35 per cent of such cases, however, the patient later develops other manifestations of multiple sclerosis.

Ophthalmoscopic changes in the retinal arteries and veins may also have diagnostic importance. In *retinal arteriosclerosis,* which may be a part of cerebral or of generalized arteriosclerosis, the arteries may be straight or tortuous. There is proliferation of the intima, and an endarteritis or a periarteritis. The lumens of the vessels, especially the arteries, are narrowed, with widening of the reflex stripe and slight indentation of the veins at the arteriovenous crossings. As the process progresses, white lines seen along the borders of the arteries give an appearance of "silver-wire" arteries. Hemorrhages are frequently scattered along the blood vessels.

Obstruction of the central artery may cause sudden blindness. Within a few hours the entire fundus is pale and edematous, and the arteries are extremely thin and can be followed only a short distance from the disk. The veins are pale and may appear to be beaded, and there is a bright cherry-red spot at the fovea. Within a few days there may be degeneration of the retina, and within a few weeks atrophy of the nerve and of the retina. In *thrombosis of the central vein* there is marked distention of all the retinal veins, and the entire fundus may be covered with hemorrhages. The arteries are attenuated. The disk is blurred and may be elevated. Subhyaloid and vitreous hemorrhages are commonly encountered in patients with *subarachnoid hemorrhage.*

In *hypertension* retinal changes occur early and may be of prognostic significance. There is angiospasm, which progresses to angiosclerosis. The arteries are narrowed, the diameter ratio of arteries to veins is reduced, there is an increase in the reflex stripe, and there are localized areas of irregularity in the lumens of the arteries owing to spasm, in addition to arteriovenous compression, proliferation, and peri-arterial sheathing. As the process progresses the areas of spasm become more marked, with definite zones of constriction, straightening of the normal curves, and shortening of the arteries, so that the distal arteriolar segments are not seen. There may be hemorrhages and edema of the retina and the nerve head, which cause a diffuse angiospastic retinitis accompanied by exudation and elevation of the disk. Whitish deposits, or "cotton-wool patches," form in the retina, edema develops in the macula, and a partial or complete star-shaped figure made up of white dots appears with the fovea as its center. Keith and Wagener have classified the retinal changes in hypertension and have expressed the belief that much information concerning the status of the patient, differential diagnosis, and prognosis, especially in cases of so-called malignant hypertension, can be derived from the retinal examination.

With *cerebrovascular insufficiency,* of either the carotid or vertebrobasilar arterial systems, visual symptoms may be prominent. Amaurosis fugax, or brief, recurrent attacks of binocular loss of vision, and transient hemianopic defects may occur with insufficiency of the vertebrobasilar system. With atherosclerotic stenosis and insufficiency of either the common or internal carotid artery there may be attacks of transient, ipsilateral, monocular blindness (also called amaurosis fugax) due to temporary retinal ischemia, decrease in the retinal artery pressure, or even occlusion of the central retinal artery. Occulusion of any of the arteries that supply the visual pathways or the cortex may cause permanent field defects. Atherosclerotic plaques at the bifurcations of the retinal arteries have been described in patients with carotid artery disease. In patients with extensive vascular disease (so-called pulseless disease) any of the above may be present, and in addition there may be multiple microaneurysms of the retinal arteries and dilated veins. *Ophthalmodynamometry,* or the measurement of the pressures in the central artery of the retina, is discussed in Chapter 3.

Ocular angiospasm, or *angiospastic retinopathy,* has also been described in association with other conditions. This and periphlebitis of the retinal veins may be present in individuals with Buerger's and Raynaud's diseases or other types of peripheral vascular disease. Central angiospastic retinopathy has been described as a disease entity, either of the autonomic nervous system or of psychosomatic origin. The attacks of spasm are accompanied by edema of the macula and by a marked disturbance of vision. The spasm may lead to ischemia and degeneration of the macular area. As the edema subsides, a mottled irregularity of pigmentation is noted in the region of the macula, frequently with discrete, punctate, yellowish spots around the fovea. The condition may progress to the development of a sharply outlined, punched-out hole in the macula. There may be a residual central scotoma. With temporal arteritis there may be visual defects due to ischemia of the optic nerve or retina. In patients with multiple sclerosis who have some visual impairment there may be increased blurring of vision immediately after exercise. Some observers have suggested that this may be secondary to transient retinal arteriolar spasm. Rucker has reported sheathing of the retinal veins with plaque formation and narrowing of the lumen in about 10 per cent of patients with multiple sclerosis.

Congenital defects of the retina may occur, especially in *albinism*. In the *infantile form of amaurotic family idiocy* (Tay-Sachs disease) there is atrophy with lipoid infiltration of the retinal ganglion cells, and the normal choroid at the macula stands out as a distinct red spot in contrast to the pale retina; there is also optic atrophy. In the *late infantile* and *juvenile* varieties of this disease there is a pigmentary degeneration of the retina, with deposits of black pigment in the periphery of the fundus and atrophy of the disk and retina. *Pigmentary degeneration of the retina* need not necessarily be associated with progressive intellectual deterioration, but it is often associated with other congenital anomalies such as deafness, mental deficiency, etc., and is a part of the *Laurence-Moon-Biedl syndrome,* which consists of retinitis pigmentosa, adiposogenital dystrophy, polydactyly, syndactyly, skull defects, and idiocy. Other degenerations of the retina may consist of macular degeneration, colloidal changes, or fatty deposits. In *tuberous sclerosis* there may be retinal tumescences of glial or vascular origin that are called phakomas. In *Recklinghausen's disease* glial elevations may appear on the disk or retina. Choroiditis, especially in the macular areas, is significant in the diagnosis of *toxoplasmosis.*

Inflammatory changes are rarely limited to the retina, but are associated with disease of the choroid, *chorioretinitis,* or of the optic nerve, *neuroretinitis.* Syphilitic *neuroretinitis* and *chorioretinitis* are characterized by choroidal changes, pigment deposits, degenerative changes in the blood vessels, and areas of atrophy in the retina. In *military tuberculosis* retinal tubercles may appear. In *exudative retinopathy* (Coat's disease) there are areas of cicatricial tissue, the result of hemorrhages in the deep layers of the retina. *Retinal vasculitis* (Eales's disease) is a condition marked by recurrent hemorrhages into the retina and vitreous.

In *nephritis* and *diabetes* there are characteristic changes that result in the so-called *albuminuric* and *diabetic neuroretinitides,* with tortuosity of the vessels, hypermia and edema of the retina (especially in the macular area), flame-shaped hemorrhages, exudation, redness of the disk with striation of its margins, and at times elevation of the disk. The changes are similar to those occurring in hypertensive retinopathy. In *anemia* there may be pallor or even ischemia. Distention of the retinal vessels and cyanosis with hemorrhages are present in *polycythemia* and congenital heart disease. Dilatation and tortuosity of the vessels, with numerous hemorrhages, are common in *leukemia.* In *systemic vascular diseases* there may be retinal changes, with distention of the vessels or embolic or thrombotic phenomena. *Angiomatosis of the retina,* von Hippel's disease, is frequently accompanied by hemangioblastomatosis of the cerebellum, Lindau's disease. There are, of course, numerous ocular and intraocular conditions, among the more important of which are glaucoma, separation of the retina, retinal and orbital tumors, and various congenital and traumatic eye conditions, all of which can be differentiated from neurologic disease largely by ophthalmoscopy.

SUBJECTIVE ANOMALIES OF VISION

In a complete discussion of the optic nerve one should also mention subjective anomalies of vision. The *scintillating scotomas* of migraine have already been referred to. In migraine there may also be photophobia, blurring of vision, and transient hemianopias that cannot be confirmed objectively. *Visual hallucinations* and *metamorphopsias* occur in psychotic states and may constitute the aura of an epileptic attack, especially if the epileptogenic focus is in the visual cortex or temporal lobe. In lesions of the striate cortex the hallucinations are vague and unformed, such as flashes of light, but with involvement of the parastriate or peristriate cortex or temporal lobe there may be formed hallucinations or visual illusions. In the psychoses, toxic states, and delirium, formed visual hallucinations are common. In epilepsy and in certain psychoneurotic states there may be perversions of vision such as *macropsia* or *micropsia,* conditions in which objects seem larger or smaller than they really are. *Diplopia* is caused by dysfunction of the ocular nerves, although monocular diplopia may occur. *Aniseikonia* is a condition in which the ocular image of an object as seen by one eye differs in size and shape from that seen by the other; *metamorphopsia* is a distortion of objects seen. The visual *aphasias* and *agnosias* are discussed in "Aphasia, Agnosia, and Apraxia" (Chapter 53).

LOCALIZATION OF DISORDERS OF VISUAL FUNCTION

Disturbances of vision may result from disease processes in the eye, anywhere along the course of the optic nerve, at the optic chiasm, along the optic tract or radiations, or in the visual cortex. *Disease of the retina* may cause visual difficulty owing to involvement of the peripheral neurons, the rods and cones. In retinitis, chorioretinitis, vascular disease, hemorrhages, exudation, and separation of the retina there may be patchy or complete loss of vision in the involved eye, especially if the disease process is in the region of the macula.

Diseases of the optic nerve owing to optic atrophy, degenerative conditions, optic or retrobulbar neuritis, infection, neoplasm, toxins, trauma, pressure, or vascular insufficiency may cause unilateral loss of vision progressing from a central scotoma or a partial field defect to complete blindness (Fig. 23, *A*). If there is total loss of vision in one eye because of optic nerve disease, the direct light reflex is lost in this eye, but its consensual reflex is retained. If the lesion is immediately anterior to the chiasm, there may be a minimal field defect in the opposite eye, especially in the upper temporal quadrant, as well as blindness of the eye involved.

A lesion at the optic chiasm may bring about a loss of acuity progressing to blindness. If the lesion is at the center of the chiasm, there is a bitemporal field defect (Fig. 23, *B*), usually with loss of the upper quadrants before the lower quadrants; this may progress to optic atrophy. A lesion at one side of the chiasm causes a unilateral nasal hemianopic defect (Fig. 23, *C*), while lesions at both sides of the chiasm produce bilateral nasal defects. Adenomas of the pituitary gland, craniopharyngiomas, meningiomas arising from the tuberculum sella, third ventricle tumors, meningovascular syphilis, and optochiasmatic arachnoiditis may cause defects in vision due to chiasmal involvement. The visual changes may vary from unilateral or bilateral concentric contraction to sectoral, quadrantic, altitudinal, or hemianopic defects, or to complete blindness. Occasionally a homonymous hemianopia occurs with pituitary or parasellar lesions.

Involvement of the optic tract from the chiasm to the geniculate body results in a contralateral hemianopic defect, with loss of the light reflex when a pencil of light is focused on the blind portion of the retina (Fig. 23, *D*). Lesions of the geniculate body or of the optic radiations from the geniculate body to the cortex of the occipital lobe produce a hemianopic defect involving the contralateral fields, without loss of the light reflex when the light is focused on the blind portion of the retina (Fig. 23, *G*). If the radiations through the temporal lobe, especially in their lower portion, are more affected, the upper quadrants of vision will be more involved, and if those subserving the upper portions of the retina are more affected, the lower quadrants of vision will be more involved (Fig 23, *E* and *F*). Lesions at these sites may be associated with intracranial neoplasms, abscesses, or granulomas, or may be caused by subdural hematomas or vascular involvement. The field defect appearing with tumors may be due either to direct involvement of the radiations or to interference with blood supply. The anterior part of the optic tract is supplied by many branches from the arterial circle of Willis, and is not apt to be involved in vascular disease. The posterior part of the tract and the anterior portion of the radiations, especially the lower fibers, are supplied by the anterior choroidal artery. The middle cerebral artery supplies the middle portion of the radiations, and the middle cerebral and the calcarine branch of the posterior cerebral artery supply the posterior portion of the radiations. The geniculate bodies are supplied by the anterior choroidal artery and by the thalamogeniculate branches of the posterior cerebral. The striate cortex is supplied by the calcarine branch of the posterior cerebral and by other cortical branches of the posterior cerebral as well as cortical branches of the middle cerebral. Hemorrhage, thrombosis, embolism, spasm, or sclerosis of the arteries may cause visual changes.

Lesions of one occipital lobe will cause a contralateral hemianopic defect. If the involvement is localized to the cuneus or the upper lip of the calcarine fissure, there is a lower quadrantanopia, and if it is limited to the lingual gyrus or the lower lip of the calcarine fissure, there is an upper quadrantanopia. A lesion at the occipital pole will mainly affect central vision; focal lesions of the occipital poles may produce localized loss of central vision. Occasionally sparing of the macula is seen in hemianopias associated with involvement of the posterior portion of the occipital lobe. Lesions slightly peripheral to the striate cortex may cause difficulty with fixation and with maintaining visual attention, loss of following and reflex ocular movements, loss of stereoscopic vision, impairment of visual memory and recall, difficulty in accurate discernment or localization of objects, disturbances in the spatial orientation of the visual image in the homonymous field, and loss of ability to discriminate with respect to size, shape, and color. There may be errors in the patient's ability to localize himself or stationary or moving objects in space, with a loss of visual perception of motion and of spatial relationships (visual spatial agnosia). Simultagnosia is the ability to perceive only one object, or specific details but not a picture in its entirety, at one time. In the Charcot-Wilbrand syndrome there is loss of ability to recall visual images and to draw or construct from memory (Chapters 50 and 53). With bilateral lesions of the striate cortex there may be either marked loss of visual orientation or cortical blindness, often with anosognosia, or denial of blindness (Anton's syndrome). Lesions farther forward, in the region of the angular or supramarginal gyri, may cause other disturbances of visual perception, recognition, and comprehension. If they are in the dominant hemisphere they cause alexia (word blindness) or visual receptive aphasia. Such lesions may be neoplastic, vascular, or traumatic in origin. Stimulation or irritation of the calcarine cortex produces unformed visual hallucinations, such as flashes of light, in the corresponding field of vision, and irritation of the surrounding areas may cause formed visual hallucinations.

Psychogenic disturbances of vision may be of various types. There may be photophobia, blurring of vision, ocular fatigue, polyopia, monocular diplopia, tubular or spiral field defects, amblyopia, or blindness. Asthenopia is a weakness or fatigability of the visual organs. Central angiospastic retinopathy may be of psychogenic origin. Field changes like those in hysteria have been reported in patients with frontal lobe tumors.

REFERENCES

ADLER, F. H.   Physiology of the Eye: Clinical Application (ed. 3).   St. Louis, C. V. Mosby Company, 1959.

BARTLEY, S. H.   Vision: A Study of Its Basis. New York, D. Van Nostrand Company, 1941.

BEHRMAN, S.   Pathology of papilledema.   *Neurology* 14:236, 1964.

BENDER, M. B.   "Neuroophthalmology," in BAKER, A. B. (ed.), Clinical Neurology (ed. 2).   New York, Hoeber Medical Division, Harper & Row, 1962, vol. 1, pp. 275–349.

BERENS, C.   The fundus changes and the blood pressure in the retinal arteries in increased intracranial pressure: Papilledema and optic atrophy.   *A. Res. Nerv. & Ment. Dis., Proc.* (1927) 8:263, 1929.

BERK, M. M.   A critical evaluation of color perimetry.   *Arch. Ophth.* 63:966, 1960.

BRESLIN, D. J., GIFFORD, R. W., JR., FAIRBAIRN, J. F. II, and KEARNS, T. P.   Prognostic importance of ophthalmoscopic findings in essential hypertension.   *J.A.M.A.* 195:335, 1966.

BRICKNER, R. M., and FRANKLIN, C. R.   Visible retinal arteriolar spasm in multiple sclerosis.   *Tr. Am. Neurol. A.* 70:74, 1944.

BRODAL, A.   The Cranial Nerves: Anatomy and Anatomico-clinical Correlations. Springfield, Ill., Charles C Thomas, 1959.

COGAN, D. G.   Neurology of the Visual System.   Springfield, Ill., Charles C Thomas, 1966.

COPENHAVER, R. M., and BEINHOCKER, G. D.   Objective visual field testing: Occipital potentials from small visual stimuli.   *J.A.M.A.* 186:767, 1963.

GANS, J. A.   The automation of visual fields.   *Tr. Sect. Ophth., A.M.A.* 1962, pp 34–39.

GARDNER, W. J., SPITLER, D. K., and WHITTEN, C.   Increased intracranial pressure caused by increased protein content in the cerebrospinal fluid.   *New England J. Med.* 250:932, 1954.

GIFFORD, S. R.   An evaluation of ocular angiospasm.   *Arch. Ophth.* 31:453, 1944.

GLEW, W. B.   The pathogenesis of papilledema in intracranial disease: A review of some of the literature.   *Am. J. M. Sc.* 239:221, 1960.

HARRINGTON, D. O.   The Visual Fields: A Textbook and Atlas of Clinical Perimetry (ed. 2). St. Louis, C. V. Mosby Company, 1964.

HOLLENHORST, R. W. Neuro-ophthalmologic examination of children. *Neurology* 6:739, 1956.

HOLLENHORST, R. W. Significance of bright plaques in the retinal arteries. *J.A.M.A.* 178:23, 1961.

HOYT, W. F., and BEESTON, D. The Ocular Fundus in Neurologic Disease. St. Louis, C. V. Mosby Company, 1966.

HOYT, W. F., and PONT, M. E. Pseudopapilledema: Anomalous elevation of the optic disk. *J.A.M.A.* 181:191, 1962.

HUGHES, B. The Visual Fields. Oxford, Blackwell Scientific Publications, 1954.

KAHN, E. A., and CHERRY, G. R. The clinical importance of spontaneous retinal venous pulsations. *Univ. Michigan Med. Bull.* 16:305, 1950.

KEITH, N. M. Cardiovascular diseases in relation to the retina. *Tr. Am. Acad. Ophth.* 37:37, 1932.

KENNEDY, F. The symptomatology of temporosphenoidal tumors. *Arch. Int. Med.* 8:317, 1911.

KESTENBAUM, A. Clinical Methods of Neuro-Ophthalmologic Examination (ed. 2). New York, Grune & Stratton, 1961.

LARSEN, H. W. Atlas of the Fundus of the Eye. Copenhagen, Munsgaard, 1964.

LODER, L. L. Fundus and visual field changes accompanying lesions of the optic chiasm. *Univ. Hosp. Bull., Ann Arbor* 6:2, 1940.

MILES, P. W. Testing visual fields by flicker fusion. *A. M. A. Arch. Neurol. & Psychiat.* 65:39, 1951.

MILLER, S. J. H., SANDERS, M. D., and FFYTCHE, T. J. Fluorescein fundus photography in the detection of early papilloedema and its differentiation from pseudo-papilloedema. *Lancet* 2:651, 1965.

OATMAN, E. L. Diagnostics of the Fundus Oculi. Troy, New York, Southworth Company, 1913.

PARKER, W. R. The relation of the tension of the eyeball to the first appearance of papilledema. *A. Res. Nerv. & Ment. Dis., Proc.* (1927), 8:256, 1929.

PATON, L., and HOLMES, G. The pathology of papilloedema: A histological study of sixty eyes. *Brain* 33:389, 1911.

PETROHELOS, M. A., and HENDERSON, J. W. The ocular findings in intracranial tumors: A study of 358 cases. *Am. J. Ophth.* 34:1387, 1951.

POLYAK, S. L. The Retina. Chicago, University of Chicago Press, 1941; The Vertebrate Visual System. Chicago, University of Chicago Press, 1957.

REED, H. The Essentials of Perimetry. London, Oxford University Press, 1960.

RUCKER, C. W. Sheathing of the retinal veins in multiple sclerosis. *J.A.M.A.* 127:970, 1945.

SMITH, J. L. (ed.) The University of Miami Neuro-ophthalmology Symposium. Springfield, Ill., Charles C Thomas, 1964.

TRAQUAIR, H. M. An Introduction to Clinical Perimetry (ed. 6). London, Henry Kimpton, 1949.

UZMAN, L. L., and JAKUS, M. A. The Kayser-Fleischer ring: A histochemical and electron microscope study. *Neurology* 7:341, 1957.

WAGENER, H. P., and KEITH, N. M. Diffuse arteriolar disease with hyptertension and associated retinal lesions. *Medicine* 18:317, 1939.

WALSH, R. B. Clinical Neuro-Opthalmology. (ed. 2) Baltimore, The Williams & Wilkins Company, 1957.

WELCH, R. C.   Finger counting in the four quadrants as a method of visual field gross testing.   *Arch. Ophth.* 66:678, 1961.

WILLIAMS, D., and GASSEL, M. M.   Visual function in patients with homonyous hemianopia.   *Brain* 85:175, 1962.

ZELIGS, M. A.   Central angiospastic retinopathy: A psychosomatic study of its occurrence in military personnel.   *Tr. Am. Neurol. A.* 71:23, 1946.

ZUCKERMAN, J.   Perimetry.   Philadelphia, J. B. Lippincott Company, 1954.

CHAPTER 11

THE OCULAR NERVES

SINCE THE OCULOMOTOR, trochlear, and abducens nerves all function in regulation of the eye movements, they are here referred to as the "ocular nerves" and are examined together. The cervical portion of the sympathetic (thoracicolumbar) division of the autonomic nervous system functions with the third nerve in the innervation of the eyelid and of the pupil and, consequently, it also should be considered in the appraisal of the ocular nerves.

ANATOMY AND PHYSIOLOGY

THE OCULOMOTOR NERVE

The *oculomotor,* or *third cranial, nerve* has its nuclei of origin in the mesencephalon, or midbrain. These nuclear centers are situated in the periaqueductal gray matter just anterior to the aqueduct of Sylvius, at the level of the superior colliculi (anterior quadrigeminal bodies). There are two, and possibly more, separate nuclear groups (Fig. 50). The paired *lateral nuclei* are the largest, and are situated anterior and lateral to the others; their median portions are fused into an unpaired mass. These contain large cells, the neuraxes of which supply the superior rectus, inferior rectus, medial rectus, inferior oblique, and levator palpebrae superioris muscles. Although it may be assumed that the fibers destined for the individual muscles originate in different groups of nerve cells, evidence for accurate localization is conflicting. In general, two types of representation of the cells of origin for the fibers to the various muscles have been described: a series of specific areas placed successively in both a rostrocaudal and a dorsoventral arrangement, and a series of longitudinally running columns of gray matter, with some overlap in a dorsoventral pattern. It may be that the oculomotor fibers have diffuse origin, with only limited relation to various groups. Each third nerve receives fibers from the contralateral as well as the homolateral nucleus, but the amount of decussation is also a matter of dispute. Early studies indicated that the fibers to the levator and superior rectus were uncrossed,

159

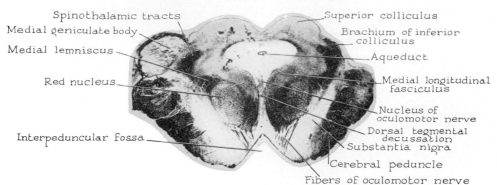

FIG. 50. Section through mesencephalon at level of superior colliculus (anterior quadrigeminal body) and oculomotor nucleus.

those to the medial rectus mainly uncrossed, those to the inferior oblique mainly crossed, and those to the inferior rectus entirely crossed, but more recent investigations have indicated that the fibers to the levator and superior rectus are the only ones to cross. A small but distinct nuclear mass sometimes found between the two lateral nuclei has been called the *central nucleus of Perlia,* and is said to be a center for convergence. It appears doubtful, however, whether there is either a distinct nucleus of Perlia or a center for convergence in the midbrain.

Posterior to the lateral nuclei, or somewhat between them at their rostral and dorsal extremities, are the *Edinger-Westphal nuclei* which are made up of smaller cells and are a part of the craniosacral, or parasympathetic, division of the autonomic nervous system. There is a paired rostral portion and an unpaired medial and caudal portion that is sometimes called the *anteromedian nucleus.* Preganglionic fibers from these nuclei go to the ciliary ganglion. Postganglionic fibers related to cells in the rostral part of the nucleus supply the sphincter, or constrictor, of the pupil, and those related to the anteromedian nucleus supply the ciliary muscle and function in accommodation.

The fibers from these various nuclei course anteriorly through the mesencephalon, traversing the medial portion of the red nucleus, the substantia nigra, and the cerebral peduncle, and make their exit from the anterior surface of the midbrain. Shortly after leaving the brain stem these filaments are united to form the third nerve on each side. This nerve emerges just above the pons, between the superior cerebellar and the posterior cerebral arteries (Fig. 20). It penetrates the dura just lateral and anterior to the posterior clinoid processes and enters the cavernous sinus, where it lies in the superior aspect, close to the lateral wall (Fig. 51). Here it is medial to the temporal lobe of the brain and lateral to the carotid artery. It enters the orbit through the superior orbital fissure, where it separates into superior and inferior divisions. The former supplies the levator palpebrae superioris and superior rectus muscles, while the latter supplies the medial and inferior rectus and the inferior oblique muscles and also sends the short root to the ciliary ganglion, from which postgangionic fibers go as the short ciliary nerves to supply the ciliary muscle and the sphincter pupillae (Fig. 52).

The superior, medial, and inferior recti and the inferior oblique are extraocular muscles. The *superior rectus* elevates the eyeball, especially if it is in abduction, and adducts it to a certain extent; it turns the eyeball upward and inward and rotates the adducted globe so that the upper end of the vertical axis is inward. The *medial, or internal, rectus* is an adductor of the eyeball. The *inferior rectus* depresses the eyeball, especially if it is in abduction, and adducts it to a certain extent; it turns the eyeball downward and inward and rotates the adducted globe so that the upper end of the vertical axis is outward. The *inferior oblique* elevates the eye, especially if it is in adduction, and abducts the eyeball; it turns the eye upward and outward and rotates the abducted globe so that the upper end of the vertical axis is outward (Fig. 53). The *levator palpebrae superioris* supplies the striated musculature of

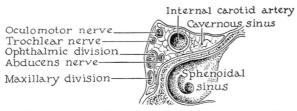

FIG. 51. Oblique section through right cavernous sinus. (After Gray.)

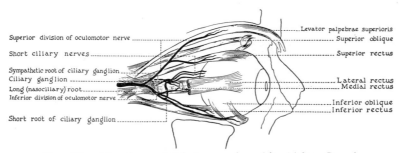

FIG. 52. Muscles and third nerve in orbit. (After Gray.)

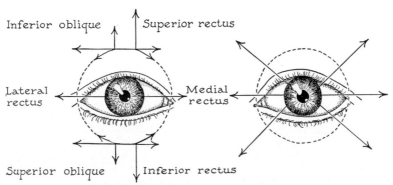

FIG. 53. Action of the ocular muscles.

the eyelid, which it elevates. All of the striated musculature of the eyelid, however, is not innervated by the levator; some is supplied by the orbicularis oculi with which the fibers of the levator are closely intermingled. The *sphincter pupillae* causes constriction of the pupil. Contraction of the *ciliary muscle* causes relaxation of the ciliary zonule and decrease in the tension of the lens capsule, followed by an increase in the convexity of the lens to adjust the eye for near vision. This change in the shape of the lens is accompanied by convergence of the eye and constriction of the pupil.

A complete paralysis of the third nerve results in ptosis, or drooping of the upper eyelid, paralysis of medial and upward gaze, paresis of downward gaze, and dilatation of the pupil (Fig. 54). A patient so afflicted is unable to raise his eyelid, and he is unable to turn the eyeball medially, downward, or laterally and upward. The eyeball is deviated laterally and somewhat downward, and can be moved still farther laterally owing to the function of the lateral rectus, and downward and laterally owing to the function of the superior oblique, but in no other directions. The completely dilated pupil does not react to light or in accommodation. The power to vary the curvature of the lens for near and distance vision is lost.

It is stated that the third nerve may also send some fibers to the orbicularis oculi, and as a result some weakness of this muscle may be present in third nerve lesions.

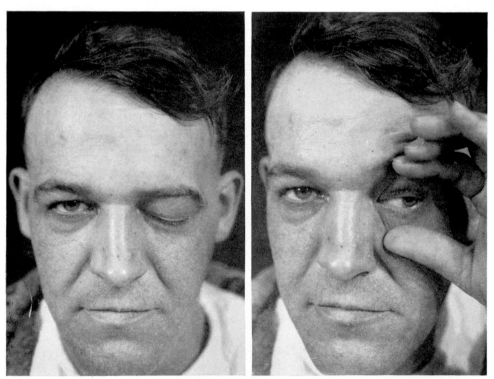

Fɪɢ. 54. Paralysis of left oculomotor nerve in patient with aneurysm of left internal carotid artery.

A third nerve paralysis need not be complete; there may be paresis rather than paralysis of function, and only certain functions may be involved whereas others remain intact. If the lesion which causes dysfunction of the nerve is within the midbrain, where the nuclear centers and their neuraxes are still separated, or within the orbit, after the nerve has redivided, only certain portions or functions may be involved. If, however, the lesion is along the course of the nerve between its emergence from the midbrain and its division within the orbit, there is apt to be paralysis of all functions. Paralysis of only the sphincter pupillae and ciliary muscle is called *internal ophthalmoplegia*; paralysis of the extraocular muscles is called *external ophthalmoplegia*.

THE TROCHLEAR NERVE

The *trochlear,* or *fourth cranial, nerve* is the smallest of the cranial nerves. Its nuclei are situated just anterior to the aqueduct in the gray matter of the lower mesencephalon immediately above the pons (Fig. 55). They extend from the level of the lower part of the anterior quadrigeminal bodies to the lower pole of the posterior quadrigeminal bodies and are immediately caudal to the lateral nucleus of the third nerve, but separated from it by a short distance. The fibers of the trochlear nerve curve posteriorly and caudally around the aqueduct and decussate in the anterior medullary velum. It is the only cranial nerve whose fibers emerge from the posterior aspect of the brain stem. The nerve then circles around the pons, the brachium conjunctivum, and the cerebral peduncle. It penetrates the dura just behind and lateral to the posterior clinoid processes, goes through the cavernous sinus, where it is lateral and inferior to the third nerve (Fig. 51), and enters the orbit through the superior orbital fissure. It terminates on the *superior oblique muscle* on the side opposite to the nucleus of origin. This muscle depresses the eye, especially if it is in adduction, abducts the eyeball, and rotates the abducted globe so that the upper end of the vertical axis is inward (Fig. 53). In paralysis of the

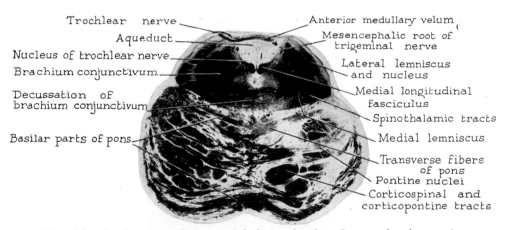

FIG. 55. Section through mesencephalon at border of pons, showing trochlear nucleus and nerve.

fourth nerve these functions are lost. In a nuclear lesion of the fourth nerve, the contralateral superior oblique muscle is paralyzed, but in a lesion along the course of the nerve, after its decussation, the ipsilateral muscle is involved.

THE ABDUCENS NERVE

The *abducens,* or *sixth cranial, nerve* arises in the gray matter anterior to the fourth ventricle in the dorsal part of the tegmentum of the lower pons (Fig. 56). The nucleus is situated just posterior to the nucleus of the facial nerve but within its looping fibers. The neuraxes of the sixth nerve leave the pons medially to those of the facial nerve (Fig. 20). They emerge from the brain stem as a single nerve at the junction between the pons and the medulla, and as they emerge they cross the internal auditory artery (the posterior branch of the basilar artery). The sixth nerve has the longest intracranial course of all the cranial nerves. It passes anteriorly, lying between the pons and the clivus; it finally pierces the dura at the dorsum sellae, where it lies between the posterior clinoid process and the apex of the petrous bone, in close relationship to the gasserian ganglion. In the cavernous sinus it is below and medial to the third nerve and lateral to the internal carotid artery (Fig. 51). It also enters the orbit through the superior orbital fissure, and it supplies a single muscle, the *lateral,* or *external, rectus,* which functions to abduct the eyeball, or deviate it laterally (Fig. 53). In paralysis of the sixth nerve the eyeball is turned medially, and it cannot be moved laterally (Fig. 57). Because of its long intracranial course, this nerve is more frequently involved in disease processes than are the other cranial nerves, and increase in intracranial pressure or exudate from inflammatory processes or hemorrhage may cause it to be pressed between the pons and the clivus and thus interrupt its continuity. In such circumstances there may also be bilateral sixth-nerve involvement.

Small groups of cells close to the motor cells of the abducens nucleus are sometimes termed the *parabducens nucleus,* from which impulses are relayed through the

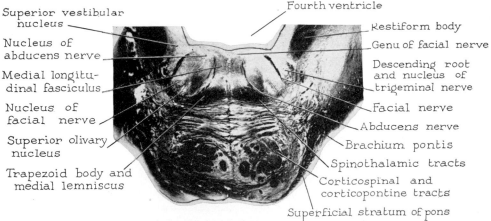

FIG. 56.   Section through pons, showing the fibers of abducens and facial nerves.

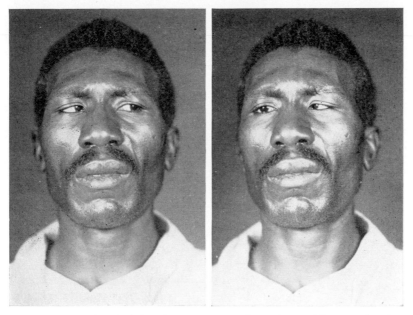

F̲ɪɢ. 57.   Paralysis of right abducens nerve in patient with posterior fossa
tumor: *Left,* patient looking to left; *Right,* patient attempting to look in direction of action of paralyzed muscle.

medial longitudinal fasciculus to the oculomotor nucleus. This connection coordinates the contraction of the lateral rectus of one eye with the medial rectus of the
other, so that both eyes move together in the same horizontal plane (conjugate
deviation) toward the side of the contracting lateral rectus.

THE MEDIAL LONGITUDINAL FASCICULUS

The oculomotor, trochlear, and abducens nuclei are situated one below the other
in a more or less columnar arrangement in the brain stem. They are united, for
coordinated and conjugate action, by the *medial longitudinal fasciculus,* which also
connects them with the nuclei of the vestibular and cochlear portions of the eighth
nerve, the trigeminal and facial nerves, the spinal accessory nerve, the hypoglossal
nerve, the motor nuclei of the upper cervical nerves, the nucleus of the posterior
commissure (nucleus of Darkshevich), and the nucleus of the medial longitudinal
fasciculus (interstitial nucleus of Cajal), as well as with higher centers (Fig. 58).
Owing to the function of this correlating mechanism, no isolated action of any eye
muscle is ever possible, and movements of one eye are correlated with those of the
other. Also, through the action of this fiber tract, head and even body movements
are correlated with eye movements. Thus, in response to visual, auditory, sensory,
vestibular, and other stimuli, there is conjugate deviation of the eyes and the head.
This pathway has important functions in auditory-ocular reflexes, vestibular-ocular
reflexes, and righting reflexes.

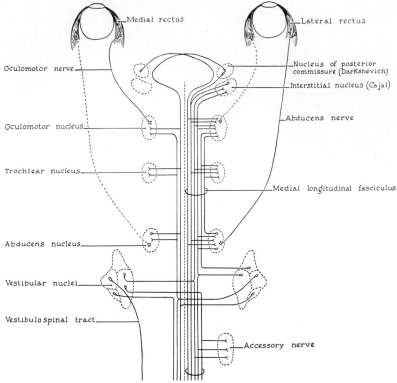

FIG. 58. Medial longitudinal fasciculus.

SYMPATHETIC INNERVATION

The cervical portion of the sympathetic (thoracicolumbar) division of the autonomic nervous system has its origin in the intermediolateral group of cells of the spinal cord extending from the eighth cervical or first thoracic segment through the upper four, five, or six thoracic segments. Those fibers which control oculopupillary action probably arise from the eighth cervical and the first and second thoracic segments (ciliospinal center). The preganglionic fibers go to the inferior, middle, and superior sympathetic ganglia in the neck, and the postganglionic fibers follow the course of the internal carotid artery into the head to the cavernous sympathetic plexus and then travel with the ophthalmic division of the fifth nerve into the orbit (Fig. 59). The sympathetic division supplies the sympathetic root of the ciliary ganglion, carried through the long ciliary nerves; fibers may pass without interruption through the ciliary ganglion into the short ciliary nerves. The cervical sympathetic nerves innervate the dilator of the pupil and also supply the tarsal muscles and the orbital muscle of Müller. The former are smooth muscle sheets in the upper and lower eyelids; the latter is a structure which, in the lower forms at least, keeps the globe of the eye forward in the orbit.

Paralysis of the cervical portion of the sympathetic division causes a *Horner's syndrome*. This is characterized by miosis resulting from paralysis of the dilator of

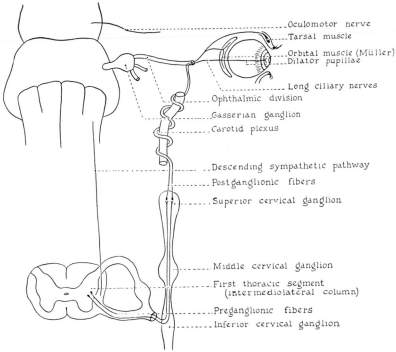

Oculomotor nerve
Tarsal muscle
Orbital muscle (Müller)
Dilator pupillae
Long ciliary nerves
Ophthalmic division
Gasserian ganglion
Carotid plexus
Descending sympathetic pathway
Postganglionic fibers
Superior cervical ganglion
Middle cervical ganglion
First thoracic segment
(intermediolateral column)
Preganglionic fibers
Inferior cervical ganglion

FIG. 59.   Cervical portion of sympathetic division of autonomic nervous system.

the pupil, a partial or pseudoptosis owing to paralysis of the upper tarsal muscle, enophthalmos owing to paralysis of the muscle of Müller, and often a slight elevation of the lower lid because of paralysis of the lower tarsal muscle (Fig. 60). The enophthalmos may be apparent rather than real. In addition, in a complete Horner's syndrome, there is ipsilateral dilatation of the vessels of the face, head, neck, conjunctiva, and arm, with ipsilateral anhidrosis. There may be ocular hypotony with an acute Horner's syndrome, and heterochromia of the irides and atrophy of the side of the face if the defect dates from birth or is of long duration. Although there may be decreased sensitivity to atropine, this drug will usually dilate the pupil in a Horner's syndrome, owing to its action in paralyzing the sphincter of the pupil, but cocaine, which stimulates the sympathetic endings, will not act as a mydriatic, and the ciliospinal reflex is lost. There may be hypersensitivity to epinephrine, especially if the lesion is a postganglionic one. Horner's syndrome may be the result of the interruption of the descending sympathetic pathways in the brain stem or spinal cord, of lesions either in the cord at the level of the ciliospinal center or of the preganglionic fibers as or after they leave the cord, of injury to the cervical sympathetic ganglia, or of involvement of the postganglionic fibers.

Some authorities have expressed the belief that control of the pupillary diameter is almost, if not entirely, through the increased or decreased activity of the parasympathetic fibers, and that the sympathetic nervous system and the dilator muscle, if

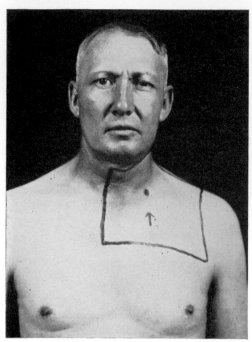

Fɪɢ. 60.   Horner's syndrome in patient with left superior pulmonary sulcus tumor.

actually present in the iris, have little role in the normal phasic activity producing changes in the size of the pupil. More recent work, however, indicates that the sympathetics contribute actively to dilatation and to maintaining the size of the dark-adapted pupil.

CORTICAL CONTROL

The principal cortical center for the regulation of function of the ocular nerves is situated in the posterior portion of the second and third frontal convolutions, just anterior to the precentral fissure (area 8 $\alpha\beta\gamma$). The impulses go through the corona radiata, internal capsule, and cerebral peduncle, from whence they descend with the aberrant pyramidal fibers. It is probable that they terminate on the centers for lateral gaze in the lower pons, and possibly on the vestibular nuclei, from which structures impulses of the next order ascend through the medial longitudinal fasciculus to the other nuclei concerned with ocular movement. There is almost complete decussation, and the cortical center of one hemisphere supplies the opposite ocular nuclei. This frontal center is concerned with *volitional control of conjugate ocular movements,* and stimulation of it causes a rapid deviation of the eyes to the opposite side, which may be accompanied by conjugate movement of the head. If the lower portion of this area is stimulated, the eyes are deviated upward as well as laterally, and if the upper portion is stimulated, the eyes are turned downward and laterally. Destruction or ablation of this area is followed by paralysis of conjugate gaze to the opposite side with turning of the eyes toward the involved side and transient visual hemiagnosia. This center may also have a regulatory effect over the levator palpebrae superioris, and when it is stimulated opening of the eyelids may accompany conjugate movements of the eyes.

The zone immediately surrounding the area striata, corresponding to fields 18 and 19 of Brodmann, especially the latter, is the cortical center for *optically induced eye movements and optic fixation reflexes* (Fig. 61) Corticofugal fibers from this center pass through the optic radiations in the posterior limb of the internal capsule to the cerebral peduncle, and then follow the same course as those from the frontal lobes. Stimulation of this center also produces deviation of the eyes to the opposite side, but the movements are slower and less forceful; ablation is followed by loss of following movements and optic fixation reflexes, with retention of voluntary control. It is a reflex rather than a volitional center, and is important in fixation and in maintaining visual attention. Stimulation of the dorsal part of area 19 or the ventral part of area 18 results in upward conjugate deviation of the eyes, and stimulation of the ventral part of area 19 or the dorsal part of area 18 causes downward conjugate movement. There are association pathways from the occipital to the frontal cortical areas, with radiation of some impulses to the frontal cortex before they descend to the brain stem. Still other centers for ocular movement have been described in the angular gyrus and temporal lobe (Chaper 50). Cortical areas for ocular deviation may also function in eye-centering, as may areas in the diencephalon, brain stem, and cerebellum. A pontine center for lateral gaze has been described in the vicinity of the abducens nucleus, one for vertical gaze is presumably at the level of the superior colliculi, and one for convergence has been said to be in the nucleus of Perlia, but the existence of this latter is doubted. The basal ganglia and the vestibular complex also play important parts in the regulation of ocular movements.

Cortical centers that control pupillary responses have also been described. Dilator impulses originating in the hypothalamus are conveyed to the frontal cortex, probably also to area 8 $\alpha\beta\gamma$, from whence they descend to the ciliospinal center at the eighth cervical and upper thoracic segments of the spinal cord, where they synapse with the cells of the intermediolateral column. Stimulation of area 8 causes pupillary dilatation. Pupilloconstrictor fibers may descend from the peristriate area to the Edinger-Westphal nucleus; stimulation of area 19 has been observed to produce pupillary constriction. The pupillodilator fibers and the afferent pathways that carry light reflex impulses from the retina are in close proximity in the midbrain.

FIG. 61. Cortical centers related to vision and ocular movement. (After Foerster.)

CLINICAL EXAMINATION OF THE OCULAR NERVES AND THE CERVICAL SYMPATHETIC SYSTEM

In examining the functions of the oculomotor, trochlear, and abducens nerves, and the cervical sympathetic fibers to the intraocular structures, it is necessary to consider individually the pupils, the eyelids, the extraocular movements, and the position of the eyeball within the orbit.

THE PUPILS

One must consider the size, shape, equality, and position of the pupils, and their reflex responses. The pupils should be round, regular, equal, and concentric, and should have specific reflex responses. Clinical observation is usually sufficient, and complicated procedures, such as pupillography, are used mainly for research.

Size: The size of the pupils varies greatly with the intensity of the surrounding illumination, but in lighting of average intensity they are usually from three to four millimeters in diameter. The use of a small ruler with holes varying from one to seven millimeters in diameter aids in estimating the size of the pupils. They are small and react poorly at birth and in early infancy. They are normally larger in young individuals, and some texts state that in moderate illumination the pupils of adolescents are about four millimeters in diameter and perfectly round. In middle age they are three and a half millimeters in diameter and slightly irregular, and in old age they are three millimeters or less in diameter and are quite irregular.

When the pupils are small (less than two millimeters in diameter) they are said to be *miotic.* They may be miotic in senility, arteriosclerosis, and syphilis, sometimes in hyperopia, occasionally in alcoholism, and frequently in drug intoxications, especially those associated with use of morphine or other opium derivatives. Miosis is also present in sleep, deep coma, increased intracranial pressure, and brain stem lesions with bilateral interruption of dilator fibers; the pupils may be pinpoint in size with acute pontine lesions. Miosis is present unilaterally with irritation of the third nerve or paralysis of the cervical portion of the sympathetic nervous system, and in association with corneal or intraocular foreign bodies. The pupils constrict slightly on expiration.

Dilatation of the pupils (more than five millimeters in diameter) is called *mydriasis.* The pupils may be dilated in anxiety, fear, pain, hyperthyroidism, midbrain lesions, certain stages of coma and drug intoxication, cardiac arrest and cerebral anoxia, after the use of such drugs as atropine and belladonna, and sometimes in myopia. They also dilate with muscular activity, in response to loud noises, and in deep inspiration. Unilateral mydriasis accompanies paralysis of the third nerve, irritation of the cervical sympathetic nerves, and conditions in which there is decrease in visual acuity or reduction in the amount of light reaching the retina. On lateral deviation there may be slight dilatation of the pupil of the abducting eye. Stimulation of the hypothalamus or of the frontal motor eye fields is followed by pupillary dilatation.

Persons with light irides have larger pupils than those with dark irides. In so-called vagotonic individuals, with cold skin, bradycardia, and low blood pressure, the pupils are constricted owing to overaction of the parasympathetic nervous system; in sympathicotonic individuals, with warm skin, rapid pulse, and hypertension, there is mydriasis (Chapter 43). Patients with anxiety psychoneuroses and some with schizophrenia belong to this latter group. Because certain drugs influence the size of the pupils, one should inquire about the use of these if patients have abnormally large or small pupils.

There is normally a certain amount of alternate fluctuation in the size of the pupil, designated as *pupillary unrest;* when this is present to an excessive degree, it is called *hippus,* or a rhythmic contraction and dilatation of the pupils. Hippus has been said to be associated with respiratory rhythm, but probably in most cases is an evidence of imbalance of the sympathetic and parasympathetic divisions of the autonomic nervous system. It may be present during recovery from a third nerve paralysis. It is occasionally encountered in organic disease of the central nervous system, such as syphilis, neoplasms, and multiple sclerosis, but usually is of no significance in either diagnosis or localization.

Shape: The shape, or outline, of the pupil is also important in neurologic diagnosis. Normally the pupil is round and is regular in outline. Any irregularity, abnormality in shape, notching, or serration may be significant. Gross abnormalities in shape are usually the result of ocular disease such as iritis. There may be anterior synechiae with adhesions to the lens, a congenital coloboma, or defects owing to trauma or a previous iridectomy. A slight change in shape, however, such as an oval pupil, slight irregularity in outline, serration of the border, or slight notching, may be pertinent in neurologic disease. Such findings are often among the earlier objective manifestations of syphilis of the central nervous system and of atrophy of the iris owing to syphilis.

Equality: Equality of the pupils is also an important criterion. Comparison of the size of the two pupils may have more significance than the observation of size alone. There may be a slight difference in the size of the pupils in 15 to 20 per cent of normal individuals, on a congenital basis, and minimal inequality is sometimes found in neuroses and psychoses, but if this is at all marked it is noteworthy. A difference in the size of the pupils may also be caused by errors of refraction and unequal illumination. The physiologic basis of inequality can often by demonstrated by parallel reflex reactions of the two pupils to all stimuli and to drugs such as atropine. Alternating anisocoria has been observed with various nervous system diseases.

Gross inequality of the pupils is called *anisocoria.* A sympathetic paralysis on one side will, of course, cause a smaller pupil on that side, and sympathetic stimulation will cause mydriasis. A third nerve paralysis produces dilatation, and stimulation of the oculomotor nerve, contraction. Unequal pupils may be caused by iritis. The pupil of an amblyopic or blind eye is often larger, and acuity of vision should be noted in evaluating the size and equality of the pupils. The pupillodilator fibers are in close proximity to the tympanic plexus in the inner ear, and there may be ipsilateral constriction of the pupil in inner ear disease.

Unequal pupils or unilateral dilatation and fixation of one pupil are frequently seen after cerebral vascular accidents or in association with severe head trauma. It has been said that the presence of a dilated and fixed pupil in a comatose individual may give presumptive localization of a lesion in the ipsilateral cerebral hemisphere. If the dilatation is marked and the pupil is fixed, one may assume direct pressure on the third nerve, probably the result of herniation of the hippocampal gyrus through the incisura of the tentorium cerebelli causing pressure on the third nerve as it crosses the body of the sphenoid bone. On the other hand, involvement of the descending pupillodilator fibers from the frontal area as they pass through the internal capsule may cause miosis on the opposite side rather than an ipsilateral mydriasis. In a hemianopia secondary to optic tract involvement the ipsilateral pupil may be dilated.

Position: The position of the pupil may also be significant. The pupil is usually situated in the center of the iris. Eccentric pupils, or ectopia of the pupils, may be the result of trauma or iritis and need not be pathognomonic of neurologic disease; the phenomenon, however, should be noted because it may give some clue to the underlying process. Some individuals have bilaterally eccentric pupils.

Reflexes: The evaluation of the pupillary reflexes is one of the most important parts of the neurologic examination. It is to preserve these reflexes that the use of a mydriatic is avoided if possible in carrying out the fundus examination. The principal reflex responses are those to light, in accommodation and covergence, and to pain, but others are also important.

1. THE LIGHT REFLEX: The normal pupil contracts promptly when light is focused on the homolateral retina, and dilates when the light is withdrawn—the *direct light reflex*. The afferent pathway is through the optic nerve, and the efferent fibers carried by the oculomotor nerve through the ciliary ganglion. As a result of the semidecussation of fibers, both in the optic chiasm and to the Edinger-Westphal nuclei, the contralateral as well as the homolateral pupil responds—the *crossed,* or *consensual, light reflex.* Thus in a third nerve lesion the direct and consensual light reflexes are absent on the involved side, owing to paralysis of the sphincter of the pupil, but the consensual and the direct reflexes remain in the opposite eye. A blind eye does not respond directly to light, nor does its mate respond consensually, but a blind eye does respond consensually if its third nerve is intact and if the other eye and its optic nerve are not involved. In paralysis of the sympathetic pathway the light response is diminished, and dilatation is imperfect, but the pupil still contracts in response to light.

Each eye should be tested individually for both the direct and the consensual reflexes, and it should be noted whether the responses are prompt, sluggish, or absent. For most accurate testing a distant source of light should be used; if a bright light is focused directly into the eye, the accommodation-convergence response as well as the light reflex is brought into action. The light reflex is best tested if the examiner stands behind and somewhat above the patient, who is asked to gaze at a lighted window or at some other distant source of light. The examiner then places his hands in front of the patient's eyes in such a way as to cut off the source of light, yet at a sufficient distance to enable him to see the size of each pupil. The hands are withdrawn alternately, and the light is allowed to focus on the retina; as the hand is withdrawn on each side, the response of the homolateral pupil (direct reflex) and that of the contralateral pupil (consensual reflex) are noted. A *reflex response to darkness* has also been described, but it is difficult to state whether this is a true reflex or a tonic dilatation due to relaxation of the sphincter on withdrawal of the light stimulus. The reaction to light is a relative phenomenon. If an eye is subjected to a light of a certain intensity after having been adapted to less intense light, the pupil contracts. This same intensity of light, however, causes dilatation of the pupil in an eye previously adapted to light of greater intensity.

An *Argyll Robertson pupil* is one which does not react to light, though it does react in accommodation. The retina is sensitive to light, but the pupil is fixed. This condition is also spoken of as *reflex iridoplegia*. It has been said that the Argyll Robertson pupil is pathognomonic of syphilis of the central nervous system, but it has also been observed in multiple sclerosis, encephalitis, diabetes, alcoholic encephalopathy, syringobulbia, neoplasms of the posterior portion of the third ventricle or the pineal body, and lesions at the level of the superior colliculus, and in senile and vascular conditions. The true Argyll Robertson pupil is said to be less than three millimeters in diameter, and to show little variation in size. Wilson, however, states that the pupil is not necessarily miotic. Both the direct and the consensual reflexes are absent. There is an active reaction in accommodation for near objects, and the convergence response may be increased and sustained. Dilatation in response to pain is diminished, psychic and sensory responses are diminished or absent, the pupil dilates poorly in response to atropine, and there may be associated atrophy of the iris. The condition is usually bilateral, although the pupils are not necessarily equal. Transmission of light impulses through the optic nerve must be intact. Less diagnostic than the Argyll Robertson pupil but also significant are pupils with a sluggish reaction to light, a reaction to light through a small excursion, a paradoxical reaction in which there is dilatation rather than contraction, or a contraction followed immediately by dilatation.

Various sites have been suggested for the lesion which causes the Argyll Robertson pupil, but it is quite obvious that such a lesion must involve both the afferent pathways carrying light reflex fibers from the retina and the autonomic connections. If a single lesion is responsible, it must occur at the point where these fiber tracts converge. It is believed by most observers that the phenomenon results from an inflammatory or a degenerative lesion in the periaqueductal region at the level of the anterior quadrigeminal bodies just ventral to the posterior commissure. At this area the light reflex fibers from the pretectal nuclei, which semidecussate to supply both Edinger-Westphal nuclei, run close to the sympathetic pupillodilator fibers. A lesion at this site interrupts both the pathway from the retina which goes to the pretectal area and thence to the Edinger-Westphal nucleus and through the third nerve to the iris, and the adjacent pathway of the sympathetic pupillodilator fibers that are descending from the hypothalamus and frontal cortex through the midbrain to the oculopupillary center in the upper thoracic spinal cord, and thence through the cervical sympathetic chain to the iris. The syndrome may be the result of a single lesion near the anterior quadrigeminal bodies, such as a tumor of the pineal gland, or there may be bilateral or more widespread lesions, as may be the case in a syphilitic ependymitis. Reliable observers differ, however, in their opinions on the site of the lesion that causes the Argyll Robertson pupil; it has been variously placed in the optic nerves, optic tracts, along the course of the third nerve, in the ciliary ganglion, and in the iris. Fulton has stated that the clinical syndrome of the Argyll Robertson pupil has never been reproduced experimentally.

In *Adie's syndrome* there is also an impaired pupillary reaction to light and a better response in accommodation and convergence. The light reaction, however, is not absent, and there is slow constriction on prolonged exposure to a bright light, especially if the patient has been in a dark room, with a gradual dilatation after the stimulus has been withdrawn. The accommodation response is also slow and may be incomplete. The abnormality is unilateral in about 80 per cent of cases, and the tonic, or myotonic, pupil is dilated in average light. The iris is not atrophic. The response to miotic and mydriatic drugs is normal, but the affected pupil is abnormally sensitive to methacholine (Mecholyl) and constricts rapidly after a few drops of a freshly prepared 2.5 per cent solution have been instilled in the conjunctival sac. This drug, in such concentrations, has no effect on normal pupils. Various sites have been suggested for the lesion responsible for the abnormality, but the increased sensitivity to cholinergic drugs suggests that the postganglionic parasympathetic fibers are affected, either in the ciliary ganglion or peripheral to it.

Adie's syndrome is a benign disorder, occurring most frequently in women. Because the tendon reflexes are often absent, it has been referred to as "tonic pupils with absent tendon reflexes," and at one time was said to be easily confused with central nervous system syphilis. The above description, however, shows that the pupillary abnormality is quite different from the Argyll Robertson pupil. Furthermore, it is not the impaired response to light that brings the disorder to clinical attention, but the unilaterally dilated pupil, which sometimes seems to have an abrupt onset. It is not an uncommon cause for anisocoria. In addition to the change in tendon reflexes, the patient may exhibit some depression or emotional instability. Because progressive anhidrosis may also occur in patients with Adie's syndrome, there is some evidence to suggest that it may be a part of a widespread autonomic disturbance.

After an oculomotor ophthalmoplegia the pupil may contract on convergence but not to light; this may simulate the Argyll Robertson pupil. Under such circumstances, however, it may be observed that the pupil also contracts with other movements of the eyeball and with movements of the eyelid. Consequently, this abnormality of pupillary response, sometimes noted after head injury complicated by a third nerve involvement, has no etiologic relationship to the classical reaction described by Argyll Robertson, but is, rather, a synkinetic reaction. *Wernicke's hemianopic phenomenon,* in which light focused on one half of the retina causes no pupillary response, is present in hemianopias in which the interruption of the pathways is anterior to the departure of the fibers to the pretectal region (Chapter 10). In retrobulbar neuritis there may be a partial dilatation of the pupil, which may react to light but not hold the reaction, or, paradoxically, may dilate slowly (the Marcus Gunn pupillary sign); the consensual reflex may be better than the direct one. These changes can be brought about by rapid alternate stimulation of the eyes with a bright light.

2. THE ACCOMMODATION REFLEX: The accommodation reflex, or the *accom-*

modation-convergence synkinesis, is elicited by having the patient shift his gaze to some near object after he has relaxed his accommodation by gazing in the distance. This is followed by a *thickening of the lens, convergence of the eyes,* and *constriction of the pupils.* There are two principal theories in regard to the *mechanism of accommodation.* The most generally accepted theory is that of Helmholtz, who expressed the belief that contraction of the ciliary muscle reduces or relaxes the tension of the zonular muscle, and thus permits the elastic capsule of the lens to shape the lens and to increase its convexity in order to adjust the eyes for near vision. Tscherning, on the other hand, stated that the force of the ciliary muscle, acting through the zonule, tightens the zonule, and the vitreous forcefully molds a relatively plastic lens into the accommodated form. *Convergence* is produced by the action of both medial rectus muscles. The *constriction of the pupils* is called a reflex response, but many observers, including Wilson, believe that the decrease in size of the pupils on accommodation and convergence is not a reflex in the ordinary use of the term, but part of a synkinesis, or associated movement. The response depends upon the conduction of afferent impulses through the optic nerve and efferent impulses through the oculomotor nerve; afferent impulses may also be conducted through proprioceptive fibers from the extraocular muscles. It is generally believed, however, that there is also a cortical factor. The impulse probably reaches the occipital cortex by passing through the optic tract, lateral geniculate body, and optic radiations. It may then be carried directly to the superior colliculus through the internal corticotectal pathway, or it may pass by way of association fibers to the frontal cortex, and by way of descending pathways to the superior colliculus and the nuclear center of the oculomotor nerve. The contraction of the pupil accompanies accommodation even when convergence is prevented by prisms, and it accompanies convergence even when accommodation is prevented by atropine.

The constriction of the pupil in accommodation is occasionally lost in a postdiphtheritic paralysis of the ciliary mechanism, and in encephalitis. In both of these conditions there may also be a paralysis of convergence and some weakness of function of the medial rectus muscles. The pupil may continue to contract on accommodation in conditions where there is loss of convergence due to paralysis of the medial recti. There is no loss of pupillary response on accommodation in the Argyll Robertson pupil. It may be that there are two separate paths for pupillary contraction, and that the efferent pathway subserving the accommodation response differs from that for the light response. It has been said that the efferent pathway that has to do with pupillary constriction in the accommodation-convergence synkinesis goes through the third nerve to the episcleral ciliary ganglion and thence to the ciliary body without passing through the ciliary ganglion.

3. THE PAIN REFLEXES: The pupil may respond to a painful stimulus directed toward either a neighboring or a distant portion of the body.

a. The *ciliospinal reflex* consists of a dilatation of the pupil on painful stimulation of the skin of the neck on the ipsilateral side. In comatose states a similar response follows painful pressure on the cheek just below the orbit. The afferent impulses are relayed through the cervical (and trigeminal) nerves, and the efferent impulses through the cervical portion of the sympathetic division of the autonomic nervous system. The dilatation is so minimal that it may be difficult to see in the normal individual, and it is best elicited in dim light, since in bright illumination the light reflex may interfere with the response. The reflex is absent in lesions of the cervical sympathetic fibers.

b. The *oculosensory reflex* consists of either constriction of the pupil or dilatation followed by constriction in response to painful stimulation of the eye or its adnexa. It occurs in the presence of corneal or intraocular foreign bodies and in injuries to the eye or the side of the face. The afferent impulses are carried through the trigeminal nerve, and the efferent impulses through the oculomotor nerve. This is also called the *oculopupillary reflex.*

c. The so-called *paradoxical pupillary reaction of Byrne* consists of dilatation of the pupil in response to pain in the lower portion of the body, usually in the opposite lower extremity or in the opposite sciatic nerve. This dilatation, like the ciliospinal reflex, is doubtless a response to sympathetic stimulation.

4. THE ORBICULARIS REFLEX: Forceful closing of the eyes, closing of the eyes in sleep, and upward deviation of the eyeballs are followed by constriction of the pupils. The response is in all probability an associated movement. A variation of the orbicularis reflex is *Westphal's pupillary reaction,* which consists of pupillary contraction on attempts to close the eyes while the examiner holds them open.

5. THE COCHLEAR OR COCHLEOPUPILLARY REFLEX: Either a dilatation or a constriction followed by dilatation of the pupils occurs in response to a loud noise.

6. THE VESTIBULAR OR VESTIBULOPUPILLARY REFLEX: This consists of either a dilatation of the pupils in response to stimulation of the labyrinthine system, or a constriction during stimulation followed by dilatation.

7. THE GALVANIC REFLEX: Galvanic stimulation to the region of the temple causes constriction of the pupil. The mechanism is probably similar to that in the oculosensory reflex.

8. THE PSYCHIC REFLEX: There is a dilatation of the pupils in response to fear, anxiety, mental concentration, and sexual orgasm. It results from stimulation of the sympathetic division of the autonomic nervous system.

9. THE DRUG REFLEXES: The variations in size of the pupils in response to pharmacologic preparations may be designated the drug reflexes. These consist of dilatation on either stimulation of the sympathetic division of the autonomic nervous system or paralysis of the parasympathetic division, and constriction on either paralysis of the sympathetic elements or stimulation of the parasympathetic. Atropine, homatropine, and scopolamine act as mydriatics by a paralyzing action on structures innervated by postganglionic cholinergic nerves; epinephrine, ephedrine, amphetamine, and cocaine dilate the pupil by stimulation of structures innervated by postganglionic adrenergic nerves. Pilocarpine, Mecholyl, and muscarine constrict the pupil by stimulation of structures innervated by postganglionic cholinergic nerves, and physostigmine (eserine) and neostigmine (Prostigmin) by inhibition of the action of cholinesterase. Ergot derivatives act as constrictors by blocking the action of postganglionic adrenergic nerves. Histamine may constrict the pupil by direct stimulation of the sphincter fibers. Nicotine has an irregular effect, depending upon whether the sympathetic or the parasympathetic endings are more stimulated. In man nicotine poisoning results in constriction followed by dilatation. These

responses are discussed further under the examination of the autonomic nervous system (Part VI). They may be utilized in the neurologic examination. Cocaine, for instance, will not dilate a miotic pupil if the miosis is secondary to sympathetic paralysis, but atropine will. Cocaine will cause further dilatation of a mydriatic pupil if the mydriasis is due to paresis of the sphincter, but not if it is secondary to sympathetic stimulation. A myotonic pupil is abnormally sensitive to Mecholyl.

THE EYELIDS

The function of the eyelids is examined by having the patient close his eyes, both without and against resistance. The size of the palpebral fissures should be noted, as should associated contractions of the frontalis muscle. Paralysis of the levator palpebrae superioris causes *ptosis,* or drooping of the eyelid. This may be partial or complete. In lesions of the cervical sympathetic pathways there is *pseudoptosis,* owing to paralysis of the upper tarsal muscles; there is drooping of the lid to or below the margin of the pupil, but the patient can raise it completely by voluntary effort. There may also be slight elevation of the lower lid (Fig. 60). In true ptosis, however, the striated, or voluntary, muscle is affected. If it is complete, there is loss of ability to elevate the lid (Fig. 54); if partial, the lid is elevated only in part, and by voluntary effort. In evaluating ptosis and partial ptosis one notes the amount

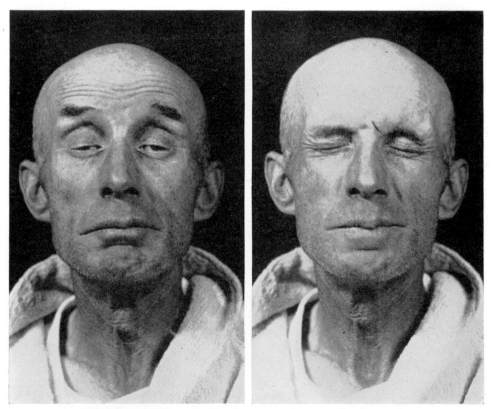

FIG. 62.   Bilateral ptosis in patient with myasthenia gravis.

of iris or pupil covered by the lid. Slight weakness may become more apparent if the patient alternately elevates and depresses his lids through a small excursion. Partial ptosis may often be diagnosed by observing the contraction of the frontalis muscle when the patient attempts to open his eye on the involved side. If the examiner fixes the frontalis muscle with his finger, the patient may be unable to raise his eyelid. In ptosis of long standing there may be wrinkles in the forehead on the involved side, owing to constant contraction of the frontalis (Fig. 62). In hysterical ptosis there is no associated overaction of the frontalis.

Any inequality of the palpebral fissures should be noted. The narrower fissure may denote a third-nerve or sympathetic involvement on one side, and the wider fissure may indicate a seventh-nerve (orbicularis oculi) paresis on the opposite side. A slight but perceptible difference in the width of the palprebral fissures occurs in 30 to 35 per cent of normal individuals. In the absence of organic disease there is at times an appearance of ptosis in fatigue states. In myasthenia gravis there may be actual ptosis, either unilateral or bilateral, when the patient is fatigued, as well as weakness of the orbicularis; these may almost disappear after either a period of rest or the administration of neostigmine (Fig. 63). Partial ptosis of congenital origin is present in the *Marcus Gunn phenomenon,* or *jaw-winking reflex;* the patient can raise the lid voluntarily and on upward gaze, but jaw movements are accompanied by exaggerated elevation (Chapter 12). In Parkinson's disease there is infrequent blinking and there may be some lid retraction. *Lid lag* (von Graefe's sign)

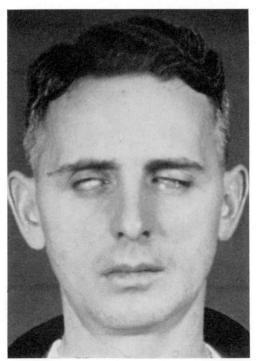

Fig. 63.   Myasthenia gravis before administration of neostigmine.

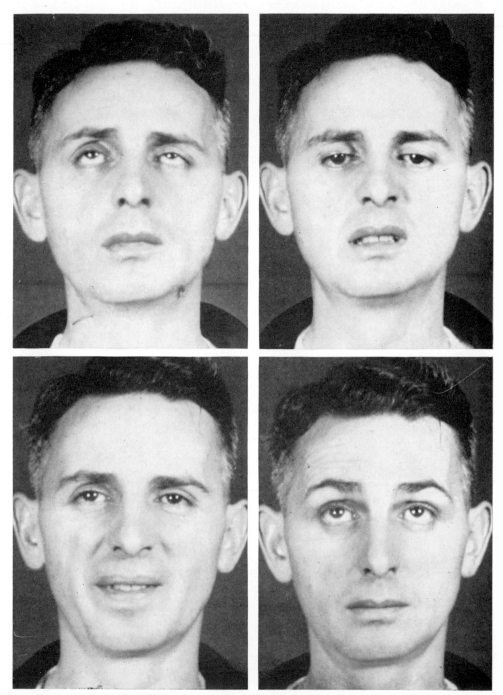

FIG. 63 (*Continued*).   *Top*, myasthenia gravis before the administration of neostigmine. *Bottom*, after the administration of neostigmine.

and *increased width of the palpebral fissures* (Dalrymple's sign) may be seen in hyperthyroidism. Loss of tone of the levator may cause a partial ptosis, but the eyelid can be elevated on upward gaze. With *myotonia* of the lids there may be difficulty raising them immediately after forced closure; in the *myotonic lid lag* the upper lids remain retracted briefly and then descend slowly on looking downward immediately after a period of upward gaze. In *apraxia of lid opening,* which accompanies some extrapyramidal disorders, the patient has difficulty initiating lid elevation although there is no paralysis of the levator. *Spasm* of the eyelids may occur in psychogenic disorders, and a fine tremor of the lids (Rosenbach's sign) is seen in hyperthyroidism and hysteria. *Blepharospasm,* or spasmodic contraction of the orbicularis oculi and the levator, is a common psychogenic phenomenon, but it may be a reflex response to pain in the eye or irritation of the cornea or iris, or may be due to an abnormal sensitivity or intolerance to light (photophobia); it sometimes occurs as a postencephalitic phenomenon.

THE OCULAR MOVEMENTS

The ocular movements are tested by having the patient look in the six cardinal directions—laterally, medially, upward and laterally, upward and medially, downward and laterally, and downward and medially, as well as directly upward and downward (Fig. 53), and then convergence is tested. Voluntary movements in response to a verbal command, and following movements using the examiner's finger, a flashlight, or a pointer for a guide, are first observed, and then reflex movements in which the patient fixes on a target and the head is passively moved from side to side and upward and downward are observed. Abnormalities of gaze may sometimes be brought out by having the patient perform a circular movement, following the slowly moving finger of the examiner. The range, speed, and smoothness of motion are noted, as well as the power to sustain lateral and vertical gaze. The *cover,* or *screening, test* may aid in the demonstration of ocular muscle weakness. The eyes are focused on a light held at a reading distance, and they are alternately covered with a card. When an eye with a paretic muscle is covered, it will deviate away from the field of action of the affected muscle; when uncovered, it will move back to the parallel position in order to focus on the light. When the sound eye is screened and the one with the paretic muscle is made to fix, the sound eye will deviate in a direction which is opposite to that of the paretic eye, and will return to the parallel position when uncovered.

The movements of individual muscles are first observed, and isolated pareses and paralyses noted; an attempt should be made to differentiate between nerve and muscle involvement. Then the conjugate movements are investigated for abnormalities of conjugate gaze and dissociation of movements. Certain reflex responses should be watched for, as well as the association between eye movements and contraction of the levator and frontalis muscles, and between eye and head movements. Finally, pathologic eye movements are evaluated. In examining infants, it should be borne in mind that binocular fixation is not established before the age of six months; by the age of four months, however, following movements and convergence can be tested. The cover test is especially helpful in evaluating ocular palsies in children. In both infants and comatose patients, reflex movements can be investigated; rapid passive turning of the head produces contralateral ocular deviation (the oculocephalic or vestibulo-oculogyric reflex, or the doll's head phenomenon).

The eyeball rotates in its socket around one or more of three primary axes that intersect each other at right angles near the center of the globe. One axis is vertical, and around it the lateral movements of abduction and adduction take place in the horizontal plane. A second is transverse, and is the axis of rotation for upward and downward movements. The third axis is in the anteroposterior plane, and torsion movements in the frontal plane take place around it. The eyes are said to be in their primary position, or position of rest, when their direction is maintained by the tone of the ocular muscles and gaze straight ahead and far away. The visual axes are then parallel. When the eyes view some definite object, they are turned by the contraction of the ocular muscles and are converged so that the visual axes meet at the observed object. An image of the object falls upon a corresponding point on each macula. This movement of the eyes for acute observation is called *fixation*. The point where the visual axes meet is called the *fixation point*.

Paralysis of the individual ocular muscles produces a series of phenomena. Owing to loss of function of the individual muscle there is (1) *loss or limitation of certain movements of the eyeball*. It must be borne in mind that there are no simple eye movements that are the result of the contraction of a single muscle, and that for any movement it is necessary to have not only the contraction of the prime movers, but also the relaxation of the antagonists. Consequently, paresis or paralysis of one muscle or of a group of muscles is followed by (2) *secondary contraction of the antagonists*. The pull of the nonaffected muscle or muscles results in (3) *primary deviation of the eyeball* from parallelism with the normal eye, or *noncorrespondence of the visual axes*. This produces *squint, or strabismus*. If the patient attempts to fix his gaze on an object in the direction requiring the action of the affected muscle, and at the same time is prevented from seeing it with the normal eye, this eye will deviate too far in the required direction, owing to the increased effort resulting from the attempt to move the affected eye. Thus there is (4) *secondary deviation of the unaffected eye*. As a result of the deviation there occurs (5) an *erroneous projection of the field of vision*, always in the direction that the paralyzed muscle normally pulls the eye. Consequently, there is (6) a *false image*, with (7) *double vision, or diplopia*, owing to failure of the image of the object toward which the eyes are directed to fall on corresponding points of the two retinas. The false image is in the direction of the plane or planes of action of the paralyzed muscles. If the false image is on the same side as the eye which sees it, there is *homonymous diplopia;* if the image is on the opposite side, there is *crossed diplopia*. The farther the eyes are moved in the direction of the pull of the paralyzed muscles, the greater the separation of the images. Inasmuch as the face may be rotated and the head moved or tilted in the direction of action of the paralyzed muscle in an attempt to minimize the diplopia, there may be (8) an *abnormal posture, or attitude, of the head*. Tilting of the head, however, occurs less frequently than the other manifestations. Vertigo and nausea may also be present.

Diplopia is usually preceded by blurring of vision. The patient's account of the two images seen in diplopia, especially if he is an intelligent observer, will give much information about the paretic muscles or nerves. If he sees double, he should be asked the relationship of the two objects to each other—whether they are on the same horizontal plane, the same vertical plane, or separated both horizontally and vertically. He should also be asked whether the diplopia is present at all times, or noted only when looking upward, downward, or to one side. It should be borne in mind that diplopia is not always the result of paralysis of ocular muscles; it may occur in conditions in which there is abnormality of the position of the eyeball, as in orbital inflammations or tumors. Monocular diplopia and polyopia usually signify hysteria, although monocular diplopia may be present in ocular conditions such as cataracts, subluxation of the lens, and retinal detachment, and in cerebral lesions with dissociated visual projections or hemianopia of cortical origin. Slight monocular diplopia is said to be present in many eyes with normal vision, probably due to slight refractive differences in the lens substance; one image is much fainter than the other. *Aniseikonia,* a difference in the size and shape but not the position of objects seen with the two eyes, is due to intraocular abnormality and not related to dysfunction of the ocular muscles.

A patient with diplopia may keep one eye closed to avoid seeing double, or may tilt his head to minimize the difficulty. In diplopia of long standing he may learn to suppress the vision of one eye. The diplopia is made more marked and the distance between the true and the false images increases as the eyes are moved in the direction of the action of the paretic muscle. Diplopia is tested by holding a pencil or some other object, or, best, a small light in front of the patient; the relative position of the two objects is noted when the eyes are at rest and when they are deviated in all directions of gaze. Then one eye is closed suddenly, and the patient is asked which object has disappeared. Minimal diplopia is increased and the images are more clearly differentiated if a colored glass (usually red) is placed before one eye and the patient asked to look at a small light held at a distance of one meter. By moving the light into the various quadrants of vision, one can determine where the separation of images is the greatest. The relative positions of the two images may be recorded on a Lancaster chart (Fig. 64). A carefully made diplopia chart helps to

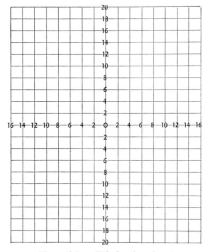

FIG. 64.   Diplopia chart.

identify the affected muscles; it also gives a permanent record of the degree of involvement, and thus aids in evaluating progression or improvement. Diplopia can also be tested by having the patient fix on an object with the paretic eye while the good eye is covered. Then the involved eye also is covered, and the patient is asked to point quickly at the object. If a muscle is paretic, he will point past the object in the direction of the apparent image when he looks in the direction of the pull of the paralyzed muscle.

An *isolated paralysis* of one or more of the extraocular muscles or nerves indicates the presence of either a *nuclear* or an *infranuclear* lesion, that is, a lesion affecting the nucleus of the involved nerve, the course of the nerve from the nucleus to the muscles it supplies, or the muscle itself. In a paralysis of the *superior rectus* the eye is turned down and slightly outward. Upward movement is limited, especially when the eyeball is abducted. There is crossed diplopia on looking upward and laterally, and the secondary image is oblique; it is above and tilted away from the true image. The head may be deviated backward and rotated toward the affected side; the chin is elevated. In paralysis of the *medial rectus* the eyeball is turned laterally and cannot be deviated medially. Diplopia occurs on looking medially; it is horizontal and crossed, corresponding to the field of vision of the unaffected eye; the secondary object is vertical, and the face is turned toward the unaffected side. When the *inferior rectus* is involved the eyeball is deviated upward and slightly laterally, and cannot be moved downward when the eye is in abduction. Diplopia occurs on looking downward and laterally; it is crossed, and the false image is oblique, below the true image, but tilted toward it. The head may be tilted forward and toward the affected side; the chin is depressed. When the *lateral rectus* is paralyzed the globe is turned medially and cannot be abducted. Diplopia occurs on looking to the ipsilateral side, the two objects are on the same horizontal plane, and the false image is lateral, vertical, and homonymous. The face is turned toward the side of the involved muscle. In paralysis of the *inferior oblique* the eyeball is deviated down and slightly medially, and cannot be moved upward when in adduction. Homonymous diplopia occurs on attempts to gaze upward and nasally, and the secondary image is oblique, above, and tilted away from the true image. The head is tilted backward and toward the shoulder of the affected side; the chin is elevated. With paralysis of the *superior oblique* there may be little deviation of the eyeball, but there is limitation of downward movement when the eye is adducted and there is no intorsion of the eye on looking downwards in abduction. Homonymous diplopia, with the secondary object oblique, occurs on looking downward and nasally; the secondary image is below and lateral, and tilted toward the true image. The head may be deviated forward and toward the unaffected side, with the chin tilted toward the shoulder of the involved side. In all the above, the position of the secondary object may vary, depending on whether the patient is fixing with his paretic or nonparetic eye. It is often difficult to differentiate isolated palsies of the cyclovertical muscles, except immediately after onset or when severe. Also, individual variations, incomplete or multiple involvement, and secondary contractures of opposing muscles may cause alterations in the position of the eyeballs or of the false image.

Nuclear and infranuclear involvement must be differentiated by noting associated signs and symptoms, or their absence. In a nuclear third-nerve lesion there may be paralysis of individual extraocular muscles without palpebral involvement or associated internal ophthalmoplegia. Infranuclear affections usually result in a complete third-nerve paralysis, unless the lesion is within the orbit, when isolated involvement may again occur. It is difficult to differentiate between nuclear and infranuclear fourth-nerve abnormalities, but a nuclear fourth-nerve lesion causes a contralateral paralysis, where as an infranuclear paralysis is ipsilateral. A nuclear sixth-nerve involvement is usually differentiated from an infranuclear paralysis by the associated seventh-nerve symptoms. Owing to the proximity of the nuclei of these nerves to the medial longitudinal fasciculus, nuclear lesions often result in complicated syndromes, and isolated nuclear palsies are rare.

Isolated palsies should be differentiated from apparent paralysis due to refractive errors, ocular or orbital disease, and muscular imbalance that causes strabismus, or squint. *Strabismus* is defined as deviation of one eye from its proper direction so that the visual axes of the two eyes cannot both be directed simultaneously at the same objective point. There is lack of parallelism of the ocular axes. The deviation may be divergent, convergent, upward, or downward, and may be unilateral or alternating. It may be latent, occurring only when one eye is occluded, or manifest, occurring when both eyes are open. It may be occasional, incipient, or constant. It may be concomitant, with the same amount of deviation regardless of the direction the eyes are looking, or nonconcomitant. Strabismus may be paralytic in disease of the ocular nerves, but in nonparalytic strabismus the involved eye can be moved throughout its complete range of movement, following the fixing eye with a constant error, even though it may diverge or converge at rest. In paralytic strabismus the defect is increased by deviation of the eyes in the direction of the action of the paralyzed muscle. Since most strabismus is present from birth or early childhood, the patient learns to suppress one image, and usually develops amblyopia in the involved eye. *Heterotropia* is a generic term synonymous with strabismus, or squint, with a manifest deviation of the eyes. The term *esotropia* is used for convergent strabismus, or the turning inward of the visual axis of an eye; *extropia,* for divergent strabismus; and *hypertropia,* for vertical strabismus with one visual axis elevated above the other. *Heterophoria* is a generic term indicating a latent tendency to imperfect binocular balance rather than manifest involvement. *Hyperphoria* is a tendency for the visual axis of one eye to deviate above that of the other; *esophoria,* a tendency for the visual axes to deviate inward (latent convergent strabismus); and *exophoria,* the tendency to deviate outward (latent divergent strabismus). Esophoria may occur in individuals with hyperopia; exophoria, in those with myopia.

Normally the eye movements are *conjugate,* or *coordinated,* and there can be no isolated action of any ocular muscle. By means of the coordinating mechanism of the medial longitudinal fasciculus, various muscles of each eye contract and their antagonists relax in order to carry out any movement and, furthermore, the two eyes move together. In order to look to the right, for instance, the right lateral rectus and the other abductors, the superior and inferior obliques, contract, while the medial rectus and the associated adductors, the superior and inferior recti, relax, and thus the eyeball is deviated. At the same time, the left eye moves to the right by means of the contraction of the medial, superior, and inferior recti and the relaxation of the lateral rectus and the superior and inferior obliques (Fig. 65).

Supranuclear involvement of ocular motion indicates the presence of a lesion either in the pathways connecting the various nuclei or in the higher centers. Disturbances of conjugate gaze may be found in association with midbrain, pontine, or cerebral lesions, resulting in paresis but rarely paralysis of conjugate gaze; there is a paresis of movement rather than paralysis of muscles. The visual axes remain parallel, and there is neither strabismus nor diplopia.

Cerebral lesions may be either irritative or paralytic. *Stimulation* of the *frontal motor eye field* causes strong, rapid, involuntary conjugate deviation of the eyes to the opposite side, which may be accompanied by conjugate movement of the head and rotation of the trunk, usually of short duration. This occurs with irritation of either the cortex of the descending neuraxes, and may be part of a jacksonian convulsion. *Destructive lesions* of this cortical center or its descending fibers cause paresis of gaze to the opposite side, usually not complete, with deviation of the eyes toward the side of the lesion. This deviation may be of considerable magnitude, but is usually of short duration, spontaneous recovery taking place within a few weeks. The head is turned in the same direction as the eyes, paralysis of associated muscles is symmetrical, and there is paresis of the face and extremities on the side toward which there is paresis of gaze.

With destructive frontal lesions only voluntary motion is affected; the patient cannot turn his eyes laterally on command, but lateral following and reflex movements are intact. Vertical gaze may also be affected. Although the patient is unable to deviate his eyes, they will follow a test object that is moved slowly in the direction of paresis of gaze. They remain fixed on a stationary object when the head is

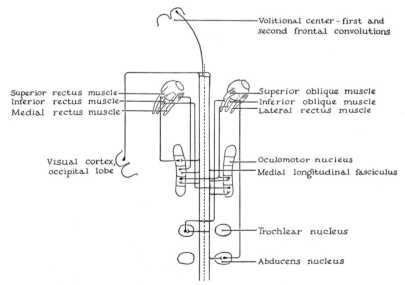

FIG. 65.   Mechanism for conjugate lateral gaze. (Modified after Riley.)

passively rotated in the opposite direction (optic fixation reflex). Also, reflex movements in response to visual, vestibular, and acoustic stimuli and to turning movements of the head and body are retained or even exaggerated, as are the tonic neck reflexes. In *congenital ocular motor apraxia,* which occurs mainly in males, there is loss of voluntary horizontal eye movements, but random and involuntary movements are preserved; the quick phase of optokinetic nystagmus is absent in the horizontal plane. There are associated jerky head movements and reading difficulties. This syndrome is thought to result from a lesion of the cortical center for voluntary eye movements or of its connections with lower centers. In the *pseudo-ophthalmoplegia* described by Ford and Walsh there is loss of lateral or even vertical gaze; but the eyes move with passive rotation of the head; this phenomenon is brought about by optic fixation and labyrinthine and otolith reflexes, and may result from a lesion in the tectum.

Irritative and destructive lesions of eye movement centers in the *occipital lobe,* and probably also in the temporal lobe and angular gyrus, cause similar conjugate deviation and paresis of conjugate gaze. With *destructive lesions* of the *occipital centers* (areas 18 and 19), however, voluntary movements may be little affected, but there is loss of following and reflex movements. Owing to associated involvement of the striate cortex or optic radiations, there may be difficulty with fixation and with maintaining visual attention, as well as field defects. Stereoscopic vision and visual memory may be lost. Balint's syndrome ("psychic" paralysis of visual fixation, optic ataxia and disturbance of visual attention) is said to be caused by bilateral parieto-occipital lesions.

Pontine and midbrain lesions are usually paralytic rather than irritative. With *irritative lesions* affecting centers concerned with lateral gaze (the vestibular complex, the medial longitudinal fasciculus, secondary vestibular fibers destined for this tract, or the so-called parabducens nucleus), there is ipsilateral deviation of the eyes. With *destructive lesions* of these structures there is paresis of gaze toward the side of the lesion, with contralateral deviation of the eyes that is of small magnitude, but usually permanent; as with frontal lesions, voluntary motion is affected more than reflex and following movements. An abnormal position of the head is not a typical symptom, and the head may be turned in the direction opposite to the ocular deviation. Paralysis of associated muscles may be asymmetrical, and that of the face, if present, is collateral with the eye muscle paralysis, whereas paralysis of the extremities is on the opposite side; there may be additional nuclear palsies. Occasionally there is paralysis of conjugate gaze with retention of convergence.

A lesion at the level of the *superior colliculi* (anterior quadrigeminal bodies) causes paralysis of conjugate upward gaze; this symptom complex is known as *Parinaud's syndrome,* and is found in tumors of the pineal gland or posterior portion of the third ventricle, encephalitis, vascular lesions, multiple sclerosis, and other conditions (Fig. 66). Because the internal corticotectal fibers from the occipital lobes are more superficial than the corticobulbar fibers in the superior colliculus, following and reflex movements are usually lost before voluntary movements; this is especially true in the case of tumors that press down upon the rostromedial portion of the colliculi; occasionally, with infiltrating lesions of the midbrain, voluntary

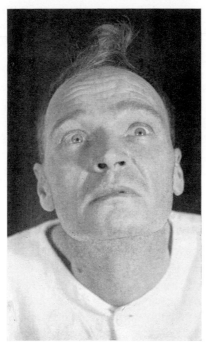

FIG. 66. Paresis of upward gaze in patient with tumor of posterior portion of third ventricle.

movements are lost first. If there is pressure on the caudolateral portion of the colliculi, following movements in a downward direction may be impaired.

It has been generally stated that a lesion of the nucleus of Perlia causes *paralysis of convergence,* although the individual medial rectus muscles may function normally in conjugate lateral gaze. While the presence of this nucleus and of a convergence center in the midbrain is doubtful, lesions in the periaqueductal gray matter of the midbrain may cause impairment of convergence, and this is seen in encephalitis, both acute and chronic, multiple sclerosis, trauma, vascular disease, and other conditions. Paralysis of convergence has also been reported with occipital and frontal lesions. Paralysis of divergence has also been described with lesions of the periaqueductal gray matter, and in brain tumors and extrapyramidal syndromes.

Partial loss of conjugate lateral movements and mixed gaze palsies are found with internuclear involvement. If there is a lesion of the medial longitudinal fasciculus that interrupts the impulses from the center for lateral gaze in the lower pons to the third nerve nucleus in the midbrain, there is paralysis of the medial recti on attempted conjugate lateral gaze. If the lesion is near the midbrain level (*anterior* or *superior internuclear ophthalmoplegia,* the syndrome of Lhermitte, or ophthalmoplegia internuclearis of Spiller), there is paralysis of adduction of the contralateral eye on attempted lateral gaze to one side, and there is usually associated paresis of convergence. With a more caudal lesion (*posterior* or *inferior internuclear ophthalmoplegia*) there is paresis of abduction of the ipsilateral eye on attempted lateral gaze, which may be more marked than the paresis of adduction of the contralateral eye, and the latter may converge normally. In both of these syndromes the paretic muscles may respond to vestibular stimulation. Nystagmus usually is present, especially with posterior lesions, and while it may be either horizontal, rotatory, or vertical, it is most often the first and is more marked in the abducted eye. The internuclear ophthalmoplegias are often grouped together as the *syndrome of the medial longitudinal fasciculus*. In the classical syndrome there is paralysis of adduction of the contralateral eye on attempted lateral gaze to one side, with normal convergence of that eye, together with variable paresis and monocular nystagmus of the abducting eye (dissociated, or "ataxic," nystagmus); there may be vertical nystagmus of both eyes on upward gaze. Convergence may be lost if the lesion is near the midbrain level. The syndrome is most often bilateral, and bilateral involvement is usually considered indicative of multiple sclerosis. Unilateral involvement is more often the result of a vascular lesion. Either unilateral or bilateral internuclear ophthalmoplegias, however, may be present with vascular, neoplastic, inflammatory, or degenerative lesions of the brain stem or compression of the latter by neoplasms in the posterior fossa; under such circumstances there are usually symptoms and signs indicating involvement of neighboring centers and pathways.

Dissociation of eye movements is found in deep sleep and in coma, and it is often of serious prognostic significance in meningitis. In *skew deviation,* which is seen occasionally in cerebellar disease and posterior fossa lesions, the homolateral eye is turned downward and inward whereas the contralateral eye is deviated upward and outward. With *cerebellar lesions,* or involvement of cerebellar connections with other centers, there may be disturbances of ocular fixation with resulting ataxia or asynergy of extraocular movement. *Ocular dysmetria* is an overshooting of the eyes on attempted rapid fixation of gaze toward either side or on returning to the primary position; there may also be overshooting in following movements when the object of regard is suddenly stopped.

Normally the conjugate following movements of the eyes (also called pursuit movements) are smooth and uniform. Occasionally, however, they assume a jerky, irregular character, and the eyes follow the moving visual object in a series of short steps, remain fixed for a moment, and then move again. They may overshoot the target or advance ahead of it before coming to a jerky stop. These are termed *saccadic movements*; they are brought out most effectively if the target is moved slowly across the visual field. They are seen principally in Parkinson's disease, especially the postencephalitic type, and are sometimes referred to as "cogwheel" movements. They may also be present in multiple sclerosis, posttraumatic and toxic states, and other organic cerebral disorders. The ocular movements have a saccadic character during the first few months of life.

Reflex movements of the eyes may be divided into two classes: movements that are carried out involuntarily but involve the mediation of consciousness, and true reflexes that are subserved by a subcortical mechanism. The first group consists of the movements of fixation, *optically induced movements,* or the *visual,* or *psycho-optical, reflexes*. These result from stimulation of the retina. When a light falls upon a peripheral portion of the retina the eye is moved reflexly in such a way that the image strikes the fovea, unless the intensity of the light is such that it causes closing of the eye. Both eyes respond in a coordinated manner, and the movement is a rapid one. There may be associated turning of the head. The afferent pathway travels through the optic tracts to the occipital cortex, whereas the efferent pathway goes to the superior colliculus and thence to the nuclei of the ocular nerves and other motor nuclei. Attention and a conscious appreciation of the stimulus are probably necessary to the response. There may be a tendency for the eyes to remain directed on the object in central vision; this is sometimes termed the *optic fixation reflex*. With impairment of voluntary movement of the eyes, or with frontal lesions in which there is loss of cortical inhibition, this reflex may become exaggerated or dominant, and the patient may have difficulty in disengaging his vision from any point on which it is directed. Individuals with macular deficiencies or other severe ocular difficulties dating from birth may show, instead of fixation, gross, roving movements of the eyes ("ocular" nystagmus). The *fusion reflex* determines the accurate directing of the eyes so that the images of the object toward which vision is directed fall on corresponding points of the two retinas. The *emergency light reflex* consists of pupillary constriction, closing of the eyes, lowering of the eyebrows, and sometimes even a bending of the head or an elevation of one arm in response to a sudden, strong visual stimulus. The afferent pathway goes through the optic tracts to the occipital cortex, and the efferent impulses go through the oculomotor, facial, accessory, and upper cervical nerves. It is a modification of the visual-palpebral or blink reflex (Chapter 13).

True reflex movements are produced by stimulation of the vestibular apparatus, otoliths, acoustic mechanism, or conjunctiva or cornea, and by changes in the position of the head or the body (postural reflexes, righting reflexes, and tonic neck reflexes). These latter are responses to proprioceptive impulses arising from the muscles of the neck or from the body as a whole, and in them eye movements are correlated with bodily responses and movements of the head and neck (Part V). The *vestibulo-oculogyric reflex (labyrinthine reflex)* consists of either a lateral deviation of the eyeballs or nystagmus on stimulation of the labyrinthine apparatus or on sudden passive turning of the head (the *oculocephalic reflex* or doll's head phenomenon). *The auditory-oculogyric reflex (cochlear reflex)* consists of a lateral deviation of the eyes in the direction of a sudden noise. In both of these responses the impulse travels through the constituent portion of the eighth nerve and its nuclei to the medial longitudinal fasciculus, and thence to the nuclei of the ocular nerves. The *corneo-oculogyric* or *sensory reflex* consists of a contralateral or upward deviation of the eyes and a contraction of the orbicularis in response to irritation of the cornea. The afferent impulses are carried through the trigeminal nerve, and the efferent pathway is through the ocular and facial nerves. This response is related to the corneal reflex (Chapter 12). The *oculogyric-auricular reflex* consists of a slight retraction of both auricles, greater on the opposite side, on lateral gaze toward one side. Proprioceptive impulses are carried through the oculomotor and abducens nerves, with the efferent pathway going through the facial nerve (Chapter 13).

There are *associated movements* between the ocular muscles, the levator palpebrae superioris, and the muscles of facial expression. Upward gaze is associated not only with elevation of the eyelid, but also with contraction of the frontalis. Elevation of the lid is associated with contraction of the frontalis. On contraction of the orbicularis oculi, with resultant closing of the eye, the eyeballs rotate upward; this occurs not only in voluntary closing of the eye, but also in sleep. This oculo-facial associated movement is sometimes called the *palpebral-oculogyric reflex;* proprioceptive impulses are carried through the facial nerve to the medial longitudinal fasciculus, and efferent impulses are relayed to the superior rectus muscles. The response is exaggerated in *Bell's phenomenon,* in which, in the presence of paralysis of the orbicularis, the eyeball rotates upward as the patient attempts to close his eye (Chapter 13). Association between eye and face or head movements may be observed in the vestibular, cochlear, sensory, and postural reflexes as well as in stimulation of the cortical or pontine centers, and there is absence of these movements in paralytic or destructive cerebral or brain stem lesions.

PATHOLOGIC EYE MOVEMENTS

NYSTAGMUS

Nystagmus is a frequent manifestation in diseases of the nervous system, and it is also observed in diseases of the eye and the inner ear. It may, however, be a normal phenomenon under certatin circumstances or may be induced experimentally or as part of the clinical examination. There are many varieties of nystagmus, and in order to evaluate its significance in any individual instance, one must understand the underlying mechanisms and the mode of production of the phenomenon.

Nystagmus or, as it is sometimes called, talantropia, may be defined as an involuntary oscillation or trembling of the eyeball. The term "rhythmic" is often included in the definition, but nonrhythmic varieties may be seen. Certain observers object to the inclusion of the adjective "involuntary," as nystagmus of volitional origin has been described. Nystagmus is a coordinated movement, and usually both eyes move synchronously over a virtually equal range. Unilateral nystagmus, however, may occur, or there may be dissociation of movements or disproportion between the movements on the two sides. The motor response involves not only the contraction of certain muscles, but the relaxation of their antagonists by reciprocal innervation, with alternating activity of agonists and antagonists.

Nystagmus may be described in various ways: by type, form, direction, rate, amplitude, duration, and intensity, and by relationship of the response to movements of the eyes, head, and body. It may be rhythmic or pendular in *type*. *Rhythmic* or *resilient nystagmus,* also known as *jerky, biphasic, directed,* or *spring* nystagmus, is characterized by alternate slow and quick ocular excursions, resulting in a jerky, unequal oscillation of the eyeballs. Usually there is a rapid movement in the direction of gaze which is followed by a slower return movement away from the point of fixation. *Pendular* or *undulatory nystagmus* is characterized by more or less regular to-and-fro movements of approximately equal range and velocity toward each side of a central point.

Nystagmus may be horizontal, vertical, oblique, rotatory, or mixed in *form,* and to the right, left, upward, or downward in *direction*. In the rotatory variety the direction is recorded as clockwise or counterclockwise. Retraction nystagmus is occasionally seen. Nystagmus may be slow, medium, or rapid in *rate* or *velocity*. If the movements are from ten to forty per minute, the nystagmus is slow; it is medium if they are between forty and a hundred per minute, and rapid if over a hundred per minute. The oscillations may be fine, medium, or coarse in *amplitude*. The movements may be so gross that they cannot be overlooked, or so fine that they cannot be seen with the naked eye and are visualized only when the eye is examined with the ophthalmoscope or when a plus 20.00 D. lens is placed in front of the eye. The convex lens not only magnifies the nystagmus but also eliminates fixation. If the movements are of less than five degrees or the excursions are less than one millimeter in amplitude, the nystagmus is fine; if they are over fifteen degrees or more than three millimeters in amplitude, the nystagmus is coarse; if they are between these, it is considered medium.

Nystagmus may be either abortive or sustained in *duration*. It is also classified by *intensity*. It is of first-degree intensity if present only when the patient looks in the direction of the quick component; second-degree, if present not only when looking in the direction of the quick component, but also while the eyes are in the neutral position; third-degree, if present even when looking in the direction of the slow component.

Nystagmus may be either *congenital* or *acquired;* it may be *spontaneous* or *artificial (induced);* it may be present at rest, on fixation, or on deviation of the eyeballs. It may be *associated* or *conjugate,* with the movements symmetrical in the two eyes, or *dissociated,* with the movements of the two eyes unrelated. In *unilateral* nystagmus the movements take place only on one side. In *disjunctive* nystagmus, which is rare, the movements are symmetrically opposite. A movement that appears to be simple to the naked eye may be irregular or complex when visualized through an ophthalmoscope or a lens. Nystagmus may vary from time to time in the same individual, depending upon the position of the body, head, and eyes, and other factors. It may be maintained or unimpaired in the presence of extensive ocular palsies. Rhythmic head movements may accompany it. Patients with nystagmus may notice blurring of vision and a sensation of movement at the onset of the manifestation, or they may notice a constant movement of the objects within the field of vision; this subjective manifestation, which is known as *oscillopsia,* is relatively rare.

Various methods have been described for the delineation and recording of nystagmus. A tambour may be placed against the closed eyelid, and a pneumatic tube used to transmit the movements of the eyeball to a kymograph. A photoelectrical cell can record variations in an infrared beam focused on the eyeball. Cinematography may be used. The character and extent of the oscillations may be studied by means of the slit lamp and biomicroscope. Electronystagmography, however, gives the most detailed information about the rate, amplitude, type, duration, and intensity of the nystagmus and, furthermore, provides a permanent record. Electrodes may be attached to the outer and inner canthi, the margins of the orbit, the anethetized conjunctiva, or the ocular muscles, and the electrical potentials are recorded on an oscillograph or electroencephalograph. Both spontaneous and induced nystagmus may be studied, as well as other abnormalities of ocular movement.

There are many types of nystagmus that appear to serve widely diverse purposes. The position of the eyes is influenced reflexly by impulses coming from the retinas, the ocular muscles, the labyrinths, and the cochlea, and by proprioceptive impulses initiated by movements of the head or the body. It is also influenced by impulses relayed from the cerebral cortex. Nystagmus may, in most instances, be considered a compensatory reaction of the eyeballs to defective or abnormal impulses from any of these sources. It may have many apparent purposes: to retain a specific field of vision, that is, to keep the eyes as long as possible in the same position in relation to the visual field; to increase incoming impulses; to aid in ocular fixation; to assist in orientation in space.

If the head moves or if the field of vision moves, the eyes move in the opposite direction in in attempt to remain fixed in the original field, to maintain as long as possible the same position relative to the visual field, or to preserve the image of the fixed object on the retina. Because of the limited excursion of the eyes, however, the original field cannot be held, and at their maximal deviation the eyes are jerked back to take up a new focus. If one labyrinth is stimulated, there is a slow movement of the eyes, again in an attempt to retain the original field of vision (Fig. 67). The eyes cannot, however, be held in this position, and they are jerked back to take up a new focus in relation to the environment. If either of these movements persists, nystagmus results.

If, owing to poor macular vision, inadequate visual acuity, or inadequate illumination, the impulses focused on the macula are not sufficient to allow adequate perception, the eyes move from side to side in an attempt to increase or reinforce the incoming visual impulses, to find the sharpest image, or to achieve adequate fixation, with no relation to movement of the head or of the field of vision. Here, also, a nystagmus results, but the movements toward each side are equal in amplitude and rate. If nystagmus is the result of movement of the field of vision or of attempts to increase vision, it is a reflex response to retinal stimulation and may be called an *oculocerebral reflex*. If it is the result of movement of the head or the body or of irritation of the labyrinth, it is a reflex response to vestibular stimulation and may be called a *vestibulocerebral reflex*. Other mechanisms in the production of nystagmus will be described under the discussion of specific varieties. Owing to the integrative action of the various components of the nervous system and their correlation

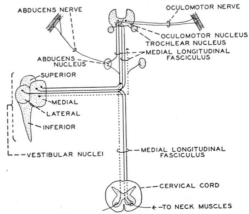

Fig. 67.   Relationship of vestibular system to production of conjugate lateral gaze.

and interdependence upon each other, it is often impossible to separate visual, sensory (proprioceptive), vestibular, and other factors.

The *slow phase* of rhythmic nystagmus is said to be of peripheral or vestibular origin. The reflex arc involves the labyrinths, vestibular nuclei, medial longitudinal fasciculus, nuclei of the extraocular muscles, and the ocular muscles themselves. There has been little agreement about the source of the *rapid phase,* which is often referred to as the cerebral or central component, but it probably is of brain stem origin. It has been found that all of the rapid discharges are mediated by the reticular formation. Nystagmus may disappear during anesthesia and return with the return of consciousness. It may still be elicited after extirpation of the hemispheres, and even after section of the brain stem to the level of the nucleus of the oculomotor nerve. It has been demonstrated that the only portions of the central nervous system essential for the production of the slow and quick phases of nystagmus are the vestibular and oculomotor nuclei and the connections between them, although other regions and structures may exert a profound influence on the phenomenon. Clinicians, in referring to rhythmic nystagmus, usually name it from the direction of the rapid component, because this movement is more readily noticed and is more striking. The slow phase, however, represents the more active physiologic determinant, and in experimental literature it is used to indicate the direction of the nystagmus.

In the appraisal of nystagmus, the eyes should be inspected in the resting position and on deviation in all directions, and with the patient both seated and recumbent. The direction, rate, amplitude, type, form, duration, and intensity of the nystagmus should be noted, and some of these features can be recorded graphically (Fig. 68). One should also observe the relationship of the nystagmus to position or movement of the eyes, head, and body. It may change in direction or type or may even be brought on by change in position of the head or body. Nystagmoid jerks may be difficult to differentiate from clinical nystagmus. Some individuals have spontaneous rhythmic ocular movements during mental concentration while their eyes are

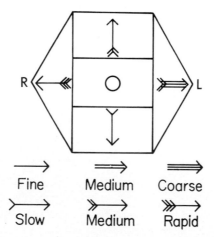

FIG. 68. Scheme for recording direction, rate, and amplitude of nystagmus.

gazing into the distance. There is no generally accepted classification of nystagmus, and interpretations of the mechanism for and significance of different types vary widely. So-called physiologic varieties may appear in the presence of disease of the nervous system, and varieties usually considered to be pathologic are not always the result of a definite disease process. All types may be influenced by visual and vestibular stimuli, postural and tonic neck reflexes, the position of the head and eyes, and changes in the state of attention or alertness. The following classification includes the more commonly encountered and important categories; there may be mixed forms and irregular manifestations.

1. INDUCED NYSTAGMUS: Nystagmus may be produced clinically or experimentally by certain tests or methods of stimulation. The response is usually considered to be physiologic, and may be induced in normal individuals. Changes occur, however, in disease processes.

a. *Optokinetic* or *Optomotor Nystagmus:* When a person in a rapidly moving vehicle directs his eyes toward fixed objects, a jerky type of physiologic nystagmus appears. This is a conjugate or conjunctive response of the eyes to a succession of moving visual stimuli and has been known as optic, railway, or elevator nystagmus. When tested for clinically it is called optokinetic or optomotor nystagmus and is elicited by means of either an optokinetic drum or optokinetic tape. The drum, painted with vertical black and white stripes, is rotated rapidly in front of the eyes, or the tape, a series of two-inch square red patches placed two inches apart

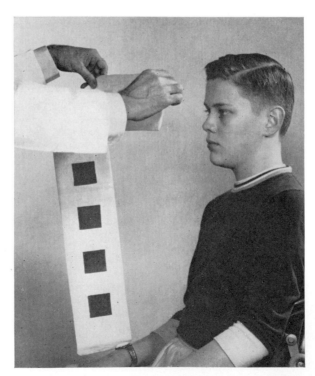

FIG. 69.   Testing for optokinetic nystagmus using optokinetic tape.

on a white tape a yard long, is drawn across the patient's field of vision (Fig. 69). The stimulus may be directed from the right or the left to elicit horizontal nystagmus, and from above or below to elicit vertical nystagmus. The slow phase is in the direction of the movement of the drum or tape, with the quick return in the opposite direction. Thus the slow phase seems to indicate the pursuit of the moving object, with a quick return in an attempt at fixation on a new oncoming object. The nystagmus is fine, rapid, and rhythmic. The response is intensified if the subject looks in the direction of the quick phase. This phenomenon is a reflex response to retinal stimulation or to proprioceptive impulses from the eye muscles, and has been believed to be cortical in origin. It probably represents a cortical or an oculocerebral reflex, dependent on the continuity of the association pathways between the occipital and frontal cortices. There may be both active (cortical) and passive (subcortical) varieties. Optokinetic nystagmus is a physiologic response and its absence must be regarded as pathologic. The rotating drum test is used to demonstrate feigned or simulated blindness in a malingerer, to diagnose hysterical blindness, and to test for the presence of vision in an infant. In some disease states optokinetic nystagmus may be accompanied by vertigo, turning of the body, or irregular eye movements.

b. *Labyrinthine Nystagmus:* This is a physiologic response that follows the stimulation of the semicircular canals by rapid rotation of the body, spraying the external auditory canal with warm or cold water, galvanic stimulation, or pressure changes. It, too, is rhythmic in type. Its direction depends upon which semicircular canals are stimulated, and is thus dependent upon the position of the head during stimulation. The direction also varies with the type of stimulus used. The slow phase is said to be the resultant effect of the stimuli caused by the movement of the endolymph in the semicircular canals of the labyrinth. The head and eyes, and sometimes the body, are deviated in the direction of the endolymph current, and the slow phase of the nystagmus corresponds; the rapid phase is in the opposite direction. This variety of nystagmus is a reflex response to stimulation of the labyrinth, and thus is a vestibulocerebral reflex; pathologic variations may accompany disease processes. The details of the vestibular tests, and the resulting nystagmus, are presented in "The Acoustic Nerve" (Chapter 14).

c. *Chemical* or *Toxic Nystagmus:* Nystagmus is known to result from the use of drugs and from association with various toxins. Chemical stimulation may also be used to produce experimental, or induced, nystagmus, and certain drugs, including some of those that cause nystagmus, may alter or abolish pathologic nystagmus (see below).

It is stated that rhythmic nystagmus may be produced by loud auditory stimuli *(reflex acoustic nystagmus)* or by painful stimulation to the ear, face, or eye *(reflex sensory nystagmus)*. These are rarely elicited and are of only theoretical interest.

Optokinetic and labyrinthine nystagmus may be either altered or absent with lesions of various parts of the central nervous system. Contralateral optokinetic nystagmus is defective or diminished with cerebral lesions affecting the temporal, occipital, and parietal areas, especially the latter. This is true whether or not there is a hemianopic defect. With brain stem lesions there may be a dissociation of vertical responses or between vertical and horizontal responses, or a depression or unilateral defect of optokinetic nystagmus. On the other hand, there is a directional preponderance (i.e., increase in duration and intensity) of caloric or rotational nystagmus to the side of the lesion with involvement of the posterior portion of the temporal lobe, when tested with optic fixation maintained, but absence or reversal of this preponderance when optic fixation is abolished. These alterations of induced nystagmus in the presence of disease indicate that centers in various portions of the nervous system may either inhibit or exert directional control over these ocular movements.

2. PATHOLOGIC NYSTAGMUS: This, in most instances, indicates the presence of some abnormal process in the eyes or the ocular muscles, or in the central connections concerned with ocular movement or bodily equilibrium. It is *spontaneous* and usually of clinical significance.

a. *Nystagmus Associated With Disease of the Eye or Its Adnexa:* (1) *Nystagmus of optic derivation:* Nystagmus may be associated with deficient vision, resulting either from impaired visual acuity or inadequate illumination and retinal fatigue. It is usually pendular rather than rhythmic in type, and the movements appear to result from an attempt to maintain fixation of vision in spite of deficient acuity or insufficient light. It may appear in early infancy or may be acquired; it is not congenital.

(a) *"Ocular" nystagmus:*   This is of the pendular type and is usually coarse and slow, although sometimes rapid. It is characterized by to-and-fro movements, often of equal range and velocity, toward each side of a central point. The movements may be wide and aimless and of the so-called "searching," "wandering," or "roving" type. They may be highly irregular, and occasionally there is a rhythmic component. They are usually horizontal, sometimes vertical, and rarely rotatory. This variety of nystagmus occurs in persons who have had markedly deficient vision since birth, whose vision has failed before fixation is learned or whose fixation is deficient, or in color-blind individuals or those with increased sensitivity to light. Thus it may be observed in persons with congenital cataracts, corneal scars owing to ophthalmia neonatorum or interstitial keratitis, congenital corneal leukomas, macular deficiencies, chorioretinitis, high errors of refraction (especially high-grade myopia), and albinism. It develops shortly after birth, and it does not occur in persons who are blind from birth. It probably begins when the infant first attempts fixation. As a result of poor vision or imperfect macular vision, a "searching" movement of the eye develops as the infant attempts to increase the incoming impulses, to find the sharpest image, or to achieve adequate fixation. The nystagmus is an adaption to attain fixation in spite of defective vision. Sometimes there is an associated nodding of the head. "Ocular" nystagmus probably does not develop in adults. When bilateral visual defects (especially loss of macular vision) are acquired late in life, there may be slow, seemingly aimless eye movements, which are not definitely pendular; these probably represent voluntary attempts at fixation rather than a true nystagmus. Unilateral nystagmus may occur in unilateral optic atrophy or other visual defects. An inconstant nystagmus is sometimes seen in homonymous hemianopic visual field defects, particularly when the patient is looking to the blind side. This is probably not entirely ocular in origin, as it usually is of the rhythmic type, and it may vary with position.

(b) *Occupational nystagmus:* Eye strain caused by deficient illumination, repeated movements of the eyes, or retinal fatigue may cause nystagmus. This has been reported most frequently in miners, and is commonly referred to as "miners' nystagmus." It develops after long exposure to poor illumination, especially after working in a stooped position with the eyes deviated upward, and is probably the result of insufficiency of binocular fusion. Only the rods are used for vision in imperfect light, and as there are no rods at the macula, there is inefficient macular vision in poor illumination; as a result, there is constant shifting of the axis of the eyes. Miners' nystagmus is usually pendular but occasionally rotatory. The movements are rapid or slow, constant or inconstant, and usually vertical in direction and increased on upward gaze; they may not be conjugate. There is defective fixation and there may be associated spasm of the levator palpebrae superioris. There often are associated symptoms of tremor, vertigo, and photophobia. Occupational nystagmus may develop in compositors, draftsmen, jewelers, train dispatchers, crane workers, painters, and others whose work necessitate movement of the eyes and strain on the ocular muscles or results in retinal fatigue. The movements may be either vertical or horizontal, are usually pendular, and show marked variation in rate; there may be associated blepharospasm, visual impairment, and ocular discomfort.

(c) *Spasmus nutans:* This condition is seen in babies of from six months to two years of age. It consists of a rhythmic nodding or rotatory tremor of the head, tilting of the head, and a fine, rapid, pendular, or occasionally rhythmic, type of nystagmus. It is usually horizontal in direction, but it may be vertical. The movements may be unilateral or dissociated, and may vary with the direction of gaze. Closing of the eyes may either reduce or increase the tremor, while forceful control of the tremor may increase the nystagmus. The condition has been ascribed to rickets, but it is known to occur in children who live in dark dwellings where no sunlight penetrates, regardless of the presence of rickets. It may be of complex origin, both ocular and central; it is usually self limited.

(2) *Nystagmus of neuromuscular origin:* In a large percentage of normal persons a few fine, rapid nystagmoid movements are seen upon extreme deviation of the eyes. They are more marked on lateral gaze and are usually horizontal in direction. The rapid movement is in the direction of gaze, and the slow return represents the reflex contraction of the overstretched antagonists in an attempt to return the eyes to the central position. These movements are irregular and are usually transient; they may disappear gradually after five to ten jerks. This type of oscillation is sometimes referred to as *Endstellungsnystagmus,* or *end-position nystagmus,* inasmuch as the movement is present only on extreme deviation of the eyes. The terms *fixation nystagmus, positional nystagmus,* and *pseudonystagmus* are also used, and some authorities prefer to designate the movements as *nystagmoid jerks,* since they may not constitute a true nystagmus. These movements may occur in normal persons when they attempt to fix their eyes on an object outside the field of vision without turning the head, or when they suddenly change the field of vision. The movements disappear when fixation has been established. The tendency toward the phenomenon is increased in fatigue states, paresis of the ocular muscles, and abnormal attempts at fixation, and is often seen in nervous individuals. Exaggerations occur under the following circumstances:

(a) *Paretic nystagmus:* A rhythmic nystagmus often occurs near the limit of the range of movement of a weak ocular muscle. When the subject is looking toward the paretic side, the weak agonist pulls the eyeball outward with a rapid jerk to avoid diplopia, and the antagonistic muscles slowly pull the eyeball back to the neutral position. There may be dissociation between the movements in the paretic and the normal eye. Paretic nystagmus may also occur with paresis of conjugate gaze.

(b) *Fatigue nystagmus:* This is similar to paretic nystagmus. It may follow excessive use of or increased fatigability of certain extraocular muscles, and may occur in general fatigue states and asthenia. It is usually observed only at extremes of lateral gaze and is usually abortive rather than sustained. It may occur when an individual attempts to hold his eyes in any extreme position for too long a period of time. In patients with myasthenia gravis one may observe nystagmus that may be either the paretic or the fatigue variety.

(c) *Latent nystagmus:* This variety appears on covering one eye in subjects with poor visual acuity or without binocular vision, especially in those with unilateral amblyopia. The nystagmus is associated; the rapid component is in the direction of the open eye. Latent nystagmus may be partially of ocular origin, inasmuch as it represents an attempt to aid vision, but the rhythmicity suggests that it is basically a neuromuscular phenomenon.

b. *Nystagmus Associated With Disease of the Central Nervous System:* Nystagmus is a frequent finding and is often of diagnostic import in association with diseases of the central nervous system. It is sometimes of localizing significance, but on most occasions it is not possible to identify the exact site or etiology of the lesion responsible for the nystagmus, even though its presence indicates that a pathologic process exists. Eye movements are influenced by the cortical centers in the frontal and occipital lobes, the corticofugal pathways from these centers, the basal ganglia and thalamus, the superior colliculi, the nuclei of the ocular nerves, the cerebellum, the vestibular mechanism, and the medial longitudinal fasciculus. Most pathologic nystagmus, however, appears to be associated with involvement of either the medial longitudinal fasciculus or the vestibular mechanism. Cortical irritation may cause conjugate jerking movements of the eyes, but this is not a true nystagmus, and it is probable that cerebral lesions do not cause nystagmus, although they may influence the type and directional preponderance of that which appears with disease in other parts of the nervous system.

Nystagmus of "central" origin is rhythmic in type and may occur in any direction. It may vary in form, rate, amplitude, and intensity. It may be spontaneous and present at rest, or it may occur only on fixation, at extremes of gaze, or on change of position of the head or body. It is of most significance if it is mixed or rotatory in form or if there is dissociation or disproportion of movements. Rhythmic head movements may accompany or even be present in place of nystagmus. In some of the varieties of nystagmus associated with disease of the central nervous system it is possible to localize fairly well the site of the pathologic process.

(1) *Vestibular nystagmus:* This is a pathologic variation of induced labyrinthine nystagmus, and may be caused by either irritation or destruction of the semicircular canals, vestibular nerves, or vestibular nuclei. Afferent impulses pass from the

labyrinths to the vestibular nuclei and thence to the nuclei of the ocular muscles, and the efferent path is relayed to the individual muscles. The vestibular nuclei of the two sides are in tonic equilibrium, each nucleus tending to turn the head and eyes to the opposite side. Synergistic relationship between the cortical motor eye fields and the vestibular nuclei is necessary for conjugate movements. Stimulation of the labyrinths, specific semicircular canals, or the vestibular nerves or nuclei by a toxic process, pressure, edema, or inflammation produces essentially the same type of response as stimulation of these centers by rotation, heat or cold, or the galvanic current, and the response depends upon the type of stimulus and the part of the vestibular system that is stimulated; the slow phase is usually to the opposite side. Destruction of one labyrinth or of one vestibular nerve results in a rhythmic, spontaneous nystagmus, the slow phase of which is toward the injured side, and there may be associated deviation of the eyes and head toward this side. The labyrinths are antagonistic, so that elimination of one acts as a stimulus to the other. The amplitude of the nystagmus is increased when the patient turns his eyes in the direction of the rapid phase or when fixation is eliminated by placing strong lenses in front of the eyes. Nystagmus that follows destruction of one labyrinth gradually diminishes and disappears. It may last only two or three days and is usually gone in a week, as the loss of one labyrinth is compensated for by processes in the correponding vestibular nuclei. The nystagmus that appears after destruction of one labyrinth disappears if the other labyrinth is rendered functionless. Lesions of the lateral or medial vestibular nuclei produce a horizontal nystagmus, which may have a rotatory component. Lesions of the superior vestibular nuclei cause a vertical or oblique nystagmus. Vestibular nystagmus is always accompanied by vertigo.

Hemorrhage into the labyrinth, suppuration of the labyrinth secondary to middle ear disease, increased or decreased pressure of the labyrinthine fluid, pressure on the inner ear, trauma to a vestibular nerve as a result of skull fracture, intracranial hemorrhage, meningitis, involvement of a vestibular nerve by a neoplastic process such as a neurinoma of the cerebellopontine angle, or toxic or inflammatory involvement of the labyrinths or the vestibular nerves may produce nystagmus that may be temporary or persistent. The nystagmus associated with toxic labyrinthitis may be caused by stimulation of the vestibular end organs by the toxic process, or it may be of the *compression variety,* a result of increased pressure of the labyrinthine fluid in the semicircular canals. In Ménière's syndrome the nystagmus may be associated with increased secretion of endolymph or with a change in the acid-base or electrolyte balance. It may be possible to differentiate between nystagmus due to irritation and that due to destruction of a labyrinth by caloric stimulation of the external auditory canal. With the former the nystagmus will be increased, whereas with the latter no reflex nystagmus will be elicited, and there will be no change in the nystagmus already present. In many disease processes, as in tumors of the cerebellopontine angle, multiple sclerosis, and lesions of the pons and medulla, vestibular nystagmus may be complicated by the existence of nystagmus resulting from involvement of the medial longitudinal fasciculus or other structures.

(2) *Cerebellar nystagmus:* This may be an ocular expression of cerebellar asynergia or ataxia, a result of synergic disorders of fixation of cerebellar origin, or

it may result from involvement of the cerebellar connections with the vestibular apparatus, the medial longitudinal fasciculus, or higher centers. The portions of the cerebellum most closely related to the vestibular complex are the flocculonodular lobe and the fastigial nuclei; these both receive fibers from and discharge to the vestibular nuclei. The pyramis, however, and even the hemispheres, have some regulatory effect on vestibular function. With lesions of the cerebellum the eyes at rest are deviated ten to thirty degrees toward the unaffected side. When the subject attempts to focus on an object directly in front of him, the eyes wander slowly back to the resting position and are returned to the midline by means of quick jerks. When he looks toward either side, there are quick jerks toward the point of fixation with slow return movements to the resting point. The rapid movements are always in the direction of gaze, and the slow movements are toward the position of rest. The nystagmus is always more marked and the movements are slower and of greater amplitude when the patient looks toward the side of the lesion. It is said that cerebellar nystagmus is dependent upon fixation, in contrast to vestibular nystagmus, which is increased when fixation is eliminated by the use of strong lenses. In vestibular nystagmus the slow phase is toward the injured side, whereas in cerebellar nystagmus the slow phase depends upon the position of the eyes.

Nystagmus is a common symptom in patients with cerebellar lesions of various etiologies, but owing to the multiplicity of connections between the cerebellum and other centers, it may be difficult to determine the exact site of the lesion responsible. Its presence usually indicates, however, that the vestibulocerebellar pathways are affected, and therefore most often suggests involvement of either the vermis region or the inferior cerebellar peduncle. The nystagmus with hemispheric lesions may be a pressure phenomenon or may represent an asynergia rather than a true nystagmus. Nystagmus is usually not present in parenchymatous cerebellar degenerations. With a tumor of the cerebellopontine angle the nystagmus is coarse on looking toward the side of the lesion, and fine and rapid on gaze to the opposite side.

(3) *Nystagmus with lesions of the medial longitudinal fasciculus:* Interruption of the impulses between the center for lateral gaze in the pons and the oculomotor nuclei *(internuclear ophthalmoplegia)* may cause dissociated lateral gaze palsies and dissociated nystagmus. In the *syndrome of the medial longitudinal fasciculus* there is paralysis of adduction of the contralateral eye on attempted lateral gaze to one side, and a coarse monocular nystagmus of the abducting eye with the rapid movement in the direction of gaze. This is termed dissociated, or "ataxic," nystagmus; there may also be vertical nystagmus. This syndrome, especially if bilateral, is often considered to be pathognomonic of multiple sclerosis, but it may also be found in vascular, neoplastic, and other lesions of the brain stem.

(4) *Other types of "central" nystagmus:* It is often not possible to localize accurately the lesion responsible for nystagmus associated with various pathologic processes. Nystagmus of pathologic significance is produced mainly by lesions affecting structures in the region of the fourth ventricle, either its roof or floor, or by involvement of the brain stem, principally the zone between the oculomotor and the vestibular nuclei. Cerebral lesions probably do not cause spontaneous nystagmus, unless there is associated pressure on or involvement of other structures; they may,

however, influence or alter induced nystagmus and that produced by lesions elsewhere.

The presence of unequal movements in the two eyes, or of dissociated or disjunctive nystagmus, is usually indicative of interruption of impulses within the brain stem, but sometimes occur with other lesions in the posterior fossa. *Vertical nystagmus* usually indicates involvement of the superior vestibular nuclei or their connections in the medial longitudinal fasciculus, but it may be present with peripheral labyrinthine lesions or even cerebellar disease. *Convergence nystagmus* (a rhythmic oscillation with slow abduction of the eyes followed by a quick adduction) occurs with anterior midbrain, posterior third ventricle, and periaqueductal lesions and is often seen with Parinaud's syndrome; the nystagmus may be precipitated by attempts at upward gaze. *Retraction nystagmus* (an oscillatory retraction of the eyeballs) is found with lesions in the region of the aqueduct, and also in Parinaud's syndrome; it may be brought out by testing for vertical optokinetic nystagmus with the stimulus directed downward. *See-saw nystagmus* is a vertical disjunctive variety in which one eye moves upward while the other moves down; there usually are associated torsional movements. Most cases have occurred in patients with tumors of the suprasellar region or anterior third ventricle or other lesions affecting the optic chiasm and causing a bitemporal hemianopia, although some investigators feel that a brain stem lesion can also cause this type of nystagmus.

The nystagmus of posterior fossa lesions is not necessarily the result of direct irritation or destruction of the structures mentioned above, but may be caused by pressure on them, edema, or interruption of blood supply. The presence of associated signs and symptoms, such as cranial nerve palsies, conjugate gaze pareses, coordination difficulties, and sensory changes, may aid in the localization of the lesion. The nystagmus with conditions such as multiple sclerosis, Friedreich's ataxia, olivopontocerebellar atrophy, syringobulbia, encephalitis, and vascular, neoplastic, and degenerative diseases may be caused by lesions in various sites, and sometimes is the result of disseminated involvement.

c. *Miscellaneous Varieties of Nystagmus:* (1) *Toxic nystagmus:* The ingestion or injection of various drugs and toxins may cause nystagmus, which can appear with the use of barbiturates, acetanilid and related drugs, diphenylhydantoin sodium, lead, nicotine, chloroform, quinine, and alcohol. The movement is usually rhythmic, horizontal but occasionally vertical, rather coarse, and increased on lateral gaze, with the rapid component in the direction of gaze. The site of action of these drugs is not known, but they probably affect the vestibular connections and the brain stem; toxins associated with infectious states may affect the labyrinths. The nystagmus seen in patients with epilepsy may be due to the anticonvulsant medication rather than a manifestation of the underlying disease process. The appearance of nystagmus in a patient receiving diphenylhydantoin sodium (Dilantin) does not call for withdrawal of the drug, but an increase in the nystagmus along with either vertigo or diplopia may be the first sign of intoxication.

The intravenous administration of barbiturates or mephenesin (Tolserol) or the injection of curare causes nystagmus to appear promptly. Coarse nystagmus on lateral gaze appears first, then on vertical gaze, and finally there is nystagmus on direct forward gaze. Such administration of these drugs also causes inability to maintain gaze on voluntary deviation of the eyes, and abolishes optokinetic nystagmus. These drugs also alter induced and pathologic varieties of nystagmus. Small doses of barbiturates abolish optokinetic nystagmus and larger doses first increase and then abolish vestibular nystagmus. Barbiturates may also abolish the nystagmus on direct forward gaze in such conditions as multiple sclerosis and diseases of the brain stem; they may temporarily stop latent and some types of congenital nystagmus; they may alter the nystagmus of chronic alcoholics, and produce a fine, shimmering variety.

(2) *Congenital or hereditary nystagmus:* This variety, which dates from birth, must be differentiated from "ocular" nystagmus, which does not develop until fixation is attempted. It is not associated with grossly defective vision, and is usually rhythmic, rapid, and either horizontal or rotatory. It may vary in form and rate, however, and occasionally is vertical; it may be pendular at rest and rhythmic on lateral gaze, with the rapid component in the direction of gaze. It is probably the result of hypoplasia or some other developmental abnormality of the central nervous system. Congenital nystagmus may be inherited as an autosomal recessive trait; it may be sex-linked, occurring only in males, or it may be irregularly dominant, occurring in both sexes. It may be associated with partial albinism.

(3) *Nystagmus due to involvement of the cervical portion of the spinal cord:* Lesions of the spinal cord, usually above the fourth cervical segment, may produce nystagmus. This is uncommon, but has been reported in syringomyelia, tumors, and other lesions. It may indicate involvement of the medial longitudinal fasciculus or of the spinovestibular pathways, or may be related to the tonic neck reflexes and their effect on ocular movement.

(4) *Positional nystagmus:* Nystagmus secondary to organic disease may be present only with alterations of the position of the head or body. One variety which is usually transient has been reported with posttraumatic vertigo and certain nonprogressive lesions of the nervous system; this has been termed positional nystagmus of the benign, paroxysmal type, and may be secondary to involvement of the utricle. Another variety which persists as long as the critical head position is maintained, but may be accompanied by less severe vertigo, has been reported with metastatic involvement of the cerebellum and brain stem; this has been called positional nystagmus of the central type. Many of the other varieties of pathologic nystagmus may be altered or influenced by changes in the position of the head or body.

(5) *Hysterical nystagmus:* This has been described, but its actual existence is doubtful. The movements are said to be jerky and irregular, and occasionally accompanied by spasm of the orbicularis oculi and medial rectus muscles. If it does occur, it may be caused by inadequate neuromuscular control of the lateral eye movements and failure of alternate contraction of the agonists and antagonists on deviation of the eyes. It may be brought on by emotional strain, but it must be borne in mind that a true pathologic nystagmus may be increased by nervous tension, and nervous and fatigued individuals are especially apt to show nystagmoid movements or fixation nystagmus when they attempt to deviate their eyes and to fix them on some object.

(6) *Voluntary nystagmus:* Simulated nystagmus, or that of voluntary origin, has

also been described. It is usually pendular and horizontal, and may be either unilateral or bilateral. The movements are extremely rapid; they are increased by
fixation, convergence, and increasing the width of the palpebral fissures. The nystagmus disappears when the subjects's attention is distracted or when vision is blurred
by a convex lens placed in front of each eye. It is doubtful whether these voluntary
movements of the eyeballs should be considered a variety of nystagmus.

OTHER ABNORMAL MOVEMENTS

Oculogyric Crises: These consist of attacks of involuntary conjugate upward
deviation of the eyeballs (Fig. 70). Occasionally there is also some deviation to one
side, or the eyes may be turned downward. The attacks may be transitory or last for
hours, until the patient is able to get to sleep. He may be able to turn the eyeballs
downward for short periods of time, but be unable to keep them down. These
phenomena are usually found in postencephalitic syndromes, and there may be
associated weakness of upward gaze between attacks, weakness of convergence, and
jerkiness of ocular movements. Oculogyric crises may also occur with the use of
certain of the phenothiazine drugs. In *petit mal* seizures there may be brief spasms of
upward gaze.

Spasmodic Lateral Deviation of the Eyes: Irritation of the cerebral centers controlling conjugate gaze may cause spasmodic lateral deviation of the eyes (Fig. 71).
There may be associated turning of the head to the same side. This phenomenon is
often seen in jacksonian convulsions, and it may be of localizing significance if it
precedes generalized convulsions. A pseudospasm of conjugate gaze may be a
symptom of pontine lesions in which there is paralysis of gaze to the opposite side.
Reflex deviation of the eyes in response to labyrinthine, cochlear, retinal, trigeminal,
and postural stimulation has been mentioned above.

Opsoclonus: The term opsoclonus has been given to rarely occurring coarse, ir-

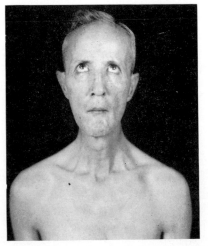

F IG . 70.   Oculogyric crisis in patient with postencephalitic parkinsonism.

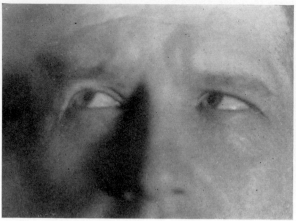

FIG. 71.   Forced conjugate gaze to the right with paralysis of conjugate gaze
to the left in patient with neoplasm of right frontal lobe.

regular, nonrhythmic, "agitated" oscillations of the eyeballs in both horizontal and
vertical planes. The movements, when present, may persist for long periods of time.
They have been observed in encephalitis, cerebellar and brain stem disorders, and
comatose states. A description of other somewhat related and also rare abnormalities
of ocular movement follows. Brief periods of *flutter-like* or *shimmering oscillations*
are sometimes present with cerebellar lesions as well as on attempts to fix the eyes
in a defective field of vision; they are also seen on occasion without disease in tense
and nervous individuals. With some of the spinocerebellar degenerations there may
be both flutter-like oscillations and dysmetria in pursuit movements. Brief bursts
of rapid, horizontal to-and-fro movements, called *lightning movements* or *ocular
myoclonus,* may occur with midbrain or cerebellar lesions. Intermittent periods of
coarse, synchronous, downward "bobbing" movements of the eyes have been observed in coma and with pontine lesions.

Rapid eye movements, which can be seen through the closed lids, occur periodically during sleep. During a normal night's sleep most individuals have four or five
periods of what has been called paradoxical or activated sleep which takes up 20 to
25 per cent of the sleeping time. The rapid eye movements (REM) are present
during these periods (Chapter 55).

EXOPHTHALMOS AND ENOPHTHALMOS

Either exophthalmos or enopthalmos may occur in disease of the nervous system
and may be of significance in neurologic diagnosis. *Enophthalmos* has already been
referred to under the discussion of paralysis of the cervical portion of the sympathetic
division; it may also occur in intraorbital disease with loss of orbital tissue.

Exophthalmos may be bilateral, as it usually is in hyperthyroidism, but unilateral
exophthalmos is more significant in the diagnosis of neurologic disease. It may be
due to hypertonus of the smooth muscle of the orbit secondary to sympathetic over-
stimulation, but more frequently is a pressure manifestation. In the appraisal of

exophthalmos one should note such phenomena as *von Graefe's sign,* or lid lag; *Möbius' sign,* or insufficient convergence; *Dalrymple's sign,* or increased width of the palpebral fissures; and *Stellwag's sign,* or infrequent winking. Malignant exophthalmos may occur spontaneously or following thyroidectomy; there may be associated ocular muscle palsies. Bilateral exophthalmos occasionally occurs in patients with increased intracranial pressure. Unilateral exophthalmos may be present in hyperthyroidism, but it is usually indicative of some localized intracranial or intraorbital disease. It may be seen in brain tumors, especially meningiomas of the sphenoidal ridge and olfactory groove. It may occur in association with a tumor or mucocele within the orbit, orbital cellulitis, or deformities of the skull. *Pulsating exophthalmos* may be caused by an intracranial aneurysm, angioma, or arteriovenous fistula; a pulsation may be felt or bruit heard over the protruded eye. *Proptosis,* a marked forward displacement of the eyeball, is an exaggerated degree of exophthalmos. When it occurs in cavernous sinus thrombosis there is associated chemosis, or edema of the conjunctiva, together with edema of the eyelids and paralysis of the third, fourth, and sixth nerves. In determining slight degrees of exophthalmos and enophthalmos an exophthalmometer may be used.

DISORDERS OF THE OCULAR NERVES

In appraising lesions of the nerves of ocular movement, one must differentiate between isolated involvement of a single nerve or of part of a nerve and involvement of these nerves in various combinations, and between infranuclear, nuclear, and supranuclear lesions. By noting in detail the manifestations of disordered function of these nerves, together with evidences of involvement of associated structures, one may be able to decide whether the pathologic lesion is in the cerebrum, midbrain, pons, medulla, or spinal cord; outside the brain or brain stem but within the skull; in the middle cranial fossa, or within the cavernous sinus or the orbit.

Paralysis of the *third nerve* may be either partial or complete. If the lesion is within the midbrain or within the orbit, the involvement is incomplete, but one along the course of the nerve may cause a complete paralysis. Nuclear lesions may be accompanied by involvement of the superior colliculus, red nucleus, substantia nigra, cerebral peduncles, medial longitudinal fasciculus, or ascending sensory pathways (see below). Among the more frequent causes of third nerve palsy are intracranial aneurysms, diabetes, trauma, neoplasms, syphilis, compression of the nerve trunk by an atheromatous posterior cerebral artery, and compression by hippocampal herniation; since the pupilloconstrictor fibers are in the upper portion of the nerve, hippocampal herniation may affect only these, and there is pupillary dilatation but no ptosis or ocular palsy. Incomplete palsies produce a variety of impaired movements; all may be weakened, or some may be defective and others paralyzed. One muscle only may be involved, or all except one. There may be paralysis of only the ciliary muscle, with resulting cycloplegia, or of the sphincter iridis, with resulting iridoplegia, or both may be involved. If the voluntary muscles are paralyzed, there may be either an external ophthalmoplegia or ptosis, or both. The pupil is often spared in a diabetic oculomotor palsy. With faulty regeneration and misdirection of oculomotor fibers following third nerve paralysis certain synkinetic movements may appear; retraction of the upper lid, medial rotation of the eye, and constriction of the pupil take place on downward gaze (*the pseudo-Graefe syndrome*). If there is a residual partial ptosis, there may also be elevation of the lid on attempted medial and upward gaze, and the ptosis may increase with abduction.

An isolated *fourth nerve* paralysis is difficult to diagnose, since the ocular movements are only slightly disturbed and there is little deviation of the eyeball. The defect in function of the superior oblique may be hidden by the collateral action of the lateral and inferior reciti. There is, however, a deviation of the face forward, downward, and toward the unaffected side, and the chin is tilted toward the shoulder of the involved side. The patient may complain of difficulty in descending stairs. In a nuclear palsy of the fourth nerve the defect is on the contralateral side, but in involvement of the nerve itself it is ipsilateral.

Isolated paralysis of the *sixth nerve* occurs more frequently than does that of the third or the fourth nerve, and bilateral sixth nerve paralysis may be present without localizing significance with increased intracranial pressure, diabetes, vascular disease, brain stem displacement, meningitis, and trauma to the skull. In a nuclear lesion of the sixth nerve there often is involvement of other nuclei, such as that of the seventh nerve, or of other pathways, such as the medial longitudinal fasciculus.

Nuclear involvement of the ocular nerves may be the result of vascular lesions, such as hemorrhages or thromboses within the brain stem or vertebrobasilar artery insufficiency, or of inflammatory lesions, deficiency states, neoplasms, trauma, metabolic disorders, multiple sclerosis, syringobulbia, or other disorders of the midbrain and brain stem. Any or all of the nerves may be affected. Even though only one nerve may be paralyzed, there are usually associated manifestations that indicate extension of the process to involve the medial longitudinal fasciculus, the descending pyramidal pathways, the ascending sensory tracts, the cerebellar connections, or neighboring cranial nerve nuclei.

Infranuclear lesions, resulting from involvement of the nerves after they have left the brain stem, may be caused by lesions within the skull, in the middle cranial fossa, in the cavernous sinus, or in superior orbital fissure or the orbit. Involvement within the skull may be produced by meningitis, basal hemorrhage, trauma to the skull, or concussion. Neuritic palsies may have the same etiologies as other polyneuritides—deficiency states, metabolic disorders, exposure to or ingestion of toxins, diphtheria and other infections, collagen disorders, amyloidosis, and others; they may be a part of polyradiculoneuritis or the Guillain-Barré syndrome. Any or all of the nerves may be involved with lesions within the cavernous sinus or in the region of the superior orbital fissure, and with intracranial aneurysms, especially those involving the internal carotid artery or its branches. All may be involved, but in a different manner, in neoplasms or infections within the orbit. Pathologic changes within the muscles themselves, such as those associated with trichinosis, rheumatic infiltrations, myositis, fatty degeneration, and other strictly muscular disorders, may also produce disturbances of ocular movement.

Supranuclear lesions that cause disturbances of function of the ocular nerves may occur in the cerebral cortex, basal ganglia, internal capsule, midbrain, or brain stem. Tumors, neoplasms, vascular lesions, inflammations, trauma, and degenerative changes of the cerebrum may affect the ocular nerves through involvement of either the cerebral centers which regulate their function or of the infracortical connections. Irritative lesions cause abnormalities of movement (Fig. 71), whereas destructive lesions cause paresis of conjugate gaze and may also cause abnormalities of induced nystagmus. In disease of the extrapyramidal system there may be dyskinesias of ocular movement, such as the oculogyric crisis, along with slowness of jerkiness of movement.

In states of lowered consciousness and coma it may be possible to test for reflex ocular movements even though voluntary motion is absent. The oculocephalic reflex (doll's head phenomenon) is tested by holding the eyes open and passively but rapidly turning the head from side to side; if the eyes move in a direction opposite to that in which the head is moved, the reflex is intact. Absence of movement to one side suggests the presence of paresis of conjugate gaze to that side, and dissociation of response suggests the presence of brain stem involvement. The reflex is absent in deep coma and severe brain stem disease. Optokinetic nystagmus can be tested in states of lowered consciousness and caloric nystagmus in some stages of coma. Abnormalities of caloric response indicate interruption of brain stem pathways. The caloric responses are absent in deep coma and severe brain stem disease.

Disturbances in function of the ocular nerves may also occur on a *psychogenic basis*. Paresis of the ocullar muscles or the levator rarely occurs, but there may be spasm of these muscles (Chapter 56). Spasm of convergence is most frequently encountered. Hysterical ptosis has been described; this is probably the result of spasm of the orbicularis (blepharospasm) rather than of paresis of the levator. Diplopia, if present, may be monocular, or there may be polyopia. The existence of hysterical nystagmus is doubtful. In anxiety states and some psychoses the pupils may be large.

Abnormalities of the ocular nerves are especially important in the diagnosis of many diseases of the nervous system. In *multiple sclerosis* there may be nystagmus, ocular palsies with diplopia, ptosis, and pupillary abnormalities. The nystagmus is a very frequent finding; it is rhythmic, usually horizontal, but occasionally rotatory or mixed, and is relatively coarse. The presence of dissociated, or "ataxic," nystagmus is significant. Inasmuch as multiple sclerosis may also be accompanied by retrobulbar neuritis, optic atrophy, scotomas, and changes in the retinal arteries and veins, the examination of the eyes is of extreme importance in its diagnosis.

In *syphilis of the central nervous system* the pupillary reflexes are especially important, but there may also be a third nerve paralysis, isolated palsies, ptosis, and other ocular manifestations. Most characteristically one finds Argyll Robertson pupils, but a sluggish or paradoxical pupillary response, anisocoria, or irregularity of the pupils may be significant. The manifestations may be caused by vascular, inflammatory, or degenerative changes associated with the syphilitic involvement. Optic atrophy is also found in central nervous system syphilis, and cerebral involvement by gummas or thromboses may cause defects in the visual fields. Interstitial keratitis has been considered to be almost exclusively the result of congenital syphilis, but in *Cogan's syndrome* there is sudden onset of vertigo, tinnitus, and deafness accompanied by photophobia, blurred vision, and interstitial keratitis.

which is nonsyphilitic; the etiology is unknown, but it may either be of infectious origin or related to polyarteritis nodosa.

Congenital and developmental abnormalities may cause dysfunction of ocular motility and related phenomena. Strabismus and ocular imbalance present from birth may be of muscular rather than neurologic origin. Ptosis may be congenital. A large precentage of patients with cerebral palsy of various types have strabismus, ocular palsies, or motor imbalance. There may be associated mental deficiency and epilepsy. All of these symptoms result from cortical or cerebral damage prior to, during, or immediately after delivery. Similar ocular signs, along with nystagmus, optic atrophy, and other visual defects, may play an important part of the clinical picture in such inherited, developmental, and degenerative conditions as congenital hydrocephalus, craniostenosis, mongolism, albinism, Schilder's disease, and the lipoidoses.

Diplopia and ocular palsies are important in the diagnosis of *acute encephalitis. Polioencephalitis superior hemorrhagica,* or *Wernicke's polioencephalitis,* is characterized by ocular palsies, nystagmus, ataxia, and disturbances of consciousness. It occurs mainly with chronic alcoholism, but also with hyperemesis gravidarum and other states of malnutrition, and is the result of thiamin deficiency. Diplopia, nystagmus, pupillary changes, and even complete ocular nerve palsies are sometimes found in acute *bulbar poliomyelitis.* In *polioencephalitis inferior* and *botulism* the initial symptom may be difficulty with convergence, followed by ptosis, dilated pupils, and paralysis of extraocular muscles. In *postdiphtheritic paralysis* there is loss of accommodation, often with associated weakness of convergence; blurring of vision for near objects is a common symptom.

In *chronic progressive external ophthalmoplegia* there is a gradually increasing weakness of the muscles of the eyelids and the extraocular muscles; the condition may be familial. In most instances this is associated with progressive muscular alterations, rather than degeneration of nuclear centers, and is a myopathy or dystrophy of the ocular muscles; other evidences of muscular dystrophy may accompany or follow the ocular involvement. In *dystrophia myotonica* there may be ptosis along with baldness and changes in the facial expression and voice; occasionally there is either myotonia of the lids or a myotonic lid lag. The earliest symptoms of *myasthenia gravis* are often referable to the muscles supplied by the ocular nerves, and the patient may notice diplopia and ptosis that come on with activity and are relieved by rest; the amount of ptosis and ocular muscle weakness may fluctuate during a brief period of examination. There is often weakness of the frontalis and orbicularis oculi as well as of the levator. The neostigmine test may confirm the diagnosis. In *hyperthyroidism* or excessive production of pituitary thyrotropic hormone there may be paralysis of extraocular muscles in addition to the exophthalmos and associated signs mentioned above; hypothyroidism may cause edema of the eyelids that simulates ptosis.

Diabetes mellitus is one of the more common causes of paralysis of the third and other ocular nerves; the pupil is often spared. In diabetes there may also be an abnormality of the pupillary response of the Argyll Robertson type. Recurring cranial nerve palsies may be seen in sarcoidosis. Paralysis of the abducens nerve, and sometimes of other ocular nerves, may be complications or sequelae of *spinal anesthesia* and spinal puncture. Variable ophthalmoplegias have been reported with angioneurotic edema. Recurrent ocular palsies occur in *ophthalmoplegic migraine* and in *periodic palaysis* of the familial type; both may result in permanent paralysis. There may be partial ptosis and miosis during the attacks of so-called cluster headaches. Cyclic oculomotor paralysis has been described.

In *Friedreich's ataxia, Marie's ataxia,* and *cerebellar* and *labyrinthine lesions* nystagmus is an important finding. In *Gerlier's disease,* or paralyzing vertigo, diplopia and ptosis are often present. *Ocular torticollis* may be associated with involvement of one or more of the ocular nerves, especially paralysis of the trochlear nerve. Ocular torticollis may date from birth or from the time of the development of fusion; the deformity can usually be corrected voluntarily. In *Parkinson's disease* there may be saccadic or jerky ocular movements, sometimes referred to as "cogwheel" in type, and weakness of convergence or of upward gaze. There often is infrequent blinking and associated lid retraction, but repeated blinking movements may appear when threatening movements are made toward the eyes or the bridge of the nose is tapped with a reflex hammer (Myerson's sign). These phenomena, together with oculogyric crises, blepharospasm, and abnormalities of the pupillary responses, occur more frequently in postencephalitic than in idiopathic parkinsonism. Abnormalities of ocular motility may also be present in Wilson's disease and other extrapyramidal disorders.

In *meningitis* and *trauma to the skull* one finds various ocular palsies and pupillary changes. Ptosis, photophobia, and dissociation of ocular movements may also be present with meningitis. These same manifestations are seen in *subarachnoid hemorrhage. Aneurysms of the internal carotid artery* or of the circle of Willis may affect any or all of the ocular nerves. Such involvement in a patient who has had a subarachnoid hemorrhage usually indicates the presence of a localized aneurysmal dilatation; supraclinoid carotid aneurysm is one of the most common causes of an isolated oculomotor paralysis. *Thrombosis of the cavernous sinus* and *intraorbital neoplasms* or *infections* may produce proptosis with ocular palsies. The typical syndrome of cavernous sinus thrombosis consists of ipsilateral proptosis, chemosis, edema of the eyelid and orbital tissues, paralysis of the third, fourth, and sixth nerves, and involvement of the upper divisions of the trigeminal nerve; papilledema is sometimes present.

Intracranial neoplasms, abscesses, granulomas, hematomas, hemorrhages, and *thromboses* may cause disturbances of function of the ocular nerves, and also of the optic nerves, which aid not only in diagnosis but also in localization. Significant findings include extraocular muscle palsies, disturbances of conjugate gaze, pupillary changes, and nystagmus, and also, as far as the second nerve is concerned, papilledema, optic atrophy, and field defects. Increased intracranial pressure alone may cause either unilateral or bilateral abducens palsy; the ipsilateral pupil may be dilated and fixed with expanding intracranial lesions, owing to compression by hippocampal herniation. Hemorrhages, thromboses, and tumors of the brain stem are also important causes of ocular nerve dysfunction, as well as of transient blurring of vision, field defects, and conjugate gaze palsy. Brain stem hemorrhages and thromboses frequently cause marked miosis, owing to bilateral interruption of descending dilator pathways. Ocular palsies, nystagmus, and involvement of neighboring cranial nerves or ascending or descending pathways may aid in localization.

Many syndromes have been described in which there is involvement of the nerves of ocular movement and the cervical sympathetic pathways. *Horner's syndrome* has been mentioned above. By evaluating the signs and symptoms of involvement of neighboring structures, it is often possible to localize, within the brain stem or spinal cord or along the sympathetic pathway, the responsible lesion. This syndrome may occur, for instance, in thrombosis of the posterior inferior cerebellar artery, with associated fifth and tenth nerve and spinothalamic involvement, or in Raeder's paratrigeminal syndrome, with associated motor and sensory changes in the trigeminal nerve. It has also been reported in association with thrombosis of the internal carotid artery. *Parinaud's syndrome,* or paralysis of conjugate upward gaze, has also been mentioned; there may be, in association, fixed pupils or pupils which react in accommodation but not to light, and there often is paralysis of convergence. There may be convergence or retraction nystagmus. This symptom complex is caused by lesions at the level of the anterior quadrigeminal bodies, and it is sometimes referred to as the *syndrome of the superior colliculus,* or the *"pineal" syndrome;* it is found in encephalitis and in tumors of the pineal gland, the posterior portion of the third ventricle, and the mesencephalon. *Gradenigo's syndrome* consists of a lateral rectus palsy associated with pain, swelling, and tenderness behind the ipsilateral ear; it indicates inflammatory involvement of the petrous pyramid.

Benedikt's syndrome, or *the tegmental syndrome of the midbrain,* is caused by a lesion of the midbrain involving the third nerve as it passes through the red nucleus. It is characterized by an ipsilateral oculomotor paralysis with contralateral ataxia, tremor, and hyperkinesis of the upper extremity. If the cerebral peduncle is also involved, there is a contralateral hemiparesis, and extension to the medial lemniscus produces loss of proprioceptive sensation and diminished tactile sensation on the opposite side of the body. In *Claude's syndrome,* limited to the third nerve and red nucleus, there is an ipsilateral oculomotor paresis with contralateral ataxia and tremor. *Weber's syndrome,* or *superior alternating hemiplegia,* consists of an ipsilateral third nerve paralysis and a contralateral paresis of the lower face, tongue, and extremities. This is caused by involvement of the oculomotor nerve as it passes through the cerebral peduncle. In the *Nothnagel syndrome* there is a unilateral oculomotor paralysis combined with ipsilateral cerebellar ataxia, owing to involvement of the third nerve and the brachium conjunctivum. In the *syndrome of the mesencephalic gray matter* there are bilateral internal and external ophthalmoplegias, because of total bilateral oculomotor paralyses. The *syndrome of the interpeduncular space* consists of bilateral third nerve paralyses together with a spastic tetraparesis; there is involvement of the emerging fibers of both oculomotor nerves and of both cerebral peduncles.

Raymond's syndrome consists of an ipsilateral sixth nerve paralysis and a contralateral paresis of the extremities. More frequent is the *Millard-Gubler syndrome,* or *middle alternating hemiplegia;* in this there is an ipsilateral lateral rectus paralysis, probably because of nuclear involvement, with an ipsilateral facial paralysis, probably owing to involvement of the root fibers, and a contralateral pyramidal hemiplegia resulting from involvement of the corticospinal fibers. The *Foville syndrome* is characterized by an ipsilateral facial paralysis owing to involvement of the root fibers, an ipsilateral paralysis of lateral gaze because of involvement of the parabducens nucleus or the medial longitudinal fasciculus, and a contralateral pyramidal hemiplegia. There is contralateral deviation of the eyes, and sometimes of the head as well. According to some authorities, there is paresis of conjugate gaze and lateral rotation of the head contralateral to the lesion, with ipsilateral deviation, resulting from involvement of the aberrant oculogyric and cephalogyric pyramidal fibers. In any of the last three syndromes there may be individual variations; involvement of the medial lemniscus causes loss of proprioceptive sensation and diminished tactile sensation on the opposite side of the body. The *internuclear ophthalmoplegias* and the *syndrome of the medial longitudinal fasciculus* have been described above.

The *Raymond-Cestan syndrome* has been described variously. Characteristically there is ipsilateral paralysis of conjugate gaze or contralateral ocular deviation, because of involvement of the parabducens nucleus or the medial longitudinal fasciculus, with contralateral hemiplegia and loss of proprioceptive and diminished tactile sensations, resulting from involvement of the pyramidal pathways and the medial lemniscus. In addition, there may be ipsilateral ataxia and dyssynergy as a result of involvement of the inferior cerebellar peduncle. Occasionally there is bilateral spastic paresis, with paralysis of lateral gaze in both directions and dissociation of eye movements, owing to involvement of both pyramidal pathways and both medial longitudinal fasciculi. This syndrome follows a hemorrhage or a thrombosis of the basilar artery or its pontine branches. Conditions in which the primary involvement is in the medulla may also influence eye movements. These are discussed in Chapter 18.

In *Gerhardt's syndrome* there is a bilateral abducens palsy. *Möbius' syndrome* is characterized by paralysis or paresis of the ocular muscles, especially the abducens, together with paralysis or paresis of the facial muscles; this is generally felt to be due to aplasia or hypoplasia of the nuclear centers in the brain stem, although some investigators postulate the presence of a supranuclear lesion. In *Duane's syndrome* there is widening of the palpebral fissure on abduction and narrowing on adduction of the affected eye. There is also limitation of lateral gaze, and there may be retraction and elevation of the globe on adduction. This has been explained on the basis of either aplasia of the abducens nerve with anomalous innervation of the lateral rectus by the oculomotor nerve or fibrosis of the lateral rectus and levator muscles. In the *syndrome of Foix*, found in cavernous sinus lesions and in periostitis, fractures, tumors, and aneurysms in the region of the superior orbital fissure, the third, fourth and sixth nerves and the ophthalmic division of the trigeminal nerve are involved. The *syndrome of the tentorial notch,* or the *uncal syndrome,* occurs with herniation of the uncus and/or the hippocampal gyrus through the incisura of the tentorium cerebelli, usually due to increased intracranial pressure or a mass lesion in the ipsilateral cerebral hemisphere. The first sign of this is a dilated pupil, which may not react to light, on the side of the compression. Later a complete third nerve paralysis appears, along with signs of lateral midbrain compression, causing a contralateral pyramidal paresis, progressive coma, and, finally, decerebrate rigidity. Compression of the posterior cerebral artery may cause a hemianopia. Occasionally there is a so-called central syndrome with Cheyne-Stokes respirations, constricted pupils, and bilateral pyramidal tract involvement. Pupillary dilatation with passive neck flexion may indicate transient compression of the brain stem or its vascular supply, and thus may be a sign of impending uncal herniation.

REFERENCES

ADIE, W. J.   Tonic pupils and absent tendon reflexes: A benign disorder *sui generis*; its complete and incomplete forms.   *Brain* 55:98, 1932.

ADLER, F. H.   Physiology of the Eye; Clinical Application (ed. 2).   St. Louis, C. V. Mosby Company, 1953.

ANDERSON, J. R.   Ocular Vertical Deviations and the Treatment of Nystagmus (ed. 2). Philadelphia, J. B. Lippincott Company, 1959.

ASCHAN, G., BERGSTEDT, M., and STAHLE, J.   Nystagmography, *Acta otolaryng.*   Suppl. 129, 1956, p. 5.

ATKIN, A., and BENDER, M. B.   'Lightning eye movements' (ocular myoclonus).   *J. Neurol. Sc.* 1:2, 1964.

BAILEY, C. J., and GUTH, L.   Role of the sympathetic nervous system in the pupillary response to darkness.   *Exper. Neurol.* 1:66, 1959.

BENDER, M. B.   "Neuroophthalmology," in Baker, A. B. (ed.), Clinical Neurology (ed. 2).   New York, Hoeber Medical Division, Harper & Row, 1962, vol. 1, pp. 275–349.

BENDER, M. B. (ed.)   The Oculomotor System.   New York, Hoeber Medical Division, Harper & Row, 1964.

BIELSCHOWSKY, A.   Lectures on Motor Anomalies.   Hanover, N.H., Dartmouth College Publications, 1940.

CARMICHAEL, E. A., DIX, M. R., and HALLPIKE, C. S.   Lesions of the cerebral hemispheres and their effects upon optokinetic and caloric nystagmus.   *Brain* 77:345, 1954.

CARPENTER, M. G., McMASTERS, R. E., and HANNA, G. R.   Disturbances of conjugate horizontal eye movements in the monkey.   *Arch. Neurol.* 8:231, 1963.

CAWTHORNE, T., and HINCHCLIFFE, R.   Positional nystagmus of the central type as evidence of subtentorial metastasis.   *Brain* 84:415, 1961.

COGAN, D. G.   Neurology of the Ocular Muscles (ed. 2). Springfield, Ill., Charles C Thomas, 1956.

COGAN, D. G.   Syndrome of nonsyphilitic interstitial keratitis with vestibuloauditory symptoms.   *Arch. Ophth.* 33:144, 1945; A type of congenital ocular motor apraxia presenting jerky head movement.   *Am. J. Ophth.* 36:433, 1953; Ocular dysmetria, flutter-like oscillations of the eyes, and opsoclonus.   *Arch. Ophth.* 51:318, 1954; Convergence nystagmus.   *Arch. Ophth.* 62:295, 1959.

CROSBY, E. C.   Nystagmus as a sign of central nervous system involvement.   *Ann. Otol. Rhin. & Laryng.*   62:1117, 1953.

CROSBY, E. C., and HENDERSON, J. W.   The mammalian midbrain and isthmus regions: II. Fiber connections of the superior colliculus; B.   Pathways concerned in automatic eye movements.   *J. Comp. Neurol.*   88:53, 1948.

DAROFF, R. B., and SMITH, J. L.   Intraocular optic neuritis with normal visual acuity. *Neurology* 15:409, 1965.

DAVIDOFF, R. A., ATKIN, A., ANDERSON, P. J. and BENDER, M. B.   Optokinetic nystagmus and cerebral disease.   *Arch. Neurol.* 14:73, 1966.

DAVSON, H (ed.)   The Eye: Vol. 3, Muscular Mechanisms.   New York, Academic Press, Inc., 1962.

DEJONG, R. N.   Horner's syndrome: A report of ten cases.   *Arch. Neurol. & Psychiat.* 34:734, 1935; Nystagmus: An appraisal and a classification.   *Arch. Neurol. & Psychiat* 55:43, 1946.

DUKE-ELDER, W. S.   Text-Book of Ophthalmology.   St. Louis, C. V. Mosby Company, 1934, vol. 1; 1938, vol. 2; 1941, vol. 3; 1949, vol. 4.

DYKEN, P. R.   Extraocular myotonia in families of dystrophia myotonica.   *Neurology* 16:738, 1966.

FINCHAM, E. F.   Monocular diplopia.   *Brit. J. Ophth.* 47:705, 1963.

FISHER, C. M.   Ocular bobbing.   *Arch Neurol.* 11:543, 1964.

FORD, R. F., and WALSH, F. B.   Tonic deviation of the eyes produced by movements of the head, with special reference to otolith reflexes.   *Arch. Ophth.* 23:1274, 1940.

GOLDSTEIN, J. E., and COGAN, D. G.   Apraxia of lid opening.   *Arch. Ophth.* 73:155, 1965.

GREEN, W. R., HACKETT, E. R., and SCHLEZINGER, N. S.   Neuro-ophthalmologic evaluation of oculomotor nerve paralysis.   *Arch. Ophth.* 72:154, 1964.

HÉCAEN, H., and DE AJURIAGUERRA, J.   Balint's syndrome (psychic paralysis of visual fixation) and its minor forms.   *Brain* 77:373, 1954.

HENDERSON, J. W.   Optokinetic and other actors modifying vestibular nystagmus.   *Arch. Ophth.* 37:459, 1947; The anatomic basis for certain reflex and automatic eye movements.   *Am. J. Ophth.* 32:232, 1949.

HENDERSON, J. W., and CROSBY, E. C.   An experimental study of optokinetic responses.   *A.M.A. Arch. Ophth.* 47:43, 1952.

HOLLENHORST, R. W.   Neuro-ophthalmologic examination of children.   *Neurology* 6:739, 1956.

HOYT, W. F., and NACHTIGÄLER, A.   Anomalies of ocular motor nerves.   *Am. J. Ophth.* 60:433, 1965.

KAPP, J., and PAULSON, G.   Pupillary changes induced by circulatory arrest.   *Neurology* 16:225, 1966.

KESTENBAUM, A.   Clinical Methods of Neuro-Ophthalmologic Examination (ed. 2).   New York, Grune & Stratton, 1961.

KILOH, L. G., and NEVIN, S.   Progressive dystrophy of the external ocular muscles (ocular myopathy).   *Brain* 74: 115, 1951.

LANCASTER, W. B.   Physiology of disturbances of ocular motility.   *Arch. Ophth.* 17:983, 1937.

LANGWORTHY, O. R.   General principles of autonomic innervation.   *Arch. Neurol. & Psychiat.* 50:590, 1943.

LOWENSTEIN, O., and LOEWENFELD, I. E.   Role of sympathetic and parasympathetic systems in reflex dilatation of the pupil: Pupillographic studies.   *Arch. Neurol. & Psychiat.* 64:313, 1950.

LYLE, D. J.   Neuro-Ophthalmology (ed. 2).   Springfield, Ill., Charles C Thomas, 1954.

MCCABE, B. F.   The quick component of nystagmus.   *Laryngoscope* 75:1619, 1965.

MCNEALY, D. E., and PLUM, F.   Brainstem dysfunction with supratentorial mass lesions.   *Arch. Neurol.* 7:10, 1962.

MERRITT, H. H., and MOORE, M. The Argyll Robertson pupil: An anatomic-physiologic explanation of the phenomenon, with a survey of its occurrence in neurosyphilis. *Arch. Neurol. & Psychiat.* 30:357, 1933.

NATHANSON, M., BERGMAN, P. S., and ANDERSON, P. J. Significance of oculocephalic and caloric responses in the unconscious patient. *Neurology* 7:829, 1957.

NORRIS, F. H., JR., and FAWCETT, J. A. A sign of intracranial mass with impending uncal herniation. *Arch. Neurol.* 12:381, 1965.

PETER, L. C. The Extra-Ocular Muscles (ed. 3). Philadelphia, Lea & Febiger, 1941.

PETROHELOS, M. A., and HENDERSON, J. W. The ocular findings of intracranial tumor: A study of 358 cases. *Am. J. Ophth.* 34:1387, 1951.

REA, R. L. Neuro-Ophthalmology (ed. 2). St. Louis, C. V. Mosby Company, 1941.

REID, W. L., and CONE, W. V. The mechanism of fixed dilatation of the pupil resulting from ipsilateral cerebral compression. *J.A.M.A.* 112:2030, 1939.

ROBERTSON, D. ARGYLL. On an interesting series of eye-movements in a case of spinal disease, with remarks on the action of belladonna on the iris, etc. *Edinburgh M. J.* 14:696, 1869; Four cases of spinal myosis; with remarks on the action of light on the pupil. *Ibid.,* 15:487, 1869.

SANDBERG, L. E., and ZILSTORFF-PEDERSEN, K. Directional preponderance in temporal lobe disease. *Arch. Otolaryng.* 73:139, 1961.

SCOBEE, R. G. The Oculorotary Muscles (ed. 2). St. Louis, C. V. Mosby Company, 1952.

SILVERSTEIN, H., and WEINER, L. M. Effect of unilateral cerebral lesions on nystagmus. *Arch. Otolaryng.* 81:64, 1965.

SMITH, J. L. Optokinetic Nystagmus. Springfield, Ill., Charles C Thomas, 1963.

SMITH, J. L. (ed.). The University of Miami Neuro-ophthalmology Symposium. Springfield, Ill., Charles C Thomas, 1964.

SMITH, J. L., and COGAN, D. G. Internuclear ophthalmoplegia: A review of 58 cases. *Arch. Ophth.* 61:687, 1959.

SMITH, J. L., DAVID, N. J., and KLINTWORTH, G. Skew deviation. *Neurology* 14:96, 1964.

SMITH, J. L., and MARK, V. H. See-saw nystagmus with suprasellar epidermoid tumor. *Arch. Ophth.* 62:280, 1959.

SPIEGEL, E. A., and SOMMER, I. Neurology of the Eye, Ear, Nose and Throat. New York, Grune & Stratton, 1944.

TOGLIA, J. U., and COLE, W., JR. Electronystagmography in clinical neurology. *Dis. Nerv. Syst.* 26:630, 1965.

TOROK, N., GUILLEMIN, V., JR., and BARNOTHY, J. M. Photelectric nystagmography. *Ann. Otol. Rhin., & Laryng.* 60:917, 1951.

VAN ALLEN, M. W., and BLODI, F. C. Neurologic aspects of the Möbius syndrome. *Neurology* 10:249, 1960.

WALKER, A. E. The syndromes of the tentorial notch. *J. Nerv. & Ment. Dis.* 136:118, 1963.

WALSH, F. B. Clinical Neuro-Ophthalmology (ed. 2). Baltimore, The Williams & Wilkins Company, 1957.

WARWICK, R. The so-called nucleus of convergence. *Brain* 78:248, 1955; Representation of the extra-ocular muscles in the oculomotor nuclei of the monkey. *J. Comp. Neurol.* 98: 449, 1953.

CHAPTER 12

THE TRIGEMINAL NERVE

ANATOMY AND PHYSIOLOGY

THE TRIGEMINAL, or *fifth cranial, nerve* is a mixed nerve, or one that carries both motor and sensory fibers. It is the largest of the cranial nerves, and, due to connections with the third, fourth, sixth, seventh, ninth, and tenth cranial nerves and with the sympathetic nervous system, one of the most complex. The nuclei of the trigeminal nerve are situated in the midportion of the pons (Fig. 72).

THE MOTOR PORTION

The *motor nucleus* of the trigeminal nerve is a prominent mass of large motor cells situated just anterior and medial to the outgoing fibers of the nerve in the lateral part of the reticular formation of the pons, near the floor of the fourth ventricle. The motor root, or portio minor, emerges from the lateral aspect of the pons in close association with, but anterior and medial to, the sensory root. It passes beneath the gasserian ganglion and leaves the skull through the foramen ovale. It joins the mandibular division immediately after leaving the skull, but soon separates from it to supply the muscles of mastication and associated muscles.

The *cerebral center* which controls the motor functions of the trigeminal nerve is situated in the lower third of the posterior frontal convolution. Each cerebral center probably has bilateral connections with the motor nuclei. Impulses travel through the corona radiata, the internal capsule, and the cerebral peduncle to the pons, where many of them decussate before supplying the motor nuclei. There is also extrapyramidal supranuclear innervation from the premotor cortex and the basal ganglia.

The principal function of the motor division of the trigeminal nerve is the innervation of the muscles of mastication, namely, the masseter, temporal, and internal and external pterygoid muscles. The *masseter muscles* elevate the mandible,

215

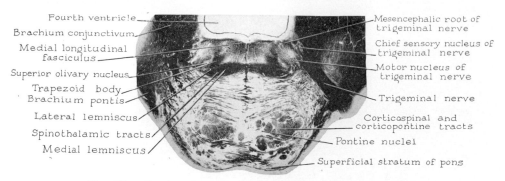

FIG. 72.   Section through pons at level of trigeminal nuclei.

and by means of their superficial fibers protrude it to a slight extent. The *temporal muscles* also elevate the mandible, and their posterior fibers serve to retract it; possibly the anterior fibers aid in protrusion. When the *external pterygoid muscles* act together they protrude and depress the mandible; when one acts alone it causes lateral movement to the opposite side. When the *internal pterygoid muscles* act together they elevate the mandible and assist the external pterygoids in protruding it; when one acts alone, it draws the mandible forward and causes deviation to the opposite side. Mastication consists of upward and downward movements of the jaw to open and close the mouth, together with forward, backward, and lateral motion. The masseters, temporals, and internal pterygoids elevate the mandible; the external pterygoids, assisted by the mylohyoids, digastrici, geniohyoids, and the other depressors of the hyoid bone, and also by gravity, depress the jaw; the internal and external pterygoids, assisted by the masseters and possibly the temporals, protrude the mandible; the temporals, assisted by the digastrici, retract the jaw, and the pterygoids produce side to side movement.

The trigeminal nerve also supplies the *mylohyoid muscle* and the *anterior belly of the digastricus*. The former draws the hyoid bone upward and forward and raises the floor of the mouth, thus pressing the base of the tongue against the palate; if the hyoid bone is fixed, the mylohyoid tends to depress the mandible. The anterior belly of the digastricus raises and advances the hyoid bone if the jaw is fixed, or depresses and retracts the mandible if the hyoid bone is fixed by the antagonist muscles; if the mandible is fixed, it also assists the mylohyoid in drawing the base of the tongue upward and forward and pressing it against the palate during the first portion of the act of deglutition.

The *tensor veli palatini* and the *tensor tympani* are two smaller muscles which are also supplied by the trigeminal nerve but have less clinical significance. The former tenses the soft palate, draws it to one side, and raises it to a certain extent. This muscle aids in preventing food from passing from the oral to the nasal pharynx and also dilates the eustachian tube. The tensor tympani draws the manubrium of the malleus and the tympanic membrane medialward, thus tensing the tympanic membrane.

THE SENSORY PORTION

The cells of origin of the sensory portion of the trigeminal nerve have their nuclei in the gasserian (semilunar) ganglion. The neuraxes which carry extroceptive sensation terminate in the sensory nuclei in the pons and medulla.

The *main,* or *chief, sensory nucleus,* or the *pontine nucleus,* is situated lateral and posterior to the motor nucleus in the lateral part of the reticular formation of the pons. It receives only tactile impulses, but receives both the general and the discriminatory and localized types of tactile sensibility. Only a small percentage of the trigeminal roots enter this nucleus. After a synapse here, the neuraxes which carry both discriminatory and general tactile sensations ascend to the thalamus near the medital lemniscus in the *dorsal secondary ascending tract* of the fifth nerve (Fig. 73). This is both crossed and uncrossed. Those neuraxes which carry general tactile sensation also descend and enter the ventral secondary ascending tract (see below). Tactile impulses carried in the trigeminal pathway have central connections similar to those from other parts of the body (Fig. 10). In the nucleus ventralis posteromedialis of the lateral nuclear mass of the thalamus they terminate in a position medial to those conveying touch from the rest of the body, and on the parietal cortex they are below and lateral to those from the rest of the body.

The *nucleus of the descending root,* or *spinal tract,* of the trigeminal nerve extends

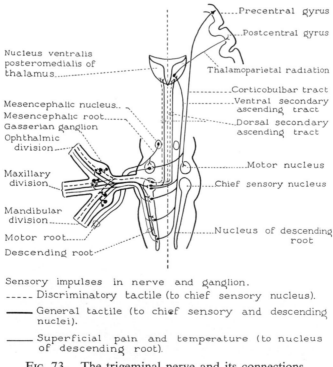

Sensory impulses in nerve and ganglion.
- - - - - Discriminatory tactile (to chief sensory nucleus).
——— General tactile (to chief sensory and descending nuclei).
——— Superficial pain and temperature (to nucleus of descending root).

FIG. 73.   The trigeminal nerve and its connections.

downward from the chief sensory nucleus, through the lower pons and medulla, and into the spinal cord, as far as the third or even fourth cervical segment. The descending root fuses with Lissauer's tract, and its adjoining nucleus fuses with the substantia gelatinosa rolandi. Pain, temperature, and general tactile impulses terminate on this tract and nucleus. The fibers from the maxillomandibular areas are in the dorsal part of the tract, and those from the ophthalmic area in the ventral part. The exteroceptive components of the facial, glossopharyngeal, and vagus nerves join the descending tract at their specific levels of entrance into the brain stem. The fibers descend for varying distances, depending upon the segmental distribution, but finally synapse, and neuraxes of the neurons of the next order cross and ascend to the thalamus in the *ventral secondary ascending tract* of the trigeminal nerve, or the *trigeminothalamic tract* (Fig. 73). These terminate in the nucleus ventralis posteromedialis of the lateral nuclear mass of the thalamus, those carrying pain and temperature being somewhat rostral to those conveying touch. In the thalamus the trigeminal fibers are medial to those from the rest of the body, whereas on the parietal cortex they terminate laterally on the inferior portion of the postcentral gyrus (Figs. 6 and 8).

A third sensory component, the *mesencephalic root* of the trigeminal nerve, runs with the motor root and then extends posteriorly and cephalad from the level of the motor nucleus into the mesencephalon. It carries proprioceptive impulses (including deep pain) from the muscles supplied by the trigeminal nerve and possibly also from muscles supplied by other cranial nerves.

The *gasserian,* or *semilunar, ganglion* (Fig. 73) of the trigeminal nerve occupies a cavity (cavum mecklii) in the dura mater near the apex of the petrous portion of the temporal bone. Here it lies lateral to the internal carotid artery and the posterior part of the cavernous sinus. The ganglion cells are unipolar and the fibers bifurcate. The internal branches pass into the substance of the pons to terminate on the chief sensory and spinal nuclei, and the external branches pass outward as the sensory root (portio major) of the trigeminal nerve, which then forms its three constituent divisions.

The upper, or *ophthalmic, division* is the smallest of the three branches. It passes forward through the lateral wall of the cavernous sinus, where it lies beneath the third and fourth nerves and lateral to the sixth nerve (Fig. 51); it enters the orbit through the superior orbital fissure, but just before leaving the cavernous sinus it gives off the tentorial and anastomotic branches and then divides into its lacrimal, frontal, and nasociliary branches.

The *maxillary division* passes through the lateral part of the wall of the cavernous sinus and leaves the skull through the foramen rotundum. Then it crosses the pterygopalatine fossa, enters the orbit through the inferior orbital fissure, traverses the infraorbital canal and groove, and appears on the face at the infraorbital foramen. Before leaving the skull the maxillary division gives off the middle, or recurrent, meningeal nerve which supplies the dura mater of the middle cranial fossa. The sensory root to the sphenopalatine ganglion and the zygomatic and posterior superior alveolar branches arise in the pterygopalatine fossa, and the middle and anterior superior alveolar branches, in the infraorbital canal. On the face, after leaving the infraorbital foramen, it divides into the terminal inferior palpebral, external and internal nasal, and superior labial branches.

The *mandibular division,* the largest of the branches, leaves the skull through the foramen ovale. The *motor root* of the trigeminal nerve, which lies in front of and medial to the sensory root, passes beneath the gasserian ganglion and also leaves the skull through the foramen ovale. Immediately after leaving the skull it joins the mandibular division to form a large trunk which directly divides into a small anterior, or chiefly motor, branch and a large posterior branch which is mainly sensory. Before dividing, the mandibular nerve gives off two branches. One is the spinous, or recurrent, branch which enters the skull through the foramen spinosum and supplies the dura mater, the greater wing of the sphenoid bone, and the lining membrane of the mastoid cells; the other is the nerve to the internal pterygoid muscle. The muscles supplied by the anterior portion have been listed; the sensory filaments of the anterior portion go to make up the buccinator nerve. The posterior portion of the mandibular nerve divides into three large branches. Two of these, the lingual and the auriculotemporal, are exclusively sensory, but the third, the inferior alveolar, also carries motor fibers to the mylohyoid muscle and the anterior belly of the digastricus.

The sensory portion of the trigeminal nerve carries exteroceptive sensations (Fig. 74). The *ophthalmic division* supplies the skin of the forehead, temple, and scalp as far as the vertex; the upper eyelid; and the skin over the anterior and part of the lateral surface of the nose. It also supplies the eyeball; the upper conjunctiva; the cornea, ciliary body, and iris, and the mucous membrane lining of the frontal sinus, parts of the sphenoid and ethmoid sinuses, and the upper part of the nasal cavity. It sends the sensory root to the ciliary ganglion, and branches to the lacrimal gland, the tentorium cerebelli, and the oculomotor, trochlear, and abducens nerves.

The *maxillary division* supplies the skin on the side and posterior half of the nose, the lower eyelid, upper cheek, anterior temporal region, and upper lip. It innervates the mucous membranes of the lower conjunctiva, maxillary sinus, parts of the sphenoid and ethmoid sinuses, lower nose, upper lip and cheek, oral part of the hard palate, soft palate except for its posterior border, uvula, and nasopharynx. According to most authorities the maxillary nerve supplies the tonsillar areas and the fauces, but these regions are also innervated by the ninth and tenth nerves. Its alveolar branches innervate the upper gingival areas, alveolar ridge, and teeth. The maxillary division also supplies the dura of the middle cranial fossa through

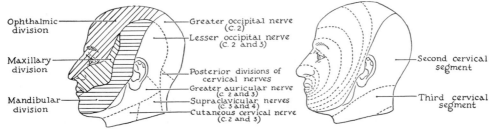

FIG. 74.   Peripheral and segmental cutaneous distributions of trigeminal nerve.

the middle meningeal nerve, and sends the sensory root to the sphenopalatine ganglion where it communicates with the geniculate ganglion of the seventh nerve and the sympathetic nervous system through the vidian and greater superficial and deep petrosal nerves. The *mandibular division* supplies the skin of the side of the head, the posterior part of the cheek and temporal areas, the anterior portion of the pinna, the upper and outer walls of the external auditory canal, the anterior half of the tympanum, and the lower lip and chin, and the mucous membranes of the lower lip, the lower portion of the buccal surface, the tongue, and the floor of the mouth. The inferior alveolar nerve supplies the lower gingival area, lower alveolar ridge, and teeth. Its recurrent, or meningeal, branch innervates the dura of the middle and anterior cranial fossae, the greater wing of the sphenoid, and the mucous membrane lining of the mastoid cells. The mandibular division also supplies the temporomandibular joint and sends branches to the otic and submaxillary ganglia.

These three branches, or divisions, of the trigeminal nerve supply sensation to the entire side of the face except for the angle of the jaw, which is supplied by the second and third cervical nerves through the great auricular nerve. There is some midline crossing by the trigeminal nerve, but less than is found in the nerves supplying the trunk. Although the fifth nerve, through the lingual branch of the mandibular division, supplies the mucosa of the tongue, it is generally conceded that taste sensation to the anterior two-thirds of the tongue is a function of the seventh nerve, even though carried through the lingual nerve to the chorda tympani (Chapter 13).

With a lesion of the lingual nerve there will be loss of taste and of exteroceptive sensation on the anterior surface of the tongue. The various mucous membranes, including those of the palpebral conjunctiva, nose, and mouth, are supplied by pain, temperature, and tactile sensations. Only free sensory endings have been demonstrated in the cornea, but end bulbs of Krause are also present at the corneal limbus. It is said that the cornea is sensitive only to pain stimuli, but light stimulation with cotton does cause an unpleasant sensation, and most current observers believe that with careful testing tactile, pain, and temperature sensations can be differentiated on the cornea. Some corneal sensation and a diminished corneal reflex may persist after trigeminal tractotomy and medullary lesions; under these circumstances those impulses which descend in the spinal root are interrupted, whereas those tactile impulses going to the chief sensory nucleus remain intact.

The *segmental distribution* of the trigeminal nerve to the skin and mucous membranes of the face differs somewhat from the peripheral supply of the ophthalmic, maxillary, and mandibular divisions. Pain and temperature sensations, and to a lesser extent tactile sensations, were said by Dejerine to assume an "onion skin" distribution (Fig. 74). The perioral area is supplied by those fibers whose neurons synapse and cross highest in the descending root of the nerve, whereas the fibers which descend for varying distances before they synapse and decussate supply a somewhat concentric distribution in gradually widening circles over the face and head, the most posterior and outermost segment, and that closest to the cervical sensory distribution, being innervated by those fibers which descend to the lowest portion of the spinal tract and nucleus. On the other hand, studies based on operative section of the spinal tract of the trigeminal nerve have suggested that the segmental representation in this tract may instead be in terms of, but inverse to, the peripheral divisions of the nerve, with the ophthalmic fibers descending to the most caudal part of the tract and the mandibular fibers terminating the most cephalad. This conclusion has been reached in part by the fact that section of the caudal part of the tract has caused analgesia which is limited to the territory of the ophthalmic division. This may be a misinterpretation, however, because it is known that mandibular and maxillary fibers (at least in part) as well as ophthalmic fibers descend to cervical levels. A possible explanation for the above-mentioned results of caudal tractotomy may be arrived at anatomically. The ophthalmic fibers are situated in the most ventral part of the tract, with the maxillary and mandibular fibers more dorsal and dorsomedial; consequently, an incomplete tractotomy may sever mainly the ophthalmic fibers, with partial sparing of those from the other divisions of the nerve.

Proprioceptive impulses from the muscles supplied by the trigeminal nerve are probably carried through the mandibular division and thence to the mesencephalic root of the nerve. This conveys muscle sense, motion and position sensations, and other kinesthetic impulses. The mesencephalic root of the trigeminal nerve may also carry proprioceptive impulses from the muscles supplied by the oculomotor, trochlear, abducens, facial, and other motor cranial nerves.

The divisions of the trigeminal nerve supply filaments to four *ganglia* in the head. The *ciliary ganglion,* situated in the posterior part of the orbit, receives its sensory innervation from the nasociliary branch of the ophthalmic division (the long root of the ciliary ganglion); it receives its motor (parasympathetic) supply from the Edinger-Westphal nucleus through the inferior division of the oculomotor nerve (the short root), and its sympathetic supply from the cavernous sympathetic plexus, running through the long ciliary nerves. Its branches, the short ciliary nerves, supply the ciliary muscle, sphincter and dilator of the pupil, and cornea. Involvement of these structures may follow a lesion of the ciliary ganglion.

The *sphenopalatine ganglion,* placed deep in the pterygopalatine fossa, receives its sensory innervation from the sphenopalatine branches of the maxillary division; it receives its motor (parasympathetic) supply from the facial nerve (nervus intermedius) through the greater superficial petrosal nerve, and its sympathetic supply from the internal carotid plexus through the deep petrosal nerve. These two latter nerves join to form the vidian nerve, or nerve of the pterygoid canal, before their entrance into the ganglion. The sphenopalatine ganglion sends ascending, or orbital, branches to the periosteum of the orbit and the mucous membrane of the posterior ethmoidal and sphenoidal sinuses; descending, or palatine, branches to the hard and soft palates, tonsils, and uvula; medial branches to the nasal mucosa; and posterior, or pharyngeal, branches to the mucous membrane of the nasopharynx. Fibers concerned with lacrimation pass along the zygomaticotemporal branch of the maxillary division to the lacrimal branch of the ophthalmic, and thence to the lacrimal gland.

The *otic ganglion,* situated just below foramen ovale in the infratemporal fossa, receives a motor and possibly a sensory branch from the mandibular division; motor (parasympathetic) and sensory branches from the glossopharyngeal nerve and to a lesser extent from the facial nerve, both through the lesser superficial petrosal nerve from the tympanic plexus, and sympathetic innervation from the plexus surrounding the middle meningeal artery. It may also communicate with the nerve of the pterygoid canal and the chorda tympani. It sends motor branches to the tensor tympani and tensor veli palatini muscles and secretory fibers to the parotid gland through the auriculotemporal nerve.

The *submaxillary ganglion,* situated on the medial side of the mandible between the lingual nerve and the submaxillary gland, receives its sensory supply from the lingual branch of the mandibular division, its motor (parasympathetic) supply from the superior salivatory nucleus of the facial nerve through the chorda tympani, and its sympathetic branch from the sympathetic plexus around the external maxillary artery. It sends secretory fibers to the submaxillary and sublingual glands and the mucous membrane of the mouth and tongue; those preganglionic fibers from the chorda tympani which supply the submaxillary gland pass through the ganglion to synapse on terminal ganglion cells in the hilus of the gland.

CLINICAL EXAMINATION

EXAMINATION OF THE MOTOR FUNCTIONS

The principal motor functions of the trigeminal nerve are examined by testing the motor power of the muscles of mastication. In disturbance of function of the motor division of the nerve there is ipsilateral paresis or paralysis of the masticatory muscles. There is weakness or loss of power in raising, depressing, protruding, retracting, and deviating the mandible. The jaw is deflected toward the side of the involved nerve, and the patient is unable to deviate it toward the nonparalyzed side (Fig. 75). In bilateral paresis the jaw droops, due to the pull of gravity, and all muscle power is lost.

The function of the muscles of mastication may be tested by carrying out the following procedures: (1) The patient clenches his jaws while the examiner palpates the contraction of the masseter and temporal muscles on each side; if there is either weakness or paralysis on one side, there will be either impairment or absence of contraction on that side. (2) He opens his mouth; owing to the action of the pterygoids, especially the external pterygoids that draw forward the condyle of the mandible and protrude the jaw, paralysis of the muscles of mastication will be evidenced by deviation of the jaw to the side of the paralyzed muscles. Deviation is appraised by noting the relation between the upper and lower incisor teeth when the jaw is opened and closed, not by the position of the lips. If the examiner places a ruler or pencil in a vertical position in front of the nose, he may be able to tell whether there is deviation of the mandible. In paralysis of the facial nerve there may be an apparent deviation of the jaw because of weakness of the muscles of facial expression. (3) The patient moves his jaw from side to side against resistance; in paralysis of the fifth nerve on one side he is able to move the jaw to the paralyzed, not to the nonparalyzed side. (4) He protrudes and retracts the jaw, and any tendency toward deviation is noted. (5) He bites on a tongue depressor with his molar teeth, and the depth of the tooth marks is noted and compared on the two sides; if the examiner can pull out the tongue blade while the patient is biting on it,

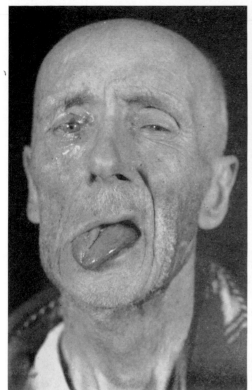 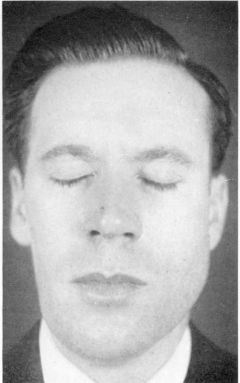

FIG. 75 (*Left*). Infranuclear paralysis of right trigeminal, facial, and hypoglossal nerves in patient with metastatic carcinoma; deviation of tongue and mandible to the right.

FIG. 76 (*Right*). Infranuclear paralysis of right trigeminal nerve with atrophy of muscles of mastication.

there is weakness of the muscles of mastication. (6) The jaw reflex is tested (see below). (7) The tone, volume, and contour of the muscles of mastication are noted, fasciculations are sought for, and the electric reactions tested. If there is atrophy of these muscles, there are visible or palpable concavities above and below the zygoma.

Paresis or paralysis of the muscles of mastication is most marked in nuclear or infranuclear lesions, and in such it is followed by atrophy (Fig. 76). Due to the fact that the motor nuclei of the trigeminal nerve have mainly bilateral supranuclear innervation, there is rarely any marked degree of paresis of the muscles of mastication in a unilateral cerebral, or upper motor neuron, lesion. There may, however, be slight to moderate unilateral weakness of the masticatory muscles with deviation to the side of the paretic muscles, weakness of deflection to the opposite side, and exaggeration of the jaw reflex on the paretic side. The amount of involvement is dependent upon the extent of decussation. In bilateral supranuclear lesions there may be marked paresis (see below).

The other muscles which are supplied by the fifth nerve cannot be adequately examined, but if possible their function should be evaluated. If there is paralysis of the mylohyoid and anterior belly of the digastricus, one may be able to note, on palpation, some flabbiness or flaccidity of the floor of the mouth. If there is paralysis of tensor veli palatini, the uvula may be slightly tilted to the affected side, and the palatal arch on that side may appear broader and lower than normal. The levator veli palatini is more important than the tensor palatini, however, in elevation of the soft palate, and paresis of the tensor is masked if the muscles supplied by the tenth nerve are intact. In paralysis of the levator, some movement of the palate may be retained by the intact tensor. Paralysis of the tensor tympani is not apparent objectively, but the patient may complain of difficulty in hearing high tones and of dysacousis for high tones.

EXAMINATION OF THE SENSORY FUNCTIONS

In testing sensation in the distribution of the trigeminal nerve, both skin and mucous membranes are examined. The various exteroceptive modalities, namely superficial pain, hot, cold, and light touch sensations, are examined individually in the same manner as elsewhere on the body. ("The Sensory System," Part II), and changes in them are charted. The cornea, conjunctiva, nostrils, gums, tongue, and insides of the cheeks are also examined. With lesions of the sensory portion of the nerve there will be areas altered or absent sensation. One should attempt to differentiate between sensory changes of peripheral origin, that is, those resulting from lesions of one or more of the primary divisions of the nerve, and changes in the segmental distribution that result from lesions of the cerebrospinal axis (Fig. 74). More important than the finding of an "onion skin" distribution with involvement of the descending root, however, is the dissociation of sensation with such a lesion; there may be loss of pain and temperature, but sparing of discriminatory and localized tactile sensations. In differentiating organic from hysterical anesthesias of the face, it is important to recall that there is less crossing at the midline on the face than there is elsewhere on the body, and that the skin over the angle of the jaw is not supplied by the fifth nerve, but by the second and third cervical nerves through the great auricular nerve. In trigeminal neuralgia and in certain neuritides there is an increased sensitivity at the emergence of the various sensory branches through their individual fascial sheaths and foramina, and stimulation of these "trigger" or "dolorogenic" zones may precipitate attacks of pain. Proprioceptive sensations carried by the trigeminal nerve cannot be adequately tested, but it may be of value to test for extinction and the ability to identify figures written on the skin.

EXAMINATION OF THE REFLEXES

The trigeminal nerve participates in many reflex responses. Since it is the principal sensory nerve of the face, in most instances the afferent portion of the reflex arc is carried through the nerve, but in some of the responses it conveys the efferent portion of the arc as well.

The Jaw, Masseter, or Mandibulbar Reflex: To elicit the jaw (or jaw muscle) reflex the examiner places his index finger over the middle of the patient's chin, holding the mouth slightly opened. He then taps his finger with the reflex hammer. The response is a contraction of the masseter and temporal muscles, causing a sudden closing of the mouth. The chin itself may be tapped, or the examiner may place a tongue blade over the base of the tongue or the lower incisor teeth and tap the protruding end. All the above call forth a bilateral response. A unilateral response may sometimes be elicited by tapping the angle of the jaw or by placing a tongue blade over the lower molar teeth and tapping the protruding end. The afferent impulses for this reflex are carried through the sensory portion of the trigeminal nerve, possibly through the mesencephalic root, and the efferent impulses through its motor portion; the reflex center is in the pons. The response is a rather minimal one, and occasionally it is very slight or even absent in normal individuals. The jaw reflex is absent in nuclear and peripheral lesions of the trigeminal nerve, and is exaggerated with supranuclear lesions, or those affecting the pyramidal pathways above the motor nucleus, especially if bilateral. It is sometimes possible to elicit jaw clonus.

In the *zygomatic reflex,* which may be considered as a modification of the jaw reflex, percussion over the zygoma results in ipsilateral deviation of the mandible. Both the sensory and motor portions of the reflex are carried by the fifth nerve. This response can be elicited only in the presence of supranuclear lesions.

The Head Retraction Reflex: With the head bent slightly forward, the upper lip is sharply tapped just below the nose. If the reflex is present, there is a quick, involuntary backward jerk of the head. This reflex is usually not elicited in normal individuals, but is obtained if there is exaggeration of the deep reflexes. It is present in bilateral supracervical lesions of the pyramidal tract. The sensory impulse is carried through the trigeminal nerve and the motor response through the upper cervical nerves to the retractor muscles of the neck. The reflex center is in the upper cervical portion of the spinal cord.

The Corneal Reflex: To elicit the corneal reflex, the examiner touches the cornea lightly with a wisp of cotton, a piece of string, or a hair; it is best to moisten the cotton to avoid irritating the cornea (Fig. 77). The patient should turn his eye in the opposite direction and the examiner should approach from the side to eliminate the blink, or visual-palpebral, reflex. Both the upper and lower portions of the cornea should be tested. In response to this stimulus there is a blinking, or closing of the ipsilateral eye, the *direct corneal reflex,* and also a closing of the opposite eye, the *consensual corneal reflex.* The afferent portion of the reflex arc is mediated by the ophthalmic division of the trigeminal nerve, whereas the efferent or motor response is a function of the facial nerve that conveys the impulse to the orbicularis oculi. The reflex center is in the pons.

In a unilateral trigeminal lesion, with resulting corneal anesthesia, stimulation fails to produce either the direct response on that side or the consensual response on the opposite, but stimulation on the opposite side elicits both responses. With a seventh nerve lesion and paralysis of the orbicularis oculi, the direct response is absent on that side, but the contralateral consensual reflex is maintained; when the opposite cornea is stimulated the direct response is present but the consensual reflex

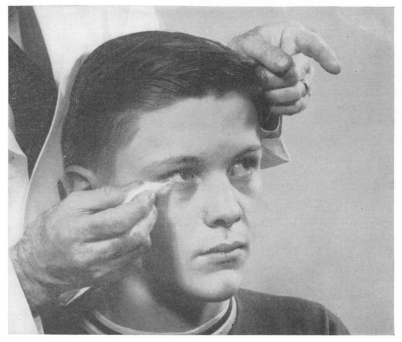

FIG. 77.   Method of eliciting corneal reflex.

is absent. On occasion the bulbar conjunctiva, rather than the cornea, is stimulated —the *conjunctival reflex;* this may be absent in normal individuals, especially those with a high threshold for pain, and is often absent in hysteria. It is much less significant clinically than the corneal reflex. Loss of the corneal reflex is an early sign of trigeminal nerve involvement, and indicates interruption of the sensory impulses carried through the ophthalmic division. The lesion may be in the ophthalmic division or its branches to the cornea or in the gasserian ganglion. With lesions of the nucleus of the descending root of the trigeminal nerve the reflex may be retained, but the response is diminished. It is believed that the corneal reflex also may be absent in hysteria, but in most instances loss of this reflex, especially if unilateral, indicates the presence of an organic lesion. The corneal reflexes are widely used as an index of the depth of anesthesia and of coma.

Modifications of the corneal reflex are as follows: The *oculosensory,* or *oculopupillary, reflex* is characterized by a constriction of the pupil, or dilatation followed by constriction, in response to a painful stimulus directed toward the eye or its adnexa. The afferent impulses are carried through the trigeminal nerve and the efferent impulses through the oculomotor nerve. The *corneo-oculogyric reflex* consists of a contralateral or an upward deviation of the eyes in response to stimulation of the conjunctiva or cornea. There is associated contraction of the orbicularis. Here the impulses are carried through the fifth and the third and seventh nerves. The *corneomandibular reflex* consists of contralateral deviation of the mandible, the result of ipsilateral contraction of the external pterygoid muscle, when one cornea is stimulated. Both the afferent and efferent portions of the reflex arc are carried through the trigeminal nerve. This response, also known as the "winking jaw phenomenon," may be an associated movement rather than a true reflex; its presence indicates supranuclear interruption of the ipsilateral corticotrigeminal tract.

The Nasal, Sneeze, or Sternutatory Reflex: Stimulation of the nasal mucous membrane by tickling it with a hair or some similar object is followed by contraction of the nasopharyngeal and thoracic muscles with a violent expulsion of air from the nose and mouth. The afferent portion of the reflex arc is carried from the nasal mucous membrane through the trigeminal nerve, and the efferent impulses are carried through the trigeminal, facial, glossopharyngeal, and vagus nerves, and through the motor nerves of the cervical and thoracic portions of the spinal cord. There is also a visceral component relayed through the sympathetic nervous system. The reflex center is situated in the brain stem and in the upper portion of the spinal cord. The nasal mucosa may be stimulated not only mechanically, but also by the use of irritating inhalants such as pepper, acetic acid, ammonia, and formaldehyde. The effect of these upon the fifth nerve supply to the mucous membrane of the nose has been discussed in Chapter 9. Mechanical and gaseous stimuli and infections of the nasal mucosa and even bright light in some persons, may evoke not only the above reflex response, but also lacrimation, vasomotor reactions with increased secretion of mucus, and respiratory inhibition.

A modification of the above reflex is the *nasal reflex of Bechterew*. In this, tickling of the nasal mucosa causes contraction of the ipsilateral facial muscles. The afferent impulse is carried through the trigeminal nerve, and the efferent impulse through the facial nerve to the muscles of facial expression.

The *trigeminobrachial reflex*, found only in the presence of lesions involving both the corticospinal pathways and the sensory nuclei of the trigeminal nerve in the brain stem, consists of contralateral flexion and supination of the forearm following stimulation of an area in the distribution of one trigeminal nerve. The *trigeminocervical reflex* may be found in the presence of involvement of the corticobulbar pathways and the brain stem trigeminal nuclei; in this there is contralateral turning of the head following stimulation of an area in the distribution of one trigeminal nerve.

There are many other responses in which the afferent portion of the reflex arc is carried through the trigeminal nerve. These are described, however, under the discussion of the nerves that play the major role in the responses. The more important ones are the following: orbicularis oculi, nasomental, trigeminofacial, and lacrimal reflexes, Chapter 13; palatal, sucking, and oculocardiac reflexes, Chapter 15.

DISORDERS OF FUNCTION

Lesions of the trigeminal nerve may be manifested by any or all of the following: motor changes, either irritative or paretic in nature; sensory alterations, consisting of diminution or loss of sensation, hyperesthesia, dysesthesias, or pain; abnormalities of the reflexes innervated by the trigeminal nerve; trophic or secretory changes.

Irritative Motor Phenomena: These may be either tonic or clonic in nature, and are usually the result of supranuclear lesions. An irritative focus in the pre-central gyrus may produce a jacksonian convulsive seizure limited to the muscles of mastication; this is manifested by a clenching of the jaws with biting of the tongue or the cheeks. In diseases of the extrapyramidal system there may be involvement of the masticatory muscles; a rhythmic tremor of the jaws is seen in Parkinson's disease, and arrhythmic movements in the choreas. Sometimes in basal ganglion disease there are yawning, gasping, "fish gaping," and champing movements, the result of either irritative or release phenomena. In *trismus,* as seen in tetanus, and sometimes in encephalitis, hydrophobia, and tetany, there is irritability with marked spasm of the muscles of mastication; the teeth are tightly clenched, the muscles are hard and firm, and the patient is unable to open his jaws. Trismus may also occur in hysteria. Spasms of the mucles of mastication are also seen in strychnine poisoning, and chattering of the jaws in chills and under emotional stress. Chewing movements and grinding of the teeth are sometimes present in deteriorating psychoses, and chewing or tasting movements in psychomotor or temporal lobe seizures.

Paretic Motor Phenomena: Due to the fact that the motor nuclei of the trigeminal nerve have mainly bilateral cerebral innervation, there is rarely any marked degree of paresis of the muscles of mastication in a unilateral *supranuclear lesion,* although there may be slight weakness of the contralateral muscles with an exaggerated jaw reflex. There may be a transient deviation of the jaw to the paralyzed side in acute involvement. In bilateral supranuclear lesions, however, there often is marked paresis, and in bilateral cortical or internal capsule lesions, as in pseudobulbar palsy or amyotrophic lateral sclerosis, there is striking weakness of the muscles of mastication with a grossly exaggerated jaw reflex. There is no atrophy in supranuclear lesions; there are no fasciculations, and there is no reaction of degeneration.

In lesions of the *motor nucleus* there is unilateral involvement, and if the lesion in a destructive one, the paresis is usually accompanied or followed by the development of atrophy and fasciculations in the involved muscles. The jaw reflex is absent. Irritative lesions of the motor nuclei may cause spasm of the muscles of mastication.

In *infranuclear lesions* there is unilateral paralysis with absence of the jaw reflex. The paralysis may be followed by atrophy of the involved muscles, but rarely by fasciculations. In both nuclear and infranuclear lesions the paralysis and atrophy of the muscles of mastication may be present to a marked degree (Fig. 76). Lesions at the myoneural junction or of the muscles themselves also cause paralysis of the muscles of mastication.

Sensory Involvement: Sensory changes in the distribution of the trigeminal nerves are rarely the result of supranuclear lesions, although with involvement of the parietal lobe or sensory radiations there may be some raising of the sensory threshold of the contralateral face, especially for the discriminative elements, and with a thalamic lesion there is hypesthesia with hyperpathia of the face.

Nuclear involvement is followed by loss of sensation of both skin and mucous membrane in the segmental distribution, and by loss of those reflexes whose afferent arc is mediated by the trigeminal nerve. Lesions of the chief sensory nucleus result in diminished tactile sensation on the involved side of the face, and in those of the tract or nucleus of the descending root there is dissociation of sensation, with principally a disturbance of the pain and temperature modalities, and possibly to a lesser extent of tactile sense.

Involvement of the sensory portion of the trigeminal nerve after it leaves the pons is characterized by disturbance of all types of exteroceptive sensation. There may be loss or diminution of sensation, dysesthesias or paresthesias, or spontaneous pain. If the lesion is central to or at the gasserian ganglion, all three divisions are affected, but if it is peripheral to the ganglion, only isolated divisions are involved. In irritative lesions there is usually hyperesthesia of the peripheral branches at their points of exit from the skull, as at the supraorbital, infraorbital, mental, and alveolar foramina, and stimulation of these "trigger zones" may precipitate attacks of pain. If the painful lesion is a neuritis, there will be evidences of sensory change in the involved branches, together with reflex changes, such as absence of the corneal, sneeze, or palatal reflexes. If, however, it is a neuralgia, the routine examination will fail to show objective evidence of nerve involvement.

Trophic Phenomena: Trophic and sensory changes may also occur in disease of the trigeminal nerve. In lesions of the ophthalmic division there is anesthesia of the cornea, and this is sometimes followed by the development of corneal ulcerations and inflammation which may result in ophthalmia. This neuroparalytic keratitis may follow rhizotomy of the fifth nerve for the relief of tic douloureux. It is necessary to protect the eye very carefully whenever the cornea is anesthetic. Corneal ulcerations also occur in herpes ophthalmicus (see below). In anesthesia of the nose there is inability to recognize such substances as ammonia and acetic acid; this is often accompanied by a dryness of the nasal mucosa which may result in complete loss of smell. There may be trophic changes in the nasal mucosa and adjacent structures, sometimes with resulting erosion of the ala nasi. Caries of the jaw bone and loosening of the teeth may also be manifestations of a trophic disturbance.

Abnormalities in lacrimal, salivary, and mucous secretion, either a decrease or an increase in secretion, may be associated with lesions of the trigeminal nerve. This nerve, however, does not have secretory functions and does not normally produce these secretions. Lacrimation is a function of the facial nerve, and salivation and mucous production are functions of the facial and glossopharyngeal nerves and the sympathetic division of the autonomic nervous system. The fifth nerve, however, is intimately connected with these nerves through reflex centers and through the ganglia described above, and these various secretions may be reflex responses to stimuli mediated through the trigeminal nerve. Taste, too, which is not a function of the fifth nerve, is intimately connected with it and is carried through the lingual nerve to the chorda tympani. A Horner's syndrome, with characteristic eye findings and with vasodilatation and loss of sweating on the involved side of the face, may be seen with lesions of the fifth nerve, especially of the gasserian ganglion. This, however, is the result of involvement of the sympathetic plexus which surrounds the carotid artery rather than of the nerve itself.

Disorders of function of the trigeminal nerve may be the result of lesions at various sites in the central or peripheral nervous systems. Some of the more frequent or important are as follows:

Supranuclear involvement of the trigeminal nerve is usually due to vascular lesions, neoplasms, degenerative changes, or inflammatory reactions affecting the cerebral center, internal capsule, basal ganglia, cerebral peduncle, or pons above the nuclear areas. The manifestations are predominantly motor in type, usually without profound paralysis unless there is bilateral involvement. There are no fasciculations or atrophy. The jaw reflex is exaggerated. There may be irritative motor phenomena in cortical or extrapyramidal lesions. In pseudobulbar palsy and amyotrophic lateral sclerosis there may be pronounced bilateral weakness. The former is usually the result of bilateral cerebral thromboses or hemorrhages, but is also found in association with cerebral neoplasms, encephalitis, or vascular inflammatory, or neoplastic lesions involving the midbrain or pons above the motor nucleus. In thalamic lesions there may be anesthesia dolorosa of the contralateral facial area.

Nuclear lesions may be of various types. Pontine neoplasms, inflammations, and degenerative and vascular lesions may affect either the motor or the sensory nuclei or both. The motor weakness may be considerable and accompanied by atrophy and loss of the jaw reflex. In progressive degenerations, such as progressive bulbar palsy and syringobulbia, there are also fasciculations of the paretic muscles. Due to the prolonged extension of the descending root and nucleus of the fifth nerve through the pons and medulla into the upper portion of the cervical cord, lesions far below the middle portion of the pons may cause sensory changes in the segmental distribution of the nerve. Multiple sclerosis, syringomyelia, syringobulbia, polioencephalitis, and vascular lesions in the brain stem may affect the trigeminal nerve and may cause dissociation of sensation, absence of the corneal reflex, and pain in the distribution of the various divisions of the nerve, together with motor changes. Nuclear lesions are almost always accompanied by other symptoms referable to the pons or brain stem, such as involvement of other nuclei or centers, or interference with ascending or descending pathways. Inasmuch as the ascending lateral spinothalamic tract lies in close approximation to the tract of the descending root of the trigeminal, a lesion of one may involve the other, resulting in anesthesia of the ipsilateral side of the face and the contralateral side of the body. In thrombosis of the posterior inferior cerebellar artery and other medullary syndromes there are changes of fifth nerve function (Chapter 18). The spasms which occur in toxic conditions and in tetany may result from nuclear involvement.

Infranuclear lesions also may involve the sensory filaments, the motor nerve, or both. In meningitis and in skull fractures, stab wounds, or other traumatic lesions, the trigeminal nerve may be injured just after its exit from the pons. Tumors of the cerebellopontine angle and other neoplasms or gummas involving the base of the skull or the meninges commonly affect the sensory branches with resulting pain, anesthesia, and loss of the corneal reflex. Various branches may be affected by lesions within the cavernous sinus, aneurysms of the circle of Willis or the internal carotid artery, caries of the petrous bone, orbital cellulitis or tumors, polyneuritis, or tumors or abscesses in the temporal lobe or middle cranial fossa. Branches of the trigeminal nerve are frequently involved in neoplasms of the nasopharynx and in metastatic malignancies (Fig. 75). Neoplasms such as neurinomas of the fifth nerve usually occur at the gasserian ganglion but may involve the nerve itself. These cause not only pain and sensory changes, but loss of motor power as well, and due to the proximity of the ganglion to the carotid artery and to its sympathetic plexus, there may be ptosis, miosis, and other evidences of a cervical sympathetic paralysis. The term *paratrigeminal* or *Raeder's syndrome* is used when a Horner's syndrome is present along with ipisilateral motor and sensory trigeminal nerve dysfunction; this is usually found with neoplasms of the gasserian ganglion or middle cranial fossa. Involvement of the muscles themselves or of the myoneural junction causes motor weakness without sensory change. In myasthenia gravis the paresis may be so profound that the patient may have to use his hand to assist in closing his jaw when chewing.

Pains referred to the various branches of the trigeminal nerve occur frequently. They may be of reflex origin. A careful examination should always be made to determine a local cause. As a general rule, the radiation of pain is at first confined to one division, and search for the cause of the pain should always commence with a thorough investigation of those parts supplied by that division. In cases of severe pain, however, there is radiation over the branches of the other main divisions. There may be associated spasm and contraction of muscles. Pain of this type may be associated with dental caries, alveolar disease, sinus involvement, glaucoma, and malignant disease within the sinuses. Neuritis of the trigeminal nerve is a result of the same processes which cause neuritis elsewhere in the body—infections, toxic processes, vitamin deficiencies, etc. It is usually predominantly sensory in nature. A specific type of neuritis may be associated with the industrial use of trichlorethylene, and a similar neuritis results if trichlorethylene is used in the treatment of tic douloureux. Stilbamidine isethionate, first used in the therapy of kala-azar and later for tic douloureux, also causes a neuritis confined largely to the distribution of the fifth nerve. *Herpes zoster* of the trigeminal nerve is an extremely painful condition, both in its acute stage and in the form of a postherpetic neuralgia. Usually seen in elderly people, it most often affects branches of the ophthalmic division, and is known as *herpes ophthalmicus*. The pain and vesicles are distributed over the forehead, eyelid, and cornea, and the involvement of the latter may be followed by ulcerations and keratitis, resulting in corneal opacities and often in ophthalmia and blindness. There may be associated involvement of the motor division and the seventh and eighth cranial nerves, and occasionally there are encephalitic manifestations.

Perhaps the most frequent lesion of the trigeminal nerve, if one excepts the limited reflex involvements associated with disease of the teeth or sinuses, is *trigeminal neuralgia,* or *tic douloureux,* sometimes called Fothergill's neuralgia. This condition usually occurs in elderly people, and is characterized by sudden attacks of excruciating, lancinating pain of momentary duration in the distribution of one or more of the major divisions of the nerve. The attacks are usually brought on by stimulation of the trigger zones described above, and accordingly the patient may refuse to eat, talk, wash his face, shave, or brush his teeth for fear of initiating an attack. Exposure to cold may also precipitate the pain. Objective examination shows no evidences of impairment of function of the nerve, and sensory tests, motor power, and reflexes are all normal. The symptoms may stop spontaneously for a period of time, but usually recur. The underlying etiology of and exact mechanism for this pain are still not known, but both central and peripheral pathophysiologic alterations have been suggested as possible explanations for the syndrome. It is sometimes associated with multiple sclerosis.

The pain of tic douloureux may be temporarily relieved by injection of the involved divisions of branches with procaine, or relieved for some months by the injection of alcohol, but for permanent relief the nerve must be sectioned centrally to the gasserian ganglion—a retrogasserian neurectomy or rhizotomy. Complete anesthesia and analgesia in the distribution of the sectioned branches also occur, however, and there often are associated dysesthesias that may be distressing to the patient. A neuroparalytic keratitis may follow this operation. It is sometimes possible to cut only those fibers that enter into the maxillary and mandibular divisions of the nerve, and spare those to the ophthalmic, which is less frequently affected. The intramedullary tractotomy (Sjöqvist) avoids these undesirable sequelae. The descending root of the trigeminal nerve is sectioned by a small incision at the posterolateral edge of the medulla at the level of the lower one third of the olivary nucleus, just caudal to the lowest filaments of the vagus nerve and the lower end of the fourth ventricle. There is loss of pain but not complete loss of tactile sensations, and because of the preservation of the latter the face does not feel cold, stiff, or numb. Distressing dysesthesias are less common, and since some sensation remains in the eye, the patient is less apt to develop a neuroparalytic keratitis. Pain in the distribution of the ipsilateral facial, glossopharyngeal, and vagus nerves is also relieved. If the incision is extended ventrally, the ascending lateral spinothalamic tract may be sectioned. The ventral secondary ascending tract may also be sectioned, along with the lateral spinothalamic tract, in the mesencephalic tractotomy (Dogliotti). The incision is made at the level of the superior colliculus (anterior quadrigeminal body), across the brachium of the inferior colliculus to the base of the superior colliculus. The pain conducting pathways at this site may also be interrupted by electrolytic lesions (mesencephalotomy). Rhizotomy and tractotomy are also used to relieve intractable facial pain, such as that secondary to carcinomatous infiltrations.

Recent developments in the treatment of tic douloureux seem to give promise of relief and also may contribute to further understanding of the mechanism of the pain. The decompression of the posterior trigeminal root and gasserian ganglion as devised by Taarnhøj controls the pain in a large percentage of cases and causes little if any postoperative sensory change. Gangliolysis is a modification of the decompression procedure. Compression of or minor trauma to the ganglion or posterior root has also brought relief from the pain, as has the injection of boiling water into the ganglion, as well as cervical and great auricular nerve block. It is too early to postulate the permanent relief from pain that may result from these procedures. Treatment by medical measures has also been used, but in the past has not been very effective. The therapeutic value of trichlorethylene and stilbamidine, both of which cause a trigeminal neuritis, is to be questioned. Recently diphenylhydantoin (Dilantin), mephenesin, and carbamazepine (Tegretol), an iminostiblene derivative, have been found to give relief in many cases; these may either decrease conduction of peripheral nerves or inhibit polysynaptic reflex transmission.

Pain similar to, if not identical with, tic douloureux is sometimes found in multiple sclerosis, syringobulbia, and tabes dorsalis. There are many atypical facial neuralgias that resemble tic douloureux but must be differentiated from it. *Sluder's syndrome,* or *neuralgia of the sphenopalatine ganglion,* is said to be characterized by pain in the orbital area, cheek, roof of the mouth, root of the nose, upper jaw, and teeth, and sometimes extending to the ear, occiput, neck, shoulder, and arm. The pain is said to be relieved by novocaine infiltration of the sphenopalatine ganglion, but the existence of such a symptom complex is questioned. So-called *vidian neuralgia* has a similar distribution, but pain in the ear is a more prominent symptom; this has been said to be due to irritation of the vidian nerve by infection in the sphenoid sinus. *Costen's syndrome* consists of unilateral pain in the face and head accompanied by pain in the ear, impaired hearing, tinnitus, and vertigo; this symptom complex results from distortion of and destructive changes in the temporomandibular joint, secondary to malocclusion. Many of the *atypical facial neuralgias* may be reflex in origin, occasionally involving connections between the trigeminal nerve and other cranial afferent and cervical nerves, and others may be associated with autonomic nervous system disorders; often the pain is deep, boring, and agonizing, and is not relieved by section of the fifth nerve. Those of psychogenic origin are termed psychalgias. Migraine, especially of the hemicranial type, may simulate a neuralgia of the ophthalmic division of the fifth nerve, as may the so-called cluster headache (atypical migraine, Horton's headache, or histamine cephalgia). This latter syndrome has on occasion been relieved by section of the greater superficial petrosal nerve; there is also loss of lacrimation and mucus secretion in the area supplied by the sphenopalatine ganglion. In neuritis of the fifth nerve resulting from various toxic, infectious, and deficiency factors there may be attacks of pain similar to those of the neuralgias, but there is residual pain between attacks, and a detailed examination should show impairment of sensation and loss of reflexes.

The *Marcus Gunn phenomenon,* or *jaw-winking reflex,* occurs with partial ptosis of congenital origin; opening of the mouth and chewing and lateral movements of the jaw cause an exaggerated reflex elevation of the ptotic lid. This is probably a pathologic associated, or synkinetic, movement, and proprioceptive impulses from the pterygoid muscles are relayed to the oculomotor nucleus. The automatic closure of one eye on opening the mouth has been called the inverted Marcus Gunn phenomenon, or the *Marin Amat syndrome*. This has been explained as an associated movement involving the facial and masticatory muscles, but inasmuch as it is seen only in patients who have had a peripheral facial paralysis, it is probably an intra-facial associated movement.

The *auriculotemporal syndrome* (Frey) consists of flushing, warmness, and excessive perspiration over the cheek and pinna on one side following the ingestion of highly seasoned food. It is usually a sequel of trauma or infection of the parotid gland, with injury to the regional nerves, and there may be associated trigeminal sensory changes. It is probable that in regeneration of the severed auriculotemporal nerve the secretory fibers to the parotid gland become misdirected to the sweat glands and the vasodilator endings, or there may be abnormal local irritability of cholinergic fibers. The symptoms have been relieved by interruption of the efferent arc by means of either alcohol injection or surgical section of the auriculotemporal nerve or intracranial section of the glossopharyngeal nerve. In the so-called *encephalotrigeminal angiomatosis* (Sturge-Weber syndrome, or Parkes-Weber-Dimitri disease) there are congenital nevi or angiomas over the side of the face in the trigeminal distribution with associated ipsilateral leptominingeal angiomas and intracortical calcifications; there is cerebral hemiatrophy with contralateral hemiparesis and focal convulsions (Fig. 78). *Progressive facial hemiatrophy* is described in Chapter 13.

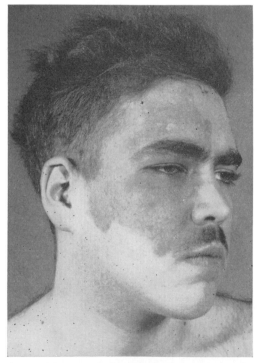

Fig. 78. A patient with encephalotrigeminal angiomatosis (Sturge-Weber syndrome). (Courtesy of Dr. K. R. Magee.)

REFERENCES

BRODAL, A. Central course of afferent fibers for pain in facial, glossopharyngeal and vagus nerves: Clinical observations. *Arch. Neurol. & Psychiat.* 57:292, 1947.

COGAN, D. G., and GINSBERG, J. Representation of corneal and conjunctival sensation in the central nervous system. *A. M. A. Arch. Ophth.* 47:273, 1952.

DOGLIOTTI, A. M. First surgical sections, in man, of the lemniscus lateralis (pain-temperature path) at the brain stem, for the treatment of diffuse rebellious pain. *Anes. & Analg.* 17:143, 1938.

GARDNER, W. J. Concerning the mechanism of trigeminal neuralgia and hemifacial spasm. *J. Neurosurg.* 19:947, 1962.

GARDNER, W. J., and MCCUBBIN, J. W. Auriculotemporal syndrome. *J.A.M.A.* 160:272, 1956.

GARDNER, W. J., STOWELL, A., and DUTLINGER, R. Resection of the greater superficial petrosal nerve in the treatment of unilateral headache. *J. Neurosurg.* 4:105, 1947.

GUNN, R. MARCUS. Congenital ptosis with peculiar associated movements of the affected lid. *Tr. Ophth. Soc. U. Kingdom* 3:283, 1883.

JAEGER, R. Permanent relief of the tic douloureux by gasserian injection of hot water. *A.M.A. Arch. Nuerol. & Psychiat.* 77:1, 1957.

KERR, F. W. L. The etiology of trigeminal neuralgia. *Arch. Neurol.* 8:15, 1963.

KUGELBERG, E., and LINDBLOM, U. The mechanism of pain in trigeminal neuralgia. *J. Neurol., Neurosurg., & Psychiat.* 22:36, 1959.

LELE, P. P., and WEDDELL, G. The relationship between neurohistology and corneal sensibility. *Brain* 79:119, 1956.

LIST, C. F., and WILLIAMS, J. R. Pathogenesis of trigeminal neuralgia. *A. M. A. Arch. Neurol. & Psychiat.* 77:36, 1957.

MAGLADERY, J. W., and TEASDALL, R. D. Corneal reflexes: An electromyographic study in man. *Arch. Neurol.* 5:269, 1961.

MCINTYRE, A. K., and ROBINSON, R. G. Pathway for the jaw-jerk in man. *Brain* 82:468, 1959.

OLIVECRONA, H. Tractotomy for relief of trigeminal neuralgia. *Arch Neurol. & Psychiat.* 47:544, 1942.

RAEDER, J. G. Paratrigeminal paralysis of the oculopupillary sympathetic. *Brain* 47:149, 1924.

SHELDEN, H. C., PUDENZ, R. H., FRESHWATER, D. B., and CRUE, B. L. Compression rather than decompression for trigeminal neuralgia. *J. Neurosurg.* 12:123, 1955.

SJÖQVIST, O. Studies on pain conduction in the trigeminal nerve: A contribution to the surgical treatment of facial pain. *Acta. psychiat. et neurol.*, 1938, supp. 17, p. 1.

SLUDER, G. Etiology, diagnosis, prognosis and treatment of sphenopalatine ganglion neuralgia. *J.A.M.A.* 61:1201, 1913.

STOOKEY, B. P., and RANSOHOFF, J. Trigeminal Neuralgia: Its History and Treatment. Springfield, Ill., Charles C Thomas, 1959.

SZENTÁGOTHAI, J. Functional representation in the trigeminal nucleus. *J. Comp. Neurol.* 90:111, 1949.

SZENTÁGOTHAI, J., and KISS, T. Projection of dermatomes on the substantia gelatinosa. *Arch. Neurol. & Psychiat.* 62:734, 1949.

TAARNHØJ, P. Decompression of the trigeminal root and the posterior part of the ganglion as treatment in trigeminal neuralgia. *J. Neurosurg.* 9:288, 1952.

TOWER, S. S.   Unit for sensory reception in cornea with notes on nerve impulses from sclera, iris, and lens.   *J. Neurophysiol.* 3:486, 1940.

WALKER, A. E.   Anatomy, physiology and surgical considerations of the spinal tract of the trigeminal nerve.   *J. Neurophysiol.* 2:234, 1939.

WARTENBERG, R.   Head retraction reflex.   *Am. J. M. Sc.* 201:553, 1941.

CHAPTER 13

THE FACIAL NERVE

ANATOMY AND PHYSIOLOGY

THE FACIAL, or *seventh cranial, nerve* is probably involved in disease processes more frequently than any other nerve in the body. It is predominantly a motor nerve and innervates the muscles of facial expression. In addition, however, it carries parasympathetic secretory fibers to the salivary and lacrimal glands and to the mucous membranes of the oral and nasal cavities, and it conveys various types of sensation, including exteroceptive sensation from the region of the ear drum, taste sensation from the anterior two-thirds of the tongue, general visceral sensation from the salivary glands and mucosa of the nose and pharynx, and proprioceptive sensation from the muscles it supplies. Anatomically the motor division of the nerve is separated from that portion which carries sensation and parasympathetic fibers; this latter part is frequently referred to as the *nervus intermedius,* or the *pars intermedia of Wrisberg.* Some authorities consider this a distinct nerve, although it is usually classed as part of the facial nerve.

THE MOTOR PORTION

The *motor nucleus* of the seventh nerve lies deep in the reticular formation of the lower part of the pons, medial to the nucleus of the descending root of the fifth nerve, anterior and lateral to the nucleus of the sixth nerve, and posterior to the superior olivary nucleus (Fig. 56). Two groups of cells have been described; the dorsal group supplies the frontalis, upper facial, and zygomatic muscles, and the upper half of the orbicularis oculi; the ventral group supplies the lower half of the orbicularis oculi, the lower face, and the platysma. The intrapontine root of the nerve arises from the dorsal surface of the nucleus and runs dorsomedially toward the floor of the fourth ventricle. It then passes upward, encircling the nucleus of the abducens nerve and producing an elevation, the facial colliculus, in the rhomboid fossa; this is the first genu of the facial nerve. The fibers then proceed forward, downward, and laterally through the pons, close to the facial nucleus, to emerge at the lateral aspect of the caudal border of the pons, between the pons and

237

medulla and between the inferior olivary body and the inferior cerebellar peduncle. Here the nerve lies in the cerebellopontine angle lateral to the exit of the sixth nerve and medial to the eighth. It enters the internal auditory meatus above the eighth nerve, with the pars intermedia between the acoustic and facial nerves. At the bottom of the meatus the nerve enters the facial canal, or fallopian aqueduct. It is at first directed lateralward, between the cochlea and vestibule, toward the medial wall of the tympanic cavity. It then turns suddenly backward, at its second genu, and arches downward behind the tympanic cavity to emerge from the stylomastoid foramen. After leaving the skull it runs forward in the substance of the parotid gland and divides behind the ramus of the mandible into its constituent parts (Fig. 79).

The *cortical center* of the muscles of facial expression is in the lower third of the precentral convolution. Impulses arising in the pyramidal cells are carried through the corona radiata, the genu of the internal capsule, and the medial portion of the cerebral peduncle, into the pons, where they decussate; the majority supply the facial nucleus on the opposite side. That portion of the nucleus which innervates the lower half to two thirds of the face has predominantly crossed, unilateral supranuclear control, whereas the portion that supplies the upper third to half has bilateral control. The facial nuclei also receive bilateral innervation from the extrapyramidal cortex and the basal ganglia, and possibly from the hypothalamus; this is concerned with the maintenance of tone in the facial muscles, and with automatic and emotional movements.

The motor branches of the facial nerve supply all the muscles of facial expression from the scalp and forehead through the platysma, including the extrinsic and intrinsic muscles of the ear, and in addition supply the stapedius, the posterior belly of the digastricus, and the stylohyoid muscles. The branch to the stapedius originates

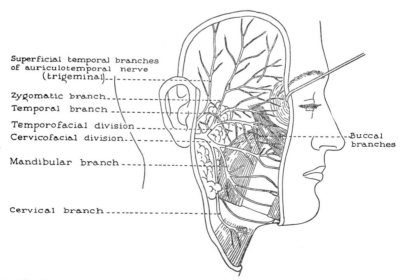

Fig. 79. Branches and distribution of facial nerve. (After Pollock and Davis.)

within the facial canal. At its exit from the stylomastoid foramen the facial nerve gives off the posterior auricular, digastric, and stylohyoid branches. The posterior auricular branch supplies the occipitalis, posterior auricular, and transverse and oblique auricular muscles. The digastric and stylohyoid branches supply respectively the posterior belly of the digastricus and the stylohyoid muscles.

Within the substance of the parotid gland the facial nerve divides into its *temporofacial and cervicofacial divisions* at the so-called *pes anserinus*. The former divides into the temporal, zygomatic, and upper buccal branches and the latter into the lower buccal, mandibular, and cervical branches. The *temporal branch* innervates the frontalis and corrugator muscles, the upper part of the orbicularis oculi, the anterior and superior auricular muscles, and the intrinsic muscles on the lateral surface of the ear. The *zygomatic branch* is distributed to the lower and lateral part of the orbicularis oculi and some of the muscles of the nose and upper lip; it supplies in part the quadratus labii superioris, nasalis, caninus, risorius, and zygomaticus muscles. The *buccal branches,* which are larger than the zygomatic, also supply part of the orbicularis oculi, nasalis, caninus, risorius, and zygomaticus muscles, and in addition innervate the other muscles of the nose and upper lip, namely the procerus, dilators nares, orbicularis oris, and buccinator muscles. The *mandibular branch* supplies the muscles of the lower lip and chin, namely, the lower part of the orbicularis oris, the quadratus labii inferioris, mentalis, and triangularis. The *cervical branch* supplies the platysma.

The *muscles of facial expression* are responsible for all voluntary and involuntary movements of the face, except those associated with movement of the jaws, and for all play of emotions upon the face. The *frontalis* raises the eyebrows and the skin over the root of the nose and draws the scalp forward, throwing the skin of the forehead into transverse wrinkles. The *occipitalis* draws the scalp backward. These two, with their aponeurotic connection, are called the *epicranius,* and acting together they cause movement of the entire scalp. The *orbicularis oculi,* or *orbicularis palpebrarum,* is the sphincter of the eyelids. The palpebral portion causes narrowing of the palpebral fissure and gentle closing of the lids. The orbital portion draws the skin of the forehead, temple, and cheek toward the medial angle of the orbit; it pulls down the eyebrow and draws up the skin of the cheek in order to close the eye firmly and give increased protection to the eyeball. The *corrugator* (*corrugator supercilii*) draws the eyebrow down and medially, producing vertical wrinkles in the forehead; it is the "frowning" muscle.

The muscles of the nose are as follows: The *procerus* (*pyramidalis nasi*) draws the medial angle of the eyebrows downward and produces transverse wrinkles over the bridge of the nose. The *nasalis* (*compressor naris*) depresses the cartilaginous portion of the nose and draws the ala toward the septum. The *depressor septi* draws the ala down and constricts the apertures of the nares. The *dilators nares posterior* and *anterior* enlarge the apertures of the nares.

The *orbicularis oris* is the sphincter of the mouth; it closes the lips. By its superficial fibers it causes the lips to protrude, whereas with its deep fibers it draws them in and presses them against the teeth. The *quadratus labii superioris* elevates the upper lip and dilates the nostril, the *caninus* (*levator anguli oris*) muscle raises the angle of the mouth, and the *zygomaticus* draws the mouth backward and upward; all three of these aid in the formation of the nasolabial fold. The *risorius* retracts or draws out the angle of the mouth. The *buccinator* compresses the cheeks and keeps the food under pressure of the cheeks in chewing. The *quadratus labii inferioris,* or *depressor labii inferioris,* draws the lower lip downward and lateralward. The *mentalis, or levator menti,* raises and protrudes the lower lip and wrinkles the skin of the chin. The *triangularis,* or *depressor anguli oris,* depresses the angle of the mouth. The *platysma* draws down the lower lip and the angle of the mouth; it also depresses the lower jaw and raises and wrinkles the skin of the neck.

The extrinsic muscles of the ear are the *posterior auricular* which retracts the pinna, the *superior auricular* which elevates it, and the *anterior auricular* which draws it upward and forward. The intrinsic muscles on the lateral surface of the ear, the *helicis major, helicis minor, tragicus,* and *antitragicus,* and those on the cranial surface of the ear, the *transverse* and *oblique auriculars,* are vestigial remnants and probably have little remaining function.

Additional muscles which are supplied by the facial nerve but are not muscles of facial expression are the *stapedius,* the *posterior belly of the digastricus,* and the *stylohyoid.* The former draws the head of the stapes backward and rotates it toward the posterior wall of the tympanic cavity; this increases the tension of the middle ear ossicles and of both the membrane which closes the fenestra ovalis and the tympanic membrane. The digastricus and stylohyoid act together to raise and draw backward the hyoid bone and thyroid cartilage. They also elevate and retract the base of the tongue, aid in swallowing, and pervent the return of food into the mouth in the second act of deglutition.

It is the opinion of some authorities that there is close functional connection between the nuclei of the facial and the hypoglossal nerves, and that the orbicularis oris receives some fibers from the twelfth nerve, whereas the facial nerve partially innervates the hyoglossus, genioglossus, and styloglossus muscles. Consequently there may be some weakness of the orbicularis in twelfth nerve paralysis and some deviation of the tongue in a seventh nerve lesion. The opinion has also been expressed that some fibers go from the third or sixth nerve nuclei to the orbicularis oculi, corrugator, and frontalis. Neither of these contentions has been verified.

THE NERVUS INTERMEDIUS

The *nervus intermedius,* or sensory and parasympathetic root of the facial nerve, is lateral and inferior to the motor root (Fig. 80). Within the internal auditory meatus it lies between the motor root and the eighth nerve. The sensory cells are situated in the geniculate ganglion, at the bend of the facial nerve within the facial canal, and their neuraxes enter the pons with the motor root. The geniculate ganglion is continued distally as the chorda tympani nerve which carries taste and general visceral afferent fibers as well as preganglionic parasympathetic fibers. The chorda tympani leaves the trunk of the facial nerve a short distance above the stylomastoid foramen. It goes forward and slightly upward in a minute canal in the posterior wall of the tympanic cavity and then enters and crosses the cavity. It passes to the

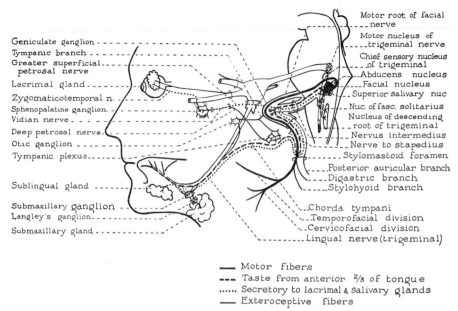

Geniculate ganglion
Tympanic branch
Greater superficial petrosal nerve
Lacrimal gland
Zygomaticotemporal n.
Sphenopalatine ganglion
Vidian nerve
Deep petrosal nerve
Otic ganglion
Tympanic plexus
Sublingual gland
Submaxillary ganglion
Langley's ganglion
Submaxillary gland

Motor root of facial nerve
Motor nucleus of trigeminal nerve
Chief sensory nucleus of trigeminal
Abducens nucleus
Facial nucleus
Superior salivary nuc
Nuc. of fasc. solitarius
Nucleus of descending root of trigeminal
Nervus intermedius
Nerve to stapedius
Stylomastoid foramen
Posterior auricular branch
Digastric branch
Stylohyoid branch
Chorda tympani
Temporofacial division
Cervicofacial division
Lingual nerve (trigeminal)

— Motor fibers
--- Taste from anterior ⅔ of tongue
...... Secretory to lacrimal & salivary glands
— Exteroceptive fibers

FIG. 80.   Course and branches of facial nerve.

base of the skull where it goes downward and forward to join the posterior border of the lingual nerve, a branch of the mandibular division of the trigeminal nerve.

The fibers which carry *exteroceptive sensation* have their cell bodies in the geniculate ganglion and terminate on the descending root and the nucleus of the descending root of the trigeminal nerve; their central connections are identical with those of the trigeminal nerve. It has been said that the pathway of the *proprioceptive* impulses is with the mesencephalic root of the fifth nerve, but the fibers which carry these impulses probably have their cells of origin in the geniculate ganglion, and terminate in the motor nucleus of the facial nerve. The fibers which carry *gustatory* and *general visceral* sensation terminate on the fasciculus solitarius and its nucleus. Secondary neurons pass from this structure to the superior and inferior salivatory nuclei, from which parasympathetic impulses go to the salivary glands. Other neurons pass to the reticular gray matter and descend in the ipsilateral and contralateral reticulospinal tracts to synapse with preganglionic sympathetic neurons in the intermediolateral column of the upper thoracic portion of the spinal cord; the neuraxes of these cells ascend to the superior cervical ganglia, and postganglionic fibers go to the salivary glands. Impulses which carry gustatory sensation to consciousness probably ascend with the contralateral medial lemniscus to the thalamus, and then, after a further synapse, terminate on the cortex of either the hippocampal gyrus or the pararolandic operculum in the lower part of the postcentral gyrus (area 43). Other impulses go to the hypothalamus for reflex stimulation of salivation. It is generally conceded by anatomists and physiologists that smell and taste are functionally related, and that the central connections dealing with gustatory sensation are correlated with those for olfactory sensation, not only in the uncinate cortex and the hippocampus, but also in the thalamus and hypothalamus. Börnstein, on the other hand, does not believe that smell and taste are functionally related. He has expressed the belief that the cortical center for taste is not in the hippocampal gyrus or uncus, with that for olfactory sensation, but in the parietal operculum. He states that there is more anatomic similarity between tactile and gustatory sensations than between olfactory and gustatory, and that gustatory sensation is conducted to the thalamus with tactile sensation and thence to the parietal lobe.

The *sensory distribution of the facial nerve* is not as definitely established as the motor supply, but it is generally accepted that the nerve carries mixed sensations. *Exteroceptive sensations* are conducted from part of the external auditory canal, tympanic membrane, and lateral surface of the pinna, and a small area behind the ear and over the mastoid process. There is a marked individual variation in this distribution. *Taste sensation* from the anterior two thirds of the tongue is carried through the lingual nerve to the chorda tympani, and thence to the geniculate ganglion. The seventh nerve may also carry taste sensation from the mucosa of the soft palate through the sphenopalatine ganglion. Some observers are of the opinion that there are alternate pathways for gustatory sensation through the trigeminal nerve, or that both carry taste, but most anatomic evidence indicates that taste sensation from the anterior two thirds of the tongue is mediated by the seventh nerve. *General visceral sensations* are probably carried through the facial nerve from the lacrimal and salivary glands and the mucosa of the mouth and pharynx. *Proprioceptive sensations* may be mediated from all the muscles supplied by the nerve. The seventh nerve may also carry impulses of deep pain and deep pressure from the face.

The *efferent preganglionic parasympathetic fibers* that initiate salivary, lacrimal, and mucous secretion are also situated in the nervus intermedius. Those that stimulate salivary secretion arise in the *superior salivatory nucleus* in the pons. They pass through the nervus intermedius, geniculate ganglion, and chorda tympani, and terminate in the *submaxillary ganglion* and ganglion cells in the hilus of the submaxillary gland (Langley's ganglion). Postganglionic fibers carry secretory and vasodilator impulses to the *submaxillary* and *sublingual glands* and the mucous membrane of the mouth and tongue (Fig. 80). These glands also receive a sympathetic supply from the thoracic autonomic division through the superior cervical ganglion and the carotid plexus. Stimulation of the parasympathetic fibers causes the formation of thin, watery saliva, and vasodilatation, whereas stimulation of the sympathetics causes the formation of a scant supply of thick, turbid saliva, and vasoconstriction. Also, dry, acid, and sour foods call out a copious, watery secretion, whereas moist foods cause the production of a scant, thick secretion. There is a central regulatory mechanism for salivary flow in the hypothalamus. Olfactory and gustatory impulses are received in the hypothalamus, and discharge paths go to the salivatory and sympathetic nuclei.

Impulses that stimulate lacrimation arise from a part of the superior salivatory nucleus or in a related nuclear mass which is sometimes called the *lacrimal nucleus* (Fig. 80). *Preganglionic fibers* pass through the nervus intermedius and the geniculate ganglion into the greater superficial petrosal nerve. This goes forward through the hiatus of the facial canal and joins the deep petrosal nerve from the carotid sympathetic plexus to form the vidian nerve, or the nerve of the pterygoid canal. It supplies the motor, or parasympathetic, root of the *sphenopalatine ganglion*. *Postganglionic fibers* then travel in the zygomaticotemporal branch of the maxillary division to the lacrimal branch of the ophthalmic, and thus to the *lacrimal gland*. Stimulation of the trigeminal nerve in the eye or the nose produces tear secretion. Psychic stimuli also cause lacrimation. There may be central stimulation or inhibition of tear secretion.

CLINICAL EXAMINATION

EXAMINATION OF THE MOTOR FUNCTIONS

The examination of the motor functions of the facial nerve consists of an appraisal of the action of the muscles of facial expression. First the face is inspected, mobility of facial expression observed, and any asymmetry or abnormality of the muscles noted. A one-sided appearance while talking or smiling, inequality of the palpebral fissures, infrequent or asymmetrical blinking, smoothness of the face and absence of normal wrinkling, or increased wrinkling may all give clues to facial nerve involvement. It should be noted whether the abnormality is more marked during emotional stress or during voluntary effort.

In making a detailed examination the patient is asked to contract the various muscles individually and in unison. He is asked to frown, wrinkle his forehead, raise his eyebrows, and corrugate his brow; to close his eyes, both singly and bilaterally, first lightly, then tightly, and then against resistance; to draw back the angles of his mouth, show his teeth, grimace, blow out his cheeks, purse his mouth, whistle, and retract the chin muscles. Retraction of the angles of the mouth is noted both on voluntary effort and on smiling, and voluntary and emotional responses of all muscles are compared. The patient may smile spontaneously after attempting to whistle. Function of the auricular muscles cannot be tested in most individuals, although some individuals can voluntarily contract the extrinsic muscles. The same is true of the occipitalis and scalp movements. Function of the platysma is tested by having the patient open his mouth against resistance or bite his teeth together firmly. The tone of the muscles of facial expression is noted, and atrophy and fasciculations are looked for. In many instances the electrical reactions should be evaluated and electromyography carried out. Abnormal movements such as tremors, spasms, tics, grimacing, and athetoid, myoclonic, and choreiform movements should be recorded. Immobility, or masking, of the face should be appraised. Special tests of motor function and confirmatory signs of facial paresis or paralysis, including the examination in stuporous patients, are discussed under disorders of function of the nerve. In infants, facial movements are observed during crying. Articulation of the labial sounds is discussed in Chapter 19.

The function of the stylohyoid muscle and the posterior belly of the digastricus cannot be adequately tested, but in paralysis of these there may be some weakness of deglutition with regurgitation of food. Weakness of the stapedius muscle is not apparent objectively, but the patient may complain of hyperacusis, especially for low tones.

EXAMINATION OF THE REFLEXES

Certain reflexes should be elicited in the examination of the facial nerve. The corneal and nasal reflexes and their modifications are discussed in Chapter 12, the sucking reflex in Chapter 15, and the palmomental reflex in Chapter 36. The following responses are those in which the seventh nerve plays the major role, and which, therefore, may be considered tests for its function.

The Orbicularis Oculi Reflex: Percussion at the outer aspect of the supra-orbital ridge, over the glabella, or around the margin of the orbit, or a sudden stretching of the orbicularis muscle is followed by a reflex contraction of this muscle, with resulting closing of the eye. The response is usually bilateral. This reflex has been known by a number of names, such as the *supraorbital (McCarthy's),* the *glabellar,* or the *nasopalpebral reflex,* depending upon the site of application of the stimulus. It can sometimes be elicited by percussion of the forehead as far as the border of the hair, or by tapping the root of the nose. It is best tested by pulling back, between the thumb and index finger, a fold of skin on the temple lateral to the external canthus, and then applying a brisk tap to the thumb. There is an immediate contraction of the orbicularis, accompanied, to a milder degree, by a contralateral response. This is a deep, or muscle stretch, reflex, and the corneal reflex may be considered as its superficial counterpart. The afferent portion of the arc may be carried through both the facial nerve (as proprioceptive impulses) and the trigeminal nerve; the efferent impulses pass through the facial nerve, and the reflex center is in the pons. The strength of response varies in individuals, but the reflex is diminished to absent in nuclear and peripheral lesions of the facial nerve and absent in coma, and is preserved or exaggerated in supranuclear varieties of facial palsy and pyramidal lesions above the nucleus of the seventh nerve. It is also exaggerated in extrapyramidal disease, in which condition the response may continue with repeated stimuli, whereas in the normal it disappears after a few stimulations; this persistent response is sometimes referred to as *Myerson's sign.*

The Palpebral Reflexes: Reflex contraction of the orbicularis oculi muscle and consequent closing of the eye may be a response to other stimuli. A reflex closing of the eyes in response to a sudden loud noise is known as the *auditory-palpebral, auro-* or *acoustico-palpebral, cochleopalpebral,* or *cochleo-orbicularis reflex.* The response usually is a bilateral one, more marked on the ipsilateral side. The sensory impulse is carried through the cochlear nerve, and the efferent portion of the reflex arc is mediated through the facial nerve. A reflex closing of the eyes in response to a strong light or a sudden visual stimulus is the *visual-palpebral, visual-orbicularis, opticofacial, blink,* or *menace reflex.* In this response the afferent portion of the reflex arc is carried from the retina through the optic nerve to the visual cortex, and thence to the facial nuclei. In a modification of this, the *emergency light reflex,* the closing of the eyes is accompanied by constriction of the pupils, lowering of the eyebrows, bending of the head, and, sometimes, elevation of the arm (Chapter 11). Closing of the eyes in response to a painful stimulus to the face or in the region of the eye is known as the *trigeminofacial, trigeminopalpebral,* or *trigemino-orbicularis reflex.* Here the afferent portion of the reflex arc is carried through the trigeminal nerve, and this response is similar to the corneal and orbicularis oculi reflexes. The trigeminofacial reflex may also be elicited by a sudden gust of air, or by cold or heat. The *palatopalpebral reflex* is a closing of the eyes in response to stimulation of the palate. Here the afferent impulse may be carried by the trigeminal, glossopharyngeal, or vagus nerves.

The Oculogyric-Auricular Reflex: This consists of a retraction of the auricle and a curling back of the helix on lateral gaze in the extreme opposite direction, or a retraction of both auricles, more on the opposite side, on lateral gaze to one side. Here the afferent impulse is a proprioceptive one carried through the ocular nerves, and the efferent impulse is conveyed through the facial nerve to the auricular muscles.

The Palpebral-Oculogyric Reflex: On contraction of the orbiculares and closing of the eyes, the eyeballs turn upward; this occurs not only with voluntary closing of the eyes, but also in sleep. It is actually an associated movement and not a reflex, but proprioceptive impulses are carried through the facial nerve to the medial longitudinal fasciculus, and efferent impulses are relayed through the oculomotor nerves to the superior rectus muscles. An exaggeration of this response is known as *Bell's phenomenon* and is seen in peripheral types of facial palsy. The *orbicularis reflex,* a constriction of the pupils on either closing or upward deviation of the eyes, is discussed with the pupillary reflexes.

The Orbicularis Oris Reflex: Percussion over the upper lip or the side of the nose is followed by a contraction of the ipsilateral quadratus labii superioris and caninus (levator anguli oris) muscles. An elevation of the upper lip and angle of the mouth follows. If the mentalis (levator menti) muscles are also stimulated, there is, in addition, an elevation and protrusion of the lower lip and wrinkling of the skin of the chin. This reflex, which is also known as the *perioral, oral, buccal,* or *nasomental reflex,* is mediated through the trigeminal (sensory) and facial (motor) nerves. It is not present to any degree in normal persons except during the first year of life, but is present and often exaggerated with pyramidal tract lesions above the nucleus of the seventh nerve and also with disease of the extrapyramidal system. A slight or brief response to a single stimulus may not be significant. On the other hand, a strong stimulus in patients with pyramidal disease may evoke, in addition, either the jaw reflex when the lower lip is tapped or the head retraction reflex on stimulation of the upper lip. The reflex is difficult to test in edentulous patients.

When the response is increased, tapping of the upper or lower lip, or even sweeping a tongue blade briskly across the upper lip, is followed by contraction of both the upper or lower portions of the orbicularis as well as the muscles about the base of the nose, causing a puckering or protrusion of the lips known as the *snout reflex.* This is seen in bilateral supranuclear lesions and diffuse cerebral degenerations, and is related to the sucking reflex (Chapter 15). The *palmomental reflex,* in which there is ipsilateral contraction of the mentalis and orbicularis oris muscles following stimulation of the thenar area of the hand, is described in Chapter 36.

Chvostek's Sign: This is a spasm, or tetanic, cramplike contraction, of the ipsilateral facial muscles that appears on tapping over the exit of the facial nerve anterior to the ear. Degrees of response are discussed in Chapter 40. This is an important sign in tetany, but it is also observed in other conditions in which there is increased reflex irritability. This may be either a trigeminofacial reflex, or a reflex involving only the facial nerve, the afferent impulses being proprioceptive ones carried by this nerve. Electromyographic studies of latency time, however, indicate that the response is due to direct mechanical stimulation of motor fibers in the nerve.

The Stapedius Reflex: Contraction of the stapedius muscle increases the tension of the middle ear ossicles and of the tympanic membrane. In the stapedius reflex a loud sound is directed to one ear and the effect on the other ear is evaluated by an instrument which measures acoustic impedance. This has been used experimentally in the study of peripheral facial paralysis but cannot be considered a part of the routine neurologic examination.

EXAMINATION OF THE SENSORY FUNCTIONS

The sensory functions of the seventh nerve are not easily tested. The *exteroceptive sensations* supply relatively inaccessible areas, namely the external auditory canal and the tympanic membrane, and these same areas also receive exteroceptive innervation from the trigeminal, glossopharyngeal, vagus, and great auricular (second and third) cervical nerves, with an overlap in distribution. As a result, no adequate examination can be made. *General visceral, proprioceptive,* and *"deep"* sensibilities cannot be evaluated. Consequently, the sensory examination of the seventh nerve is limited to the testing of taste.

Gustatory sense, or taste, is closely associated with smell, and it is known that the flavor of many foods is a combination of both olfactory and gustatory sensation, together with somatic sensations experienced in the mouth, nasopharynx, and adjacent structures. Many anosmic patients complain of loss of taste rather than of smell, because of inability to perceive the finer flavors of foods, but some anosmic persons can identify and enjoy the flavors of many foods. There are, however, only four fundamental tastes: sweet, salty, sour, and bitter. Sweet taste is conveyed by many monosaccharides and disaccharides and by some alcohols, saccharine, and chloroform; salty taste is most characteristically found in chlorides and bromides; sour taste is conveyed by various acids, and bitter by many alkaloids and glucosides. Some observers add alkaline and metallic tastes. The flavors of foods are probably blends of the above primary tastes, or combinations of them with olfactory sensations, tactile stimuli, etc. There is a difference for various substances in the latent period and in the threshold—man is most sensitive to bitter tastes, then to sour, sweet, and salty ones. The peripheral organs of taste are the taste buds embedded in the epithelium of the tongue, and to a lesser extent in the soft palate and epiglottis. It is possible that some taste buds respond to only one taste quality, whereas others respond to more than one. It is said that sweet and salt are perceived best in the region of the vallate papillae and on the dorsum of the tip of the tongue, sour along the borders and at the tip, and bitter at the back of the tongue and on the soft palate. Taste is also carried through the glossopharyngeal nerve and probably through the vagus nerve. These three nerves which convey taste act as one part of the afferent pathway for salivation.

Taste is tested by using the four common flavors; solutions of sugar, sodium chloride, acetic acid, and quinine are most frequently utilized. For semiquantitative tests, Börnstein used a 4 per cent solution of glucose, a 2.5 per cent solution of sodium chloride, a 1 per cent solution of citric acid, and a 0.075 per cent solution of quinine hydrochloride. It is important in testing taste to examine the anterior and posterior portions of each half of the tongue individually. In examining the functions of the facial nerve the examiner must be certain that the test substance is placed only on the anterior two-thirds of the tongue, without flowing to or communicating with the posterior third or the opposite half. Each time the patient speaks, he retracts his tongue into his mouth. This allows the saliva to flow over it, and possibly carries the test substance to the posterior third or the opposite half. For this reason, the tongue should be protruding during the entire test and the patient should not be allowed to speak during the examination. For an accurate test the words "sweet," "salt," "sour," and "bitter" are written on a piece of paper. The various test substances are then placed upon the portion of the tongue that is being tested, and the subject is asked to point to the word that signifies the taste that he perceives. The test substances may be placed on the tongue either by using a cotton applicator that has been dipped in the solution or by the use of a pipette. Powdered test substances are sometimes utilized, but their use is more difficult. The mouth should be rinsed with water between tests. Bitter substances should be tested last because they leave the most aftertaste. Taste may also be tested by the use of a galvanic current, applying the naked copper electrode to the tongue. The anode is applied to the tongue and a current of from 2 to 4 milliamperes is used. A galvanic current gives a sour, metallic taste. Krarup has designed an electrogustometer by means of which the galvanic taste stimulus can be regulated with a potentiometer; this can be used to determine taste thresholds and carry out quantitative testing.

Loss and diminution of taste are called respectively *ageusia* and *hypogeusia*. Perversions or abnormal perceptions of taste are *parageusias*. There is marked individual variation in taste. Complete ageusia is rare unless there is also loss of smell. Age, wasting diseases, certain drugs, coating of the tongue, and excessive smoking diminish the power of taste. If there is loss of taste one should first eliminate the possibility of disease of the tongue.

EXAMINATION OF THE SECRETORY FUNCTIONS

The secretory fibers of the facial nerve can usually be evaluated by questioning the patient and by observation. Increased lacrimation is usually apparent, and decrease in lacrimation may be determined from the history. The amount of tear secretion may be evaluated by hanging a strip of litmus or filter paper on each lower lid, and noting the amount of moistening on each side (Schirmer's test). In the so-called *lacrimal reflex* a secretion of tears, usually bilateral, is produced either by stimulating the cornea or by mechanical or chemical stimulation of the nasal mucosa (the *nasolacrimal reflex*). For the latter, irritating substances such as ammonia or formaldehyde may be used. Increase and decrease in salivation are also apparent

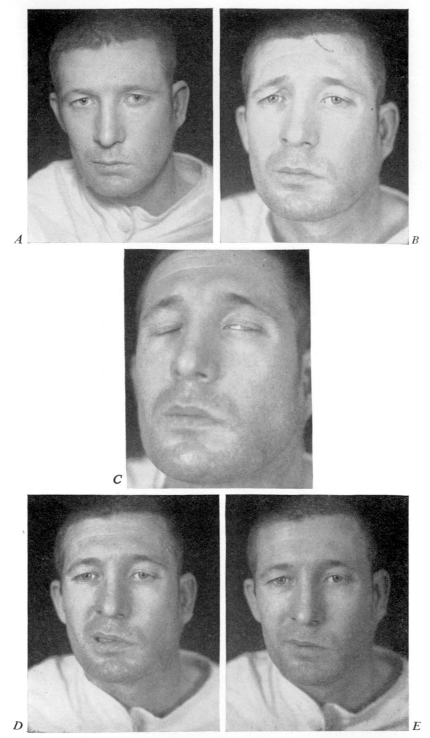

FIG. 81. Left peripheral facial paralysis; *A*, face at rest; *B*, patient attempting to elevate brow; *C*, patient attempting to close eye; *D*, patient attempting to retract angle of mouth; *E*, patient smiling.

from the history. The secretory fibers to the submaxillary and sublingual glands may be examined, if the occasion arises, by placing highly flavored substances upon the tongue. The patient is then asked to elevate his tongue, and if there is no inter-ference with secretory functions, a copious supply of saliva is seen to flow from the submaxillary duct. This may be called the *salivary reflex*. It is possible also to measure the submaxillary salivary flow through fine polyethylene tubes introduced into the submaxillary ducts. The patient may be given a gustatory stimulus, such as a lemon drop, and the amount of flow from each side during a five-minute period is compared.

DISORDERS OF FUNCTION

Lesions of the facial nerve are most commonly evidenced by motor changes, either paresis or spasm, although there may also be changes in sensation and in the secretory functions.

Paretic Motor Phenomena: Paralysis of the facial nerve is of two general varie-ties. The *peripheral* type is the result of a lesion involving either the nucleus or the nerve peripheral to the nucleus; the *central* type follows supranuclear lesions.

Peripheral Facial Paralysis: In a peripheral facial paralysis, or *prosopoplegia,* there is flaccid paralysis of all the muscles of facial expression on the involved side, and the paralysis is usually complete. There is loss of function of the frontalis, cor-rugator, and orbicularis oculi muscles, the nasal muscles, the muscles of the mouth, and the platysma, together with paralysis of the stylohyoid, the posterior belly of the digastricus, the auricular muscles, and in some instances, the stapedius. The affected side of the face is smooth, there are no wrinkles on the forehead, the eyebrow droops, the eye is open, the inferior lid sags, the nose is flattened or deviated to the opposite side, and the angle of the mouth may be depressed (Fig. 81). The patient is unable to raise his eyebrow, wrinkle his forehead, frown, close his eye, laugh, smile, show his teeth, blow out his cheek, whistle, purse his mouth, retract the angle of the mouth, or retract the chin muscles on the involved side. He talks and smiles with one side of the mouth, and the mouth is drawn to the sound side on attempted movement. The lips are narrower on the paretic than on the normal side. Food accumulates between the teeth and the paralyzed cheek. The cheek is flaccid and hollowed out; it "puffs out" in expiration, and the patient may bite his cheek or lip in chewing. He cannot drink liquids or retain them in the mouth, but is able to swallow. Saliva may drip from the paretic side of the mouth. The tongue may be protruded in the midline but is pushed to one side by the paretic angle of the mouth, so that there is an apparent deviation. If the facial nerve does send some fibers to the tongue, there may be slight ipsilateral weakness of this organ.

In a peripheral facial paralysis there is difficulty with articulation, especially in pronouncing the labials and the vowels which are produced by pursing the lips. The nasolabial fold is shallower than normal, or may be absent. The ala nasi is sunken and shows no active movement on respiration. The platysma is seen to be weak when the patient depresses his chin against passive resistance. The palpebral fissure is wider than normal, owing to lagophthalmos, or inability to close the eye. In blinking the involved lid fails to close or lags behind the opposite one. When the patient attempts to close his eye on the involved side the eyeball turns upward until the cornea is hidden; it is first deviated slightly inward, and then slightly outward (Fig. 81). This is known as *Bell's phenomenon*, and is said to be a synkinesis of central origin in which the levator palpebrae superioris, the superior rectus, and the inferior oblique muscles participate. It is an exaggeration of the palpebral-oculogyric reflex. Owing to sagging of the lower lid there is epiphora, or an overflow of tears down the cheek; there may be increased lacrimation secondary to constant irritation of the cornea. The eye may be open at all times, even in sleep. If the patient had been able to move his scalp or ear voluntarily, he will have lost this power. Involvement of the scalp muscles and extrinsic muscles of the ear, however, can seldom be demonstrated. Paralysis of the stylohyoid muscle and the posterior belly of the digastricus is not easy to identify, but there may be some weakness of deglutition, and the base of the tongue may be depressed. When the stapedius is paralyzed there is hyperacusis, especially for low tones, and these sound louder and higher.

All of the above evidences of muscular weakness are present both on voluntary and involuntary contraction. The manifestations become especially marked when the patient talks or smiles, and on such occasions the asymmetry becomes much more obvious. The paralysis may result in atrophy of the muscles, and an electrical reaction of degeneration appears in the involved nerve and muscles. The various reflexes that involve motor responses of the muscles supplied by the facial nerve are absent. The face may feel numb, but there is no objective evidence of reduction of cutaneous sensibility.

Certain confirmatory signs of facial paresis may be elicited when the peripheral paralysis is not a complete one. The patient, for instance, may be able to close his eye but unable to close it against the resistance of the examiner's fingers. The examiner may find it easier to open the eye on the involved side against the patient's resistance than that on the normal side. If the lids are passively opened and then allowed to close, the normal lid closes quickly but the closing is retarded and incomplete on the affected side. The patient should be asked to close each eye individually, and inability to close the one on the involved side without simultaneously closing its mate may indicate a facial weakness or may be the only residual of a facial palsy. If the weakness is minimal, decreased or absent winking on the affected side may have diagnostic significance. In semicomatose or comatose patients the function of the facial nerve can be tested and the presence of a facial paralysis can be elicited by noting the response to painful pressure on the supraorbital ridge. In normal individuals this is followed by a bilateral contraction of the facial muscles with closing of the eyes and retraction of the angles of the mouth. In paralysis of the facial nerve this response is obtained only on the normal side. The *levator sign* of Dutemps and Cestan is elicited by having the patient look down and then close his eyes slowly; when present, the upper lid on the paralyzed side moves upward slightly, being elevated by the levator palpebrae superioris whose function is no longer counteracted by the orbicularis. In *Negro's sign* the eyeball on the paralyzed side deviates outward and elevates more than the normal one when the patient raises his eyes; this is due to overaction of the superior rectus and inferior oblique. The *Bergara-Warten-*

berg sign is the diminution or absence of palpable vibrations in the orbicularis oculi as the examiner attempts to open the closed eyelids against resistance; it is an early and sensitive sign of facial palsy, both peripheral and central. In the *platysma sign of Babinski* there is failure of the platysma to contract on the involved side when the mouth is opened. In facial paralysis the corneal reflexes, both direct and consensual, are absent on the involved side, a result of impairment of the motor portion of the reflex arc. The consensual reflex remains on the sound side when the cornea is touched on the involved side. The orbicularis oculi, nasomental, palmomental, and other facial reflexes are also absent on the involved side.

A minimal facial paresis on one side must be differentiated from a facial contracture on the opposite side; if the latter is present, the normal side appears to be the weaker. It must also be differentiated from developmental asymmetry and facial hemiatrophy. Unequal palpebral fissures resulting from ptosis on one side may suggest the presence of a facial weakness on the opposite side. The reaction of degeneration is found only in peripheral facial palsy. Various special testing procedures are used in differentiating between peripheral and central types of facial palsy and in determining the prognosis of the former type. These include measurement of nerve conduction time in response to percutaneous electrical stimulation, nerve excitability tests, and electromyography, and, on occasion, electrogustometry, evaluation of lacrimal and salivary flow, and testing of the stapedius reflex.

There are different varieties of peripheral facial paralysis, depending upon the site of the lesion. The involvement may be *nuclear,* within the pons, or *infranuclear,* anywhere along the course of the nerve. These different types may be identified and the site of pathologic change localized by noting the involvement of associated structures (Fig. 80). These varieties are as follows:

1. *Nuclear or infranuclear involvement within the pons:* Lesions within the pons may affect either the nucleus of the facial nerve or its emerging root fibers. There is a complete or peripheral facial paralysis, often with evidence of disease of contiguous structures. There usually is preservation of sensation and secretory functions. In degenerative nuclear lesions such as progressive bulbar palsy and syringomyelia, fasciculations appear in the muscles supplied by the facial nerve. Owing to the proximity of the nucleus of the seventh nerve, and especially of its root fibers, to the nucleus of the sixth nerve, pontine lesions frequently cause both an ipsilateral facial paralysis and an ipsilateral lateral rectus paralysis. In the *Millard-Gubler syndrome* a lateral rectus paralysis, probably on the basis of nuclear involvement, is accompanied by an ipsilateral facial paralysis, probably caused by a lesion of the root fibers, and a contralateral hemiplegia because of involvement of the corticospinal pathway. In the *Foville syndrome* a facial paralysis resulting from involvement of root fibers accompanies an ipsilateral paralysis of conjugate gaze caused by a lesion of the parabducens nucleus or the medial longitudinal fasciculus, and a contralateral pyramidal hemiplegia; involvement of the ascending afferent pathways may cause sensory changes (Chapter 11).

2. *Infranuclear involvement just peripheral to the pons or between the pons and the facial canal:* The seventh nerve lies with the eighth nerve in the cerebellopontine angle and the internal auditory meatus. In lesions at these sites there may

be involvement of the entire face, together with tinnitus, deafness, and vertigo; the nervus intermedius may be affected with loss of taste on the anterior two thirds of the tongue and diminution of salivary and lacrimal secretion. Lesions in the cerebellopontine angle commonly extend to the fifth nerve, cerebellar peduncles, and cerebellum, and cause ipsilateral pain or sensory changes, ipsilateral ataxia, and nystagmus.

3. *Involvement within the facial canal between the internal auditory meatus and the geniculate ganglion:* When lesions occur at this site, there commonly is a peripheral type of facial paralysis together with involvement of the nervus intermedius. Consequently ipsilateral loss of taste and diminution of lacrimal and salivary secretions accompany the palsy. There often is associated hyperacusis owing to paralysis of the nerve to the stapedius. The distance between the internal auditory meatus and the geniculate ganglion is very short, however, and lesions at this site are not common.

4. *Involvement of the facial nerve at the geniculate ganglion:* A complete facial paralysis, hyperacusis, loss of taste, impairment of secretory functions, and pain in the region of the ear drum follow a lesion of the facial nerve at the geniculate ganglion. There may be an herpetic eruption; the vesicles are present on the ear drum and in the external auditory meatus. This geniculate neuralgia, with or without herpes, is called *Hunt's neuralgia,* or the *Ramsay Hunt syndrome.*

5. *Involvement of the facial nerve peripheral to the geniculate ganglion but central to the departure of the nerve to the stapedius:* When a lesion occurs at this site, there is a peripheral facial paralysis accompanied by hyperacusis, loss of taste, and diminution of salivation. Lacrimation is not affected.

6. *Involvement of the facial nerve within the facial canal between the departure of the nerve to the stapedius and the departure of the chorda tympani:* Lesions here cause a peripheral type of facial paralysis, together with loss of taste on the anterior two thirds of the tongue and diminution of salivary secretion. Neither hearing nor lacrimation is affected.

7. *Involvement of the facial nerve within the facial canal peripheral to the departure of the chorda tympani:* In lesions peripheral to the departure of the chorda tympani there is only a peripheral type of facial paralysis, with no accompanying changes.

8. *Involvement of the facial nerve in the parotid gland after the emergence of the nerve from the stylomastoid foramen:* Lesions of the facial nerve after it has left the stylomastoid foramen may cause partial involvement, because only certain branches of the pes anserinus are affected, thereby paralyzing some of but not all the muscles of facial expression.

Facial Paralysis of Central Origin: In a *central,* or *supranuclear, facial palsy* there is paresis of the lower portion of the face, with relative sparing of the upper portion. The paresis is rarely complete and it is always contralateral to the pathologic lesion. As explained above, the nuclear center that controls the upper portion of the face has both contralateral and ipsilateral supranuclear connections; in other words, it has cortical connections from both hemispheres. The nuclear center that supplies the lower portion of the face, on the other hand, has mainly contralateral supranuclear innervation. As a result, a cortical or subcortical lesion in one cerebral hemisphere will cause paralysis of the lower part of the face on the opposite side, but there is relative sparing of the upper portion. It must be borne in mind that there is a great deal of individual variation in facial innervation, and the extent of involvement in a palsy of the central type may vary from the lower half to two thirds of the face. There is usually a little weakness of the lower part of the orbicularis oculi, so that the palpebral fissure is wider on the involved side; there may also be some weakness of the upper portion of the orbicularis, although the frontalis and the corrugator are rarely or minimally involved. The inability to close the eye on the involved side without closing its mate may be the only defect of the upper face. The levator sign and Negro's sign may be present in the central type as well as the peripheral type, and the patient may be unable to close his eye against resistance. The Bergara-Wartenberg sign and the platysma sign of Babinski are also present. Bell's phenomenon, however, is usually absent, the corneal reflex is usually present, and the orbicularis oculi reflex may be exaggerated. The lower portion of the face is smoother than normal, and the nasolabial fold is shallow. There is probably some bilateral innervation to the lower face as well as to the upper, and the paralysis of the lower face is never as marked in a central palsy as it is in a peripheral one. In a central palsy one rarely finds drooping of the angle of the mouth, blowing out of the cheek, difficulty in drinking liquids, and difficulty with the articulation of labials. There is some preservation of function, even in the involved muscles, and the central variety may be called a *paresis* of the lower face, whereas the peripheral variety is a *paralysis* of the entire face. The differentiation between the two is rarely a difficult one. If, however, the supranuclear innervation is entirely crossed, it may be difficult to distinguish between a central type of palsy and a peripheral one. Occasionally in a central facial palsy one finds an exaggerated reaction of the angle of the mouth and closing of the eye as an automatic synkinetic movement with great bodily exertion, but, on the other hand, the weakness may be apparent only in the associated facial movements and grimacing that may accompany bodily exertion.

There are two principal varieties of central facial palsy, the *volitional* and the *emotional* types. In the *volitional palsy* the involvement is most marked on voluntary contraction, and the paresis becomes apparent when the patient attempts to bare his teeth or retract the angle of the mouth. On involuntary contraction, such as spontaneous smiling, crying, or other expressions of emotion, there is preservation of function and there may be little or no evidence of paresis (Fig. 82). In fact, these automatic or involuntary movements may not only be preserved, but at times there is an exaggeration or dissociation of responses on smiling. This variety of paresis results from involvement of either the cortical center in the lower third of the precentral convolution that controls facial movements or the pathway between this center and the motor nucleus of the facial nerve. The lesion thus may be either in the cortex or in the subcortical pyramidal pathways as they go through the internal capsule, the cerebral peduncle, or the pons above the facial nucleus.

In the *emotional* or *mimetic type of facial palsy,* or *amimia,* the impairment is most marked on smiling and weeping, and the patient can voluntarily retract his

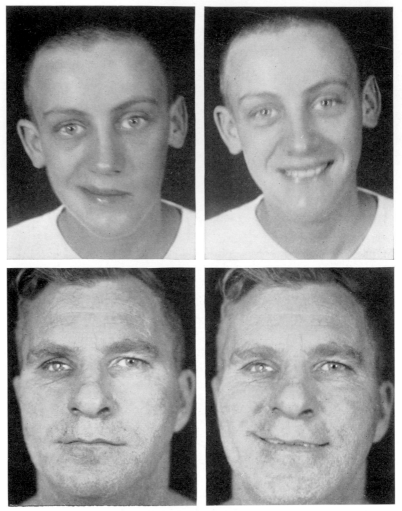

FIG. 82 (*Top*).   Volitional type of facial paresis on the left associated with neoplasm of right frontal lobe: *Left,* patient attempting to retract angle of mouth; *Right,* patient smiling.

FIG. 83 (*Bottom*).   Emotional type of facial paresis on the left following cerebral thrombosis: *Left,* face at rest; *Right,* patient smiling.

mouth or blow out his cheeks without difficulty (Fig. 83). This type of palsy is considered to be the result of a deep-seated lesion, perhaps owing to extrapyramidal, basal ganglion, thalamic, or even hypothalamic, involvement. It has also been described in lesions of the frontal lobe anterior to the precentral convolution and of the reticular portion of the pons just above the facial nucleus. The fibers carrying stimuli that produce an emotional response may go through pathways other than the pyramidal tracts. There is probably a close association between the centers or pathways controlling the emotional movements and those associated with respiration, and a smile may be accompanied by an arrest of respiration and laughter by a series of respiratory arrests and accelerations. The associated facial and respiratory pathway may pass from the thalamus to the anterior part of the frontal lobe, and thence to the lenticular nucleus.

In many cases of central palsy there is both volitional and emotional involvement. In pseudobulbar palsy the paresis may be either voluntary or mimetic, but is usually predominantly the latter, and the involvement is bilateral. In addition there may be forced laughter and crying that are either unmotivated and spontaneous or precipitated by the slightest or most indifferent stimulus. This may be due to a short-circuiting from the ventral nucleus of the thalamus to the hypothalamus, or may be a result of failure of corticothalamic inhibition.

The *masked face* that is seen in Parkinson's disease and other related parkinsonian syndromes (Fig. 84) is sometimes classed as a third type of central facial paresis. Here there is no real paresis, either of voluntary or emotional response, but the face is smoother than normal, the facial features are flattened, and the normal emotional responses are absent. There is loss of associated movements, with infrequent blinking and smiling. The patient is able to smile, however, and when he does he frequently shows an exaggerated, "frozen" smile. In this variety also there may be forced or unmotivated laughing and crying. The masked face is seen with degenerative and inflammatory diseases of the basal ganglia and extrapyramidal system and is often present in pseudobulbar palsy. In all probability this condition is the result of involvement of the putamen or globus pallidus, and it is sometimes called a "pallidal" variety of facial palsy.

Paresis or paralysis of facial nerve may result from a wide variety of lesions, and these lesions may be widely distributed throughout the central or peripheral nervous systems. Neoplasms, vascular lesions, degenerative changes, and inflammations involving the motor cortex, the internal capsule, the basal ganglia, the cerebral peduncle, or the upper pons may cause one of the varieties of central palsy; lesions of the lower pons, the cerebellopontine angle, within the facial canal, or lesions

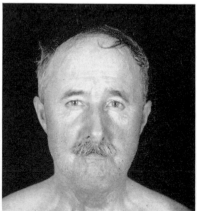

FIG. 84.   Masked face in patient with Parkinson's disease.

affecting the nerve after its exit may cause the peripheral variety. Pontine lesions are apt to be vascular in origin, but there may be involvement of the facial nuclei with neoplasms, polioencephalitis, multiple sclerosis, syringobulbia, and degenerative processes such as progressive bulbar palsy, in which there are also atrophy and fasciculations. Either unilateral or bilateral facial paralysis may be of congenital origin. When this is associated with paralysis of extraocular muscles, especially the external rectus, it is known as *Möbius' syndrome,* or congenital oculofacial paralysis; this is usually the result of hypoplasia or aplasia of the nuclear centers (Fig. 85). There may also be paresis of the muscles of mastication and other muscles innervated by cranial nerves, and other developmental defects.

Just after its exit from the pons the facial nerve may be involved in meningitides of various types, basal skull fractures, neoplastic changes, basilar aneurysms, extra-dural abscesses, gummas, or diseases of the base of the skull. The facial nerve is frequently affected in acoustic neurinomas and with other neoplasms such as meningiomas and chordomas in the cerebellopontine angle or at the base of the brain. It is involved early in chemodectomas or tumors of the glomus jugulare, and the paralysis may be a progressive one. Tumors of the nerve itself are rare, and the nerve is not frequently affected by organization and exudate following a subarachnoid hemorrhage.

Within the facial canal many processes may affect the nerve. Inflammatory conditions at the geniculate ganglion, such as herpes zoster, may cause the Ramsay Hunt

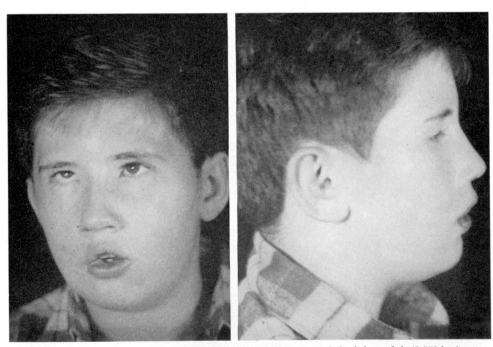

FIG. 85.   Patient with aplasia of right abducens and facial nuclei (Möbius' syndrome).

syndrome, and it is very probable that many of the instances of spontaneous facial paralysis without herpes are due to a neurotropic virus infection. The facial nerve may be involved in various infectious processes, such as mumps, uveoparotid fever, scarlet fever, malaria, focal infections, and polyneuritis cranialis; in diabetic, alcoholic, and vitamin deficiency neuritides; in vascular insufficiency; or by metastatic neoplasms and lymphosarcomatous growths. Owing to the proximity of the facial canal to the middle ear and the mastoid process, the facial nerve is frequently involved in disease of the middle ear and its adnexa. Facial paralysis is seen as a complication of otitis media, petrositis, mastoiditis, and suppuration of the temporal bone, and in association with a cholesteatoma; the ear should be examined in every case of peripheral facial paralysis, whether or not there are symptoms of ear disease. A facial paralysis may develop following a mastoidectomy if the nerve has been exposed during the process of the operation or if the suppurative process has extended to the facial canal.

Paralysis of the peripheral branches of the nerve, after its emergence from the stylomastoid foramen, may result from disease or tumors of the parotid gland and from trauma to the face, especially that associated with cuts, slashes, or stab or gun shot wounds. Trauma at birth, especially a forceps delivery, may cause such an involvement. A neuritis of the great auricular nerve in the parotid gland has been said to cause facial palsy even though the seventh nerve is not directly affected. Paralysis of the terminal branches of the nerve is said to be characteristic of leprosy; here there is involvement of individual muscles, often with extreme hypotonia and ectropion of the eye and mouth.

Bilateral peripheral facial paralysis is occasionally seen, especially in various types of peripheral neuritis, and facial diplegia may be one of the characteristic findings in the Guillain-Barré syndrome (Fig. 86). Facial diplegia has also been described in aneurysm of the basilar artery, and it may occur in polioencephalitis, and in myasthenia gravis and the myopathies (see below).

The term *Bell's palsy* is often used as a synonym for the peripheral variety of facial paralysis, but the term should be used only if the paralysis is the result of a lesion peripheral to the geniculate ganglion, that is, one without neuralgia or herpes. Taste may or may not be affected. This usually develops spontaneously, and the patient may not be aware of the paralysis until he sees his face in a mirror or notices difficulty drinking or holding liquids in his mouth. Occasionally there is mild pain in the ear or some subjective numbness or stiffness of the face. There is sometimes a history of exposure to cold or wind on the affected side or of a mild systemic infection prior to the onset of the paralysis, but the relationship of these to its etiology is not known. Most clinicians feel that either compression of the nerve by edema or periostitis of the facial canal or ischemia secondary to arteriolar spasm of the nutrient vessels is responsible for most cases of idiopathic Bell's palsy. Either of these may cause either a physiologic or an anatomic block of the nerve. There is also evidence to suggest, however, that inflammatory involvement of the nerve (possibly viral, even in the absence of herpetic features) is responsible for a certain percentage of cases. The prognosis varies. In the majority of cases recovery is fairly prompt and complete. In a somewhat smaller group improvement is delayed; re-

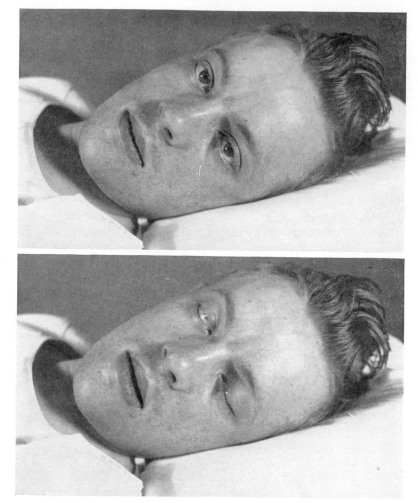

FIG. 86. Facial diplegia in patient with Guillain-Barré syndrome: *Top,* face at rest; *Bottom,* patient attempting to close eyes and retract angles of mouth.

covery may or may not be complete, or regeneration may be faulty with the development of facial spasms. In a still smaller group there is very little or no recovery. The prognosis for the speed and degree of recovery may often be determined by electrical and electromyographic testing. Bell's palsy is sometimes recurrent. *Melkersson's syndrome* is characterized by recurring facial palsy, recurring facial edema, and a congenitally fissured tongue; it is sometimes familial.

The muscles of facial expression may be involved in various other disease processes. In progressive bulbar palsy and amyotrophic lateral sclerosis there may be atrophy and fasciculations of the facial muscles; the atrophy is often difficult to recognize because the bulk of the facial musculature is small. In myasthenia gravis there often is marked weakness of the facial muscles, with a weak or "myasthenic" smile; the patient has difficulty in both closing and opening his eyes. In the "myopathic facies," seen in the facioscapulohumeral type of muscular dystrophy of Landouzy and Dejerine, the eyelids droop and cannot be tightly closed, and the lips cannot be pursed, but protrude and droop tonelessly giving the "bouche de tapir" (Fig. 87). On smiling the risorius pulls at the angle of the mouth, but because the zygomaticus is unable to elevate the lips, there results a "transverse smile." In *facial hemiatrophy,* or *progressive facial hemiatrophy,* there is either underdevelopment of congenital origin or a progressive atrophy of the muscles of mastication and facial expression and other muscles of one half of the face, together with trophic

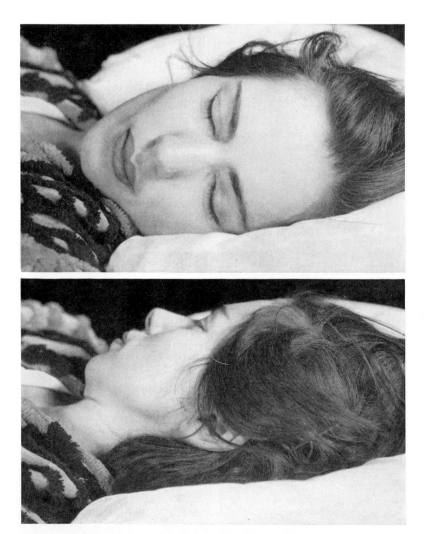

FIG. 87. Myopathic facies in patient with the facioscapulohumeral type of muscular dystrophy of Landouzy-Dejerine.

changes in the skin, subcutaneous fat, connective tissue, cartilage, and bone. Those in the skin include atrophy of the papillary layer with disappearance of subcutaneous fat and resulting scleroderma; trophic changes in the hair consist of loss of pigmenta-tion and circumscribed alopecia (Fig. 88). Occasionally instead of hemiatrophy there is *hemihypertrophy*. These processes probably have a central origin, and are due to a disturbance of development of the involved nuclei or their supranuclear centers, but the changes in the skin, subcutaneous tissues, bone, etc., may be asso-ciated with some disturbance of the sympathetic nervous system. This, too, how-ever, may have central origin, and there may be involvement of the higher centers which leads to increased and unregulated activity of the lower centers.

Irritative Motor Phenomena: Irritation of the facial nerve causes abnormal motor manifestations rather than paralysis. *Localized,* or *jacksonian, convulsive attacks* occur with irritative lesions of the cortical center in the prerolandic convolu-tion; tonic spasm or clonic movements of the contralateral facial muscles may be accompanied or followed by similar movements of the arm or leg or a conju-gate turning of the head and eyes. *Disease of the basal ganglia* or extrapyramidal system can cause various hyperkinesias of the facial muscles—choreiform, athetoid, dystonic, grimacing, or myoclonic movements. Tremors of the face may accompany the masking of parkinsonism.

Irritation of the nucleus or of the nerve itself may cause contraction of the face, or *spasm* of the facial muscles. A facial spasm on one side with a pyramidal paralysis opposite is called *Brissaud's syndrome;* this is said to occur in the presence of irrita-

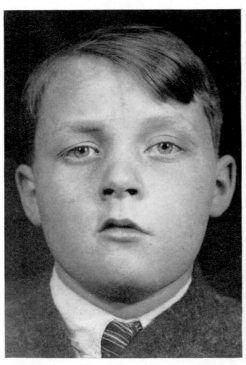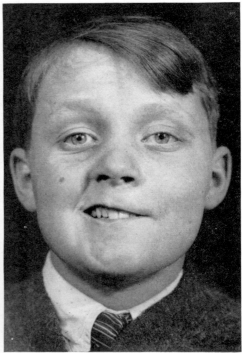

Fig. 88.   Right facial hemiatrophy, showing scleroderma and alopecia.

tion of the facial nucleus, and is usually due to an inflammatory or neoplastic process. Irritation of the facial nerve anywhere along its course may cause spasm of the muscles it supplies. Reflex spasm may be a result of pain in the involved side of the face or irritation of the trigeminal nerve. Such spasm is sometimes seen with dental infections, tic douloureux, other painful affections of the face, and diseases of the parotoid gland and mastoid. In *Chvostek's sign* (see p. 245) there is marked hyperirritability of the facial nerves and muscles. In the *risus sardonicus* of tetanus there is increased activity of the muscles supplied by the facial nerve.

Abnormal associated or *synkinetic movements* resulting in *facial spasm*s and even *facial contracture* may follow incomplete or faulty regeneration of the seventh nerve consequent to a peripheral type of palsy. It may first be noted that voluntary efforts to close the eye are accompanied by associated elevation of the corner of the mouth, contraction of the platysma, or wrinkling of the forehead; on baring the teeth there is an associated closing of the ipsilateral eye. These may be termed *abnormal associated movements*. If the disorder progresses, the patient may exhibit a more or less rhythmic elevation of the corner of the mouth; on close inspection, however, it may be seen that this movement is synchronous with rhythmic blinking of the eye, and it may be noted that movements of the mouth, as in talking and smiling, are accompanied by narrowing of the palpebral fissure on the same side. These movements may progress to a stage of *facial spasm,* with repetitive, hyperkinetic, recurrent, spasmodic, clonic and occasionally tonic contractions of the muscles of the involved side of the face. The mouth twists to the affected side, the nasolabial folds deepens, the eye closes, and there is contraction of the frontalis muscle (Fig. 89). The spasm may involve the entire nerve or only certain branches; it may be propagated from one branch to another. Instead of spasm, there may be a *facial contracture;* here one observes, instead of weakness of the involved side of the face, an apparent overactivity, with wrinkling of the forehead, narrowing of the palpebral fissure, drawing up or twisting of the angle of the mouth, and increased depth of the nasolabial fold. On casual inspection of a patient who has a facial contracture following a facial paralysis, one may gain the faulty impression that there is weakness instead of the opposite side. Careful testing, however, will show that the affected muscles are still somewhat paretic, even though in a state of contracture. It is generally believed that faulty regeneration or misdirection of outgrowth of regenerating fibers is responsible for the above phenomena; some fibers destined for the orbicularis oculi go to the orbicularis oris, and vice versa. Some observers do not accept this explanation, however, and express the belief that these are release phenomena resulting from either a central or a nuclear lesion. Both the postparalytic and the more rare "cryptogenic" hemifacial spasms have on occasion been relieved either temporarily or permanently by neurolysis or decompression of the facial nerve. Section of the nerve will relieve the spasm but cause a permanent motor defect, but selective neurotomy of the branches most affected may afford relief without causing a significant motor deficit.

A true facial spasm, which is an organic condition, should be differentiated from the *tic,* or *habit spasm,* which is not organically initiated. In the latter there may be retraction of the angle of the mouth or contraction of the orbicularis oculi, which may resemble that in the true spasm, but the movements are somewhat more bizarre

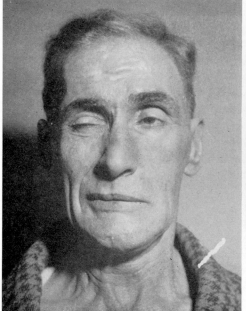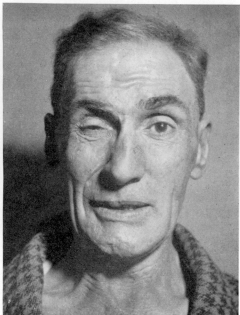

FIG. 89. Facial spasm following right peripheral facial paralysis: *Left,* patient voluntarily closing the eye; *Right,* patient voluntarily retracting the angle of the mouth.

and more purposeful, and other muscles aside from those supplied by the facial nerve are brought into action. The eyebrow may be depressed instead of elevated. *Blepharospasm,* or nictitating spasm, is characterized by movements which involve principally the orbicularis oculi and frontalis muscles. This may start as a reflex response, associated with the presence of a foreign body in the eye, but may continue as a habit spasm. Bizarre grimacing movements of the face are also often habit spasms. Another type of reflex blepharospasm occurs in patients with organic brain disease and may appear following a cerebrovascular accident; voluntary opening of the eye is not impaired, but there is an exaggerated blink response to sensory and threatening stimuli. When this occurs the examiner may have difficulty carrying out the ophthalmoscopic examination, because the stimulus of lifting the lid or focusing light in the eye causes an involuntary closing of the palpebral fissure. Blepharospasm may also be present in photophobia and in postencephalitic parkinsonism.

Tremors of the face may be diagnostic of certain conditions. Perioral tremors are frequently seen in general paresis and alcoholism. General facial tremors, especially of the eyelids, occur in psychogenic states. In Rosenbach's sign, seen in both hyperthyroidism and hysteria, there is a fine tremor of the closed eyelids. Fascicular tremors are present in progressive bulbar palsy and amyotrophic lateral sclerosis. There also may be choreiform, athetoid, myoclonic, and myokymic movements of the face.

Sensory Involvement: Sensory phenomena are less frequently associated with lesions of the facial nerve than motor phenomena, and are less easily diagnosed. Loss of exteroceptive, general visceral, and proprioceptive sensations may not be apparent to the patient and may not be elicited by the examination procedures.

In destructive lesions of the geniculate ganglion, or of the chorda tympani or the facial nerve central to its departure, there is loss of taste on the anterior two thirds of the tongue on the involved side; in irritative lesions there is *geniculate neuralgia*. with paroxysmal bouts of pain, first deep in the ear, later radiating to the face. "Tic douloureux of the chorda tympani" has also been described. In lesions of the lingual nerve there is loss of taste together with loss of exteroceptive sensation on the involved side of the tongue, and there is usually subjective numbness. Bilateral ageusia has been described in unilateral facial palsy; parageusias have been reported following recovery from Bell's palsy.

In *herpes zoster oticus,* or the *Ramsay Hunt syndrome,* there is, in addition to the peripheral facial paralysis and the sensory and secretory abnormalities described (loss of taste on the anterior two thirds of the tongue, hyperacusis, and diminution of salivary and lacrimal secretion), pain behind and in the ear, and there may be vesicles on the tympanum and in the external auditory canal, and also on the lateral surface of the pinna and in the cleft between the auricle and the mastoid process. Hunt has described two varieties of the syndrome—the otalgic form of geniculate neuralgia with pain in the ear, and the prosopalgic form with pain deep in the face, principally in the posterior orbital, palatal, and nasal regions. This latter variety is said to be the result of involvement of the sensory fibers which are carried through the greater superficial petrosal nerve to the sphenopalatine ganglion. Deep geniculate prosopalgia is usually accompanied by geniculate otalgia. More recent observers, however (Denny-Brown, *et al.*), on the basis of pathologic studies, doubt the presence of a true geniculate ganglionitis, and they express the belief that the herpes zoster syndromes accompanied by palsy of the facial nerve are dependent upon the concurrent involvement of two or more cranial nerves, including the acoustic and trigeminal, and possibly involvement of the cervical nerves.

There is said to be no loss of sensation in central lesions, but there may be parageusias or perversions of taste or gustatory hallucinations. Hypergeusia and parageusias may be characteristic of certain psychoses and of hysterical states. Gustatory hallucinations may occur in tumors of or near the region of the uncinate or hippocampal gyri or the parietal operculum, or as a part of a seizure of the so-called psychomotor or temporal lobe variety. Thus they are valuable in cerebral localization. There may be associated smacking of the lips and chewing movements before or during loss of consciousness in psychomotor seizures. Frequently gustatory and olfactory hallucinations occur together. Bender has demonstrated extinction of taste sensation on double simultaneous stimulation in a patient with a parieto-occipital tumor, although the taste threshold was normal with single stimulations. Elderly persons sometimes complain of either loss of taste or disagreeable tastes which may lead to anorexia. In pernicious anemia there may be perversions or loss of taste for certain foods. In both diabetes and familial dysautonomia abnormalities of the taste threshold have been described. Some drugs, such as thiouracil, cause loss of taste. Inability to taste phenylthiocarbamide is a mendelian recessive trait.

Secretory Changes: Abnormalities of secretory function may be produced by lesions of the facial nerve. Peripheral involvement of nervus intermedius, the greater superficial petrosal nerve, the chorda tympani, or of the sphenopalatine or submaxillary ganglia may cause diminution or loss of lacrimal, salivary, or mucous secretion. There may also be vasomotor changes. Irritative lesions of the brain stem at the level of the superior salivatory nucleus may cause an increase in secretion, whereas destructive lesions may cause a decrease in flow. There is never absence of salivation, however, unless there are bilateral lesions. Changes in secretion may also be the result of central lesions, especially those involving the hypothalamus or the autonomic connections. Irritation of the rostral end of the hypothalamus produces an increase in salivation, whereas irritative lesions of the posterior end or destructive lesions of the rostral regions cause a decrease in salivary flow with dry mouth and perversions of taste. Sialorrhea, hydrostomia, or ptyalism are conditions in which there is an excess of saliva. Sialorrhea is somewhat characteristic of Parkinson's disease. There is also ptyalism in the various types of bulbar palsy; this may be caused by excessive secretion of saliva or may be due to inability to swallow. Atropine and other drugs used in the treatment of Parkinson's disease often cause an unpleasantly dry mouth. In *Sjögren's syndrome* there is deficient secretion of the lacrimal, salivary, and mucosal glands, with resulting keratoconjunctivitis and dryness of the mouth and upper respiratory tract.

An increase or decrease in lacrimal or salivary secretion may occur on a psychogenic basis. Lacrimation, of course, is most frequently the result of a psychic stimulus. The secretion of saliva may be stimulated, not only by the smell or taste of food, but also by the thought or sight of food. Excitement may produce an increase in saliva; in nausea there is increased salivation. Depressed and anxious patients often complain of decrease in salivation with dry mouth and perversions or loss of taste. An abnormal dryness of the mouth, of either central or peripheral origin, is referred to as *xerostomia.*

The *syndrome of crocodile tears* is an unusual residual of a peripheral facial palsy. It is a paradoxic gustatory-lacrimal reflex, and is characterized by the appearance of tears when strongly flavored foods are placed on the tongue. It is probably due to a faulty regeneration of the nerve fibers, in which filaments having to do with salivary secretion have grown along the pathway to the lacrimal gland. There may be abnormal local irritability of cholinergic fibers. The condition has been treated by section of the greater superficial petrosal nerve. In the chorda tympani syndrome there is unilateral sweating and flushing in the submental region after eating. The somewhat similar auriculotemporal syndrome is discussed in Chapter 12.

REFERENCES

BENDER, M. B., and FELDMAN, D. S. Extinction of taste sensation on double simultaneous stimulation. *Neurology* 2:195, 1952.

BLATT, I. M. Bell's palsy: Diagnosis and prognosis of idiopathic paralysis by submaxillary salivary gland flow and chorda tympani nerve testing. *Laryngoscope* 75: 1081, 1965.

BLUM, M., WALKER, A. E., and RUCH, T. C. Localization of taste in the thalamus of Macaca Mulatta. *Yale J. Biol. & Med.* 16:175, 1943.

BÖRNSTEIN, W. S. Cortical representation of taste in man and monkey: I. Functional and anatomical relations of taste, olfaction, and somatic sensibility. *Yale J. Biol. & Med.* 12:719, 1940; II. The localization of the cortical taste area in man and a method of measuring impairment of taste in man. *Ibid.,* 13:133, 1940.

BOYER, F. C., and GARDNER, W. J. Paroxysmal lacrimation (syndrome of crocodile tears) and its surgical treatment. *Arch. Neurol. & Psychiat.* 61:56, 1949.

BUCHTHAL, F. Electromyography in paralysis of the facial nerve. *Arch. Otolaryng.* 81:463, 1965.

CLARK, E. C., and DODGE, H. W., JR. Extraolfactory components of flavor. *J.A.M.A.* 159:1721, 1955.

DASTUR, D. K. The relationship between terminal lingual innervation and gustation. *Brain.* 84:499, 1962.

DENNY-BROWN, D., ADAMS, R. D., and FITZGERALD, P. J. Pathologic features of herpes zoster: A note on "geniculate herpes." *Arch. Neurol. & Psychiat.* 51:216, 1944.

FISHER, C. M. Reflex blepharospasm. *Neurology* 13:77, 1963.

FURSTENBERG, A. C., and CROSBY, E. C. Disturbance of the function of salivary glands. *Ann. Otol., Rhin. & Laryng.* 54:243, 1945.

GARDNER, W. J., and SAVA, G. A. Hemifacial spasm—A reversible pathophysiologic state. *J. Neurosurg.* 19:240, 1962.

GORMAN, W. Flavor, Taste and the Psychology of Smell. Springfield, Ill., Charles C Thomas, 1964.

HUNT, J. R. On herpetic inflammations of the geniculate ganglion: A new syndrome and its complications. *J. Nerv. & Ment. Dis.* 34:73, 1907.

KETTEL, K. Melkersson's syndrome. *Arch. Otolaryng.* 46:341, 1947.

KRARUP, B. On the technique of gustatory examination. *Acta oto-laryng.,* Supp. 140, 1958, p. 195; Electro-gustometry: A method for clinical taste examination. *Acta oto-laryng.* 49:294, 1958.

KUGELBERG, E. The mechanism of Chvostek's sign. *A. M. A. Arch. Neurol. & Psychiat.* 65:511, 1951; Facial reflexes. *Brain* 75:385, 1952.

LAUMANS, E. P. J. Nerve excitability tests in facial paralysis. *Arch. Otolaryng.* 81:478, 1965.

LITTLE, S. C. Abnormal Movements of the Face. University, Ala., University of Alabama Press, 1954.

LITTON, W. B., and WORK, W. D. Otoneurology in otorhinolaryngology. *Univ. of Michigan Med. Center J.* 30:283, 1964.

MacKENZIE, I. C. K. A simple method for testing taste. Lancet 1:377, 1955.

MONRAD-KROHN, G. H. On the dissociation of voluntary and emotional innervation in facial paresis of central origin. *Brain* 47:22, 1924.

PEIRIS, O. A., and MILES, D. W. Galvanic stimulation of the tongue as a prognostic index in Bell's palsy. *Brit. M. J.* 2:1162, 1965.

PFAFFMANN, C. "The sense of Taste," in FIELD, J., MAGOUN, H. W., and HALL, V. E. (eds.), Handbook of Physiology. Washington, D.C., American Physiological Society, 1959, Vol. 1, pp. 507–533.

SOGG, R. L., HOYT, W. F., and BOLDREY, E. Spastic paretic facial contracture: A rare sign of brain tumor. *Neurology* 13:607, 1963.

266 THE NEUROLOGIC EXAMINATION

SzENTÁGOTHAI, J. The representation of facial and scalp muscles in the facial nucleus. *J. Comp. Neurol.* 88:207, 1948.

TAVERNER, D. Electrodiagnosis in Bell's palsy. *Arch. Otolaryng.* 81:470, 1965.

WARTENBERG, R. A sign of facial palsy. *Arch. Neurol. & Psychiat.* 41:586, 1939; Progressive facial hemiatrophy. *Ibid.,* 54:75, 1945; Associated movements in the oculomotor and facial muscles. *Ibid.,* 55:439, 1946; Hemifacial Spasm: A Clinical and Pathophysiological Study. New York, Oxford University Press, 1952.

WEIL, A. A., and NOSIK, W. A. Electrophysiologic and clinical observations in hemifacial spasms. *Neurology* 6:381, 1956.

WEINGROW, S. M. Facial reflexes. *Arch. Pediat.* 50:234, 1937.

ZWIELOCKI, J. Some inpendence measurements on normal and pathological ears. *J. Accoust. Soc. America* 29:1312, 1957.

CHAPTER 14

THE ACOUSTIC NERVE

THE EIGHTH CRANIAL, *acoustic,* or *auditory, nerve* is composed of two fiber systems which are blended into a single nerve trunk. These are the *cochlear nerve,* or the nerve of hearing, and the *vestibular nerve,* which subserves equilibration, coordination, and orientation in space. These nerves originate in separate peripheral receptors and have distinct central connections. Even though they are united along their course through the skull, they differ so greatly both in their anatomic relationships and in their respective functions that they should be considered as separate nerves.

THE COCHLEAR NERVE
ANATOMY AND PHYSIOLOGY

The receptors, or end organs, of the cochlear nerve are the hair cells, or auditory cells, in the organ of Corti, within the cochlea of the internal ear. Impulses are carried to the bipolar cells of the spiral ganglia of the cochlea, from which the central fibers pass as the cochlear nerve. This traverses the internal auditory meatus, where it is lateral and inferior to the facial nerve; it crosses the subarachnoid space between the pons and medulla, and enters the upper medulla at its junction with the pons (Fig. 90). Its neuraxes pass around the restiform body to terminate on the dorsal and ventral cochlear nuclei at the dorsolateral and ventrolateral aspects of this body in the lower pons. Fibers from the dorsal cochlear nucleus cross the floor of the fourth ventricle under the striae medullares acousticae (fibers of Piccolomini to the cerebellum), after which they pass ventrally into the pons, near the superior olivary nucleus, to terminate on the lateral lemniscus of the opposite side (Fig. 91). Some of the fibers from the ventral nucleus cross the pons as trapezoid fibers to the contralateral lateral lemniscus, and others communicate with the ipsilateral and contralateral olivary bodies, and through them with the nuclei of the third, fourth, and sixth cranial nerves. There are also communications with the nucleus of the trapezoid

267

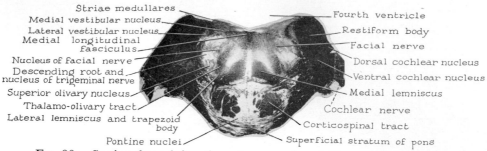

Striae medullares
Medial vestibular nucleus
Lateral vestibular nucleus
Medial longitudinal fasciculus
Nucleus of facial nerve
Descending root and nucleus of trigeminal nerve
Superior olivary nucleus
Thalamo-olivary tract
Lateral lemniscus and trapezoid body
Pontine nuclei

Fourth ventricle
Restiform body
Facial nerve
Dorsal cochlear nucleus
Ventral cochlear nucleus
Medial lemniscus
Cochlear nerve
Corticospinal tract
Superficial stratum of pons

FIG. 90.   Section through junction of pons and medulla at level of cochlear nuclei.

body and the nucleus of the lateral lemniscus. A few fibers from each cochlear nucleus, especially the dorsal, pass to the ipsilateral lateral lemniscus. The lateral lemnisci ascend to the inferior colliculus (posterior quadrigeminal body) and the medial geniculate body. The former is an auditory reflex center, and the fibers from the latter, a station in the central auditory pathway, pass through the posterior limb of the internal capsule as auditory radiations to terminate on the cortex of the transverse temporal convolutions (Heschl), especially the anterior part, and the adjacent portion of the superior temporal convolution.

The cochlear nerve has but one function, that of hearing. Sound waves stimulate the special sensory receptors in the organ of Corti; impulses are carried along the nerve to the cochlear nuclei, and then centrally to terminate on the auditory cortex in the temporal lobes of the same and the opposite sides. It is not within the scope of this work to discuss in any detail the physics of sound or the physiology of sound conduction or recognition. Suffice it to say, however, that sound is a form of motion produced by some vibrating medium. A sound wave is a series or chain of alternate condensations and rarefactions in the surrounding air, by which the vibratory movements of the sounding body are conveyed to the tympanic membrane of the ear and then transmitted by the auditory ossicles to the inner ear. The *pitch,* or relative position of sound in the musical scale, depends upon the frequency or rapidity with which the vibrations follow one another. The pitch is raised as the number of vibrations per second is increased. The human ear normally appreciates and recognizes tones of between 8 to 16 and 30,000 to 35,000 vibrations per second. The *intensity* with which a sound wave impresses the perceptive mechanism depends upon the amplitude of vibration. There is a physical law which declares that the intensity of sound is proportional to the square of the amplitude. The *quality,* or *timbre,* is that property of sound by which one distinguishes between two tones of the same pitch or intensity. Sound is brought to the organ of hearing in two ways. It is conveyed by *air conduction* when the vibrating body is at some variable distance from the ear and the sound waves are transmitted through the medium of the surrounding air into the external auditory meatus and to the tympanic membrane. It is conveyed by *bone conduction* when the vibrating medium is in contact with the skull or the bones of the body, and waves are transmitted through the medium of the cranial bones.

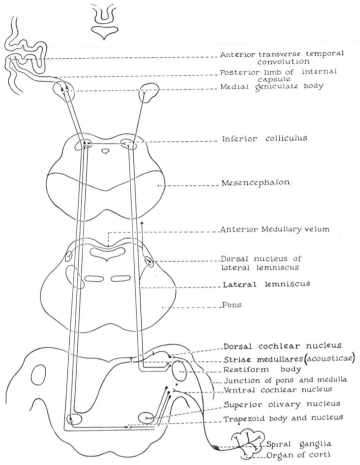

Anterior transverse temporal convolution
Posterior limb of internal capsule
Medial geniculate body
Inferior colliculus
Mesencephalon
Anterior Medullary velum
Dorsal nucleus of lateral lemniscus
Lateral lemniscus
Pons
Dorsal cochlear nucleus
Striae medullares (acousticae)
Restiform body
Junction of pons and medulla
Ventral cochlear nucleus
Superior olivary nucleus
Trapezoid body and nucleus
Spiral ganglia
Organ of corti

FIG. 91.   The cochlear pathway.

CLINICAL EXAMINATION

Hearing is tested in a variety of ways. Much information may be obtained by observation of the patient. His ability to understand soft and loud tones and low and high pitches is noted. Signs of deafness, such as a tendency to turn the head in listening, lip reading, speaking with a loud voice, or inability to hear high or low tones, may give valuable information. If there is any history of difficulty in hearing, or if hearing tests are to be made, the external auditory canal should be examined with an otoscope to eliminate the presence of wax, pus, blood, foreign bodies, and exudate, and to determine whether the tympanic membrane is intact. The mastoid region should be examined for swelling and tenderness.

In carrying out tests of hearing, the examiner may first note the distance from each ear at which the subject is able to hear either the *whispered* or the *spoken voice*. In carrying out the test one ear is kept closed, preferably with the moistened tip of the little finger, and the patient's head is turned so that he cannot see the examiner's lips. It is said that a whisper, if used, should be so light that the thyroid cartilage does not vibrate. This test, however, is not very accurate, since the intensity and pitch of the voice varies in individuals, and in the same individual from time time. It must be recalled that certain tones are heard more loudly and at a greater distance than others. Sibilants and the short vowels such as *a, e, i,* are heard at a greater distance than broad consonants such as *l, m, n,* and *r,* and such vowels as *o* and *u*. "Seventy-six" and "sixty-seven" can be heard at a greater distance than "ninety-nine" and "fifty-three." Monosyllables should be used rather than stock questions, such as "How are you," for hearing a single word of a group may enable the patient to understand the entire question. Words and numbers should be used alternately. The voice test is inaccurate, but since it is more important to hear the human voice than any other sound, it may be more valuable from a practical point of view to test acuity for the spoken voice than to measure hearing accurately in terms of intensity or decibels. The voice test, if properly applied, can be useful and reliable.

Hearing may be tested by noting the patient's ability to perceive the noise made when the examiner rubs his thumb and index finger together in front of the external auditory meatus, but for more critical evaluation a *watch* is used. This is first held outside the range of hearing of one ear while the other one is closed; it is then brought toward the ear until the patient is first able to hear it tick. The distance from the ear is noted, and the examiner compares the patient's acuity of hearing with his own. It is important to recall that because watches differ in size and form and in the thickness of the case, any examiner, if he wishes to use a watch as a standard, should consistently use the same one. Inasmuch as the sound of a watch is high pitched, this test is impractical in nerve deafness and in testing hearing in elderly individuals. Some acuity for high tones is lost as early as the fifth decade. The Politzer's acoumeter, an instrument which gives a clicking sound similar to that of a watch but louder, may be used if the patient is unable to hear a watch. For testing high tones the monochord, the range of which extends to 20,000 vibrations, or the Galton whistle (42,048 vibrations) is sometimes employed.

The use of a *tuning fork* also gives more specific information. The examiner may compare the patient's hearing with his own and note the patient's relative auditory acuity on each side. Air conduction is tested by placing the tuning fork in front of the external auditory meatus, and bone conduction by placing it on the mastoid process. Both the intensity, or quantity, of the sound and the duration are noted. In evaluating bone conduction, one must be certain that the patient *hears* the tuning fork rather than feels its vibration. In the *Schwabach test* a tuning fork of 128, 256, or 512 vibrations per second (C^0, C^1, C^2) is used, and the patient's bone conduction is compared with that of the examiner. The 512 tuning fork is preferred for this test because the subject is more apt to hear it than feel its vibrations. The duration of perception of tone is noted; the vibrating tuning fork is placed against the patient's mastoid process until he no longer hears it, and then is transferred to the observer's mastoid. The test can then be repeated for evaluation of air conduction.

In the *Rinné test* the patient's air conduction and bone conduction are compared. The tuning fork is placed firmly against the mastoid process and the patient is asked to indicate when he no longer hears it; it is then placed in front of the external auditory meatus, and the period of time during which it is heard there is noted. In the normal individual, or in the *positive Rinné,* the tuning fork is heard twice as long by air as by bone conduction. In conductive deafness, the *Rinné* is *negative*; air conduction is diminished and bone conduction is retained, and the fork is heard better when it is placed over the mastoid process. Often in deafness of this type the bone conduction may even be exaggerated beyond the normal, due to the fact that occlusion of the external auditory meatus converts the cavity of the middle ear into a resonating chamber. In sensorineural deafness both bone and air conduction are diminished, but they retain their normal relationship and the Rinné is positive; if the deafness is severe, however, the bone conduction may be absent.

The *Weber test* is carried out by placing a vibrating tuning fork over the forehead or the vertex of the skull. In the normal individual this is heard equally well in both ears, or is not lateralized. If one ear is occluded, it is heard better or more loudly on that side. In conductive deafness the sound is lateralized to the involved side, and the Weber test is said to be *positive*. In sensorineural deafness the fork is heard by the uninvolved ear, or the Weber test is *negative*.

In testing loss of hearing throughout a wide range of pitch, a series of tuning forks varying from 64 to 2048 double vibrations per second (C^{-1} to C^4) may be used, but this is a complicated and often an unsatisfactory procedure.

For an accurate, quantitative test of hearing, the electric *audiometer* is used and an audiogram is made (Fig. 92). By means of this instrument, "pure tones" are

FIG. 92.   Electric audiometer. (The Microtone Company).

produced as musical notes which vary in frequency of vibration, or pitch, and the intensity, or loudness, may be varied at any frequency. The vibrations are produced by means of electrical oscillators, and an ordinary telephone receiver transforms the electrical energy of the audiometer into sound waves which are conveyed by air conduction through the external auditory meatus. For bone conduction an especially constructed receiver is provided. The normal range of hearing is said to be from 8 to 16 vibrations per second to 32,768, or some eleven or twelve octaves, although few adults, especially in late life, are able to hear above 16,000 vibrations per second. With the audiometer, frequencies of from 128 to 11,584, calibrated in octaves or half octaves, are tested. This includes the normal speech range, which is from about 200 to 3000 vibrations per second. The ear is normally more sensitive to the middle of the pitch range where the practical hearing range is situated. Both air and bone conduction are tested, first without masking and then with one ear masked by producing a sound in it so that it cannot perceive the stimulus that is being directed to the opposite ear. The masking is done by an electric buzzer, the intensity of which may be varied by calibrated steps. It may not be possible to eliminate the normal ear if it has forty decibels more hearing than the ear being tested. Audiometric examinations should be carried out in sound proof rooms or with the use of rubber receiver caps if such rooms are not practicable.

Intensities of sound on the audiometer are measured in dynes per square centimeter, and loss in ability to detect tones is charted in decibels. The amount of loss of hearing throughout in various ranges may thus be charted in a curve. The audiometer and the audiogram not only are important as aids in the detection and differentiation of acoustic deficiencies and in the recognition of obscure perceptive defects, but they are also valuable in affording a permanent record which is of aid in evaluating the progress of a hearing defect and its response to treatment, and in the prescribing of hearing aids. The audiometer has in general supplanted the watch, acoumeter, tuning fork, rods, bells, and whistles in the testing of hearing. It must be stated, however, that there are many varieties of audiometers, and that the instruments, or the interpretation of them, may not be without error. The making of an accurate audiogram takes patience and observation, and hastily made audiometric records may be valueless. In spite of the scientific accuracy of the instruments, the human element enters in.

In testing large numbers of people, especially in the examination of school children, the "group audiometer" is sometimes used. This is a phonograph with an electric "pick-up" to which as many as forty earpieces can be connected. Recordings of monosyllables or of numbers at different pitches are played, and the subjects are asked to write down those that they hear. Thus the number of mistakes or omissions shows the hearing defect.

Additional acoustical procedures are valuable in the differentiation of certain types of deafness. These are usually carried out by the otologist or audiologist, and include the following: speech audiometry, including determination of the speech reception threshold and speech discrimination score; Fowler's binaural loudness balance test and determination of the loudness recruitment phenomenon; testing of auditory adaption and fatigue and tone decay; the use of various modifications of the von Békésy continuous frequency automatic audiometer; determination of the short increment sensitivity index and of the comfortable and uncomfortable loudness levels; appraisal of sound localization; electrophysiologic testing, including determination of the psychogalvanic skin response. Special tests for psychogenic deafness are described in Chapter 56.

It should be stressed again that the ability to hear and understand the human voice is the most important functional aspect of audition. In certain types of deafness that are clinically significant the pure tone and even the speech thresholds are normal, but there is a decrease of speech discrimination.

In the evaluation of hearing in the infant, in semicomatose individuals, in hysteria, and in malingering, certain reflex responses may be utilized. The *auditory-palpebral,* *auro-* or *acousticopalpebral, cochleopalpebral,* or *cochleo-orbicularis reflex* consists of a slight blink, or contraction of the eyelids (more marked on the ipsilateral side) or even a reflex closing of the eyes in response to a loud, sudden noise. The *cochleo-pupillary reflex* is either a dilatation of the pupils, or a contraction followed by dilatation, in response to a loud noise. The *auditory-oculogyric reflex* consists of a deviation of the eyes in the direction of a sound. The *general acoustic muscle reflex* is a generalized jerking of the body in response to a loud, sudden sound.

DISORDERS OF FUNCTION

Disturbances in the function of the cochlear nerve and its connections are usually manifested by either diminution or loss of hearing (hypacusis or anacusis), with or without tinnitus. More rarely there may be such disturbances as hyperacusis, paracusis, auditory hallucinations, or auditory aphasia. There are two principal varieties of hearing loss: *sensorineural* (also known as *nerve* or *perceptive*) *deafness* due to disease of the cochlea, the cochlear nerve or its nuclei, or the central pathways concerned with hearing; and *conductive* (also known as *obstructive* or *transmission*) *deafness* due to interference with transmission of sound to the cochlea, usually the result of obstruction of the external auditory canal or disease of the middle ear.

In *sensorineural deafness* air and bone conduction are both diminished, but they may retain their normal relationship so that the Rinné is positive, the Schwabach is shortened, and the Weber is negative, or is referred to the sound side. The hearing loss is especially marked for the higher tones as tested by the audiometer (Fig. 93) or by Galton's whistle, and the individual has most difficulty with sibilants, sharp consonants, and short vowels. He has special difficulty with the letters *s* and *t* and the vowels *e, a,* and *i,* and will show loss of ability to recognize such words as *sister, fish, twenty, water,* and *date.* Occasionally the audiogram will show loss of only certain ranges of speech, with "islands" in the chart (Fig. 94). In elderly individuals there is often a progressive loss of high tones, called *presbycusis,* that indicates an increasing sensorineural defect. This may not involve serviceable hearing at the outset, and may not be noticed by the patient until the loss reaches the 2,048 vibration range (Fig. 95).

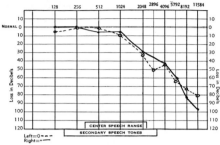

FIG. 93. Audiogram in patient with sensorineural deafness.

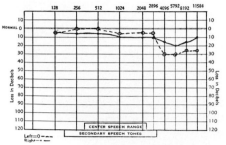

FIG. 94. Audiogram in patient with early sensorineural deafness not affecting serviceable hearing.

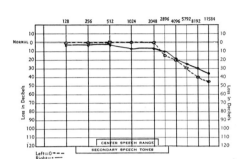

FIG. 95. Audiogram in patient with presbycusis.

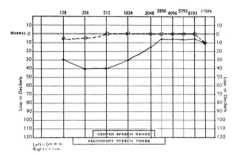

FIG. 96. Audiogram showing the auditory defect in a case of conductive deafness.

Ancillary diagnostic testing may be used to differentiate sensorineural hearing loss due to disease of the cochlea or inner ear (end organ deafness) from that secondary to involvement of the nerve itself or more central structures (retrocochlear deafness). In the former the following may be found: loss of acuity for pure tones with parallel impairment of speech discrimination; recruitment of loudness, especially for tones of high frequency; near superposition of normal amplitudes of pulsed and steady tone Békésy tracings (type II Békésy audiogram) (Fig. 97); a positive short increment sensitivity index; absence of significant tone decay; a lowered overload threshold but no threshold fatigue; diplacusis. With retrocochlear deafness the following are present: more loss of discrimination for speech than for pure tones; absence of or reverse recruitment; absent or minimal short increment sensitivity responses; more impairment in the ability to hear continuous rather than pulsed tones in Békésy recordings (type III and IV Békésy audiograms); abnormal auditory adaptation by tone decay test; abnormal spread of masking; threshold fatigue.

In *conductive deafness* there is primarily a loss of air conduction, and bone conduction may be preserved or even exaggerated; consequently the Rinné is negative. The Schwabach is shortened; the Weber is referred to the involved side, or is positive. Low tones are lost, as are some of the broad or flat consonants and vowels such as *m, n, l, r, o,* and *u,* but in general speech discrimination is quite good and parallels the loss for pure tones. The hearing loss is usually in the range of from 128 to 1,024 vibrations, and in pure conductive defects there is rarely loss of more than twenty to thirty decibels in this range (Fig. 96). There is no recruitment, tone decay is within normal range, and short increment sensitivity responses are absent or minimal. The pulsed and continuous tones are interwoven (type I Békésy audiogram).

One should always attempt to determine the type of deafness, but it is necessary to remember that there may be combined deafness with both nerve and middle ear involvement. If there is loss of over twenty-five to thirty decibels, affecting both the higher and lower ranges, there is a mixed type of deafness with both conductive and sensorineural involvement (Fig. 98).

In deafness due to *otosclerosis* there is usually very gradual but progressive bilateral impairment of hearing. This condition is an hereditary one, characterized by replacement of the normal compact bone of the otic capsule by cancellous bone, causing deafness when there is obliteration of the oval window and immobilization of the stapes. Secondary changes may cause gradual degeneration of the fibers of the cochlear nerve and alterations in the organ of Corti. Early in the course of the disease there may be either loss only of low tones or mild impairment of hearing throughout the entire range with preserved bone conduction and a negative Rinné, suggesting a conductive hearing loss. With the development of secondary changes, however, there is increasing loss of higher tones as well, and evidences of an associated sensorineural type of deafness (Fig. 99). Otosclerosis is further characterized

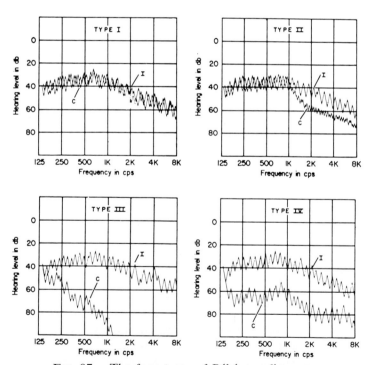

FIG. 97.   The four types of Békésy audiograms.

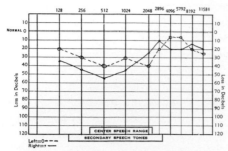 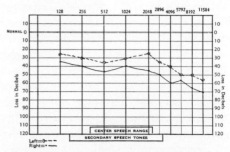

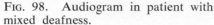

FIG. 98. Audiogram in patient with mixed deafness.

FIG. 99. Audiogram in patient with far-advanced otosclerosis.

by severe and persistent tinnitus without vertigo and by *paracusis willisiana,* or the ability to hear better in the presence of loud noises. This differentiates the condition from nerve deafness, for most patients with involvement of the cochlear nerve complain of profound inability to hear in the presence of noise.

Tinnitus aurium is characterized by the perception of abnormal sounds in the ear. It is a sensation of noise caused by the abnormal excitation of the auditory apparatus or its afferent pathways. It may vary in pitch and intensity, and may be continuous or intermittent. It is described in different instances as a singing, ringing, buzzing, blowing, whistling, humming, beating, pounding, ticking, swishing, or roaring sound. Tinnitus is commonly associated with deafness. It may be present in either conductive or sensorineural deafness, and is a constant accompaniment of otosclerosis. Various factors may be responsible for the different types of tinnitus, and the mechanism underlying many types is not known. Stimulation or irritation of the diseased nerve or central pathways may cause the symptom, much as irritation of a peripheral nerve or afferent pathways causes paresthesias; total deafness then could be likened to the anesthesia that is produced by interruption of the continuity of the nerve.

Tinnitus due to external factors may be caused by wax or water in the external auditory canal or obstruction of the eustachian tube. It may be present in acute otitis media, and persist after the infection has subsided. It is most commonly associated with irritation or disease of the cochlea, the cochlear nerve or nuclei, or the supranuclear pathways and centers, and is found in circulatory disturbances of the internal ear or the central connections, as in anemia, arteriosclerosis, or hyperpiesia, and in toxic and inflammatory involvement of the cochlear nerve. Tinnitus is frequently found in presbycusis and in other types of sensorineural deafness. It may disappear by the time the deafness is complete, but may become apparent even before the deafness is noted, and increase after hearing is lost. Occasionally the symptom itself interferes with hearing. Tinnitus is often more noticeable at night when objective noises are diminished, and may interfere with sleep. To the patient it may be more distressing than the accompanying deafness, and may cause marked depression in elderly individuals. Occasionally patients prefer to have the eighth nerve sectioned, with resulting complete and permanent loss of hearing, rather than to subject themselves to the constant noises.

In the evaluation of tinnitus, an attempt should be made to determine its type and pitch, and to learn whether it seems to come from one or both ears, or to arise within the head without localization. Tinnitus associated with conductive hearing loss is said to be low pitched, while that associated with sensorineural loss may be of higher or of any pitch. Loudness of tinnitus is not related to type of hearing loss. True or intrinsic tinnitus, which is always associated with impaired hearing, should be differentiated from so-called extrinsic tinnitus, caused by extraneous noises. A pulsating or intermittent tinnitus synchronous with the pulse may be present with hypertension or arteriosclerosis, but is more often associated with angiomas or aneurysms of the internal carotid and vertebral arteries. It is in reality a bruit rather than a tinnitus, and is occasionally relieved by compression of the internal carotid artery. Muscle spasm, contraction of the tensor tympani, nasopharyngeal sounds, and "clicking jaw" may also simulate tinnitus. Disease of the temporal cortex, principally that associated with arteriosclerosis, hypertension, or cerebral anemia or hyperemia, may cause the perception of abnormal sounds which, however, are more complex than those perceived in a true tinnitus and may even take the form of *auditory hallucinations*. Tinnitus may be psychogenic.

Hyperacusis, or pathologic increase in auditory acuity, occurs with paralysis of the stapedius muscle, but is also present in the aura of an epileptic attack, in migraine, and in certain psychic states, especially the psychoneuroses. *Dysacusis* is impairment of hearing that is not primarily a loss of auditory sensitivity. *Diplacusis* is of two types. In the binaural type there is an apparent difference in the pitch or intensity of the same sound as heard in the two ears. The type in which a single sound is heard as two or as a group of sounds may be either monaural or binaural. Diplacusis is usually caused by disease of the inner ear, but disturbances elsewhere in the auditory pathway may also cause it.

Loss of hearing and/or tinnitus may be the result of disease processes anywhere along the course of the auditory pathways. *Conductive deafness* may be caused by obstruction of the external auditory canal by foreign bodies; the presence of cerumen, water, blood, or exudate against the tympanic membrane; perforation of the tympanic membrane; disease of the middle ear; or disease of the nasopharynx with obstruction of the eustachian tube. *Sensorineural deafness* may be produced by disease of the cochlea, the cochlear nerve or nuclei, or of the central auditory pathways. *Sensory,* or *inner ear, deafness* is caused by damage to the hair cells in the organ of Corti or the bipolar cells in the cochlea; this may follow acoustic trauma, Ménière's disease, and certain infections and congenital abnormalities, such as the deafness resulting from rubella acquired by an infant from its mother during the first trimester of pregnancy. *Retrocochlear deafness* is that which follows lesions central to the inner ear. *Nerve deafness* is caused by degeneration and other pathologic alterations of the nerve itself; tumors of the nerve, injury associated with skull fracture, meningitis, syphilis, and various toxins cause this type of deafness.

Nuclear lesions, either vascular, inflammatory or neoplastic, occasionally cause impairment of hearing. *Presbycusis* may have many causes. The sensory type results from atrophy of the organ of Corti and the nerve itself in the cochlea; the neural type is caused by loss of neurons in the auditory nerve and pathway; metabolic and mechanical etiologies have also been described. Owing to the fact that the supra-nuclear pathways are both crossed and uncrossed, unilateral lesions in the brain stem or the temporal lobes are rarely followed by clinical loss of hearing, although detailed audiometric testing may show defects of the type found in sensorineural deafness. Bilateral deafness may result, however, from midbrain lesions or from tumors of the posterior third ventricle or the aqueduct region with compression of either the medial geniculate bodies or the inferior colliculi. Impairment of localization of sound has been described in the auditory field contralateral to a temporal lobe lesion. Bizarre types of tinnitus are found in cerebral lesions, and auditory hallucinations may occur in lesions of the temporal lobe. These frequently constitute epileptic auras. More bizarre hallucinations occur in psychotic states. *Auditory receptive aphasia* may be a manifestation of disease of the temporal lobe; it is characterized by inability to interpret or comprehend spoken words even though hearing is normal (Chapter 53). In hysteria and other psychogenic disturbances there may be either partial or total and either unilateral or bilateral loss of hearing, with or without tinnitus; this is discussed in Chapter 56.

THE VESTIBULAR NERVE

ANATOMY AND PHYSIOLOGY

The receptors of the vestibular nerve are situated in the neuroepithelium in the cristae of the ampullae of the semicircular canals and in the maculae of the utricle and saccule in the inner ear. Impulses are carried to the bipolar cells of the vestibular ganglia of Scarpa in the internal auditory meatus, from which central fibers pass as the vestibular nerve. This traverses the internal auditory meatus with the cochlear nerve and enters the medulla just below the pons (Fig. 100). Along their peripheral courses the two nerves are enclosed within a single sheath; the vestibular is larger. As they enter the brain stem the vestibular nerve is ventromedial to the restiform body and lies between it and the superior olivary body. The cochlear nerve is lateral and slightly caudal to the vestibular. Within the internal auditory meatus the facial nerve and pars intermedia lie medially to and above the acoustic nerve. The peripheral fibers of the vestibular ganglia are composed of three branches; the

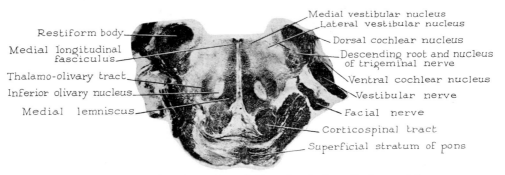

FIG. 100.   Section through medulla at level of vestibular nuclei.

superior branch arises from the sensory epithelium of the macula of the utricle and the ampullae of the superior (anterior vertical) and lateral (horizontal) semicircular canals; the fibers of the inferior branch arise from the macula of the saccule, and the fibers of the posterior branch arise from the ampulla of the posterior (posterior vertical) semicircular canal. It is sometimes stated that the cochlear nerve supplies the saccule and the posterior vertical canal, but these are probably supplied by vestibular fibers which appear to run with the cochlear nerve.

The majority of the vestibular fibers terminate on the four vestibular nuclei: the lateral, or Deiters', nucleus; the chief, dorsal, or medial nucleus, or nucleus of Schwalbe; the superior nucleus of Bechterew, and the inferior, spinal, or descending, nucleus (Fig 101). Some of them, however, go without synapse into the cerebellum; these pass through the direct vestibulocerebellar pathway, which is one of the components of the inferior cerebellar peduncle. All four of the vestibular nuclei communicate with the medial longitudinal fasciculus of the same or of the opposite side. This pathway, through connections with the nuclei of the oculomotor, abducens, and trochlear nerves, and the nuclei of the accessory and upper cervical nerves, is important in regulating movements of the eyes, head, and neck in response to stimulation of the semicircular canals (Fig. 58, p. 166). Impulses from the superior and medial nuclei go into the cerebellum as the indirect vestibulocerebellar pathway, whereas the lateral nucleus receives cerebellovestibular fibers. Fibers from the lateral nucleus go down the spinal cord as the ipsilateral lateral, or direct, vestibulospinal pathway which is important in the regulation of muscle tone and posture.

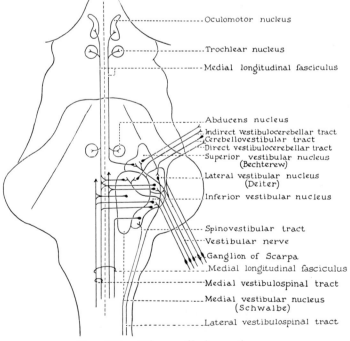

FIG. 101.   The vestibular pathway.

Impulses from various vestibular nuclei descend to the cervical cord through the crossed medial vestibulospinal tract. The medial vestibular nucleus also has connections with the reticular gray of the brain stem and through this with the dorsal efferent nucleus of the vagus nerve and with the spinal cord.

There is no defined tract or pathway from the vestibular nuclei to the thalamus or to the cerebral cortex, and there is no known central localization for the perception of vestibular impulses, but some of them may terminate on the temporal cortex. Ordinarily, however, the activities of the vestibular apparatus are not clearly represented in consciousness, and the equilibratory reactions excited from the semicircular canals are usually unconsciously performed. Even though there is no vestibulocortical tract, there may be connections between the vestibular centers and the hemispheres via the cerebellum and the cerebellorubrothalamic pathway.

The labyrinth is composed of the semicircular canals and the utricle and saccule. The bony labyrinth comprises a series of osseous canals situated in the petrous portion of the temporal bone (Fig. 102). Within the bony canals (Fig. 103) are membranous tubes which contain endolymph and are separated from the osseous canals by perilymph (Fig. 104). There are three sets of semicircular canals, each at right angles to the other two. The lateral, or horizontal, canals are almost on the horizontal plane of the head, but are tilted thirty degrees upward in their anterior

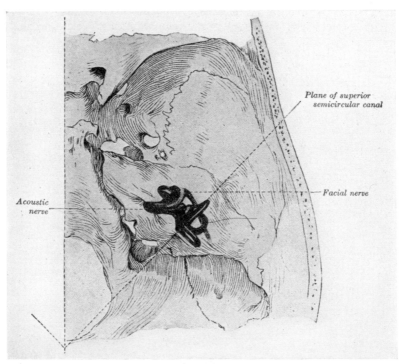

Fig. 102.   The right osseous labyrinth in temporal bone, viewed from above. (Spateholz, Werner: Hand-Atlas of Human Anatomy. Philadelphia, J. B. Lippincott Company, 1943.)

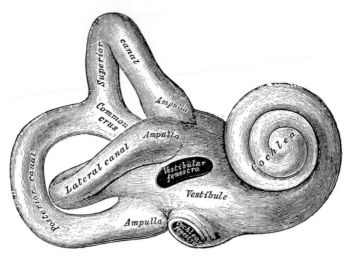

Fig. 103. The right osseous labyrinth, lateral view. (Gray's Anatomy of the Human Body. Philadelphia, Lea & Febiger, 1948.)

arcs. The superior, or anterior vertical, canals are midway between the frontal and sagittal planes of the body, at an angle of forty-five degrees with the sagittal plane of the head and transverse to the long axis of the petrous portion of the temporal bone. Their outermost portions are anterior, and the canals run inward and backward. The posterior, or posterior vertical, canals are also at an angle of forty-five degrees with the sagittal plane of the head and are parallel to the posterior surface of the temporal bone. Their outermost portions are posterior and the canals run inward and forward. The vertical canals are arranged in two diagonal pairs at right

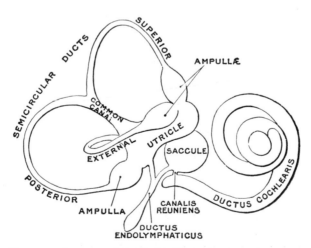

Fig. 104. The membranous labyrinth. (Gray's Anatomy of the Human Body. Philadelphia, Lea & Febiger, 1948.)

angles to the lateral canals and at right angles to each other. The posterior canal on one side is parallel to the superior canal on the opposite side. If the head is placed thirty degrees forward, the lateral canals are horizontal and the vertical canals are vertical. Each semicircular canal has an ampulla, or dilated portion, which is twice the diameter of the rest of the canal. The ampullae lie at the anterior extremities of the horizontal canals and at the lateral extremities of the vertical canals. Within the ampullae are the cristae with the specialized epithelium, or hair cells, which are vestibular receptors. These are stimulated by movement of the endolymph.

The semicircular canals are excited by movement in space and by changes in the direction and velocity of movement. They are influenced especially by rotatory motion of the head and rotatory acceleration. Stimulation of them gives evidence of the slightest alteration in the position of the body, and any change automatically calls for the appropriate motor response, a *kinetic labyrinthine reflex*. They are, thus, proprioceptive centers and regulate *kinetic equilibrium*. The semicircular canals and the vestibular apparatus are also important in the control of *ocular movements, ocular reflexes* which follow changes in the position of the head and body, and *ocular fixation* (Fig. 67). It is said by certain authorities that each canal has a major control over that pair of ocular muscles which moves the eyes in the plane of the canal (Fig. 105). It is probable, however, that each labyrinth, directly

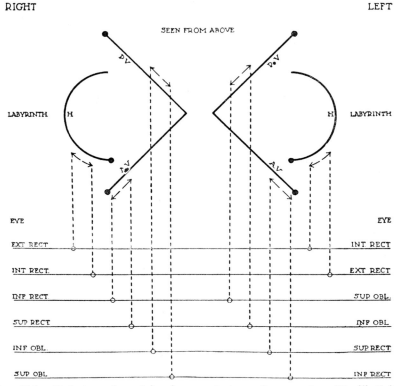

Fig. 105. Relation of semicircular canals to ocular muscles. (Favill, John: *Arch. Neurol. & Psychiat.* 19:318, 1928.)

or indirectly, has connections with all the ocular muscles of each eye through the medium of the medial longitudinal fasciculus, without a special relationship between canals and muscles.

Within the osseous vestibule are two membranous sacs, the utricle and saccule. Receptors similar to those in the semicircular canals are situated in these structures. The hair cells of the maculae are in contact with small calcareous masses, the otoliths. The otoliths of the utricles are known as the lapilli, and those of the saccules as the sagittae. The maculae of the utricle and saccule are stimulated by alterations of the position of the head and body in space, linear acceleration, gravity, and centrifugal force. The position of the otoliths with reference to the hair cells varies under the influence of gravity. The lapilli function synergistically, whereas the sagittae are opponents. When the head is erect the two saccular maculae are in the horizontal plane and the utricular maculae are perpendicular to them. The otolith mechanism, thus, conveys information concerning the position of the head and body in space, motion in a linear plane, and movement either with or against gravity. It exerts a tonic influence on the body musculature, reinforces muscle tone, and excites the muscular contractions necessary for the maintenance of equilibrium. It functions in *static equilibrium,* and is essential to the *static, postural, tonic neck,* and *righting reflexes* (Chapter 38).

The vestibular apparatus, thus, has multiple and complex functions. Kinetic impulses which have their origin in the semicircular canals stimulate motor responses which involve compensatory movements of *equilibrium.* Impulses which arise from the otolith apparatus give information about *orientation in space* and evoke reflexes which serve to maintain equilibrium in any posture. As a result of these functions and of its close relationship to the cerebellum, the vestibular complex plays an essential part in coordination, especially in the coordination of movements of the trunk and limbs in response to stimulation of the semicircular canals. The otolith mechanism, through the descending vestibulospinal pathways, is important in the regulation of *muscle tone* and is essential to postural and righting reflexes. Through the medial longitudinal fasciculus and its connections with the ocular and cervical muscles, the vestibular apparatus is essential to *ocular reflexes and fixation and to the conjugate movements of the head and eyes* which enable the individual to keep his gaze on stationary objects while his head and body are in motion.

The most characteristic symptom in disease of the vestibular system is dizziness, or *vertigo.* This is a sensation of movement, and is often accompanied by feelings of unsteadiness and loss of balance. True organic, or vestibular, vertigo is usually rotatory in type, and has been described as objective if external objects seem to be rotating around the individual, and as subjective if the individual himself seems to be rotating. All vertigo, however, is subjective, a sensation of a disturbed relationship with one's environment in some definite plane, often accompanied by a false sense of motion in that plane. Instead of a subjective sensation of rotation, the patient may notice a feeling of vertical or horizontal movement, or a sense of tipping, tilting, or of being pushed or pulled. Vertigo should be differentiated from giddiness or faintness, and from swimming, reeling, light-headed, or drunken sensations which may be interpreted as dizziness but are not true vertigo. In addition to vertigo there are often disturbances of equilibrium, manifested by unsteadiness and staggering. If the dysfunction is unilateral, the staggering is toward one side, and there is postural deviation, often accompanied by kinetic deviation, or past pointing. If the vertigo is severe, it may be accompanied by nausea, vomiting, diaphoresis, tachycardia, pallor, hypotension, and even shock and loss of consciousness. In most instances vestibular irritation or disease is accompanied by ocular deviation and nystagmus.

CLINICAL EXAMINATION

The clinical examination of the vestibular nerve should be preceded in every instance by a careful appraisal of the patient's symptoms. If the patient complains of dizziness, the examiner should attempt to determine whether there actually is vertigo rather than light-headedness or giddiness, sometimes referred to as pseudo-vertigo. If vertigo is present, it is essential to know whether it is objective or subjective, episodic or constant, lateralized, and related to change of position. The presence of associated symptoms, such as nausea, vomiting, staggering, deviation of the eyes, disturbances of balance, prostration, or loss of consciousness, is important. The type, form, direction, rate, amplitude, duration, and intensity of spontaneous nystagmus should be noted, as well as abnormalities of coordination and of station and gait.

Certain tests of vestibular function and vestibular reflexes are closely related to the examination of other portions of the nervous system and are discussed elsewhere. Coordination *per se* is considered in detail in the examination of motor functions; muscle tone is also discussed in the motor examination; postural and righting reflexes are described in "The Reflexes," Part V; ocular movements are considered in detail in Chapter 11. The *vestibulopupillary reflex* consists of either dilatation of the pupil or constriction followed by dilatation in response to stimulation of the labyrinthine system. The *vestibulo-oculogyric reflex* is a part of the response to vestibular stimulation to be described below. Lateral movements of the eyes in response to vestibular stimulation occur even when there is paralysis of volitional movement. Certain *vestibulospinal reflexes* may be investigated by *Fukuda's stepping test*. The blindfolded subject is placed in the center of two concentric circles divided into angles of thirty degrees, and is asked to mark time for one minute. His rotation of his own axis and any movement forward, backward, or to the sides is noted; in normal individuals there is only minimal rotation and movement.

Tests for vestibular function essential to the neurologic appraisal are those which are carried out by stimulation of the semicircular canals or of vestibular nerve endings. The otolith organs are not available to direct testing by the clinician. The labyrinths, particularly the semicircular canals and/or the vestibular receptors, may be stimulated in four ways: by the use of the rotating chair, change in temperature, galvanic stimulation, and pressure changes. All of these are often called Bárány tests, but possibly the term should be restricted to caloric examination.

In all of these tests the vestibular symptoms of vertigo, nausea, vomiting, and sometimes diaphoresis and prostration are reproduced, and the objective manifestations of deviation of the eyes, nystagmus, postural deviation, and past pointing are noted. It is believed that stimulation of the labyrinth by rotation or by the use of hot or cold water sets up a current or lymphokinesis in the endolymph within the semicircular canals, and that this, in turn, stimulates the vestibular nerves. Galvanic stimulation and pressure changes may act upon the vestibular nerve endings directly. It cannot be definitely stated whether the endolymph is static in the resting individual and is in motion only on stimulation of the labyrinth, or whether the fluid is bidirectional in the resting individual and becomes unidirectional by stimulation. Some authorities express the belief that there is no circulation in the fluid, but that pressure changes stimulate the cristae ampullaris. It is generally accepted, however, that the movement of the endolymph completely and consistently explains and accounts for the resulting phenomena.

The *nystagmus* which results from vestibular stimulation is rhythmic in type. Its direction depends upon the semicircular canals stimulated, and is thus dependent upon the position of the head during the examination. The slow phase is in the direction of the endolymph flow. It is said to be caused by stimuli initiated by the movement of the endolymph. The head and eyes, and sometimes the body, are deviated in the same direction. The vertigo, or hallucinated movement, is compensatory and is in the opposite direction, as is the rapid phase of the nystagmus. The excitation of a single semicircular canal produces nystagmus only in a plane parallel with the plane of that canal (Flourens' law), and the relationship between the direction of the flow of the endolymph and the direction of the nystagmus is a definite and constant one. Reversal of the flow of the endolymph causes a reversal in the direction of the nystagmus. Stimulation of more than one canal produces a more complex response and a more complex type of nystagmus. It is stated that a horizontal semicircular canal is maximally stimulated by a movement of the endolymph within the canal toward its ampulla, and a vertical canal is maximally stimulated by a movement of the endolymph away from its ampulla (Ewald's first law). Furthermore, maximal stimulation of a semicircular canal results in nystagmus with the rapid component toward the stimulated side, while minimal stimulation causes nystagmus with the rapid component toward the opposite side (Ewald's second law). The interval of time between the stimulation and the onset of the nystagmus should be noted, as well as the type, form, direction, duration, and intensity of the response. The amplitude of the nystagmus is increased on turning the eyes in the direction of the rapid phase. Placing a strong convex lens in front of the patient's eyes will aid in the observation of the nystagmus by magnifying it, and will be of further value by preventing the patient from fixing on any point or object. Electronystagmography may aid in the evaluation of the responses.

Postural deviation is a tilting or reactive movement of the entire body in the direction of the flow of the endolymph. It is tested by having the patient stand with his feet together and noting persistent falling in any one direction. The patient may be asked to walk along a straight line or to walk tandem, placing one heel directly in front of the other foot, and any deviation is noted. *Past pointing,* or kinetic deviation, is a reactive movement of the extremities in the direction of endolymph flow. It is tested by having the patient place his extended index finger on that of the examiner; the eyes are then closed, and the hand is either lowered or raised and then brought to touch the examiner's finger again. Motion should take place at the shoulder joint. The degree of deviation to either side is noted. On repeated movements the amount of deviation may increase. Past pointing should be tested in both upper extremities. The direction of deviation should be symmetrical, although the degree may be more marked on the side toward which deviation takes place. The nystagmus, postural deviation, and past pointing which follow vestibular stimulation must be differentiated from those signs of disease which may have been present before the tests were carried out. It is also valuable, in appraising the vestibular tests, to note the presence of such manifestations as subjective vertigo, nausea, vomiting, diaphoresis, and other symptoms. The patient may contribute information by comparing the vertigo which follows vestibular stimulation with vertiginous symptoms he may have had previously. Since the vestibular tests may be followed by unpleasant symptoms, it is best to carry them out after the neurologic examination has been completed. In many clinics these examinations are made by the otologists.

Rotation Tests: In the rotating-chair tests the patient is seated in the Bárány chair and is rotated rapidly, about ten times in twenty seconds, and the movement is then abruptly stopped. The head is fixed by a head rest, and the eyes are closed to prevent the development of optokinetic nystagmus. On the completion of rotation the eyes are opened so that nystagmus may be seen, and postural deviation and past pointing are tested. In the beginning of rotation, owing to inertia, the endolymph moves less rapidly than the body, and there is an apparent movement in the direction opposite to that of the body. As a consequence, during rotation the eyes are drawn to the opposite side, and the slow phase of the nystagmus is opposite to the direction of rotation. This, however, is difficult to observe. Later the endolymph moves in the same direction as the body, and when the rotation ceases abruptly, the momentum of the labyrinthine fluid causes it to continue to flow in the direction of the recently completed movement of the body, even though the head is now stationary. This causes the after-nystagmus, which is what one observes clinically, and it is opposite in direction to the primary nystagmus. The slow phase of the nystagmus, deviation of the eyes, postural deviation, and past pointing are all correlated with endolymph displacement and are in the direction of the recently completed movement, whereas the vertigo is in the opposite direction.

In order to test the lateral (horizontal) canals, the head is tilted forward thirty degrees so that these canals are on a horizonal plane. This plane is reached when a line drawn through the middle of the eye and the external auditory meatus is parallel with the floor. If the patient is rotated to the right, past pointing and postural deviation develop to the right, while vertigo develops to the left (Table 1). The after-nystagmus is characterized by a slow movement to the right with the quick phase to the left; it is horizontal in type. The opposite results are obtained by rotation to the left. The duration and intensity of the nystagmus and the degree of vertigo, nausea, and other symptoms depend upon the rapidity of rotation, the degree of sensitivity of the vestibular apparatus, and the duration of rotation. In the normal individual the nystagmus lasts from twenty-five to thirty seconds. This test involves the semicircular canals and vestibular apparatus on both sides, but the canal on the side toward which the subject is rotated is stimulated the more.

TABLE 1. VESTIBULAR TESTS

ROTATION TESTS: MANIFESTATIONS FOLLOWING ROTATION TO THE RIGHT (OPPOSITE RESULTS ON ROTATION TO THE LEFT)

Position of head (patient seated)	Canals stimulated	Nystagmus: slow phase (after-nystagmus)	Falling (postural deviation) (after head is brought up)	Past pointing (kinetic deviation)	Vertigo (hallucinated movement)
30° forward	lateral superior	horizontal to right	to right	to right	to left
90°–120° forward		rotatory to right	to right	to right	to left
60° backward	superior	rotatory to left	to left	to left	to right
90° toward right shoulder	posterior	vertical upward	backward	upward	forward
90° toward left shoulder	posterior	vertical downward	forward	downward	backward

CALORIC TESTS: MANIFESTATIONS FOLLOWING DOUCHING OF RIGHT EAR WITH COLD WATER (OPPOSITE RESULTS ON DOUCHING WITH HOT WATER; OPPOSITE RESULTS ON DOUCHING LEFT EAR)

Position of subject and head	Canal stimulated	Nystagmus: slow phase	Falling (postural deviation) (after head is brought up)	Past pointing (kinetic deviation)	Vertigo (hallucinated movement)
Lying down, head 30° forward	lateral	horizontal to right	to right	to right	to left
Seated, head 60° backward	lateral	horizontal to right	to right	to right	to left
Seated, head 90°–120° forward	lateral	horizontal to left	to left	to left	to right
Seated, head 30° forward	superior	rotatory to right	to right	to right	to left

Rotatory and vertical nystagmus are produced by stimulation of the vertical canals, and diagonal or mixed nystagmus by stimulating more than one set of canals. The superior (anterior vertical) canals are placed in the plane of rotation and are stimulated by tilting the head either forward ninety to one hundred and twenty degrees so that the chin is against the chest, or backward sixty degrees. The posterior (posterior vertical) canals are stimulated if the head is flexed ninety degrees laterally toward the shoulder during rotation. The results which follow the stimulation of the vertical canals or of various combinations of the canals are sometimes confusing and are difficult to evaluate. If the patient is rotated to the right with the head ninety to one hundred and twenty degrees forward there is rotatory nystagmus with the slow phase to the right, with postural deviation and past pointing to the right and vertigo to the left. If he is rotated to the right with the head extended sixty degrees, there is rotatory nystagmus with the slow phase to the left, with vertigo to the right and deviation and past pointing to the left. If he is rotated to the right with the head bent ninety degrees toward the right shoulder, there is vertical nystagmus with the slow phase upward, with a sensation of falling forward, past pointing upward, and, after the head is again erect, a tendency for the patient to fall backward. If he is rotated toward the right with the head ninety degrees toward the left shoulder, there is vertical nystagmus with the slow phase downward, with vertigo backward, past pointing downward, and a tendency to fall forward after the head is erect. Nystagmus and deviation in opposite directions are produced by rotation to the left. Mixed and diagonal types of nystagmus are elicited following rotation with the head in the other positions, so that more than one set of canals is stimulated.

Caloric Tests: In the caloric, or thermal, tests the external auditory canal is douched with cold or hot water or air. It is said that a thermal stimulation of the auditory canal produces a change in the temperature of the endolymph. This sets up a convection current and causes the endolymph to circulate. Only those canals in the vertical plane are affected. Cold water causes the endolymph to flow from above downward, away from the ampulla, and toward the side stimulated, whereas hot water has the opposite effect. The advanatge of the caloric test is that the vestibular apparatus on each side can be examined individually.

Before doing the caloric test the canal must be examined for the presence of cerumen or blood, and the tympanic membrane for perforations or other abnormalities. If the drum is perforated, air or an antiseptic solution should be used. If the drum is retracted, the response is accentuated. The patient's eyes should be fixed on a stationary object. In the original test water at seven to eight degrees centigrade above or below normal body temperature was used, and either allowed to flow slowly into the canal through a rubber tube attached to a vessel suspended about two feet above the level of the ear, or injected gently from a large syringe. One hundred cubic centimeters or more may be necessary to elicit a response. The water may be allowed to run in the ear for forty seconds and this may be repeated if there is no response, or it may be injected until vertigo appears. In order to facilitate the test and to avoid the use of large amounts of water, many examiners use ice water (zero to five degrees centigrade). Five cubic centimeters are injected, and if there is no response the procedure is repeated with ten cubic centimeters. This may be repeated until a response is obtained. This method is less annoying to the patient, and less time consuming. Warm water may be used first as a rough screening test; if similar responses are obtained bilaterally, the cold water stimulus can be omitted. When cold water is used, the past pointing and postural deviation develop toward the side of stimulation, and the slow phase of the nystagmus is in that direction. Hot water produces opposite effects. The nystagmus may be recorded graphically (Fig. 106).

In order to stimulate the lateral canals and obtain horizontal nystagmus, the patient must either be lying down with his head tilted thirty degrees forward, or seated with his head tilted forward ninety to one hundred and twenty degrees or backward sixty degrees, so that the lateral canals are in a vertical plane. If the lateral canal of the right ear is stimulated with cold water when the patient is either lying down with his head thirty degrees forward or seated with his head sixty degrees backward, there is nystagmus with the slow phase to the right, with past pointing and postural deviation to the right and vertigo to the left. If the right ear is stimulated with cold water when the patient is seated with his head ninety to one hundred and twenty degrees forward, the vertigo is to the right, and the slow phase of the nystagmus, postural deviation, and past pointing are to the left. The nystagmus is horizontal on these occasions. The superior canals are stimulated and rotatory nystagmus is obtained when the patient is seated with his head tilted forward thirty degrees, or when the patient is lying down with his head tilted forward ninety to one hundred and twenty degrees or backward sixty degrees. If the right ear is stimulated with cold water when the patient is seated with his head forward thirty degrees, there is rotatory nystagmus with the slow phase to the right, with postural deviation and past pointing to the right and vertigo to the left. The posterior canals are too far distant from the middle ear for stimulation in this test. If there is destruction of one labyrinth, or of the eighth nerve on that side, there is no response following caloric stimulation.

Galvanic Tests: The galvanic test is carried out with the patient standing upright with his feet together and his eyes closed. The cathode is placed in the patient's hand or over the sternum or back, and the anode over the mastoid prominence. Normally a current of from five to seven milliamperes causes nystagmus with the slow phase toward the side stimulated and slight swaying and past pointing toward that side. The nerve endings in all the semicircular canals are stimulated directly, and the movement of the endolymph in the semicircular canals is not ordinarily affected; the nystagmus is of a mixed type, both horizontal and rotatory. If one to two milliamperes evoke a response, there is hyperirritability of the labyrinth, and if ten to fifteen milliamperes are needed, there is impairment of function. Inasmuch as the galvanic stimulus may act directly on the vestibular nerve, there may be a

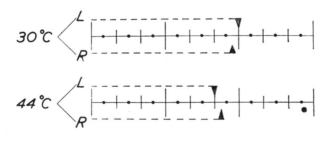

FIG. 106. Graphic record of normal caloric nystagmus. Each continuous line represents a three-minute period. (Carmichael, E. A., Dix, M. R., and Hallpike, C. S.: *Brain* 77:246, 1954.)

response to the galvanic stimulation even though the labyrinth is destroyed and the caloric test is negative. Opposite results are obtained when the cathode is used as the stimulus.

Mechanical Tests: Compression of the external auditory meatus or the production of pressure changes in the semicircular canals by the introduction of a pipet manometer into one of them causes stimulation of the labyrinth. These methods are used in cases where there is a fistula between the middle ear and the labyrinth. They are more valuable in otologic than in neurologic diagnosis. An increase in pressure causes a nystagmus with the slow phase to the opposite side, and a decrease in pressure results in nystagmus with the slow phase to the same side.

Of all the above tests, the caloric is the most practicable and the easiest to evaluate. The disadvantage of the rotation tests in neurologic diagnosis is that both labyrinths are stimulated simultaneously. Unilateral vestibular disease may be diagnosed more readily by the caloric, galvanic, and mechanical tests, which stimulate each side individually. The caloric test, which sets the endolymph in motion and thus stimulates the end organ, is probably more valuable than the galvanic test, which may stimulate the nerve directly. Furthermore, specific canals are affected by caloric stimulation, whereas all the canals on one side are influenced by galvanic stimulation. Mechanical tests are rarely used in neurologic diagnosis. In all instances the nystagmus, past pointing, etc., which may have existed prior to the test, must be differentiated from those which develop during the examination. Caloric, rotation and galvanic stimulation may also be used to modify the stepping test; the patient's body rotates on its own axis in the direction of the slow phase of the nystagmus.

With hyperirritability of the vestibular system there is an exaggerated response to all of the above tests, and there are marked subjective symptoms in the form of vertigo, nausea, and vomiting. There is an individual variation in vestibular responses, which may be apparent clinically in the susceptibility of certain persons to motion sickness. With impaired vestibular function there is a diminished response on the affected side, especially in the caloric and galvanic tests. With destruction of the labyrinth or its connections or of the vestibular nerve on one side, there is absence of response to caloric or galvanic tests; there is no nystagmus, past pointing, postural deviation, or vertigo following stimulation of individual canals or of all canals on that side. Caloric testing can also be done in comatose patients; there is usually tonic conjugate deviation of the eyes without nystagmus, but it may be possible to bring out evidence of ocular muscle palsies, paresis of conjugate gaze, or abnormalities such as internuclear ophthalmoplegia.

With central lesions there may be a dissociation of responses, such as the presence of certain manifestations and the absence of others, lack of reaction to stimulation of certain semicircular canals but response of others, and perversion or inversion of reflex nystagmus. If there is interruption of connections with the medial longitudinal fasciculus on one side, stimulation of individual canals or of all canals on that side causes vertigo, past pointing, and postural deviation, but no nystagmus. With an intrapontine lesion there may be normal reactions from one set of canals and absence of response from others; there is especially apt to be absence of response to stimulation of the vertical canals. With a lesion of the inferior cerebellar peduncle on one side there is nystagmus following stimulation of the lateral canal on that side, but no vertigo, past pointing, or postural deviation. With a lesion of the middle cerebellar peduncle on one side there is nystagmus following stimulation of the superior canal on that side, but no vertigo, past pointing, or falling. With a unilateral cerebellar lesion there is nystagmus following stimulation of all canals on that side, but no vertigo, past pointing, or falling. With a lesion of the midbrain there may be nystagmus following stimulation of all canals on both sides, but no vertigo, past pointing, or postural deviation. It must be emphasized, however, that one should not depend upon the vestibular tests alone for the localization of nervous system lesions. The other neurologic findings and the clinical history are essential to the diagnosis.

DISORDERS OF FUNCTION

As has been stated, vertigo is the most characteristic symptom of vestibular disease. Irritation or destruction of the labyrinths and increase or decrease in the pressure of the endolymph may cause vertigo, which may be accompanied by the objective signs of unsteadiness, staggering, incoordination, ocular deviation, and nystagmus, and by symptoms of nausea, vomiting, and prostration. Vestibular manifestations may be caused by disease of the labyrinths themselves, the vestibular nerve, the vestibular nuclei, or the supranuclear connections. Vertigo may also, however, be a symptom of general rather than focal disease, and in such cases it has no localizing value. The history is very important, and one should determine whether the patient experiences an actual sensation of rotation or movement, either of himself or of the environment; if such is present, one should inquire about its pattern, periodicity, direction, severity, and relationship to posture or change of position, as well as about associated ataxia, falling, deafness, and tinnitus.

Since the labyrinths are antagonistic to each other, the elimination of one acts as a stimulus to the other. If one labyrinth is destroyed there is nystagmus, usually with the slow phase toward the involved side, and there are associated deviations of the eyes, head, body, and extremities in the same direction. These manifestations do not persist, but are compensated for by processes within the corresponding vestibular nuclei and by visual and other nonlabyrinthine reflexes. It is often difficult to differentiate between manifestations associated with destruction and those secondary to irritation of the labyrinths or vestibular nerves, and between underactivity on one side and hyperactivity on the opposite side. In hyperirritability, however, the rapid phase of the nystagmus is usually toward the involved side, whereas in diminished irritability it is toward the opposite side. Hyperactivity and hypoactivity of the labyrinth may be caused by the same process. Shortly after the onset of a lesion there may be symptoms caused by irritation, whereas later those of destruction may predominate.

The labyrinths may be affected by inflammation, hemorrhage, edema, pressure changes, etc. Middle ear disease or mastoiditis with extension to the inner ear may cause a purulent or serous labyrinthitis, with vertigo and the attendant subjective and objective manifestations. The labyrinthitis may be either circumscribed or diffuse. Hemorrhage into the labyrinth may cause intense vertigo which may persist for a long period of time. The term *Ménière's disease* has been used for both suppurative labyrinthitis and hemorrhage into the labyrinth, but currently it is applied to labyrinthine hydrops, which was once known as Ménière's syndrome. Skull fractures through the labyrinth and labyrinthine fistulas may cause symptoms of vestibular dysfunction.

In *motion sickness* of various types—sea, air, train, and car sickness—the vertigo is probably the result either of the continuous motion of the endolymph in the semicircular canals or of the stimulation of the utricles by linear acceleration in the vertical plane of the head. There is a marked individual variation in vestibular response, and such stimulation in especially susceptible individuals, or in those with hyperactive labyrinthine systems or sensitive vestibular mechanisms, causes vertigo, disturbances of equilibrium, drowsiness, nausea, vomiting, and pallor, perspiration, and other autonomic nervous system disturbances. Vision and psychic factors influence the symptoms. Nystagmus is usually absent in motion sickness.

Ménière's disease is characterized by paroxysmal apoplectiform attacks of labyrinthine vertigo, usually associated with unilateral tinnitus and deafness. The vertigo is often accompanied by nausea, vomiting, and unsteadiness, and may even result in prostration and loss of consciousness. At times the attacks are precipitated by change of position or sudden movements of the head. The patient is free from vertigo between the attacks. The manifestations most frequently appear in middle age, and cochlear symptoms precede those of labyrinthine involvement. The disease is usually unilateral, but occasionally becomes bilateral. Hearing tests show an inner ear or end organ type of deafness, and the vestibular responses are usually decreased on the affected side. There are many theories concerning etiology. Most authorities express the belief that edema of the labyrinth with increased pressure of labyrinthine fluid (labyrinthine or endolymphatic hydrops) is responsible in most cases. Vasomotor changes (vasodilatation or vasospasm), overproduction of endolymph, increase in the permeability of the capillaries with associated increase in intralabyrinthine pressure, disturbances of the autonomic nervous system, allergy, and changes in acid-base equilibrium with retention of sodium have all been listed as possible etiologies. Pathologically there are degenerative changes in the hair cells of the cochlea and the neuroepithelium of the semicircular canals. Individual cases seem to have been relieved by dehydration, restriction of sodium or increased intake of potassium, and the use of vasodilator and antihistamine drugs. In severe cases the acoustic nerve or its vestibular portion has been sectioned as a therapeutic measure. Other approaches for relief of the symptoms by surgical and allied procedures include decompression of the labyrinth, fenestration and surgical destruction of the membranous labyrinth, ultrasonic destruction or electrocoagulation of the labyrinth, stellectomy and dorsal sympathectomy, and section of the chorda tympani and/or tympanic plexus.

The terms *labyrinthitis* and *vestibular neuronitis* are used to signify disease processes in which the predominant symptom is vertigo, often with recurring attacks and usually without an associated cochlear disturbance. In the acute attacks there may be nausea and vomiting as well as nystagmus and kinetic and postural deviation. The vertigo is often brought on or increased by sudden movements or change in position of the head; it may be present only when the patient is in a certain position, as when recumbent, with positional nystagmus. There may be persisting dizziness between attacks. There may be either decreased or increased response to caloric testing on one or both sides; if the response is increased, the test may reproduce the symptoms. The syndrome may be associated with or follow some nonspecific infection, and occasionally occurs as so-called epidemic vertigo, but in most cases the etiology is not known and the condition is self-limited. The pathologic process may be in the labyrinth or in the vestibular nerve or nuclei. The symptoms may be due to stimulation of the vestibular end organs by infection or by some endogenous toxin.

In addition to its peripheral origin, vertigo may also be of central, or even cortical, origin, or a symptom of disease elsewhere in the body, or of general disease. It is common in disease of the brain stem and cerebellum, and may occur with cerebral tumors and abscesses, increased intracranial pressure, and intracranial aneurysms. Inasmuch as there may be associated symptoms of cochlear nerve dysfunction in such cases, these are discussed more in detail in the following paragraphs. Vertigo may be a prominent symptom in posttraumatic states, probably the result of focal injury to the vestibular pathways. In benign paroxysmal vertigo the symptom may be related to the position of the head or body, usually with rotatory nystagmus and vertigo when the patient assumes the supine position; the responsible lesion may be in the utricle or in the connections between the labyrinth and the brain stem. Ocular vertigo may be associated with imbalance of the extraocular muscles, ocular muscle palsies, and errors of refraction; vertigo experienced in high places may have visual origin, but changes in atmospheric pressure may also be responsible. Systemic diseases such as arteriosclerosis, hypertension, sudden fall in blood pressure, cardiac abnormalities, anemia, metabolic disturbances such as hypothyroidism and hypoglycemia, allergy, drug sensitivity, febrile states, and infections may cause vertigo. It may be difficult to differentiate between labyrinthine symptoms caused by peripheral lesions and those due to central nervous system changes or general or systemic disease. Those of peripheral origin, however, are usually episodic in character, aggravated by changes in posture, and accompanied by nystagmus. Vertigo of "central" origin is more apt to be continuous; it is less clearly defined, and is rarely accompanied by nystagmus; there may be evidence of other central nervous system changes.

Dizziness is a common symptom in hysteria and the anxiety states. In these conditions, however, the patient rarely complains of true rotatory vertigo, but rather of giddiness or unsteadiness. The manifestations may be bizarre, and often are poorly described; there is no nystagmus; true postural deviation is rarely seen; and there are associated manifestations of the anxiety state.

LESIONS OF THE EIGHTH NERVE AND ITS CONNECTIONS

Although diseases of the peripheral apparatus, the cochlea and labyrinth, or diseases within the central nervous system may cause involvement of only one portion of the acoustic nerve or its connections, diseases of the nerve itself show evidence

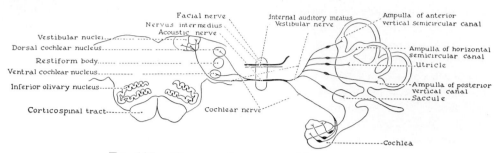

FIG. 107. The acoustic nerve and its connections.

of impairment of function or irritation of both portions (Fig. 107). There are both tinnitus and deafness resulting from disturbance of cochlear function, and vertigo, abnormalities of equilibration, and nystagmus as a result of disturbance of vestibular function. There may be symptoms of involvement of both branches in disease of the external, middle, or internal ear, with both vertigo and deafness. In obstruction of the external auditory canal by foreign bodies there is conductive deafness but there may also be vertigo. Otitis media, either acute or chronic and either catarrhal or suppurative, and obstruction of the eustachian tube, may cause symptoms referable to both branches. Mastoid disease, suppuration of the petrous apex, cholesteatomas, vascular lesions, angioneurotic edema, and trauma may cause both vestibular and cochlear symptoms. In otosclerosis there occasionally is vertigo as well as tinnitus and deafness.

The end organs of both nerves within the cochlea and semicircular canals may be affected by various processes. Both are involved in Ménière's disease and in certain infections and congenital abnormalities, such as rubella occurring early in pregnancy. Acoustic trauma, such as either blast injuries or repeated exposure to loud noises, as experienced in certain occupations, affects predominantly the cochlear endings. Streptomycin and its analogues frequently cause both vertigo and deafness. Streptomcyin itself affects mainly the sensory epithelium of the semicircular canals, with secondary changes in the vestibular ganglia and later damage to the cochlea. If discontinued as soon as tinnitus is noted, serious deafness may be prevented; the effects are somewhat reversible, and the patient may learn to compensate for the labyrinthine dysfunction. Dihydrostreptomycin and kanamycin have their major action on the organ of Corti, causing tinnitus and deafness; occasionally irreversible deafness develops without the warning of tinnitus.

The acoustic nerve itself may be affected in many types of disease processes. It is frequently involved in basal skull fractures, and deafness and vestibular dysfunction may follow such a fracture or other types of cerebral or cranial trauma. Other diseases of the base of the brain and its coverings, such as meningitis, arachnoiditis, intracranial aneurysms, subarachnoid hemorrhage, and neoplasms, may involve the nerve, as may bone lesions such as Paget's disease and periostitis. Nerve deafness is one of the frequent sequelae of epidemic meningitis and it is one of the commoner stigmas of congenital syphilis. The eighth nerve is especially susceptible to various toxins, among which are quinine, lead, arsenic, alcohol, barbiturates, acetanilid, aminopyrine, hyoscine, chloroform, ether, carbon monoxide, salicylates, cinchophen, and nicotine, as well as to endotoxic processes associated with disease of the gastrointestinal tract and uremia. It may be affected by either focal or systemic infections, and eighth nerve symptoms are common in any acute febrile illness. Progressive degeneration of the nerve may occur with increasing age, on a familial basis, or as a complication of central nervous system syphilis. It may also be affected in anemia, diabetes, gout, nephritis, leukemia, hypothyroidism, allergic states, avitaminosis, and myxedema and other hormonal imbalances.

Lesions of the brain stem may involve the nuclei or the central connections of either the cochlear or the vestibular nerve, but the latter are more commonly affected. The internal auditory artery supplies the entire inner ear, and the pontine branches of the basilar artery supply the nuclei of the eighth nerve. Intermittent insufficiency of the vertebrobasilar arterial system may cause recurring attacks of vertigo with or without hearing impairment and tinnitus. Thrombosis, aneurysms, angiomas, and other lesions of these or of other vessels of the pons or adjacent areas may cause both attacks of vertigo and deafness. Equilibrium is often affected; the nystagmus is often coarse and protracted and may be more marked toward one side or may be vertical in direction; there may be associated involvement of other cranial nerves or of the motor and sensory pathways that traverse the brain stem. Multiple sclerosis commonly causes vertigo and may cause either nerve deafness or "islands" of hearing loss; the damage may be in the nuclei or the ascending pathways. Other brain stem lesions that may cause similar symptoms include encephalitis and other inflammatory diseases, neoplasms, gummas, abscesses, tuberculomas, tabes dorsalis and other forms of central nervous system syphilis, Friedreich's ataxia, syringobulbia, and platybasia. Cerebellar lesions are often characterized by vertigo which may be the result of involvement of the vestibular pathways, but the symptom may also be associated with the ataxia and unsteadiness produced by the cerebellar dysfunction. Nystagmus, deviation, and past pointings are commonly encountered with cerebellar lesions. Patients with ataxia often complain of dizziness when referring to their sense of unsteadiness and lack of coordination.

Cerebral disturbances such as cerebral anemia, hyperemia, arteriosclerotic or senile changes, concussion, and increasing intracranial pressure may cause both vestibular and cochlear symptoms, as may cerebral neoplasms, abscesses, vascular accidents, and degenerative cerebral disease, especially if they involve the temporal lobes. Both tinnitus and vertigo may be present with migraine or as the aura of an epileptic attack. Vertigo and either unformed or formed auditory hallucinations may precede or accompany temporal lobe seizures. Vertigo is a common symptom in generalized cerebral disease, and may not have localizing value. Both tinnitus and vertigo have been produced by stimulation of the chorda tympani nerve. Both deafness and vertigo may be of psychogenic origin; the deafness is usually variable and inconsistent, whereas the vertigo may be vague and atypical.

There are a few neurologic syndromes in which involvement of the eighth nerve is especially significant. Perhaps the most important of these is the *cerebellopontine angle neoplasm,* usually a neurinoma or a neurofibroma, although occasionally a meningioma. The tumor arises on the eighth nerve within the internal auditory meatus, and its first symptoms are those of irritation or of loss of function of the nerve, namely, deafness and tinnitus, and later there are recurring attacks of vertigo. As the tumor grows in size there is involvement of the fifth nerve, with ipsilateral pain and anesthesia of the face and loss of the corneal reflex. Pressure on the cerebellum or its peduncles causes ataxia and coordination difficulties. There may be involvement of the seventh nerve with a peripheral facial palsy, and of the sixth, ninth, and tenth nerves. Later there are signs of increased intracranial pressure with headache, ocular manifestations, and occasional loss of consciousness. There are usually roentgen signs of erosion of the internal auditory meatus. On examination a sensorineural type of deafness is found, and the labyrinth on the involved side fails to respond to caloric or galvanic stimulation. There may, however, be atypical manifestations, with little impairment of hearing and unusual vestibular responses. Nystagmus is a common sign; it is coarse and slow on gaze toward the side of the lesion, and fine and rapid on gaze toward the opposite side. Acoustic neurofibromas are occasionally a part of Recklinghausen's disease, or generalized neurofibromatosis. Inflammatory lesions in the cerebellopontine angle may be difficult to differentiate from neoplasms. In the former, however, motor symptoms predominate, whereas neoplasms affect sensory functions earlier and more serevely.

Partial deafness may be an early symptom of a *tumor of the glomus jugulare* (*chemodectoma*); later there may be tinnitus, vertigo, and involvement of the facial, vagus, and other lower cranial nerves. On examination a vascular polyp may be found in the auditory canal or evidence of hemorrhage behind the tympanic membrane. *Bonnier's syndrome* consists of vertigo, nystagmus, and pallor, owing to involvement of Deiter's nucleus; these are often accompanied by contralateral hemiplegia, apprehension, tachycardia, and somnolence, and there may be evidence of associated involvement of the ninth, tenth, fifth, and third nerves. In *Lermoyez's syndrome* there are sudden attacks of dizziness which occur after increased deafness and are followed by improvement of hearing. In *Gerlier's disease,* or paralyzing vertigo, there are sudden transient attacks of vertigo accompanied by ptosis, paralysis of the arms and legs, pain in the back and neck, and muscular contractions. *Brun's syndrome* consists of vertigo, vomiting, headache, and visual disturbances on change of position of the head; this is usually associated with a cysticercus infection of the fourth ventricle or with midline tumors of the cerebellum, and the symptoms are probably the result of disturbances of function of the vestibular pathways in the brain stem. In *deaf-mutism* there is severe impairment of hearing from birth or from an early age, so that normal speech has not been acquired; there may or may not be impairment of vestibular function. There are many causes of deaf-mutism. Congenital deaf-mutism is usually inherited as a mendelian recessive trait, and may be due to aplasia of the cochlea and/or the labyrinth. In *Cogan's syndrome* there are vestibular and auditory symptoms (vertigo, tinnitus, and deafness) along with a nonsyphilitic interstitial keratitsis and some manifestations of systemic disease; this may be of infectious origin or a localized manifestation of polyarteritis nodosa.

REFERENCES

ALEXANDER, E., JR., BEAMER, P. R., and WILLIAMS, J. O. Tumor of the glomus jugulare with extension into the middle ear. *J. Neurosurg.* 8:515, 1951.

ALPERS, B. J. Vertigo and Dizziness. New York, Grune & Stratton, 1958.

ATKINSON, M. Tinnitus aurium: Some considerations concerning its origin and treatment. *Arch. Otolaryng.* 45:68, 1947.

BÁRÁNY, R. Physiologie und Pathologie (Funktions-Prüfung) des Bogengang-Apparates beim Menchen; Klinische Studien. Leipzig u. Wein, F. Deuticke, 1907; The relationship between semicircular canals and the eye muscles: The central mechanism in vestibular nystagmus. *Tr. Internat. Otol. Cong.* 9:592, 1912.

VON BÉKÉSY, G. Experiments in Hearing. New York, McGraw-Hill Book Company, 1960.

BERNSTEIN, L. Simplification of clinical caloric test. *Arch. Otolaryng.* 81:347, 1965.

BRODAL, A., POMEIANO, O., and WALBERG, F. The Vestibular Nuclei and Their Connections. Springfield, Ill., Charles C Thomas, 1962.

BUNCH, C. C. Clinical Audiometry. St. Louis, The C. V. Mosby Company, 1943.

CAWTHORNE, T. E., FITZGERALD, G., and HALLPIKE, C. S. Studies in human vestibular function: III. Observations on the clinical features of "Ménière's disease," with especial reference to the results of the caloric tests. *Brain* 65:161, 1942.

COGAN, D. G., and DICKERSEN, G. R. Nonsyphilitic interstitial keratitis with vestibulo-auditory symptoms. *Arch. Ophth.* 71:172, 1964.

CUSHING, H. Tumors of the Nervous Acusticus and the Syndrome of the Cerebello-pontile Angle. Philadelphia, W. B. Saunders Company, 1917.

DAVIS, H., and SILVERMAN, S. R. (eds.) Hearing and Deafness (ed. 2). New York, Holt, Rinehart & Winston, 1960.

DeWEESE, D. D. Dizziness: An Evaluation and Classification. Springfield, Ill., Charles C Thomas, 1954.

DeWEESE, D. D., and SAUNDERS, W. H. Textbook of Otolaryngology (ed. 2). St. Louis, The C. V. Mosby Company, 1964.

FAVILL, J. The Relationship of Eye Muscles to Secicircular Canal Currents in Rotationally Induced Nystagmus. Chicago, privately printed, 1936.

FIELDS, W. S., and ALFORD, B. R. Neurological Aspects of Auditory and Vestibular Disorders. Springfield, Ill., Charles C Thomas, 1964.

FISCHER, J. J. The Labyrinth: Psysiology and Functional Tests. New York, Grune & Stratton, 1956.

FORD, F. R. A clinical classification of vestibular disorders. *Bull. Johns Hopkins Hosp.* 87:299, 1950.

FORD, F. R., and WALSH, F. B. Clinical observations upon the importance of the vestibular reflexes in ocular movements. *Bull. Johns Hopkins Hosp.* 58:80, 1936.

FUKUDA, T. The stepping test. *Acta oto-laryng.* 50:95, 1959.

GLORIG, A. (ed.) Audiometry: Principles and Practices. Baltimore, The Williams & Wilkins Company, 1965.

GRAHAM, J. T., and NEWBY, H. A. Acoustical characteristics of tinnitus. *Arch. Otolaryng.* 75:162, 1962.

HOLMGREN, L. Hearing tests and hearing aids: A clinical and experimental study. *Acta oto-laryng.* Supp. 34, 1939.

HOUSE, W. F. (ed.) Transtemporal bone microsurgical removal of acoustic neuromas. *Arch. Otolaryng.* 80:559–756, 1964.

JONGKEES, L. B. W., and GROEN, J. J.   The nature of the vestibular stimulus.   *J. Laryng. & Otol.* 61:529, 1946.

KLINGON, G. H.   Caloric stimulation in localization of brain-stem lesions in a comatose patient.   *A. M. A. Arch. Neurol. & Psychiat.* 68:233, 1952.

KLINGON, G. H., and BONTECOU, D. C.   Localization in auditory space. *Neurology* 16:879, 1966.

KOBRAK, H. G.   The present status of objective hearing tests.   *Am. Otol. Rhin. & Laryng.* 57:1018, 1948.

LEVY, I., and O'LEARY, J. L.   Incidence of vertigo in neurological conditions.   *Ann. Otol., Rhin. & Laryng.* 56:557, 1947.

LEWY, A., SHAPIRO, S. L., and LESHIN, N.   Functional examination of hearing. *A. M. A. Arch. Otolaryng.* 59:608, 1954.

McNALLY, W. J.   Five lectures on the physiology of the ear.   *Ann. Otol., Rhin. & Laryng.* 38:1163, 1929, and 39:248, 1930.

POOL, J. L., and PAVA, A. A.   The Early Diagnosis and Treatment of Acoustic Nerve Tumors.   Springfield, Ill., Charles C Thomas, 1957.

QUIX, F. H.   The function of the vestibular organ and the clinical examination of the otolithic apparatus.   *J. Laryng. & Otol.* 40:425, 493, 1925.

RASMUSSEN, G. L., and WINDLE, W. F. (eds.)   Neural Mechanisms of the Auditory and Vestibular Systems.   Springfield, Ill., Charles C Thomas, 1961.

ROSEN, S.   Ménière's disease: Successful treatment by chorda tympanectomy.   *A.M.A. Arch Neurol. & Psychiat.* 72:682, 1954.

RUBEN, R. J.   Anatomic diagnosis of nonconductive deafness by physiological tests. *Arch Otolaryng.* 78:47, 1963.

SANCHEZ LONGO, L. P., FORSTER, F. M., and AUTH, T. L.   A clinical test for sound localization and its applications.   *Neurology* 7:655, 1957.

SCHUKNECHT, H. F.   Further observations of the pathogenisis of presbycusis.   *Arch Otolaryng.* 85:369, 1964.

SPIEGEL, E. A., and SOMMER, I.   Neurology of the Eye, Ear, Nose and Throat.   New York, Grune & Stratton, Inc., 1944.

STEVENS, S. S., and DAVIS, H.   Hearing: Its Psychology and Physiology.   New York, John Wiley & Sons, Inc., 1938.

SZENTÁGOTHAI, J.   The elementary vestibulo-ocular reflex arc.   *J. Neurophysiol.* 13: 395, 1950.

VINNIKOV, Y. A., and TITOVA, L. K.   The Organ of Corti. (Davis, H., trans.)   New York, Consultants Bureau, 1964.

WOLFSON, R. J. (ed.)   The Vestibular System and Its Diseases.   Philadelphia, University of Pennsylvania Press, 1965.

ZILSTORFF-PEDERSEN, K., and PEITERSEN, E.   Vestibulospinal reflexes.   *Arch Otolaryng.* 77:237, 1963.

CHAPTER 15

THE GLOSSOPHARYNGEAL AND VAGUS NERVES

THE GLOSSOPHARYNGEAL and vagus, or *ninth* and *tenth cranial, nerves* are intimately associated with each other and are similar in function. Both have motor and autonomic branches with nuclei of origin in the medulla. Both conduct exteroceptive and general and special visceral sensations to similar or identical fiber tracts in the brain stem. The two nerves leave the skull together and course through the neck in a similar manner, and in many instances they both supply the same structures. The two are frequently affected by the same disease process. Often involvement of one may be difficult to differentiate from that of the other. For these reasons these two nerves are considered together.

THE GLOSSOPHARYNGEAL NERVE

ANATOMY AND PHYSIOLOGY

The *glossopharyngeal nerve,* as its name implies, is distributed principally to the tongue and pharynx. Its *motor fibers* originate in the cells of the *nucleus ambiguus,* which is situated in the reticular formation of the lateral part of the medulla, dorsal to the inferior olivary nucleus and ventromedial to the nucleus of the descending root of the trigeminal nerve (Fig. 108). The fibers first go posteriorly and medially toward the floor of the fourth ventricle, and then sweep laterally and somewhat forward to form the emergent root strands. The nucleus ambiguus, which extends from the level of entrance of the cochlear nerve at the upper border of the medulla to the level of the decussation of the medial lemniscus, or even to that of the beginning of the pyramidal decussation, gives rise also to motor constituents of the vagus and accessory nerves.

The motor elements of the glossopharyngeal nerve go to the pharynx, but probably supply only the *stylopharyngeus muscle.* This muscle draws the posterior wall and the sides of the pharynx upward and lateralward, thus elevating the pharynx and increasing its transverse diameter. The stylopharyngeus also elevates the larynx in the act of swallowing and aids in closing the epiglottis. Certain authorities (Stookey and others) state that the glossopharyngeal nerve innervates also the palato-pharyngeus and palatoglossus muscles, and to a certain extent the superior con-strictor of the pharynx. It is generally accepted, however, that these latter muscles are supplied by the vagus nerve through the pharyngeal plexus, or possibly by the bulbar portion of the accessory nerve, fibers of which are distributed through the vagus. The *cortical center* which regulates the motor function of the ninth nerve is in the lower part of the precentral gyrus; the supranuclear innervation is bi-lateral but mainly crossed, and the motor path traverses the internal capsule, cerebral peduncle, and pons to the medulla.

Autonomic efferent fibers of the glossopharyngeal nerve have their origin in the portion of the dorsal efferent nucleus which is known as the *inferior salivatory nucleus* (Fig. 108). The preganglionic fibers pass through Jacobson's nerve, the tympanic plexus, and the lesser superficial petrosal nerve to the otic ganglion, and the postganglionic fibers through the auriculotemporal branch of the fifth nerve to the parotid gland. The glossopharyngeal nerve carries secretory and vasodilating impulses to the parotid gland. Salivation is also influenced by the sympathetic di-vision of the automatic nervous system, and is stimulated by gustatory and olfactory stimuli, by drugs such as pilocarpine, and by visual and psychic stimuli. The glosso-pharyngeal nerve may, with the facial nerve, supply secretory impulses to the mucous membrane of the posterior and inferior portions of the pharynx and buccal cavity.

The *sensory branches* of the glossopharyngeal nerve have their nuclei in the *petrous ganglion,* situated in a depression in the lower portion of the petrous bone just below the jugular foramen, and in the *superior,* or *jugular, ganglion,* which is less constant and may be a part of the petrous ganglion. Fibers that carry *exterocep-tive sensation* have peripheral pain and temperature endings in the posterior por-tions of the tympanic membrane and the external auditory canal. After passing

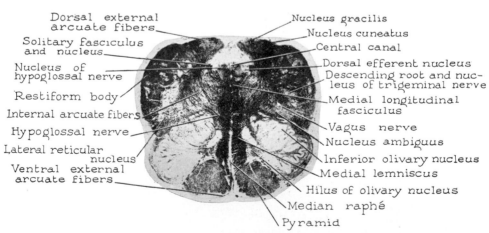

FIG. 108.   Section through medulla at level of inferior olivary nucleus.

through the petrous ganglion they terminate on the descending root of the trigeminal nerve and its nucleus within the medulla; their central connections are identical with those of the other cranial nerves that carry exteroceptive sensation. Fibers that carry *general visceral sensation* from the mucous membrane of the pharyngeal wall, posterior and lateral portions of the soft palate, fauces, uvula, tonsils, tympanic cavity, mastoid cells, eustachian tube, posterior third of the tongue, and carotid body also pass through the petrous ganglion, but terminate on the fasciculus solitarius and its nucleus. Fibers that carry *special visceral,* or *taste, sensation* have receptors in taste buds on the posterior third of the tongue and also terminate on the fasciculus solitarius and its nucleus.

The glossopharyngeal nerve emerges from the medulla by means of three or four to six rootlets which are situated in the groove between the inferior olivary nucleus and the inferior cerebellar peduncle, below the emerging fibers of the seventh nerve and above and in line with those of the tenth (Fig. 20). After leaving the medulla these rootlets unite to form the single nerve which leaves the skull through the jugular foramen with the tenth and eleventh nerves but within a separate sheath of the dura. It is lateral to and in front of these other nerves. Within the jugular foramen are situated the petrous ganglion and the smaller superior, or jugular, ganglion which may be a part of the petrous. At its exit from the skull the nerve passes forward between the internal jugular vein and internal carotid artery and descends in front of the latter vessel, but medial to the vein. It dips beneath the styloid process and follows the posterior border of the stylopharyngeus muscle with which it passes between the internal and external carotid arteries. It curves forward, forming an arch on the side of the neck, and reaches the lateral wall of the pharynx. It then disappears under the hyoglossus muscle, and divides into its constituent branches. The ninth nerve has intimate connections with the fifth, seventh, and tenth nerves and the cervical portion of the sympathetic division of the autonomic nervous system.

The branches of distribution of the glossopharyngeal nerve are the tympanic nerve and the carotid, pharyngeal, muscular, tonsillar, and lingual branches. The *tympanic nerve, or Jacobson's nerve,* arises from the petrous ganglion as its most important branch. It ascends to the tympanic cavity through a small canal on the under surface of the temporal bone, between the carotid canal and the jugular fossa. In the tympanic cavity it divides into branches which form the *tympanic plexus* (Fig. 80). This plexus gives off the lesser superficial petrosal nerve and a branch to the greater superficial petrosal nerve; it receives sensory impulses from the mucous membrane lining of the tympanic cavity, the mastoid air cells, and the auditory canal. The *lesser superficial petrosal nerve* is a continuation of the tympanic nerve, supplemented by a filament from the geniculate ganglion of the facial nerve. It supplies motor (parasympathetic) and sensory roots to the otic ganglion, where there are further communications with the trigeminal and cervical sympathetic nerves. Postganglionic fibers pass in the auriculotemporal branch of the fifth nerve to the parotid gland. *Carotid branches* descend along the internal carotid artery to communicate with the pharyngeal branch of the vagus and the sympathetic nerves. They supply sensation to the carotid body and sinus for reflex control of respiration, heart rate, and blood pressure. *Pharyngeal branches* join those of the vagus and the sympathetic nerves to form the *pharyngeal plexus,* situated opposite the middle constrictor. Glossopharyngeal branches of this plexus supply the mucous membrane of the pharynx and possibly its muscles. The *muscular branch* supplies the stylopharyngeus muscle. *Tonsillar branches* supply the tonsils, the soft palate, and the palatine arches. The *lingual branches* are the terminal divisions. They supply the circumvallate papillae and mucous membrane of the base and posterior third of the tongue, the glosso-epiglottic and pharyngo-epiglottic folds, and the lingual surface of the epiglottis, and they communicate with the lingual nerve.

CLINICAL EXAMINATION

The various functions of the ninth nerve are difficult to test, principally because the areas of distribution are also supplied by other, more important, nerves, and also because many of the structures it supplies are inaccessible.

The *motor supply* of the ninth nerve probably goes to only the *stylopharyngeus muscle.* The only objective manifestation of a motor lesion of the ninth nerve may be a slight unilateral lowering of the palatal arch at rest, although the two sides elevate equally well on effort. The lateral wall of the pharynx may be neither elevated nor retracted. The "curtain movement" or "rideau phenomenon," described under "The Vagus Nerve," is probably associated with a lesion of the tenth rather than the ninth nerve.

The *autonomic functions* of the glossopharyngeal nerve can be evaluated by noting the function of the parotid gland. If highly seasoned foods are placed on the tongue, a copious flow of saliva may be seen to issue from Stenson's duct. This may be called the *salivary reflex;* afferent impulses are carried through the facial and glossopharyngeal nerves, and efferent impulses are conducted from the inferior salivatory nucleus to the parotid gland. Secretion by the gland can also be stimulated by the introvenous injection of five milligrams of pilocarpine. An instrument, the *sialometer,* has been described for the quantitative testing of salivary secretion. This is a two-chambered disk which is about the diameter of a dime and three times as thick. It has an outer suction compartment and an inner collecting chamber, each connected with a rubber tube. The disk is held in place over the nipple of Stenson's duct by mouth suction on the tube leading to the outer compartment. The tube is then clamped off, and the disk remains comfortably in place. The tube leading from the inner chamber is attached to a pipette, and the salivary secretion is measured in hundredths of a cubic centimeter per five-minute period.

The *sensory functions* of the glossopharyngeal nerve can be examined somewhat more readily than the motor functions. Some of these, however, are also difficult to test. The areas to which branches of the glossopharyngeal nerve supply *exteroceptive sensation* are the posterior portion of the tympanic membrane and the posterior wall of the external auditory meatus; these regions are also supplied by the fifth, seventh, and tenth cranial nerves, and, in addition, are inaccessible to clinical testing. The glossopharyngeal nerve supplies *special visceral sensation, taste,* to the posterior third of the tongue, and possibly with the vagus to the epiglottis, the region of the arytenoid cartilage, the hard and soft palates, the anterior pillars, and the posterior pharyngeal wall. This function may be tested in a similar manner to the testing of taste described in Chapter 13, but is examined more satisfactorily by the use of a galvanic current.

The function of the glossopharyngeal nerve said to be most avaliable to clinical testing is that concerned with *general visceral sensation*. Certain areas of this supply, too, are inaccessible, but it is possible to test sensation in the region of the tonsils, fauces, opening of the eustachian tubes, lateral and posterior pharyngeal walls, posterior third of the dorsum of the tongue, and the lateral surfaces and a narrow rim along the inferior margin of the soft palate. With a lesion of the glossopharyngeal nerve these areas may be anesthetic, although owing to overlapping of supply in the throat by the tenth nerve and over the soft palate by the fifth, there may be a border of hypesthesia around the anesthetic zone. It has been found clinically, however, that in a large percentage of patients who have had a rhizotomy of the ninth nerve for glossopharyngeal neuralgia there is little or no objective sensory loss in the above distributions, and it is possible that the pharynx may derive a large part of its sensory innnervation from the tenth nerve.

The examination of the *pharyngeal and palatal reflexes* is an important part of the examination of the glossopharyngeal nerve. The *pharyngeal* or *gag reflex* is elicited by applying a stimulus, such as a tongue blade or an applicator, to the posterior pharyngeal wall, tonsillar region, faucial pillars, or even the base of the tongue. The stimulus should be applied to each side of the pharynx. If the reflex is present, there will be elevation and constriction of the pharyngeal musculature, accompanied by retraction of the tongue. This reflex is used physiologically to initiate deglutition. The afferent impulses of the reflex arc are carried through the glossopharyngeal nerve, whereas the efferent element is conducted through the vagus. The ninth may, however, contribute to the motor portion of the reflex arc, while the tenth may contribute to the sensory. The reflex center is in the medulla.

The *palatal* or *uvular reflex* is tested by stimulating the lateral and inferior surface of the uvula, or soft palate, with a tongue blade or a cotton applicator. Elevation of the soft palate and retraction of the uvula occur simultaneously. If the stimulus is directed toward one side of the soft palate, there is greater elevation on that side, together with ipsilateral deviation. The center for this reflex is also in the medulla. The motor portion of the reflex arc is carried through the vagus (and possibly the glossopharyngeal) nerve and the sensory component through the glossopharyngeal (and possibly the vagus) nerve. The trigeminal nerve, however, also supplies a part of the soft palate, and for this reason the palatal reflex may occasionally be retained in ninth nerve lesions.

These reflexes are absent if there is interruption of either the afferent or the efferent pathway. Occasionally their absence is without pathologic significance, but it usually indicates a lesion of the glossopharyngeal nerve, a finding which is most significant if it is unilateral. In some individuals they are markedly exaggerated. They may be either absent or increased in hysteria. When they are exaggerated, gagging and even retching and vomiting may occur. With pharyngeal anesthesia, whether due to hysteria or an organic lesion, no gagging results.

The *carotid sinus reflex,* which affects control of respiration, blood pressure, and heart rate, also receives its afferent supply from the glossopharyngeal nerve, but since this reflex is more closely related to vagal function, it is discussed in "The Vagus Nerve," as are the *cough* and *swallowing* reflexes.

In summing up the examination of the glossopharyngeal nerve, it should be repeated that the most important as well as the most readily available tests are the evaluation of sensation of the posterior pharyngeal wall and the soft palate, and the appraisal of the pharyngeal and palatal reflexes. Tests of the motor power of the stylopharyngeus muscle, the secretion of the parotid gland, exteroceptive sensations, and taste on the posterior third of the tongue usually are not a part of the routine neurologic examination.

DISORDERS OF FUNCTION

Lesions of the glossopharyngeal nerve, especially isolated lesions, are not common. The nerve is small and is well protected. In fact some authorities state that isolated lesions of the ninth nerve are almost unknown, and that the nerve is involved only in association with the tenth, eleventh, twelfth, and other nerves. It is stated that a lesion of the glossopharyngeal nerve may be followed by slight but transient difficulty in swallowing, especially of dry foods, due to paralysis of the stylopharyngeus muscle, but no disturbance of speech. There is slight difficulty in retracting the lateral pharyngeal wall, and there may be slight lowering of the palatal arch at rest. The tenth nerve is much more important than the ninth in both deglutition and articulation. A lesion of the ninth nerve may be followed by a temporary diminution in secretion of the parotid gland. From a clinical point of view, disturbances of salivation caused by disorders of function of the glossopharyngeal nerve are not differentiated from those caused by disturbances of the facial nerve (Chapter 13). Anesthesia in the distribution of the glossopharyngeal nerve rarely causes clinical symptoms, nor does loss of taste on the back of the tongue. Reflex swallowing and coughing may be lost in glossopharyngeal lesions, due to sensory involvement, as may reflex salivation, due to interference with both taste and salivary secretion. The cough reflex elicited by stimulation of the tympanic membrane or the external auditory meatus is also lost.

Supranuclear lesions contribute to the syndrome of pseudobulbar palsy, but only if bilateral, and since the motor functions of the ninth nerve are minimal, there is not much involvement of this nerve in pseudobulbar lesions. In *nuclear lesions,* such as progressive bulbar palsy, syringobulbia, multiple sclerosis, polioencephalitis, neoplasms, vascular lesions, syphilis, tuberculosis, and botulism, there is usually associated involvement of the other medullary nerves, especially the tenth. *Infranuclear lesions,* such as gunshot or stab wounds in the neck, tumors, thrombosis of the jugular vein, peripheral neuritides, gummas, aneurysms of the carotid artery, skull fractures, and meningitis, also involve the tenth, eleventh, and other nerves. Tumors of the ninth nerve are rare, and usually also affect other nerves. Diseases of the middle ear, pharyngeal abscesses, neoplastic metastases, and cervical adenopathy may cause disorders in the function of the nerve. Herpes zoster of the petrous ganglion has been described, but is rare. The vesicles are said to be present over the pharynx and fauces, and occasionally on the tympanic membrane and in the external auditory canal, with pain deep within the ear. The otalgia which frequently accompanies throat disease is probably in most instances due to reflex involvement of the glossopharyngeal nerve. On the other hand, there is sometimes a disturbance of taste with increased salivation in diseases of the middle ear, due to involvement of the tympanic plexus. Other disorders of taste, such as gustatory hallucinations and parageusias, are described in Chapter 13, as are changes in salivary secretion. Bonnier's syndrome, in which there is involvement of the eighth, ninth, and tenth nerves, is discussed in Chapter 14; the syndromes of Vernet, Villaret, Collet, Sicard, and Babinski-Nageotte, in Chapter 18; and the auriculotemporal syndrome, in Chapter 12.

Perhaps the most important lesion of the ninth nerve is *glossopharyngeal neuralgia,* or "tic douloureux of the ninth nerve." In this condition the patient experiences attacks of severe lancinating pain which originate in the lateral portion of the throat or the tonsillar region and radiate along the course of the eustachian tube to the tympanic membrane, external auditory canal, and adjacent portion of the ear. As is the case in trigeminal neuralgia, there may be trigger zones; they are usually in the pharyngeal wall, fauces, tonsillar regions, or base of the tongue. The pain may be brought on by talking, eating, swallowing, or coughing. The syndrome occasionally initiates or is associated with cardiac arrest, syncope, or convulsions, because of stimulation of the carotid sinus reflex; associated hypersecretion of the ipsilateral parotid gland has also been reported. The condition must be differentiated from neuralgia of the auriculotemporal or superior laryngeal nerves, and symptomatic pain secondary to irritation of the nerve by neoplasms or other disease must always be considered before a diagnosis of glossopharyngeal neuralgia is made. Some authorities differentiate between glossopharyngeal neuralgia, in which the pain radiates from the throat to the ear, and Jacobson's neuralgia, in which the pain is limited to the ear and eustachian tube. The condition is treated by intracranial section of the glossopharyngeal nerve, central to the petrous ganglion; this may be followed by little or no sensory deficit in the throat or loss of taste on the posterior portion of the tongue, in spite of complete relief of pain. Pain in the distribution of the glossopharyngeal nerve may also be relieved by intramedullary tractotomy (Chapter 12).

THE VAGUS NERVE

ANATOMY AND PHYSIOLOGY

The *vagus nerve* is the longest and most widely distributed of the cranial nerves. The nuclei of origin of the vagus nerve are similar to and in many respects identical with those of the glossopharyngeal nerve, and the functions of the tenth parallel those of the ninth nerve.

THE MOTOR PORTION

The *motor fibers* of the tenth nerve have their nuclei in the vagal portion of the *nucleus ambiguus* (Fig. 108). These fibers follow the same course through the medulla as the motor fibers of the glossopharyngeal, and leave the skull through the jugular foramen. The vagus nerve, or the vagus nerve with the bulbar portion of the accessory, supplies all of the striated musculature of the *soft palate, pharynx,* and *larynx* with the exception of the tensor veli palatini and the stylopharyngeus. The tensor veli palatini, which renders the soft palate tense, is discussed in Chapter 12, and the stylopharyngeus, which raises and dilates the pharynx, in the earlier part of this chapter. It is often stated that the levator veli palatini, musculus uvulae, palatoglossus, salpingopharyngeus, palatopharyngeus, and the superior and middle constrictors of the pharynx are supplied by the accessory nerve through the pharyngeal plexus, or that the palatopharyngeus, palatoglossus, and superior constrictor are supplied by the glossopharyngeal nerve. It is more probable, however, that these muscles are supplied by the vagus, or possibly by fibers of the bulbar portion of the accessory nerve which are distributed through the vagus. The *cortical center* which regulates the motor functions of the vagus nerve is in the lower part of the precentral gyrus; the supranuclear innervation is bilateral but predominantly crossed.

The *levator veli palatini* raises the soft palate and pulls it backward; it blocks off the nasal passages in swallowing. The *musculus uvulae,* or *azygos uvulae,* shortens and bends the uvula backward and raises its tip; it helps to block off the nasal passages. The *palatoglossus* elevates the posterior part of the tongue and narrows the fauces in swallowing by approximating the anterior pillars; it also depresses the soft palate. The *palatopharyngeus* draws the pharynx and the thyroid cartilage upward and depresses the soft palate; it approximates the pharyngopalatine arches and closes the posterior nares and faucial orifice. The *salpingopharyngeus,* which blends with the palatopharyngeus, raises the upper and lateral portions of the pharynx. The *superior, middle,* and *inferior constrictors of the pharynx* flatten and contract the pharynx in swallowing. They play an important part in the final acts of deglutition by forcing the food into the esophagus and initiating the peristaltic waves that run through the digestive tract. Since the pharynx may be regarded as a resonator, and alterations of its form result in modifications of the voice, the constrictors of the pharynx are important agents in the production of modulation of speech.

The process of *deglutition* is a complicated one. During the first stage the bolus of food is driven back into the fauces by the pressure of the tongue against the hard palate. At the same time the base of the tongue is retracted and the larynx is raised with the pharynx. During the second stage the entrance to the larynx is closed by the drawing of the arytenoid cartilages forward toward the epiglottis. After leaving the tongue, the bolus passes onto and glides along the posterior surface of the epiglottis for a certain distance. Then the palatoglossi contract behind the bolus and constrict the fauces. The palatine velum is slightly raised by the levator and is made tense by the tensor veli palatini. The palatopharyngei, by their contraction, pull the pharynx upward over the bolus; they nearly come together, and the small interval between them is filled by the uvula. By these means food is prevented from passing into the nasopharynx. The stylopharyngei draw the sides of the pharynx upward and laterally so as to increase its transverse diameter, and its anteroposterior diameter is increased as the tongue and larynx are carried forward in their ascent. The epiglottis is pushed back over the entrance to the larynx, which is closed. The bolus of food is then directed downward and backward into the pharynx. As soon as it is received there the elevator muscles relax, the pharynx descends, the constrictors contract on the bolus, and it is conveyed downward into the esophagus.

All the *intrinsic laryngeal muscles* are supplied by the recurrent nerves, with the exception of the cricothyroid, which is innervated by the external branch of the superior laryngeal nerve. Possibly the arytenoid receives some motor filaments from the internal branch of the superior laryngeal. The laryngeal muscles function by regulating the tension of the vocal cords and by opening and closing the glottis (abducting and adducting the vocal cords). The cricothyroids, posterior and lateral cricoarytenoids, and thyroarytenoids are paired muscles. The *cricothyroids* are the chief tensors of the vocal cords; they stretch, or elongate, the cords by drawing up the arches of the cricoid cartilages and tilting back the upper borders of their laminae; they increase the distance between the vocal processes and the angle of thyroid. The *posterior cricoarytenoids* are the chief abductors; they separate the vocal cords and consequently open the glottis by rotating the arytenoid cartilages outward. The *lateral cricoarytenoids* are the chief adductors; they close the glottis by rotating the arytenoid cartilages inward, so as to approximate the vocal processes. The *thyroarytenoids* draw the arytenoid cartilages forward toward the thyroid, and thus shorten and relax the vocal cords. The deeper portions of the thyroarytenoids (*vocales*) may also, if acting alone, modify the tension and elasticity of the vocal cords, and the external portions may act as adductors and narrow the rim of the glottis by roating the arytenoid cartilages inward. The *arytenoid,* which is unpaired, approximates the arytenoid cartilages and closes the opening of the glottis, especially its posterior aspect. It is composed of oblique and transverse parts. The *oblique arytenoid* acts as sphincter of the upper larynx, whereas the *transverse arytenoid* closes the posterior portion of the glottis. The extrinsic muscles of the larynx include those going to the hyoid bone, which is physiologically a part of the voice apparatus. These muscles are discussed with the infrahyoid muscles (Chapter 17).

THE PARASYMPATHETIC PORTION

The *parasympathetic,* or *visceromotor, constituents* of the vagus nerve arise from the *dorsal efferent nucleus,* a long column of cells, dorsolateral to the hypoglossal nucleus, which extends from the upper pole of the inferior olivary body to the lowest portion of the medulla. In its upper portion it occupies the ala cinerea of the rhomboid fossa, and it extends into the closed part of the medulla along the lateral side of the central canal. The fibers go ventromedially and join those from nucleus ambiguus, and leave the medulla as preganglionic fibers of the craniosacral portion of the autonomic nervous system. They terminate on ganglia close to the viscera they supply and send postganglionic fibers directly to the muscular and glandular structures which they innervate. There may be bilateral cortical innervation, but central control is largely from the hypothalamus.

The *parasympathetic functions* of the vagus nerve are multiple and significant. The vagus is the largest and most important parasympathetic nerve in the body. It is essential to the regulation of *heart action.* It inhibits and depresses the activities of the organ by slowing the beat and weakening the contraction. It is also a vaso-constrictor of the coronary musculature. Vagus stimulation produces bradycardia, whereas vagus paralysis results in tachycardia. Vagus stimulation causes contraction of the smooth muscle of the *trachea, bronchi,* and *bronchioles,* with narrowing of the lumens of these structures, and it also stimulates the glands of the bronchial mucosa. Bronchial spasm may be relieved by the administration of a drug which inhibits vagus action. The vagus nerve supplies the *alimentary tract* from the pharynx through the esophagus, stomach, and small intestine; it also innervates the ascending and transverse colons, and extends to the descending colon. In general it acts as a stimulant to alimentary function. It stimulates the secretion of gastric and pancreatic juices; it contracts the musculature of the gastrointestinal tract to render peristalsis more active; and it relaxes the sphincters of the upper alimentary tract. Through the lienal plexus the vagus stimulates the spleen; through the hepatic plexus it stimulates the liver and gall bladder; and through the celiac plexus it acts on the kidneys and suprarenal bodies. It inhibits suprarenal secretion. It must be remembered, however, that although the vagus nerve has a regulatory effect—motor, secretory, and inhibitory—on many important viscera, the vagus centers in the medulla that control these functions are themselves under the control of higher centers in the cortex and hypothalamus. Furthermore, the functions of the parasympathetic division of the autonomic nervous system cannot be studied without including the study of the sympathetic division. The parasympathetic portion of the vagus nerve is considered in more detail in "The Autonomic Nervous System," Part VI.

THE SENSORY PORTION

The *sensory branches* of the vagus nerve have their nuclei in the jugular ganglion and ganglion nodosum. Fibers which carry *exteroceptive sensation* from the posterior portion of the external acoustic meatus, the adjacent part of the tympanic membrane, and a small area on the posterior aspect of the pinna have their first cell bodies in the jugular ganglion and terminate on the descending root of the trigeminal nerve and its nucleus. Fibers which carry *pain sensation* from the dura mater of the posterior cranial fossa and the transverse sinuses also go through the jugular ganglion to the trigeminal root, although it may be that some of these terminate on the fasciculus solitarius.

Fibers which carry *gustatory sensation* from the anterior and posterior surfaces of the epiglottis and the arytenoids, and with the glossopharyngeal nerve from the hard and soft palates, the anterior pillars, and the posterior pharyngeal wall, have their nuclei in the ganglion nodosum and terminate on the fasciculus solitarius and its nucleus. Fibers which carry *general visceral sensation* from the lower pharynx, the larynx, and probably from all the viscera to which the vagus nerve sends parasympathetic efferent impulses, pass through the ganglion nodosum and terminate on the fasciculus solitarius and its nucleus.

The *jugular ganglion* is situated in the upper part of the jugular foramen. It communicates by means of several delicate twigs with the cranial portion of the accessory nerve, and also with the petrous ganglion of the glossopharyngeal nerve, the facial nerve, and the superior cervical sympathetic ganglion. The *ganglion nodosum* lies just beneath the jugular foramen. The internal branch of the accessory nerve passes through it to fuse with the vagus nerve, and this ganglion communicates with the hypoglossal nerve, the superior cervical sympathetic ganglion, and the loop between the first and second cervical nerves.

DISTRIBUTION AND BRANCHES

The vagus nerve leaves the medulla in the dorsolateral sulcus between the inferior cerebellar peduncle and the inferior olivary body. There are eight or ten filaments that are in line with the ninth nerve above and the eleventh nerve below (Fig. 20). These unite to form a single flattened trunk which courses outward beneath the flocculus of the cerebellum and leaves the skull through the jugular foramen with the ninth and eleventh nerves. It is behind the former and in the same dural compartment as the latter. The vagus nerve passes vertically down the neck within the carotid sheath. It lies between the internal jugular vein and the internal carotid artery as far as the upper border of the thyroid cartilage, and then between the internal jugular vein and the common carotid artery to the base of the neck. Branches leave the nerve in the jugular foramen to supply the meninges and the ear, and other branches leave just below to supply the pharynx and larynx, but the major portion of each vagus nerve goes into the thorax.

The *branches of distribution* of the vagus nerves are as follows: The meningeal and auricular branches arise from the jugular ganglion. The *meningeal branch* follows a recurrent course upward through the jugular foramen to supply the dura mater of the posterior fossa of the skull, especially in the vicinity of the transverse and occipital sinuses. The *auricular branch,* or *nerve of Arnold,* receives a filament from the petrous ganglion of the glossopharyngeal, passes behind the internal jugular vein, and enters the mastoid canaliculus. It then crosses the facial canal, passes between the mastoid process and the external auditory meatus, and divides into two branches. One communicates with the posterior auricular branch of the facial nerve; the other supplies exteroceptive sensation to the posterior part of the tympanic membrane and external acoustic meatus and the skin of the posterior part of the pinna. The pharyngeal and superior laryngeal branches arise from ganglion nodosum. The *pharyngeal branches* pass across the internal carotid artery to the upper border of the middle constrictor of the pharynx, where they divide into numerous filaments which join with branches from the glossopharyngeal and superior laryngeal nerves and sympathetic nerves to form the *pharyngeal plexus.* From this plexus the vagus sends motor nerves to all the muscles of the soft palate and the pharynx, with the exception of the stylopharyngeus and the tensor veli palatini, and sensory nerves are distributed to the mucous membrane of the pharynx. The *superior laryngeal nerve* passes medial to the external and internal carotid arteries and then divides into external and internal laryngeal branches. The *external laryngeal branch* is the smaller and descends on the larynx, beneath the sternothyroid, to innervate the cricothyroid muscle. It supplies branches to the pharyngeal plexus and the inferior constrictor of the pharynx and communicates with the superior cardiac nerve. The *internal laryngeal branch* passes between the middle and inferior constrictors of the pharynx, enters the larynx through the thyrohyoid membrane, and supplies sensory filaments to the mucous membrane covering the pharyngeal and internal surfaces of the larynx as far as the vocal cord, and branches to the mucous membranes of the epiglottis, the base of the tongue, and the aryepiglottic fold.

The *superior cardiac branches* arise from the vagus in the upper and lower parts of the neck. They communicate with the cardiac branches of the sympathetic division to form the *cardiac plexus*. The *recurrent nerves* are given off in the upper thorax and ascend to the larynx. That on the right arises in front of the subclavian artery, winds backward around it, and passes between the esophagus and the trachea and behind the common carotid artery and the thyroid gland. The left recurrent nerve arises on the left of the arch of the aorta, winds below the aorta, ascends to the side of the trachea, and follows a course similar to that of its fellow nerve. Both nerves pass under the lower border of the inferior constrictor of the pharynx and enter the larynx behind the articulation of the inferior cornu of the thyroid cartilage with the cricoid. They are distributed to all the muscles of the larynx except the crico-thyroid; they communicate with the internal branch of the superior laryngeal nerve, and supply sensation to the mucous membrane of the lower part of the larynx and the trachea. The *inferior cardiac branches* arise on the right from the trunk of the vagus and from the recurrent and on the left from the recurrent only, and end in the cardiac plexus.

Within the thorax, *bronchial* and *pulmonary branches* communicate with filaments from the sympathetic division to form the *pulmonary plexuses; esophageal branches* unite with each other and with filaments from the splanchnic nerves and thoracic sympathetic ganglia to form the *esophageal plexus;* and *pericardial branches* are given off by the vagus nerves and the pulmonary and esophageal plexuses. Within the abdomen branches of the two vagus complexes enter the *gastric, lienal, celiac,* and *hepatic plexuses.*

CLINICAL EXAMINATION

In spite of its great size, its many functions, and its importance in the regulation of essential visceral processes, clinical testing of the vagus nerve is carried out with difficulty, and means for its examination are inadequate.

EXAMINATION OF THE MOTOR FUNCTIONS

The *motor branches* of the vagus nerve, which supply the soft palate, pharynx, and larynx, are more available to clinical testing than are most of the other branches of the nerve.

The Soft Palate: In the examination of the soft palate one observes the position of the soft palate and uvula at rest, and the position and movements during quiet breathing and on phonation. Congenital asymmetries or surgical absence of the uvula are noted, the *palatal reflex* is tested, and the character of the voice and the ability to swallow are appraised. Special attention should be paid to dysarthria and to dysphagia for liquids or solids.

Normally the uvula hangs in the midline and rises in the midline on phonation. In a *unilateral vagus paralysis* there is weakness of the soft palate, owing to disturbance of function of the levator veli palatini and musculus uvulae on the involved side. There is unilateral lowering with flattening of the palatal arch, and the medial raphé is deviated to the normal side. On phonation the uvula is retracted to the nonparalyzed side (Fig. 109). The normally functioning tensor veli palatini, which is innervated by the trigeminal nerve, may prevent marked drooping of the palate. The palatal reflex is lost on the involved side, in this instance owing to interruption of the motor rather than the sensory pathways. There usually is little difficulty with articulation or deglutition, although in acute unilateral lesions there may be a "nasal" quality to the speech, dysphagia, more marked for liquids than solids, and some regurgitation of fluids into the nose when swallowing; these are usually transient.

In *bilateral vagus paralysis* the palate cannot be elevated on phonation although it may not droop markedly, owing to the action of the normally functioning tensors of the palate. The palatal reflex is absent bilaterally. The nasal cavity is not closed from the oral cavity, and on speaking air escapes from the latter into the former. The resonance mediated by the nasal cavity gives speech a characteristic "nasal" quality. There is special difficulty with palatal and guttural sounds such as *k, q,* and *ch.* The sound *b* becomes *m, d* becomes *n,* and *k* becomes *ng.* The speech is similar to that of a patient with a cleft palate. There may be marked dysphagia, especially for liquids, and fluids may be regurgitated into the nose on attempts to swallow.

The Pharynx: Functions and disorders of the pharynx are tested by noting the contraction of the pharyngeal muscles on phonation, by observing the eleva-

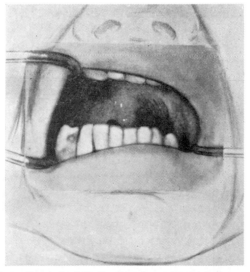

Fig. 109.   Unilateral paralysis of soft palate. (Purves-Stewart J.: The Diagnosis of Nervous Diseases. Baltimore, Williams & Wilkins Company, 1945.)

tion of the larynx on swallowing, by testing the pharyngeal reflex, and by noting the character of the patient's speech; he should also be given both liquids and solids to swallow, and any difficulty noted. If the superior constrictor of one side is not functioning, one may observe Vernet's "rideau phenomenon," or a "curtain movement" of the pharyngeal wall toward the nonparalyzed side, on testing the pharyngeal reflex or at the beginning of phonation. Normally the larynx is elevated on swallowing; in paralysis of the middle and inferior constrictors this is absent or it may occur once or twice, but not repeatedly. The pharyngeal reflex is absent on one side in unilateral lesions, on both in bilateral lesions, owing to interruption of the motor portion of the reflex arc.

In paresis of the pharynx there may be some dysarthria, but this usually is minimal unless there is associated involvement of the soft palate or the larynx. Coughing may be impaired, and there may be loss of the cough reflex. There may also be difficulty in swallowing, especially in swallowing solid foods. Dysphagia, however, is marked only in acute unilateral or in bilateral lesions.

The Larynx: In the examination of the larynx the character and quality of the voice, abnormalities of articulation, difficulty with respiration, and impairment of coughing are noted. A mirror examination of the larynx or a direct laryngoscopic examination should be carried out if there is hoarseness which is not readily explained by an acute inflammatory process, if there is dysarthria, or if there are any suggestions of vagus nerve involvement. Normally the vocal cords are abducted during inspiration (Fig. 110) and are adducted on phonation and coughing. In addition, there is reflex adduction on irritation of the larynx. In examining the larynx one notes the appearance and position of the vocal cords at rest, their movements during phonation and inspiration, and their response on coughing and irritation. One may also test sensation of the upper larynx, a function of the internal branch of the superior laryngeal nerve. In paralysis of the laryngeal musculature there is often difficulty in speaking, but occasionally there is almost complete involvement of the larynx on one side without an appreciable effect on the voice.

In *paralysis of the cricothyroids,* which are supplied by the superior laryngeal nerve, there is defective tension, with elongation of the vocal cord in phonation (Fig. 111); high tones are lost, and the voice is deep and hoarse and fatigues easily. Inspiration is normal, and there is neither dyspnea nor stridor. In *paralysis of the thyroarytenoid* there is little difficulty with abduction, but adduction is slightly impaired. In *bilateral thyroarytenoid paralysis* the glottis has an oval instead of linear appearance during phonation (Fig. 112); the voice is hoarse, but there is neither dyspnea nor stridor. In *paralysis of the arytenoid* the glottis is closed only anteriorly, and the larynx shows a small triangular slit posteriorly during phonation (Fig. 113); inspiration is normal.

In *unilateral abductor palsy* the involved cord lies close to the midline and cannot be abducted on inspiration (Fig. 114). The voice may be hoarse, but in general phonation and coughing are little affected, since adduction is normal (Fig. 115). There is little dyspnea for the normal cord is abducted in inspiration, but there may be some inspiratory stridor. In *bilateral abductor paralysis* both cords lie close to the midline and cannot be abducted. The voice may be hoarse, but phonation

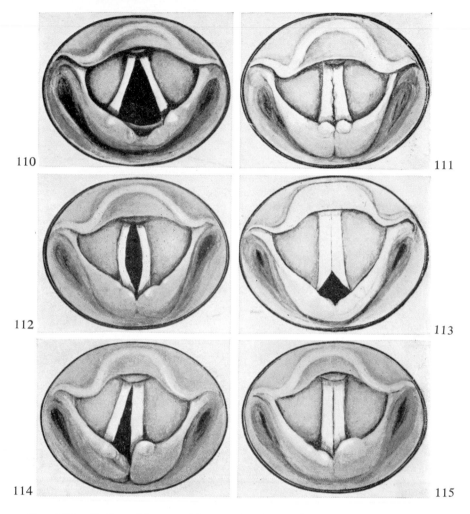

FIG. 110. Reflected image of larynx showing position of vocal cords during normal deep inspiration.

FIG. 111. Reflected image of larynx in a case of paralysis and superior laryngeal nerves, with weakness of cricothyroid muscles and wrinkling and defective tension of vocal cords on phonation.

FIG. 112. Reflected image of vocal cords in a case of bilateral thyroarytenoid paralysis, seen during phonation.

FIG. 113. Reflected image of vocal cords in a case of paralysis of the arytenoid, seen during phonation.

FIG. 114. Reflected image of vocal cords in a case of left abductor paralysis, seen during inspiration.

FIG. 115. Reflected image of vocal cords in a case of left abductor paralysis, seen during phonation. (Fig. 110–118 from: Jackson, C., and Jackson, C. L.: Diseases of the Nose, Throat, and Ear, Including Bronchoscopy and Esophagoscopy. Philadelphia, W. B. Saunders Company, 1945.)

is often only slightly affected because both cords can still be adducted, and coughing is normal. There is severe dyspnea with inspiratory stridor, since the cords are drawn even closer on inspiration, but expiration is not affected.

In *adductor palsy* the cords are not adducted in phonation (Fig. 116) although they meet in the midline in coughing. Abduction is unimpaired and inspiration is normal. There is neither stridor nor dyspnea, and coughing is normal, but the voice is either lost or cannot be raised above a whisper. The loss of voice is usually sudden. The difficulty is almost always bilateral, and is generally of psychogenic origin. Unilateral adductor palsy is occasionally seen in trauma and in peripheral neuritides; there is paralysis of one lateral cricoarytenoid, with hoarseness and also impairment of coughing.

In a *total unilateral palsy* both adduction and abduction are affected and the involved cord lies in the cadaveric position, motionless in midabduction. The voice is low-pitched and hoarse and there is difficulty in coughing, but phonation may not be much affected since the normal cord may cross the midline (Fig. 117). There is little or no dyspnea, and inspiratory stridor is absent or is slightly present on deep inspiration. In *bilateral palsy* both cords are in the cadaveric position and phonation and coughing are lost (Fig. 118). There is marked dyspnea with stridor, especially on inspiration.

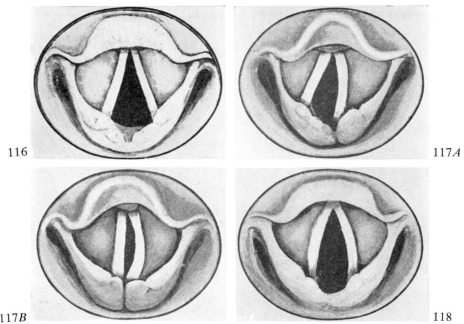

116   117*A*

117*B*   118

Fig. 116.   Reflected image of vocal cords in a case of bilateral adductor paresis, seen during attempted phonation.
Fig. 117.   Reflected image of vocal cords in a case of left unilateral paralysis, seen during: *A*, inspiration; *B*, phonation. The affected cord is in the cadaveric position.
Fig. 118.   Reflected image of vocal cords in a case of bilateral incomplete paresis. Both cords are in the cadaveric position.

The most common type of laryngeal palsy is the result of a *unilateral recurrent nerve lesion*. Three stages have been described in a recurrent paralysis. The first manifestation is lessened abduction on the involved side, due to isolated involvement of the posterior cricoarytenoid; next there is tension, or secondary contracture, of the adductors; and finally there is complete paralysis with the cord in the cadaveric position. The uninvolved cord crosses the midline on adduction. The voice may be coarse and husky, and there is loss of the ability to sing. Coughing may be ineffective, but there is little dyspnea or stridor. There never is aphonia, however, for the healthy side crosses the midline to meet the parlyzed cord. Owing to anatomic variability of the recurrent nerves, especially of their terminal divisions, the paralyses with lesions of these nerves may be complex and varied. With slight weakness of the vocal cords or pharynx, hoarseness and dysphagia may be apparent only on turning the head to either side. With *bilateral recurrent paralysis* there is stridor, and the dyspnea may be so marked that tracheotomy is necessary. The absence of laryngeal movements in bilateral recurrent palsy is called *Gerhardt's sign*.

EXAMINATION OF THE AUTONOMIC FUNCTIONS

Although the vagus nerve is the most important parasympathetic nerve in the body, its *autonomic functions* are not easily tested clinically. Certain functions, however, must be evaluated, and special attention should be paid to the cardiac and respiratory rates and rhythms in every neurologic examination. Because the pulse may be slowed with medullary compression or increased intracranial pressure, the rate should be followed closely in all patients with intracranial disease.

Since the vagus nerve is the inhibitor of the heart, paralysis of it causes tachycardia, whereas stimulation causes bradycardia. It is apparent, however, that abnormalities of cardiac rate may be due to many other causes. The heart rate and, to a certain extent, the respiratory rate may be slowed slightly by pressure on the eyeball or by painful stimulation of the skin on the side of the neck. This is called the *oculocardiac reflex*. The afferent portion of the reflex arc is carried through the trigeminal nerve and the efferent portion through the vagus nerve. The reflex is inconstant, unstandardized, and influenced by emotion. Usually the pulse is not slowed more than five to eight beats per minute, and it may be necessary to test the response during electrocardiography in order to be certain of the results. The slowing may be accompanied by extra systoles. The oculocardiac reflex is an index of vagal hyperirritability; it is absent in vagus paralysis and increased in vagotonic individuals. It is said to be decreased in sympathicotonia and either exaggerated or diminished in hyperthyroidism. It may be absent in tabes and in complete heart block, and may be abolished by the use of atropine. It is demonstrated to a significant degree only in such pathologic conditions as paroxysmal tachycardia, where the overactivity of the heart may on occasion be controlled by vagus stimulation. The oculocardiac reflex is also called *Aschner's ocular phenomenon*.

Vagus paralysis may also cause depression, acceleration, or irregularities of the respiratory rate and alterations of gastrointestinal function. Detailed investigations of cardiac abnormalities, of pulmonary function and vital capacity, and of the gastrointestinal tract are usually not considered as parts of the neurologic examination.. Some of the autonomic functions of the vagus nerve can be tested by pharmacologic means, and are discussed in "The Autonomic Nervous System," Part VI. It is common knowledge that the bronchial spasms present in asthma may be relieved by atropine, a drug which has a paralyzing effect on structures innervated by postganglionic cholinergic nerves, and that cardiospasm or spasm of the intestine may also be relieved by atropine or belladonna, whereas peristalsis may be stimulated by the use of physostigmine or neostigmine.

EXAMINATION OF THE SENSORY FUNCTIONS

The *sensory elements* of the vagus nerve cannot be adequately tested. The *exteroceptive* branches supply the tympanic membrane, part of the external acoustic meatus, and part of the pinna. These areas are difficult to examine, and furthermore are also supplied by the fifth, seventh, and ninth cranial nerves. Sensation to the meninges cannot be tested. *Taste* in the region of the epiglottis is difficult to examine, and is probably of no clinical significance. The *general visceral afferent* supply, too, is distributed to areas that are inaccessible for testing, except for the lower pharynx and larynx. The vagus nerve also carries some sensation from the tonsillar area and posterior pharyngeal wall; the ninth nerve is considered to be more important in this respect, and while there is rarely anesthesia of the pharynx in isolated vagus lesions, preserved sensation after interruption of the ninth nerve indicates that the vagus also contributes to pharyngeal sensation.

EXAMINATION OF THE REFLEXES

The vagus nerve plays a part in many *autonomic,* or *visceral, reflexes,* and loss of these reflexes may follow a lesion of the tenth nerve.

The Vomiting Reflex: The palatal and pharyngeal reflexes have already been mentioned. Exaggeration of these reflexes may cause the *retching, vomiting,* or *regurgitation reflex,* also carried through the ninth and tenth nerves. Excessive stimulation or hyperirritability may initiate reverse peristalsis in the esophagus and stomach, with forceful ejection of material from the stomach. The reflex center is probably in the region of the dorsal efferent nucleus; such a center has been described in the dorsolateral border of the lateral reticular formation of the medulla. The vomiting reflex may also be produced by stimulation of the wall of the lower pharynx, the esophagus, the stomach, the duodenum, or the lower gastrointestinal tract, in all of which the sensory portion of the reflex arc is carried through the tenth nerve to the fasciculus solitarius. From there the impulse is relayed to the dorsal efferent nucleus, and also down the spinal cord to innervate the diaphragm and the abdominal muscles, as well as sympathetic centers. The cardiac sphincter is inhibited by impulses mediated through the vagus nerve, and the pyloric sphincter is constricted by impulses which leave the spinal cord through the splanchnic nerves. Vomiting may also be precipitated by stimulation of the internal ear (vestibular portion of the eighth nerve). There may be associated phenomena such as salivation, hyperhidrosis, and pallor resulting from stimulation of vasomotor and secretory centers.

The Swallowing Reflex: Stimulation of the pharyngeal wall or back of the tongue initiates swallowing movements. The afferent impulses are carried through the fifth, ninth, and tenth nerves, and the efferent impulses through ninth, tenth, and twelfth nerves. Food is moved into the esophagus by action of the tongue, palatine arches, soft palate, and pharynx. The presence of the bolus of food acts as a stimulus for the various stages of the process of deglutition.

The Cough Reflex: Stimulation of the mucous membrane of the pharynx, larynx, trachea, or bronchial tree, or stimulation of the tympanic membrane or external auditory canal elicits a cough response. The afferent portions of the reflex arc are carried by the glossopharyngeal and vagus nerves to the fasciculus solitarius. and efferent impulses descend to the pharyngeal muscles, tongue, palate, and larynx, and to the diaphragm, intercostals, and abdominal muscles. The reflex response consists of a deep inspiration followed by forced expiration with the glottis momentarily closed by approximation of the vocal bands. There is spasm of the diaphragm and throat. The pressure of the abdominal muscles and the diaphragm continues until sufficient tension is exerted to open the vocal cords.

The Nasal, Sneeze, or Sternutatory Reflex: A violent expulsion of air through the nose and mouth occurs in response to stimulation of the nasal mucous membrane. The afferent impulse is carried through the fifth nerve and the efferent through the vagus and phrenic nerves with associated function of the fifth, seventh. ninth, and upper thoracic nerves, and the sympathetic pathways. The reflex center is in the brain stem and upper spinal cord. The reflex response is similar to that in coughing, but there is also contraction of the faucial pillars with descent of the soft palate, so that the air is directed chiefly through the nose.

The Sucking Reflex: In the infant, stimulation of the lips is followed by the production of a series of sucking movements which involve the lips, tongue, and jaw. The afferent impulses are carried through the fifth and ninth nerves, and the efferent through the fifth, seventh, ninth, tenth, twelfth, and spinal nerves. The response is elicited by touching, stroking, or tapping the lips near the buccal angle. The baby will turn his head toward the stimulus, open his mouth, and make sucking movments with the lips and tongue. If an object, such as a nipple or finger, is placed at the mouth, it is grasped by the upper and lower lips, hard palate, tongue, and mandible. The pharynx is closed off from the nasal cavity and the mandible is depressed, causing a partial vacuum. Respirations are interrupted only during deglutition. This reflex is normally present at birth, but is lost after infancy. Like the snout reflex, it is present in adults with supranuclear pyramidal tract involvement and those with diffuse brain disease and severe cerebral degenerations. Under such circumstances, testing for the orbicularis oris reflex causes not only puckering or protrusion of the lips, but also sucking and even tasting, chewing, and swallowing movements. This exaggerated response is also known as the *Atz, mastication,* or *"wolfing" reflex.* When present, it may be elicited by lightly touching, stroking, or tapping the lips, stroking the tongue, or stimulating the palate. When grossly exaggerated, there may be automatic opening of the mouth and smacking and chewing movements even when an object is brought near the lips.

Hiccup or Singultus: This is a sudden reflex contraction of the diaphragm causing a forceful inspiration. There is an associated laryngeal spasm with sudden arrest of the inspiration by closure of the glottis, which produces the peculiar inspiratory sound. The phenomenon usually results from some irritation of the stomach wall or the diaphragm or occasionally the pharynx. The phrenic nerves are the important pathways, but the vagus nerve may also play a part, through both its sensory and motor functions.

Yawning: Yawning is deep prolonged inspiration, usually involuntary, through the open mouth; it is often accompanied by stretching movements of the neck and body. Under most circumstances it can be considered a complex respiratory reflex which occurs during sleepiness and fatigue, usually a response to chemical stimulation. It may serve to restore depleted oxygen in the blood. Yawning may be a symptom of encephalitis or brain stem or cerebral disorders, it may also be brought on by suggestion and boredom.

The Carotid Sinus Reflex: Stimulation of the carotid sinus or of the carotid body by digital pressure at the bifurcation of the common carotid artery (either unilateral or bilateral) causes reflex stimulation of the vagus nerve and of the cerebral centers governing vegetative functions. The afferent impulses are carried through the carotid branch of the glossopharyngeal nerve to the medulla, and efferent impulses are carried through the vagus and sympathetic nerves. Normally, pressure on or massage over the carotid sinus or body causes no change in vegetative functions, but in certain susceptible individuals, usually those with arteriosclerosis or hypertension, such stimulation may cause slowing of the heart rate, fall in blood pressure, decrease in cardiac output, and peripheral vasodilatation; this is the *hyperactive carotid sinus reflex.* In pathologic states, such stimulation may cause vertigo, pallor, loss of consciousness (*carotid sinus syncope*), and occasionally convulsions. It must be borne in mind, however, that in individuals with extensive atherosclerotic involvement of the carotid and/or vertebrobasilar arterial systems, pressure on one carotid artery may cause syncope and sometimes convulsions or contralateral hemiplegia secondary to cerebral ischemia. If either hyperactivity of this reflex or carotid artery stenosis is suspected, pressure over the sinus and artery should be carried out with caution, and only unilateral stimulation should be used. Three types of pathologic carotid sinus syndrome responses have been described: the vagal type, in which the predominant response is slowing of the heart rate; the depressor type, in which the fall in blood pressure is the principal manifestation, and the cerebral type, characterized by syncope or loss of consciousness. Receptors similar to those in the carotid sinus and body are found in the aortic sinus and body. Impulses aroused by stimulation of these latter structures are probably carried through the vagus nerve. Both the carotid and aortic receptors respond to chemical as well as mechanical stimuli, and are important in the regulation of both circulation and respiration. Carotid sinus syncope has been relieved by either denervation of the carotid body or intracranial section of the glossopharyngeal nerve.

In summing up the examination of the vagus nerve, it should be stated that the motor functions are the most readily available ones for clinical testing. The soft palate is examined at rest and on phonation, and the palatal reflex is tested. The pharynx is examined during speaking and swallowing, and the pharyngeal reflex is elicited. Dysphagia and dysarthria are appraised. If there is any disturbance of speech, the larynx is examined directly or indirectly. Of the autonomic functions, those most available to testing are the regulation of heart and respiratory rates. The most important autonomic reflexes, as far as the examination is concerned, are the oculocardiac and carotid sinus reflexes, although the integrity of the vagus nerve is essential to many important visceral reflexes. The sensory functions are not significant in the clinical examination.

DISORDERS OF FUNCTION

Total paralysis of one vagus nerve is followed by paresis of the soft palate, pharynx, and larynx on the involved side, together with certain sensory and autonomic changes. The paresis of the soft palate and pharynx are not marked, but there may be minimal difficulty in swallowing both liquids and solids. The voice may be moderately impaired, with either a nasal quality or hoarseness. The only definite sensory change is an anesthesia of the larynx due to involvement of the superior laryngeal nerve, although it is sometimes possible to demonstrate loss of sensation behind the pinna and in the external auditory canal. The palatal and pharyngeal reflexes are absent on the involved side, but such autonomic reflexes as those which lead to vomiting, coughing, and sneezing are usually retained in unilateral lesions. Heart action may be increased and the oculocardiac reflex may be lost on the involved side, but usually there are few cardiac symptoms. Gastric disturbances are slight.

Bilateral vagus paralysis is not compatible with life. It causes complete paralysis of the palate, pharynx, and larynx, with marked dysphagia and dysarthria; rapid, irregular heart action; slow, irregular, dyspneic breathing; loss of hunger and thirst, vomiting, abdominal pain, and dilatation and atonia of the stomach and intestines.

There may be paralysis of any branch of the vagus nerve. Involvement of the meningeal and auricular branches causes changes which are entirely sensory. Paralysis of the pharyngeal branches produces difficulty in swallowing. The function of the superior and middle constrictors of the pharynx is especially affected, and there may be paralysis of the soft palate; palatal and pharyngeal reflexes are lost. Paralysis of the superior laryngeal nerve causes anesthesia of the larynx if the internal branch is involved, and paralysis of the cricothyroid if the external branch is involved. There may also be weakness of the inferior constrictor of the pharynx. Paralysis of the recurrent nerve, which is the most common type of vagus lesion, has been discussed in detail. Isolated involvement of the visceral branches with sparing of the others is unusual.

Irritation of the vagus nerve may be followed by slowing of the pulse, reflex coughing and vomiting, and hypertonus of the gastrointestinal tract. The tachycardia and projectile vomiting which occur with increased intracranial pressure may be the result of vagal irritation. Various respiratory disturbances associated with vagus nerve involvement include Cheyne-Stokes', Biot's, and Kussmaul's breathing; respiratory tics, forced yawning, and other anomalies of breathing seen in chronic encephalitis; and the hyperventilation syndrome that occurs in hysteria.

This latter may lead to changes in acid-base equilibrium with symptoms suggestive of tetany.

Spasm of the constrictors of the pharynx, also known as pharyngismus or crico-pharyngeal spasm, may be associated with central nervous system disorders, such as rabies, or may be present secondary to local irritation. It is frequently of psychogenic origin, and is responsible for the so-called *globus hystericus* in which there is a feeling of constriction or of a foreign body in the throat. Spasm of the larynx may be present in rabies and tetany and possibly in hysteria, although in the latter the spasm is in adduction. It may also follow irritation of the larynx and excessive use of the voice. In laryngismus stridulous in children there is the sudden development of laryngeal spasm with "crowing" respiration and cyanosis. This may occur either as an independent disease, especially in connection with rickets, or in laryngeal inflammations. A partial laryngeal spasm may result in stuttering, with explosive speech, or in tic-like or compulsive coughs. The "epileptic cry" is probably due to spasm of the larynx. In asthma and in acute allergic states such as anaphylactic shock there may be spasm not only of the larynx, but also of the bronchi and bronchioles. Spasm of the esophagus, cardia, pylorus, and intestinal tract may be caused by organic and nonorganic factors. Myoclonus, or "nystagmus," of the palate and sometimes of the pharynx and larynx is seen in lesions of the olivodentorubrometencephalic pathways. This is rhythmic, and the contractions may be from 50 to 240 per minute.

In *neuralgia of the superior laryngeal nerve* there are lancinating pains which radiate from the larynx to the ear. This bears some resemblance to glossopharyngeal neuralgia, but the trigger zone is usually in the region of either the pyriform sinus or the thyroid cartilage, and the pain is brought on by talking or swallowing. Occasionally the pain radiates to the angle of the jaw before going to the ear. Similar pain may be present on a reflex basis. Pain from a sore throat may radiate to the ear owing to vagus stimulation, as it does in stimulation of the glossopharyngeal nerve. Laryngeal crises have been described in tabes. There may be hyperesthesia of the tragus in vagus irritation, and pressure on the external auditory meatus may cause coughing.

The so-called vasovagal attacks described by Gowers are characterized by palpitation, peripheral vasomotor constriction, nausea, faintness, dyspnea, gastric distress, slow pulse, cold extremities, flatulence, increased gastric motility and acidity, precordial distress, respiratory arrhythmia, and often by fear of impending death. He expressed the belief that these symptoms were the result of overactivity of the vagus system, but it is recognized today that they are manifestations of imbalance of the divisions of the autonomic nervous system, and that they are probably of psychogenic rather than organic origin. They often appear in association with anxiety and may constitute the predominant symptoms of the anxiety psychoneurosis; they may contribute to the syndrome of hyperventilation. Somewhat similar symptoms are present in the so-called diencephalic seizures, and may be an important part of temporal lobe seizures. The syndromes of *vagotonia* and *sympathicotonia* are discussed in "The Autonomic Nervous System," Part VI.

Vagus involvement may result from supranuclear, nuclear, or infranuclear lesions. *Supranuclear involvement* is significant mainly when it is bilateral. In pseudobulbar palsy the dysphagia and dysarthria are due in part to bilateral supranuclear vagus involvement. Irritative supranuclear lesions are rarely encountered. Extrapyramidal supranuclear involvement may cause difficulty with swallowing and talking, and in postencephalitic states there may be tics and anomalies of respiratory rhythm. Laryngeal spasm with stridor may be present with Parkinson's disease.

Nuclear involvement may occur in progressive bulbar palsy (glossopalatolabial palsy), polioencephalitis inferior, bulbar poliomyelitis, the Guillain-Barré syndrome, neoplasms, vascular lesions such as thromboses and hemorrhages, multiple sclerosis, amyotrophic lateral sclerosis, diphtheria, developmental anomalies of the base of the skull, tabes dorsalis, and many other conditions. In botulism there may be dysphonia, dysphagia, vomiting, dry mouth, and respiratory difficulties. If the nuclear lesion is a degenerative one, such as occurs in progressive bulbar palsy, amyotropic lateral sclerosis, and syringomyelia, there may be fasciculations in the palatal, pharyngeal, and laryngeal muscles. If there is medullary compression at the foramen magnum due to trauma, increased intracranial pressure, or edema of the brain, there may be marked slowing of the heart and respiratory rates, projectile vomiting, and increased or decreased blood pressure. This syndrome, along with progressive bulbar and pseudobulbar palsies and such specific nuclear syndromes as those of Avellis, Schmidt, Tapia, Babinski-Nageotte, and Cestan-Chenais, etc., are described in Chapter 18.

Infranuclear involvement may follow lesions at the base of the brain, in the jugular foramen, or along the course of the vagus nerves. Extramedullary but intracranial involvement occurs in association with meningitis, basal hemorrhages, extramedullary tumors, intracranial aneurysms, and skull fractures. Lesions at the jugular foramen or in the retroparotid space may involve also the ninth, eleventh, twelfth, and cervical sympathetic nerves. Such lesions may be due to stab wounds, gunshot wounds, periostitis, thrombosis of the jugular bulb, retroparotid abscesses, etc., and may result in the syndromes of Vernet, Villaret, Sicard, or Collet (Chapter 18). Either intracranially or extracranially the vagus may be involved in polyneuritis cranialis or in the toxic, deficiency and other multiple neuritides that affect peripheral nerves in other parts of the body. Diphtheritic involvement of the tenth nerve is not rare; in this condition there is often paralysis of the soft palate with nasal speech and regurgitation of fluids. Individual branches of the vagus nerve may be involved by disease processes in the neck, upper mediastinum, thorax, and abdomen. Tumors occasionally affect the vagus nerve, but the diagnosis may be difficult. The vagus, along with the other lower cranial nerves, is often affected in tumors of the glomus jugulare or chemodectomas. Involvement of the esophageal musculature in dystrophia mytonica may cause difficulty in swallowing.

The *recurrent nerve* is the most frequently affected. This may be damaged by tumors in the neck, especially carcinoma of the thyroid, cervical adenopathy, metastatic lesions, Hodgkin's disease, lymphosarcoma, aortic aneurysms, mitral stenosis with enlargement of the left auricle, pericarditis, mediastinal and apical tumors, stab wounds in the neck, or accidental trauma during a thyroidectomy or phrenicectomy. The *superior laryngeal* and *pharyngeal branches* may be involved in trauma, or in neoplasms or abscesses in the neck. Muscular weakness of the pharynx and larynx with dysphagia and dysarthria may be prominent symptoms in myasthenia gravis.

Psychogenic disturbances frequently affect the structures innervated by the vagus nerve. Loss of palatal and pharyngeal reflexes occurs in hysteria; this may be of diagnostic value. In the so-called globus hystericus, pharyngismus, esophagismus, or cricopharyngeal spasm, the patient may complain not only of constriction and a sense of a lump in the throat but also of dysphagia. In hysterical aphonia or dysphonia there is paresis of the adductors of the larynx. Cardiospasm, pylorospasm, spastic constipation, and various forms of functional dyspepsia may in part be due to vagus involvement. Asthma, respiratory tics, and other anomalies of respiration may result from psychogenic involvement, and irregularity in the heart rate, tachycardia, bradycardia, and palpitation may be a reflection of psychogenic influence on the cardiac system. The syndrome of vagotonia and the vasovagal attacks have been mentioned.

Interest has recently been revived in the treatment of gastric and duodenal ulcers by vagotomy. Incomplete vagotomies performed in the past were not followed by beneficial effects, but complete vagotomies, done by either the supradiaphragmatic or the transabdominal approach, have been effective in relieving the symptoms in a large percentage of patients. There is relief of pain with healing of the ulcer, probably because of reduction of gastric motility and decrease in the volume and acidity of gastric secretion. The interruption of the efferent autonomic impulses to the stomach may have other, less tangible, beneficial effects. Thus far there have been no reports of complications which may be associated with interruption of vagus impulses to other abdominal structures. Vagotomy has also been performed for the treatment of ulcerative colitis and regional enteritis and for the relief of the pain with gastric crises of tabes dorsalis. The cough reflex has been interrupted and bronchial pain relieved by section of the vagus nerves below the origin of the recurrent nerves.

REFERENCES

AMOLS, W., and MERRITT, H. H.   Vomiting: Neural mechanisms and control by chlorpromazine.   *Neurology* 5:645, 1955.

ATKINSON, M., KRAMER, P., WYMAN, S. M., and INGELFINGER, F. J.   The dynamics of swallowing: I. Normal pharyngeal mechanisms.   *J. Clin. Investigation* 36:581, 1957.

BARBIZET, J.   Yawning.   *J. Neurol., Neurosurg. & Psychiat.* 21:203, 1958.

BOYD, A. K.   Vagotomy and the anatomic variations in the vagus nerve.   *Am. J. Surg.* 78:4, 1949.

BRODAL, A.   Central course of afferent fibers for pain in facial, glossopharyngeal and vagus nerves.   *Arch. Neurol. & Psychiat.* 57:292, 1947.

DRAGSTEDT, L. R.   Vagotomy for gastroduodenal ulcer.   *Ann. Surg.* 122:973, 1945.

ENGEL, G. L.   On the existence of the cerebral type of carotid sinus syncope.   *Neurology* 9:565, 1959.

FAY, T.   Observations and results from intracranial section of the glossopharyngeus and vagus nerves in man.   *J. Neurol. & Psychopath.* 8:110, 1927.

FERRIS, E. B., JR., CAPPS, R. B., and WEISS, S.   Relation of the carotid sinus to the autonomic nervous system and the neuroses.   *Arch. Neurol. & Psychiat.* 37:365, 1937.

FURSTENBERG, A. C., and MAGIELSKI, J. E.   A motor pattern in nucleus ambiguus: Its clinical significance. *Ann. Otol., Rhin. & Laryng.* 64:788, 1955.

GURDJIAN, E. S., WEBSTER, J. E., HARDY, W. G., and LINDNER, D. W.   Nonexistence of the so-called cerebral form of carotid sinus syncope.   *Neurology* 8:818, 1958.

HOLT, G. W.   Clinical syndromes of the glossopharyngeus.   *Am. J. Med. Sc.* 238:85, 1959.   The vagi: Medical and surgical implications.   *Ibid.* 251:86, 1966.

JACKSON, C., and JACKSON, C. L.   Diseases and Injuries of the Larynx: A Textbook for Students and Practitioners.   New York, The Macmillan Company, 1942.

JACKSON, C., and JACKSON, C. L.   Diseases of the Nose, Throat, and Ear, Including Bronchoscopy and Esophagoscopy.   Philadelphia, W. B. Saunders Co., 1945.

JACKSON, R. G.   An anatomic study of the vagus nerves, and a technic of transabdominal gastric vagus resection.   *Univ. Hosp. Bull., Ann Arbor* 13:31, 1947.

LINN, L., and SPIEGEL, L. A.   Disturbances in parotid secretion in an unusual neurologic syndrome.   *Arch. Neurol. & Psychiat.* 49:548, 1943.

LOURIE, R. S.   Rate of secretion of the parotid glands in normal children: A measurement of function of the autonomic nervous system.   *Am. J. Dis. Child.* 65:455, 1943.

MONTAGU, A.   On yawning.   *J.A.M.A.* 182:732, 1962.

MORRISON, L. F.   Recurrent laryngeal nerve paralysis.   *Ann. Otol., Rhin. & Laryng.* 61:567, 1952.

MORTON, D. R., KLASSEN, K. P., and CURTIS, G. M.   The effect of high vagus section upon the clinical physiology of the bronchus.   *Tr. Am. Neurol. A.* 75:143, 1950.

NEGUS, V. E.   The Mechanism of the Larynx.   St. Louis, The C. V. Mosby Company, 1929.

PEET, M. M.   Glossopharyngeal neuralgia.   *Ann. Surg.* 101:265, 1935.

PENIDO, J. R. F., DODGE, H. W., JR., CLAGGETT, O. T., and STARR, G. F.   Tumors of the vagus nerve.   *Proc. Staff Meet., Mayo Clin.* 32:239, 1957.

RAY, B. S., and STEWART, H. J.   Role of the glossopharyngeal nerve in the carotid sinus reflex in man; Relief of carotid sinus syndrome by intracranial section of the glossopharyngeal nerve.   *Surgery* 23:411, 1948.

REICHERT, F. L., and POTH, E. J.   Recent knowledge regarding the physiology of the glossopharyngeal nerve in man with an analysis of its sensory, motor, gustatory and secretory functions.   *Bull. Johns Hopkins Hosp.* 53:131, 1933.

RICH, A. R.   The innervation of the tensor veli palatini and levator veli palatini muscles.   *Bull. Johns Hopkins Hosp.* 31:305, 1920.

RILEY, H. A., GERMAN, W. J., WORTIS, H., HERBERT, C., ZAHN, D., and EICHNA, L.   Glossopharyngeal neuralgia initiating or associated with cardiac arrest.   *Tr. Am. Neurol. A.* 68:28, 1942.

STOOKEY, B. P.   Glossopharyngeal neuralgia: Surgical treatment, with remarks on the distribution of the glossopharyngeal nerve.   *Arch. Neurol. & Psychiat.* 20:702, 1928.

TURNER, W. A.   On the innervation of the muscles of the soft palate.   *J. Anat. & Physiol.* 23:523, 1889.

WEISS, S., and BAKER, J. P.   The carotid sinus reflex in health and disease: Its role in the causation of fainting and convulsions.   *Medicine* 12:297, 1933.

CHAPTER 16

THE SPINAL ACCESSORY NERVE

ANATOMY AND PHYSIOLOGY

THE SPINAL ACCESSORY, or *eleventh cranial, nerve,* is composed of two distinct parts. The *cranial part,* or the *ramus internus* or *accessory portion,* is the smaller of the two, and is accessory to the vagus. It arises from the cells within the caudal prolongation of the nucleus ambiguus and the dorsal efferent nucleus, probably mainly from the former. Its fibers emerge from the medulla as four or five delicate rootlets below the roots of the vagus. The nerve goes laterally to the jugular foramen, where it becomes united with the spinal portion for a short distance and also communicates with the jugular ganglion of the vagus nerve. It leaves the skull through the jugular foramen, separate from the spinal portion, passes through the ganglion nodosum without interruption, and blends with the fibers of the vagus nerve (Fig. 119). It is distributed principally with the pharyngeal and superior laryngeal branches of the vagus. It is stated by many authorities that the levator veli palatini, musculus uvulae, palatoglossus, palatopharyngeus, salpingopharyngeus, and the superior and middle constrictors of the pharynx are supplied by the cranial portion of the accessory nerve, but it is more probable that these are supplied by the vagus nerve, possibly by accessory fibers which distributed through the vagus. A few fibers from the accessory nerve are also said to innervate the intrinsic muscles of the larynx with the recurrent nerve, and possibly a few fibers which originate in the dorsal efferent nucleus carry parasympathetic impulses and join the cardiac branches of the vagus.

The major portion of the eleventh nerve is the *spinal portion,* or *ramus externus.* Its fibers arise from the motor cells of the accessory nuclei in the central cell group of the ventral horn of the spinal cord from the lower end of the medulla to the fifth or even the sixth cervical segment. Rootlets from these nuclei pass through the lateral funiculus of the cord and unite to form a single trunk which ascends within the dura between the dentate ligament and the posterior roots of the spinal nerves. This trunk enters the skull through the foramen magnum and is directed toward the jugular foramen, where it joins the cranial portion of the nerve for a short distance, and probably receives one or two filaments from it (Fig. 119). It leaves the skull as does the cranial portion, through the jugular foramen. It is within the same dural sheath as the vagus nerve, but separated from it by a fold of arachnoid. It descends in the neck behind or in front of the internal jugular vein and behind the digastricus and stylohyoid to the upper part of the sternocleidomastoid. It pierces this muscle and supplies filaments to it, and then courses obliquely across the posterior triangle of the neck to end in the deep surface of the trapezius. In the neck it unites with the second and third cervical nerves, and beneath the trapezius it forms a plexus with the third and fourth cervical nerves. The nuclei of the spinal portion of the accessory nerve communicate with the nuclei of the oculomotor. trochlear, abducens, and vestibular nerves through the medial longitudinal fasciculus (Fig. 58). The *cerebral center* which governs the action of the spinal accessory nerve is in the lower portion of the precentral gyrus. The supranuclear innervation is bilateral in part, but comes largely from the contralateral hemisphere.

The eleventh nerve is entirely motor in function. The accessory portion operates with the glossopharyngeal and vagus nerves, and cannot be distinguished from them. It is in reality an integral part of the vagus. The spinal portion of the nerve supplies two important muscles, the *sternocleidomastoid* and the upper portion of the *trapezius*. The innervation of the former muscle is almost entirely by the eleventh nerve, although it may be supplied by a few fibers from the anterior divisions of the second and third cervical nerves. The amount of innervation to the trapezius differs in individuals, but only the upper part is supplied by the accessory; the lower part is innervated by the third and fourth cervical nerves.

The *sternocleidomastoid muscles* function with the other cervical muscles in

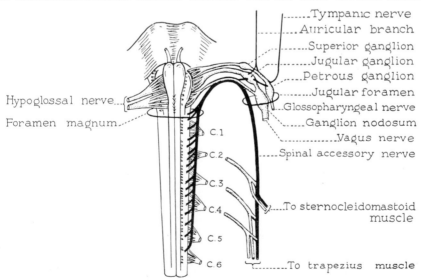

FIG. 119. Relationship of cranial and spinal portions of accessory nerve to vagus and glossopharyngeal nerves.

flexing the head and in turning it from side to side. When the muscle on one side contracts, the head is drawn toward the ipsilateral shoulder and is rotated so that the occiput is pulled toward the side of the contracting muscle, while the face is deviated in the opposite direction, carried forward, and tilted upward. Acting together from their sternoclavicular attachments the two muscles flex the cervical part of the vertebral column and bring the head forward and downward; they also rotate the head from side to side. When the head is fixed, the two muscles assist in elevating the thorax in forced inspiration.

The *trapezius* retracts the head and draws it to the corresponding side. It also elevates, retracts, and rotates the scapula, and assists in elevating the abducted arm above the horizontal. When the muscle on one side contracts while the shoulder is fixed, the head is drawn to that side. When the two muscles act together, the head is drawn backward and the face is deviated upward. When the head is fixed, the upper and middle fibers of the trapezius elevate, rotate, and retract the scapula and shorten the distance between the occiput and the acromion. The lower fibers depress the scapula and draw it toward the midline.

The sternocleidomastoid and trapezius muscles act together to rotate the head from side to side and to flex and extend the neck.

CLINICAL EXAMINATION

The functions of the cranial portion of the eleventh nerve are so closely allied to those of the vagus nerve that they cannot be distinguished from them clinically or examined separately. As a consequence, the examination of the spinal accessory nerve is limited to an evaluation of the functions of the sternocleidomastoid and trapezius muscles.

The *function of the sternocleidomastoid* is appraised by inspection and palpation as the patient rotates his head against resistance. The muscle usually stands out well, and its contours are distinct even at rest; its contractions can be seen and felt (Fig. 120). In unilateral paresis there may be little change in the position of the head in the resting state and rotation and flexion can be carried out fairly well by the other cervical muscles, but a weakness of rotation can be observed if the examiner places his hand against one side of the patient's chin and the patient is asked to counteract this resistance. In a complete unilateral paralysis the occiput cannot be pulled toward the paralyzed side, and as a result the face is turned toward that side by the contralateral muscle and cannot be turned toward the normal side. If the chin is bent down against resistance there is further deviation of the face toward the paralyzed side, and contraction of the platysma may be observed. The paralyzed muscle is flat and does not contract, and it no longer stands out or becomes tense when attempts are made to turn the head toward the opposite shoulder or to flex the neck against resistance. There may be contracture of the contralateral normally functioning muscle. The two sternocleidomastoid muscles can be examined simultaneously by having the patient flex his neck while the examiner exerts pressure under the chin, or by having the patient turn the head from side to side. If both are paralyzed there is difficulty in anteroflexion of the neck and the head assumes an extended position.

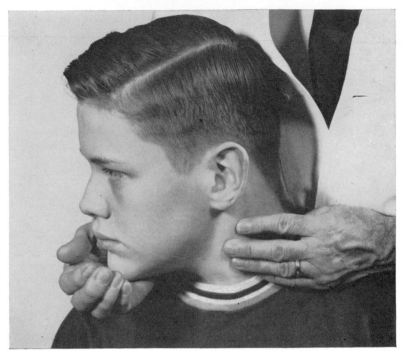

Fig. 120. Examination of the sternocleidomastoid muscle; on turning the head to the right against resistance, the contracting muscle can be seen and palpated.

In addition to testing the motor power of the sternocleidomastoids, one should note the tone, volume and contour, and electrical reactions (see "The Motor System," Part IV). In a nuclear or infranuclear lesion there may be atrophy, and fasciculations may be seen in the former. The *sternocleidomastoid reflex* may be elicited by tapping the muscle at its clavicular origin. Normally there is a prompt contraction. The reflex is innervated by the accessory and upper cervical nerves, and is lost in disease of these nerves.

The *function of the trapezius* is tested by having the patient shrug and retract his shoulders against resistance. The movements may be observed and the contraction may be seen and palpated (Fig. 121). Muscle power should be compared on the two sides. In unilateral paralysis of the trapezius the shoulder cannot be elevated and retracted, the head cannot be tilted toward that side, and the arm cannot be elevated above the horizontal. There is a dropping of the arm on the affected side, and the finger tips touch the thigh at a lower level than on the normal side; if the palms are placed together with the arms extended anteriorly and slightly below the horizontal, the fingers on the affected side will extend beyond those of the normal side. There is a tendency for the upper portion of the scapula to fall laterally while its inferior angle is drawn inward, and there may be some "winging" of the scapula when the arm is extended anteriorly below the horizontal; this is less marked, however, than the "winging" with a paralysis of the serratus anterior, which is most marked when the arm is extended anteriorly above the horizontal (Chapter 27).

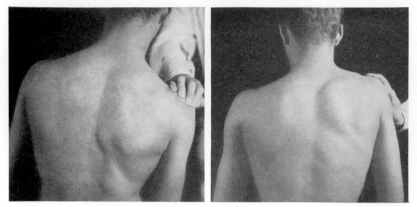

FIG. 121.   Examination of motor power of trapezius muscle; on elevating shoulder against resistance, the contracting upper portion of the muscle can be seen and palpated.

The outline of the neck is changed; there is a depression or drooping of the shoulder contour, and the levator scapulae bcomes subcutaneous (Fig. 122). The paralyzed muscle becomes atrophic, fasciculations may be seen, and there may be abnormal electrical reactions. In unilateral paralysis of the trapezius there may be contracture of the normal muscle. The two trapezius muscles can be examined simultaneously by having the patient extend his neck against resistance. In paralysis of both trapezei there is weakness of extension of the neck and the head may fall forward; the patient is unable to raise his chin, and the shoulders appear to be square as a result of atrophy of both trapezius muscles. The relationship of the trapezius muscle to

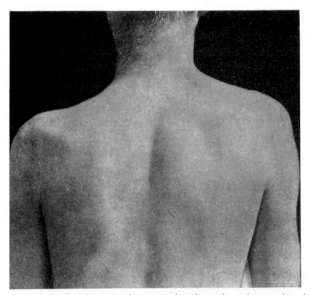

FIG. 122.   Paralysis of left trapezius muscle; there is a depression in shoulder contour, with downward and lateral displacement of scapula.

the movements of the shoulder girdle and the examination of the functions of its lower fibers are discussed in "The Motor System," Part IV.

In bilateral paralysis of the spinal accessory nerves there is diminished ability to rotate the neck and the head may fall either backward or forward, depending upon whether the sternocleidomastoids or the trapezei are the more involved. Inasmuch as other cervical muscles, among which are the scaleni, splenii and obliqui capitis, recti capitis, and longi capitis and colli, are also of importance in rotation, deviation, flexion, and extension of the head and neck, there is never a complete paralysis of the neck muscles in lesions of the spinal accessory nerve.

DISORDERS OF FUNCTION

Paralysis or paresis of the muscles supplied by the spinal portion of the accessory nerve may be caused by supranuclear, nuclear, or infranuclear lesions.

Supranuclear involvement in the cerebrum and brain stem may cause only moderate loss of function since central regulation of the accessory nerve is in part bilateral. In hemiplegia there is usually no deviation of the head, but on testing there may be slight weakness of the sternocleidomastoid (or sometimes marked weakness in acute hemiplegia), with difficulty in turning the face to the side opposite the paralysis. There is often, however, moderate drooping of the shoulder and weakness of the trapezius on the affected side. There is no atrophy and there are no fasciculations. Cerebral vascular accidents, degenerations, neoplasms, and inflammatory conditions, among others, may cause a supranuclear palsy. More frequent than paralytic supranuclear lesions are irritative ones, which cause a turning of the head, and often of the head and eyes, in the direction opposite to the involved hemisphere. This turning of the head or head and eyes is seen in jacksonian epilepsy, and is often the first manifestation of the fit. Extrapyramidal lesions may also involve the sternocleidomastoid and trapezius muscles, principally the former, with resulting rigidity, akinesis, or hyperkinesis (Part IV). Deviation of the head is a frequent postencephalitic manifestation, and abnormal movements of the head and neck are seen in chorea, athetosis, and dystonia musculorum deformans. Lesions of the brain stem above the accessory nuclei may cause dysfunction of the sternocleidomastoid and trapezius muscles, either through involvement of the supranuclear (pyramidal or extrapyramidal) pathways, or through involvement of the medial longitudinal fasciculus. This tract, which connects the nuclei of the third, fourth, sixth, and eleventh nerves with the cochlear, vestibular, and other centers, is important in controlling conjugate deviation of the head and eyes in response to auditory, vestibular, and other stimuli. Destructive lesions of this pathway may cause paresis of rotation of the head to the ipsilateral side, with involuntary deviation to the opposite side; irritative lesions may cause ipsilateral rotation.

Nuclear involvement of the accessory nerve is not frequently encountered, but it may occur in such conditions as progressive bulbar palsy, progressive spinal muscular atrophy, syringobulbia, and syringomyelia. In nuclear lesions there not only is paresis of the involved muscles, but also atrophy, fasciculations, and electrical reactions of degeneration. The Schmidt, Avellis, Jackson, Babinski-Nageotte, and Cestan-Chenais syndromes (Chapter 18) occur in the presence of lesions of the accessory nuclei and of other medullary structures. The Jackson and Schmidt syndrome may be produced by radicular (infranuclear) involvement.

Infranuclear, or *peripheral, lesions,* either extramedullary but within the skull, in the jugular foramen, or in the neck, are the most common causes of impairment of function of the accessory nerve. They produce paralysis followed by atrophy of the muscles it supplies. Basal skull fractures, meningitis, exudation from intra-cranial hemorrhage, syphilis, osteitis, or extramedullary neoplasm may affect the nerve within the skull or at the foramen. There is usually evidence of involve-ment of other structures, principally the vagus, glossopharyngeal, or hypoglossal nerves (Chapter 18). Within the neck the accessory nerve may be affected by cer-vical adenitis, neoplasms, trauma, abscesses, or external pressure. The nerve is occasionally traumatized in operations on the cervical areas. Among other causes of peripheral accessory involvement are dislocations and caries of the cervical spine, lesions in the mediastinum and at the pulmonary apices, and multiple neuritis. Injuries to the nerve in the posterior cervical triangle will impair only the supply to the trapezius. Muscular disorders which affect the sternocleidomastoid and trapezius muscles include the myopathies, myasthenia gravis, and myositis. Atrophy of both sternocleidomastoid muscles is a prominent symptom in dys-trophia myotonica (Fig. 123).

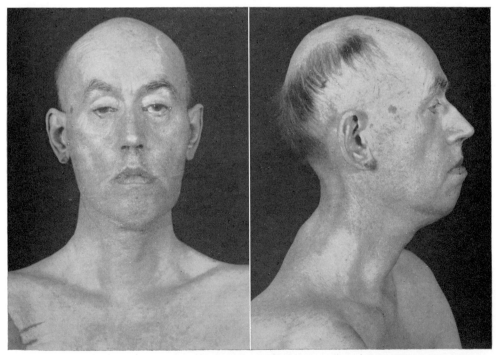

FIG. 123.   A patient with dystrophia myotonica; there is atrophy of the sternocleidomastoid muscles. (Courtesy of Dr. K. R. Magee.)

TORTICOLLIS

Hyperkinetic manifestations with tonic or clonic spasm of the muscles supplied by the accessory nerve are encountered more frequently than paralytic phenomena. The involvement is most marked in the sternocleidomastoid muscles, but the trapezius and the other muscles of the neck may also be affected. The muscular contractions cause a turning, or deviation, of the head or neck, known as wryneck, or *torticollis*. The head and occiput are pulled to one side, and the face is turned toward the opposite side (Fig. 124). The movements may be jerky, clonic, or spasmodic at first, and may be present only in attacks. They may present the manifestations of a tic. Later the difficulty becomes tonic, with constant deviation. The hyperkinesis usually starts in one sternocleidomastoid, but in far developed cases there is some involvement on both sides and the other cervical muscles are also affected. The trapezius may pull the head backward or the shoulder upward on the involved side, and the obliqui capitis, recti capitis, and splenii capitis may also be implicated. The involved muscle or muscles may become tense and firm and may hypertrophy in the course of time.

In a fully developed torticollis there is a more or less stereotyped deviation of the head into an abnormal position. It may vary from a slow twisting movement to a complete deviation with sustained muscular contractions. In spite of the spasmodic turning of the head to one side, it can usually be deviated voluntarily to the midline or to the opposite side, especially if the patient is allowed to press some object against his chin. A minimal amount of manual assistance may aid in deviation of the head to the opposite side. The turning of the head in spasmodic torticollis is usually painless, but occasionally there is pain in the contracted muscles. Though

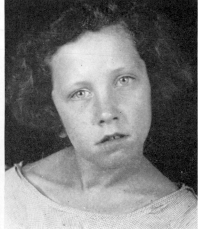

FIG. 124.   Spasmodic torticollis: *Left,* of psychogenic origin; *Right,* of congenital origin. In both cases there is contraction of the right sternocleidomastoid muscle, with deviation of chin toward left shoulder.

the deviation is most frequently a lateral one, there may be a backward (retrocollis) or a forward (anterocollis) deviation.

There are many causes and varieties of torticollis, and the syndrome should not be considered an entity. Congenital, structural, traumatic, and myogenic factors include birth injury, congenital atrophy or hypertrophy of one sternocleidomastoid muscle, congenital fusion of the cervical vertebrae, the Klippel-Feil syndrome, spina bifida, rickets, fracture or dislocation of the cervical spine, cervical arthritis, and trauma to the muscles. Symptomatic, or reflex, torticollis may be secondary to occipital neuralgia, vascular lesions, tumor or scar formation in the neck, neoplastic metastases to the cervical lymph nodes, or some infectious process such as cervical adenitis, caries of the cervical spine, lesions of the mediastinum or pulmonary apex, retropharyngeal or retrotonsillar abscesses, myositis, arthritis, or synovitis. Professional torticollis may occur in cobblers and tailors.

The more important varieties of torticollis, however, from a neurologic point of view, are those associated with disease, either organic or functional, of the nervous system. *Paralytic torticollis* may follow either a lower motor neuron or an upper motor neutron paresis. *Ocular torticollis* is associated with paresis of one or more of the extraocular muscles; there is no true contracture of the sternocleidomastoid muscle, the deformity can usually be corrected voluntarily, and there is no facial assymetry (Chapter 11). *Neonatal torticollis* may be secondary to trauma associated with other asymmetries and developmental anomalies, or due to fibrous tumors of the sternocleidomastoid. *Aural* or *labyrinthine torticollis* is secondary to involvement of the cochlear or the vestibular mechanisms, including the medial longitudinal fasciculus and the vestibulospinal pathways. *Involvement of the extrapyramidal system,* especially of the basal ganglia, is probably the most frequent cause of neurologic torticollis. The manifestation is seen in encephalitis and in dystonia; it may be the only symptom, or there may be associated rigidity or spasticity, deviation of the eyes, or athetoid movements. Torticollis has been produced experimentally by lesions in the mesencephalic tegmentum. In some instances spasmodic torticollis may develop on a *psychogenic basis,* possibly as a conversion mechanism. It may start as a tic, nodding spasm, negation tremor, or compulsive turning of the head to one side, but later there is spasmodic or tonic deviation of the head.

Spasmodic torticollis has been treated surgically by section of the involved muscles or of the involved spinal accessory nerve, sometimes combined with section of the anterior roots or even posterior divisions of the upper cervical nerves. Such measures, however, have often failed to afford permanent relief; not only does a surprising amount of stability and motility of the neck remain after such procedures, but the spasmodic movements may persist at well. More recently torticollis has been relieved in some cases by selective thalamotomy. Psychotherapy has failed to relieve the symptoms in many instances in which the difficulty was known to be of psychogenic origin; in such cases the surgical approach is sometimes used.

The eleventh nerve is sometimes anastomosed with the facial in the treatment of peripheral facial paralysis.

REFERENCES

COOPER, I. S.   Effect of thalamic lesions upon torticollis.   *New England J. Med.* 270:967, 1964.

DANDY, W. E.   An operation for treatment of spasmodic torticollis.   *Arch. Surg.* 20: 1021, 1930.

FOLTZ, E. L., KNOPP, L. M., and WARD, A. A., JR.   Experimental spasmodic torticollis. *J. Neurosurg.* 16:55, 1959.

HERZ, E., and HOEFER, P. F. A.   Spasmodic torticollis: I. Physiologic analysis of involuntary motor activity.   *Arch. Neurol. & Psychiat.* 61:129, 1949.

HERZ, E., and GLASER, G. H.   Spasmodic torticollis: II. Clinical evaluation.   *Arch. Neurol. & Psychiat.* 61:227, 1949.

PATTERSON, R. M., and LITTLE, S. C.   Spasmodic torticollis.   *J. Nerv. & Ment. Dis.* 98:571, 1943.

PUTNAM, T. J., HERZ, E., and GLASER, G. H.   Spasmodic torticollis: III. Surgical treatment.   *Arch. Neurol. & Psychiat.* 61:240, 1949.

SORENSON, B. F., and HAMBY, W. B.   Spasmodic torticollis: Results in 71 surgically treated cases.   *J.A.M.A.* 194:706, 1965.

STRAUSS, W. L., JR., and HOWELL, A. B.   The spinal accessory nerve and its musculature. *Quart. Rev. Biol.* 11:387, 1936.

CHAPTER 17

THE HYPOGLOSSAL NERVE

ANATOMY AND PHYSIOLOGY

The hypoglossal, or *twelfth cranial, nerve,* which is the motor nerve to the tongue, has its origin in the cells of the hypoglossal nucleus. This is an upward extension of the anterior column of the spinal cord, and consists of a long column of large, multipolar cells, similar to those in the anterior horns. It extends almost the entire length of the medulla; its upper portion lies just underneath the floor of the fourth ventricle, close to the midline, under the medial aspect of the trigonum hypoglossi (Fig. 108), and its lower portion is situated in the gray matter on the ventro-lateral aspect of the central canal (Fig. 125). Numerous fibers connect the nuclei of the two sides. The nerve roots leave the ventral side of the nucleus and go forward and laterally through the reticular formation to emerge from the medulla in the anterolateral sulcus between the pyramid and the inferior olivary body, medially to the ninth, tenth, and eleventh nerves (Fig. 108).

The hypoglossal nerve leaves the medulla in ten to fifteen rootlets (Fig. 20). These are collected into two bundles which perforate the dura mater separately, pass through the hypoglossal canal, and then unite. This united nerve descends through the neck to the level of the angle of the mandible, and it then passes forward to supply the extrinsic and intrinsic muscles of the tongue. In the upper portion of its course it is situated beneath the internal carotid artery and internal jugular vein, and is intimately connected with the vagus nerve. It then passes forward between the artery and vein, loops around the occipital artery, and crosses the external carotid and lingual arteries. It goes forward above the hyoid bone, beneath the tendon of the digastricus, deep to the stylohyoid and the mylohyoid and lateral to and above the hyoglossus, and breaks up into a number of fibers to supply the various muscles of the tongue.

The hypoglossal nerve communicates with the ganglion nodosum of the vagus nerve shortly after it leaves the skull, and it also gives a filament to the pharyngeal plexus. In the neck it communicates with the superior cervical ganglion of the sym-

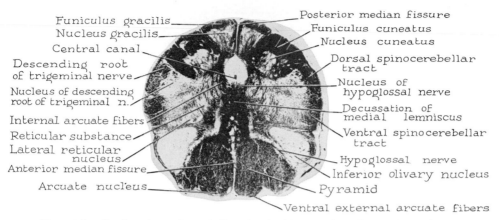

Funiculus gracilis

Nucleus gracilis

Central canal

Descending root
of trigeminal nerve

Nucleus of descending
root of trigeminal n.

Internal arcuate fibers

Reticular substance

Lateral reticular
nucleus

Anterior median fissure

Arcuate nucleus

Posterior median fissure

Funiculus cuneatus

Nucleus cuneatus

Dorsal spinocerebellar
tract

Nucleus of
hypoglossal nerve

Decussation of
medial lemniscus

Ventral spinocerebellar
tract

Hypoglossal nerve

Inferior olivary nucleus

Pyramid

Ventral external arcuate fibers

FIG. 125.   Section through medulla at level of decussation of medial lemniscus.

pathetic trunk and is joined by a filament from the first or first and second cervical nerves. Lower in the neck it communicates with the descending cervical branch from the second and third cervical nerves. At the base of the tongue it communicates with the lingual branch of the mandibular nerve. Although the twelfth nerve is purely a motor nerve, through communications with other nerves it also may aid in conveying sensations.

The branches of the hypoglossal nerve are the meningeal, descending, thyrohyoid, and muscular. The *meningeal branches* send filaments to the dura mater in the posterior cranial fossa and to the diploë of the occipital bone; since the hypoglossal nerve is entirely motor, these branches are doubtless supplied by the first and second cervical nerves. The *descending ramus* leaves the hypoglossal nerve as it loops around the occipital artery and descends in front of or in the sheath of the carotid vessels. It gives a branch to the superior belly of the omohyoid and then joins the descending cervical communicating branch from the second and third cervical nerves to form the loop known as the ansa hypoglossi (Fig. 126), which supplies the inferior belly of the omohyoid and the sternohyoid and sternothyroid muscles and may communicate with the phrenic and cardiac nerves. The *thyrohyoid branch* arises near the posterior border of the hyoglossus and supplies the thyrohyoid muscle. The descending and thyrohoid branches may carry hypoglossal fibers to a limited extent, but they are innervated mainly by the cervical plexus.

The *muscular,* or *lingual,* branches constitute the real distribution of the hypoglossal nerve. They supply the genioglossus, styloglossus, hyoglossus, and chondroglossus muscles, the intrinsic muscles of the tongue, and possibly the geniohyoid.

The *cerebral center* for the regulation of tongue movements is situated in the lower portion of the precentral gyrus near and within the sylvian fissure. The supranuclear fibers pass through the knee of the internal capsule and the middle of the cerebral peduncle. Supranuclear control to the genioglossus muscle is almost entirely crossed, while the supply to the other muscles is bilateral.

The hypoglossal nerve controls the movements of the tongue. It supplies all of the extrinsic muscles of the tongue with the exception of the palatoglossus, the intrinsic muscles, and possibly the geniohyud muscle (Fig. 126). The extrinsic muscles pass from the skull or the hyoid bone to the tongue, all are in pairs and are symmetrical; the intrinsic muscles arise and end within the organ.

The *extrinsic muscles* of the tongue and their functions are as follows: The *genioglossi,* by means of their posterior fibers, draw the root of the tongue forward and thus protrude the apex. The anterior fibers draw the tongue back into the mouth and tend to depress and retract the organ. The two work together to draw the tongue downward and make its superior surface concave from side to side. The posterior fibers of the genioglossus on one side push the tongue toward the opposite side. The *hyoglossi* retract the tongue and depress the sides; they make the superior surface convex. The *chondroglossus* is sometimes described as a part of the hyoglossus, and

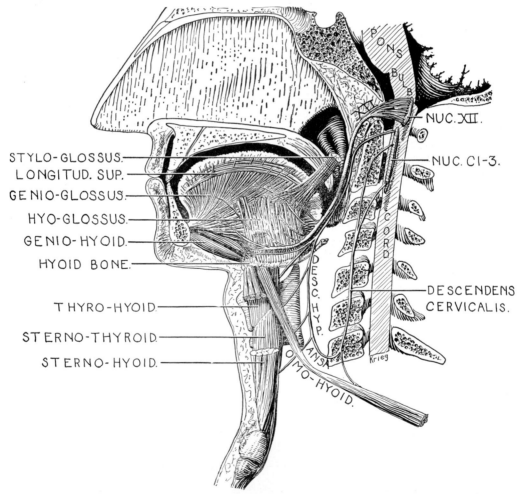

Fig. 126. Ansa hypoglossi and muscles supplied by hypoglossal nerve. (Krieg, W. J. S.: Functional Neuroanatomy. Philadelphia, The Blakiston Company, 1942.)

is a depressor and retractor. The *styloglossi* draw the tongue upward and backward; they retract the organ and elevate the root. They also elevate the sides, and thus aid in the production of transverse concavity of the dorsum. The *palatoglossus,* which aids in drawing the root of the tongue upward, may also be classified as one of the extrinsic muscles of the tongue. It is more closely associated in location and function, however, with the muscles of the soft palate. It is innervated by the vagus nerve (see discussion of vagus nerve).

The *intrinsic muscles* of the tongue are the superior and inferior longitudinales, transversus, and verticalis. They are mainly concerned with altering the shape of the tongue; they cause it to become shortened, narrowed, or curved in different directions. Both *longitudinales* shorten the tongue; the *superior longitudinalis* also turns up the tip and sides to make the dorsum concave, whereas the *inferior longitudinalis* pulls the tip down and makes the dorsum convex. The *transversus* narrows and elongates the tongue, and the *verticalis* flattens and broadens it.

The *suprahyoid group of muscles* also influence the movement of the tongue by bringing about the movement of the hyoid bone. The *geniohyoid* raises and advances the hyoid bone and the base of the tongue during deglutition; it depresses the mandible when the hyoid bone is fixed. Many anatomists state that this muscle is supplied by the hypoglossal nerve, but other authorities express the belief that its innervation is derived mainly from the first and second cervical segments of the spinal cord through the cervical plexus, although the fibers are carried through the hypoglossal nerve. The other suprahyoid muscles, which function with the geniohyoid in raising the hyoid bone and the base of the tongue and in depressing the jaw when the hyoid is fixed, are the mylohyoid and anterior belly of the digastricus, which are discussed with the trigeminal nerve, and the stylohyoid and the posterior belly of the digastricus, which are discussed with the facial nerve.

The *infrahyoid group of muscles* have no specific action on the tongue, but through their innervation they are related to the hypoglossal nerve. The *sternohyoid* depresses the hyoid bone and the larynx after these structures have been drawn up by the pharynx in the act of deglutition. The *sternothyroid* acts as a depressor of the thyroid cartilage of thc larynx. The *omohyoid* depresses the hyoid bone which it carries backward and to one side; it also contracts and renders tense the cervical fascia. The *thyrohyoid* elevates the thyroid cartilage when the hyoid bone ascends; it draws the thyroid cartilage up and behind the hyoid bone. These muscles are innervated by the first three cervical nerves through the descending and thyrohyoid branches of the hypoglossal and the ansa hypoglossi. They may receive some innervation from the hypoglossal nerve as well.

CLINICAL EXAMINATION

The examination of the hypoglossal nerve consists of an evaluation of the motor functions of the tongue. Motor power is tested; the position of the tongue on protrusion and at rest, and the strength and rapidity of movement in all directions are noted; weakness, paralysis, atrophy, and abnormal movements are observed.

The position of the tongue when at rest in the mouth is first noted, and the patient is then asked to protrude it, to move it in and out, from side to side and upward and downward, both slowly and rapidly, and to press it against each cheek while the strength of this pressure is tested with the finger placed on the outside of the cheek. He may also be asked to curl it upward and downward over the lips, and to elevate the lateral margins. If there is unilateral paralysis or paresis of the tongue muscles, the organ deviates toward the involved side on protrusion (Fig. 75), owing to the action of the normal genioglossus which produces a stronger movement than do the other tongue muscles. It protrudes the apex of the tongue by drawing the root of the organ forward and pushing the distal portion outward and, at the same time, toward the paretic side. As the tongue lies in the mouth at rest it may deviate or curl slightly toward the healthy side, owing to the unopposed action of the styloglossus which draws the organ upward and backward. There is diminution or loss of ability to deviate the protruded tongue toward the nonparetic side and of ability to push it against the cheek on the sound side, but the patient is able to push it against his cheek on the paralyzed side. He may be unable to remove food from between his teeth and the cheeks on either side. If the paralysis is not accompanied by atrophy, the tongue may appear to bulge slightly and to be higher and somewhat more voluminous on the paralyzed side, but when atrophy supervenes the paralyzed side becomes smaller and the tongue may become curved toward the paralyzed side with a sickle-shaped deformity. In bilateral paralysis of the tongue the patient may be able to protrude the organ only slightly or not at all. If there is paralysis of the facial muscles or of the muscles of mastication, it may be difficult to evaluate deviation of the tongue. The paretic angle of the mouth may have to be retracted by the examiner, so that the relationship of the tongue to the central incisors can be compared. With either weakness or coordination difficulties, rapid movements may be impaired. The presence of unilateral atrophy may be confirmed by palpation of the tongue. In myotonia, sharp percussion of the tongue may cause the formation of a dimple which disappears slowly.

Trophic changes and abnormalities of movement should be thoroughly appraised. In atrophy there is loss of muscle substance, first apparent at the borders or at the tip. The tongue is wrinkled, furrowed, and obviously wasted, and the epithelium and mucous membrane on the affected side are thrown into folds. The protruded tongue may curve toward the atrophic side (Fig. 127). Atrophy may be accompanied by fasciculations, which at times may give the appearance of a wriggling mass of worms. Fine, rapid tremors seen in general paresis and toxic states may be difficult to differentiate from fasciculations when the tongue is protruded, but the tremors usually disappear when the tongue is lying at rest in the mouth, whereas the fasciculations persist. Coarse tremors of the tongue are present in parkinsonism, but they may also be seen in fatigue states. In psychogenic disorders there may be medium to coarse tremors. All tremors may be brought out or accentuated by protrusion of the tongue or by talking. Other hyperkinesia of the tongue are observed in various diseases of the motor system. In chorea there may be irregular, jerky movements of the tongue, and often the patient is unable to keep his tongue protruded. Athetoid and dystonic movements, habit spasms, and tics may involve the tongue; lingual spasm has been described in tetanus and in the psychoneuroses.

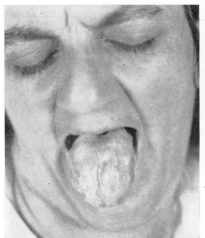

FIG. 127. Nuclear and infranuclear paralysis of muscles supplied by hypoglossal nerve: *Left,* atrophy and fibrillations of tongue in patient with progressive bulbar palsy; *Right,* unilateral atrophy and deviation of tongue in peripheral hypoglossal paralysis.

The examination of the sensory functions is not a part of the appraisal of the hypoglossal nerve. General sensation to the tongue is carried through the lingual branches of the trigeminal and glossopharyngeal nerves, and taste by the facial and glossopharyngeal nerves. Proprioceptive sensations from the tongue musculature may travel with the hypoglossal nerve, but there are no methods for testing them. Some sensation is carried from the meninges of the posterior fossa through the meningeal branch of the hypoglossal nerve. This area is not available for clinical testing, and furthermore this is probably a function of the first and second cervical nerves through the hypoglossal nerve rather than of the hypoglossal nerve itself. The fact that sensation from the meninges is carried through the hypoglossal nerve, however, accounts for the pain that may be experienced in the occipital region and in the back of the neck in posterior fossa tumors.

Morphologic changes in the tongue may be of diagnostic significance. Ankyloglossia, or tongue-tie, may simulate paresis. Macroglossia is seen in cretinism and mongolism. There may be hypertrophy of the tongue in conditions such as paralysis agitans and other dyskinesias where there is constant protrusion. The presence of coating or lack of coating, fissuring, redness, scars, mucous patches, atrophy or hypertrophy of the papillae, etc., may give some clue in the diagnosis of physical disease. The term *atrophic glossitis* is used to designate changes that occur in the tongue in certain deficiency states. In these, however, the atrophy involves only the papillae, and there is no neurogenic atrophy of the musculature. The tongue of pernicious anemia has been described as smooth and translucent with atrophy of the fungiform and filiform papillae; in some stages of the disease the tongue is pale and in other stages is red, but in all there is lack of coating. In pellagra and niacin deficiency the tongue is smooth, and there is atrophy with desquamation of the papillae; in acute stages it is scarlet-red and swollen, but in chronic or mild deficiency stages the papillae are mushroomed and the organ is not so deeply red. Fusion and atrophy of the papillae and fissuring may produce the so-called geographic, or scrotal, tongue. In riboflavin deficiency the papillae are flattened and the tongue may be a purplish or magenta hue. In thiamin deficiency the tongue is smooth, shiny, atrophic, and reddened.

DISORDERS OF FUNCTION

Lesions of the hypoglossal nerve or its central connections cause paresis or paralysis of the tongue. A unilateral paralysis may cause few symptoms. Speech and swallowing are little affected. In bilateral paralysis the tongue cannot be extended or moved laterally; the first stage of deglutition is impaired, and there is difficulty in articulation, especially in pronouncing the linguals. With bilateral nuclear or infranuclear lesions swallowing may be difficult and speech indistinct; there may be respiratory difficulty, as the tongue tends to slip back into the throat. There are no sensory changes with lesions of the hypoglossal nerve. Glossodynia, or burning of the tongue, is often accompanied by parageusias, or abnormalities of taste, and by repeated movements of the tongue against the teeth; these symptoms are not related to lesions of the hypoglossal nerve, but may be secondary to arteriosclerosis, psychogenic disorders, and other conditions.

Paralysis of the tongue, or *glossoplegia,* may be due to a supranuclear, a nuclear or an infranuclear lesion. In supranuclear involvement there is paresis, with deviation but no atrophy. The impairment of power is rarely complete. Since the genioglossus, the principal protractor of the tongue, has mainly crossed supranuclear innervation, the tongue protrudes toward the paralyzed side, but to the side opposite the cerebral lesion. In nuclear and infranuclear lesions there is atrophy of the involved side in addition to paralysis and deviation, and there may be an electrical reaction of degeneration. The protrusion is toward the paralyzed side, which is also the side of the lesion. If the nuclear lesion is a degenerative or progressive one, such as progressive bulbar palsy, amyotrophic lateral sclerosis, or syringobulbia, there are also fascicular tremors.

Supranuclear paralysis of the tongue may follow lesions of the cerebral cortex, the internal capsule, the cerebral peduncle, or the pons. The paresis is usually the result of a destructive lesion of the cortex or the pyramidal pathway. If the lesion is an irritative one, there may be involuntary protrusion of the tongue to the opposite side, which may be seen in jacksonian convulsions. In dystonia, athetosis, and chorea there may be abnormal movements, and in other extrapyramidal disorders there may be slowing of tongue movements, with thickness of speech and difficult protrusion. In pseudobulbar palsy there is bilateral paralysis; the tongue may be small and the patient may be unable to protrude it beyond the teeth. Patients with aphasia may have apraxia of tongue movements, and often are unable to protrude the organ on command.

Nuclear lesions may be of the progressive varieties described above, or may be due to neoplasms, vascular lesions, or toxic or inflammatory conditions such as polioencephalitis, multiple sclerosis, syphilis, abscesses, tuberculosis, or botulism.

In progressive bulbar palsy and amyotrophic lateral sclerosis the atrophy may be so marked that the tongue cannot be protruded, and it is seen lying on the floor of the mouth, exhibiting extensive fasciculations. It is stated by some anatomists that the uppermost part of the hypoglossal nucleus sends a few fibers to the facial nucleus for innervation of the orbicularis oris, just as the facial nucleus sends a few fibers to the tongue. Consequently some associated paresis of the orbicularis on the involved side sometimes accompanies a nuclear lesion. Similarly some paresis of the tongue is occasionally seen in peripheral facial palsies. In nuclear lesions there may be evidence of involvement of contiguous structures, such as the ascending sensory or descending motor pathways. In the hypoglossal alternating hemiplegia (Chapter 18) there is a nuclear paralysis of the tongue on the side of the lesion, and a contralateral spastic hemiplegia. The syndromes of Jackson and Tapia may follow either nuclear or radicular lesions.

Infranuclear lesions may be extramedullary but within the skull, within the hypoglossal canal, or in the neck. Basal skull fractures, subarachnoid or intracranial hemorrhage with exudation and organization, meningitis of various types, syphilis, tuberculosis, periostitis, extramedullary neoplasms or abscesses, basilar impression, compression of the medulla into the foramen magnum by increased intracranial pressure, or dislocation of the upper cervical vertebrae may affect the nerve before it leaves the skull. After the exit of the nerve from the hypoglossal canal or within the neck it may be injured by trauma of various types, stab or gunshot wounds, carotid aneurysms, infections in the retroparotid or retropharyngeal spaces, tumors of the neck, adenitis, tumors of the base of the tongue, salivary gland tumors, or operations on the neck, mouth, or tongue. The hypoglossal nerve may also be involved in multiple neuritis, and primary tumors of the twelfth nerve have been reported. When the hypoglossal nerve is involved with the ninth, tenth, and eleventh, and occasionally with the cervical sympathetic nerves in lesions in the retroparotid space, the syndromes of Collet, Sicard, or Villaret are seen.

Weakness of the tongue may be a symptom of myasthenia gravis. The tongue may be protruded a few times, but soon fatigues. Progressive lingual atrophy may occur with facial hemiatrophy. The localized contraction following percussion in myotonia has been described above. In psychogenic paralysis of the tongue the patient may appear unable to deflect it to the paralyzed side, but instead protrudes it to the nonparalyzed side.

Hyperkinetic manifestations of the tongue have already been mentioned. Tremors, fasciculations, and choreiform and athetoid movements may be manifestations of supranuclear, nuclear, or psychogenic disturbances. Forced deviation of the tongue may be a part of a jacksonian convulsion. More frequent than hysterical paralysis are such psychogenic manifestations as tics, lingual spasm, lisping, stammering, and other speech anomalies. *Aphthongia* is the name given to a form of spasm occurring in speakers and similar in nature to writer's cramp. Either tonic or clonic spasm of the tongue may be seen in hysteria, as a result of reflex irritation, or in tetanus or rabies.

The hypoglossal nerve, instead of the accessory, is sometimes anastomosed with the facial nerve in the treatment of peripheral facial paralysis.

CHAPTER 18

MEDULLARY AND RELATED SYNDROMES

THE MEDULLA, or medulla oblongata, may be considered either the caudalmost portion of the brain stem or an upward projection of the spinal cord. The caudal portion of the posterior cerebral vesicle of the embryo is called the myelencephalon. This term implies functions of both spinal cord and brain, or transition from spinal cord to brain. The medulla and the lower part of the fourth ventricle develop from the myelencephalon.

The medulla extends from the bulbopontine sulcus and the striae medullares (acousticae), above, to the lowermost roots of the hypoglossal nerve and the lowest plane of the pyramidal decussation, just rostral to the highest rootlet of the first cervical nerve. It is from twenty-four to thirty millimeters in length. The medulla contains the motor nuclei of the glossopharyngeal, vagus, cranial portion of the accessory, and hypoglossal nerves; the parasympathetic nuclei of the glossopharyngeal and vagus nerves; and the nuclei of termination of the sensory components of the glossopharyngeal and vagus nerves. Some of the vestibular nuclei are in the medulla, and the cochlear nuclei are situated at the junction between the medulla and the pons. It also contains the nuclei of gracilis and cuneatus, inferior olivary bodies and accessory olives, reticular formation, inferior cerebellar peduncles, arcuate fibers, and sensory and pyramidal decussations. Structures which pass through the medulla are the pyramidal (corticobulbar and corticospinal) pathways, lateral and ventral spinothalamic tracts, medial lemniscus, descending tract and nucleus of the trigeminal nerve, medial longitudinal fasciculus, fasciculus solitarius, ascending spinocerebellar and spinovestibular and descending vestibulospinal pathways, descending sympathetic pathways, and other fibers of passage.

The functions of the medulla are various. The presence of the nuclei of the ninth, tenth, and twelfth nerves make it an important center in the control of the reflex action of the pharynx, larynx, and tongue, and thus of articulation and degluti-

342

tion. It receives taste and visceral sensations and is concerned with many visceral reflexes such as coughing, swallowing, sneezing, salivation, sucking, and vomiting, and various secretory responses. It contains the medial longitudinal fasciculus and its connections with the accessory nerve, as well as the olivary bodies, all of which are important in the regulation of head and neck movements and of coordinated movements of the head and eyes. It is in part a center of cochlear and vestibular responses, and is a relay station for the nerves concerned with these. It is a region of passage for long ascending and descending pathways which relate it to lower and higher centers, and it is the region of decussation of certain of these pathways. The reticular formation plays an important part in the facilitation and suppression of motor activity, in the regulation of tone and conduction of sensation, in postural and other reflex activity, and in the control of consciousness and of visceral and autonomic functions. In addition, through the dorsal efferent nucleus and the vagus nerve, the medulla regulates respiratory, cardiovascular, digestive, and other metabolic processes of the body. There are secondary centers under the influence of the hypothalamus which, through the vagus nerves, exert an important control over such vital functions as heart rate, respiratory rate and rhythm, muscular and secretory activities of the gastrointestinal tract, and sugar metabolism.

Due to the small size and compact form of the medulla, a focal lesion may affect structures which have widely varying functions, and thus may lead to definite and pronounced symptoms and signs. Such a lesion may involve the *nuclear centers* and cause specific and multiple cranial nerve palsies. It may damage the *fiber tracts* and produce motor and sensory changes of the face and body. It may affect the vital functions and bring about bradycardia, hypotension, abnormalities of respiration such as Cheyne-Stokes breathing, disturbances in gastrointestinal function, and hyperglycemia. Usually, owing to the proximity of the relationships, a very small lesion of the medulla involves all three and causes neurologic syndromes which include cranial nerve palsies, sensory changes, pyramidal tract and cerebellar dysfunction, and oftentimes anomalies of respiration, circulation, and digestion. Involvement of the ninth, tenth, and twelfth nerves may cause regurgitation, dysphagia, and dysarthria. In unilateral lesions, however, there is never complete paralysis of deglutition or of articulation, but in extensive or bilateral lesions there may be profound impairment of these functions. Since the pyramidal and sensory pathways decussate in the medulla, unilateral lesions may produce ipsilateral paralysis of individual cranial nerves, together with contralateral motor and sensory changes. The signs referable to the ipsilateral cranial nerve dysfunction indicate the level of the lesion. Involvement of the fibers of passage may result in monoplegia, hemiplegia, alternating hemiplegia, or sensory dissociation. Due to the proximity of the two pyramidal pathways, there may be a paraplegia or a decerebrate type of rigidity. Involvement of the dorsal efferent nuclei or of both vagus nerves or pressure on the medullary centers may lead to profound disturbances in cardiac function, blood pressure, and respiratory action, and convulsions and/or coma and death may result. If death does not take place at once, there may be some recovery, but the residual paralysis of deglutition may lead to an eventual aspiration pneumonia.

Specific syndromes of the midbrain and pons are not dealt with in this chapter, but those in which there is also medullary involvement are described. The *midbrain,* which is the seat of the nuclei of origin of the oculomotor and trochlear nerves, also contains the red nucleus, substantia nigra, cerebral peduncles, superior cerebellar peduncles, the geniculate and quadrigeminal bodies in part, and ascending and descending pathways. The syndromes involving specific cranial nerves are discussed with those nerves, and disturbances of motor function associated with lesions of the red nucleus and substantia nigra or their connections are described in "The Motor System," Part IV.

The cranial nerve nuclei from the trigeminal through a part of the acoustic are situated within the *pons.* The pons also contains, in addition to the long ascending and descending pathways, the pontine nuclei and the brachium pontis (middle cerebellar peduncle). Syndromes characterized by cranial nerve involvement are described with those nerves. Owing, however, to the proximity of the pons to the medulla, and to the fact that the two structures may be supplied by the same blood vessels, pontine involvement may occur in medullary lesions, and it may be difficult to differentiate the two. Many pontine lesions, such as those which produce alternating hemiplegia and hemianesthesias, are very similar to medullary syndromes, and in many vascular lesions there may be involvement of both structures. Those pontine syndromes which occur with medullary ones and those of specific vascular origin are considered in this chapter.

A lesion of the medulla or of the medullary nerves may be *acute, subacute,* or *chronic* in course, and may vary in etiology and in site of pathologic change. *Intramedullary lesions* involve the cranial nerve nuclei and fibers of passage directly; *extramedullary lesions* within the posterior fossa affect the roots of the cranial nerves and also cause pressure manifestations; *supranuclear lesions* interrupt the continuity of the corticobulbar pathways; *extrinsic lesions,* that is, those outside the skull or within the neck, involve the peripheral course of the bulbar nerves in various combinations.

Neoplasms may be either intramedullary (gliomas or ependymomas) or extramedullary (neurofibromas, meningiomas, hemangiomas, or metastatic tumors). The symptoms and signs vary from case to case, but the course is progressive; occasionally increase of intracranial pressure appears late, and there sometimes is a paucity of neurologic signs in spite of the large size of the tumor. Extrinsic metastases and neoplasms that spread by direct extension from the nasopharynx and neighboring sites may cause widespread cranial nerve involvement and bone erosion without signs of medullary compression. Tuberculomas, gummas, and other granulomas may cause symptoms similar to those present with neoplasms. *Vascular lesions,* such as those secondary to hemorrhage, thrombosis, embolism, or focal softening, are intramedullary in site and usually acute in onset. Aneurysms of the basilar or vertebral artery or their branches and hemangiomas, however, may cause extramedullary compression and cranial nerve involvement. Extravasation of blood about the base of the brain from either subarachnoid or intracerebral hemorrhage may affect the cranial nerves as they leave the skull. Hemorrhages into the midbrain, pons, and medulla may cause hyperthermia, respiratory difficulties, coma, and finally death in patients with brain tumors, subarachnoid hemorrhage, cerebral hemorrhage, trauma, or other conditions with acute increase in intracranial pressure. The venous drainage from the medulla goes caudally into the venous plexus surrounding the spinal cord, and that from the pons and midbrain goes cephalad into middle cranial fossa; consequently compression at either the foramen magnum or tentorium may cause bleeding into the brain stem.

Other causes of intramedullary involvement include polioencephalitis inferior, bulbar polioencephalitis accompanying poliomyelitis, multiple sclerosis, syringobulbia or syringomyelia, tabes dorsalis, progressive bulbar palsy, congenital abnormalities and disturbances of development, and many other infectious, toxic, and degenerative processes. Extramedullary syndromes may be caused by trauma, basal skull fractures, abnormalities of skeletal development, acute and chronic meningeal inflammations, and sudden increase of intracranial pressure causing herniation of the medulla into the foramen magnum. Extrinsic lesions include, in addition to neoplastic invasion, trauma, cervical adenitis, tuberculosis, and aneurysms. Some of the above will be discussed in detail in the following paragraphs.

VASCULAR LESIONS

Vascular lesions of the medulla (and/or pons) may be either intermittent in course or abrupt in onset. The medulla receives its blood supply from the vertebral arteries; the pons, from the basilar (Fig. 128). These arteries, however, also supply the cerebral peduncles and the major portion of the cerebellum, and the terminal posterior cerebral branches of the basilar supply the occipital lobes, part of the temporal lobes, the hypothalamus, and the posterior portions of the thalamus and internal capsule (Chapter 52). With vascular insufficiency of the vertebral and/or basilar arteries, caused by atherosclerotic involvement of these vessels or of the subclavian arteries from which the vertebrals arise, there may be transient ischemic attacks which are characterized by temporary dysfunction of the nuclear centers, ascending and descending pathways, and other structures supplied by them. These may take the form of brief episodes of unilateral or bilateral weakness of the limbs, fleeting dimness or loss of vision or visual field defects, diplopia or paresis of conjugate gaze, nystagmus, nausea and vomiting, vertigo, ataxia, deafness or tinnitus, sensory changes involving either the trigeminal distribution or the extremities, dysphagia, dysarthria, drowsiness, mental confusion, and coma. Recurring episodes may cause increasingly severe deficits, and permanent occlusion of the branches of these vessels may cause the syndromes described below. Extensive involvement of the major vessels, however, may lead to sudden death due to circulatory or respiratory involvement. It must be recalled that there is wide individual variation in the vascular supply of the brain stem, and as a result the symptom complex that follows either occlusion or hemorrhage of these vessels may differ in individual cases.

The *anterior spinal artery* is formed by the union of branches from each vertebral artery; the site of union may vary. It supplies the pyramids, medial lemniscus, and emerging hypoglossal fibers. Thrombosis of this artery is usually followed by either an *alternating hypoglossal hemiplegia,* or an *alternating hypoglossal hemianesthetic hemiplegia.* In the former, also known as *crossed hypoglossal paralysis,*

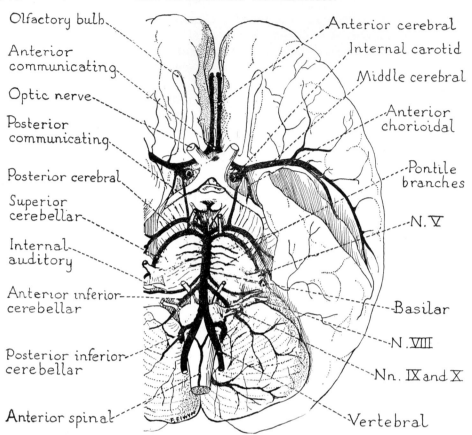

Olfactory bulb

Anterior communicating

Optic nerve

Posterior communicating

Posterior cerebral

Superior cerebellar

Internal auditory

Anterior inferior cerebellar

Posterior inferior cerebellar

Anterior spinal

Anterior cerebral

Internal carotid

Middle cerebral

Anterior chorioidal

Pontile branches

N. V

Basilar

N. VIII

Nn. IX and X

Vertebral

FIG. 128.   Basal surface of brain, showing main cerebral arteries and some of their branches. (Strong, O. S., and Elwyn, A.: Human Neuroanatomy. Baltimore, Williams & Wilkins Company, 1948.)

or the *syndrome of the pyramid and the hypoglossal nerve,* there is an ipsilateral flaccid paralysis of the tongue due to involvement of the hypoglossal nucleus or the emerging root fibers of the hypoglossal nerve, with a contralateral pyramidal paresis of the arm and leg, a result of involvement of the pyramidal tract before decussation. In the latter, also known as the *syndrome of the pyramid, the medial lemniscus, and the hypoglossal nerve,* there is in addition a contralateral loss of proprioceptive sensibility and diminution of tactile sensation due to involvement of the medial lemniscus. The spinothalamic tract is spared in most instances, so that there is no loss of pain and temperature sensations, and as a consequence there is a dissociation of sensory loss. The lesion may cross the midline and both pyramidal tracts or both medial lemnisci may be involved in either syndrome. In *bilateral anterior spinal thrombosis,* in which the circulation is cut off on both sides or in instances in which only one anterior spinal artery exists, there are double hemiplegia and hemianesthesia (tactile and proprioceptive sensations), with a bilateral or alternating paralysis of the tongue, usually more marked on one side. Both the paralysis and the sensory change spare the face. Lesions of the anterior spinal artery do not always involve the hypoglossal nerve. They may affect the medial longitudinal fasciculus and cause nystagmus. They frequently cause a disturbance of bladder and bowel function. All of the above are sometimes referred to as *Dejerine's anterior bulbar syndromes*.

In *hemiplegia cruciata, crossed hemiplegia,* or the *syndrome of the decussation,* there is a lesion at the level of the decussation of the pyramids (Fig. 129), with a contralateral spastic paresis of the lower extremity due to involvement of the corticospinal fibers to the leg which have not yet decussated, and an ipsilateral spastic paresis of the upper extremity attributable to damage to those fibers to the arms which have already crossed. There may also be ipsilateral flaccid paresis and atrophy of the sternocleidomastoid and trapezius (partial) muscles, and occasionally ipsilateral paralysis of the tongue. The crossed hemiplegia may also be the result of anterior spinal artery involvement, or it may be of traumatic origin. A more extensive lesion or one just above the decussation may produce a spastic tetraplegia.

The *posterior inferior cerebellar artery,* usually a branch of the vertebral artery, comes off just below the union of the two vertebrals to form the basilar artery; occasionally it is a branch of the basilar artery. It supplies the inferior cerebellar peduncle (restiform body), the dorsolateral tegmentum of the medulla, and the inferior surface of the vermis and adjacent cerebellar cortex. Thrombosis of this artery, the *lateral medullary* or *Wallenberg's syndrome,* is the most frequently encountered medullary syndrome (Fig. 130). There is involvement of the nucleus ambiguus and the emerging fibers of the ninth and tenth nerves, the descending tract and nucleus of the trigeminal nerve, the descending sympathetic pathways, the restiform body and the afferent spinocerebellar tracts, and the lateral spinothalamic tract. The resulting manifestations include ipsilateral paralysis of the soft palate, pharynx, and larynx with dysphagia and dysphonia; ipsilateral anesthesia of the face for pain and temperature sensations with loss of the corneal reflex; ipsilateral Horner's syndrome, and ipsilateral cerebellar asynergia and hypotonus. There is controlateral loss of pain and temperature sensations on the limbs and trunk. Sixth, seventh, and eighth nerve involvement on the side of the lesion have occasionally been reported. The vestibular nuclei as well as the solitary fasciculus and the olivary connections may be affected. There may be headache or pain in the back of the neck at the time of the occlusion; vertigo, nausea, vomiting, nystagmus, conjugate deviation of the eyes, and singultus are frequent manifestations. The patient may be unable to talk and swallow at the onset. If he survives, which is usually the case, there is a certain amount of improvement; he regains his ability to swallow and talk, although there may be residual hoarseness and persistent ataxia and sensory changes. Due to the individual variation in the blood supply to the brain stem, this syndrome may be the result of occlusion of the vertebral rather than of the posterior inferior cerebellar artery. It has also been described secondary to aneurysms, hematomas, and metastatic neoplasms.

The *anterior inferior cerebellar artery* supplies the lateral tegmentum of the upper medulla and lower pons, restiform body, lower portion of the middle cerebellar peduncle (brachium pontis), flocculus, and inferior surface of the cerebellar hemisphere. This vessel is usually a branch of the basilar artery, but is the most variable

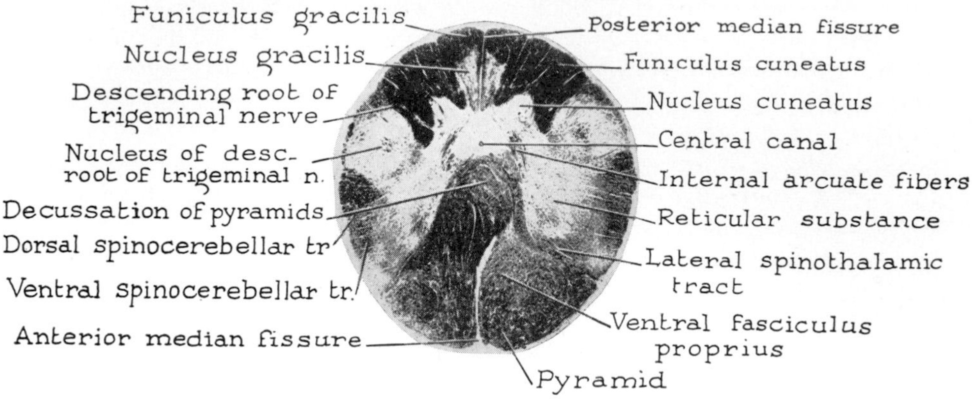

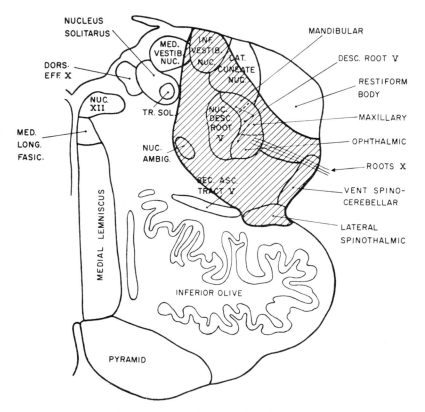

Funiculus gracilis — Posterior median fissure

Nucleus gracilis — Funiculus cuneatus

Descending root of trigeminal nerve — Nucleus cuneatus

Nucleus of desc. root of trigeminal n. — Central canal

Decussation of pyramids — Internal arcuate fibers

Dorsal spinocerebellar tr. — Reticular substance

Ventral spinocerebellar tr. — Lateral spinothalamic tract

Anterior median fissure — Ventral fasciculus proprius

Pyramid

FIG. 129.   Section through medulla at level of decussation of corticospinal tracts.

NUCLEUS SOLITARUS

MED. VESTIB. NUC.

INF. VESTIB. NUC.

LAT. CUNEATE NUC.

MANDIBULAR

DORS. EFF. X

DESC. ROOT V

RESTIFORM BODY

NUC. XII

TR. SOL.

NUC. DESC. ROOT V

MAXILLARY

MED. LONG. FASIC.

NUC. AMBIG.

OPHTHALMIC

ROOTS X

SEC. ASC. TRACT V

VENT SPINO-CEREBELLAR

MEDIAL LEMNISCUS

LATERAL SPINOTHALMIC

INFERIOR OLIVE

PYRAMID

FIG. 130.   Hemisection of the medulla illustrating typical variety of lateral medullary syndrome associated with thrombosis of the posterior inferior cerebellar artery. (Currier, R. D., Giles, C. L., and DeJong, R. N. *Neurology* 11:778, 1961.)

of the cerebellar arteries. Thrombosis of this artery causes, on the same side as the lesion, cerebellar asynergia, loss of pain and temperature sensations and diminished light touch sensation on the face, a Horner's syndrome, deafness, and a peripheral type of facial palsy. Contralaterally there is incomplete loss of pain and temperature sensations on the limbs and body. Postoperative thrombosis of this artery may follow excision of an acoustic neuroma.

The *superior cerebellar artery* supplies the lateral part of the tegmentum of the pons and midbrain, upper portion of the brachium pontis, brachium conjunctivum (superior cerebellar peduncle), superior surface of the cerebellum, and cerebellar nuclei. In thrombosis of this artery (which is in no respect a medullary syndrome) there is ipsilateral cerebellar asynergia with hypotonus and involuntary movements, often choreiform or choreoathetoid in type, and there is an ipsilateral Horner's syndrome. Contralaterally there is loss of pain and temperature sensations on the face and body owing to involvement of the spinothalamic tract and the ventral secondary ascending tract of the trigeminal nerve, and there may be a central type of facial palsy, and, occasionally, partial deafness.

Lesions of the *vertebral artery* may be either partial or complete. A thrombosis of this artery may cause immediate death, but various syndromes compatible with life have been described with and explained on the basis of a vertebral thrombosis. The *syndrome of Avellis* may follow thrombosis of the vertebral artery, and is characterized by involvement of the spinothalamic tract and of the nucleus ambiguus, usually with associated involvement of the bulbar nucleus of the accessory nerve. In some instances there is coincidental involvement of the medial lemniscus and the tract of the solitary fasciculus. There is ipsilateral paralysis of the soft palate, pharynx, and larynx, with contralateral loss of pain and temperature sensations on the trunk and extremities. There may also be loss of proprioceptive sensibility and diminution of tactile sensation on the opposite side of the body, and ipsilateral anesthesia of the pharynx and larynx and loss of taste. An ipsilateral Horner's syndrome and a contralateral pyramidal tract paralysis have also been described with this syndrome.

The *syndrome of Cestan-Chenais* is caused by occlusion of the vertebral artery below the point of origin of the posterior inferior cerebellar artery. Involvement of the nucleus ambiguus, restiform body, and descending sympathetic pathways causes paralysis of the soft palate, pharynx, and larynx, with cerebellar asynergia and a Horner's syndrome on the side of the lesion, while involvement of the corticospinal tract and the medial lemniscus produces hemiplegia with loss of proprioceptive sensibility and diminution of tactile sensation on the opposite side of the body. This differs from the posterior inferior cerebellar thrombosis principally in the presence of pyramidal signs and medial lemniscus involvement and the absence of changes in pain and temperature sensations. Occasionally, however, the symptoms in the syndrome of Cestan-Chenais may be extensive and variable. There may be involvement of the nuclei of the eleventh and twelfth nerves, with ipsilateral paralysis of the sternocleidomastoid and trapezius muscles and of the tongue; there may be involvement of the descending root of the trigeminal nerve, with ipsilateral loss of pain and temperature sensations on the face; and there may be spinothalamic involvement, with loss of pain and temperature sensations on the opposite half of the body. The syndrome may be caused by multiple lesions.

The *syndrome of Babinski-Nageotte* is in many respects similar to that of Cestan-Chenais, but it is believed to be caused by multiple or scattered lesions, chiefly in the distribution of the vertebral artery. There is usually involvement of the nucleus ambiguus, solitary fasciculus, descending root of the trigeminal nerve, restiform body, sympathetic pathways, pyramidal tract, and medial lemniscus, and often of the hypoglossal nucleus as well. There is ipsilateral paralysis of the soft palate, pharynx, and larynx, and sometimes of the tongue, with loss of taste on the posterior third of the tongue, loss of pain and temperature sensations on the face, cerebellar asynergy, and Horner's syndrome, together with contralateral spastic hemiplegia, loss of proprioceptive sensibility, and diminution of tactile sensation. There may be contralateral loss of pain and temperature sensations of the trunk and limbs if the lateral spinothalamic tract is involved. According to some authorities the Cestan-Chenais syndrome differs from that of Babinski-Nageotte in that there is tenth nerve involvement in the former but not in the latter. There is a wide variability in the descriptions of the syndromes.

Occlusion of the basilar artery may have a gradual onset or a somewhat fluctuating course, with some prodromata, but often the symptoms appear precipitously, and death may occur within a short period of time There are bilateral cranial nerve and long tract abnormalities. With total occlusion there is either a hemiplegia on one side and a partial hemiplegia on the other, or a quadriplegia; this is accompanied by bilateral involvement of the supranuclear fibers to the bulbar nuclei as well as of the ascending sensory pathways. As a result there is a picture of pseudobulbar palsy with severe dysphagia and dysarthria (see below), together with disturbance of both deep and superficial sensations on the body and extremities and sometimes on the face. The pupils are usually miotic. There may be decerebrate rigidity, either profound coma or akinetic mutism, and respiratory and circulatory difficulties. The symptoms of basilar artery hemorrhage are similar, but warning symptoms are less apt to occur. Hemorrhages into and edema of the brain stem may also occur following intracranial surgery or cerebral trauma or with sudden increase of intracranial pressure, subarachnoid hemorrhage, and rapidly expanding supratentorial mass lesions.

Thrombosis of the *medial pontine branches* may cause involvement of the nuclei of the sixth and seventh nerves or their emergent fibers, medial longitudinal fasciculus, pyramidal tract, and medial lemniscus, with ipsilateral facial paralysis and paralysis of lateral rectus movement or of conjugate lateral gaze, and contralateral hemiplegia, loss of proprioceptive sensibility, and diminution of tactile sensation. The *lateral pontine branches* supply the middle cerebellar peduncle, superior olivary body, facial nucleus, vestibular and cochlear nuclei, and in part the motor and sensory nuclei of the trigeminal nerve, medial longitudinal fasciculus, and spinothalamic tract. Thrombosis of these branches causes ipsilateral cerebellar asynergia with symptoms referable to the fifth, seventh, and eighth cranial nerves, often with contralateral loss of pain and temperature sensations on the trunk and limbs. There may also be contralateral hemiplegia and loss of tactile and proprioceptive sensations. With thrombosis of the *upper pontine branches* of the basilar artery there is a contralateral pyramidal hemiplegia, including the face and tongue, with contralateral loss of pain, temperature, and proprioceptive sensations and diminished tactile sensation on the face, trunk, and extremities, due to involvement of the pyramidal tract, the medial lemniscus, the spinothalamic tract, and the ventral and dorsal secondary ascending tracts of the trigeminal nerve. Thrombosis of the *internal auditory artery* produces ipsilateral deafness and loss of vestibular function.

SYNDROMES OF INTRAMEDULLARY OR OF EXTRAMEDULLARY INVOLVEMENT

There are many other specific syndromes which are characterized by involvement of the medullary nerves and pathways in various combinations. They may be the results of either intramedullary or extramedullary lesions, and may be of vascular origin, or found in association with syringobulbia, syringomyelia, multiple sclerosis, polioencephalitis, trauma, or neoplasms. They have been described by and associated with the names of the individual observers, but the descriptions in the literature vary widely, and in many instances there is a difference of opinion regarding the specific characteristics of each. The *syndrome of Jackson,* or the *vago-accessory hypoglossal paralysis,* is caused by a nuclear or radicular lesion of the tenth (nucleus ambiguus), eleventh, and twelfth nerves on one side; there is ipsilateral flaccid paralysis of the soft palate, pharynx, and larynx, with flaccid weakness and atrophy of the sternocleidomastoid and trapezius (partial) muscle, and of the tongue. The *syndrome of Schmidt,* or the *vago-accessory syndrome,* is caused by a lesion of the nucleus ambiguus and of the bulbar and spinal nuclei of the eleventh nerve and/or their radicular fibers; there is ipsilateral paralysis of the soft palate, pharynx, and larynx, with flaccid weakness and atrophy of the sternocleidomastoid and trapezius (partial) muscles. Inasmuch as the sternocleidomastoid and trapezius muscles are involved in both the above syndromes, it is unlikely that a nuclear lesion in the lower third of the medulla is responsible. Both are probably caused by extramedullary lesions which involve the fibers before they leave the skull. The *syndrome of Tapia,* or *vago-hypoglossal palsy,* is characterized by ipsilateral paralysis of the soft palate, pharynx, and larynx, and paralysis and atrophy of the tongue. This has been attributed to a tegmental lesion in the lower third of the medulla involving the ambiguus and hypoglossal nuclei, but since the soft palate and pharynx may be spared, this syndrome, as is the case with the two above, is more likely the result of an extramedullary lesion with involvement of the hypoglossal and vagus nerves high in the neck. The *syndrome of Avellis,* characterized by involvement of nucleus ambiguus and the bulbar nucleus of the accessory nerve, together with the spinothalamic tract and the medial lemniscus, has been described above.

The *syndrome of Vernet* is caused by a lesion at the jugular foramen, and is characterized by ipsilateral paralysis of the ninth, tenth, and eleventh nerves. It is usually of traumatic origin and may follow a basilar skull fracture; however, vascular and neoplastic lesions, thrombosis of the jugular bulb, aneurysms of the internal carotid artery, syphilis, tuberculosis, and adenitis may also be etiologic factors. The *syndrome of Villaret* is the result of a lesion in the retropharyngeal or the retro-parotid space. There is ipsilateral paralysis of the ninth, tenth, eleventh, and twelfth nerves and of the cervical sympathetic fibers (Horner's syndrome). The *syndromes of Collet and Sicard* are similar to that of Villaret, with the exception of the Horner's syndrome. Some authorities, however, state that the syndromes of Villaret, Collet, and Sicard are the same. In the *syndrome of Garel and Gignoux* there is involve-ment of the vagus and accessory nerves below the jugular foramen. With *tumors of the glomus jugulare* (*chemodectomas*) there may be involvement of the ninth, tenth, and eleventh nerves at the jugular foramen, as well as evidence of seventh and eighth nerve dysfunction. In *Garcin's syndrome* there is paralysis of all of the cranial nerves (or only the third through the tenth nerves), usually on one side but occasionally on both; this is most often the result of involvement by metastatic neoplasm, but may also be caused by invasion by neoplasm of the nasopharynx or retropharyngeal space or by granuloma or infection.

CHRONIC MEDULLARY SYNDROMES

Chronic medullary syndromes occur more frequently than either the acute and subacute or the localized varieties. The two principal types, progressive bulbar palsy and pseudobulbar palsy, bear some resemblance to each other. In both the outstand-ing symptoms are dysphagia and bulbar dysarthria, and both run a chronic course.

Progressive, or *true, bulbar palsy* is a relentlessly progressing degenerative disease which involves the motor nuclei within the medulla and sometimes those within the pons and midbrain. It is closely related to progressive spinal muscular atrophy, in which the process is limited to the anterior horn cells of the spinal cord, and to amyotrophic lateral sclerosis, in which there is involvement of the bulbar nuclei, the anterior horn cells, and the pyramidal cells within the motor cortex. Progressive bulbar palsy is usually a disease of late adult life; most frequently the onset is in the sixth and seventh decades, although younger individuals may be affected. The degen-erative process in the motor nuclei causes atrophy of the muscles supplied by the specific nerves, and this atrophy is accompanied by fasciculations and progressive paralysis. Inasmuch as the centers which supply the tongue, pharyngeal muscula-ture, palate, and sometimes the lips are predominantly involved, the condition is often referred to as glossopalatolabial, glossolabiolaryngeal, or glossopharyngeolabial paralysis.

The disease usually starts in the nucleus of the twelfth nerve and ascends. Among the first manifestations may be atrophy, fasciculations, and paralysis of the tongue. These symptoms are bilateral from the onset; in the beginning there may be fatigabil-ity of the tongue, but in far advanced cases the patient may be unable to protrude his tongue or to push food back into his mouth. The lingual involvement is followed or accompanied by dysphagia, usually for both liquids and solids, and by dysarthria. Regurgitation of fluids is an outstanding symptom, and it may lead to choking and aspiration. The defect in articulation is of the bulbar type, and is the result of involvement of the soft palate, the larynx, and the tongue. It is best described as a "thick" speech with a definite nasal factor—the speech observed in edema of the throat or when the mouth is filled with soft food. At the outset the most pronounced difficulty is in the pronunciation of the linguals and palatals, but later the labials, too, are affected. In far-advanced cases speech is reduced to unmodified laryngeal noises that are quite unintelligible. There is often marked drooling of saliva. Sometimes atrophy and fasciculations may be seen in the palate and pharynx as well as in the tongue, and the condition may ascend to the facial muscles and even the muscles of mastication. Occasionally the sternocleidomastoid and trapezius muscles are affected, and there may be autonomic involvement with tachycardia. The palatal and pharyngeal reflexes disappear early. There are no sensory changes, and no pyramidal tract manifestations unless amyotrophic lateral sclerosis develops. The condition is a progressive one, and there is no known cure. Death is usually caused by aspiration pneumonia. Progressive bulbar palsy may be associated with progressive spinal muscular atrophy, or it may be the first manifestation of amyotrophic lateral sclerosis. It is occasionally familial.

Progressive bulbar palsy is also a manifestation, often the terminal aspect, of *Werdnig-Hoffmann paralysis,* or progressive muscular atrophy of infancy and early childhood. Progressive bulbar paralysis of childhood, which may show a clinical course similar to that of the adult type, is known as *Fazio-Londe's disease. Congenital flaccid bulbar palsy* may be related to either Möbius' syndrome or the congenital myopathies.

In *pseudobulbar* (supranuclear) palsy there are difficulties with articulation, mastication, and deglutition which resemble those of progessive bulbar palsy, but the underlying mechanism is entirely different. Pseudobulbar palsy is caused by bilateral lesions which interrupt the pathways of the suprasegmental fibers to the bulbar nuclei. The pathologic process is supranuclear, but the symptoms are referred to the medulla. Since the bulbar nuclei are bilaterally innervated, or receive impulses from both the ipsilateral and the contralateral motor cortices, a unilateral supranuclear lesion rarely causes much difficulty in talking, eating, or swallowing. Bilateral lesions, however, which interrupt the pathways on both sides, do cause such difficulties. The most common causes of pseudobulbar palsy are repeated, bilateral cerebral vascular lesions which may be caused by multiple hemorrhages, thromboses or emboli. The syndrome may also occur in encephalitis, multiple sclerosis, multiple or diffuse neoplasms, or other disease processes that interrupt the pyramidal pathways on both sides. The lesions may be at the cortex, in the corona radiata or internal capsule, in the basal ganglia, in the cerebral peduncle, or in the pons or medulla above the nuclear centers involved. They are situated most frequently, however, in the internal capsule. There is usually a history of a vascular lesion that caused paralysis or paresis of one side of the body, but was followed by improvement. At the time of the original attack there may have been slight and transient impairment of speech, chewing, or swallowing. A later vascular lesion on the opposite side, with involvement of the remaining supranuclear fibers to the bulbar nuclei, causes the syndrome of pseudobulbar palsy. There is a bulbar type of dysarthria similar to that in progressive bulbar palsy. The speech is thick and slurred, but is more frequently explosive in type. There is difficulty in swallowing, with regurgitation, choking, holding of food in the mouth, and drooling. Even though the dysarthria is marked, there is a lesser tendency to choke than in progressive bulbar palsy, since the palatal and pharyngeal reflexes are preserved. There is neither atrophy nor fasciculations of the tongue, but the patient may be unable to protrude his tongue beyond his lips because of bilateral paralysis. The palate rises only slightly. There may be weakness and spasticity of the muscles of mastication, with an exaggerated jaw reflex, snout and sucking reflexes, and paresis of the muscles of facial expression, with masking of the face. Pyramidal tract signs are present in every case, and sensory changes are common. There frequently is deficient emotional control with spontaneous, or unmotivated, laughter and crying. The prognosis is more favorable than in progressive bulbar palsy, but the outcome is dependent upon the etiologic factor in the individual case and the possibility of further cerebral damage. Aspiration pneumonia may also terminate the illness in this syndrome.

Two types of pseudobulbar palsy have been described, that due to scattered lesions which affect the corticobulbar fibers, and that due to involvement of the basal ganglia or the extrapyramidal pathways. In both there is disturbance in function of the tongue, pharynx, larynx, lips, cheeks, and muscles of mastication, with difficulties in articulation, phonation, mastication, and deglutition. On occasion respirations may be severely affected, and swallowing may evoke a cough reflex. There may be evidences of further cerebral involvement with aphasia, extensive motor and sensory changes, incontinence, and dementia. In striatal pseudobulbar palsy there are additional signs of basal ganglion involvement with rigidity, hyperkinesias, and a parkinsonian attitude. A *progressive supranuclear palsy* has recently been described in which, in addition to pseudobulbar palsy, there are paralysis of vertical gaze, dystonia of the neck muscles, and progressing dementia; degenerative lesions are found in the brain stem, basal ganglia and cerebellum.

In *myasthenia gravis,* or *asthenic bulbar paralysis,* there may be dysarthria and dysphagia of the bulbar type which may resemble those of bulbar palsy. There may also, however, be weakness and fatigue of the facial and masticatory muscles, the extraocular muscles, the levator palpebrae superioris, and the general skeletal musculature. Ptosis, diplopia, difficulty in chewing, and general weakness are frequent symptoms. All of these manifestations are brought on by use of the involved muscles and are symptoms of abnormal fatigability; they are relieved by rest. Myasthenia gravis is not a true bulbar disease, but is rather a disease of the myoneural junction (Chapter 21).

MISCELLANEOUS SYNDROMES

Diphtheritic palsy is frequently manifested by a bulbar syndrome with involvement of the soft palate and pharynx, and sometimes of the tongue. There is nasal speech, with regurgitation of fluids due to paresis of the soft palate, and sometimes there is difficulty in swallowing solids due to weakness of the pharynx. If the laryngeal musculature is involved, hoarseness and even aphonia may be present. There often is associated paralysis of accommodation and of convergence. Furthermore, there frequently are manifestations of either a peripheral neuritis or an ascending myelitis, and of cardiac involvement. The pathogenesis of these changes is not entirely understood, but they are believed to be caused by the selective action of the diphtheritic toxin, chiefly on the peripheral nerves.

Botulism causes a polioencephalitis of the bulbar centers, often with associated involvement of some of the higher nuclear groups. After a short period of incubation, symptoms of dysarthria, dysphonia, and dysphagia develop, with paresis of the tongue, palate, pharynx, and ocular movements. Photophobia, vertigo, diplopia, ptosis, vomiting, and generalized muscular weakness are other important symptoms. In *tetanus* spasm of the pharynx may accompany trismus. In *rabies* spasmodic contractions of the muscles of the throat, face, and mouth and of the respiratory muscles are brought on by attempts to swallow.

Central pontine myelinosis runs a fulminating course. It may start with diplopia, dysphagia, dysarthria, and other evidences of brain stem involvement, followed by quadriplegia and by mutism and extensor rigidity before its fatal termination. Most cases have been reported in chronic alcoholics or in patients with severe malnutrition or chronic debilitating disease, although in some instances there appears to have been a relationship to infection. Pathologically there is widespread, symmetrical myelin loss within the central portion of the pons and occasionally of the adjacent midbrain and medulla. No etiology is known other than the above-mentioned precipitating factors.

In *akinetic mutism* (Chapter 55) the patient is speechless and motionless and makes little response to stimuli. He appears to be asleep, but can be aroused, and his eyes will follow moving objects and deviate in the direction of loud noises. This syndrome, also referred to as *coma vigil*, occurs with basilar artery thrombosis, Wernicke's syndrome, encephalitis, and traumatic and neoplastic lesions of the upper brain stem, all of which may cause involvement of the reticular activating system at midbrain and upper pontine levels.

Pressure on the midbrain and brain stem secondary to supratentorial mass lesions can cause either the syndrome of the tentorial notch (uncal syndrome) with third nerve involvement and signs of lateral midbrain compression (Chapter 11) or the so-called central syndrome with constricted pupils, Cheyne-Stokes respirations, bilateral pyramidal tract involvement, decorticate rigidity, and progressive impairment of diencephalic, midbrain, pontine, and medullary function.

In *bulbar poliomyelitis,* or *polioencephalitis,* there is paralysis of the throat, tongue, and respiratory muscles. In *epidemic encephalitis* there may be true bulbar or pseudobulbar involvement. *Syringomyelia* and *syringobulbia* may cause varying syndromes of medullary involvement, as may *multiple sclerosis, tabes dorsalis,* and *bulbar neoplasms.* Medullary manifestations are also seen in such conditions as Friedrich's ataxia, Marie's cerebellar ataxia, and olivopontocerebellar atrophy, but in these the cerebellar symptoms are more outstanding. So-called palatal myoclonus is discussed in Chapters 15 and 31.

The *syndrome of the herniation of the medulla and the cerebellar tonsils into the foramen magnum* may occur in association with increased intracranial pressure. It may take place precipitously following the removal of cerebrospinal fluid by the lumbar route in the presence of increased intracranial pressure, especially if the increased pressure is caused by posterior fossa tumors and abscesses. Compression of the medulla produces impairment of vital functions, with profound bradycardia, slow or rapid respirations, fall or marked rise in blood pressure, soaring temperature, unconsciousness, and death. On postmortem examination a "pressure cone" may be seen on the medulla.

Developmental or congenital anomalies of the occipital bone, atlas, and axis frequently cause medullary involvement, with characteristic neurologic syndromes. The bony walls of the foramen magnum and upper portion of the vertebral canal have a close anatomic relationship with the medulla, upper cervical portion of the spinal cord, and cerebellum. The neurologic manifestations may be produced by mechanical compression of the medulla and spinal cord by the bony deformity; there may be associated malformations of the nervous system, or both factors may be important. The bony abnormalities consist of malformations of the occipital foramen, basilar impression or imagination, platybasia, malformation or occipitalization of the atlas, fusion of the atlas with the occiput, abnormal position of the axis in relation to the occiput and the atlas, absence of one or more of the cervical vertebrae and fusion of certain of the cervical vertebrae (the Klippel-Feil syndrome), and cervical spina bifida. The principal nervous system anomalies are the *Arnold-Chiari deformity* with caudal displacement of the cerebellar tonsils and/or the inferior portion of the vermis and of the lower medulla and fourth ventricle into the spinal canal; maldevelopment and heterotopic changes in the brain stem and cerebellum; dysraphic conditions with incomplete closure of the medullary tube; hyrobulbia or syringobulbia; meningocele. The skeletal and nervous system development anomalies usually occur together. In severe cases there may be associated hydrocephalus. The neurologic picture consists of bulbar and cerebellar signs, with palsies of the ninth through the twelfth cranial nerves, involvement of the pyramidal tracts or sensory pathways, nystagmus, cerebellar manifestations, and signs of compression of the spinal cord at the foramen magnum; there may be signs of increased intracranial pressure. Some of the neurologic anomalies are entirely developmental, whereas others may arise on a mechanical basis secondary to traction. In the *Dandy-Walker syndrome* there is dilatation of the fourth ventricle and associated hydrocephalus. This arises following maldevedopment in fetal life and has been attributed to atresia of the foramina of Luschka and Magendie. There are usually associated anomalies of the cerebellar vermis, and in some cases this, rather than or in addition to atresia of the foramina, may be responsible for the syndrome.

REFERENCES

ADAMS, R. D.   Occlusion of the anterior inferior cerebellar artery.   *Arch. Neurol. & Psychiat.* 49:765, 1943.

ADAMS, R. D., VICTOR, M., and MANCALL, E. L.   Central pontine myelinolysis.   *Arch. Neurol. & Psychiat.* 81:154, 1959.

ARING, C. D.   Supranuclear (pseudobulbar) palsy.   *Arch. Int. Med.* 115: 198, 1965.

ATKINSON, W. J.   The anterior inferior cerebellar artery: Its variations, pontine distribution, and significance in the surgery of cerebello-pontine angle tumours.   *J. Neurol., Neurosurg. & Psychiat.* 12:137, 1949.

BENDA, C. E.   The Dandy-Walker syndrome or the so-called atresia of the foramen of Magendie.   *J. Neuropath. & Exper. Neurol.* 13:14, 1954.

BIEMOND, A.   Thrombosis of the basilar artery, and the vascularization of the brain stem.   *Brain* 74:300, 1951.

BHARUCHA, E. P., and DASTUR, H. M.   Craniovertebral anomalies. *Brain* 87:469, 1964.

BRAY, P. F., CARTER, S., and TAVERAS, J. M.   Brainstem tumors in children. *Neurology* 8:1, 1958.

BROWN, H. W., and PLUM, F.   The neurologic basis of Cheyne-Stokes respiration. *Am. J. Med.* 30:849, 1961.

BROWN, J. R., and BAKER, A. B.   Poliomyelitis: I. Bulbar poliomyelitis: A neurophysiological interpretation of clinicopathological findings.   *J. Nerv. & Ment. Dis.* 109:54, 1949.

BULL, J. W. D., NIXON, W. L. B., and PRATT, R. T. C.   The radiological criteria and familial occurrence of primary basilar impression.   *Brain* 75:229, 1955.

CANNON, B. W.   Acute vascular lesions of the brain stem: A complication of supratentorial space-occupying lesions.   *A. M. A. Arch. Neurol. & Psychiat.* 66:687, 1951.

COOPER, I. S., KERNOHAN, J. W., and CRAIG, W. McK.   Tumors of the medulla oblongata.   *A. M. A. Arch. Neurol. & Psychiat.* 67:269, 1952.

CURRIER, R. D., GILES, C. L., and DE JONG, R. N.   Some comments on Wallenberg's lateral medullary syndrome.   *Neurology* 11:778, 1961.

D'AGOSTINO, A. N., KERNOHAN, J. W., and BROWN, J. R.   The Dandy-Walker syndrome.   *J. Neuropath & Exper. Neurol.* 22:450, 1963.

DAVISON, C.   Syndrome of the anterior spinal artery of the medulla oblongata.   *Arch. Neurol. & Psychiat.* 37:91, 1937.

DAVISON, C., GOODHART, S. P., and SAVITSKY, N.   Syndrome of the superior cerebellar artery and its branches.   *Arch. Neurol. & Psychiat.* 33:1143, 1935.

GILLILAN, L. A.   The correlation of the blood supply to the human brain stem with clinical brain stem lesions.   *J. Neuropath. & Exper. Neurol.* 23:78, 1964.

GOMEZ, M. R. CLERMONT, V., and BERNSTEIN, J.   Progressive bulbar paralysis in childhood (Fazio-Londe's disease).   *Arch. Neurol.* 37:297, 1961.

GOODHART, S. P., and DAVISON, C.   Syndrome of the posterior inferior and anterior inferior cerebellar arteries and their branches.   *Arch. Neurol. & Psychiat.* 35:501, 1936.

GRAHAM, P. J.   Congenital flaccid bulbar palsy.   *Brit. M. J.* 2:26, 1964.

KRAYENBÜHL, H., and YAŞARGIL, M. G.   Die vaskulären Erkrankungen in Gebeit der Arteria vertebralis und Arteria basialis.   Stuttgart, Georg Thieme Verlag, 1957.

KUBIK, C. S., and ADAMS, R. D.   Occlusion of the basilar artery: A clinical and pathological study.   *Brain* 69:73, 1946.

LIST, C. F.   Neurologic syndromes accompanying developmental anomalies of occipital bone, atlas, and axis.   *Arch. Neurol. & Psychiat.* 45:577, 1941.

McNEALY, D. E., and PLUM, F.   Brainstem dysfunction with supratentorial mass lesions. *Arch. Neurol.* 7:10, 1962.

O'CONNELL, J. E. A., and TURNER, J. W. A.   Basilar impression of the skull. *Brain* 73:405, 1950.

OLSZEWSKI, J., and BAXTER, D.   Cytoarchitecture of the Human Brain Stem.   Philadelphia, J. B. Lippincott Company, 1954.

PEACH, B.   Arnold-Chiari malformation: Anatomic features of 20 cases.   *Arch. Neurol.* 12:613, 1965.

SIEKERT, R. G., and MILLIKAN, C. H.   Syndrome of intermittent insufficiency of the basilar arterial system.   *Neurology* 5:625, 1955.

SPILLANE, J. D., PALLIS, C., and JONES, A. M.   Developmental abnormalities in the region of the foramen magnum   *Brain* 80:11, 1957.

STEEGMANN, A. T.   Primary pontile hemorrhage.   *J. Nerv. & Ment. Dis.* 114:35, 1951.

STEELE, J. C., RICHARDSON, J. C., and OLSZEWSKI, J.   Progressive supranuclear palsy. *Arch Neurol.* 10:333, 1964.

STOPFORD, J. S. B.   The arteries of the pons and medulla oblongata.   *J. Anat. & Physiol.* 50:131 and 255, 1916; and 51:252, 1917.

SVIEN, H. J., BAKER, H. L., and RIVERS, M. H.   Jugular foramen syndrome and allied syndromes.   *Neurology* 13:797, 1963.

TYLER, H. R.   Botulism.   *Arch. Neurol.* 9:652, 1963.

WHITE, H. H.   Brain stem tumors occurring in adults   *Neurology* 13:292, 1963.

CHAPTER 19

DISORDERS OF
ARTICULATION

THE TERMS PHONATION, speech, and articulation are often used synonymously. In correct usage, however, they must be distinguished. *Phonation* is the production of vocal sounds without word formation; it is entirely a function of the larynx. *Speech* is defined as the utterance of vocal sounds which convey ideas, or as the faculty of expressing thoughts by words (articulate sounds which symbolize and communicate ideas). It is the whole process by which meanings are comprehended and expressed in words; it involves psychologic as well as physiologic factors, and is largely a function of the cerebral cortex. *Articulation,* on the other hand, is the enunciation of words and phrases, or the power of forming words by the larynx together with the pharynx, tongue, palate, teeth, and lips; it is a motor action whereby words, having been formulated, are audibly expressed. It is largely a function of the organs and muscles innervated by the medullary nerves.

Various types of abnormalities in sound production and word formulation may be produced by organic lesions of the nervous system. Disorders of function of the larynx may cause disorders of the volume, quality, or pitch of the voice, called *dysphonia*; complete loss of voice is *aphonia*. Lesions of the cerebral centers and connections which deal with word formulation and power of expression by speech, even though articulation may be adequate, cause *dysphasia* or *aphasia*. Involvement of the organs and muscles of articulation, the nerves to them, the nuclei of these nerves, or the central regulation of the nuclei (pyramidal, extrapyramidal, or cerebellar) causes *dysarthria,* or the imperfect utterance of sounds or of words; verbal formulation is normal, phonation is preserved, but enunciation of words is faulty owing to difficulty in performing the coordinated muscular movements necessary for the production of the vowels and consonants which make up syllables and words. If the disorder is so marked that it causes total inability to articulate, because of a defect in the control of the peripheral speech musculature, there is

359

anarthria. Dyslalia is a disturbance of utterance in which there is no organic neurologic defect, but there is either structural abnormality of the organs concerned with speech or a disorder of articulation without dysfunction of the articulatory apparatus. In *mutism* there is inability to speak or loss of power of speech; usually the patient appears to make no attempt to speak or make sound. Mutism is usually of psychogenic origin, but may occur in association with central nervous system lesions. In the present discussion only the motor components of word production are considered. The central control of speech and its disorders are discussed elsewhere ("Aphasia, Agnosia, and Apraxia," Chapter 53).

Sounds are produced by the expiration of a current of air from the lungs, through the trachea and upper air passages, and over the diaphragm formed by the movable vocal cords. For true articulated speech it is necessary to have coordination of the diaphragm, intercostal muscles, lungs, air passages, larynx, pharynx, soft palate, tongue, lips, and facial and masticatory muscles. Respiratory movements determine the strength and rhythm of voice. Variations in pitch are effected by alterations in the tension and length of the vocal cords and the rate and character of the vibrations transmitted to the column of air which passes between them. Modifications in sound are produced by changes in the size and shape of the glottis, pharynx, and mouth, and by changes in the position of the tongue, soft palate, and lips. The pharynx, nasopharynx, and mouth act as resonating chambers and further influence the timbre and character of the voice. Toneless speech may be possible in the absence of vocal cords, and whispered speech may be carried out in inspiration as well as in expiration.

Many *cranial nerves* are involved in articulation, and for an adequate appraisal of speech the function of each must be considered. The trigeminal nerves control the muscles of mastication and thus open and close the mouth. The facial nerves control the functions of the muscles of facial expression, especially in this regard the muscles of the mouth and the orbicularis oris. The vagus nerves, assisted to some degree by the glossopharyngeal and accessory nerves, supply the soft palate, pharynx, and larynx, and the hypoglossal nerves regulate the functions of the tongue. Thus articulation may be considered as one of the important bulbar functions. The upper cervical nerves, which have communications with the ninth, tenth, eleventh, and twelfth nerves and in part supply the infrahyoid and suprahyoid muscles, are also essential, as are the cervical sympathetic nerves which in part supply the pharyngeal plexus, and the phrenic and intercostal nerves.

In order to understand the production of disturbances in articulation, it is important to understand some of the more important *types of sound formation. Voiced sounds* are produced when the glottis is narrowed so that the vocal cords approach each other or touch lightly. *Voiceless sounds* are made while the glottis is open for outgoing breath. Both types of sound may be modified by changes in the size, shape, and position of the passageways through which the air must pass after leaving the larynx. *Vowels* are largely of a laryngeal origin, but are modified by the resonance of the vocal cavities. *Consonants* may be either voiced or voiceless; they are formed chiefly by the organs of articulation and are characterized in enunciation by constriction or by closure at one or more points in the breath channel. This distinction between vowels and consonants, however, is not absolute. Fricative sounds (either voiced or voiceless) are characterized by a frictional rustling of the breath as it is emitted with the oral passage largely closed.

From the point of view of phonetics, speech sounds may be placed in various categories. From the anatomic point of view, however, it is more important to recognize the individual organs which are chiefly responsible for the various sounds. The *articulated labials* are consonants which are formed principally by the lips; they are *b, p, m,* and *w.* The *modified labials* are vowels which are altered by contraction of the lips, mainly through the action of the orbicularis oris; they are *o* and *u,* and to a lesser extent *i, e,* and *a. Dentolabials* are formed by placing the teeth against the lips; *f* and *v* belong to this group. The *linguals* are sounds which are formed with the aid of the tongue. *T, d, l, r, n,* and *th* are *tongue-point,* or *alveolar, sounds* and are formed by contact of the tip of tongue with the upper alveolar ridge. *S, z, sh, zh, ch,* and *j* are *dentals,* or *tongue-blade* or *palato-alveolar sounds.* The *velars,* or *tongue-back, sounds (gutturals)* are articulated between the back of the tongue and the velum, or soft palate; they are *k, g,* and *ng. The palatals* are formed when the dorsum of the tongue is approximated to the hard palate; they include the German *ch* and *g,* and the French *gn.* Certain vowel sounds such as *i, a,* and *y* are modified by the palate and the velum. Whispered sounds are entirely articulatory. Humming with the mouth open is solely phonation.

Normal articulation is dependent upon a number of factors. Not only is the proper neuromuscular control of the organs of articulation and phonation necessary, but also normal cerebral synthesis and correlation. A proper development of the tongue, larynx, and soft palate, and adequate hearing are essential to correct enunciation. A normal attention span and adequate intelligence are also important. In appraising speech one must take into consideration the cultural background and the emotional make-up of the individual. It must be borne in mind that there are normal variations in enunciation and articulation which are results of training or which may be associated with certain geographic areas. No two individuals possess the same speech patterns. This is true not only in pitch and timbre, but also in the quality, duration, and intensity of tones and sounds, and in the ability to pronounce certain words and syllables. Some individuals never acquire the ability to formulate certain sounds. Education and training both enter into speech, and the uneducated, the illiterate, and the mentally deficient may mispronounce letters and syllables even though their powers of articulation are normal. Persons of foreign birth or those who learned to speak some other tongue before learning English may never learn to enunciate certain English sounds. Even within the United States there are marked regional variations, as shown in the pronunciation of the vowels and many of the consonants.

EXAMINATION OF ARTICULATION

In the examination of the articulatory process the patient's spontaneous speech in normal conversation is observed first. This may be done while the history is being taken. Then the patient may be asked to read aloud some simple printed matter.

The mode of expression, character of enunciation, rate of speech, and prosody (variations in pitch, rhythm, and stress of pronunciation) are noted. Any abnormalities of articulation such as tremulousness, stammering or stuttering, slurring or eliding of letters or words, scanning, explosive characteristics, and difficulties with specific sound formation should be observed.

For a detailed examination of articulation, the patient may be asked to repeat some of the so-called test phrases. These have been selected to test principally the labials and linguals—phrases containing such letters as *l*, *r*, *b*, *p*, *t*, and *d*—and as the patient repeats them, various aspects of dysarthria may become evident. These phrases are time-honored—perhaps above their actual value—and are to a certain extent colloquial, but many of them serve a need in testing articulation. The more commonly used are such phrases as "Truly rural," "Third riding artillery brigade," and "Methodist Episcopal," but such phrases as "Liquid electricity," "Voluntary retribution," and "Irretrievable" are also valuable. Among the other phrases used are "National Hospital for Paralyzed and Epileptic," "Magnolia Petroleum Corporation," "Constantinople is the capital of Turkey," "'Round the rugged rock the ragged rascal ran," "Peter Piper picked a peck of pickled peppers," "Voluntary contributions," "British constitution," "National Intelligencer," "Biblical criticism," and "Hippopotamus." More accurate evaluation of articulation can be made, however, by the use of weighted words, phrases, and sentences in which the individual consonants and vowels are placed in the initial, medial, and final positions. Ataxia and so-called scanning of speech are brought out most effectively by having the patient repeat a fairly long sentence. Weakness and fatigability of articulation, as well as disturbances in rhythm and quality, may be made evident by having the patient count loudly and quickly to thirty or beyond. Disturbances of laryngeal function and of rhythm may also be elicited by having the patient attempt prolonged phonation with an "ah" or "ee" sound.

DISORDERS OF ARTICULATION

Abnormalities of articulation may be caused by a number of different pathologic conditions. Disturbances in the respiratory rhythm produce an interference with speech. Paresis of the respiratory muscles causes an enfeebled voice with abnormalities in regularity and rhythm. Laryngitis, neoplasms of the larynx, or other abnormalities of the voice box may be responsible for severe impairment, but whispered speech may be possible in the presence of extensive disease of the larynx. Local disturbances, congenital or acquired, such as cleft palate, harelip, ankyloglossia, adenoids, edentulism, stomatitis, nasal obstruction, or perforated nasal septum may cause abnormalities in sound production. Speech is affected when there is interference with the symbolic formation of ideas, but articulation may be normal in spite of the presence of aphasia.

Neurologic disturbances of articulation or vocalization may be caused by involvement of the myoneural junction or the muscles of the tongue, larynx, and pharynx; by disease of the lower motor neuron—either the motor nucleus or the peripheral nerves which supply the muscles of articulation; by dysfunction of the cerebellum, the basal ganglia, or the upper motor neurons; by difficulties in symbol formulation or word expression; by psychomotor disturbances; and by abnormalities of rhythm in vocal expression or respiratory control.

Diseases of the *neuromuscular level* (those which involve the *lower motor neuron* or the *myoneural junction)* produce various changes, dependent upon the specific nerves or muscles that are involved. With lesions of the *hypoglossal nerve,* especially of the nucleus or the peripheral nerve, or with specific disorders of the tongue such as ankyloglossia, there is special difficulty pronouncing the lingual sounds, although there may be impairment of all enunciation. The speech is lisping in character and is clumsy and indistinct. With *paralysis of the larynx* the voice may be hoarse, and the patient may not be able to speak above a whisper. There is special difficulty with vowel sounds. A similar change in articulation occurs in laryngitis and in tumors of the larynx. In a unilateral laryngeal palsy, or in recurrent paralysis, the voice is low-pitched and hoarse, but occasionally there is almost complete unilateral paralysis without appreciable effect on phonation, owing to unimpaired adduction and to crossing of the midline by the normal vocal cord. With slight weakness of the vocal cords, hoarseness may become evident by having the patient talk with his head turned to one side. In bilateral abductor paralysis speech is moderately affected, but in bilateral total palsy it is lost. In paralysis of the crico-thyroid, which is supplied by the superior laryngeal nerve, the voice is hoarse and deep and fatigues quickly. In adductor palsy, usually psychogenic, the loss of speech is out of proportion to the involvement. Disturbances of voice production due to lesions of the laryngeal apparatus are called *dysphonias.* If the dysfunction is so extensive that no voice sounds can be made, the condition is known as *aphonia.*

If the paralysis is limited to the *pharynx,* there is little impairment of articulation, but in *paralysis of the soft palate* there is marked involvement, with resulting "nasal" speech, or rhinolalia, caused by undue patency of the posterior nares, or inability to shut off the nasal cavity from the mouth. An abnormal nasal resonance is added to all voice sounds. There is special difficulty with the velar sounds, but those formed by the lips and tongue are also weakened, for much of the air which should be used for their production escapes through the nose. The speech is similar to that encountered in a patient with a cleft palate. Characteristically *b* becomes *m, d* becomes *n,* and *k* becomes *ng.* The dysarthria is more marked when the head is tipped forward; it is less evident when the patient is lying with his head back, for then the paralyzed soft palate falls back by its own weight and closes off the naso-pharynx. A postdiphtheritic paralysis is one of the most common causes of this type of speech difficulty.

With *paralysis of the seventh nerve* there is difficulty in pronouncing the labials and the dentolabials. This defect is very noticeable only in peripheral facial involvement. Sometimes in a Bell's palsy there may be a marked dysarthria because of inability to close the mouth, purse the lips, and distend the cheeks. Similar articulatory defects are found in myopathies involving the labial muscles, especially the facioscapulo-humeral type, and in harelip and wounds of the lips. Tremors of the lips, such as those of dementia paralytica and toxic states, may interfere with speech. There is not much impairment of articulation in paralysis of the *trigeminal nerves* unless the involvement is bilateral, and in such instances there usually are other characteristics of bulbar speech. In trismus, such as occurs in tetanus, speech may be affected because the patient is unable to open his mouth. Lesions of the *ninth* and *eleventh nerves* have little effect on articulation.

Diseases of the lower motor neuron which may cause difficulties in articulation of the types just described may occur in neuritides of the cranial nerves, in polioencephalitis, or in many of the medullary syndromes. They may also occur in neuromuscular disorders such as the myopathies and myasthenia gravis and other disorders of the myoneural junction. In *myasthenia gravis,* prolonged speaking such as counting may cause progressive weakness of the voice with a decrease in volume and at times the development of a bulbar or nasal quality, which may even proceed to anarthria; the speech may vary with use and improve with rest. An occasional myasthenic patient may have to close his jaw with his hand in order to enunciate. In *progressive bulbar palsy* the defect is the result of multiple cranial nerve paralyses which affect the tongue, larynx and pharynx, soft palate, and, to a lesser extent the facial muscles, lips, and muscles of mastication. Both articulation and phonation may be affected; speech is slow and hesitant with failure of correct enunciation, and all sounds and syllables may be indistinct. The patient talks as though his mouth were filled with soft food, and the resulting change in articulation is often known as the "hot mush" or "hot potato" speech. It is thick and slurred, often with a definite nasal quality. It may have a halting, drawling, monotonous character. The tongue lies in the mouth, more or less immobile; the palate rises very little, and swallowing is difficult. The impairment may progress to a stage in which speech is reduced to unmodified laryngeal noises that are quite unintelligible. If the disease is so extensive that the patient is completely unable to talk, there is *anarthria.*

Supranuclear lesions, or involvement of the corticobulbar pathways, may cause disturbances of speech or of articulation. Unilateral cortical lesions do not usually affect speech unless they are in the dominant hemisphere and cause dysphasia, although occasionally some dysarthria accompanies dysphasia. Both dysarthria and dysprody have been described with localized frontal lobe lesions; these may be due to a dyspraxia of speech. In acute hemiplegia there may be transient slurring or thickness of speech, dependent upon the degree of weakness of the face and tongue. *Bilateral cortical lesions,* however, or bilateral lesions of the corona radiata, internal capsule, cerebral peduncles, pons, or upper medulla (vascular, inflammatory, neoplastic, degenerative, etc.) may cause *pseudobulbar palsy,* with its characteristic dysarthria. There is a thick, bulbar type of speech, similar to that in progressive bulbar palsy, but somewhat more explosive in nature; it rarely progresses to complete anarthria. The muscles which govern articulation are weak and spastic, the tongue is smaller than normal and is protruded with difficulty, and there may be spasticity of the muscles of mastication. In *spastic diplegia,* especially congenital spastic paraplegia, the speech may be slow and slurred, with poor enunciation, and there may be spasm of the pharyngeal muscles; owing to an abnormal breathing rhythm, there is poor correlation between breath control and voice production, so the speech is irregular and jerky.

Articulation may be affected in lesions of the *basal ganglia*. In *athetosis* the grimaces of the face and tongue interfere with speech. Irregular spasmodic contractions of the diaphragm and other respiratory muscles, together with spasm of the tongue and pharynx, may give the speech a curious jerky and groaning character. In addition there may be a pseudobulbar element with slurred, spastic, indistinct speech. In *chorea* the violent movements of the face, tongue, and respiratory muscles may make the speech jerky, irregular, and hesitant; the patient is unable to maintain phonation. Occasionally there is loss of ability to speak. In *paralysis agitans* and the *parkinsonian syndrome* associated with encephalitis there is *bradylalia;* speech is feeble, slow, and slurred owing to muscular rigidity and immobility of the lips and tongue. There is dysprosody, or a defect in rhythm, melody, and pitch, and the speech lacks inflections, accents, and modulation. The patient speaks in a monotone, and the words are slurred and run into one another. The voice becomes increasingly weak as the patient talks, and he may become unable to speak above a whisper; as the speech becomes more indistinct it may become inaudible or practically disappear. Tremor of the voice may be apparent; words may seem to be chopped off, and there may be clonic blocks and hesitations, or the speech may stop abruptly. There may be repetition of syllables, or palilalia. Like the gait associated with the disease, the speech may show festination with a tendency to hurry toward the end of sentences or long words. It may be further affected by respiratory tics and anomalies.

With *cerebellar lesions* there is a defect of coordination, or asynergy, of the speech, which is slow, slurred, irregular, labored, intermittent, and jerky. It is often explosive or staccato in character. Words are enunciated with irregular force and speed, with variations in loudness and pitch. Often the words or syllables are broken up, causing a jerky, syllabic, sing-song cadence, the so-called scanning type of speech which resembles the scanning of poetry. It may be accompanied by grimaces and irregular respirations. In patients with *voice tremor,* or tremor of phonation, there are rhythmic alterations in loudness and pitch; there may be associated essential tremor of the extremities or head or other signs of neurologic dysfunction, or the condition may be of psychogenic origin. Organic voice tremor is often an inherited condition.

Specific types of speech defects or anomalies of articulation may be observed in association with various organic diseases of the nervous system. The exact type of disorder in articulation may vary in individual cases, and depends upon the site of the predominant pathologic change. Many varieties of dysarthria have been described. In *pararthria* there is imperfect or disturbed utterance of speech in which single sounds or syllables cannot be pronounced in proper succession. *Bradyarthria,* or *bradylalia,* is slow or labored speech. *Magiarthria* is ataxic speech. *Alalia,* or *mutism,* is usually of psychogenic origin if present in a patient who appears to be conscious, but may also occur with lesions of the cerebrum and brain stem. In akinetic mutism, also referred to as coma vigil, there is complete immobility, except for movements of the eyes, in addition to lack of speech.

In *dementia paralytica* there is a tremulous, slurring type of dysarthria; there are special difficulties with the linguals and labials. The defect is brought out when the patient repeats the various test phrases. He hesitates and repeats. He omits letters, syllables, and phrases, or he elides them, or runs them together. The speech is slovenly, with ataxia, stumbling, and alliteration. Tremors of the lips, tongue, and face are increased when talking. Articulation may be made more difficult by the presence of aphasia and memory loss. In *multiple sclerosis* the speech is characteristically scanning in type; there are explosive and staccato elements, with slowness, stumbling, halting, slurring, and ataxia of a cerebellar type. The spacing of the sounds with perceptible pauses between words and irregular accenting of the syllables give the sing-song or scanning character which has been described as pathognomonic of the disorder. In *Friedreich's ataxia* the ataxic, staccato, and explosive elements predominate. Speech is clumsy, often scanning in type, and the pitch may be suddenly changed in the middle of a sentence.

In *alcoholic intoxication* the speech is slurred and indistinct. There is difficulty with the labials and linguals and there may be tremulousness. Furthermore, the conversation is often characterized by a tendency toward garrulousness, and the patient may repeatedly utter words that he can pronounce and enunciate correctly, whereas he avoids the use of other words. In *delirium tremens* the speech is tremulous, and it is frequently characterized by reference to hallucinations. In various *toxic states,* such as bromism and barbiturate intoxication and the early stages of anesthesia, the speech is thick and slurred. In *myotonia* the speech may be impaired by hypertonicity of the muscles, and a like difficulty may be encountered in *tetanus.* In *myxedema* the speech is low-pitched, harsh and husky, slow, and monotonous.

Dyslalia associated with damage to or structural abnormalities of the external speech organs or the articulatory apparatus may be caused by wounds of the lips, tongue, palate, or floor of the mouth; maxillofacial injuries; perforation of the palate; congenital harelip and cleft palate; abnormal shortness of the frenulum of the tongue; tumors of the palate or tongue; enlarged tonsils and adenoids, and dental malalignment. Secondary speech disturbances may also occur without abnormalities or specific dysfunction of the articulatory apparatus. These are seen in individuals with hearing defects, delayed physical development, mental retardation, and psychogenic disorders. The nature and degree of speech disorders resulting from hearing loss depends largely upon the amount of loss and the individual's ability to cope with it; it may vary from a mild abnormality of articulation to the indistinct and often unintelligible speech of *deaf-mutism.* A child with slow physical development or psychological problems may retain childish speech until later years. In delayed puberty and in enunuchism the male voice retains the juvenile or feminine characteristics, while in the virile woman it may be low-pitched and coarse. In mild mental retardation, also, childish speech may be retained. In imbecility the speech may be indistinct and difficult to understand; it is slow and labored, develops late, and the vocabulary is limited. Similar characteristics may be observed in cretinism and mongolism. In idiocy the speech is babbling and grunting in character, with a tendency toward echolalia.

Emotional and psychologic factors influence articulation. In agitation the speech may be broken and tremulous. In nervous tension it may be high-pitched, uneven, and characterized by breathlessness. In *hysterical dysphonia* the speech defect may vary in type from time to time. It often is bizarre in character, and does not correspond to any organic impairment of function. Oftentimes there is an abrupt onset of the difficulty with sudden periods of remission. The speech may be rapid and jumbled (tachyphemia or tachylalia), or there may be stuttering, lalling, "baby talk," or mutism. In hysterical aphonia there is imperfect adduction or even paresis of adduction of the vocal cords; even though the speech difficulty is profound, there is no disturbance of coughing or of respiration. In *habit spasms* and *obsessive-compulsive states* there may be articulatory tics which are characterized by grunts, groans, or barking sounds. In *lingual spasm* there is marked difficulty with articulation. *Aphthongia* is a type of anarthria due to spasm of the speech muscles; it occurs in speakers and is similar in nature to writer's cramp. The term *dysphemia* may be used for any type of speech disorder due to psychoneurosis.

In *manic states,* with psychomotor acceleration, there may be a rapid flow of words, often with an abrupt change of ideas from one subject to another. In *depressed states* there may be marked slowing of speech, sometimes with *mutism.* In *schizophrenia* there may be hesitancy with blocking, or there may be negativism with resulting *mutism,* or *alalia.* Palilalia, echolalia and perseveration are usually psychotic manifestations. *Palilalia* is the pathologic repetition of words and phrases. *Echolalia* is the meaningless repetition by a patient of the words addressed to him. *Perseveration* is the persistence of one reply or one idea in response to various questions; this may also be observed in certain aphasias. *Neologisms,* or the invention of new or meaningless words, is often a psychotic manifestation. Alliteral sentences, reduplication, and confusion are found in delirious and in psychotic states. *Idioglossia* is imperfect articulation with utterance of meaningless vocal sounds; the individual may speak with a vocabulary of his own. Idioglossia may be observed in patients with partial deafness, aphasia, and congenital word-deafness. The term *dyslogia* is used for disorders of speech, or impairment of reasoning power and speech, due to mental disease.

Stuttering is a variety of faltering or interrupted speech which is characterized by difficulty in enunciating and joining together syllables. Speech is stumbling and hesitant in character, with habitual and spasmodic repetitions of consonants or syllables, alternating with pauses which interfere with communication. *Stammering* is also a faulty, spasmodic, interrupted speech; there are involuntary hesitations in which the subject is unable to produce the next expected sound. *Cluttering* is characterized by sudden irregular accelerations of speech with shifting of stress and syllable division. Stuttering and stammering are often considered to be synonyms although the term stuttering is said to be more emphatic. Stammering often indicates embarrassment or hesitation, whereas stuttering suggests a more marked emotional quality. In both the flow of speech is broken by pauses during which articulation is entirely arrested. There may be localized cramps, spasms, and tic-like contractions of the muscles essential to articulation, and these may be accompanied by grimaces, spasms and contractions of the muscles of the head and extremities, and spasm and incoordination of the respiratory muscles. The individual may be unable to pronounce certain consonants, and there is special difficulty with dentals and labials. Often the first syllable or consonant of a word is repeated many times. There is a failure of coordination between the laryngeal and oral mechanisms of speech, and between voice production and respiratory rhythm. There may be a spasm of the articulatory apparatus and the individual may remain with his mouth open until the spasm relaxes, when the words rush out in an explosive manner until the breath is gone. He then takes another breath, and the process is repeated. The difficulty is markedly influenced by emotional excitement and by the presence of strangers. In spite of his difficulty in speaking, the individual may be able to sing without hesitation. There are many theories regarding the etiology of stammering and stuttering, or spasmophemia as the two are sometimes called, and both organic and psychological factors are cited. Delay in the myelinization of cortical areas concerned with speech and blocking of the control of the cortex over lower centers have been suggested as possible neurologic bases for stuttering. There is often a history of corrected left-handedness or of some disturbance in cerebral dominance. On the other hand, stuttering has been considered to be an emotional or personality disorder, or a habit that is learned in early childhood. Apparently organic factors may be of major importance in some cases, and psychological elements in others, and even in cases where there seems to be an organic basis for the disorder, emotional and environmental factors may play a part in the development and perpetuation of the difficulty.

In *lalling,* or *lallation,* the utterance is childish or infantile in type; it is characterized by a lack of precision in pronouncing certain consonants, especially the letters *r* and *l.* A uvular is substituted for a lingual-palatal *r,* so that "broken reed" is pronounced "bwoken weed." The diphthong *ow* or other letters may be substituted for the letter *l,* or sometimes *l* may be substituted for *r. T* and *d* may be substituted for *k, c, s,* and *g.* In *lisping* the sibilants are imperfectly pronounced, and *th* is substituted for *s;* a similar defect in articulation may be associated with partial edentulism. Lalling (sometimes also termed dyslalia) may occur secondary to hearing defects, mental or physical retardation, or psychogenic disorders. If that is not the case, it and lisping are usually due to imperfect adjustment of the organs or articulation (as in children), persistent faulty habits of articulation, imitation of faulty patterns of articulation, poor speech training, habit, or affectation.

REFERENCES

BERRY, M. F., and EISENSON, J.   Speech Disorders: Principles and Practices of Therapy. New York, Appleton-Century-Crofts, Inc., 1956.

BLEUMEL, C. S.   Stammering and Allied Disorders.   New York, The Macmillan Company, 1935.

BROWN, J. R., and SIMONSON, J.   Organic voice tremor: A tremor of phonation. *Neurology* 13:520, 1963.

COBB, S.   Speech disorders and their treatment.   *Bull. New York Acad. Med.* 19:34, 1943.

GREENE, J. S., and WELLS, E. J.   The Cause and Cure of Speech Disorders.   New York, The Macmillan Company, 1927.

GREENE, M. C.   The Voice and Its Disorders.   Philadelphia, J. B. Lippincott Company, 1964.

INGRAM, T. T. S.   A description and classification of the commoner disorders of speech in children.   *Arch. Dis. Child.* 34:444, 1959.

KAPLAN, H. M.   Anatomy and Physiology of Speech.   New York, McGraw-Hill Book Company, Inc., 1960.

LILLYWHITE, H.   Doctor's manual of speech disorders.   *J.A.M.A.* 167:850, 1958.

MONRAD-KROHN, G. H.   The prosodic quality of speech and its disorders. *Acta psychiat. et neurol.* 22:255, 1947.

MORLEY, M. E.   The Development and Disorders of Speech in Children. Edinburgh and London, E. & S. Livingstone, Ltd., 1957.

ORTON, S. T.   Reading, Writing and Speech Problems in Children.   New York, W. W. Norton and Company, Inc., 1937.

PEACHER, W. G.   Speech disorders in World War II: VII. Treatment of dysarthria. *J. Nerv. & Ment. Dis.* 106:66, 1947.

PEACHER, W. G., and PEACHER, G. M.   Speech disorders in World War II: IV. Dysarthria and dyslalia, methods of examination.   *J. Nerv. & Ment. Dis.* 103:484, 1946.

TRAVIS, L. E.   Speech Pathology: A Dynamic Neurological Treatment of Normal Speech and Speech Deviations. New York, D. Appleton and Company, 1931.

WEST, R., KENNEDY, L., CARR, ANNA, and BACKUS, O. L.   The Rehabilitation of Speech (ed. 2).   New York, Harper & Brothers, 1947.

WHITTY, C. W. M.   Cortical dysarthria and dysprody of speech.   *J. Neurol., Neurosurg. & Psychiat.* 27:507, 1964.

PART FOUR

The Motor System

Section I. *Components of the Motor System*

CHAPTER 20

LEVELS OF MOTOR ACTIVITY

THE EXAMINATION of motor functions involves many factors and is often a complex process. It includes not only the determination of muscle power, but also an evaluation of tone and bulk, a study of coordination and gait, an observation of abnormalities of movement, and, on occasion, special electrical and chemical tests. Many constituent parts of the peripheral and central nervous systems participate in motor activity, and these various functional components may have to be examined individually.

By means of our motor system we move our bodies in space and the various parts of the body in relation to each other. We also maintain postures and attitudes in opposition to gravity and other external forces. All movements, except for those of the body viscera and other structures supplied by the autonomic nervous system (Part VI), are effected by contractions of striated muscles through the control of the nervous system.

The intricate organization of the motor system and its evolutionary development from the simple responses of unicellular organisms to the patterns of behavior of animals and man account for the complexity of motor function. From anatomic and functional standpoints it may be demonstrated that there are certain phylogenetic levels, or stages of development, which increase in intricacy as we ascend the phylogenetic scale. In the lower vertebrates all motor activities are effected through subcortical centers, but with the greater development of the cerebral cortex in higher mammals, some of these functions are transferred to it. The older centers, however, retain their original functions, although they are modified by cortical control. They are not replaced, but are incorporated into an elaborate motor system, subordinate to the cortex. They continue to function as *levels of motor activity*. They all work together, however, and the efficiency of each depends upon its collaboration with the others. Certain diseases of the nervous system may involve, or predominantly involve, these individual levels; various segments or functional units may be affected while others are spared. In other clinical conditions, however, a complexity of motor phenomena may be encountered, and it may be difficult to separate the actions of different mechanisms which may be involved simultaneously. An understanding of the relationship between certain anatomic structures of the nervous system and their functional activity is necessary to adequate comprehension of disease of the motor system.

The various approaches to the understanding of the different aspects of motor disorders make a clear-cut analysis difficult. Overschematization of syndromes and rigid ascription of certain symptoms to particular anatomic systems may interfere with knowledge. It is believed, however, that in order to understand the function of the motor system as a whole, and to evaluate changes in motor activity that occur in disease, one is justified in analyzing first the morphology and function of the constituent parts and the changes in each that result from pathologic processes. Then one can synthesize them and correlate their functions. This does not mean that any one of them ever acts individually. Each does, however, have its own functions and its changes in disease processes, and an understanding of each part may aid in comprehension of motor function as a whole. In this text the description of the individual components is followed by a discussion of the examination of the various motor functions.

THE LEVELS OF MOTOR FUNCTION

There are many varieties of movement; some of them are independent of consciousness, whereas others are directly under the influence of the will. Certain neurologists have referred to the various stages, or levels, of nervous, and especially of motor, function. Hughlings Jackson described the "hierarchy or evolution of the motor centres" and listed three levels of the central nervous system, each sensorimotor and each representing impressions and movements from all parts of the body. The first, or lowest, level consists of the anterior horn cells in the spinal cord and their homologues, the motor nuclei in the brain stem; it is that sensorimotor division of the nervous system to and from which pass nerves to every part of the body. It is the lowest level in the evolution of the central nervous system and, in its motor elements, represents the simplest movements of all of the parts of the body. His second, or middle, level was placed in the motor centers of the cerebral cortex, possibly including the basal ganglia. This level mediates more complex movements. He named as his highest motor centers those which have their origin in the prefrontal lobes of the brain—the motor division of the "organ of the mind."

Orton has listed six phylogenetic levels, or stages of development, which are as follows: (1) The stage of direct muscular responses in which there are no nerve responses and the muscles react directly. (2) The asynaptic level in which the nerve filaments go from cell to cell and there is a spread of response in all directions without polarity. (3) The ganglionated cord, or nerve trunk, level in which there is a pair of dorsally placed nerve trunks, one on each side of the midline; this is found first in *Crustacea*. (4) The spinal cord level in which there is a fully developed neural axis with nuclei and pathways; this is found in *Amphioxus*. (5) The midbrain level. (6) The cortical level. Cobb states that there are seven levels of motor integration: (1) The neuromuscular, or the final common path along which all impulses from above must travel to reach expression in the muscles. (2) The spinal, which is characterized by relatively simple reflexes with little if any postural element. (3) The hindbrain, which involves the simple postural and standing reflexes. (4) The midbrain, which is characterized by more complex standing and righting reflexes. (5) The striatal, where there are elaboration of locomotor reflexes and assumption of learned movements that have been automatic. (6) The cortical motor, which functions in integration of skilled movements. (7) The cortical associative, which involves such mechanisms as initiative, memory, and symbolization. The cerebellum gives coordination to the first six levels. He refers to the first five as the "old motor system" which is important in man for all automatic locomotor responses. The "new motor system" is found only in the higher forms and reaches its most complete development in man. It works on and through the lower centers.

This evolutionary development of motor function from simple to complex movements is duplicated to a certain extent in the maturation of motor skills in man. At the time of birth simple spinal and brain stem reflexes have already been established, and more complex postural and righting reflexes appear during the first few weeks of life. Then, following the maturation of the cortex and commissural pathways, acts requiring associated sensory functions (grasping and groping) are possible. Still later volitional control of movement appears, and then the ability to perform skilled acts with a high degree of precision. In order to carry out a discrete movement, the initiation of contraction of the prime mover must be accompanied by graded contraction or relaxation of the antagonists and synergists and by fixation of the more proximal muscles to free the distal ones for use. If the act is to be performed smoothly and accurately, there must be the ability for the movement to be stopped at a given degree of contraction, and either reversed or started again at a degree of contraction necessary to accomplish the desired purpose. Stereotyped and patterned movements, integrated at lower levels, can be utilized as a part of the act. Postures must be assumed that can be modified or shifted easily and instantly for adjustment to the next movement. Throughout all this, the volitional elements and purposive aspects of the act are of paramount importance. Thus, all of the above-mentioned levels of motor integration enter into precision of movement.

In the present analysis of the anatomy and physiology of the constituent portions of the motor system, the following levels will be discussed: (1) The simplest constituent part to be considered is the *spinomuscular level,* the motor impulses of which arise in the anterior horn cells of the spinal cord and the motor nuclei of the brain stem and go to the myoneural junctions and thence to the individual muscles. Pathologic processes which are situated in the motor nuclei may be considered as diseases of the *spinal level;* those placed in the motor nerves, as diseases of the *neural level;* and those which originate at the myoneural junction and within the muscles, as diseases of the *neuromuscular* and *muscular levels.* (2) The *extrapyramidal level* has its nuclei of origin in the basal ganglia and related structures. (3) The *pyramidal* or *corticospinal level* has its origin in the motor nuclei of the cerebral cortex. (4) The *cerebellar level,* not a true motor level, is the coordinating mechanism. (5) The *psychomotor level* has to do with memory, initiative, and conscious and unconscious control of motor activity; it corresponds to Jackson's highest level. Discussed with the extrapyramidal level, but considered more in detail with reflex activity, are the hindbrain and midbrain centers which give rise to the *vestibulospinal* and related pathways. These are of importance in postural mechanisms and standing and righting reflexes.

It is not herein suggested that these so-called levels are individual motor systems, or that they in any way act individually or separately. They are merely components of the motor system as a whole, and each, with its constituent cellular centers, is a part of the complex motor apparatus. Each contributes its share to control of the primary motor neuron on which, as the final common pathway, all efferent pathways converge. Disease of each is characterized by certain signs and symptoms. Many syndromes of motor involvement may, however, embrace more than one of these constituent levels of the motor system, and the newer knowledge of cerebral and motor functions shows an even closer relationship between the individual parts than was formerly suspected. Furthermore, it must always be borne in mind that all purposive movements are initiated and guided in their performance by a constant stream of afferent impulses that reach the cerebral cortex. Sensory and motor functions are interdependent in the performance of volitional movement, and it is not possible to consider the motor system apart from the sensory system. Impairment of sensation may affect all aspects of motion—volitional, reflex, postural, tonic, and phasic.

CHAPTER 21

THE SPINOMUSCULAR
LEVEL

ANATOMY AND PHYSIOLOGY

THE STRUCTURE and functions of striated muscles depend upon their connections with the central nervous system. The *spinomuscular level* of motor integration has, as its primary units, the motor nuclei in the anterior horn cells of the spinal cord and their homologues, the motor nuclei in the midbrain, pons, and medulla. Impulses which originate in these cells are carried through their neuraxes, the peripheral motor nerves, to the motor end plate of the muscles. Stimulation of the nuclear center causes contraction of the muscle which it supplies. Sherrington, in 1904, described the anterior horn cell, from the point of view of function, as the *"final common pathway"* through which all nervous impulses from higher centers must pass to reach the myoneural junction and influence striated muscle. The terms *primary motor neuron* and *lower motor neuron* are applied to this structural unit. Inasmuch as clinical symptoms may result from pathologic change in the motor unit, in its neuraxis, or peripheral to the motor unit, either at the neuromuscular junction or in the muscle itself, one may subdivide the spinomuscular level of motor activity into the *spinal, neural, neuromuscular,* and *muscular* components. There are probably no muscular reflex actions in which impulses are not relayed to the spinal cord. In ontogeny and phylogeny, nevertheless, the primitive muscular and neuromuscular levels are seen before the development of the spinal, or spinomuscular, levels.

The primary functional unit of the spinal level, or of any motor level, is the reflex, or response to a stimulus ("The Reflexes," Part V). The essential unit of the reflex is a center of adjustment, together with the conductors necessary to connect this center with the appropriate receptor and effector apparatus. The receptor is the peripheral sensory ending; the primary conductor is the afferent nerve fiber; the center of adjustment is the motor unit with its associated synapses; the secondary conductor is the efferent nerve fiber, the neuraxis of the motor neuron; the effector

377

is the muscle stimulated. There may be intermediate or interposed association and commissural neurons.

In the spinal level is found one of the most primitive of reflex arcs. The impulse is carried from a receptor in the skin, subcutaneous tissue, tendon, or periosteum, through the dorsal root ganglion and into the dorsal horn of the spinal cord, where there is a synapse and the neuron of the second order, or the intercalated neuron, carries the impulse to the anterior horn cell (Fig. 131). On stimulation of this center of adjustment the motor impulse is relayed through its neuraxis, which goes by way of the ventral root of the spinal cord and the alpha subgroup of the "A" category of nerve fibers in the peripheral motor nerve to the motor end plate of striated muscle, where it stimulates the muscle and causes it to contract. The arrival of the motor impulse at the nerve ending is associated with the liberation of acetyl- choline, which causes depolarization of the muscle membrane at the neighboring end plate. This, in turn, starts a wave of excitation with resulting contraction of the muscle fibers. There is immediate hydrolysis of the acetylcholine by cholinesterase, and the end plate returns to its former state of polarization so that the next impulse can again cause depolarization and excitation. This normally takes place repeatedly and in rapid succession. Any interruption or break in this reflex arc causes loss of muscle response. Such loss may be caused by any pathologic process that involves the peripheral sense organ, sensory nerve, or dorsal root ganglion; the spinal cord with damage to the synapse, intercalated neuron, or motor nerve; the efferent motor fiber, myoneural junction, or muscle. Disease of the motor nerve, its neuraxis, the myoneural junction, or the muscle causes not only loss of reflex response, but also loss of motor function.

The alpha motor neuron in the anterior horn of the spinal cord is the terminal neuron of the voluntary motor system. It supplies the main large muscle fibers and its neuraxis goes directly to the motor end plate, or neuromuscular junction. One alpha motor neuron innervates from fifty to two hundred individual fibers, the num- ber varying in different muscles. This group of fibers constitutes a *fasciculus;* the anterior horn cell, its neuraxis, and the fasciculus it supplies make up a *single motor*

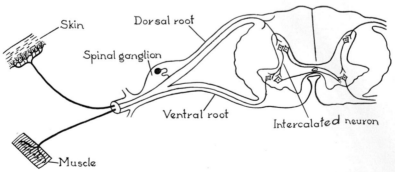

Fig. 131.   Diagrammatic section through spinal cord, showing the anterior horn cell and its afferent and efferent connections which make up the simple reflex arc.

unit. In muscles designed for discrete movement, as the ocular muscles, the ratio of nerve to muscle fibers is much smaller. All variations in the force, range, and type of movement are determined by the number and size of motor units called into activity. The gamma motor neurons in the anterior horn area are smaller in diameter than the alpha neurons and are efferent to small, specialized fibers in the muscle spindles, the intrafusal or fusiform fibers. These latter in turn act as receptor organs, and stimulation of them causes afferent impulses to be sent to the anterior horns to initiate contraction of the muscle by reflex action of the alpha motor neurons, thus producing the muscle stretch reflex. Special interneurons within the dorsal and ventral horns of the spinal cord, including the Renshaw cells, also play a part in the reflex activity of the cord, which is connected by means of synapses with interposed association and commissural neurons and with the higher levels of the nervous system. All motor impulses, whether part of the spinomuscular reflex arc or a part of a higher, more complex arc, are relayed to the muscle through the neuraxes of the anterior horn cells, which are acted upon by the corticospinal, rubrospinal, tectospinal, olivospinal, vestibulospinal, reticulospinal, intersegmental, intrasegmental, and other reflex levels (Fig. 132), and through the combined function of these various elements, normal muscular control is made possible. The part played by the fusiform (gamma efferent) system, which functions to regulate the sensitivity of muscle stretch receptors, and of special interneurons, the Renshaw cells, which have an inhibitory action on the motor neurons of the anterior horn region, are referred to here but not discussed in detail; these play an important part in the regulation of reflex activity and of tone and posture, but participate little if at all in voluntary motor function.

The arrangement of motor cells in the anterior horns was originally metameric; those of one segment innervated the muscles of the corresponding myotome. Owing, however, to complexities of development and the intermingling of the motor roots in the plexuses from which the peripheral nerves take origin, one nerve may contain fibers from several roots, and individual muscles may receive nerve impulses from more than one segment of the spinal cord. As a consequence, a disturbance of motor function which is caused by disease of the anterior horn cells may differ in distribution from one which is produced by injury of a peripheral nerve (Part VII).

A physiologic classification of the various muscles which participate in any simple movement divides them into the following groups: The *agonists,* or *prime movers* (*protagonists*), are the muscles which directly perform the desired movement; they are those whose contraction is essentially responsible for the muscular activity. The *antagonists,* or *moderators,* are those which oppose the agonists; the antagonists must be relaxed in order to have the agonists contract. The *synergists* assist the agonists and reduce unnecessary movement to a minimum; when the agonists have two or more actions and only one of these is required for a certain movement, the contraction of the synergists prevents the undesired action. The *muscles of fixation* bring about stability of the neighboring joints prior to movement in order to afford a firm base for muscular action; they place the parts of the body in a position appropriate for the movement. A single muscle may act in any of these capacities. Thus the flexor carpi ulnaris is an agonist when it flexes and adducts the wrist, an antag-

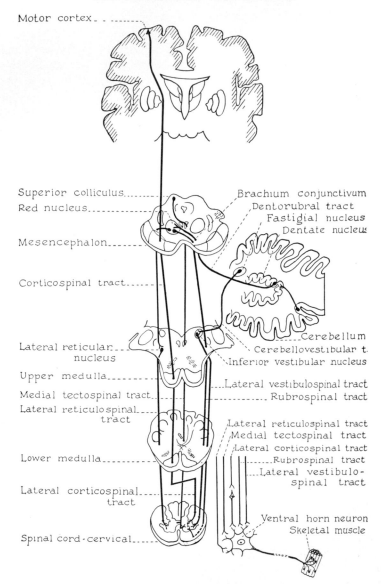

FIG. 132.   The more important descending motor pathways and their action on anterior horn cell of spinal cord (final common pathway).

onist when it resists passive extension of the wrist, a synergist when the fingers are extended with the wrist in flexion, and a fixator when it contracts to fix the pisiform bone for the action of the abductor digiti quinti. Any movement is dependent upon the combined action of all four groups—the ability of the agonists to contract while the antagonists relax, together with the associated function of the synergists and the fixators. Loss of function of any of these will impair the motor response.

CLINICAL MANIFESTATIONS OF DISEASE OF THE
SPINOMUSCULAR LEVEL

Certain specific clinical findings become manifest in disease of the anterior horn cell, its neuraxis, the myoneural junction, or the muscle itself (Table 2). In the first place, there is a *loss of motor power.* This loss of power is *focal,* or restricted, and it is *segmental,* or affects only the *muscles or muscle groups* that are supplied by the involved cells or nerves. It is dependent upon and proportional to the motor neurons (cells or neuraxes) affected, but there is *complete paralysis* of those muscle fibers no longer being stimulated. There is loss of ability to contract voluntarily and in response to stimulation, with weakness of all movements in which the affected muscle plays a part. The paralysis is characterized by a loss of tone of the involved muscles; this is spoken of as *flaccidity,* or *hypotonicity* (Chapter 28). If the motor neurons are destroyed, all the muscle fibers supplied by them undergo *atrophy,* or loss of volume; owing to degeneration of specific fibers or fasciculi, this is focal and is proportional to the degree of cell or fiber loss (Chapter 29). With denervation atrophy some 70 to 80 per cent of the original muscle mass may be lost within three months. With diminution in size, an overgrowth of connective tissue replaces the degenerated fibers. Contractures with resulting deformities may be caused either by contraction of antagonists whose action is no longer opposed by paralyzed muscles or by atrophy and fibrosis of affected muscles. Denervated muscle fibers undergo spontaneous contractions; these are known as *fibrillations,* and are too fine and rapid to be seen by the naked eye but can be demonstrated electromyographically. With certain types of motor neuron disease, such as progressive muscular atrophy, spontaneous twitching movements called *fasciculations* may be both seen through the intact skin and palpated, as well as demonstrated electromyographically. These are contractions of a bundle or fasciculus of muscle fibers, usually constituting a unit supplied by a single anterior horn cell (Chapter 31). Electrical testing will show a *reaction of degeneration* after the lesion has been present for a sufficient period of time, usually ten to fourteen days, as well as other changes in the electrical reactions, together with specific electromyographic changes (Chapter 33). Biopsy and chemical examinations of the muscles will show the presence of histologic and biochemical alterations. Finally there will be a diminution or a *loss of reflexes* in the areas involved (Part V). No *pathologic reflexes* or abnormal associated movements are found. Trophic changes in the skin, nails, hair, and bone and abnormal vasomotor phenomena may be present. There are no sensory changes if the lesion is restricted to the motor units.

Poliomyelitis may be considered as one of the more characteristic of the disease processes which involve particularly this level of the motor system. It is a disease of the *spinal portion* of the spinomuscular level. In this disorder, in which the predominant pathologic change is an acute inflammatory process in the anterior horn cells, there develops a flaccid paralysis, as described above, with focal involvement of certain muscles or muscle groups, complete for the area involved. This is accompanied sooner or later by atrophy; there is loss of tendon reflexes, without pathologic reflexes or associated movements, and a reaction of degeneration develops. There are usually no fasciculations in poliomyelitis. Eventually fibrous change takes place in the involved muscles and at the unused joints, and contractures develop. Both pain and tenderness are present in the affected muscles during the acute stage of the disease, and there has been some controversy regarding the presence of spasm in them. What has been interpreted as spasm is probably not, under most circumstances, a true sustained contraction of the muscle, but the result of multiple factors, including reflex stimulation from the spinal cord and inflamed meninges, local pathologic changes in the muscles themselves as a result of either inflammation or denervation, and increased tonus of the normal muscles in opposition to the weak or paralyzed ones. True spasm, however, may occur as a result of damage to interneurons in the spinal cord, functional disorganization of the muscle spindle, and Renshaw cell control over the surviving motor cells.

Progressive spinal muscular atrophy (chronic progressive poliomyelitis), both the adult type of Aran-Duchenne and the infantile type of Werdnig-Hoffmann, *progressive bulbar palsy,* and *amyotrophic lateral sclerosis* are related conditions in which the predominant pathologic change is a slow but progressive degeneration of the anterior horn cells and the motor nuclei within the brain stem and their

TABLE 2.   CHANGES IN MOTOR FUNCTION

	Loss of power	Tone	Atrophy	Fasciculations	Reaction of degeneration	Ataxia
SPINOMUSCULAR LESION	Focal and segmental Muscles or muscle groups Complete	Flaccid	Present	May be present	Present	Absent
EXTRAPYRAMIDAL LESION	Generalized Movements or extremities Incomplete	Rigid	Absent	Absent	Absent	Absent
PYRAMIDAL TRACT LESION	Generalized Movements or extremities Incomplete	Spastic	Absent (see text)	Absent	Absent	Absent (see text)
CEREBELLAR LESION	None Ataxia may simulate loss of power	Hypotonic (ataxia)	Absent	Absent	Absent	Present
PSYCHOGENIC DISORDER	Bizarre No true loss of power May simulate any type	Normal or variable Often increased	Absent	Absent	Absent	Absent (may simulate ataxia)

neuraxes, with resulting progressive wasting of muscle tissue (Fig. 133). Flaccid paralysis, atrophy, and areflexia are present, but the atrophy is the outstanding manifestation and it precedes the paralysis and areflexia. A reaction of degeneration appears later. One of the most characteristic manifestations in this group of disorders is the presence of fasciculations in the affected muscles (Chapter 31). Other progressive degenerations of the anterior horn nuclei, such as may occur with *syringomyelia* and intramedullary neoplasms, also cause atrophy and fasciculations. All these diseases of the anterior horn cell and motor nerve may result ultimately in trophic changes and muscular contractions. Peroneal muscular atrophy (progressive neural muscular atrophy, or Charcot-Marie-Tooth disease) causes similar changes; here, however, the pathologic alterations are in the peripheral nerves and nerve roots (Fig. 134).

Radiculitis, with irritation or disease of the ventral nerve roots, and *peripheral neuritis,* with involvement of the motor nerves, cause clinical manifestations that are similar in many respects to those in poliomyelitis. There is a lesion of the

TABLE 2. CHANGES IN MOTOR FUNCTION (*continued*)

	Reflexes	Abnormal movements	Associated movements	Trophic disturbances
SPINOMUSCULAR LESION	Deep reflexes diminished to absent Superficial reflexes diminished to absent No pyramidal tract responses	None, except for fasciculations	Normal	Present
EXTRAPYRAMIDAL LESION	Deep reflexes normal or variable Superficial reflexes normal or increased No pyramidal tract responses	Present	Absence of normal associated movements	Absent
PYRAMIDAL TRACT LESION	Deep reflexes hyperactive Superficial reflexes diminished to absent Pyramidal tract responses	None	Presence of pathologic associated movements	Usually absent
CEREBELLAR LESION	Deep reflexes diminished or pendular Superficial reflexes normal No pyramidal tract responses	May be present (intention tremor and ataxia)	Normal	Absent
PSYCHOGENIC DISORDER	Deep reflexes normal or increased (range) Superficial reflexes normal or increased No pyramidal tract responses	May be present	Normal	Absent

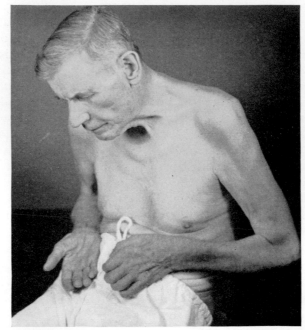

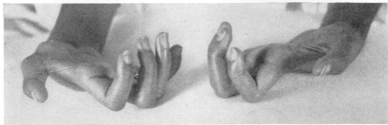

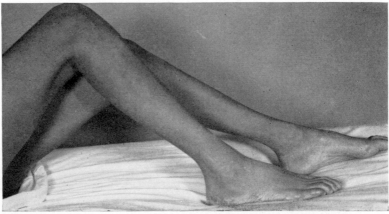

FIG. 133 (*Top*). Amyotrophic lateral sclerosis; advanced atrophy of muscles of shoulder girdle and hands.

FIG. 134 (*Bottom*). Peroneal muscular atrophy (Charcot-Marie-Tooth disease); wasting of the small muscles, with contractures of hands and feet.

neural portion of the spinomuscular level; the disease process is in the neuraxis rather than in the motor nerve, although there may be an ascending degeneration that eventually involves the nucleus as well. Owing to impairment of conduction of the motor impulse, there is a flaccid paralysis of certain groups of muscles, with atrophy, reaction of degeneration, and areflexia. Fasciculations are usually absent in neuritides, although they have been described in instances in which there is evidence of irritation of the neurons. A neuritis, however, is rarely confined to the motor nerves, and, as a consequence, there frequently are sensory changes, with pain and hyperesthesia. In the absence of associated spinal cord tract involvement, it may be difficult to differentiate between anterior root and anterior horn cell disease; in the absence of sensory changes, it may be difficult to differentiate between affections of the peripheral nerve, anterior root, and anterior horn cell.

Diseases in which the pathologic physiology is situated at the myoneural junction may be considered as illustrations of disorders of the *neuromuscular portion* of the spinomuscular level. In *myasthenia gravis* there is impairment of conduction of the motor impulse at the myoneural junction of striated muscles. This may be due to one of many causes. There may be either a failure of acetylcholine to form or a deficit in the amount of acetylcholine at the motor nerve ending, i.e., a decrease in either the synthesis or release of acetylcholine; there may be an excessive amount of cholinesterase which destroys the acetylcholine; the cholinesterase normally present may lead to a too rapid destruction of acetylcholine; there may be a deficit in the ability of the muscle to utilize acetylcholine; some curare-like substance may be present which elevates the threshold of the nerve impulses. The disease is characterized by fatigability of muscles, which is followed by a weakness and may result in pseudoparalysis or even true flaccid paralysis. There may be atrophy and areflexia. Motor and electrical tests, including chronaxie studies, show increased fatigability, without a reaction of degeneration, and specific electromyographic changes (Chapters 27 and 33). The symptoms are relieved temporarily by drugs such as neostigmine, which either retard or inhibit the destructive action of cholinesterase on acetylcholine and thus enhance the response to or increase the effectiveness of the latter. Anticurare drugs such as Tensilon (edrophonium chloride) have a stimulating effect at the myoneural junction and also give temporary relief.

Familial periodic paralysis is also a disease of the myoneural junction; there are recurrent attacks of flaccid paralysis with areflexia and a cadaveric electrical response. The symptoms come on abruptly and may last from a few hours to three or four days. There is a fall in the potassium content of the blood serum during attacks, and the symptoms are often relieved by the administration of this ion. In certain cases, at least, the syndrome is related to intermittent aldosteronism. There is retention of sodium shortly preceding an attack, which brings about a drop in potassium at the time of the onset of symptoms; the paralysis can be prevented by decreasing sodium intake. There may also be disturbances of carbohydrate, phosphorus, and thiamin metabolism. The periodic paralysis that occurs in association with hyperthyroidism is also characterized by hypokalemia. In addition, muscle weakness due to hyopkalemia may occur secondary to either urinary (renal tubular necrosis) or gastrointestinal (severe or chronic diarrhea) potassium loss.

Recently a hyperkalemic variety of familial periodic paralysis has been described —so-called hereditary episodic adynamia of Gamstorp. The attacks come on during a period of rest after activity, and there is an increase in serum potassium during them; they may be provoked by the administration of potassium. Myotonia is a symptom in some cases. More recently a third, or normokalemic type, has been reported; this is worsened by the administration of potassium and treated by the use of sodium. The muscle weakness of Addison's disease may be secondary to hyperkalemia, or there may be variations in muscle strength and muscular excitability resulting from alterations in body electrolytes, with fall and rise of intracellular and extracellular sodium and potassium as significant factors.

Other abnormalities of electrolytes and metabolites as well as the action of various drugs and toxins may cause paralysis and other evidences of motor dysfunction by their effect on the neuromuscular junction. Muscular activity is accompanied by an exchange of sodium and potassium across the cell membrane, and potassium can also excite muscular contraction by causing depolarization; consequently, abnormalities in both potassium and sodium metabolism may alter function. Increased aldosterone production causes retention of sodium with a resulting deficiency of potassium, which leads to periodic muscular weakness as well as tetany. With calcium deficiency there is heightened sensitivity of the motor end plate, causing fibrillations and a lowered threshold of muscle to both stimulation and acetylcholine. Magnesium in high concentrations causes neuromuscular depression by blocking contraction with a curarelike effect; a deficiency of magnesium results in weakness, tremors, and tetany. Curare and tubocurarine raise the threshold of the motor end plate to acetylcholine and thus prevent depolarization by acetylcholine. Decamethonium and succinylcholine cause depolarization, but this is persistent; after a brief initial stimulation a neuromuscular block occurs, and the muscle no longer responds. Other drugs such as mephenesin, which have been used clinically to produce muscular relaxation, have no effect on the neuromuscular junction, but cause central (subcortical and spinal) depression of polysynaptic neural pathways by blocking internuncial motor neuron discharges. Certain of the organic phosphates cause paralysis both by central action and by irreversible inhibition of cholinesterase. Botulinus toxin causes paralysis of muscles, possibly either by acting on the terminals of the axon rather than the end plate itself, or by causing inadequate synthesis or release of acetylcholine. The bites of certain ticks, snakes, and spiders and the toxin of some mushrooms also cause paralysis at the neuromuscular junction, but the exact mode of action is not known.

Finally there is a group of diseases which are primarily of muscular origin. These may be considered as illustrations of disturbance of the *muscular portion* of the spinomuscular level. They may be characterized by a flaccid paralysis similar to that seen in spinal (anterior horn cell) disorders, but there is no areflexia until after extensive atrophy has occurred. The most characteristic diseases of this group are the myopathies, which include pseudohypertrophic muscular dystrophy, the facioscapulohumeral type of dystrophy of Landouzy-Dejerine, the scapulohumeral form of Erb, and the distal myopathy of Gowers and Spiller. In the dystrophies, or myopathies, the anterior horn cells and the nerve trunks remain intact, but degeneration of the muscle fibers, often with replacement by connective tissue and fat, causes loss of contractility without loss of excitability (Fig. 135). The actual pathophysiology of these disorders is still unexplained, but most observers believe that there is some underlying biochemical or enzymatic dysfunction, probably related to an abnormality of electrolyte, protein, carbohydrate, creatine, or lactic acid metabolism. Amyotonia congenita, or Oppenheim's disease, is generally considered to be a type of myopathy, although changes have also been reported in the motor nuclei of the spinal cord or in the motor cortex. Related to amyotonia congenita but definitely of myopathic origin are the syndromes of congenital hypoplasia of muscle, benign congenital hypotonia, and congenital nonprogressive myopathy.

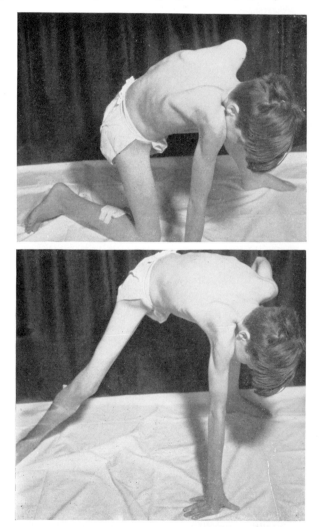

FIG. 135. Muscular dystrophy; marked wasting of musculature in shoulder and pelvic areas; atrophy and weakness of glutei cause difficulty in assuming erect position, and patient "climbs up his thighs" in order to stand erect.

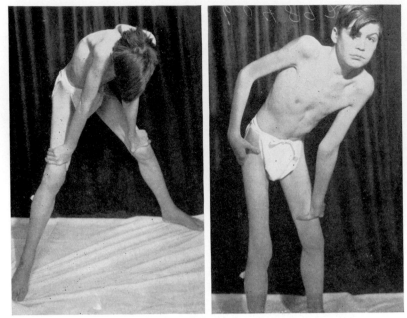

FIG. 135 (*Continued*).

Motor changes of muscular origin may also be found in the various types of myositis, such as polymyositis, dermatomyositis, fibromyositis, trichinosis, periarteritis nodosa, myositis ossificans, rheumatic myositis, vascular myosclerosis, ischemic myositis (Volkmann's contracture), thyrotoxic, carcinomatous, and steroid myopathies, diabetic amyotrophy, and localized panatrophy, as well as in other types of muscular dysfunction, such as idiopathic paroxysmal myoglobinuria and McArdle's disease (defect in muscle glycogen breakdown due to phosphorylase deficiency). In these, all of which are muscular disorders, there is no involvement of the motor neuron or its neuraxis. There may be, however, a flaccid loss of power of muscular origin, with focal involvement of certain muscles or groups of muscles. This may result in atrophy and in certain instances in areflexia and abnormal electrical reactions. In myotonia congenita and dystrophia myotonica, on the other hand, as well as in paramyotonia and occasionally in myxedema, there is an increase in muscle tone with a myotonic electrical response. In dystrophia myotonica there is muscular atrophy as well as myotonia. Electromyography and muscle biopsy are important procedures in the diagnosis of the myopathies, both primary and secondary, and in the differentiation of them from the muscular atrophies of neural and anterior horn cell origin. Enzyme and histochemical studies may also give diagnostic information.

Diseases of the sensory portion of the reflex arc, which include the sensory neuritides and tabes dorsalis, are not discussed here. It must be recalled that in such conditions there is areflexia and there may be muscular flaccidity, but if the anterior horn cell and/or its neuraxis are not involved, there is no paralysis and no atrophy or reaction of degeneration. Certain lesions of the afferent system, however, especially if they affect dorsal nerve roots, posterior columns, or parietal cortex, may cause profound impairment of voluntary motor function and interference with purposeful movement.

REFERENCES

ADRIAN, E. D.   General principles of nervous activity.   *Brain* 70:1, 1947.

ADAMS, R. D., DENNY-BROWN, D., and PEARSON, C. M.   Diseases of Muscle: A Study in Pathology (ed. 2).   New York, Hoeber Medical Division, Harper & Row, 1962.

BURGEN, A. S. V., DICKENS, F., and ZATMAN, L. J.   The action of botulinum toxin on neuro-muscular junction.   *J. Physiol.* 109:10, 1949.

COBB, S.   Foundations of Neuropsychiatry (ed. 3).   Baltimore, The Williams & Wilkins Company, 1944, pp. 43-72.

CONN, J. W., LOUIS, L. H., FAJANS, S. S., STREETEN, D. H. P., and JOHNSON, R. D.   Intermittent aldosteronism in periodic paralysis.   *Lancet* 1:802, 1957.

DALE, H.   The physiological basis of neuromuscular disorders.   *Brit. M. J.* 2:889, 1948.

GAMSTORP, I.   Adynamia episodica hereditaria.   *Acta paediat.* Vol. 45, Suppl. 108, 1956.

JACKSON, J. H.   Selected Writings (J. TAYLOR, ed.).   London, Hodder & Stoughton, 1931, vol. 1, pp. 349, 413; 1932, vol. 2, pp. 399–400.

MCARDLE, B.   Myopathy due to a defect in muscle glycogen breakdown.   *Clin. Sc.* 10:13, 1951.

ORTON, S. T.   Neuropathology.   *Arch. Neurol. & Psychiat.* 15:763, 1926.

PENRY, J. K., HOEFNAGEL, D., VAN DEN NOORT, S., and DENNY-BROWN, D.   Muscle spasm and abnormal postures resulting from damage to interneurones in spinal cord.   *Arch. Neurol.* 3:500, 1960.

POSKANZER, D. C., and KERR, D. N. S.   A third type of periodic paralysis, with normokalemia and favourable response to sodium chloride.   *Am. J. Med.* 31:328, 1961.

RIKER, W. F., JR.   Some aspects of the pharmacology of neuromuscular function.   *Am. J. Med.* 15:231, 1953.

TYLER, H. R.   Pathology of the neuromuscular apparatus in botulism.   *Arch. Path.* 76:55, 1963.

WALTON, J. N. (ed.)   Disorders of Voluntary Muscle.   Boston, Little, Brown & Company, 1964.

CHAPTER 22

THE EXTRAPYRAMIDAL LEVEL

THE "EXTRAPYRAMIDAL LEVEL" is discussed before the pyramidal level because it is phylogenetically more primitive; it has been referred to as the most highly developed portion of the "old motor system." The so-called extrapyramidal system, however, should not be regarded as an anatomic or physiologic entity; it is, instead, a functional concept, and our understanding of it has been derived mainly from clinicopathologic data on diseases characterized by disturbances of tone, movement, and/or posture. While its major or best known nuclear centers are in the basal ganglia, other important areas described below are functionally related, and it is closely allied with centers of motor integration in the brain stem, especially with the midbrain and vestibular components that are important in the regulation of tone, in primitive postural and righting reflexes, and in facilitation and inhibition of motor responses. It is also intimately connected with those portions of the cerebral cortex which have to do with motor control. According to Fulton and Kennard, the term 'extrapyramidal' should embrace all the non-pyramidal projection systems. Such a division of the projection systems is clearly useful since it allows separation of the voluntary pyramidal pathway from the other motor systems which have to do primarily with postural and other involuntary adjustments. It is not an independent neural mechanism nor a single unitary system, but a group of complex neural organizations which, while not directly concerned with the production of voluntary movement, are closely integrated with other levels of the motor system for the control of muscular activity.

ANATOMY AND PHYSIOLOGY

Until recent years it was believed that the basal ganglia were the major, or only, constituents of the extrapyramidal level, and therefore this phase of motor activity has also been referred to as the *basal ganglion, striatal, pallidal,* or *thalamopallidal*

390

level. It cannot, however, be separated functionally from related centers in the brain stem or from important connections with the cerebral cortex. It must be recalled, for clarification, that certain cortical centers other than pyramidal, especially the pre-motor centers, are also referred to as "extrapyramidal." Phylogenetically and onto-genetically the basal ganglia comprise the oldest portion of the cerebrum. They reach a high state of development in birds.

The basal ganglia which contribute most extensively to the extrapyramidal system are the *caudate* and *lenticular nuclei.* These structures lie deep in the substance of the cerebral hemispheres between the lateral ventricle and the insula (Fig. 136). The *caudate nucleus* is a pear-shaped mass of gray matter. Its head is on the lateral side of the anterior horn of the lateral ventricle, into which it bulges, and its tail runs backward in the floor of the ventricle and then downward and forward in the roof of the descending horn. The *lenticular,* or *lentiform, nucleus,* is composed of

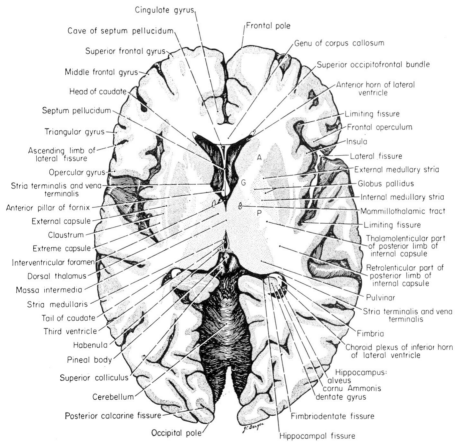

FIG. 136. Drawing of the superior surface of an unstained horizontal section of the adult human brain, through the internal capsule, basal ganglia, and thalamus. (Crosby, E. C., Humphrey, T., and Lauer, E. W.: Correlative Anatomy of the Nervous System. New York, The Macmillan Company, 1962.)

the *putamen* and *globus pallidus*. The former, which makes up the outer segment of the nucleus, is separated from the insula by a narrow zone of gray matter, the claustrum, and by the capsulae externa and extrema. The caudate nucleus is continuous with it, and histologically the two structures are identical; they contain a few large (Golgi type I) and many small (Golgi type II) ganglion cells. The globus pallidus is medial to the putamen and is separated from the thalamus and the caudate nucleus by the internal capsule. It is divided into a lateral and medial zone, and contains only large ganglion cells.

The nomenclature of these nuclei varies. The caudate and putamen are frequently referred to as the *striatum,* in contrast to the globus pallidus, or *pallidum.* Sometimes all three are classed as parts of the striatum, and the caudate and putamen are called the *neostriatum,* whereas the globus pallidus is the *archi-* or *paleostriatum.* Other structures classed as basal ganglia on an anatomic basis, the *claustrum* and the *amygdaloid nucleus,* are not functionally related to the above structures, and are not considered to be parts of the extrapyramidal system. The claustrum lies lateral to the putamen, but is separated from it by the external capsule; its functions are obscure, but it receives a cortical projection. The amygdaloid nucleus lies on the roof of the temporal horn of the lateral ventricle; it has olfactory connections.

Other structures are functionally and clinically related to the basal ganglia and must be considered parts of the extrapyramidal motor system. The *subthalamic nucleus* or *corpus Luysi* is a small, lens-shaped gray mass situated in the ventral thalamus just dorsal to the cerebral peduncle (Fig. 137). The *red nucleus* is located in the tegmentum of the midbrain at the level of the anterior quadrigeminal bodies. It contains both large and small cells. The *substantia nigra* is a gray mass that lies between the cerebral peduncle and the tegmentum of the midbrain, also at the level of the anterior quadrigeminal bodies. It is composed of two parts, the *zona compacta* that contains large melanin-bearing ganglion cells, and the *zona reticulata* that contains nonpigmented, spindle-shaped ganglion cells. The lateral and medial nuclear groups of the *reticular formation* are situated in the tegmentum of the midbrain, and other constituents of the reticular formation that either inhibit or facilitate motor responses are placed caudally in the brain stem. The *inferior olivary nucleus* is located in the medulla. The *dentate nucleus* and possibly the other nuclei of the cerebellum, the *zona incerta,* the *vestibular nuclei,* the *interpeduncular nucleus,* the *tegmental nuclei,* the *nucleus of the posterior commissure* (*Darkshevich*), *the interstitial nucleus* of Cajal, and the gray matter of the quadrigeminal plate are intimately associated with the above structures. All these are in close approximation to the *thalamus,* which is not only the sensory reception center for both the basal ganglia and the cortex, but also receives fibers from and relays impulses to most of the above-mentioned structures as well as the cerebral cortex.

The basal ganglia have rich communications with one another and with brain stem structures, as well as with certain areas of the cerebral cortex and with lower centers (Fig. 138). The *caudate nucleus* receives projections from the frontal cortex, principally from areas 4s and 8, and possibly from area 4 through collaterals from the corticospinal neurons, and from areas 2, 6, and 9. It also receives fibers from nuclei medialis dorsalis and ventralis anterior of the thalamus (thalamostriate) and from

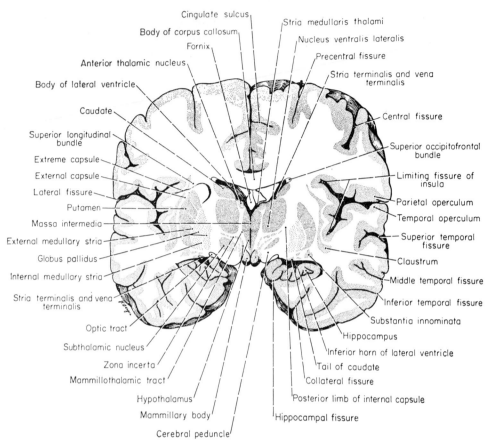

Cingulate sulcus
Body of corpus callosum
Fornix
Anterior thalamic nucleus
Body of lateral ventricle
Caudate
Superior longitudinal bundle
Extreme capsule
External capsule
Lateral fissure
Putamen
Massa intermedia
External medullary stria
Globus pallidus
Internal medullary stria
Stria terminalis and vena terminalis
Optic tract
Subthalamic nucleus
Zona incerta
Mammillothalamic tract
Hypothalamus
Mammillary body
Cerebral peduncle

Stria medullaris thalami
Nucleus ventralis lateralis
Precentral fissure
Stria terminalis and vena terminalis
Central fissure
Superior occipitofrontal bundle
Limiting fissure of insula
Parietal operculum
Temporal operculum
Superior temporal fissure
Claustrum
Middle temporal fissure
Inferior temporal fissure
Substantia innominata
Hippocampus
Inferior horn of lateral ventricle
Tail of caudate
Collateral fissure
Posterior limb of internal capsule
Hippocampal fissure

Fig. 137.   Drawing of the posterior surface of an unstained coronal section of the adult human brain, through the posterior limb of the internal capsule, basal ganglia, and mammillary bodies. (Crosby, E. C., Humphrey, T., and Lauer, E. W.: Correlative Anatomy of the Nervous System. New York, The Macmillan Company, 1962.)

putamen, and sends fibers to the thalamus (striothalamic) and to the putamen and globus pallidus. The small cells are receptor in function, and are believed to give rise to the internuncial fibers that make up short association pathways with the other basal ganglia and terminate in the putamen and globus pallidus. The large cells are said to make up the efferent striofugal system and send impulses to the globus pallidus and possibly also the subthalamic nucleus, red nucleus, and substantia nigra. The distinction between large and small cells hypothesized by Hunt has, however, never been confirmed. The connections of the *putamen* are similar; it receives fibers from cortical areas 4 and 6 and from the thalamus, and has a large connection with the caudate. It also receives fibers from the subthalamic nucleus (subthalamic fasciculus of Forel) and from the substantia nigra (comb bundle). It communicates directly with the globus pallidus, although the large cells may project as do those of the caudate. It may send some fibers to the ansa lenticularis.

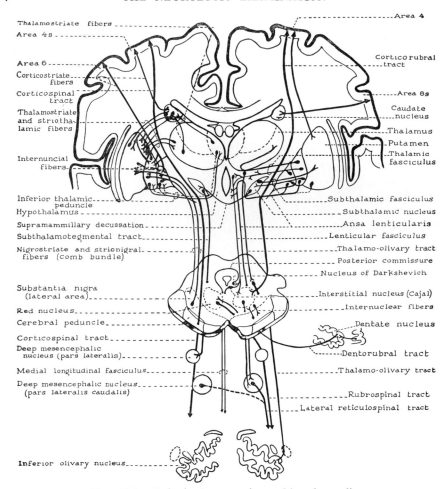

FIG. 138.   Principal connections of basal ganglia.

The *globus pallidus* receives impulses from the nuclei medialis dorsalis and ventralis anterior of the thalamus, through thalamostriate fibers and the inferior thalamic peduncle, and from area 6 of the cerebral cortex and possibly from area 4 through collaterals from the corticospinal neurons; its principal afferent innervation, however, is from the caudate and putamen. There are internuncial fibers within the ganglion. Its efferent pathways are numerous and important. The lenticular fasciculus of Forel (H_2 bundle), which emerges from the dorsal surface of the globus pallidus, is distributed to the hypothalamus, the nucleus of the posterior commissure (Darkshevich), the interstitial nucleus, the red nucleus, and the tegmentum dorsal and lateral to the rostral end of the red nucleus (deep mesencephalic nucleus, pars dorsalis and pars lateralis). The thalamic fasciculus (of Forel) carries fibers to nucleus ventralis anterior of the thalamus and probably also conveys thalamopallidal fibers. The ansa lenticularis, which emerges from the ventral surface of the globus pallidus (and also putamen), carries fibers to the hypothalamus and to the reticular formation and tegmental nuclei (deep mesencephalic nucleus, pars ventralis, pars lateralis, and pars lateralis caudalis). The subthalamic fasciculus (of Forel) conveys fibers to and from the subthalamic nucleus. The inferior thalamic peduncle carries efferent as well as afferent fibers. The globus pallidus also sends impulses to and receives them from substantia nigra, and sends impulses to the inferior olivary nucleus. Those to this latter structure arise through synapses in the field of Forel and descend in the thalamo-olivary tract; there are further synapses in the tegmental region.

The *subthalamic nucleus* receives impulses from the globus pallidus and probably the striatum and sends impulses to the globus pallidus and putamen through the subthalamic fasciculus of Forel, and to the thalamus. It communicates with the tegmentum of the midbrain (deep mesencephalic nucleus, pars lateralis) through the subthalamotegmental tract, and with the contralateral subthalamic nucleus through the supramammillary decussation of Forel. Connections with area 6 of the cerebral cortex have been described, and those with the red nucleus and substantia nigra have been hypothesized. The *red nucleus* receives impulses directly from area 4 of the frontal cortex as well as from the globus pallidus, the contralateral dentate nucleus, and possibly from the caudate and putamen. Its large cells give rise to the rubrobulbar and rubrospinal tracts that cross in the decussation of Forel and descend; the latter courses through the brain stem into the cervical portion of the spinal cord. The rubroreticular and rubro-olivary fibers from the small celled portion make up important discharge pathways; impulses relayed through them are carried down by the reticulobulbar, reticulospinal, and olivospinal tracts. In man the discharge through the rubroreticulospinal pathways is more important than that through the rubrospinal tracts. The red nucleus also sends efferent impulses to the nucleus ventralis lateralis of thalamus, the frontal cortex, the basal ganglia, the contralateral dentate nucleus, the motor nuclei of the brain stem, and possibly to substantia nigra. The *substantia nigra* receives a small communication from the globus pallidus (and possibly putamen) and also receives fibers from the tegmental nuclei and possibly from the red nucleus and subthalamic nucleus. Its efferent impulses go to globus pallidus and putamen through the comb bundle, and also to the tegmental nuclei. Cortical connections with areas 6, 8, 4s, and 4 have been described.

The basal ganglia and related centers may be considered to have their own reflex arc. Afferent impulses, which ascend through various pathways to the thalamus, go after synapse to the caudate and thence to the putamen and globus pallidus. These structures also receive afferent impulses from the frontal cortex. Internuncial fibers connect the nuclear masses. Efferent or effector fibers go from the caudate to putamen and globus pallidus and from putamen to globus pallidus. Striofugal fibers go via the ansa lenticularis and related pathways to the thalamus, hypothalamus, subthalamic nucleus, red nucleus, and substantia nigra, and also to the reticular formation and other lower centers and then, through the rubrospinal, reticulospinal, olivospinal, tectospinal, and the questionable nigrospinal and subthalamicospinal and other descending pathways, to the anterior horn cells, where they synapse and the impulses are then carried along the final common pathway to the individual muscles. Impulses that descend through these tracts may either facilitate or inhibit motor activity and influence the normal balance between the alpha and gamma motor systems.

The basal ganglia and the related structures constitute an important efferent system. Their discharges, however, are indirect and take place by means of relays. The extrapyramidal cortex and the basal ganglia discharge to the midbrain nuclei, the red nucleus, tegmentum, and substantia nigra in part, and these latter structures in turn discharge to the brain stem and spinal cord. The tegmentum is an important internode in the discharge of the basal ganglia to lower levels and an important efferent correlation center in which there is an interplay of striatal and cerebellar functioning with a conditioning cortical component. It has been demonstrated by the work of Dusser de Barenne, McCulloch, Bucy, and others that there are circuitous pathways from and back to the cortex, through the thalamus. The importance of these will be referred to under the clinical manifestations of extrapyramidal dysfunction. They are the corticocaudatopallidothalamocortical, the corticopontodentorubrothalamocortical, and the corticonigropallidothalamocortical pathways (Figs. 139, 140, and 141).

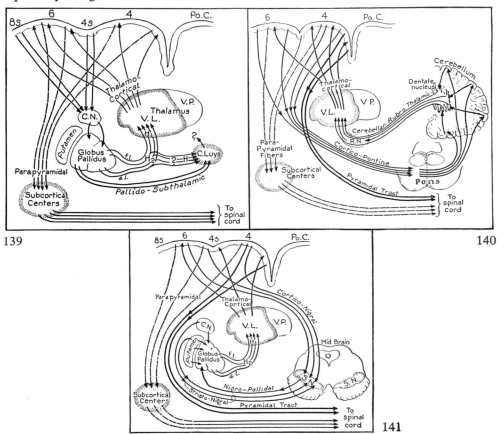

FIG. 139. The corticocaudatopallidothalamocortical pathway.
FIG. 140. The corticopontodentorubrothalamocortical pathway.
FIG. 141. The corticonigropallidothalamocortical pathway.
(FIGS. 139-141 from Bucy, P. C.: *J. Neuropath. & Exper. Neurol.* 1;224, 1942)

It may be that the above connections of the basal ganglia and related structures represent the original avenues for impulses from higher to lower portions of the nervous system, and that pathways from the cortex to the spinal cord, at first indirect, have been short circuited in the mammal through the evolution of the pyramidal system. It must be borne in mind, however, that there is a close functional relationship between the cortex, both pyramidal and extrapyramidal, and the basal ganglia, and between the cerebellum, thalamus, and brain stem structures and the basal ganglia. It may not be possible to consider disease of one part of this system-complex and overlook the others. Even in disease restricted to the basal ganglia there may be disturbance of cortical, cerebellar, thalamic, and brain stem functions.

When one considers the size and prominence of the basal ganglia, one would assume that their precise functions were better understood than they are. Stimulation of these structures in either intact animals or those with experimental lesions produces no consistent response, the effect varying to some extent with the type and intensity of the stimulus used. They exhibit no characteristic pattern of electrical activity, nor any consistent change in wave pattern in patients with so-called extrapyramidal disease. Removal or discrete lesions of them may cause little change in motor function. Both stimulation and destructive lesions of the subthalamic nucleus, red nucleus, substantia nigra, and reticular formation result in a variety of muscular contractions. There have been many attempts to reproduce the manifestations of extrapyramidal disease in experimental animals, using both destructive lesions and stimulation of the basal ganglia, red nucleus, substantia nigra, thalamus, tegmentum, reticular formation, and other areas, either singly or in combination, but thus far a perfect replica of such disease has not been obtained. With few exceptions the so-called extrapyramidal syndromes are peculiar to man, and because of the failure to produce disturbances in experimental animals sufficiently akin to those of human disease, there is still a lack of clear understanding of the functions and pathophysiology of the structures that are believed to constitute the extrapyramidal level. Consequently, our assumptions regarding the effects of disease of these structures are largely hypothetical. It was believed for many years that the principal functions of striatum and the pallidum had to do with *tone,* especially in taking and maintaining postures, and with the *control of automatic locomotor reflexes.* These structures form a postural background against which voluntary movements are executed, although they are incapable of initiating such movements. In the lower forms they are also important in movements of flight, fright, defense, and self-protection, as well as in synergistic control. Mammals with the cerebral cortex removed but with the basal ganglia intact can walk, run, and even jump in an effective though automatic manner. However, they lack initiative, spontaneity, and memory. They have few and rudimentary conditioned reflexes, and cannot react in the light of past experience.

Further investigations have shown that the functions of the basal ganglia are somewhat more complex than they were once thought to be, and that they may have to do with *highly integrated behavior patterns that may be modified by experience.* The pallidum may elaborate the simple motor and postural mechanisms of the brain stem into complex automatic motor behavior. It is probably the center for gestures of expression and reactive movements. The striatum elaborates and smooths out the coarser motor integrations of the pallidum. Both are subordinate to the functions of the extrapyramidal cortex, which exerts a controlling influence over them and must be considered an important part of the extrapyramidal system. The subthalamic nucleus, red nucleus, and substantia nigra probably have synergistic action and are important in the integration of stereotyped behavior and the control of complex muscular movements. The basal ganglia not only elaborate and integrate voluntary motor behavior and make it smooth and effective, but motor skills learned by the cortex can probably be relegated to these structures when they become automatic. The extrapyramidal system acts as a channel, in addition to the pyramidal system, through which volitional impulses are able to reach the primary motor neurons in the brain stem and spinal cord. Although dominated by the cortex, the "old motor system" has a supporting and steadying influence on volitional movements and may be utilized for the initiation and production of many involuntary or more or less automatic movements concerned with postural adjustments and reactions of defense. It is these habitual movements of daily life that are most impaired in disease of this portion of the motor system.

There is still much to be learned regarding the specific functions of the individual structures of the extrapyramidal level. Their relationship to each other and to the symptoms which appear in pathologic conditions will be discussed under the clinical manifestations of extrapyramidal disease. There may be various combinations of lesions in which one or another of the nuclear masses may predominate. Some clinical conditions may cause either paralytic or release phenomena consequent to destruction, while others may be irritative and excitatory in nature, and it is often impossible to differentiate the two. There is no refined localization of functions in these structures, and syndromes produced by disease of them are rather general in distribution and usually involve an entire half of the body.

CLINICAL MANIFESTATIONS OF DISEASE OF THE EXTRAPYRAMIDAL LEVEL

The present information regarding the functions of the basal ganglia and related extrapyramidal structures has been determined more on clinical than on experimental evidence. Diseases of the basal ganglia are common and they comprise some of the more important neurologic entities. Knowledge, however, of the pathologic change responsible for these diseases is fairly recent. Although Parkinson's disease, perhaps the most characteristic of the extrapyramidal syndromes, was first described in 1817, no anatomic or physiologic basis for the syndrome was suggested. Gowers (1888), Omerod (1890), Anton (1895), and Jelgersma (1909) noted changes in the basal ganglia in chorea, athetosis, and paralysis agitans, but the first adequate descriptions of the relationship of neurologic symptoms to lesions of the basal ganglia were made in 1911 and 1912 by Alzheimer, Vogt, Wilson, and Lewy. Cécile Vogt demonstrated the involvement of the caudate and putamen in athetosis, and Wilson, in his description of progressive lenticular degeneration, further clarified the knowledge regarding the functions of the basal ganglia. Hunt, in 1917, did important work on the extrapyramidal diseases, and Cécile and Oskar Vogt, in 1920, presented a complete pathologic and clinical classification of diseases of the basal ganglia. The epidemic of encephalitis that occured from 1917 to 1922 brought about a rich demonstration of lesions of the basal ganglia and the brain stem, even though physiologic mechanisms were not explained.

Disease of the extrapyramidal system is usually chronic and of gradual onset. It is manifested by one or more of three principal motor abnormalities: disturbance in tone, derangement of movement, and loss of associated or automatic movements. The *disturbance in tone* usually takes the form of hypertonicity or rigidity, often "cogwheel" in type, but occasionally there is hypotonicity. All muscles are affected, and often the muscles of the neck and trunk and the flexors of the extremities are most involved. The *derangement of movement* is usually a *hyperkinesia,* which may either be patterned or nonpatterned, and may take the form of a tremor or of choreiform, athetoid, dystonic, or other movements. These are independent of voluntary motion and usually disappear during sleep. Occasionally, however, there is decrease in motor activity; this may be manifested by *hypokinesia,* or poverty of movement, *bradykinesia,* or loss of speed and spontaneity of movement, or even *akinesia,* or severe deficiency of movement. There is rarely, however, a complete loss of power or paralysis, and movements of a volitional or semivolitional character persist unless there is associated pyramidal tract disease. The *loss of associated or automatic physiologic and expressive movements* may give rise to attitudinization, masking, and infrequent blinking. It is probably intimately associated with the disturbances of tone and muscular activity. In addition to these motor phenomena, there may be emotional changes and mental symptoms of various types, namely, exaggerated responses to anger or pleasure with unmotivated or spontaneous crying and laughter; compulsions, obsessions, depression, or irritability; bradyphrenia, oligophrenia, and manifestations of intellectual deterioration that lead to complete dementia in certain instances. Sensory symptoms are almost never seen unless there is associated involvement of the thalamus or of the sensory pathways. There are no characteristic reflex changes and no pathologic reflexes unless there is associated pyramidal tract involvement. There is no atrophy, and no fasciculations, reaction of degeneration, or trophic changes (Table 2, p. 354).

Diseases of the extrapyramidal level are frequently of degenerative or involutionary origin, but they may also be due to inflammatory or toxic processes, vascular disease, anoxia, neoplastic change, trauma, and disturbances of development. In most lesions that affect the basal ganglia, however, there is a diffuse disease process, with involvement of other parts of the brain as well. It is, therefore, doubtful whether a given symptom is the result of striatal disease or is due to disease elsewhere. The question has also been raised as to whether the disturbances in tone, the hyperkinetic manifestations, etc., are "release" phenomena, resulting from removal of inhibitory mechanisms or loss of control by higher centers, or whether they are manifestations of stimulation or of irritation of the basal ganglia.

The most characteristic or most representative of the extrapyramidal diseases are *Parkinson's disease* and the parkinsonian syndromes that occur following encephalitis and in association with arteriosclerosis and other conditions. In these various manifestations of the above three motor abnormalities are evident. There is marked hypertonia, or rigidity, which affects principally the spinal muscles and the proximal and flexor groups of the extremities; occasionally the rigidity is of a "cogwheel" type. There is a characteristic hyperkinesia with a coarse, pill-rolling tremor of nonintention variety. It is fairly rhythmic, gross, from two to six per second, and may involve the hands, feet, jaw, tongue, lips, and pharynx. It is usually a "resting tremor," is not affected by voluntary movement, and disappears in sleep. Occasionally the tremor is of an action type. There is slowing of all movements, and there is loss of associated and automatic movements with masking of the face, infrequent smiling and blinking, loss of swinging of the arms in walking, and micrographia. The gait is slowed and shuffling in character, with stooping, propulsion, and festination. There is muscular weakness but no true *loss of power,* such as is seen in spinal or pyramidal lesions, in spite of the synonym of paralysis agitans for the disorder. The rigidity and bradykinesia, however, may make locomotion and motor activity slow and difficult, and may produce an apparent paralysis that is *rigid* in type, is *not complete,* is *generalized,* and involves *movements* and not muscles or groups (Fig. 142). Under emotional stimulation, however, the extremities can often be used rapidly and effectively, although in some patients there is profound akinesia, with difficulty in the initiation of movement and disorders of postural fixation and righting. Abnormalities of phonation and articulation are common. There is no atrophy, and no fasciculations, reaction of degeneration, characteristic change in the deep reflexes, or pathologic reflexes (Table 2). If there is associated pyramidal tract involvement, this may cause reflex changes. There is often exaggeration of the orbicularis oculi and orbicularis oris reflexes (Chapter 13), and other special reflex phenomena are occasionally elicited (Chapter 40). The manifestations differ in each case: in some the tremor is the oustanding symptom, in others the rigidity, the bradykinesia, or the loss of associated movements. Associated involvement of the midbrain structures may cause changes in ocular movements and in pupillary reactions, and hypothalamic involvement may cause hyperhidrosis, greasy seborrhea, and somnolence.

There is not yet universal agreement about the pathologic basis of Parkinson's disease and the parkinsonian syndromes. In the so-called idiopathic variety alterations have been said to occur predominately in the pallidum and striatum, with loss of ganglion cells, gliosis, and vascular abnormalities, whereas in postencephalitis parkinsonism such changes have been observed more frequently in the substantia nigra. Greenfield and others, however, have observed alterations in the substantia nigra and locus caeruleus, namely the presence of hyaline inclusion bodies, lipochrome granules, and neurofibrillary tangles, in both conditions. The pathologic alterations, however, are often widespread, and the site of most damage probably determines whether tremor, rigidity, or loss of associated movements will be most marked. Greenfield expresses the belief that the substantia nigra is the "nodal point" of the neuronal degeneration. The etiology of idiopathic Parkinson's disease is not known; in addition to encephalitis and arteriosclerosis, parkinsonian syndromes may follow anoxia, trauma, carbon monoxide intoxication, and

FIG. 142.   Parkinson's disease; rigidity and masking.

poisoning by manganese and other toxins. Recently similar syndromes, as well as other more bizarre extrapyramidal manifestations, have been observed following the use of drugs of the phenothiazine and related groups. Tremors, rigidity, and athetoid and choreiform movements may also be symptoms of magnesium deficiency.

Other diseases of the extrapyramidal system show varying degrees of the manifestations mentioned above. In *Wilson's disease,* or *progressive lenticular degeneration,* which has its onset between the ages of ten and twenty, there are tremors, spasmodic movements of various types, hypertonia leading to contractures, and muscular weakness and wasting. The tremors may be present in the resting state and increased by voluntary action. Most characteristic, however, is a severe tremor of the outstretched upper extremities that has been called a "wing-beating" movement. This is not a true intention tremor, but is most marked with sustained positions. Other neurologic symptoms include dysarthria, dysphagia, epileptiform or apoplectiform attacks, and progressive mental deterioration. In addition there are symptoms and signs of liver disease and a Kayser-Fleisher ring, a greenish-yellow or greenish-brown deposition of pigment on the posterior surface of the cornea near the limbus. Pathologically there are symmetrical degenerations in the lenticular nuclei, together with widespread changes in both the cerebrum and cerebellum, and a nodular cirrhosis of the liver. Wilson's disease is a genetically determined disorder of copper metabolism. Inherited in a recessive manner, there is a decrease of ceruloplasmin in the blood and accumulations of copper in the brain, liver, and other organs, and the pathologic alterations and symptoms of the disease are probably the result of copper toxicity. The *pseudosclerosis of Strümpell and Westphal* may be identical with Wilson's disease, although some of the patients reported to have had this condition had a later onset of symptoms and more marked mental changes, and may have suffered from a similar but somewhat different disease process.

In *congenital athetosis,* or *mobile spasm,* there are slow, writhing, undulating, twisting movements of the distal portions of the extremities, usually the hands, fingers, and toes, with frequent grimacing. There often is associated spasticity, with increased reflexes and pyramidal signs, and there may be convulsive manifestations. The Vogts have found pathologic changes limited to the caudate and putamen, especially the latter, in these cases. These changes may be due to birth injury, anoxia, hemorrhagic disease of the newborn (erythroblastosis fetalis), intrauterine infections, toxic or inflammatory factors, or primary agenesis; the terms *status marmoratus* and *status dysmyelinatus* have been used in referring to them. Lesions of the precentral cortex may also cause athetosis. In *dystonia musculorum deformans, torsion spasm,* or *Ziehen-Oppenheim disease,* there are slow writhing movements and bizarre, grotesque torsions and twistings of the shoulder and pelvic girdles and the trunk; there may be rigidity, scoliosis, and lordosis. In this condition, too, lesions have been described in the striatum and pallidum. *Spasmodic torticollis,* in which there is spasm with dystonic movements limited to the cervical muscles, may also on occasion be a striatal disease, in some instances owing to encephalitis.

In the *syndrome of Hallervorden and Spatz* there is stiffness of all four extremities with tremors, athetoid movements, dysarthria, dementia, and emotional disturbances. Usually the condition is a familial manifestation. Pathologically there is degeneration with deposition of pigment in the globus pallidus and reticular zone of the substantia nigra; there also are diffuse cerebral and cerebellar alterations. In *progressive pallidal degeneration* there is intense rigidity with tremors; pathologically there is atrophy of the globus pallidus. In the *Creutzfeldt-Jakob syndrome, spastic pseudosclerosis,* or *corticostriatospinal* degeneration, there is a rapidly progressing mental deterioration in middle life, accompanied by signs of involvement of the extrapyramidal and pyramidal systems and occasionally of the lower motor neurons. The motor symptoms include hyperkinesias, abnormalities in tone, dysphagia, and dysarthria. The etiology is unknown. Pathologically there are degenerative changes in the cerebral cortex, the basal ganglia, and other parts of the nervous system.

The *choreas* are also extrapyramidal diseases, but show mainly hyperkinetic phenomena without rigidity—often, rather, with marked hypotonicity. *Sydenham's chorea* is a disease of children or adolescents. There are quick, irregular, involuntary, jerky, asymmetric, nonrhythmic, purposeless movements that are increased by emotional and other stimuli. Any portion of the body may be involved. There is hypotonicity with "hung" reflexes, but no loss of associated movements. In *Huntington's chorea* the movements are less jerky, more purposeful, slower and more gross, with grimacing, twisting, weaving, and lashing; the same movement may be repeated. There is also progressive intellectual deterioration. The disease is inherited as a mendelian dominant. The pathologic changes in Sydenham's chorea have never been adequately studied, but diffuse alterations have been described; these may be either degenerative or inflammatory, and seem to affect mainly the striatum and cerebral cortex. In Huntington's chorea there is profound atrophy of the caudate, putamen, and cerebral cortex, with dilatation of the lateral ventricles; microscopically there are diffuse degenerative changes in the brain. In *hemiballismus* there are unilateral wild, flail-like, writhing, twisting, or rolling movements that may be intense and may lead to exhaustion. These follow an isolated lesion, usually vascular in origin, of the contralateral subthalamic nucleus or its neighboring pathways. In *paramyoclonus multiplex* and *familial myoclonus epilepsy* there are rapid jerky movements resembling the response of a muscle to mechanical stimulation; there is no wasting and there is no disturbance of tone. Similar movements are seen in inclusion body encephalitis and the lipoid storage diseases. The pathologic changes responsible for these manifestations are not definitely known, but usually there are diffuse degenerative alterations and often inclusion bodies in the neurons, particularly in the dentate nucleus, substantia nigra, and basal ganglia. As in almost all the diseases described above, the pathologic changes are widespread and involve many different structures, even though they may predominate in specific areas.

PATHOLOGIC PHYSIOLOGY

The pathologic physiology responsible for the motor abnormalities that are associated with disease of the extrapyramidal system has not as yet been entirely explained. The earlier theories were based principally on clinical and pathologic studies, and concepts that varied widely were presented. Symptoms of extrapyramidal dysfunction are more apt to occur with mild, diffuse damage to the basal ganglia and related structures than with large circumscribed lesions of any one portion. Neoplasms affecting these structures, for instance, rarely cause the motor manifestations of extrapyramidal diseases, and it has been observed that tumors characterized by hyperkinesias and abnormalities of tone and posture are usually primarily in parts of the brain other than the so-called extrapyramidal structures. It appears that the symptoms of extrapyramidal disease result from partial rather than complete destruction of the basal ganglia, and they may be produced by slowly degenerating neural lesions capable of producing abnormal discharges; such symptoms often make their appearance long periods of time after an infection or injury. With most diseases of the basal ganglia there are widespread lesions that also involve other areas of the brain, and the lesions may vary from case to case.

Furthermore, there is a difference in the manifestations associated with the disorders involving the same structures; there may be a resting tremor with rigidity in one case, and choreiform or athetoid movements in another. Most neurologists have been of the opinion that both disturbances in tone and involuntary movements represent either the release of relatively healthy, undamaged efferent neural pathways from the controlling or inhibitory influence of specific nuclear areas, or the disordered function of intact neural structures when their connections with other areas have been interrupted. It may be, however, that abnormal discharges from degnerating neurones or imbalance between damaged and intact neural structures may be responsible. It must be concluded that there is no unanimity of opinion regarding either the exact pathophysiology or the nature or exact location of the pathologic changes responsible.

If, as has been stated, the basal ganglia and related structures are primitive motor centers that function in simple and automatic movements, support voluntary acts, aid in the integration of movements of association and expression, and control and inhibit postural reflexes, one may postulate that dysfunction of these centers will cause varying disturbances of motor control. Many theories have been suggested regarding the function of the individual portions of the extrapyramidal complex, both in their normal motor activity and in the effects of disease of each constituent part, by Wilson, Foerster, Hunt, the Vogts, Kleist, Rioch, Benda and Cobb, and others, but there has been no universal acceptance of any of them. More recent experimental work by Fulton, Kennard, McCulloch, Mettler, Magoun, Ward, Meyers, Spiegel, and others has modified the original views and contributed to present understanding, although differences of opinion are still evident. Furthermore, the so-called extrapyramidal structures are so closely integrated with other portions of the motor system, in both normal and diseased states, that it is difficult to assign certain changes in disease to a specific structure or a single, localized lesion.

An intimate relationship exists between the functions of certain portions of the cerebral cortex and those of the basal ganglia, and it may be that the activities of the latter are seldom independent of those of the former. Areas 6 and 4 of the frontal cortex both have direct connections with the extrapyramidal system, and the same may also be true of the so-called suppressor areas (4s, 8, and others), although certain concepts concerning the cortical suppression system and indeed the existence of specific suppressor areas have been questioned recently. Furthermore, there is a close integration with important midbrain and hind brain structures. Higher motor centers discharge into and through the reticular formation in the midbrain, pons, and medulla (Fig. 143). The ventromedial portion of the medullary reticular formation receives impulses from the cortex and cerebellum and from the basal ganglia by relays, and in turn discharges to the spinal cord; it has an inhibitory effect on lower motor nuclei, and tends to suppress motor activity. The excitatory mechanism is situated in the dorsolateral portion of the medulla and in the reticular formation of the midbrain and pons; it, too, receives impulses from the cortex, cerebellum and basal ganglia, and facilitates motor responses. These centers, especially those concerned with facilitation, are closely linked with the vestibular system, which plays an important part in the regulation of tone in simple postural and righting reflexes,

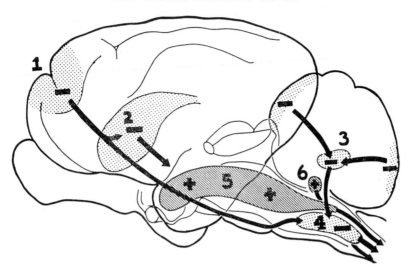

Fig. 143. Diagrammatic representation of the inhibitory and facilitatory systems in the midbrain and brain stem reticular formations. Suppressor pathways are: 1. corticobulboreticular; 2. caudatospinal; 3. cerebelloreticular; and 4. reticulospinal. Facilitatory pathways are: 5. reticulospinal and 6. vestibulospinal. (Lindsley, D. B., Schreiner, L. H., and Magoun, H. W.: *J. Neurophysiol.* 12:198, 1949.)

and in control of balance between the alpha and gamma motor systems. Normally there is an equilibrium between the activities of the suppressor and facilitatory mechanisms and between alpha and gamma control, and adjustment between them is necessary for phasic movement and postural activity. When this balance is upset by disease processes or experimentally produced lesions, involving either these centers themselves or structures or pathways discharging to them, abnormalities of tone, movement, or posture may appear.

As a consequence, disturbances in tone as well as hyperkinesias and other abnormalities of movement may result from many different alterations of either structure or function. Rigidity, which may be considered to result from an abnormal bombardment of the myoneural outflow, may be caused by pallidal lesions that interrupt the normal inhibitory effect of this structure on lower reflex arcs, impairment of conduction of impulses from the cortex to the pallidum and other basal ganglia, combined extrapyramidal and pyramidal involvement at capsular levels, interruption of pallidofugal fibers, release of lower centers from vestibular control, impairment of function of suppressor areas, or stimulation of facilitatory centers. Hyperkinesias of various types may be caused by imbalance of the reciprocal innervation between cortical and extrapyramidal centers, interruption at any site of the complex circuitous pathway between the cortex, basal ganglia, lower extrapyramidal centers, cerebellum, thalamus, and cortex (Figs. 139, 140, and 141), disease of any of the structures entering into this circuit, abnormal rhythmic activity of the reticular formation when it is released from control by higher center by means of lesions at mesencephalic or pontine levels, or alteration of normal balance between the alpha and gamma motor systems. Hypokinesia, brady-kinesia, and loss of associated movements may be the result of rigidity alone, dependent upon the extent or severity of pathologic change; it may be, however, that widespread extrapyramidal involvement interferes with the initiation of or the conduction of impulses for simple automatic activities and movements of association and expression.

Investigative and surgical approaches of various types have been made in the attempt to relieve the symptoms of extrapyramidal disease, and, incidentally, to arrive at a better understanding of the basic pathophysiology of the clinical conditions described above. It has long been known that either injection of novocaine into the involved muscles or section of either the anterior or posterior nerve roots will decrease rigidity, although these measures will not influence tremor. Both of these procedures interrupt either the afferent or efferent pathway of the proprioceptive reflex arc; neither is a suitable or practical treatment procedure. Furthermore, it is also well known that the tremor of parkinsonism is lessened or abolished by a capsular hemiplegia, at least for the duration of the paralysis, but the impairment of motor function may be more incapacitating than the hyperkinesia. Based on the above clinical observations, and more recently on the neurophysiologic demonstrations of the connections and functions of the extrapyramidal complex and its individual components, surgical measures have been ultilized in an attempt to mitigate the symptoms of diseases. Various techniques have been used, and attention has been directed to the cerebral cortex, internal capsule, basal ganglia, pallido-fugal fibers, and spinal cord. Horsley, in 1908, first excised the motor cortex for the relief of athetosis. Later resections were made of areas 6, 4, or both of the frontal cortex, or interruption of the U fibers between areas 4 and 6, for the relief of parkinsonism, intention tremor, athetosis, choreoathetosis, dystonia, and hemiballismus by Bucy, Meyers, Klemme, and others; hyperkinetic phenomena were alleviated more than rigidity. Browder made selective section of fibers in the anterior limb of the internal capsule, together with ablation of the adjacent portion of the putamen, for the relief of both tremor and rigidity in Parkinson's disease. Meyers has removed parts of the caudate and lenticular nuclei, along with interruption of fibers in the internal capsule, but later sectioned the pallidofugal fibers (fasciculus and ansa lenticularis) in parkinsonism. Electrolytic destruction (ansotomy) and coagulation of the ansa lenticularis have been carried out for Parkinson's disease and choreathetosis by Spiegel and Wycis, Fenelon, and Guiot. Walker and Meyers have sectioned the cerebral peduncle for parkinsonism and other diseases characterized by hyperkinesia, and Putnam, Ebin, and Oliver have sectioned the pyramidal and parapyramidal tracts in the spinal cord.

The most effective surgical approach to date—one that has gained fairly wide acceptance and has proved to be quite helpful in selected cases—is that advocated by Cooper, Narabayashi, Spiegel and Wycis, and others. This consists of the production of destructive lesions in the globus pallidus (pallidotomy) or the nucleus ventralis lateralis or other thalamic nuclei (thalamotomy) by the injection of procaine in oil or alcohol, by electrolysis, or by the use of ultrasound or freezing techniques (cryothalomotomy). While the permanent effect of these procedures is still to be determined, and complications of surgery have occurred in some patients, they appear to give a certain amount (and occasionally complete) relief of tremor and rigidity in many patients, although they have no effect on akinesia. Further developments in the techniques are certainly to be expected. Each new approach, furthermore, while not completely explaining the normal and pathologic physiology of the extrapyramidal complex, has contributed to our understanding of the functions of this level and its relation of the other levels of motor integration,, and has served to broaden our concepts of the anatomic and physiologic bases of the extrapyramidal disorders.

REFERENCES

BENDA, C. E., and COBB, S. On the pathogenesis of paralysis agitans (Parkinson's disease). *Medicine* 21:95, 1942.

BRAVO, G. J., and COOPER, I. S. A clinical and radiological correlation of the lesions produced by chemopallidectomy and thalamectomy. *J. Neurol., Neurosurg. & Psychiat.* 22:1, 1959.

BROWDER, J. Section of the fibers of the anterior limb of the internal capsule in parkinsonism. *Am. J. Surg.* 75:264, 1948.

BUCY, P. C. The surgical treatment of extrapyramidal diseases. *J. Neurol., Neurosurg. & Psychiat.* 14:108, 1951.

CAREY, J. H., and DeJONG, R. N. Preliminary studies on the production of Parkinson's syndrome. *Tr. Am. Neurol. A.* 79:28, 1954.

CARPENTER, M. B. Brainstem and infratentorial neuraxis in experimental dyskinesia. *Arch. Neurol.* 5:504, 1961.

COLONY, H. S., and MALAMUD, N. Sydenham's chorea: A clinicopathologic study. *Neurology* 6:672, 1956.

COOPER, E. R. A. The development of the substantia nigra. *Brain* 69:22, 1946; The development of the human red nucleus and corpus striatum. *Ibid.* 69:34, 1946.

COOPER, I. S. Parkinsonism: Its Medical and Surgical Therapy. Springfield, Ill., Charles C Thomas, 1961; Clinical and physiological implications of thalamic surgery for disorders of sensory communication: II, Intention tremor, dystonia, Wilson's disease and torticollis. *J. Neurol. Sc.* 2:520, 1965.

DE JONG, R. N., and SCHARENBERG, K. The syndrome of Hallervorden and Spatz. *Tr. Am. Neurol. A.* 77: 83, 1952.

DENNY-BROWN, D. The Basal Ganglia and Their Relation to Disorders of Movement. London, Oxford University Press, 1962.

DUSSER DE BARENNE, J. G., GAROL, H. W., and McCULLOCH, W. S. Physiological neuronography of the cortico-striatal connections. *A. Res. Nerv. & Ment. Dis., Proc.* (1940) 21:246, 1942.

EBIN, J. Combined lateral and ventral pyramidotomy in treatment of paralysis agitans. *Arch. Neurol. & Psychiat.* 62:27, 1949.

FRIEDE, R. L., and DE JONG, R. N. Neuronal enzymatic failure in Creutzfeldt-Jakob disease. *Arch. Neurol.* 10:181, 1964.

FULTON, J. F., and KENNARD, M. A. A study of flaccid and spastic paralyses produced by lesions of the cerebral cortex in primates. *A. Res. Nerv. & Ment. Dis., Proc.* (1932) 13:158, 1934.

GREENFIELD, J. G., and BOSANQUET, F. D.   The brain-stem lesions in parkinsonism. *J. Neurol., Neurosurg. & Psychiat.* 16:213, 1953.

HORSLEY, V.   The Linacre lecture on the function of the so-called motor area of the brain.   *Brit. M. J.* 2:125, 1909.

HUNT, J. R.   Progressive atrophy of the globus pallidus (primary atrophy of the pallidal system): A contribution to the functions of the corpus striatum.   *Brain* 40:58, 1917.

JAKOB, A.   The anatomy, clinical syndromes and physiology of the extrapyramidal system.   *Arch. Neurol. & Psychiat.* 13:596, 1925.

KENNARD, M. A., and FULTON, J. F.   Corticostriatal interrelations in monkey and chimpanzee.   *A. Res. Nerv. & Ment. Dis., Proc.* (1940) 21:228, 1942.

KLEMME, R. M.   Surgical treatment of dystonia, with report of one hundred cases. *A. Res. Nerv. & Ment. Dis., Proc.* (1940) 21:596, 1942.

LAURSEN, A. M.   Corpus Striatum.   *Acta physiol. scandinav.* Vol. 59, Suppl. 211, 1963.

LEWY, F. H.   Zur pathologischen Anatomie der Paralysis agitans.   *Deutsche Ztschr. f. Nervenh.* 50:50, 1913.

MAGOUN, H. W.   Recent contributions to the extrapyramidal system.   *Northwestern Univ. Bull., Med. School* 20:180, 1946; Caudal and cephalic influences of the brain stem reticular formation.   *Physiol. Rev.* 30:459, 1950.

MARTIN, J. P.   Remarks on the functions of the basal ganglia.   *Lancet* 1:999, 1959; The globus pallidus in post-encephalitic parkinsonism.   *J. Neurol. Sc.* 2:344, 1965.

MARTIN, J. P., HURWITZ, L. J., and FINLAYSON, M. H.   The negative symptoms of basal gangliar disease.   *Lancet* 2:1 and 62, 1962.

MCCULLOCH, W. S., GRAF, C., and MAGOUN, H. W.   Cortico-bulbo-reticular pathway from area 4s.   *J. Neurophysiol.* 9:127, 1946.

METTLER, F. A.   Substantia nigra and parkinsonism.   *Arch. Neurol.* 11:529, 1964.

MEYERS, R.   The extrapyramidal system: An inquiry into the validity of the concept. *Neurology* 3:627, 1953.

NARABAYASHI, H., OKUMA, T., and SHIKIBA, S.   Procaine oil blocking of the globus pallidus.   *A. M. A. Arch. Neurol. & Psychiat.* 75:36, 1956.

NASHOLD, B. S., JR., and HUBER, W. V. (eds.)   The second symposium on Parkinson's disease.   *J. Neurosurg.* 24:117–481, 1966.

PAPEZ, J. W.   A summary of fiber connections of the basal ganglia with each other and with other portions of the brain.   *A. Res. Nerv. & Ment. Dis., Proc.* (1940) 21:21, 1942.

PARKINSON, J.   An Essay on the Shaking Palsy.   London, Sherwood, Neely and Jones, 1817.

PUTNAM, T. J.   Results of treatment of athetosis by section of the extrapyramidal tracts in the spinal cord.   *Arch. Neurol. & Psychiat.* 39:258, 1938.

RANSON, S. W., and RANSON, S. W., JR.   Efferent fibers of the corpus striatum.   *A. Res. Nerv. & Ment. Dis., Proc.* (1940) 21:69, 1942.

REFSUM, S., LOSSIUS, H. M., and DIETRICHSON, P. (eds.)   The So-called Extrapyramidal System.   Oslo, Universitetsforlaget, 1963.

RIOCH, D. MCK.   Neurophysiology of the corpus striatum and globus pallidus.   *Psychiatry* 3:119, 1940.

RUSHWORTH, G.   The gamma system in parkinsonism.   *Internat. J. Neurol.* 2:34, 1961.

SCOTT, T. R., and NETSKY, M. G.   The pathology of Parkinson's syndrome.   *Internat. J. Neurol.* 2:51, 1961.

SMITH, W. O., HAMMARSTEN, J. F., and ELIEL, L. P. The clinical expression of magnesium deficiency. *J.A.M.A.* 174:77, 1960.

SPEIGEL, E. A., and WYCIS, H. T. Thalamotomy and pallidotomy for treatment of choreic movements. *Acta neurochir.* 2:418, 1952.

STERN, J. and WARD, A. A., JR. The relationship of the alpha and gamma motor systems to the efficacy of the surgical therapy of parkinsonism. *J. Neurosurg.* 20:185, 1963.

VOGT, CÉCILE. Quelques considérations générales à propos du syndrôme du corps strié. *J. f. Psychol. u. Neurol.* 18:479, 1911.

VOGT, CÉCILE, and VOGT, O. Zur Lehre der Erkrankungen des striären Systems. *J. f. Psychol. u. Neurol.* 25:631, 1920.

WALKER, A. E. Cerebral pedunculotomy for the relief of involuntary movements: I. Hemiballismus, *Acta psychiat. et neurol.* 24:723, 1949; II. Parkinsonian tremor, *J. Nerv. & Ment. Dis.* 116:766, 1952.

WALSHE, F. M. R. Observations on the nature of the muscular rigidity of paralysis agitans, and on its relationship to tremor. *Brain* 47:159, 1924.

WARD, A., JR., and JENKNER, F. L. The bulbar reticular formation and tremor. *Tr. Am. Neurol. A.* 78:36, 1953.

WILSON, S. A. K. Progressive lenticular degeneration. *Brain* 34:295, 1912; The old motor system and the new. *Arch. Neurol. & Psychiat.* 11:385, 1924.

CHAPTER 23

THE PYRAMIDAL LEVEL

THE PYRAMIDAL LEVEL of motor integration is also referred to as the *cortical level,* the *corticospinal level,* and the upper motor neuron level. It must be recalled, however, that it is only one of many motor fiber systems that converge upon the anterior horn cell and the final common pathway, and therefore it is only one of many upper motor neuron levels. It should be stated at the outset that recent experimental work, not all of which has been accepted by clinicians, has materially altered certain long-accepted concepts of the functions of the pyramidal system, its relation to the extrapyramidal system, and the changes that may be caused by disease of either of these systems. It is apparent, however, that the pyramidal level never functions independently; both in the normal state and in the presence of disease it is closely integrated with the other levels of motor activity, as well as with a constant stream of incoming sensory impulses.

ANATOMY AND PHYSIOLOGY

The pyramidal level of the motor system has been called the *new motor system.* It is found fully developed only in mammals and reaches its highest development in apes and man. In the newborn human infant the descending fibers of the pyramidal system have little or no myelin sheathing; the process of myelination starts immediately after birth and is usually complete by the age of two years. Walking and other skilled movements are learned as the pathway matures and myelination progresses. The existence of a motor area in the brain was suggested by Robert Boyle as long ago as 1691. In the seventh decade of the nineteenth century Hughlings Jackson, from a study of focal epilepsy, assumed the presence of an area in the cerebral cortex that governs isolated movements. In 1870 Fritsch and Hitzig found that galvanic stimulation of the exposed frontal cortex of the dog caused movements of the contralateral extremities. In 1873 Ferrier confirmed this work in monkeys, using faradic stimulation, and also produced paralysis by ablation of the excitable region.

Further work on localization of function of the cerebral cortex was carried out by Beevor and Horsley. The first recorded electrical stimulation of the human brain was carried out by Bartholow in 1874.

The major motor units of the pyramidal level are situated in the posterior portions of the frontal lobes of the brain. The motor cortex of primates arises in the depths of the rolandic fissure, or central sulcus, and spreads out for a variable distance rostrally over the adjacent precentral or posterior frontal convolution. It extends from the sylvian fissure up to and over the vertex and for some distance on the medial surface of the brain (Chapter 50). This area coincides cytoarchitectonically with the *area gigantopyramidalis,* Campbell's area precentralis, area 4 of Brodmann, and area FA of Economo and Koskinas (Fig. 144). It was long believed that the decending corticospinal pathway or pyramidal tract consisted entirely of the neuraxes of the Betz or giant pyramidal cells, which are found in the fifth layer of this area. The origin of the name of this pathway, however, is linked with the medullary pyramids and not with the large pyramidal cells of the motor cortex, and while there are 25,000 to 35,000 Betz cells in the precentral cortex, there are about one million fibers in the corticospinal tract at the level of the pyramids. It is probable that about 3 per cent of the pyramidal fibers arise from Betz cells, and they may not be physiologic units but only the larger members of a much more numerous group of pyramidal cells. Fulton, however, states that the excitable properties of area 4 depend largely, if not entirely, upon the integrity of the Betz cells, and that isolated movements disappear when they are destroyed and are absent if they are underdeveloped. Walshe, on the other hand, has stated that it is difficult to regard the Betz cell as a specific morphologic entity, but that it is merely the largest of the pyramidal cells. He believes that the smaller giant cells and the large pyramidal cells in the fifth layer, and possibly even the small pyramidal cells of the third layer of the motor cortex, exert a similar function, and states that the giant cells probably innervate larger motor units. The largest giant cells may mediate simple movements of the legs and trunks, whereas finer and more complex movements are subserved by the smaller giant cells and the larger pyramidal cells. Furthermore, it is probable that the parietal lobe (areas 1, 2, 3, 5, 7), areas 6 and 8 of the frontal lobe, and other portions of the brain, including the temporal and occipital lobes and certain subcortical centers, make important contributions to the pyramidal tract; it may also contain some ascending fibers. Because area 4 does not supply as many nuclei in the spinal cord as the pyramidal tract does, there are fewer degenertive changes in the anterior horn cells following cortical ablation than after section of the pyramid.

Closely related to the motor cortex, both anatomically and functionally, is the premotor region, which is also referred to as the extrapyramidal cortex. It is situated just rostral to area 4, and has been termed area 6 by Brodmann, area precentralis intermedia by Campbell, and area FB by Economo and Koskinas. It is similar histologically to the motor cortex but lacks the giant pyramidal cells. It has been demonstrated that some fibers from area 6 pass to area 4 and thence downward with the corticospinal tract, whereas others pass directly downward with the pyramidal fibers and decussate with them. There is probably less complete crossing

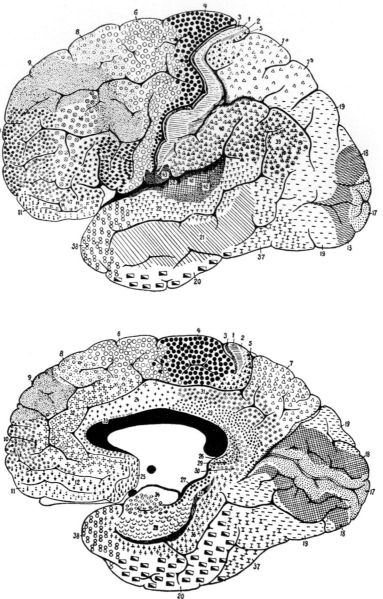

FIG. 144.   Areas of cerebral cortex, each of which possesses a distinctive structure. (Nielsen, J. M.: A Textbook of Clinical Neurology, ed. 2. New York, Paul B. Hoeber, Inc., 1946.) (After Brodmann.)

of the fibers from the premotor cortex than of those from the motor cortex. In addition, the premotor region is in direct communication with the basal ganglia and the extrapyramidal system and contributes the chief cortical component to the latter system (Fig. 138, Fig. 145). Laboratory and clinical investigations have also demonstrated the presence of secondary and supplementary motor areas with complete representation of contralateral somatic musculature. The former is situated in the parietal operculum, at the foot of the precentral gyrus, and along the upper border of the sylvian fissure; the latter, which may have bilateral representation, is in the paracentral region on the medial surface of the hemisphere, anterior to the motor cortex.

Within the motor cortex there is a definite localization of function. "Centers" have been described that control various activities. A center, however, is not a focus that has sole control of a specific function, but is the seat of greatest intensity of this function. Skeletal musculature is represented in reverse order upon the contralateral motor area. The center for the larynx and pharynx is lowest, just above the sylvian fissure, and this is followed, in an ascending direction, by centers for the palate, jaw, tongue, mouth, face, eyelids, forehead, neck, thumb, fingers, wrist, elbow, shoulder, thorax, and abdomen. The lower extremities and sacral centers

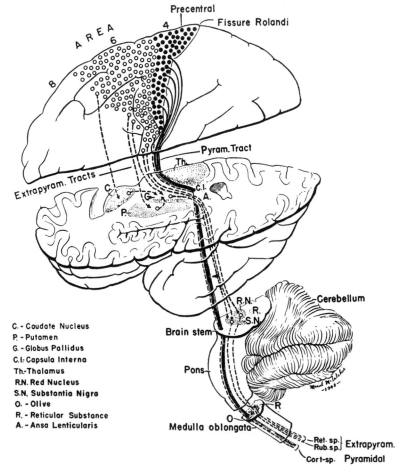

C. - Caudate Nucleus
P. - Putamen
G. - Globus Pallidus
C.I. - Capsula Interna
Th. - Thalamus
R.N. - Red Nucleus
S.N. - Substantia Nigra
O. - Olive
R. - Reticular Substance
A. - Ansa Lenticularis

FIG. 145. Diagrammatic sketch of pyramidal and extrapyramidal systems. (Benda, C. E., and Cobb, S.: *Medicine* 21:95, 1942).

are represented on the medial surface of the hemisphere. In the past it had been stated that the leg areas were also represented on the lateral surface with only the sacral centers on the medial aspect (Fig. 146). This was, however, based on evidence from experimental animals, and it is apparent that in man the motor centers for the upper extremity extend upward on the lateral surface of the brain as far as its superior border, whereas centers for the thigh and leg are represented on the medial surface of the hemisphere (Fig. 147). It has been suggested that the acquisition of speech and other forms of expression and the elaboration of new and complex

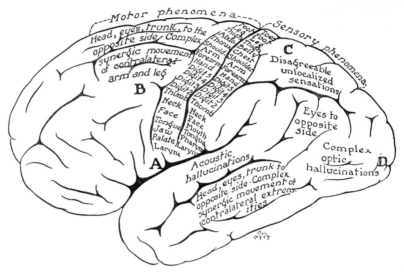

Fig. 146. Localization in cerebral cortex; principal excitable foci as determined by electrical stimulation. (Bailey, P.: Intracranial Tumors, ed. 2. Springfield, Ill., Charles C Thomas, 1948.)

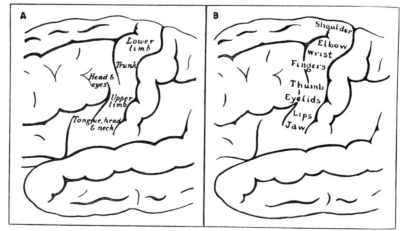

Fig. 147. Primary motor centers of brain: A, according to original experimental work; B, according to recent observations on human brain. (Scarff, J. E.: Arch. Neurol. & Psychiat. 44:243, 1940.)

functions for the upper extremities have been accompanied by corresponding expansion of cortical areas representing the tongue, mouth, lips, thumb, and fingers, with the result that the cortical representation for the leg has been forced upward and then onto the medial surface of the hemisphere. The areas for the tongue, face, and digits are exceptionally large and are out of proportion with those which control proximal musculature (Fig. 148).

The neuraxes of the motor units in the precentral convolution, or the pyramidal fibers, pass through the corona radiata into the genu and the anterior two thirds of the posterior limb of the internal capsule. Those to the face and medullary centers are anterior and are followed in a posterior direction by those to the upper extremity, trunk, and lower extremity (Fig. 149). At the midbrain level the pyramidal fibers traverse the intermediate three fifths of the cerebral peduncle, with those to medullary centers in a medial and somewhat dorsal position. The descending neuraxes then pass through the basilar portion of the pons, where they are separated by transverse fibers, and enter the medulla as the pyramidal pathway (Fig. 150). The neuraxes that convey impulses to the pontine and medullary centers are the corticopontine and cortiobulbar fibers; the majority of them decussate before synapsing with the specific nuclei, but much of the innervation to the brain stem centers is both crossed and uncrossed. The neuraxes that convey impulses to the spinal cord are the corticospinal fibers. In the caudal portion of the medulla the majority of them (70 to 90 per cent) decussate and descend through the lateral fasciculus of the spinal cord as the lateral corticospinal pathway to supply the muscles of the

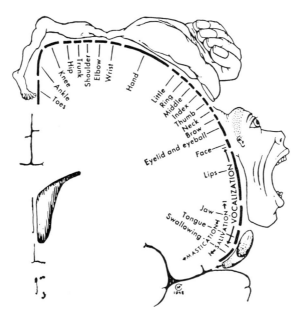

Fig. 148. Homunculus showing the relationship of motor centers to cortical representation. (Penfield, W., and Rasmussen T.: The Cerebral Cortex of man. New York, The Macmillan Company, 1950.)

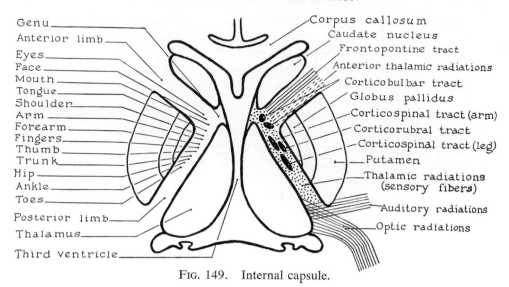

FIG. 149.   Internal capsule.

opposite side of the body. Those of the upper extremity cross more rostrally and assume a medial position in the tract. There are individual variations in the percentage of crossed fibers in the lateral corticospinal tracts, and they may contain some uncrossed fibers. In addition they also contain other corticofugal as well as some ascending fibers. About 50 per cent of the fibers of the lateral corticospinal tract terminate in the cervical region, 20 per cent in the thoracic area, and 30 per cent in the lumbosacral portion of the cord. The smaller ventral corticospinal tract descends uncrossed in the ipsilateral ventral funiculus and usually does not extend below the midthoracic region; these fibers, too, usually cross before termination. Neuraxes carried through the above pathways terminate at appropriate levels to supply the motor nuclei of the cranial nerves and the anterior horn cells of the spinal cord. Those to the cord end in the zona intermedia between the anterior and posterior horns, and there is always an intercalated neuron between the neuraxis of the corticospinal cell and the anterior horn cell. Impulses are then carried from the motor nuclei and anterior horn cells, which together with their neuraxes make up the final common pathway, to the neuromuscular junction of striated muscles. It is probable that a single pyramidal fiber innervates more than one neuron in the spinal cord, and probably some innervate many.

The pyramidal and related motor cells in the cerebral cortex may be considered motor centers, or centers of adjustment, which send effector stimuli through the pathways described above. Receptor impulses of the pyramidal arc are carried up the spinal cord and brain stem through the various sensory pathways to the thalamus. After synapse in the thalamus, impulses are relayed through the thalamic radiations to the parietal cortex, and thence to the motor cells of the cortex, stimulation of which causes muscular activity.

Excitation of the motor cortex (area 4), such as by electrical stimulation, causes

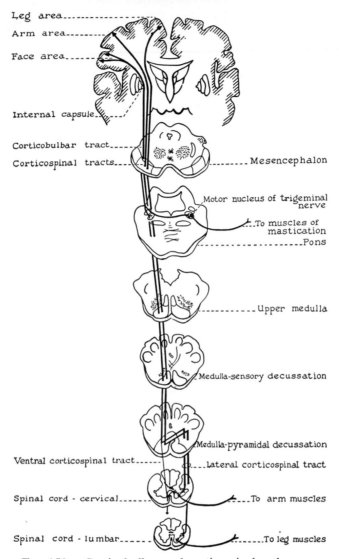

Leg area
Arm area
Face area

Internal capsule

Corticobulbar tract
Corticospinal tracts .... Mesencephalon

Motor nucleus of trigeminal nerve
To muscles of mastication
Pons

Upper medulla

Medulla-sensory decussation

Medulla-pyramidal decussation
Ventral corticospinal tract .... lateral corticospinal tract

Spinal cord - cervical .... To arm muscles

Spinal cord - lumbar .... To leg muscles

FIG. 150.   Corticobulbar and corticospinal pathways.

muscular contractions on the opposite side of the body. Although it has been generally accepted that the response is not one of simple contraction of isolated muscles, but one of movements or of groups of muscles acting harmoniously, Ruch and others were able to demonstrate that individual muscles as well as movements may be represented in the motor cortex. It is probable, however, that the response to cortical stimulation is altered by the intensity and frequency of the stimulus and the depth of anesthesia; proprioceptive impulses are also important, and alterations in the posture of a limb modify the response. In general it may be said that stimulation of area 4 causes discrete movements involving principally the digital muscles at the distal joints and the muscles supplied by the cranial nerves. The foci of localization overlap, but the centers controlling movements of the thumb, index finger, hallux, and face have widest distribution and lowest threshold. Stimulation of the premotor cortex (area 6) also causes a contralateral motor response, but a stronger stimulus is necessary. The resulting movements are more complex and consist of slow, synergic, postural or patterned contractions of a generalized type that involve large muscle groups.

Ablation of the motor cortex causes paralysis, or loss of movement, on the opposite side of the body. This affects principally the distal joints, with less involvement at the proximal joints, and finer volitional movements are entirely abolished. It has generally been accepted in the past that area 4 ablations produce a spastic paralysis with hyperreflexia and no atrophy, which will be described below as the characteristic "pyramidal syndrome." Experimental investigations during recent years, however, followed by clinical application in humans, have materially altered the older concepts of the functions of the pyramidal system and their relations to disturbances of motor control, although the entire subject is still somewhat controversial. Fulton and his co-workers have demonstrated, by means of extensive laboratory investigations, that lesions limited to the pyramidal tracts or to their cells of origin in the motor cortex, area 4 of Brodmann, yield a syndrome somewhat different from that described above. Instead of spasticity and hyperreflexia there is a flaccid motor paralysis, with transient depression of all reflexes and resulting muscular atrophy; the only pathologic reflex responses are the extensor portion of the Babinski sign and the Chaddock sign. There may be transient spasticity at the distal joints. After complete destruction of the pyramidal cells or of their tracts the signs of Babinski and Chaddock persist and there is an enduring paralysis of isolated movements, especially those of the distal joints, but the flaccidity and hyporeflexia tend to disappear with time. All these manifestations are more marked with bilateral extirpation of area 4. In no instance was permanent spasticity, a manifestation which in man is usually considered to be due to a lesion of the motor area or the corticospinal tract, observed after isolated section of area 4 in experimental animals. Section of the pyramidal tracts in the cerebral peduncle or in the medulla has also been shown to produce a hypotonic paresis, and damage to the spinal portion of the corticospinal tract in monkeys has caused a hypotonic paresis, decreased deep and superficial reflexes, exaggerated associated movements, and atrophy, especially of the distal muscles. Bucy, who sectioned the intermediate portion of the cerebral peduncle in the human for the relief of hemiballismus, found no motor impairment and no spasticity in the contralateral extremities, and only a slight increase in reflexes and an extensor Babinski response.

Ablations of area 6 or its projection fibers in experimental animals, on the other hand, are reported to give rise to a contralateral hemiparesis or hemiplegia with increased resistance to passive movement, moderately increased deep reflexes, disturbance of skilled movements, forced grasping, and vasomotor changes. There are also pathologic reflex responses in the form of the Hoffmann, Rossolimo, and Mendel-Bechterew signs, and with the fanning portion of the Babinski sign. The resistance to passive movement is of a soft, cataleptoid type, equal in quantity

through all ranges of movement and from the beginning to the end of such movement. It is approximately equal in all muscle groups. All these changes, except
the disturbance of skilled movement, are transient; all are exaggerated on bilateral
extirpation of area 6 (Fig. 151). Removal of area 6 after removal of area 4 causes
a previously flaccid extremity (or one spastic only at the distal joints) to become
highly spastic and remain so. There is a loss of voluntary power in the contralateral limbs. Deep reflexes become uniformly exaggerated, there is forced grasping,
and the Hoffmann, Chaddock, and Rossolimo signs and both the extensor and
fanning Babinski responses appear and remain permanently. Additional removal
of the homolateral postcentral gyrus or the contralateral motor area causes increase
in the paresis and spasticity.

Ablation of area 4s, which has been describd as a suppressor area exercising
an inhibitory effect over other cortical regions (especially area 4), is said to cause
spasticity, maximal in the flexors of the elbows, extensors of the knee, and adductors of the hip, with loss of fine movements and exaggeration of the stretch reflexes.
Bilateral lesions are reported to cause intense spasticity with loss of movement,
whereas stimulation causes decrease in muscle tone with relaxation of existing
muscular contractions. Woolsey and his associates have reported, on the other
hand, that bilateral ablation of the precentral areas produces only a flaccid
paresis, even if the suppressor region is included in the ablation. Bilateral simultaneous removal of the supplementary motor areas, however, especially if accom-

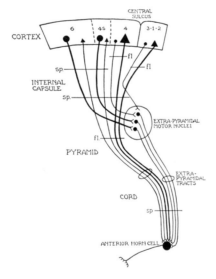

Fig. 151. Diagrammatic sketch of pyramidal and extrapyramidal projections
from cerebral cortex. Direct cells of pyramidal tract are represented in cortex
as pyramids, those of extrapyramidal tract as circles; size of pyramids and
circles represents relative number of cells in each cortical area. Letters *sp.*
indicate sites of lesions causing a spastic paralyis; letters *fl.* sites, of lesions
causing a flaccid paralysis. (Welch, W. K., and Kennard, M. A.: *J. Neurophysiology* 7:255, 1944.)

panied by ablation of the precentral regions, is followed by spasticity. They express the belief that the only motor functional parts of area 6 are those portions included in either the precentral or supplementary motor areas. Furthermore, these investigators have observed recovery of motor function following bilateral removal of areas 4 and 6, even when such ablations were carried out in fully matured monkeys.

Other investigators have reported results that are at variance with the observations described above. Denny-Brown states that ablations of area 4 lead to only transient and relative defects, but that spasticity always eventually accompanies the paralytic manifestations of such lesions and is most pronounced with total lesions. If area 6 is also removed, there is greater spasticity, with flexion of the elbow and extension of the knee and ankle. Ablation of area 6 alone produces a posture of slight flexion in both the upper and lower extremities, with a soft, plastic resistance of both flexors and extensors. He feels that the phenomenon of shock plays a part in the development of spasticity, and that more extensive ablations may be followed by a longer period of flaccidity, before the eventual appearance of spasticity. Furthermore, proprioceptive and other impulses are important to the development of hyperreflexia, the grasp reflex, and increase in tone.

It is difficult to evaluate adequately the disparity in experimental results and the differentiation between some of them and what has long been known as the "pyramidal syndrome" in man, with spasticity, hyperreflexia, and pathologic reflexes, but no resulting atrophy. Most of the experimental work has been done entirely on laboratory animals, but there has been some investigation on humans as well, and there have been isolated cases in humans in which it could be definitely established that the pathologic process was limited either to the pyramidal cortex and its pathways or to the premotor cortex and its descending tracts. The hypotonia that has been reported to occur with lesions of area 4 in lower primates is rarely seen in man except as an initial effect. There is doubtless some difference between the motor reactions in man and those in experimental animals, and it may be that in many of the reported ablations of area 6 there was some involvement of the true motor cortex. In fact, there is evidence to suggest that the physiologic motor cortex extends far into the so-called premotor area. Lassek has noted, furthermore, that there often is little evidence of destruction of pyramidal fibers with lesions of area 4 and in patients who have had a cerebral hemiplegia or hemiparesis, and states that it is difficult to correlate the clinical manifestations with the small amount of degeneration in this pathway.

In addition, it should be stated that there is serious question on the part of neurophysiologists of any relationship of the pyramidal complex to spasticity. It is generally felt, at the present time, that such increase in tone may be related more closely to dysfunction of the extrapyramidal rather than the pyramidal portion of the nervous system, or to interruption of corticofugal fibers other than pyramidal in the corticospinal pathway. Spasticity in all probability results from imbalance of the facilitatory and inhibitory centers in the midbrain and brain stem reticular formations (Fig. 143), as well as altered balance between the alpha and gamma motor systems in the spinal cord. Inhibition of suppressor impulses is followed by enhancement of facilitatory mechanisms. Within the spinal cord those impulses that lead to exaggeration of the stretch reflexes, the essential aspect of spasticity, may be carried by the reticulospinal and vestibulospinal rather than the corticospinal tracts (Chapter 28).

It should probably be assumed, on the basis of experimental data together with the clinical sources that are accumulating, that the pyramidal tract deals with discrete, isolated motor responses, especially with the finer adjustments of voluntary movement of the digits, and that disease of the pyramidal system per se results in hypotonia, areflexia, and atrophy. It is now recognized that in certain instances vascular accidents and other cerebral lesions may be followed by a paralysis that remains flaccid, with loss of tendon reflexes but with an extensor Babinski response. These manifestations probably follow a lesion limited to the pyramidal cortex or its descending pathways. The premotor cortex and its pathways are concerned with larger coordinated responses, more stereotyped movements that are partly automatic and involve the trunk and the proximal segments, and postural mechanisms. It contributes the principal cortical components to the extrapyramidal level and, as mentioned above, athetoid movements and other hyperkinesias have been relieved by section of area 6 (see p. 406). Hemiplegia in man is generally produced by combined destruction of the motor and premotor components of the upper motor neuron, and there are combinations of the foregoing symptoms, often with severe motor paralysis. In all probability the more violent reactions, such as spasticity and hyperreflexia, overshadow the flaccidity and hyporeflexia. Various pathologic responses—the forced grasping and the Hoffmann sign in the upper extremity and the Chaddock and Rossolimo signs together with both the fanning and the extensor portions of the Babinski sign—are obtained. The affected extremities may at first be flaccid with depressed reflexes (either shock or pyramidal tract effects), but spasticity, reflex exaggeration, and vasomotor changes may develop within a few days. The various pathologic responses, such as the fanning and extension of the toes and the Rossolimo and Hoffmann signs, may remain permanently.

CLINICAL MANIFESTATIONS OF DISEASE OF THE PYRAMIDAL LEVEL

In dealing with the manifestations of disease of the pyramidal level, those concepts of pyramidal function generally accepted by clinicians will be followed, and this level of the motor system will be presumed to consist of the principal efferent corticospinal neurons by which purposive movements are initiated and formed. It not only activates but also integrates highly skilled, refined, discrete movements, although it is by no means the sole cortical mechanism for movement. It is responsible for the initiation of movement of individual muscles and it also causes inhibition, or graded relaxation, of antagonistic muscles, which is necessary for the performance of skilled acts. By its integrating action individual muscular contractions are correlated into complicated motor reactions; a specific act can be started and then abruptly stopped, following which it may either be resumed or altered for the performance of a different act. It also, along with other cerebral and brain stem mechanisms, constantly supplies lower centers with tonic impulses of various types that have an inhibiting effect upon them. In disease of the pyramidal cortex or its descending pathways there is a release of this inhibiting effect, and the spinal level is allowed to respond to all stimuli. As a result there is an exaggeration of response and there is an excessive, or unbalanced, activity of the lower centers normally under cortical control.

Disease of the pyramidal pathway may be caused, as may disease elsewhere in the central nervous system, by birth injury, vascular disease, neoplasms, inflammation, degeneration, or trauma. Destruction of the neuron or of its neuraxis, whether due to involvement of the gigantropyramidal cells themselves, the internal capsule, the cerebral peduncle, the fibers as they pass through the pons or medulla, or the cortico-spinal tract, produces a definite syndrome. Inasmuch as the pyramidal pathway has an integrating and inhibiting effect upon the lower centers, the essential manifestations of such a lesion consist of a loss of skilled voluntary movements, or impairment of integration of movements, and an overactivity or exaggeration of response of the lower centers.

There is a *loss of voluntary movement* (Table 2). This loss of power, instead of being characterized by a decrease of tone, is *hypertonic,* or *spastic.* There is increased tension of the muscle masses on palpation, and increased resistance to passive movement. The paresis is *generalized* rather than focal; it involves either entire *extremities* or specific *movements* rather than individual muscles or muscle groups. In a lower motor neuron paralysis, for instance, either the short or the long flexor muscles may be paralyzed; in a pyramidal lesion, on the other hand, flexion as a whole may be paretic. It may be impossible to flex or extend one finger without flexing or extending them all. If a muscle has many functions, some of these may be affected while others are not impaired. The loss of power is *rarely complete.* There is usually *no* localized *atrophy,* although there may be some generalized loss of muscle volume, in part owing to disuse, and there may be apparent atrophy in a long-standing paralysis owing to lack of development of the involved part. If atrophy does occur, it usually affects the small muscles of the hand; it progresses rapidly if it appears early, and slowly if it appears late. There are *no fasciculations* and *no recation of degeneration.* The *deep reflexes,* instead of being lost, are *exaggerated,* and clonus may be elicited; the *superficial reflexes* are *diminished* or *lost.* Finally, there are various *pathologic reflexes,* such as the extensor Babinski response, which are often termed *pyramidal reflexes.* Some of the normal associated movements may be lost, but *abnormal associated movements* are present (Chapter 39). *Trophic changes* are rarely present, but occasionally one sees edema, desquamation, pigment changes, ulcerations, and a glossy skin.

In a paresis of central origin, which usually takes the form of a hemiparesis, the loss of power has certain characteristics. Involvement of the face is more or less limited to the lower portion (Chapter 13), and voluntary movements are affected more than emotional ones. Often there is normal movement in response to emotional stimuli. There may be only slight to moderate involvement of the sternocleidomastoid muscle, apparent as weakness in turning the head to the side opposite the paralysis, but the trapezius is usually weak. There is palsy of the affected side of the tongue, but the throat and jaw muscles function normally. Deglutition, articulation, movements of the trunk, and other acts that have bilateral supranuclear innervation are little affected. Voluntary, skilled, learned actions are most impaired, and there is loss of ability to carry out fine and isolated acts, especially those of the distal parts, with precision and delicacy. Gross movements and those that are habitual or which have little voluntary control are spared. The paresis of the extremities is spoken of as a "predilection type." In the upper limb the paresis of extension is more marked than that of flexion, and in the lower extremity paresis of flexion is more than of extension. As a result, the arm is held in a position of adduction, flexion, and slight internal rotation at the shoulder; there is flexion and pronation at the elbow, with flexion of the wrist and fingers. Still further flexion can be carried out, but there is marked weakness of extension. There is loss of isolated movements of the fingers and skilled movements of the hand, especially those that require extension of the fingers and wrist, but movements at the elbow and shoulder are less affected. In the lower extremity the leg is extended and adducted at the hip and extended at the knee and ankle. There is an equinus deformity of the foot with plantar flexion and inversion; the toes point downward and medially. There is loss of dorsiflexion and eversion of the toes and foot, and weakness of flexion at the hip and knee.

The spasticity, or increase in tone, is most marked in the flexor muscles of the upper limb and the extensors of the lower; it may become more apparent if an attempt is made to extend the muscles of the upper extremity or to flex those of the lower extremity. Passive motion can be carried out without difficulty if done through a small range of movement, but there is increasing resistance if an attempt is made to move the extremities through a greater range. On slow movement passive motion may be carried out without too much difficulty, but on rapid movement there is a "blocking" and one may at times get a waxing and waning of tone that gives the so-called "clasp knife" phenomenon. While it is stated that the spasticity, the associated movements, and the increase in reflexes are caused by the uncontrolled action of the lower centers when released from higher control, there is a sensory component as well, and in certain instances either the parietal cortex or the sensory portion of the reflex arc has been removed to relieve the spasticity in hemiplegia and paraplegia. On the other hand, pyramidal impulses from the parietal lobe (areas 3, 2, 1) may compensate for deficiency in function of area 4 following ablation.

One of the most characteristic examples of pyramidal paralysis is that which occurs following a hemorrhage, thrombosis, or embolism in the internal capsule. If the patient is examined soon after the ictus, flaccid paralysis and areflexia may be observed on the opposite side of the body, but after the period of shock is past, the above spastic syndrome of the "capsular hemiplegia" becomes apparent (Fig. 152). The lesion need not, however, be in the internal capsule, but may be cortical, in the corona radiata, or anywhere along the course of the pyramidal pathway. In the "capsular hemiplegia," which follows interruption of blood supply in the distribution of the branches of the middle cerebral artery, the arm is affected more than the face or leg. If the involvement is in the distribution of the anterior cerebral artery, the leg is affected more than the face or arm.

In spinal cord lesions of sudden onset involving the corticospinal pathways, especially if bilateral, there may also be a period of flaccidity and areflexia accompanying the paralysis that is below the level of the lesion. This is the period of "spinal shock" which sooner or later gives way, in most instances, to the pyramidal

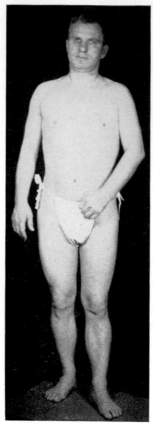

Fig. 152.   Left hemiplegia following a cerebral thrombosis.

syndrome. Occasionally in spinal lesions there develops a "paraplegia in flexion" in which there is flexion at the hips, knees, and ankles instead of extension (Fig. 153). This is indicative of a more complete interruption of conduction of descending impulses in the cord and an approach to separation of the cord below the level of the lesion from higher levels of the nervous system. Involuntary flexor spasms make their appearance, they gain in force and frequency, and finally the legs become fully flexed with the knees pressed tightly against the abdominal wall. This syndrome is probably caused by interruption of the vestibulospinal and other extrapyramidal pathways as well as the pyramidal tracts (Chapter 37).

The fact that the paresis of pyramidal lesions is rarely complete may be the result of a variety of factors, and these same mechanisms may be in part responsible for the recovery of function that follows many such lesions. Some of the distal musculature may have bilateral innervation and be supplied by both the crossed and uncrossed corticospinal tracts, or there may be incomplete decussation at the medullary pyramids; the pyramidal tracts themselves receive impulses from many regions other than the motor cortex, including areas 6, 8, 1, 2, 3, 5, and 7; many of the motor "centers" are widespread, and the foci of localization overlap; the precentral cortex and its neuraxes constitute only one portion of the motor system, and other cortical and subcortical centers are important in muscular activity; both the supplementary and secondary motor cortices may assume function in disease of the pyramidal system. Sensory components are important both in influencing the type and degree of paralysis and in contributing to motor recovery, and the prognosis for return of function is less good if there is significant sensory loss. Krynauw observed, in 1950, that hemispherectomy in patients with infantile hemiplegia produced improvement in convulsions and mental symptoms without increasing the motor deficit. This has been confirmed by others. Whereas removal of a normally developed hemisphere in adults (as for treatment of neoplasm) is followed by a spastic hemiplegia affecting principally skilled movements at distal joints, such removal in patients who have had a spastic hemiparesis since birth or early childhood is followed by a transient flaccid deficit that later becomes spastic, and the residual weakness is never worse than before operation and is sometimes less. It is probable, in these cases, that either the normal hemisphere on the opposite side and/or other cortical or subcortical structures have previously assumed a portion of the function of the diseased areas of the cortex.

Irritation of the pyramidal system, especially stimulation of the pyramidal cortex, causes an increased motor response with involuntary movements on the opposite side of the body. This may be manifested in the so-called jacksonian convulsive seizures. In the presence of cerebral neoplasms or other pathologic processes there may be a pyramidal type of paresis together with recurrent jacksonian convulsions. Section of the pyramidal pathway after it has left the cortex, however, produces only paresis, and there is no involuntary motor activity.

Time, clinical observation, and experimental data have shown that the concept of the "pure pyramidal lesion" must be changed, and that in the classical upper

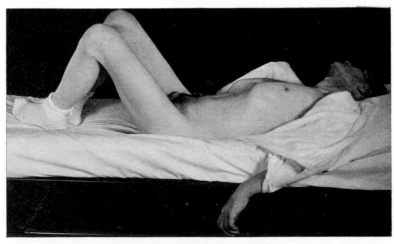

Fig. 153. Paraplegia in flexion.

motor lesion there is involvement either of both motor and premotor centers or of suppressor areas. For clinical evaluation it seems justifiable to continue to regard the manifestations of spasticity, hyperreflexia, and pathologic reflexes as signs of involvement of the pyramidal system, but to remember that in "pure" pyramidal lesions there may instead be flaccidity, often followed by atrophy. In the presence of the classical upper motor neuron syndrome with spasticity and hyperreflexia there is probably, in most instances, either simultaneous involvement of both the motor (pyramidal) and premotor cortices or interruption of their projections as they course through the internal capsule in close association with each other, or involvement of the suppressor areas or their projections.

REFERENCES

ARING, C. D. "Clinical Symptomatology," in BUCY, P. C. (ed.). *The Precentral Motor Cortex.* Urbana, Illinois, The University of Illinois Press, 1944, p. 409.

BATES, J. A. V. The individuality of the motor cortex. *Brain* 83:654, 1960.

BUCY, P. C. Max Minor Peet Lecture: The Pyramidal Tract. *Univ. Michigan Med. Bull.* 22:539, 1956; Is there a pyramidal tract? *Brain* 80:376, 1957.

BUCY, P. C., KEPLINGER, J. E., and SIGUEIRA, E. B. Destruction of the "pyramidal tract" in man. *J. Neurosurg.* 21:385, 1964.

DENNY-BROWN, D. "The Frontal Lobes and Their Functions," in FEILING, A. (ed.). Modern Trends in Neurology. New York, Paul B. Hoeber, Inc., 1951, pp. 13–89; The Cerebral Control of Movement. Springfield, Ill., Charles C Thomas, 1966.

FOERSTER, O. The motor cortex in man in the light of Hughlings Jackson's doctrines. *Brain* 59:135, 1936.

FRENCH, L. A., and JOHNSON, D. R. Observations on the motor system following cerebral hemispherectomy. *Neurology* 5:11, 1955.

FULTON, J. F., and KENNARD, M. A. A study of flaccid and spastic paralyses produced by lesions of the cerebral cortex in primates. *A. Res. Nerv. & Ment. Dis., Proc.* (1932), 13:158, 1934.

GARDNER, W. J., KARNOSH, L. J., McCLURE, C. C., JR., and GARDNER, A. K. Residual function following hemispherectomy for tumour and for infantile hemiplegia. *Brain* 78:487, 1955.

GOODDY, W. Sensation and volition. *Brain* 72:312, 1949.

KENNARD, M. A., and FULTON, J. F. The localizing significance of spasticity, reflex grasping, and signs of Babinski and Rossolimo. *Brain* 56:213, 1933.

KENNARD, M. A., VIETS, H. R., and FULTON, J. F. The syndrome of the premotor cortex in man: Impairment of skilled movements, forced grasping, spasticity and vasomotor disturbances. *Brain* 57:69, 1934.

KRYNAUW, R. A. Infantile hemiplegia treated by removing one cerebral hemisphere. *J. Neurol., Neurosurg. & Psychiat.* 13:243, 1950.

LASSEK, A. M. The Pyramidal Tract: Its Status in Medicine. Springfield, Ill., Charles C Thomas, 1954.

LIDDELL, E. G. T., and PHILLIPS, C. G. Thresholds of cortical representation. *Brain* 73:125, 1950.

McCULLOCH, W. S., GRAF, C., and MAGOUN, H. W. Cortico-bulbo-reticular pathway from area 4s. *J. Neurophysiol.* 9:127, 1946.

NATHAN, P. W., and SMITH, M. C.   Long descending tracts in man: I. Review of present knowledge. *Brain* 78:248, 1955.

NYBERG-HANSEN, R., and RINVIK, E.   Some comments on the pyramidal tract, with special reference to its individual variations in man. *Acta neurol.* 39:1, 1963.

PENFIELD, W., and RASMUSSEN, T.   The Cerebral Cortex of Man: A Clinical Study of Localization of Function. New York, The Macmillan Company, 1950.

PENFIELD, W., and WELCH, K.   The supplementary motor area of the cerebral cortex: A clinical and experimental study. *A. M. A. Arch. Neurol. & Psychiat.* 66:289, 1951.

RUCH, T. C., CHANG, H. T., and WARD, A. A., JR.   The pattern of muscular response to evoked cortical discharge. *A. Res. Nerv. & Ment. Dis., Proc.* (1946), 26:61, 1947.

SCARFF, J. E.   Primary cortical centers for movements of upper and lower limbs in man: Observations based on electrical stimulation. *Arch. Neurol. & Psychiat.* 44:243, 1940.

SUGAR, O., CHUSID, J. G., and FRENCH, J. D.   A second motor cortex in the monkey (Macaca mulatta). *J. Neuropath. & Exper. Neurol.* 7:182, 1948.

TOWER, S. S.   "The Pyramidal Tract," in BUCY, P. C. (ed.), *The Precentral Motor Cortex.* Urbana, Illinois, The University of Illinois Press, 1944, p. 149.

TRAVIS, A. M.   Neurological deficiencies after ablation of the precentral motor area in *Macaca mulatta.* *Brain* 78, 155, 1955; Neurological deficiencies following supplementary motor area lesions in *Macaca mulatta.* *Ibid.,* 78:174, 1955.

VAN CREVEL, H., and VERHAART, W. J. C.   The "exact" origin of the pyramidal tract. *J. Anat.* 97:495, 1963.

WALSHE, F. M. R.   On the "syndrome of the premotor cortex" (Fulton) and the definition of the terms "premotor" and "motor" with a consideration of Jackson's views of the cortical representation of movements. *Brain* 58:49, 1935; "The Problem of the Origin of the Pyramidal Tract," in Garland, H. (ed.), Scientific Aspects of Neurology. Baltimore, The Williams & Wilkins Company, 1961, pp. 1–15.

WOOLSEY, C. N., *et al.*   Patterns of localization in precentral and "supplementary" motor areas and their relation to the concept of a premotor area. *A. Res. Nerv. & Ment. Dis., Proc.* (1950) 30:238, 1952.

CHAPTER 24

THE CEREBELLUM

THE CEREBELLUM is not primarily a motor organ. Phylogenetically it has developed out of the primary vestibular area, and it is intimately associated with the vestibular system and the various conductors of proprioceptive impulses. Originally its functions were related entirely to the vestibular complex. The cerebellum first reaches major proportions in birds, where it is important in equilibrium and orientation in space. It reaches its greatest development, however, in mammals which have skilled movements of the extremities. The evolution of the cerebellum parallels the development of the cerebral hemispheres. It has an intimate relationship with pyramidal and extrapyramidal components of motor function as well as with the brain stem reticular formation, and plays such an important part in motor control that one is justified in referring to the "cerebellar level" of motor activity or integration.

ANATOMY AND PHYSIOLOGY

The cerebellum is situated in the posterior fossa of the skull, beneath the occipital lobe of the cerebrum from which it is separated by the tentorium cerebelli. Below and interiorly it is separated from the posterior aspect of the pons by the fourth ventricle and from the posterior aspect of the medulla and the dura mater covering the atlanto-occipital membrane by a dilatation of the subarachnoid space, the cisterna magna. From a morphologic point of view it is composed of three parts: a small, unpaired, median portion called the vermis, and two large, lateral masses, the cerebellar hemispheres, which are connected with each other by the vermis (Figs. 154, 155, and 156). Both the vermis and the hemispheres are divided, by fissures and sulci, into lobes and lobules.

The cerebellum is made up primarily of white matter which is covered with a thin layer of gray matter, the cerebellar cortex. Within the white matter are situated several gray masses, the cerebellar nuclei. The *dentate nuclei,* the largest of these, are purse-shaped structures situated within each hemisphere (Fig. 157). In the hilus of each dentate nucleus is the *emboliform nucleus,* and medial to the latter are the

428

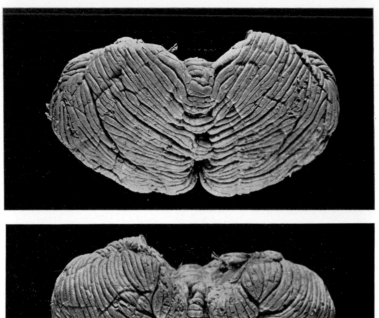

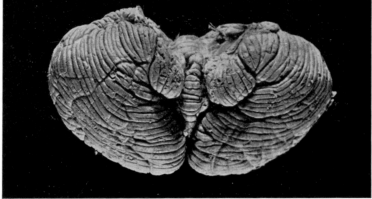

Fig. 154.   Dorsal view of human cerebellum.
Fig. 155.   Ventral view of human cerebellum. (Tilney, F. and Riley, H. A.: The Form and Functions of the Central Nervous System. New York, Paul B. Hoeber, Inc., 1938).

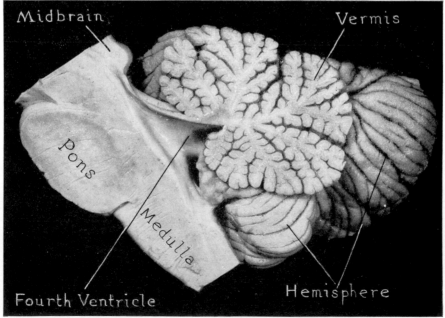

Fig. 156.   Median longitudinal section through human cerebellum. (Strong, O. S., and Elwyn, A.: Human Neuroanatomy. Baltimore, Williams & Wilkins Company, 1948.)

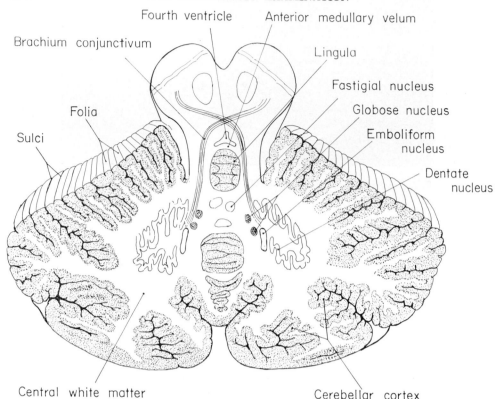

FIG. 157. Horizontal section of the cerebellum showing arrangement of cortical gray matter and locations of the central nuclei within the white matter. (After Sobotta-McMurrich.)

smaller *globose nuclei* which may consist of one or more rounded gray masses. In man these latter two nuclear groups are together called the *nucleus interpositus.* Within the medullary body of the vermis, at the roof of the fourth ventricle, are the *fastigial,* or *roof, nuclei.* Microscopically the cortex is made up of three distinct layers: the outer, nuclear, or molecular layer; the layer of Purkinje cells, and the inner, or granular, layer.

The division of the cerebellum into vermis and hemispheres is a grossly morphologic but not a physiologic one, and the division into lobes and lobules has been classified variously. According to Ingvar, the cerebellum may be divided into three lobes. The *anterior lobe,* which lies in front of the fissura prima, consists of the anterior portion of the vermis, with some lateral extensions. It is made up of the lingula, lobus centralis, and culmen. The *posterior lobe* comprises the midline pyramis, uvula, and nodule, with the flocculus and paraflocculus as lateral extensions. The *middle lobe* is situated between fissura prima and the prepyramidal sulcus; it consists of lobuli simplex, ansiformis, and paramedianus, along with the declive and tuber, and makes up the major portion of the cerebellum.

Using phylogeny and experimental physiology as bases for classification, the cerebellum has been divided into two primary divisions (Fig. 158). The vestibular *flocculonodular lobe,* or *archicerebellum,* is phylogenetically the oldest part, and its connections are primarily if not entirely vestibular. It receives fibers directly from the eighth nerve and possibly from the vestibular nuclei, and it discharges to the vestibular nuclei. The *corpus cerebelli,* from which it is separated by the fissura posterolateralis, may be subdivided into a paleocerebellar and neocerebellar portion. The *paleocerebellar portion* is the more basal region which communicates with the spinal cord, brain stem, and vestibular centers. It is composed of the anterior lobe and the posterior portion of the posterior lobe. The *anterior lobe,* which is anterior to fissura prima, is made up mainly of vermis with some lateral extensions. It consists of the lingula, lobulus centralis, and culmen. The principal afferent connections of this lobe come from the ventral spinocerebellar tract, although the lingula receives some fibers from the vestibular nuclei and the culmen some corticocerebellar fibers. The discharges are to the vestibular nuclei, brain stem, and spinal cord. The *posterior portion* of the *posterior lobe,* which lies between fissura posterolateralis and the prepyramidal sulcus, is composed of pyramis, uvula, and

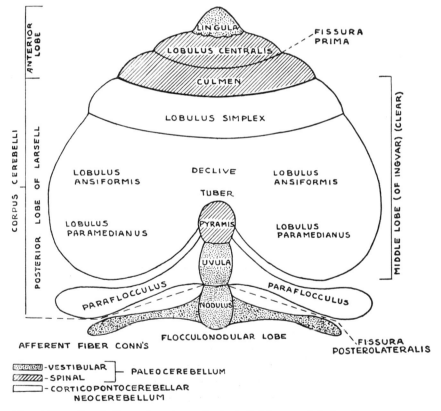

FIG. 158. Cerebellum, showing principal divisions and their afferent connections. (According to Larsell and Dow, as modified by Fulton.) (Nielsen, J. M.: A Textbook of Clinical Neurology, ed. 2. New York, Paul B. Hoeber, Inc., 1946.)

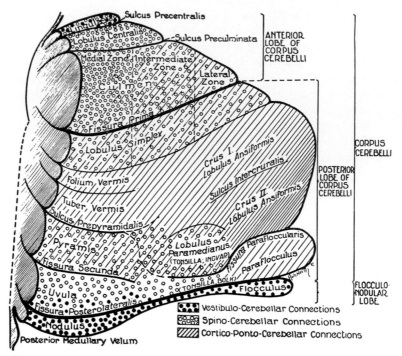

FIG. 159.   Afferent connections of cerebellum. (Dow, R. S.: *Biol. Rev.* 17:179, 1942.)

paraflocculus. It receives afferent fibers from the dorsal spinocerebellar tract and from the brain stem. The uvula also receives some vestibular fibers, and pyramis and paraflocculus, some corticocerebellar fibers. It discharges to the brain stem, vestibular nuclei, and spinal cord (Fig. 159). The *neocerebellar division* (anterior portion of the posterior lobe) is in communication with the cerebral cortex. It is made up of the lobuli simplex, ansiformis, and paramedianus, along with the declive and tuber; it constitutes the greater part of the cerebellar hemispheres, or corpus cerebelli, and extends from fissura prima to the prepyramidal sulcus. It becomes enormously developed in mammals in association with differentiation of skeletal musculature and growth of the cerebral hemispheres. In primates it is greatly elaborated and overshadows the rest of the cerebellum. Its afferent connections are principally corticopontine, or corticopontocerebellar, although lobulus simplex receives some spinocerebellar fibers; it discharges through the dentate nucleus to the red nucleus and thalamus, and thus to the cerebral cortex.

The cerebellum is connected with the rest of the central nervous system by means of the three cerebellar peduncles. The *inferior cerebellar peduncles,* or *restiform body,* connects the cerebellum with the spinal cord and the medullary centers, and through it go, as ascending fibers, the dorsal spinocerebellar tract, the dorsal and ventral external arcuate fibers from the nuclei of gracilis and cuneatus, the olivocerebellar, reticulocerebellar, nucleocerebellar, and vestibulocerebellar pathways, and direct communications from the eighth nerve. The descending, or efferent, pathways are the cerebello-olivary, cerebellospinal, cerebellovestibular, and fastigio-bulbar fibers. The *middle cerebellar peduncle,* or *brachium pontis,* connects the cerebellum with the cerebral cortex, and through it run the pontocerebellar tracts; these are the final neurons of the corticopontocerebellar pathway which comes from the frontal, temporal, etc., cortex to communicate with the contralateral cerebellar hemisphere. The *superior cerebellar peduncle,* or *brachium conjunctivum,* contains the prinicpal efferent fibers of the cerebellum, the dentorubral and the dentothalamic pathways. With it run the ventral spinocerebellar pathway, fastigiobulbar fibers (fasciculus uncinatus of Russell), and the cerebellotegmental, cerebellotectal, and tectocerebellar tracts.

The afferent fibers are distributed to the cerebellar cortex and are furnished in the main by tracts which enter through the middle and inferior peduncles. Impulses ascend to the granular and molecular layers, but ultimately impinge upon the dendrites of the Purkinje cells, the axons of which pass through the white matter of

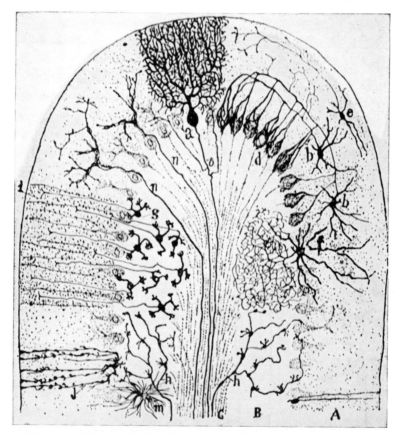

FIG. 160. Semidiagrammatic transverse section through a folium of cerebellum. *A,* molecular layer; *B,* granular layer; *C,* white matter; *a,* Purkinje cell; *b,* basket cells; *d,* pericellular baskets; *e,* superficial stellate cells; *f,* large stellate cell; *g,* granular cells, whose axons ascend and bifurcate at *i; h,* mossy fibers; *j* and *m,* neuroglia; *n,* climbing fibers. (Cajal.)

the hemispheres and are distributed to the cerebellar nuclei, chiefly to the dentate nuclei (Fig. 160). Two structurally different types of afferent terminals are found in the cerebellar cortex. *Mossy fibers,* the terminations of those neurons which enter the cerebellum through the inferior cerebellar peduncles, especially the direct spino-cerebellar, olivocerebellar, and external arcuate tracts, give off many fine collaterals around the cells of the granular layer. The axons of the granular cells enter the molecular layer where they divide and establish synaptic relations with the dendritic expansions of the Purkinje cells. *Climbing fibers,* the terminations of the neurons carried through the brachium pontis, pass out to the molecular layer and give off collaterals which come into contact with the arborizations of the Purkinje cells. The mossy fibers are thus connected indirectly with a large number of Purkinje cells, whereas the climbing fibers are in communication with only one or two Purkinje cells. The "avalanche" type of conduction from the mossy fibers, whereby certain incoming impulses are distributed to many cells, is an important characteristic of cerebellar function.

The efferent fibers from the cerebellar cortex and the Purkinje cells are nearly all relayed to the deep nuclei, where the efferent fibers from the cerebellum originate (Fig. 161). A small, phylogenetically old bundle, however, the flocculovestibular tract, goes directly from the flocculi to the vestibular nuclei. The fastigial nucleus, the oldest of the cerebellar nuclei, receives afferent fibers from the paleocerebellum and also from the vestibular nuclei and the eighth nerve. Its efferent impulses, many of them crossing in the roof, pass into the brain stem to the vestibular nuclei, especially the lateral one (Deiters'), and the reticular formation. Some of these go through the inferior peduncle, others (fasciculus uncinatus of Russell) pass with the superior peduncle. The dentate nucleus, the most important of the nuclear masses, receives its afferent fibers principally from the Purkinje cells of the neocerebellum; he emboliform nucleus receives impulses from neocerebellum and paleocerebellum; and the globose nuclei, principally from the paleocerebellum. All three of these nuclei discharge in the most important efferent system of the cerebellum, the brachium conjunctivum, which terminates in the contralateral red nucleus and nucleus ventralis lateralis of the thalamus. Impulses are then relayed to the cerebral cortex. There may also be fibers from these nuclei to the subthalamic nucleus, and impulses which go directly to the cortex.

The functions of the cerebellum were first studied by analysis of the effects of removing the entire organ. Following extirpation there appears a state similar to that seen in decerebrate rigidity, with opisthotonus, head retraction, tonic extension and abduction of the fore limbs, and clonic movements of the hind limbs. Tremors are also present, and in unilateral ablations there are forced movements toward the side of the lesion. These effects are probably due to the release of postural mechanisms from inhibitory effects normally exercised by the cerebellum. Next deficiency phenomena develop, characterized by asthenia, hypotonia, astasia, and tremor on muscular activitiy; these resemble the symptoms seen clinically with extensive damage to the cerebellum. Finally there is a gradual recovery, probably explained by the progressive assumption of cerebellar functions by the cerebrum. Stimulation of certain areas in the cerebellum is followed by localized motor responses and by either inhibition or facilitation of postural tonus and of cortically

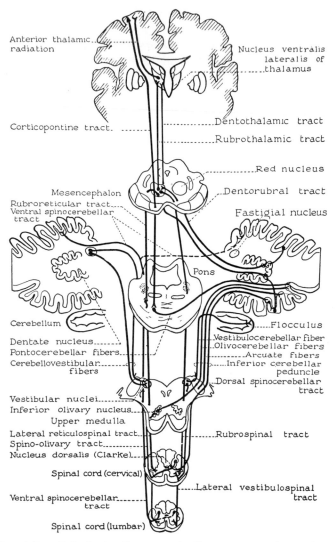

Anterior thalamic
radiation

Nucleus ventralis
lateralis of
thalamus

Corticopontine tract.

Dentothalamic tract

Rubrothalamic tract

Red nucleus

Mesencephalon

Dentorubral tract

Rubroreticular tract
Ventral spinocerebellar
tract

Fastigial nucleus

Pons

Cerebellum

Flocculus

Dentate nucleus
Pontocerebellar fibers
Cerebellovestibular
fibers

Vestibulocerebellar fiber
Olivocerebellar fibers
Arcuate fibers
Inferior cerebellar
peduncle
Dorsal spinocerebellar
tract

Vestibular nuclei
Inferior olivary nucleus
Upper medulla
Lateral reticulospinal tract
Spino-olivary tract
Nucleus dorsalis (Clarke)

Rubrospinal tract

Spinal cord (cervical)

Ventral spinocerebellar
tract

Lateral vestibulospinal
tract

Spinal cord (lumbar)

FIG. 161. Principal afferent and efferent connections of cerebellum.

and reflexly induced movements; these effects are probably produced by means of impulses which converge on the midbrain and bulbar reticular formations.

From a phylogenetic point of view, the cerebellum is primarily a highly specialized vestibular nucleus. It receives afferent impulses from the labyrinths and vestibular centers, spinal cord, and brain stem (including the reticular formation and olivary bodies), and projects to the vestibular nuclei, vestibular tracts, and reticular formation. It probably also receives fibers from and projects to the vestibular areas in the cerebral cortex. It appears that the cerebellum and vestibular centers function together in the *maintenance of equilibrium,* the *orientation of the organism in space,* and the *regulation of muscular tone and posture.*

In the mammal, however, and especially in man, the cerebellum has many important functions other than those related to equilibrium and tone. It receives proprioceptive impulses from all parts of the body and both motor and sensory impulses from the cerebrum. It either dampens or potentiates and coordinates these impulses, and then passes them on. The histologic structure of the cerebellar cortex indicates that impulses brought into it are built up and strengthened through the "avalanche" method of conduction. The major functions of the cerebellum, from a clinical point of view, are the *integration and coordination of somatic reactions.* It reinforces and resynthesizes motor impulses and graduates and harmonizes muscular contractions, both in voluntary movement and in the maintenance of posture. Responses are made stronger and more certain, and voluntary movements are made smooth and synchronous. The cerebellum is the organ through which the cerebral motor cortex achieves the synthesis of coordinated units which compose voluntary movements. Thus it plays an important part in all motor functions.

In addition to the above, it has also been shown during recent years that tactile, auditory, and visual areas exist in the cerebellum. Motor, tactile, visual, and auditory centers in the cerebrum, both cortical and subcortical, project to similar areas in the cerebellum, which in turn project back to the corresponding cerebral areas. The structure thus is neither exclusively vestibular, proprioceptive, nor motor in function, but acts either to diminish or to reinforce both sensory and motor impulses, and is an important modulator of neurologic function. It projects impulses, often indirectly, to each source from which it receives them, and accordingly appears to act as an integrating mechanism that operates through a series of feedback circuits to maintain a desired level of neural activity.

CLINICAL MANIFESTATIONS OF CEREBELLAR DYSFUNCTION

The symptoms of cerebellar disease in man are, on the whole, consistent with those produced experimentally in animals. The principal manifestations are disturbances of muscular coordination and of locomotion and equilibrium. Voluntary movement is impaired. Muscular contractions are weak and easily fatigued; they are of an intermittent and irregular character, and there is delay both in initiating and in relaxing contractions. The major disturbance, however, can be spoken of in a general way as *loss of coordination, loss of control,* or *ataxia.* Special terms have been used to describe the various aberrations of movement, muscle function, and equilibrium, that are seen in cerebellar disease, and these may be classified as follows:

1. *Asynergy* is loss of the faculty to associate more or less complex movements that have special functions. In dyssynergy and asynergy there is a lack of coordinated action between various groups of muscles or various movements which, as components of an act, are normally associated with proper degree, harmony, and sequence so that the act can be preformed smoothly and accurately. As a result, there is lack of speed and skill in performing movements which require the synchronous activity of several groups of muscles or of several movements. If the various successive components of the act are not correlated in proper sequence and degree and are not properly grouped together, there is *decomposition of movement;*

the act is broken down into its component parts and it is executed in the manner of a robot or puppet.

2. *Dysmetria* is the loss of ability to gauge the distance, speed, or power of a movement. In lack of judgment of distance, or range, of movement the act may be stopped before the goal is reached, or the subject may overshoot the desired point. In loss of judgment of rate, or speed, the movement may be carried out too slowly or rapidly. With inability to gauge force, or power, the act may be carried out with too little or too much power.

3. *Dysdiadokokinesia,* or *adiadokokinesis,* is a disturbance in the reciprocal innervation of agonists and antagonists; there is a loss of ability to stop one act and follow it immediately by its diametric opposite. This is seen when the patient attempts alternate successive pronation and supination of the hands, rapid tapping of the fingers, or alternate opening and closing of the fists. Alternate movements are carried out either slowly or irregularly and clumsily. A disturbance in reciprocal innervation is also present in the *rebound phenomenon of Gordon Holmes,* where there is a loss of the "check reflex" and a failure of the ability to relax the contraction of the flexors of the forearm and rapidly contract the antagonists, or extensors.

4. *Hypotonia,* or muscle flaccidity with decrease in resistance to passive movement of the joints, is often seen in cerebellar disease. The muscles are flabby and assume unnatural attitudes; the parts of the body can be moved passively into positions of extreme flexion or extension. There is a "hypotonic attitude" of the wrists, with a curving, downward flexion when the arms are extended. There have been some reports of the partial alleviation of the hypertonicity of parkinsonism and of congenital spastic paresis by surgical removal of either the dentate nucleus or large portions of the cerebellar hemispheres.

5. *Asthenia, fatigability,* and *slowness of movement* are characteristic manifestations. The muscles are definitely weakened and tire easily. The commencement of any voluntary movement is delayed, and both the contraction and relaxation phases are abnormally slow.

6. *Abnormal movements,* or *hyperkinesias,* are frequent symptoms of cerebellar dysfunction. One most commonly sees an *intention type of tremor* (*active or kinetic tremor*) which is not present at rest but becomes evident on purposeful movement. When this occurs in the hand, there are coarse, irregular, to-and-fro, jerky movements which increase in amplitude and coarseness as the hand approaches its objective (terminal type). There may, however, be a *resting (static) type of tremor,* characterized by regular, rhythmic oscillations which may be present when no active innervation is taking place. The movements may involve not only the extremities, but also the head or even the entire body. It has been stated that the hyperkinesias may be due to hypotonia and irregularities of muscular contraction, but these factors do not entirely explain them. There may be, however, other abnormalities of movement, secondary to unsteadiness and incoordination, which may simulate more gross hyperkinesias. The tremors and other movements probably result from involvement of the cerebellar afferent pathways in their connections with the red nucleus and thalamus (dentorubral and dentothalamic pathways, or superior cerebellar peduncle). The role, if any, of the cerebellum in the hyperkinetic

manifestations of myoclonic cerebellar dyssynergia and myoclonic epilepsy is still controversial.

7. *Abnormalities of posture and gait with abnormal attitudes and spontaneous deviation* of the head and parts of the body may be seen in cerebellar disease. In unilateral cerebellar disease there may be *deviation of the head and body* toward the affected side, with *past pointing* of the extremities toward that side. In standing the body is inclined to fall toward the side of the lesion, and in walking there is a deviation toward that side. The outstretched extremities deviate laterally, toward the affected side. There may be absence of the normal pendular movement of the arm in walking (Wartenberg). In midline, or vermis, lesions the subject may not be able to stand erect and may fall either backward or forward. The gait is staggering, reeling, or lurching in character, without laterality. Abnormal attitudes of the extremities owing to muscular hypotonicity have already been mentioned.

8. *Speech disturbances* may be noted, and articulation may be slow, ataxic, slurred, drawling, jerky, or explosive in type, owing to asynergy of the muscles of phonation. The scanning speech of multiple sclerosis and the staccato speech of Friedreich's ataxia are probably the result of cerebellar dysfunction.

9. *Nystagmus and deviation of the eyes* may be present with lesions of the cerebellum. The former is encountered frequently, but may differ in type as well as in mechanism of production. Its presence often indicates that the vestibulo-cerebellar pathways are affected, and thus suggests involvement of either the vermis region or the inferior cerebellar peduncle. On other occasions the abnormal ocular movements may be the result of involvement of the connections of the cerebellum with other centers rather than actual lesions of the cerebellum itself, or caused by pressure on other structures, or what appears to be nystagmus may actually be an ocular expression of cerebellar asynergia. With a lesion of one hemisphere the eyes at rest are deviated ten to thirty degrees toward the unaffected side. When the patient attempts to focus his vision elsewhere the eyes move toward the point of fixation with quick jerks, and there are slow return movements to the resting point. The movements are more marked and of greater amplitude when the patient looks toward the affected side. With a tumor of the cerebellopontine angle the nystagmus is coarse on looking toward the side of the lesion and fine and rapid on gaze to the opposite side. Nystagmus is usually not present with parenchymatous cerebellar degenerations (Chapter 11). Occasionally, with cerebellar lesions, there is *skew deviation* of the eyes; the homolateral eye is turned downward and inward and the contralateral eye, upward and outward.

10. *The deep reflexes* are usually *diminished* in disease limited to the cerebellum. Occasionally one may note *pendular* reflexes. If the patellar tendon is stimulated while the foot is hanging free, there is a series of jerky to-and-from movements of the foot and leg before the limb finally comes to rest; this response is normally prevented by the after-shortening of the quadriceps femoris. The hyporeflexia and the pendular response are probably caused by the hypotonicity of the flexor and extensor muscles and the lack of the restraining effect which they normally exert upon each other. The cutaneous reflexes are unaffected ("The Reflexes," Part V).

11. *Rigidity of a cataleptic type* has been described in cerebellar lesions. So-called tonic convulsions are often called "cerebellar fits." In these there is sudden rigidity, with extensor hypertonia, often of a decerebrate type, and opisthotonus, accompanied by cyanosis and unconsciousness. The arms are extended at the elbows, flexed at the wrists, and strongly pronated. The legs are extended at the hips, knees, and ankles, and the toes are plantar flexed. These tonic manifestations have been attributed to cerebellar disease and have been said to occur either on the basis of irritation or secondary to release of postural mechanisms from the normal inhibitory action of the cerebellum, but probably are the result of transient ischemia of higher centers in the brain stem and cerebrum. Portions of the cerebellum have been removed, however, in the treatment of hypertonic states.

There is no paralysis or loss of power in lesions of the cerebellum, although the ataxia may be so profound and the asthenia so marked that motor activities cannot be carried out (Table 2). There is *no atrophy,* there are *no fasiculations,* and there are *no abnormal electrical reactions.* There are no *pathologic reflexes,* and even though the cerebellum is a proprioceptive reception center there are *no* conscious or demonstrable *sensory changes* when the disease process is confined to the cerebellum. The ataxia and other abnormalities are never limited to specific muscles, muscle groups, or movements, and are apparent in an entire extremity, an entire half of the body, or bilaterally in the head, neck, trunk, or entire body.

LOCALIZATION OF CEREBELLAR DISEASE

At present, evidence for clinical localization of function within the cerebellum is inconclusive. There is no cytoarchitectonic evidence of localization. Impulses from all parts of the body are received within the cerebellum and there is projection of afferent fibers to certain centers, but these centers do not have a specific physiologic action. The vermis, for instance, is not a functional division. It is made up of distinct units, some related to older vestibular foundation of the cerebellum, others having spinal connections, and still others with newer relationships to higher centers. In the cerebellum of mammals there is so much overlapping of fibers that the primitive pattern of localization of function is largely lost or hidden. It has been stated that there are centers for motor coordination of the head, neck, and trunk in the vermis, with the center for the head anteriorly in the culmen and that for the trunk posteriorly in the uvula, and that localization of the extremities is in the hemispheres, especially the tuber. Experimental work, however, has not confirmed this.

If there is localization of function within the cerebellum, it is in relation to the efferent, not the afferent system. Experimental studies have demonstrated syndromes that follow lesions of the three major divisions of the cerebellum. Isolated lesions of the *flocculonodular lobe,* or the archicerebellum, give rise to grave disturbances of equilibrium of the entire body; these are characterized by swaying, staggering, titubation, and ataxia of the trunk, most marked in the erect position. Individual movements of the extremities are not affected, there are no tremors on volitional movement, and there are no serious reflex disturbances. The manifestations are similar to those seen in man with lesions of the vermis. Section of the inferior cerebellar peduncles causes similar symptoms. With lesions of the *anterior lobe* (paleocerebellum) there are increased stretch reflexes, exaggerated positive supporting reactions, and decerebrate rigidity (cerebellar catalepsy). There may be gross disturbances of coordination and equilibrium and nodding and weaving movements of the head and trunk. No syndrome of the anterior lobe has been adequately described in man, but the presence of the positive supporting reaction in cerebellar tumors may lead one to suspect involvement of the anterior lobe. Disease of the *neocerebellum* shows protean manifestations in the spheres of posture and movement. There are hypotonia, dysmetria, and dyssynergia, with marked disturbances in the rate, force, range, and direction of volitional movement. If the dentate nuclei or their efferent pathways are involved, there is tremor. There are no definite alterations in equilibrium. The manifestations resemble those of the syndrome of the cerebellar hemispheres.

For practical purposes it may be said that there are two characteristic cerebellar syndromes seen clinically, that of the vermis and that of the hemispheres. In the *vermis,* or *"midline," syndrome* the manifestations are primarily those that follow involvement of the flocculonodular lobe. As a result there is a large vestibular component, and the symptoms closely resemble those found in vestibular disease. In addition, since the vermis is unpaired and appears to be of importance in the regulation of the axial structures, or those which are bilaterally innervated, coordination of the head and trunk are affected. There are gross postural and locomotor disturbances of the entire body. There is truncal ataxia with swaying and unsteadiness when standing, and the subject may be unable to maintain an upright position. At times there may be loss of ability even to hold the trunk erect when seated, or to hold the neck and head in a steady and upright position. There is no lateralization and there may be a tendency to fall either backward or forward. This disturbance in equilibrium is especially marked in the gait, which may be characterized by swaying, staggering, and titubation. Again there is no lateralization, and the patient may reel in a drunken manner to either side. There is no particular involvement of the extremities, especially the upper extremities, although all coordinated movements may be poorly performed. As a part of the disturbance of posture and gait there appears to be some loss of coordination in the lower extremities, but this is a generalized impairment of function rather than specific dysmetria or dyssynergy. There may be tremor of the head, neck, or entire body, and gross impairment of muscle function, but there usually are no specific intention or resting tremors. Muscle tone is normal, as are the reflexes. Nystagmus may be present, but often is not marked. Dysarthria, however, is often evident. The most common cause of the complete vermis syndrome is the medulloblastoma of the cerebellum, which occurs most frequently in children.

The *syndrome of the cerebellar hemispheres* is essentially that described in disease of the corpus cerebelli, or neocerebellum. The manifestations are appendicular rather than axial. They are usually unilateral and occur on the side of the diseased hemisphere. There is a gross disturbance of skilled movements of the extremities, and the arm and hand are affected more than the leg and foot, regardless of the area of the hemisphere involved. Distal movements are affected more than proximal ones, and fine movements more than coarse ones. One finds a marked disturbance of isolated movements, with ataxia, dysmetria, dyssynergy, dysdiadokokinesia, hypotonicity, asthenia, and fatigability. Movements are performed irregularly, and there may be tremors of an intention type, or other hyperkinesias if the dentate nucleus or its efferent pathways are involved. The deep reflexes are diminished or are of the pendular type. Posture and gait are not impaired to the extent that one finds in the vermis syndrome, but there may be characteristic changes. There may be swaying and falling toward the side of the lesion, with deviation of the occiput toward that side. The patient may be unable to stand when using only the homolateral foot, but may retain the ability to stand when using only the contralateral foot. He may be unable to bend his body toward the involved side without falling. In walking there may be some unsteadiness, and the patient may deviate or rotate toward the involved side. There may be a "compass gait" toward the involved side, and in walking around a chair, either in a clockwise or a counterclockwise direction, there is a tendency to fall toward the affected side. There may be spontaneous deviation of the extended extremities toward the involved side, with past pointing toward that side. There may be a slurred type of dysarthria, although disturbances of articulation are more marked in vermis lesions. Nystagmus is a common finding; it is usually horizontal but may be rotatory. It is coarser and slower when the eyes are deviated toward the side of the lesion. The above syndrome is seen most characteristically in hemispheric neoplasms, as in the astrocytoma of the cerebellum.

The symptoms of cerebellar disease differ markedly in severity, depending upon the acuteness or the chronicity of the process. If the lesion is acute, the symptoms are profound; if it is slowly progressive, the manifestations of cerebellar deficiency are much less severe. There may be an extensive involvement of the hemispheres without clinical symptoms, and there may be considerable recovery from the effects of an acute lesion. The symptoms of cerebellar deficiency may be similar regardless of the etiology of the disease process, and whether the lesion is congenital or acquired. Among the causes of cerebellar disease may be included the following: congenital abnormalities such as agenesis or hypoplasia, atresia of the foramina of Luschka and Magendie with enlargement of the fourth ventricle, or cerebellar involvement associated with platybasia or basilar impression; neoplasms of either the vermis or the hemispheres, or of the brain stem or cerebellopontine angle with secondary cerebellar involvement; trauma, including cerebellar extradural hematoma; acute and chronic infectious and toxic disorders; deficiency states; vascular lesions, including intracerebellar hemorrhage and thrombosis of the posterior inferior, anterior inferior, and superior cerebellar arteries; so-called degenerative processes, including the hereditary cerebellar and spinocerebellar ataxias, olivopontocerebellar atrophy, progressive and myoclonic cerebellar dyssynergia, parenchymatous and cortical cerebellar atrophy, and hereditary ataxic polyneuritis (Refsum's syndrome). Cerebellar degenerations have also been reported secondary to or associated with alcoholism, hyperpyrexia, dilantin intoxication, carcinomatosis, and Hodgkin's disease, and with oculocutaneous telangiectasia. It must be borne in mind that on occasion symptoms suggestive of involvement of one cerebellar hemisphere may be encountered with lesions of the opposite cerebral hemisphere, and that underdevelopment or atrophy of one hemisphere may be associated with underdevelopment or involvement of the opposite cerebral hemisphere.

REFERENCES

ADRIAN, E. D. Afferent areas in the cerebellum connected with the limbs. *Brain* 66: 289, 1943.

ANGEVINE, J. B. JR., MANCALL, E. L., and YAKOVLEV, P. I. The Human Cerebellum: An Atlas of Gross Topography in Serial Sections. Boston, Little, Brown & Company, 1961.

BAILEY, P. Reflections aroused by an unusual tumor of the cerebellum. *J. Mt. Sinai Hosp.* 9:299, 1942.

BROWN, J. R. Localizing cerebellar syndromes. *J.A.M.A.* 141:518, 1949.

CHAMBERS, W. W., and SPRAGUE, J. M. Functional localization in the cerebellum: II. Somatotopic organization in the cortex and nuclei. *A. M. A. Arch. Neurol. & Psychiat.* 74:653, 1955.

DOW, R. S., and MORUZZI, G. The Physiology and Pathology of the Cerebellum. Minneapolis, University of Minnesota Press, 1958.

FULTON, J. F., and CONNOR, G. The physiological basis of three major cerebellar syndromes. *Tr. Am. Neurol. A.* 65:53, 1939.

FULTON, J. F., and DOW, R. S. The cerebellum: A summary of functional localization. *Yale J. Biol. & Med.* 10:89, 1937.

FULTON, J. F., LIDDEL, E. G. T., and RIOCH, D. McK. Relation of the cerebrum to the cerebellum: I. Cerebellar tremor in the cat and its absence after removal of the cerebral hemispheres. *Arch. Neurol. & Psychiat.* 28:542, 1932.

GREENFIELD, J. G. The Spino-Cerebellar Degenerations. Springfield, Ill., Charles C Thomas, 1954.

HOLMES, G. The Croonian lectures on the clinical symptoms of cerebellar disease and their interpretation. *Lancet* 1:1177, 1231, and 2:59, 111, 1922.

INGVAR, S. On cerebellar localization. *Brain* 46:301, 1923.

INGVAR, S. Studies in neurology. *Bull. Johns Hopkins Hosp.* 43:315 and 338, 1928.

LARSELL, O. The cerebellum: A review and interpretation. *Arch. Neurol. & Psychiat.* 38:580, 1937.

LARSELL, O. The development of the cerebellum in man in relation to its comparative anatomy. *J. Comp. Neurol.* 87:85, 1947.

SNIDER, R. S., and STOWELL, A. Receiving areas of the tactile, auditory, and visual systems in the cerebellum. *J. Neurophysiol.* 7:331, 1944.

SNIDER, R. S. Recent contributions to the anatomy and physiology of the cerebellum. *Arch. Neurol. & Psychiat.* 64:196, 1950.

TOTH, S. Effect of removing nucleus dentatus in parkinsonism. *J. Neurol., Neurosurg. & Psychiat.* 24:143, 1961.

CHAPTER 25

PSYCHOMOTOR COMPONENTS

THE FINAL or highest level of motor integration, in the present concept of motor activity, is the so-called *psychomotor level*. This is the "newest" of all motor levels, and it corresponds to the third level of Jackson—the "motor division of the 'organ of the mind' " which has its origin in the prefrontal areas of the brain. Cobb refers to it as the "cortical associative" level which involves initiative and memory, in contrast to the "cortical motor," which is herein called the pyramidal level. This latter is referred to as the center for voluntary motor activity, but by "voluntary" is meant "most highly integrated," rather than actually volitional.

The psychomotor level may be thought of as that portion of the motor system where volitional movements are initiated, but it should be considered both voluntary and involuntary, conscious and unconscious. All purposive movements are initiated and guided in their performance by a constant stream of afferent impulses that reach the cerebral cortex, following which associations take place, so that sensation and motion are interdependent in the performance of voluntary movement. The sensations, however, need not be consciously perceived. Furthermore, at this level of integration, initiative, memory, and symbolization enter into motor activity; engrams are called out and previous experiences are used to alter responses to immediate stimuli. Skilled acts can be performed with a high degree of precision, but stereotyped and automatic movements integrated at a lower level and patterned complexes learned earlier in life can be utilized as part of the response.

It is easily understood that there is a major element of voluntary control of all motor activity: movements may be initiated or stopped, inhibited or exaggerated, or in many ways altered through volitional control. Alterations in tone, changes in posture, contractures, and abnormalities of movement may all be of voluntary origin. In malingering, for instance, a paralysis, hyperkinesis, or abnormality of tone may be simulated on a voluntary basis. Reflexes may even be influenced. There are also,

443

however, alterations in motor power that originate in the psychomotor sphere but are involuntary or unconscious in origin. In hysteria, for example, there may be paralyses, hyperkinesias, changes in tone, contractures, and even resulting deformities and atrophy that are psychogenically initiated but are on an unconscious basis. The paralyses, however, are apparent rather than real, and may simulate other types of loss of power; they are often bizarre in character and fail to conform to a specific organic pattern (Table 2). The tone may be normal or variable, but is often increased. Fasciculations, primary atrophy, and electrical changes are absent, and there is no true ataxia. The reflexes are usually normal, but occasionally there is hyperactivity of both deep and superficial reflexes. There are no pathologic reflexes and associated movements are normal. Hyperkinesias, if present, can usually be differentiated from abnormal movements of organic origin. The differentiation between psychogenic disturbances of motor activity, either on a conscious or an unconscious basis, and changes in motor function secondary to organic disease is sometimes difficult (Chapter 56).

The motor manifestations seen in some of the psychoses, such as the psychomotor retardation of the depressed patient, the hyperactivity of the manic, and the bizarre motor phenomena of catatonia and some of the organic psychoses are also evidences of disturbed function of this level of motor integration, as are the automatisms and abnormal behavior of so-called psychomotor epilepsy. Finally the apraxias, in which there is loss of ability to carry out purposive acts in the absence of paralysis, may be considered disturbances of psychomotor function, regardless of whether the apraxia is motor, sensory, or idiokinetic in type (Chapter 53).

The psychomotor level of integration is the highest one in evolutionary development, and is not present in lower forms. It is a motor level, but not purely motor, since in its functioning such factors as association, memory, imitation, and coordination in the volitional sense of the word are brought into play.

In summing up our knowledge of motor integration, it can be seen that each of the components of the motor system has its part to play: the myoneural junction where the motor impulse reaches the muscle fibers; the anterior horn cells in the spinal cord and the motor nuclei in the brain stem, which act as the final common pathway along which all impulses must travel in order to reach expression in the muscles; the simple postural and standing reflexes in the hindbrain and more complex standing and righting reflexes in the midbrain; the coordinating action of the cerebellum; the function of the basal ganglia in locomotor reflexes and automatic movements; the motor and premotor cortex in integration of skilled movements; and finally the association areas in utilization of experiences and in the conscious and unconscious control of motor activity. No coordinated or integrated action can take place without simultaneous and synchronous action of all, harmoniously playing on the anterior horn cells. In order to appraise the constituent motor functions and the method of examining each, and in order to comprehend intelligently the significance of changes in movement that may occur in disease of the nervous system, we must first appreciate the combined and coordinated action of these individual components of motor activity.

Section II. Examination of the Motor System

CHAPTER 26

FUNCTIONS OF
THE MOTOR SYSTEM

MOTOR ACTIVITY is brought about by the combined and harmonious action of the various component parts of the motor system. Abnormalities of movement may be caused by *impairment* or *loss of function* of one or more of the so-called levels of motor integration; by overactivity of the lower centers as a result of their *release from* the *inhibiting action* of the higher centers; by *irritation,* or *stimulation,* of certain constituent parts, or by *partial assumption of function by healthy tissues* to compensate for impairment or disease of others. Consequently, the character of change in motor function which occurs in disease is dependent both upon the component level involved and upon the type of pathologic process which affects it. In most instances, however, the so-called levels cannot be examined, or even considered, individually, for they all act together upon the final common pathway where they are synthesized, oftentimes in a complex fashion. Even though one level may be predominantly affected by a disease process, the resulting change in function can be considered only as it influences motor activity as a whole. The character of the impairment, however, and the portion of the motor system primarily involved, give important information to aid in determining the location and diagnosis of the pathologic process.

There are many *constituent functions* of motor activity, each of which is influenced to some extent by all of the levels of motor integration. For adequate evaluation of motor function as a whole each may have to be examined and appraised individually. The most obvious function is *motor strength,* or *power,* as exhibited in active movement. If this is impaired there is increased fatigability, decreased dexterity, and abnormalities in the speed and range of movement, with resulting weakness, paralysis, and deformities. There are, however, many other important

445

elements of motor function, namely, *muscle tone,* or the resistance to passive move-ment; *muscle volume* and *contour; coordination of movement,* including such fac-tors as agility, flexibility, balance, and performance of complex and skilled acts; *posture* and *gait; abnormal movements;* and *electrical reactions.* Each of these is discussed individually; the methods of examination are presented, and the changes that occur in association with disease processes are outlined in Chapters 27 through 33. Normal and abnormal associated movements are considered in Chapter 39, and defects of purposive movement, or the apraxias, in Chapter 53.

In order to evaluate the above factors most effectively and in order to carry out a systematic examination of the various motor functions, special observations and certain tests are indicated. These are described in detail under the individual sub-jects. A few preliminary generalizations, however, should be borne in mind. As in the case of the examination of the sensory system, the motor examination is most satisfactory if the subject is alert and his mind is keen. He should understand the procedures and be ready and willing to cooperate. Their purpose and method should be explained to him in simple terms, so that he may comprehend what is expected of him. Pain, discomfort of any type, sedative or narcotic drugs, fatigue, nervous tension, and apprehension all may interfere with the observations. If the patient is in a state of confusion or lowered consciousness, or if his intelligence is impaired or he fails to understand the examiner's terminology, the procedures may be modi-fied. If fatigue and inability to concentrate occur, the examination should be stopped and resumed when the patient is rested. The possibility of conscious or unconscious (malingered or hysterical) changes must always be borne in mind.

During the examination of motor functions the patient should be warm and com-fortable. He should be undressed, if possible. The room should be well lighted. One may first, by *inspection,* observe the posture and build, muscular development and bulk, the position of the body parts at rest, active and passive movements, con-genital absence of muscles, deformities, and skeletal abnormalities. The character of the spontaneous active movements should be noted, as well as any abnormal movements. During the examination, however, one relies not only on inspection but also on *palpation,* to note volume, tone, consistency, contraction, and tenderness, and, to a lesser extent, on *percussion.* The two sides of the body should be com-pared, and any asymmetries noted. One should always inquire about handedness before testing motor power.

The examination of motor functions, if carried out adequately and in detail, is a difficult and arduous procedure. It must be painstaking and accompanied by critical evaluation. It requires the knowledge of the action of each muscle and muscle group, and varies from the testing of a single muscle to the evaluation of complex movements, coordinated functions, and skilled acts. It frequently includes electrical testing, and, on occasion, special chemical tests.

CHAPTER 27

MOTOR STRENGTH AND POWER

MOTOR STRENGTH and power indicate the capacity to exert and release force; they involve the expenditure of energy. Both the power of movement and the strength of contraction are important, not only of individual muscles, but also of groups of muscles and of movements. Power is sometimes classified as *kinetic,* the force exerted in changing position, and *static,* the force exerted in resisting movement. Both are tested, and in most disease processes both are equally affected. In certain conditions, however, as in the extrapyramidal syndromes, kinetic power may be diminished while static power remains normal.

In examining strength and power we are interested especially in *voluntary,* or *active, motility.* In general, this is tested in two ways—by having the patient carry out movements against the resistance of the examiner, and by having him resist active attempts on the part of the examiner to move fixed parts. On occasion, however, movements may have to be tested when they are carried out without resistance or even with assistance, and one may note the power to resist gravity, or even observe muscle strength when the parts are supported in water. *Passive movements* may also be tested to note range or limitation of motion. Impairment of strength and power results in *weakness,* or *paresis;* loss of strength, in *paralysis.*

Simultaneous with the testing of strength and power and the observation of impairment of them, one must note associated functions and abnormalities. *Endurance* is the ability to carry out the same act repeatedly over a period of time; loss of endurance may be an early manifestation of paresis. *Abnormal fatigability* may precede other objective manifestations of impairment of energy. The *speed,* or *rapidity,* of movement and the *range,* or *amplitude,* of motion may be impaired in weakness. If there is loss of these functions, there may be a decrease in the *flexibility,* or *suppleness,* of movement, or loss of ability to move the joints through their full range. This may be followed by *limitation of movement, contractures,* and *deformities.*

447

There is a marked individual variation in muscle strength, dependent in part upon body build, early training, and activity. As a result, a diffuse deficiency in strength of moderate degree is of little significance, but the presence of local muscle weakness or paralysis is of great importance, and recognition of such changes has definite localizing value in the diagnosis of peripheral or central nervous system lesions. If weakness is found, one should determine whether it is a *diffuse* affair or whether it is *localized*. If localized, he should determine whether it is due to involvement of a specific *muscle,* of various muscles supplied by one *nerve,* of a group of muscles supplied by a certain *segment* of the spinal cord, of a specific *movement* involving more than one muscle, or of an *entire extremity*.

Weakness is manifested not only by loss of power, but also by fatigability, variation in strength on repeated tests, diminished range and rate of movement, loss of coordination, irregularity and clumsiness of motion, tremulousness, loss of associated movements, and lack of ability to carry out skilled acts. Attempts to contract individual muscles may be accompanied by movement of an entire extremity. In comatose states the paretic extremities may be flail-like, and drop when the examiner releases them (Chapter 55). In extrapyramidal disease rigidity may interfere with apparent muscle power, and bradykinesia delays the onset of muscle contraction and causes retardation of movement. Hyperkinesias of various types and ataxia may make motor activity difficult. Loss or impairment of motion may also occur with pain, swelling, spasm, local shock, fractures, dislocations, adhesions or ankylosis of joints, contractures of either agonists or antagonists, loss of tendon or muscle sense, hysteria, and malingering.

Motor weakness, if diffuse, may be the result of poor muscular development or inadequate muscular training. On the other hand, diffuse weakness may be found in the *myopathies,* such as the dystrophies and amyotonia congenita, and in electrolyte disturbances, toxic and deficiency states, and the various type of *myositis*. Either localized or diffuse weakness may be a manifestation of *myasthenia gravis,* in which there is an increased muscular fatigability. Repeated contractions may be followed by such profound fatigue of the affected muscles that an apparent paresis develops; similar fatigability follows repeated electrical stimulation (Jolly's reaction). The *neostigmine* and *Tensilon* tests may be used to confirm the diagnosis of myasthenia gravis. The subcutaneous or intramuscular injection of 1.5 mg. of neostigmine methylsulfate (with 0.6 mg. of atropine sulfate) is followed by a spectacular improvement in the asthenia and fatigability and an increase in strength of the paretic muscles. The patient should be observed at ten-minute intervals for a period of one hour after the injection. The objective and subjective improvement may be charted. A similar increase in strength follows the intravenous injection of 10 mg. (1.0 cc.) of Tensilon (edrophonium chloride), but the improvement starts within thirty seconds and strength may reach its maximum and begin to decline before five minutes have passed. The prompt recovery of function with both of these tests differentiates myasthenia gravis from the myopathies, psychoneurosis, fatigue states, and cranial nerve palsies. Occasionally either quinine sulfate or curare is given first to cause increased weakness before the tests are carried out. Such procedures are hazardous, however, and should be considered only in carefully selected cases.

Focal loss of strength results in either a *paresis* or a *paralysis,* in the presence of which one must determine the degree, character, and distribution of the impairment of motor power. The paralysis may involve one muscle, a group of muscles, certain movements, or one or more extremities. A *monoplegia* is the paralysis of one extremity; *diplegia,* of like parts on the two sides of the body; *hemiplegia,* of one half of the body; *paraplegia,* the legs or the lower parts of the body; *quadriplegia* and *tetraplegia,* of all four extremities. *Hemiplegia alternans* affects one part on one side of the body and another on the opposite side.

When a muscle is maintained in a position of contraction or shortening for a period of time, a *contracture* may develop; the muscle cannot be stretched to normal limits without considerable pressure and the production of pain. This may be neurogenic, without alteration of muscle tissue, but in most instances there is fibrous replacement of the latter. Contractures may develop following prolonged spasm of muscles, in association with spastic paralysis, or from the overaction of one group of muscles when unopposed by weakened antagonists. They may result in periarthritic changes, ankylosis of joints, and *deformities*. Spasm, contracture, and structural fixation of joints may occur simultaneously. It must be borne in mind that contractures and deformities that resemble them may be the result of many different causes. An equinus deformity of the foot, for instance, may be produced by a foot drop resulting from a peripheral peroneal palsy; by spasm of the gastrocnemius, in a spastic paresis; by a developmental anomaly, such as a congenital clubfoot; or by trauma or arthritis. In the evaluation of contractures and deformities it is important to differentiate between those of neurogenic origin and those due to fractures and other posttraumatic lesions, arthropathies, congenital abnormalities, muscular or tendinous strain or infiltration, habitual postures, occupational factors, or other diseases that cause mechanical difficulty with movement. The periarthritic changes in the shoulder that may develop because of disuse following a hemiplegia must be differentiated from a limitation of movement in the shoulder owing to primary articular disease. The ankylosis of the wrist joint associated with a long-standing wrist drop caused by a radial nerve palsy, and the contracture of the fingers occurring with claw hand resulting from an ulnar nerve paralysis, must be differentiated from the deformities seen in arthritis, Volkmann's contracture, Dupuytren's contracture, etc. The presence of pain on passive movement is important, and one should make every effort to determine whether limitation or absence of movement is the result of paralysis, pain, muscle spasm, swelling, or fibrous or bony alterations.

EXAMINATION OF MOTOR STRENGTH AND POWER

The evaluation of motor strength and power of various muscle groups and movements is a complicated process and it requires a detailed examination. Adequate knowledge of the function of the individual muscles is necessary. Actually, however, the contraction of a single muscle is never possible, since others that have similar functions participate in almost every movement. Furthermore, in order for a muscle to contract, its antagonists must relax and the synergistic and fixating muscles must also be brought into play. The predominating action of a single muscle, however, can usually be determined. In addition to the understanding of the action of individual muscles, one must, in the neurologic appraisal of motor function, understand the combined action of groups of muscles in the performance of gross movements and comprehend the harmonious and synchronous or consecutive action of muscles in carrying out coordinated acts. The examiner must also be familiar with the peripheral nerve and segmental innervation of each important muscle in order to distinguish peripheral nerve and plexus lesions from those that involve segmental structures. Inasmuch as many muscles are innervated from more than one spinal segment, it is important to remember that involvement of the fibers from one segment does not necessarily mean a complete loss of function of the involved muscles. Certain combinations of motor deficit can point only to a peripheral nerve lesion, others to a plexus or a segmental injury. In peripheral nerve lesions muscles or groups of muscles supplied by a particular nerve may be paralyzed, whereas in radicular or segmental lesions parts of muscles innervated by different nerves may be affected. Sometimes these muscles have antagonistic functions.

In the testing of motor power, the various movements at each joint and the strength of each important muscle should be tested individually and its grade recorded, as far as is possible. The patient may be either seated or recumbent. He is instructed either to resist active attempts by the examiner to move fixed parts or to initiate and carry out movements that are resisted by the examiner. Both methods may be used interchangeably, although patients usually comprehend and cooperate better with the former; initiation of movement by the patient may be the best method of testing weak muscles. The examiner should avoid abrupt application of pressure and should gradually increase the force exerted; cooperative patients maintain a smooth resistance to pressure and this continues as the examiner decreases the force exerted and allows the joint to move. Repeated testing may be used to demonstrate the presence of fatigability. It must always be borne in mind that there is much individual variation in muscle power, that the muscles on the dominant side are usually stronger than those opposite, and that fatigue, systemic illness, lack of comprehension of the method of testing, and many other factors may result in a false impression of weakness. Much experience may be necessary before an examiner can be certain of his results in determining loss of strength or varying degrees of weakness. While judgment of the force exerted in either initiating or resisting movement is the major criterion in the evaluation of strength or weakness, observation of muscular contraction and palpation are also essential guides, especially if there is a decrease in power. By placing the finger tips over the belly of a muscle or over its tendon one may feel the contraction of the former and the movement of the latter. Even the powerless effort to move a muscle may be accompanied by a synergistic contraction of neighboring or antagonistic muscles, which may be palpated rather than seen, and in feigned paralyses the contraction of the suspected muscles may be felt when the patient is asked to carry out movements with the antagonists. By careful observation one may also judge loss of function of certain muscles by noting the alterations of movement and position and substitution of other movements for paretic ones.

Proper positioning of the patient is necessary in conducting and evaluating tests of muscle strength. The part of the body to be examined is placed in that position which will permit the muscle to act directly and at the same time inhibit as far as possible the action of muscles of similar function. It is important to fix the proximal portion of a limb when the movements of the distal portion are being tested; for instance, the humerus should be fixed when testing pronation, so that the patient does not use his shoulder to compensate for a deficiency in pronation. Paresis may be overlooked when the action of accessory muscles is substituted for that of affected ones. On the other hand, paresis may be mistaken for paralysis if the movement takes place in an unfavorable attitude, as, for instance, the overcoming of the effect of gravity. The biceps and triceps muscles can contract more easily, in the presence of weakness, if the elbow is raised outward to the height of the shoulder so that the forearm can be moved in the horizontal plane. There may be an apparent weakness of grip with a radial nerve palsy if it is tested with the wrist in flexion, but if the wrist is passively extended, it can be seen that the flexors of the fingers contract normally. Paresis of muscles must be distinguished from spasm or contracture of antagonists, and involvement of individual muscles or muscle groups from generalized weakness of major portions of the body or predominant paresis of major movement patterns, such as flexion or extension of entire extremities.

The position and attitude of the limbs, the facility, range, speed, endurance, and fatigability of the motor responses, and the regularity of voluntary and spontaneous movements should be observed. If there is a deficiency of motor response, one should note whether it is spastic or flaccid in type. If contractures or deformities are present, the examiner should attempt to determine whether these have neurogenic origin or are caused by lesions of the bones, joints, tendons, or fascia, or whether both factors are present. Both active and passive movements should be tested, and if limitation of movement is accompanied by discomfort or pain, this should be noted. *Range* of movement may be limited by fibrosis, contractures, or changes at the joints. Weakness and increased tone, however, may also affect range. *Speed* of movement in itself is not an important criterion; there is a wide individual variation in this, but it is specifically increased in hyperthyroidism and manic states, and decreased in hypothyroidism, depressed states, parkinsonism, fatigue, and various myopathies. Slowness of movement may be the first manifestation of extrapyramidal disease, but a delay in muscular contraction and a retardation of movement may be an early sign of weakness. Abnormalities in *regularity* of movement usually signify ataxia or tremor, but they may also appear in weakness.

The motor examination may have to be modified, often with only a rough estimation of function, in various disease states, confused or stuporous patients, and infants and young children. In the presence of coma, for instance, assessment of motor function may have to depend upon the presence of spontaneous movements, the position of the extremities, asymmetries of voluntary movement on the two sides, or withdrawal of an extremity in response to painful stimulation. Hemiplegia may be diagnosed in the comatose patient by noting the absence of contraction of the facial muscles on one side following pressure on the supraorbital ridge, the flail-like dropping of the wrist and forearm when the examiner releases them while the flexed elbow is resting on the bed, and the similar extension and external rotation of the thigh and leg when released after having been placed in flexion with the heel resting on the bed (Chapter 55). In infants and young children muscle function may have to be tested largely by observing spontaneous motor activity and by noting the general posture and the position of the extremities when the body is prone, supine, seated, or upright. Resistance to passive movement, the motor response to reflex testing, and palpation may provide indirect evidence of muscle strength.

The testing of motor power in suspected hysteria and malingering may also require special technics (Chapter 56). The fact that an apparent weakness is not of organic origin, however, may be suspected from various observations during the motor examination, some of which are as follows: the muscular contractions are poorly sustained and may "give way" abruptly, rather than gradually, as the patient resists the force exerted by the examiner; there may be absence of "follow-through" when the examiner withdraws his pressure; there may be increase rather than decrease in strength with repeated testing; resistance may be felt in the antagonists when the patient fails to contract the muscles under observation. On occasion "functional" testing may demonstrate the absence of weakness suspected during the routine test; that is, there may be apparent paresis of either dorsiflexion or plantar flexion of the foot when the patient is examined in the seated or recumbent position, but when upright it may be observed that he is able to stand on either the heel or the toe of that foot, and support his entire body in doing so. Weakness of hysterical origin may disappear following the intravenous injection of barbiturates, but mild or latent organic motor deficits may be made more conspicuous by this means.

It is usually possible to evaluate muscle strength and power sufficiently well by observation and palpation, without recourse to special instruments. The subjective impression of the investigator is usually sufficient. Such evaluation, however, is not quantitative; it varies with the experience and ability of the examiner, there is a large subjective element, and there may be disagreement between observers. On occasions, and for special purposes, one may resort to the use of instruments for measuring strength, especially when quantitative determinations are desired. Various dynamometers, myosthenometers, myometers, and ergometers have been described. Energy may be measured by weights, spring balances, dial or mercury gauges, strain gauge transducers, tensiometers, or electrical means, and by using a revolving drum or ink-writing apparatus one can determine the amount of work done per unit of time. These may be useful in assessment of efficiency, fatigue, and response to medication. Quantitative measurements and permanent records are of help in evaluating the progression of a disease process or the recovery of function during regeneration of a nerve lesion. It must be stated, however, that none of these mechanical devices eliminates the subjective element in testing muscle strength, and that none of them is applicable in testing certain groups, such as the rotators of the shoulder and the back and trunk muscles. With all of them the results are difficult to evaluate in the presence of fixed contractions.

Muscle function may be graded in various ways, but the following is an acceptable classification:

0: No muscular contraction.
1: A flicker, or trace, of contraction, without actual movement, or contraction may be palpated in the absence of apparent movement; no motion of joints (10 per cent).

2: The muscle moves the part through a partial arc of movement with gravity eliminated (25 per cent).

3: The muscle completes the whole arc of movement against gravity (50 per cent).

4: The muscle completes the whole arc of movement against gravity together with variable amounts of resistance (75 per cent).

5: The muscle completes the whole arc of movement against gravity and maximum amounts of resistance several times without signs of fatigue; this is normal muscular power (100 per cent).

S: Spasm of muscle.

C: Contraction of muscle.

EXAMINATION OF STRENGTH AND POWER OF SPECIAL MOVEMENTS AND INDIVIDUAL MUSCLES

A detailed outline for the motor examination of the muscles supplied by those cranial nerves which have motor functions, the oculomotor, trochlear, trigeminal, abducens, facial, glossopharyngeal, vagus, accessory, and hypoglossal nerves, has already been presented. An equally detailed examination should be directed toward the motor functions of the rest of the body. The strength and power of the individual muscles and of movements should be carefully observed, and impairment or loss of function noted. Fortunately many good anatomic texts are available which will assist the examiner in becoming familiar with the principal functions and the innervation of the various muscles. Tables or charts which give this information are also available. These, however, are not too satisfactory and tabulation is difficult as many muscles have more than one function, and some have opposite functions when extremities are placed in varying positions. Furthermore, there is a difference of opinion regarding the exact innervation of individual muscles, and occasionally there is anomalous innervation. No table of muscle functions is given as these are discussed in detail in the text. Tables 3 through 6 give the most generally accepted innervation, from the point of view of both the spinal cord segments and the peripheral nerves, of the more important muscles.

A brief outline of the major movements and individual muscles to be tested, and their innervation, follows:

EXAMINATION OF MOVEMENTS AND MUSCLES OF THE NECK

The principal neck movements are those of *flexion, extension* (*retraction*), *rotation,* and *lateral deviation* (*abduction*). These functions and their testing have already been mentioned in "The Spinal Accessory Nerve," Chapter 16. This nerve, along with the second, third, and fourth cervical segments, supplies the *sterno-cleidomastoid* and *trapezius* muscles. The former is a flexor and rotator of the head and neck, whereas the latter retracts the neck and draws it to one side. The *platysma* and the *suprahyoid* and *infrahyoid muscles* also aid in flexion. Other muscles which act on the head and neck are as follows: Muscles which *support* the *head* and *fix* the *neck* and also *flex* the *neck,* tilt it to one side, and *rotate* it are the *scaleni anterior, medius,* and *posterior,* and *longi capitis* and *colli. Rectus capitis anterior* flexes and rotates the neck, and *rectus capitis lateralis* tilts it to one side. Muscles which *fix* or *steady* the neck as well as *extend* it and *tilt* and *rotate* it are *splenii capitis* and *cervicis, semispinales capitis* and *cervicis, intertransversarii, rotatores,* and the upper portion of the *sacrospinalis* (*erector spinae*), including *iliocostalis cervicis* and *longissimi capitis* and *cervicis. Spinalis cervicis* holds the neck steady and head erect and extends the vertebral column, and the *rectus capitis posterior, obliqui capitis,* and *multifidi* extend and rotate the neck. All of these muscles are supplied by branches of the eight cervical nerves (Table 3).

TABLE 3. INNERVATION OF MUSCLES RESPONSIBLE FOR MOVEMENTS OF THE HEAD AND NECK

Muscle	Segmental innervation	Peripheral nerve
Sternocleidomastoid	Cranial XI; C (1) 2–3	Spinal accessory nerve
Trapezius	Cranial XI; C (2) 3–4	Spinal accessory nerve
Scalenus anterior	C 4–7	
Scalenus medius	C 4–8	
Scalenus posterior	C 6–8	
Longus capitis	C 1–4	
Longus colli	C 2–6	
Rectus capitis anterior	C 1–2	Suboccipital nerve
Rectus capitis lateralis	C 1	Suboccipital nerve
Rectus capitis posterior	C 1	Suboccipital nerve
Obliquus capitis inferior	C 1	Suboccipital nerve
Obliquus capitis superior	C 1	Suboccipital nerve
Splenius capitis	C 2–4 (1–6)	
Splenius cervicis	C 2–4 (1–6)	
Semispinalis capitis	C 1–4	
Semispinalis cervicis	C 3–6	
Spinalis cervicis	C 5–8	
Sacrospinalis	C 1–8	
Iliocostalis cervicis	C 1–8	
Longissimus capitis	C 1–8	
Longissimus cervicis	C 1–8	
Intertransverarii	C 1–8	
Rotatores	C 1–8	
Multifidi	C 1–8	

In testing the above movements and muscles the patient shoud be asked to flex his neck so that his chin rests upon his chest, to extend or retract it as far backwards as possible, to rotate it from side to side, and to tilt it lateralward. These are done both without resistance, and against the resistance of the examiner's hand. The examiner may then attempt passive movements while the patient resists them. Finally the muscles may be palpated to determine the degree of contraction. Flexion is tested with the patient recumbent; the examiner stabilizes the thorax by placing one hand over the lower chest, and resists attempted flexion by placing the other hand on the forehead. The contracting muscles can be seen and felt (Fig. 162). Extension is examined with the patient prone, the upper chest stabilized, and resistance against the occiput; the contracting muscles can be seen and felt, and the strength of movement can be judged (Fig. 163). Rotation and lateral movements can be evaluated by modification of these procedures. It is difficult, if not impossible, to test the function of the neck muscles individually, except, of course, for the sternocleidomastoid and trapezius. Furthermore one can appraise only weakness of movements, not of individual muscles. It must be recalled that conditions other than paralytic ones may affect these movements. Flexion of the neck, with limitation of extension, may be seen in Parkinson's disease and cervical spondylitis; retraction in meningitis and meningismus; lateral deviation and rotation in torticollis.

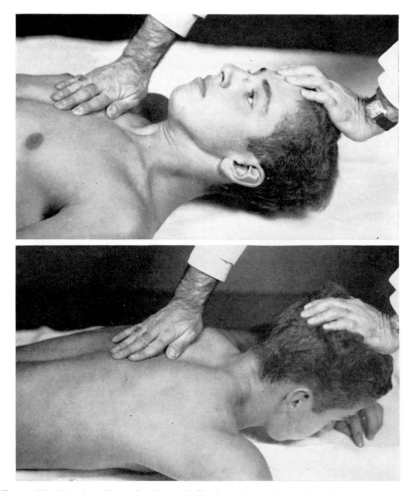

FIG. 162 (*Top*). Examination of flexion of neck; patient is attempting to flex his neck against resistance; sternocleidomastoid, platysma, and other flexor muscles can be seen and palpated.

FIG. 163 (*Bottom*). Examination of extension of neck; patient is attempting to extend his neck against resistance; contraction of trapezius and the other extensor muscles can be seen and felt, and strength of movement can be judged.

EXAMINATION OF MOVEMENTS AND MUSCLES OF THE UPPER EXTREMITIES

The Shoulder Girdle: Movements of the shoulder girdle are those which take place at the sternoclavicular and acromioclavicular joints. These consist of elevation, depression, retraction, protraction, and rotation of the scapula (Table 4).

TABLE 4. INNERVATION OF MUSCLES RESPONSIBLE FOR MOVEMENTS OF THE SHOULDER GIRDLE AND UPPER EXTREMITY

Muscle	*Segmental innervation*	*Peripheral nerve*
Trapezius Cranial XI;	C (2) 3–4	Spinal accessory nerve
Levator anguli scapulae	C 3–4	Nerves to levator anguli scapulae
	C 4–5	Dorsal scapular nerve
Rhomboideus major	C 4–5	Dorsal scapular nerve
Rhomboideus minor	C 4–5	Dorsal scapular nerve
Serratus anterior	C 5–7	Long thoracic nerve
Deltoid	C 5–6	Axillary nerve
Teres minor	C 5–6	Axillary nerve
Supraspinatus	C (4) 5–6	Suprascapular nerve
Infraspinatus	C (4) 5–6	Suprascapular nerve
Latissimus dorsi	C 6–8	Thoracodorsal nerve (long subscapular)
Pectoralis major	C 5– Th 1	Lateral and medial anterior thoracic
Pectoralis minor	C 7– Th 1	Medial anterior thoracic
Subscapularis	C 5–7	Subscapular nerves
Teres major	C 5–7	Lower subscapular nerve
Subclavius	C 5–6	Nerve to subclavius
Coracobrachialis	C 6–7	Musculocutaneous nerve
Biceps brachii	C 5–6	Musculocutaneous nerve
Brachialis	C 5–6	Musculocutaneous nerve
Brachioradialis	C 5–6	Radial nerve
Triceps brachii	C 6–8 (Th 1)	Radial nerve
Anconeus	C 7–8	Radial nerve
Supinator brevis	C 5–7	Radial nerve
Extensor carpi radialis longus	C (5) 6–7 (8)	Radial nerve
Extensor carpi radialis brevis	C (5) 6–7 (8)	Radial nerve
Extensor carpi ulnaris	C 6–8	Radial nerve
Extensor digitorum communis	C 6–8	Radial nerve
Extensor indicis proprius	C 6–8	Radial nerve
Extensor digiti minimi proprius	C 6–8	Radial nerve
Extensor pollicis longus	C 6–8	Radial nerve
Extensor pollicis brevis	C 6–8	Radial nerve

TABLE 4. INNERVATION OF MUSCLES RESPONSIBLE FOR MOVEMENTS OF THE SHOULDER GIRDLE AND UPPER EXTREMITY (continued)

Muscle	Segmental innervation	Peripheral nerve
Abductor pollicis longus	C 6–8	Radial nerve
Pronator teres	C 6–7	Median nerve
Flexor carpi radialis	C 6–7 (8)	Median nerve
Pronator quadratus	C 7– Th 1	Median nerve
Palmaris longus	C 7– Th 1	Median nerve
Flexor digitorum sublimis	C 7– Th 1	Median nerve
Flexor digitorum profundus (radial half)	C 7– Th 1	Median nerve
Lumbricales 1 and 2	C 7– Th 1	Median nerve
Flexor pollicis longus	C 8– Th 1	Median nerve
Flexor pollicis brevis (lateral head)	C 8– Th 1	Median nerve
Abductor pollicis brevis	C 8– Th 1	Median nerve
Opponens pollicis	C 8– Th 1	Median nerve
Flexor carpi ulnaris	C 7– Th 1	Ulnar nerve
Flexor digitorum profundus (ulnar half)	C 7– Th 1	Ulnar nerve
Interossei	C 8– Th 1	Ulnar nerve
Lumbricales 3 and 4	C 8– Th 1	Ulnar nerve
Flexor pollicis brevis (medial head)	C 8– Th 1	Ulnar nerve
Flexor digiti minimi brevis	C 8– Th 1	Ulnar nerve
Abductor digiti minimi	C 8– Th 1	Ulnar nerve
Opponens digiti minimi	C 8– Th 1	Ulnar nerve
Palmaris brevis	C 8– Th 1	Ulnar nerve
Adductor pollicis	C 8– Th 1	Ulnar nerve

Elevation of the scapula (scapula raised and glenoid cavity tilted upward) is carried out by the trapezius and levator scapulae muscles, assisted by the sterno-cleidomastoid and the lower portion of the serratus anterior. The *trapezius,* which is the most important elevator of the scapula and shoulder girdle, is also discussed elsewhere (see p. 327). It is innervated by the *eleventh cranial nerve* together with the *third* and *fourth* cervical segments. The upper fibers elevate, retract, and rotate the scapula and brace the shoulder, especially if the head is fixed (Fig. 121); the middle fibers rotate and retract the scapula, and the lower fibers depress it and draw it toward the midline (Fig. 164). The trapezius aids in forced respiration, and along with serratus anterior elevates the abducted arm above the horizontal. The functions of the upper fibers are tested by having the patient elevate or shrug his shoulder against resistance (Fig. 121), and the middle fibers by having him brace and retract the scapula against resistance (Fig. 164). Muscle power can be com-

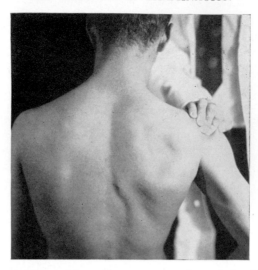

FIG. 164. Examination of trapezius; on retraction of shoulder against resistance, middle fibers of muscle can be seen and palpated.

pared with that on the normal side, and muscular contractions can be seen and
palpated. In unilateral paralysis of the trapezius the shoulder cannot be elevated and
retracted and the arm cannot be abducted above the horizontal. The upper portion
of the scapula falls laterally, the inferior angle is drawn medially, and the vertebral
border is flared (Fig. 122); this abnormal position is accentuated on attempted
abduction of the arm, but is decreased on forward elevation. The sagging of the
shoulder causes a dropping of the entire arm, and the finger tips on that side are at
a lower level than those on the normal side; this can be demonstrated by having the
patient place his palms together, slightly downward, in front of his body. The
levator scapulae (levator anguli scapulae) draws the scapula upward and rotates it so
that the inferior angle approaches the spinal column. It is also tested by observing
elevation of the scapula, but is situated more deeply than the trapezius, and its contraction cannot be seen and only occasionally palpated; it is rarely possible to detect
weakness of the levator scapulae unless the trapezius is also involved.

Depression of the scapula is carried out by the lower fibers of the trapezius and
by the pectoralis minor and subclavius muscles, assisted by the lower part of the pectoralis major and by the latissimus dorsi. The *pectoralis minor* pulls the scapula
downward and rotates it, and also aids in forced respiration. The *subclavius* depresses
the clavicle and the point of the shoulder, carrying them downward and forward.
These muscles are both concealed by the pectoralis major and consequently cannot
be adequately tested individually. Furthermore, it is difficult to distinguish depression of the scapula from similar or associated movements of the upper arm. The
pectoralis major and latissimus dorsi will be discussed below.

Retraction (adduction) of the scapula (scapula and glenoid cavity tilted backward) is carried out by the *rhomboidei major* and *minor* and the middle part of the
trapezius, assisted by the latissimus dorsi. The rhomboidei draw the scapula
upward and medialward toward the spine and rotate it so as to depress the

tip of the shoulder. These muscles, too, are situated deep to the trapezius, and their contraction is seen with difficulty. It is rarely possible to detect weakness or paralysis in them unless the trapezius is also involved. Occasionally, however, if the examiner attempts to push the elbow forward while the patient, his hand on his hip, retracts the shoulder, the contraction of the rhomboidei can be felt and seen (Fig. 165).

Protraction (abduction) of the scapula (scapula and glenoid cavity tilted forward) is carried out by serratus anterior together with pectoralis minor and the upper part of the pectoralis major. The *serratus anterior* (magnus) is supplied by the fifth through the seventh cervical segments through the *long thoracic nerve*. It keeps the vertebral border of the scapula applied to the thorax and draws the scapula forward and laterally. It rotates the scapula and raises the point of the shoulder, and fixes the scapula while other muscles abduct or flex the arm. Along with the trapezius it abducts the arm above the horizontal and aids in forced respiration. It is tested by forward elevation of the arms and pressure with the palms against some resistance, such as a wall (Fig. 166). Normally the medial border of the scapula remains close to the thoracic wall, but with weakness or paralysis of the serratus anterior the inferior angle is shifted medially and the entire vertebral border protrudes posteriorly, away from the thoracic wall, causing the deformity known as "winging" (Fig. 167); this is accentuated by the above-described testing. Abduction of the arm may cause comparatively little winging, however, which aids in differentiating a serratus palsy from the flaring of the scapula that occurs with weakness of the trapezius.

Rotation of the scapula is carried out by the trapezius, serratus anterior, pectorales, rhomboidei, and latissimus dorsi. It cannot be tested without examining

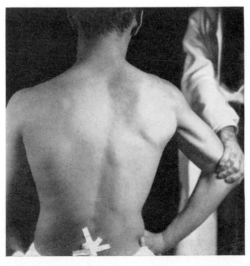

Fig. 165.   Examination of rhomboidei; with hand on hip, patient is retracting shoulder against examiner's attempt to push elbow forward; contracting muscles can be seen and palpated.

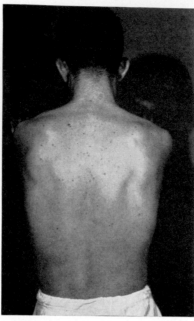

FIG 166. Examination of serratus anterior; patient is pushing against a wall while his arms are extended horizontally in front of him; normally medial border of scapula remains close to thoracic wall.

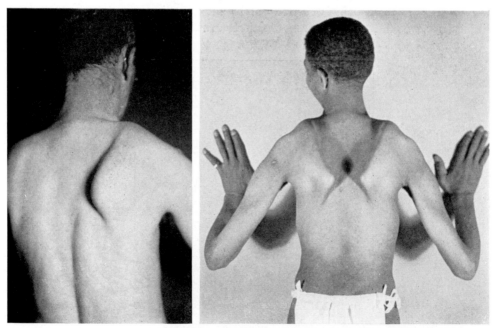

FIG. 167. "Winging" of scapula: *Left,* unilateral "winging" secondary to paralysis of right serratus anterior; *Right,* bilateral "winging" in patient with muscular dystrophy.

the other functions of these various muscles, and along with depression cannot be distinguished from similar movements at the shoulder joint. In dystrophies there often is weakness of all of the shoulder girdle muscles, and if the examiner attempts to lift the patient by grasping his elbows or upper arms or supporting him in the axillae, the shoulders are pushed upward, along the sides of the head, while the trunk remains fixed; the patient is lifted "through the shoulder blades." Bilateral winging of the scapulae is also seen in the dystrophies.

The Shoulder Joint: The principal movements at the shoulder joint are abduction and elevation, adduction, external and internal rotation, and flexion and extension of the upper arm.

The deltoid and supraspinatus muscles, aided by the subscapularis and the upper part of the infraspinatus, are the *abductors* of the shoulder. The *deltoid* is the most prominent muscle in the region of the shoulder. It is supplied by the fifth and sixth cervical segments through the *axillary nerve,* a branch of the posterior cord of the brachial plexus. When this muscle contracts as a whole the arm is abducted (raised laterally) to the horizontal plane. Further abduction, or elevation above the horizontal plane, is carried out by the associated action of the trapezius and the serratus anterior which rotate the scapula and tilt the angle of that bone upward. The posterior fibers of the deltoid also assist in extension and external rotation of the arm, and the anterior fibers in flexion and internal rotation. The anterior and posterior portions, acting together, aid in adduction of the arm. The major function of the deltoid is tested either by noting the ability of the patient to abduct the arm through a range of from fifteen to ninety degrees against resistance (Fig. 168), or by having him abduct the arm to the horizontal level, either laterally or in the forward position

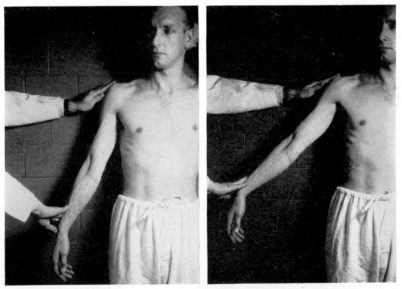

Fig. 168. Examination of deltoid; patient is attempting to abduct arm against resistance; contracting deltoid can be seen and palpated.

(the elbows may be either flexed or extended), and resist the examiner's attempt to counteract the abduction. With this latter maneuver it is possible for the examiner to test both sides simultaneously and compare their strength; this may aid in the evaluation of moderate weakness. During contraction of the deltoid the body of the muscle may be seen to stand out and can be palpated. If there is minimal weakness, the patient may be able to abduct the arm voluntarily, but not against resistance; he may move the trunk and raise the tip of the shoulder to aid in the attempt. If the weakness is more profound, active elevation to the horizontal plane may be impossible, but the passively abducted arm can be held up against the force of gravity. In complete paresis no contraction of the muscle is possible. Weakness of the deltoid is easily observed and, if it is caused by a lesion of the anterior horn cells or their neuraxes, atrophy appears quite promptly. The *supraspinatus* muscle aids the deltoid in abducting the arm, especially during the initial stages. It also has a weak action in external rotation and extension. Contraction of its muscle belly can be palpated and sometimes seen when the arm is abducted less than fifteen degrees against resistance.

The *adductors* of the shoulder are the pectoralis major and latissimus dorsi, aided by the biceps, triceps, coracobrachialis, the anterior and posterior portions of the deltoid, and the external and internal rotators. The *pectoralis major* is innervated by fibers from the fifth cervical through the first thoracic segments through the *lateral and medial anterior thoracic nerves*. It is the principal adductor of the arm, and is also a flexor and internal rotator. When the arm is fixed the muscle draws the chest upward, as in climbing; it also assists in raising the ribs in forced respiration. On attempts to adduct the horizontally abducted arm against resistance the contraction of the sternocostal and clavicular portions of the muscle can be seen and felt (Fig. 169). The muscle can also be palpated on flexion of the horizontally abducted arm and when the hands are pressed together while the arms are in a horizontal position in front of the patient. Because of the force of gravity, the arm may hang in adduction even though the pectoralis is weak.

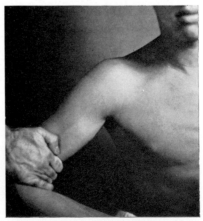

FIG. 169.   Examination of pectoralis major; patient is attempting to adduct arm against resistance; contraction of muscle can be seen and palpated.

The *latissimus dorsi* is supplied by the sixth, seventh, and eighth cervical segments through the *thoracodorsal* (*long subscapular*) *nerve*. It adducts and extends the arm and is also a medial rotator. When the humerus is fixed, the latissimus draws the pelvis and the lower part of the trunk forward and upward. When the arm is hanging by the side, it depresses, retracts, and rotates the scapula. It also aids in forced respiration. The muscle may be tested in various ways. If the patient attempts to adduct the horizontally and laterally extended arm against resistance (i.e., press the arm downward against resistance while extended horizontally), the muscle can be seen and palpated (Fig. 170). The muscle belly can also be palpated on coughing and when the patient pushes his arm downward and backward in a wood-chopping maneuver (Fig. 171).

External rotation of the arm is carried out principally by the infraspinatus and teres minor muscles, with the associated action of the posterior fibers of the deltoid. The *infraspinatus* is the chief external rotator; the upper part is also an abductor, the lower part an adductor. *Teres minor* acts with the infarspinatus to rotate the arm laterally and is also an adductor. In testing these muscles the patient attempts to move his forearm laterally and backward against resistance, and thus produce external rotation at the shoulder, while the elbow is flexed at an angle of ninety degrees and kept to the side (Fig. 172). The contraction of the infraspinatus can usually be felt.

Internal rotation at the shoulder is carried out by the subscapularis and teres major muscles, together with the action of the anterior fibers of the deltoid, and the

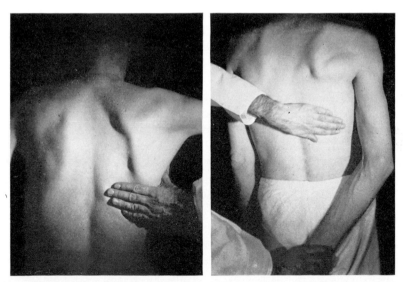

FIG. 170 (*Left*).   Examination of latissimus dorsi; on adduction of horizontally and laterally abducted arm against resistance, muscle can be seen and palpated.

FIG. 171 (*Right*).   Examination of latissimus dorsi; contraction of muscle can be seen and palpated as patient draws arm downward and backward in a wood-chopping maneuver; it can also be palpated on coughing.

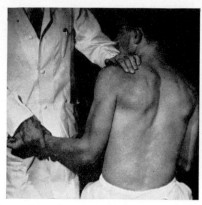

F<small>IG</small>. 172.   External rotation of arm; on external rotation of upper arm, while
forearm is flexed at elbow, contracting infraspinatus muscle can be seen and
palpated.

latissimus dorsi, pectoralis major, and biceps muscles. *Teres major* acts as an internal rotator and extensor and aids the latissimus dorsi in adducting the arm. The *subscapularis* is the chief internal rotator of the arm; it is also an extensor when the arm is at the side and a flexor when the arm is in abduction, and it assists in adduction and abduction. Internal rotation is tested by having the patient carry his arm medially and forward against resistance while the elbow is flexed and at the side.

Flexion of the arm (forward elevation) is carried out by the anterior fibers of the deltoid, and the pectoralis major, subscapularis, coracobrachialis and biceps muscles. The *corachobrachialis* flexes the arm at the shoulder and also aids in adduction. The above muscles, especially the deltoid and pectoralis, may be palpated when an attempt is made to flex the adducted or abducted arm against resistance. *Extension* of the arm (backward elevation) is carried out by the posterior fibers of the deltoid, together with the latissimus dorsi, triceps, subscapularis, and teres major muscles. This action can be tested by having the patient attempt extension of the adducted or abducted arm against resistance. The specific functions of the individual muscles concerned, however, are better examined by the above tests.

The Elbow: The principal movements at the elbow consists of flexion and extension of the forearm at the elbow joint and pronation and supination at the radioulnar joint.

Flexion at the elbow is carried out by the biceps brachii and brachialis muscles, together with the brachioradialis, extensor carpi radialis longus, flexor carpi radialis, palmaris longus, and pronator teres. The *biceps brachii* is supplied by the fifth and sixth cervical segments through the *musculocutaneous nerve,* a branch of the lateral cord of the brachial plexus. It is a flexor of the elbow and also a supinator of the forearm, especially when the latter is flexed and pronated. It also aids in flexion, medial rotation, and adduction of the upper arm. The *brachialis* is supplied by the same nerve and segments; its only function is flexion of the forearm. The *brachioradialis* is innervated by fibers from the fifth and sixth cervical segments through the *radial nerve*. It flexes the forearm when the latter is in semipronation, and also acts as a supinator when the arm is extended and pronated. When the forearm is flexed and supinated, it acts as a pronator. The functions of the biceps and brachialis muscles are tested by having the patient attempt to flex the extended and supinated forearm against resistance, or by having the examiner try to extend the forearm while the patient maintains it in flexion. During these maneuvers the contraction of the muscles, especially that of the biceps, can be seen and felt (Fig. 173). The brachioradialis is tested by attempts to flex the forearm while it is midway between pronation and supination (thumb up). When resistance is offered to this movement the belly of the muscle stands out prominently and can be palpated (Fig. 174). Even when the biceps and brachialis are completely paralyzed, the brachioradialis is still capable of flexion at the elbow, providing the forearm is in semipronation.

The *triceps brachii* is the principal *extensor* of the forearm. It is innervated by the sixth, seventh, and eighth cervical segments and possibly the first thoracic segment through the *radial nerve,* a branch of the posterior cord of the brachial plexus. It extends the elbow and holds the forearm in extension, and also extends and adducts the upper arm. The *anconeus* aids the triceps in extension. In testing these muscles the arm is abducted so that the action of gravity on the forearm is eliminated, and the forearm is placed in a position midway between flexion and extension. The subject then attempts either to extend the forearm at the elbow or to retain it in the partially extended position against the examiner's resistance (Fig. 175). During the movement the contraction of the three bellies of the muscle can be palpated. Simultaneous testing of the two sides gives a comparison of their strength and may aid in evaluating moderate weakness. The triceps is less powerful when the elbow is fully flexed, and slight weakness may be more easily detected if its function

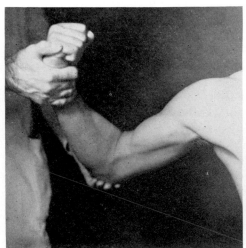

FIG. 173. Examination of biceps brachii and brachialis; on attempts to flex supinated forearm against resistance, contracting biceps muscle can be seen and palpated.

FIG. 174 (*Left*).   Examination of brachioradialis; on attempts to flex semi-pronated arm (thumb up) against resistance, muscle belly can be seen and palpated.

FIG. 175 (*Right*).   Examination of triceps; with arm held in such a position that gravity is eliminated, and with forearm in partial flexion, patient attempts to extend forearm at elbow against resistance; contraction of triceps can be seen and palpated.

is tested in this position. If the triceps is paralyzed, the forearm can assume the position of extension only through the influence of gravity.

Supination is carried out by the biceps, brachioradialis (supinator longus), supinator brevis, extensor carpi radialis longus, and extensor and abductor pollicis longus muscles. The biceps is the strongest supinator of the forearm, but its action in this respect is most marked when the forearm is flexed and pronated. The brachioradialis acts as a supinator only when the arm is extended and pronated; when the forearm is flexed and supinated it acts as a pronator. The extensor carpi radialis longus functions in a similar manner. The *supinator brevis* is less powerful as a supinator than the biceps, but it acts through all degrees of flexion and supination. Supination is tested by attempts on the part of the patient to carry out this movement against the examiner's resistance, or to hold the forearm in supination while the examiner attempts to carry out pronation. The examiner may grasp either the wrist or the back of the hand, or the subject may be asked to grip the examiner's hand. If the above maneuvers are done while the forearm is in extension, the brachioradialis may be palpated (Fig. 176), if while in flexion, the biceps may be palpated. The supinator brevis, which is one of the deep muscles of the forearm, cannot be adequately palpated.

Pronation is brought about by action of the *pronator teres,* also a weak flexor of the forearm, and *pronator quadratus*; additional muscles are the brachioradialis, palmaris longus, extensor carpi radialis longus, and flexor carpi radialis. In testing pronation the arm is externally rotated at the shoulder and the elbow is near the trunk. The patient then attempts to carry out pronation against resistance or to hold the forearm in pronation while the examiner attempts to carry out supination (Fig.

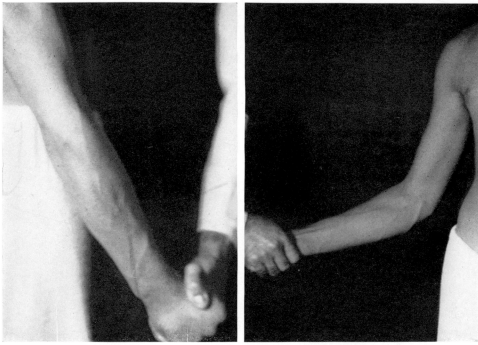

FIG. 176. Supination of forearm; on supination against resistance while forearm is in extension, brachioradialis can be palpated; if forearm is supinated while in flexion, biceps can be palpated.

177), with maneuvers similar to but in the opposite direction to those described for supination. The effect of gravity should be eliminated.

The Wrist: The principal movements at the wrist are flexion and extension of the hand, together with adduction (ulnar flexion) and abduction (radial flexion).

Flexion, or *palmar flexion,* of the hand at the wrist is carried out principally by the *flexor carpi radialis and flexor carpi ulnaris* muscles. The former, supplied by the *median nerve,* also assists in pronation and in flexion of the forearm and is a weak abductor of the wrist. The latter, supplied by the *ulnar nerve,* is also an adductor of the wrist and hand. The *palmaris longus* is also a flexor of the wrist and, in addition, is a weak flexor and pronator of the forearm. Additional muscles which aid in flexion of the hand at the wrist are flexor digitorum profundus, flexor digitorum sublimis, flexor pollicis longus, and abductor pollicis longus (see below). Flexion at the wrist may be tested by attempts to bend the hand toward the forearm against resistance (Fig. 178). The motion of both the flexor carpi radialis and flexor carpi ulnaris muscles can be seen and felt, and the contraction of the tendons of both of these muscles together with that of palmaris longus may be seen. The flexor carpi radialis can be tested individually by having the patient flex his wrist toward the radial side against resistance directed toward the thumb. Function of the flexor carpi ulnaris can be tested by having him flex the wrist toward the ulnar side while the examiner presses on the small fingers. Paralysis of the flexors of the wrist does not give rise to

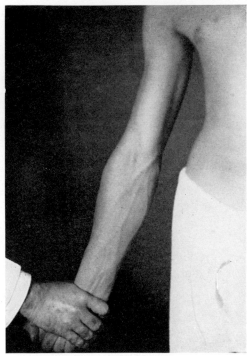

FIG. 177.   Pronation of forearm; on pronation against resistance, pronator teres can be palpated.

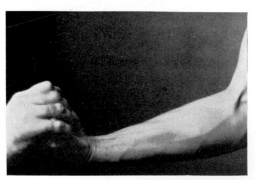

FIG. 178.   Flexion of hand at wrist; on flexing hand against resistance, tendon of flexor carpi radialis can be seen and palpated on radial side of wrist, and that of flexor carpi ulnaris on ulnar side; tendon of palmaris longus may also be seen and palpated.

any marked deformity, since the force of gravity enables the hand to assume a flexed position.

Extension (dorsal flexion) at the wrist is carried out by *extensor carpi radialis longus, extensor carpi radialis brevis, extensor carpi ulnaris,* and *extensor digitorum communis,* possibly assisted by the other extensors of the thumb and fingers. These muscles are all supplied by the sixth, seventh, and eighth cervical segments through the *radial nerve.* The extensors carpi radialis longus and brevis also abduct the hand and steady the wrist when the flexors act on the fingers, and the extensor longus is a weak flexor of the forearm and aids in pronation and supination. The extensor carpi ulnaris is also an adductor. In testing these muscles the forearm is placed in pronation (it may be resting on the arm of a chair) and the wrist is partially extended. The subject then either attempts to extend the wrist further against the examiner's resistance, or to hold it in partial extension while the examiner attempts to flex it (Fig. 179). The participating muscles and their tendons can be palpated. If the wrist is extended to the ulnar side, the extensor carpi ulnaris can be felt; if toward the radial side, the extensor carpi radialis longus; and if in the midposition, the extensor digitorum communis. Moderate weakness of the extensors results in involuntary flexion at the wrist when the patient attempts to grip his fingers; marked weakness causes a wrist drop, the outstanding symptom of a radial nerve palsy (Fig 180). Paresis of the extensors of the wrist may also be an early sign of hemiparesis.

Adduction, or ulnar deviation or flexion, at the wrist is carried out principally by the flexor carpi ulnaris and extensor carpi ulnaris muscles, assisted by flexor pollicis longus; *abduction,* or radial deviation or flexion, is carried out by the flexor carpi radialis, extensors carpi radialis longus and brevis, abductor pollicis longus, and extensors pollicis longus and brevis. These movements, too, may be tested by carrying them out against resistance.

The Hands and Fingers: Detailed muscle testing is necessary in the examination of the muscles of the hands and fingers. Innervation is complex, numerous substitution movements are possible, and misinterpretations may be made. The various muscles which supply the hands and fingers must be examined individually for flexion, extension, adduction, abduction, and opposition.

Flexion of the Fingers: The primary action of the *flexor digitorum profundus* is the flexion of the distal phalanges of the second, third, fourth, and fifth fingers. On continuing its action, however, it also flexes the remaining phalanges of these digits, and finally the hand. The radial half of this muscle is supplied by the *median nerve,* the ulnar half by the *ulnar nerve,* the fibers coming from the seventh and

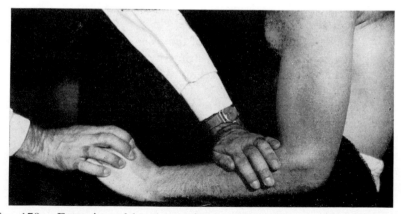

Fig. 179.   Extension of hand at wrist; on attempts to extend wrist against resistance, bellies of extensors carpi radialis longus, carpi ulnaris, and digitorum communis can be seen and palpated.

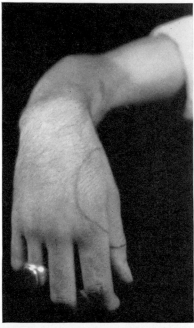

FIG. 180.   Wrist drop secondary to radial nerve palsy.

eighth cervical and first thoracic segments of the spinal cord. *Flexor digitorum sublimis,* also supplied by the *median nerve,* primarily flexes the middle phalanges of the four fingers, but a continuation of its action will result in a flexion of the proximal phalanges of these digits, and finally of the hand at the wrist. The proximal phalanges of the four fingers are flexed by the *interossei* and the *lumbricales.* The former muscles, innervated by the *ulnar nerve,* also adduct (volar interossei) and abduct (dorsal interossei) the fingers. The interossei and lumbricales together extend the middle and distal phalanges. The two lumbricales on the ulnar side of the hand are innervated by the *ulnar nerve,* and the two on the radial side of the hand by the *median nerve.* The *flexor digiti minimi brevis* flexes and slightly abducts the proximal phalanx of the little finger; two other muscles which act on the little finger are the *abductor digiti minimi* which abducts the little finger, flexes its proximal phalanx, and extends the distal phalanges, and the *opponens digiti minimi* which flexes, adducts, and slightly rotates the fifth metacarpal. These three muscles are supplied by the eighth cervical and first thoracic segments through the *ulnar nerve,* as is *palmaris brevis* which wrinkles the skin on the ulnar border of the hand and deepens the hollow of the hand.

In testing the flexor digitorum profundus the patient resists attempts to extend the distal phalanges of the individual fingers while the middle phalanges are fixed (Fig. 181). Flexor digitorum sublimis is tested by having the patient resist attempts to straighten the fingers at the first interphalangeal joints while the proximal phalanges are fixed (Fig. 182). For this test to be valid the distal phalanges should be completely flaccid, and it is not always possible to eliminate the possibility that flexion at the proximal interphalangeal joint may be produced by the flexor profundus. The function of the interossei and lumbricales in flexion at the metacarpophalangeal joint is tested with the interphalangeal joints in either flexion or extension. In paralysis of these latter muscles there is extension at the metacarpophalangeal joints and flexion of the distal phalanges, together with loss of adduction of the fingers. Flexion of the fingers at all joints is necessary to make a fist. The thumb may be in either flexion or extension (see below). The strength of the fist depends not only upon the degree of flexion at the metacarpophalangeal and interphalangeal joints, but also upon the position of the thumb and its ability to flex and to brace the fingers, and upon the synergistic action of the extensor carpi ulnaris and the radial extensors in fixation of the wrist. A firm fist can be made only with the wrist in extension. Grip, or hand grasp, should always be tested and its strength noted. For quantitative testing a *dynamometer* may be used. If successive readings are recorded, fatigability can be gauged; this is of particular importance in myasthenia gravis. On the other hand, with nonorganic weakness the strength may appear to increase with repeated testing.

Extension of the Fingers: Extensor digitorum communis extends the proximal phalanges of the second, third, fourth, and fifth fingers, and continuing its action, partially extends the interphalangeal joints and the hand. *Extensor indicis proprius* extends the proximal phalanx of the index finger and adducts this digit. *Extensor*

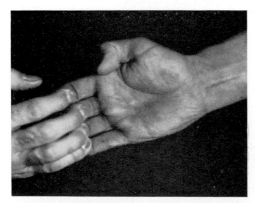 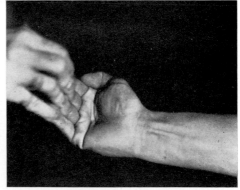

Fig. 181 (*Left*).   Examination of flexor digitorum profundus; patient resists attempts to extend distal phalanges while middle phalanges are fixed.
Fig. 182 (*Right*).   Examination of flexor digitorum sublimis; patient resists attempts to straighten fingers at first interphalangeal joints while proximal phalanges are fixed.

digiti minimi proprius extends the little finger. These three muscles are supplied by the sixth, seventh, and eight cervical segments through the *radial nerve*. The interossei and lumbricales extend the middle and distal phalanges. To test the action of the extensor digitorum communis on the fingers, the patient is asked to resist attempts to flex the fingers at the metacarpophalangeal joints while the forearm is in pronation and the wrist stabilized; the muscle belly and its tendons can be seen and palpated (Fig. 183). The function of the lumbricales and interossei is tested by having the patient attempt to extend the middle and distal phalanges against resistance while the metacarpophalangeal joints are hyperextended and fixed and the proximal interphalangeal joints are partly flexed (Fig. 184).

The Thumb and Its Muscles: The *abductor pollicis longus* abducts the thumb and extends it to a slight degree. Continuing its action it flexes and abducts the hand and aids in supination. *Extensor pollicis longus* extends the terminal phalanx of the thumb, and, continuing its action, extends the proximal phalanx and slightly adducts the thumb. It is also an abductor of the hand and an accessory muscle in supination. *Extensor pollicis brevis* extends the proximal phalanx of the thumb and abducts the thumb. It is also an abductor of the wrist. These three muscles are supplied by the sixth, seventh, and eighth cervical segments through the *radial nerve*. The abductor pollicis longus is the only flexor of the wrist that is supplied by the radial nerve. The *flexor pollicis longus* flexes the distal phalanx of the thumb, and by continuing its action also flexes the proximal phalanx and adducts the thumb;

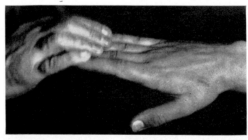

FIG. 183. Examination of extensor digitorum communis; patient resists attempts to flex fingers at metacarpophalangeal joints; muscle belly can be seen and palpated.

FIG. 184. Extension of the middle and distal phalanges; patient attempts to extend fingers against resistance while metacarpophalangeal joints are hyperextended and fixed.

it assists in flexion and adduction of the hand. The *flexor pollicis brevis* flexes and adducts the proximal phalanx of the thumb and extends the distal phalanx. The *abductor pollicis brevis* abducts the thumb, flexes the proximal phalanx, and extends the terminal phalanx. The *opponens pollicis* flexes and adducts the thumb, opposing it to the other fingers. The above four muscles are supplied by the *median nerve,* although the medial head of the flexor pollicis brevis is innervated by the *ulnar.* The segmental supply is probably mainly if not entirely from the eighth cervical and first thoracic levels. The *adductor pollicis* adducts the thumb and flexes the first metacarpal bone and the proximal phalanx; it is supplied by the eighth cervical and first thoracic segments through the *ulnar nerve.*

In testing the extensor pollicis longus the patient attempts to extend the thumb at the interphalangeal joint, or attempts to resist passive flexion of the thumb at that joint while the proximal phalanx is immobilized. This can be done with the hand palm down on the table, or with the ulnar edge down at right angles to the table. The tendon can be seen and felt (Fig. 185). The extensor pollicis brevis is tested by having the patient attempt extension or resist flexion of the thumb at the metacarpophalangeal joint while the metacarpal bone is immobilized. Again the tendon can be observed and palpated (Fig. 186). On hyperextension of the thumb, especially at both joints, the tendons of the extensors longus and brevis and that of abductor pollicis longus come into full prominence, forming the boundaries of the *anatomic snuff box.* In full extension the abductors of the thumb take part. In examining the flexor pollicis longus the patient is asked to resist an attempt to extend the flexed distal phalanx of the thumb while the proximal phalanx is flexed and immobilized and the thumb is in the position of palmar adduction (Fig. 187). In testing the flexor pollicis brevis the patient is asked to flex the proximal phalanx of the thumb and simultaneously extend the distal phalanx.

Abduction, Adduction, and Opposition of the Thumb and Fingers: Abduction of the thumb is carried out in two planes: by moving the thumb in the same plane

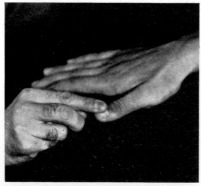 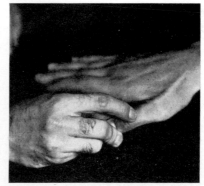

FIG. 185 (*Left*). Examination of extensor pollicis longus; patient attempts to resist passive flexion of thumb at interphalangeal joint; tendon can be seen and palpated.
FIG. 186 (*Right*). Examination of extensor pollicis brevis; patient attempts to resist passive flexion of thumb at metacarpophalangeal joint; tendon can be seen and palpated.

as that of the palm (radial abduction), and by moving it at right angles to the plane of the palm (palmar abduction). In testing radial abduction the hand may be lying in either pronation or supination on a table or it may be placed, ulnar border down, at right angles to a table. The thumb is then moved lateralward if the hand is horizontal, or upward if the hand is vertical, against resistance. This movement is carried out by the abductor pollicis longus and the extensor pollicis brevis. The tendon of the former muscle can be seen and felt (Fig. 188). In testing palmar abduction the thumb is moved at right angles to the palm and inside the radial margin of the hand, against resistance (Fig. 189). One may carry this out by plac-ing the hand on a table, dorsum down, with a pencil or some other object between the thumb and the palm, the pencil being at a plane at right angles to the hand. The patient then attempts to raise the thumb, against resistance, to a point ver-tically above its original position, keeping it parallel to the pencil and keeping the thumb nail at right angles to the palm. This latter movement is carried out by the abductor pollicis brevis, along with abductor pollicis longus, flexor pollicis brevis. and opponens pollicis. In paralysis of abduction the thumb is adducted and falls into the palm of the hand.

Adduction of the thumb is also carried out in two planes: in the plane of the palm (ulnar adduction), and in a plane at right angles to that of the palm (palmar adduction). Ulnar adduction is carried out by having the patient approximate the thumb to the palm in the same plane as the palm, the thumb nail being as nearly as possible parallel with the nails of the other fingers (Fig. 190). In palmar adduc-tion the thumb is approximated to the palmar aspect of the index finger at right angles to the palm. The thumb nail is at right angles to the nails of the other

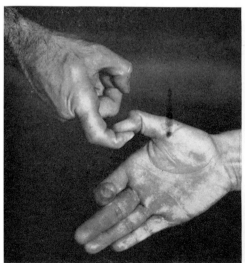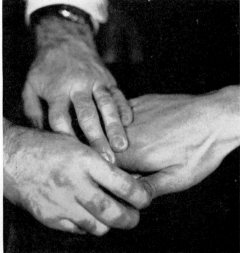

FIG. 187 (*Left*). Examination of flexor pollicis longus; patient resists attempts to extend flexed distal phalanx of thumb while proximal phalanx is fixed.
FIG. 188 (*Right*). Radial abduction of thumb; patient is attempting to abduct thumb in same plane as that of palm; tendon of abductor pollicis longus can be seen and palpated.

fingers (Fig. 191). In either or both of these tests a piece of paper may be grasped—in the former between the thumb and radial border of the index finger, and in the latter between the thumb and palmar aspect of the index finger, and the patient may try to retain this against the examiner's attempts to withdraw it. The adductor pollicis is the major muscle in both of these acts, especially the former; participating muscles are the first volar interosseous, flexors pollicis longus and brevis, and extensor pollicis longus. In weakness of the adductor the patient attempts to retain the paper between his thumb and index finger by flexion of the thumb at the interphalangeal joint (*signe de journal* of Froment); this may be a significant finding in an ulnar nerve palsy.

Opposition of the thumb is tested by having the patient attempt, against re-

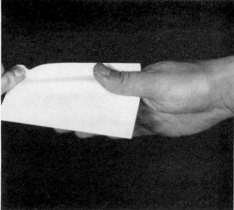

FIG. 189 (*Left*).   Palmar abduction of thumb; patient is attempting to bring thumb to a point vertically above its original position.
FIG. 190 (*Right*).   Ulnar adduction of thumb; patient is attempting to grasp a piece of paper between thumb and radial border of index finger while thumb nail is parallel to nails of other fingers.

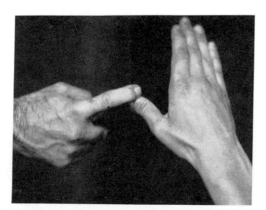

FIG. 191.   Palmar adduction of thumb; patient is approximating thumb to palmar aspect of index finger; thumb nail is kept at right angles to nails of other fingers.

sistance, to touch the tip of the little finger with the thumb (Fig. 192). The thumb nail should remain on a plane parallel to the palm and the palmar surface of the thumb should come in contact with the palmar surface of the little finger. In weakness of the opponens pollicis the patient may be able to oppose the thumb to the index finger or middle finger, but not to the little finger. In testing *opposition of the little finger* (opponens digiti minimi) the patient is asked to move the extended little finger in front of the other fingers and toward the thumb (Fig. 193). This movement is dependent not only on the ability of the little finger to move toward the radial side of the hand, but also on the palmar elevation of the head of the fifth metacarpal. When opposition is full there is cupping of the palm and rounding of the dorsal metacarpal arch. Opposition of the thumb and little finger may be tested in one ma-

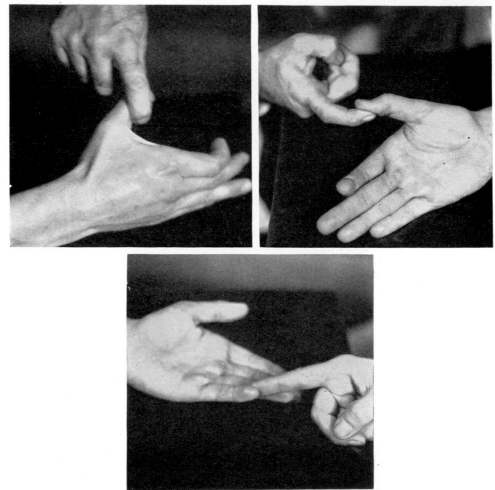

Fig. 192 (*Top*). Examination of opponens pollicis; patient is attempting against resistance, to touch tip of little finger with thumb.
Fig. 193 (*Bottom*). Examination of opponens digiti minimi; patient is attempting to move extended little finger in front of other fingers and toward thumb.

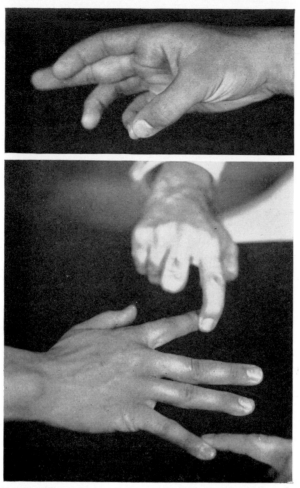

FIG. 194 (*Top*). Opposition of thumb and little finger.
FIG. 195 (*Bottom*). Adduction of fingers; patient is attempting to adduct fingers against resistance.

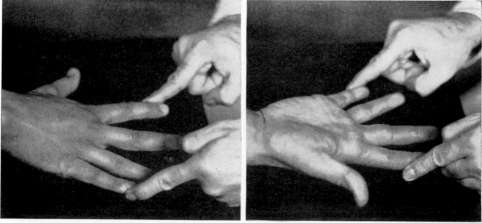

FIG. 196. Abduction of fingers; patient resists examiner's attempts to bring fingers together.

neuver. When both are opposed their extended tips meet and form an arch over the palm (Fig. 194). The strength of the combined movement may be gauged by the patient's ability to retain his grasp on a paper which is held between them while the examiner attempts to pull it away. The flexors of the thumb and little finger and the short abductor of the thumb probably enter into these movements.

Adduction of the fingers (volar interossei) is a movement which consists of bring-ing the fingers tightly together. This may be tested in various ways. While the fingers are abducted and the palm is flat on a table, the patient may try against resistance to adduct the fingers (Fig. 195). The degree of functional integrity of the adductors may be tested by having the patient attempt to retain a piece of paper between adjacent fingers while the examiner attempts to withdraw it. The examiner may interpose his fingers with those of the patient and observe the strength of adduction. In testing *abduction of the fingers* they are fully extended and spread apart and the patient either endeavors to resist the examiner's attempt to bring them together or he attempts to abduct them against resistance (Fig. 196). This is largely a function of the dorsal interossei, and the contraction of these muscles can sometimes be felt. Abduction of the little finger is a function of the abductor digiti minimi.

EXAMINATION OF MOVEMENTS AND MUSCLES OF THE THORAX, ABDOMEN, AND TRUNK

The examination of the thoracic, abdominal, and trunk muscles cannot be carried out with the detail that is used in the examination of the muscles of the upper ex-tremity. These muscles are larger and their action is often combined. As a result it may be difficult to evaluate them individually. They should, however, be examined with as much detail as possible (Table 5).

TABLE 5. INNERVATION OF MUSCLES RESPONSIBLE FOR MOVEMENTS OF THE THORAX AND ABDOMEN

Muscle	Segmental innervation	Peripheral nerve
Diaphragm	C 3–5	Phrenic nerve
Intercostal muscles (internal and external)	Th 1–12	Intercostal nerves
Levatores costarum	C 8–Th 11	Intercostal nerves
Transversus thoracis	Th 2–7	Intercostal nerves
Serratus posterior superior	Th 1–4	Intercostal nerves
Serratus posterior inferior	Th 9–12	Intercostal nerves
Rectus abdominis	Th 5–12	Intercostal nerves
Pyramidalis	Th 11–12	Intercostal nerves
Transversus abdominis	Th 7–L 1	Intercostal, ilioinguinal, and iliohypogastric nerves
Obliquus internus abdominis	Th 7–L 1	Intercostal, ilioinguinal, and iliohypogastric nerves
Obliquus externus abdominis	Th 7–L 1	Intercostal, ilioinguinal, and iliohypogastric nerves

The Muscles of the Thorax: The thoracic muscles consist of the internal and external intercostals, transversus thoracis, levatores costarum, serratus posterior superior, serratus posterior inferior, and diaphragm. In addition might be included those muscles attached to the sternum, clavicles, and scapulae which act as accessory muscles of respiration; the quadratus lumborum which draws the last rib downward; and spinal muscles in the thoracic area.

The *internal* and *external intercostals* draw the ribs upward and outward and thereby enlarge the thoracic cavity. The internal intercostals may also contract the thorax. Both sets are innervated by the anterior divisions of the twelve thoracic nerves (*intercostal nerves*). The *levatores costarum* assist in drawing the ribs upward and bend the spinal column backward and laterally and rotate it. They are innervated by the anterior division of the *eighth cervical nerve* and the first *eleven intercostal nerves*. The *transversus thoracis* is supplied by the second to the sixth or seventh *intercostal nerves;* it draws the anterior portions of the ribs downward in expiration. The *serratus posterior superior* is supplied by the first four *intercostal nerves;* it elevates the ribs to which it is attached and thus aids in inspiration. The *serratus posterior inferior* is innervated by the ninth to the twelfth *intercostal nerves;* it draws the lower four ribs downward and outward. The *diaphragm* is innervated by the third through the fifth cervical segments by means of the *phrenic nerves.* The principal muscle of respiration, it is a dome-shaped musculofibrous septum which separates the thoracic from the abdominal cavity.

During quiet inspiration the first and second pairs of ribs are fixed by the resistance of the cervical structures; the last pair by the quadratus lumborum. The other ribs are elevated, and the anteroposterior and transverse diameters of the thorax are increased. The vertical diameter is increased by the descent of the diaphragm. Expiration is effected by the elastic recoil of the walls of the thorax and by the action of the internal intercostals, latissimus dorsi, transversus thoracis, and the abdominal muscles which push back the viscera previously displaced downward by the diaphragm. In deep inspiration other muscles are brought into action. The first rib is no longer fixed, but is raised with the sternum by the scaleni and sternocleidomastoids, and all the other ribs are raised to a higher level. The shoulders, the clavicles, and the vertebral borders of the scapulae are fixed and the limb muscles and the trapezius, serratus anterior, pectorales, supraspinatus, rhomboidei, latissimus dorsi, levator scapulae, and extensors of the cervical spine are brought into play. There is an increased descent of the diaphragm, the transverse diameter of the upper part of the abdomen is greatly increased, and the subcostal angle is widened. The diaphragm also contracts before and during various expulsive acts such as coughing, sneezing, laughing, vomiting, hiccuping, urination, defecation, and parturition, and it exerts pressure on the abdominal viscera.

Paralysis of the intercostal muscles causes adduction of the costal margins and excessive protrusion of the epigastrium during inspiration. It is difficult to diagnose paralysis of the intercostals, but the presence of respiration which seems to be entirely abdominal with alternate bulging and retraction of the epigastrium may be significant. Furthermore, it may be determined by palpation that the intercostal spaces are retracted during inspiration, and that the ribs are not raised and separated. In bilateral paralysis of the diaphragm the excursion of the costal margins is increased and the epigastrium is retracted during inspiration. The abdomen cannot be protruded. The movable shadow caused by retraction of the lower intercostal region during inspiration (Litten's sign) is absent. The expulsive acts mentioned above are carried out with difficulty. In unilateral paralysis of the diaphragm the signs are not always easy to demonstrate, but it may frequently be seen during quiet inspiration that the excursion of the costal margin on the affected side is slightly increased, and that Litten's sign is absent. Fluoroscopy is an invaluable aid to the diagnosis of either unilateral or bilateral diaphragmatic paralysis. If there is either diaphragmatic or intercostal weakness or paralysis, the accessory muscles which act in deep inspiration are brought into play, and the patient breathes largely by using his scaleni, sternocleidomastoids, serrati, and pectorales.

The Muscles of the Abdomen: The abdominal muscles are the rectus abdominis, pyramidalis, transversus abdominis, and obliqui. The *rectus abdominis* flexes the thorax on the pelvis or the pelvis on the thorax, and thus aids in flexion of the vertebral column; it also compresses the abdominal viscera in such acts as defecation and parturition, and aids in forced expiration. It is innervated by the anterior divisions of the fifth to twelfth thoracic nerves (*intercostal nerves*). The *pyramidalis* tenses the linea alba; it is innervated by the anterior divisions of the eleventh and twelfth thoracic nerves. The *transversus* (*transversalis*) *abdominis* supports and compresses the contents of the abdomen; it may also contract the thorax and aid in expiration. It is innervated by the lower five or six *intercostal nerves* and by filaments from the *iliohypogastric* and *ilioinguinal nerves* (seventh thoracic through first lumbar segments). The *obliquus externus abdominis* supports and compresses the abdominal viscera and assists in expelling their contents; it also depresses the thorax in expiration, flexes the spinal column, and rotates the spinal column toward the opposite side. The *obliquus internus abdominis,* like the external oblique, supports and compresses the abdominal viscera, depresses the thorax, and flexes the spinal column; it rotates the column to the same side. Both of these muscles are supplied by the anterior divisions of the lower four to six thoracic (*intercostal*) nerves together with filaments from the *iliohypogastric* and *ilioinguinal nerves* (seventh thoracic through first lumbar segments); the external oblique may be innervated only by the intercostal nerves.

In raising the trunk from a supine to a sitting position, the thoracic and lumbar segments of the spine are flexed by the action of the spinal muscles (see below), together with the recti abdominis and the internal and external obliques, which draw the sternum closer to the pubis. In the beginning the flexors of the hips merely serve to fix the pelvis. After the shoulders have been raised about eight inches, the latter muscles contract strongly and bring the trunk to an upright position. If the abdominal muscles are weak, the trunk may be partially erected by the powerful hip flexors, but it is not possible to assume a complete sitting position unless the patient supports himself with his hand or his legs are held down by the examiner.

The abdominal muscles may be tensed and tested by having the patient raise his head against resistance (Fig. 197), cough, or attempt to rise to a sitting from a recumbent position with the hands held behind the head or the arms folded over

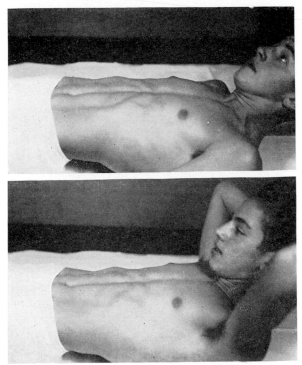

FIG. 197 (*Top*).   Examination of abdominal muscles; patient is attempting to raise his head against resistance.
FIG. 198 (*Bottom*).   Examination of abdominal muscles and flexors of spine; patient is attempting to rise from recumbent position to sitting position without use of his hands.

the chest (Fig. 198). The abdominal muscles will contract and, if the tension of the abdominal musculature is equal on the two sides, the umbilicus will remain in the midline. In weakness of the abdominal musculature these movements are carried out with difficulty, and the patient will raise his legs from the bed on attempting to rise to a sitting position. If the abdominal muscles are paralyzed on one side, the umbilicus is pulled to the normal side during these maneuvers and on inspiration, and the involved side is seen to bulge on coughing and straining. Paralysis of the upper half of the abdominal muscles is associated with downward movement of the umbilicus when the abdominal wall is tensed, and paralysis of the lower half with upward movement; this is *Beevor's sign*. In bilateral paralysis of the abdomen the umbilicus will be seen to bulge on coughing, raising the head, and attempting to sit up; expiration is affected, forced movements are no longer possible, and urination and defecation become difficult. Palpation is a valuable aid in the examination of the abdominal muscles, and by its means the contracted can be easily distinguished from the relaxed muscles.

The Muscles of the Pelvis: The muscles of the pelvis, including the urinary bladder and the perineal and external genital muscles, are not accessible for the usual clinical testing. The cremaster muscle, which is sometimes classed as an abdominal muscle, is referred to under the cremasteric reflex. The sphincter ani is mentioned under the anal reflex. The bladder musculature and some of the functions of the genitalia are discussed in The Autonomic Nervous System, Part VI.

The Muscles of the Spine: The functions of the upper portion of the spinal column have been discussed with the muscles and movements of the neck. Many of the muscles mentioned in that section continue downward and carry out similar functions for the remainder of the spinal column, the principal movements of which are *flexion, extension, lateral deviation (abduction)*, and *rotation*. The *sacrospinalis (erector spinae)* and its divisions, the *iliocostales dorsi* and *lumborum* and *longissimus dorsi,* serve, when acting on one side, to bend the spinal column toward that side. When acting on both sides they extend the spinal column. The *intertransversarii* bend the vertebral column laterally, and when acting on both sides make it rigid. The *spinalis dorsi* extends the spinal column. The *semispinalis dorsi* extends the spinal column and rotates it toward the opposite side. The *multifidi* abduct the spinal column and rotate it toward the opposite side; they act bilaterally as extensors. The *rotatores* and *interspinales* rotate and extend the vertebral column. The *quadratus lumborum* produces lateral flexion and extension of the vertebral column. All of these muscles are supplied by the posterior and occasionally by the anterior rami of the corresponding spinal nerves. In addition, the abdominal muscles and the flexors of the neck and thigh participate in flexion of the spine, and the extensors of the neck and thigh and levatores costarum participate in extension. The flexors and extensors and rotators of the shoulder as well as those of the hip and the thoracic and abdominal muscles participate in rotation. The shoulder muscles are important in lateral inclination of the spine, and the lateral abdominal muscles and the latissimus dorsi in lateral trunk raising.

The extensors of the spine are tested by having the patient lie in a prone position and attempt to raise his head and shoulders without the assistance of his hands (Fig. 199); extension is further tested if he attempts to raise the lower extremities,

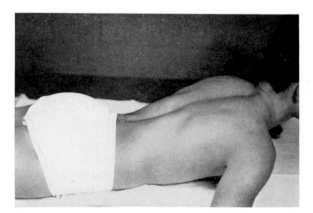

FIG. 199.   Examination of extensors of spine; patient, lying prone, is attempting to raise his head and upper part of trunk.

or if resistance is applied to the upper thorax. In paralysis of the extensors there is a moderate degree of lordosis, which disappears when the patient lies down. In sitting the spinal column has a convex posterior curve, and the patient prevents himself from falling forward by supporting himself with his hands. The flexors are tested by having him rise from a recumbent position to a seated and then a standing position without the use of the hands (Fig. 198). This tests also the flexors of the abdomen and hips. The flexors and extensors of the spine may both be tested by having the patient bend at the waist, touch his fingertips to the floor, and then resume the erect position. The rotators and lateral flexors of the spine should also be examined.

EXAMINATION OF THE MOVEMENTS AND MUSCLES OF THE LOWER EXTREMITIES

The movements of the lower extremities are less complex than are those of the upper extremities, and there are fewer substitution movements. As a result there is less chance for error in the assessment of muscle function. It is extremely important, however, to eliminate the effect of gravity in evaluating movements (Table 6).

TABLE 6. INNERVATION OF MUSCLES RESPONSIBLE FOR MOVEMENTS OF THE LOWER EXTREMITIES

Muscle	Segmental innervation	Peripheral nerve
Psoas major	L (1) 2–4	Nerve to psoas major
Psoas minor	L 1–2	Nerve to psoas minor
Iliacus	L 2–4	Femoral nerve
Quadriceps femoris	L 2–4	Femoral nerve
Sartorius	L 2–4	Femoral nerve
Pectineus	L 2–4	Femoral nerve
Gluteus maximus	L 5–S 2	Inferior gluteal nerve
Gluteus medius	L 4–S 1	Superior gluteal nerve
Gluteus minimus	L 4–S 1	Superior gluteal nerve
Tensor fasciae latae	L 4–S 1	Superior gluteal nerve
Piriformis	S 1–2	Nerve to piriformis
Adductor longus	L 2–4	Obturator nerve
Adductor brevis	L 2–4	Obturator nerve
Adductor magnus	{ L 2–4	Obturator nerve
	L 4–5	Sciatic nerve
Gracilis	L 2–4	Obturator nerve
Obturator externus	L 2–4	Obturator nerve
Obturator internus	L 5–S 3	Nerve to obturator internus
Gemellus superior	L 5–S 3	Nerve to obturator internus
Gemellus inferior	L 4–S 1	Nerve to quadratus femoris
Quadratus femoris	L 4–S 1	Nerve to quadratus femoris

TABLE 6.   INNERVATION OF MUSCLES RESPONSIBLE FOR MOVEMENTS OF THE LOWER EXTREMITIES (continued)

Muscle	Segmental innervation	Peripheral nerve
Biceps femoris (long head)	L 5–S 1	Tibial nerve
Semimembranosus	L 4–S 1	Tibial nerve
Semitendinosus	L 5–S 2	Tibial nerve
Popliteus	L 5–S 1	Tibial nerve
Gastrocnemius	L 5–S 2	Tibial nerve
Soleus	L 5–S 2	Tibial nerve
Plantaris	L 5–S 1	Tibial nerve
Tibialis posterior	L 5–S 1	Tibial nerve
Flexor digitorum longus	L 5–S 1	Tibial nerve
Flexor hallucis longus	L 5–S 1	Tibial nerve
Biceps femoris (short head)	L 5–S 2	Common peroneal nerve
Tibialis anterior	L 4–S 1	Deep peroneal nerve
Peroneus tertius	L 4–S 1	Deep peroneal nerve
Extensor digitorum longus	L 4–S 1	Deep peroneal nerve
Extensor hallucis longus	L 4–S 1	Deep peroneal nerve
Extensor digitorum brevis	L 4–S 1	Deep peroneal nerve
Extensor hallucis brevis	L 4–S 1	Deep peroneal nerve
Peroneus longus	L 4–S 1	Superficial peroneal nerve
Peroneus brevis	L 4–S 1	Superficial peroneal nerve
Flexor digitorum brevis	L 4–S 1	Medial plantar nerve
Flexor hallucis brevis	L 5–S 1	Medial plantar nerve
Abductor hallucis	L 4–S 1	Medial plantar nerve
Lumbricales (medial 1 or 2)	L 4–S 1	Medial plantar nerve
Quadratus plantae	S 1–2	Lateral plantar nerve
Adductor hallucis	L 5–S 2	Lateral plantar nerve
Abductor digiti quinti	S 1–2	Lateral plantar nerve
Flexor digiti quinti brevis	S 1–2	Lateral plantar nerve
Lumbricales (lateral 2 or 3)	S 1–2	Lateral plantar nerve
Interossei	S 1–2	Lateral plantar nerve

The Hip Joint: The movements that take place at the hip joint are flexion, extension, abduction, adduction, and internal and external rotation.

The principal *flexors* of the thigh at the hip are the psoas and iliacus muscles. The *psoas major* is innervated by branches from the trunks of the second, third, and fourth lumbar nerves. The *iliacus* is innervated by the second, third, and fourth lumbar segments through the *femoral nerve.* Occasionally there is also a *psoas minor* which is innervated by branches from the first and second lumbar nerves. These muscles together are often referred to as the *iliopsoas.* This, acting from above, is the most powerful flexor of the thigh on the pelvis, and conversely, when the thigh is fixed, acting from below it flexes the pelvis and trunk forward upon the femur. The psoas also bends the spinal column laterally and rotates the thigh inward; the iliacus rotates the thigh slightly outward. The two muscles on each side, when acting together, serve to maintain an erect posture by supporting the vertebral column and pelvis on the femurs, and they bend the trunk and pelvis forward. Accessory flexors of the hips are the rectus femoris, adductors magnus, longus, and brevis, sartorius, pectineus, tensor fasciae latae, gracilis, and anterior fibers of the glutei medius and minimus. The iliopsoas may be tested by having the patient attempt to flex the hip joint against resistance. This is carried out with the patient in the recumbent position with the knee flexed, the angle between the thigh and the trunk slightly less than ninety degrees, and the leg supported on the examiner's arm or hand. Further flexion is attempted against resistance (Fig. 200). Flexion at the hip may also be tested with the patient recumbent and the knee in extension, or with the patient seated and his legs over the edge of the examining table. The flexors of the hip may be examined along with the abdominal muscles by having the patient rise from a recumbent to a sitting position without the assistance of his hands.

The major *extensor* of the thigh is the *gluteus maximus*. This muscle, innervated

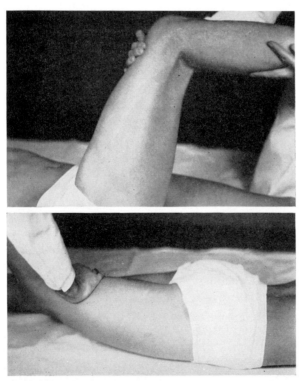

FIG. 200 (*Top*).   Examination of flexors of thigh; patient is attempting to flex hip joint against resistance; knee is flexed and leg is supported on examiner's arm.

FIG. 201 (*Bottom*).   Examination of gluteus maximus; patient, in prone position with leg flexed at knee, attempts to extend thigh at hip against resistance; contracting muscle can be seen and palpated.

by the fifth lumbar and first and second sacral segments through the *inferior gluteal nerve,* is the most powerful extensor and lateral rotator of the thigh. It not only brings the bent thigh into line with the body, but it also causes the body to assume an erect posture after stooping, and supports the pelvis. It is also an adductor of the thigh, but when the latter is flexed it is a weak abductor. Acting from below it extends the trunk. Additional extensors are the posterior fibers of the glutei medius and minimus, the lower part of the adductor magnus, the piriformis, obturator internus, and hamstrings. The gluteus maximus is important in climbing steps, jumping, and rising from a chair. In paralysis of the glutei the pelvis is bent forward as the patient attempts to get out of a chair. To test the function of this muscle the patient lies prone and lifts his lower extremity, flexed at the knee, off the table. Then he attempts to maintain it in this position while the examiner tries to press it back down. The contraction of the muscle can be palpated and can usually be seen (Fig. 201). The gluteus maximus can also be tested by having the patient lie on his side and extend the flexed hip, or by having him assume an upright from a stooped position. In the dystrophies there is marked weakness of the extensors, and the patient rises from a stooped position by using his hands to "climb up the legs" (Gowers' maneuver, Fig. 135).

Abduction at the hip is carried out by the glutei medius and minimus, piriformis, sartorius, and tensor fasciae latae. The upper fibers of the gluteus maximus and the obturator internus also aid in abduction when the thigh is flexed. The *glutei medius* and *minimus* are supplied by the fourth and fifth lumbar and first sacral segments through the *superior gluteal nerve.* Both are abductors and medial rotators of the thigh and lateral flexors of the pelvis. The anterior portion of gluteus medius is a flexor and medial rotator, whereas the posterior portion is an extensor and lateral rotator. The anterior part of gluteus minimus is a flexor, the posterior part an extensor. The *piriformis* is an abductor, lateral rotator, and weak extensor of the thigh. The *sartorius* is an abductor, flexor, and lateral rotator of the thigh, and a flexor and medial rotator of the leg. The *tensor fasciae latae* makes the fascia lata tense, flexes and abducts the thigh and rotates it medially, and flexes and abducts the pelvis. Abduction is tested by having the patient attempt to move his leg outward against resistance while he is recumbent with his leg in extension (Fig. 202); the gluteus medius and tensor fasciae latae can be palpated. It may also be tested with the patient lying on the opposite side; the strength of movement can be evaluated against both gravity and resistance. In paralysis of these muscles the thigh cannot be abducted or rotated medially; in walking the trunk bends toward the affected side, the leg swings inward, and the excessive raising and lowering of the pelvis cause a waddling gait. If the patient stands on the foot on the side of the weak glutei, there will be sagging of the opposite side of the pelvis because of gluteal insufficiency on the involved side.

Adduction of the thigh is principally a function of the three adductors, together with the pectineus, gracilis, quadratus femoris, obturator externus, hamstrings, and the lower fibers of gluteus maximus. The iliopsoas is also an adductor when the thigh is flexed. The *adductor longus* is an adductor, flexor, and medial rotator of the thigh. The *adductor brevis* is an adductor and to a lesser extent a flexor and a

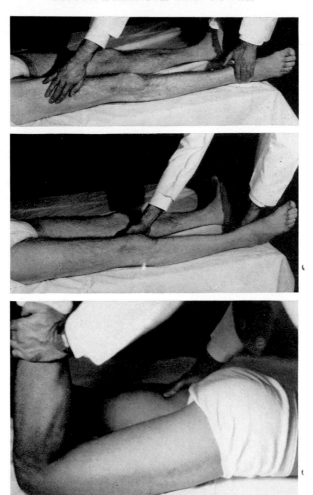

FIG. 202 (*Top*). Abduction at hip; patient, recumbent, is attempting to move extended leg outward against resistance; contraction of gluteus medius and tensor fasciae latae can be palpated.

FIG. 203 (*Middle*). Adduction at hip; patient, recumbent, is attempting to adduct extended leg against resistance; contraction of adductor muscles can be seen and palpated.

FIG. 204 (*Bottom*). Internal rotation of thigh; patient, lying prone with leg flexed at knee, is attempting to carry foot laterally against resistance, thus rotating hip medially; contraction of gluteus medius can be palpated.

lateral rotator. The *adductor magnus* is the strongest adductor; its superior and middle fasciculi are flexors and medial rotators, and its inferior fasciculi are extensors and lateral rotators of the extended thigh and medial rotators of the flexed thigh. *Gracilis* adducts, flexes, and laterally rotates the thigh; it also flexes the leg and medially rotates the flexed leg. *Pectineus* is a flexor and adductor of the thigh. The three adductors and gracilis are supplied by the second, third, and fourth lumbar nerves through the *obturator nerve,* and the adductor magnus receives an extra branch from the fourth and fifth lumbar segments through the *sciatic.* The pectineus is supplied by the second, third, and fourth lumbar segments through the *femoral nerve.* Adduction is tested while the patient is on his back with his legs in extension; he adducts the thigh while the examiner attempts to abduct it. The contraction of the adductor muscles can be palpated (Fig. 203). Adduction can also be tested with the patient lying on the homolateral side; the opposite leg is passively raised and supported, and the patient attempts to adduct the thigh against gravity and resistance.

Internal, or *medial, rotation* of the thigh is carried out principally by the anterior parts of the glutei medius and minimus and the tensor fasciae latae, together with the adductor longus, upper part of the adductor magnus, semitendinosus, and semimembranosus muscles, the lower part of adductor magnus when the thigh is flexed, and the iliopsoas when the tibia is fixed. To test internal rotation the patient lies prone with the lower leg flexed at the knee. He then attempts to carry the foot laterally, thus rotating the hip medially, while the examiner tries to pull the foot medially. During this maneuver the gluteus medius can be felt to contract (Fig. 204). Internal rotation can also be tested with the patient recumbent and his leg either extended or flexed and hanging over the edge of the examining table.

External, or *lateral, rotation* of the thigh at the hip is carried out by the gluteus maximus, obturators internus and externus, gemelli superior and inferior, quadratus femoris, and piriformis, assisted by the adductor brevis, sartorius, gracilis, iliopsoas, posterior part of the gluteus medius, long head of biceps, and lower part of adductor magnus. The *obturator internus* is a powerful lateral rotator of the thigh; it is also an extensor and abductor when the hip is flexed at a right angle. The *obturator externus* is a powerful lateral rotator and a weak adductor. *Gemelli superior* and *inferior* function as essential parts of obturator internus. *Quadratus femoris* is a powerful lateral rotator and a weak adductor. Obturator internus is supplied by a special nerve, the *nerve to the obturator internus,* from the fifth lumbar and the first, second, and third sacral segments. Obturator externus is supplied by the *obturator nerve* (second to fourth lumbar segments). The quadratus femoris is innervated by a special nerve which is derived from the fourth and fifth lumbar and first sacral nerves. The superior gemellus is supplied by a branch of the *nerve to the obturator internus* or a branch of that to quadratus femoris, and the inferior gemellus is innervated by a branch of the *nerve to quadratus femoris.* External rotation is tested by maneuvers similar to those for testing internal rotation, but the patient attempts to carry the foot medially against resistance, thus rotating the hip laterally. If these muscles are paralyzed the entire leg is turned inward.

The Knee Joint: The movements that take place at the knee joint are flexion, extension, and internal and external rotation.

Flexion of the leg at the knee is carried out by the biceps femoris, semimembranosus, semitendinosus, popliteus, gracilis, sartorius, and gastrocnemius muscles. The first three of these muscles are known as the *hamstring muscles. Biceps femoris* flexes the leg, and when the leg is flexed it is a lateral rotator. It also extends and adducts the thigh, and the long head is a lateral rotator of the thigh. The long head, acting from below, assists in extending the trunk upon the thigh. The *semi-membranosus* and *semitendinosus* muscles flex the leg and act as medial rotators. Acting from below they extend the thigh, or the trunk upon the thigh, and adduct and medially rotate the thigh. *Popliteus* flexes and medially rotates the leg. These muscles are supplied by branches of the sciatic nerve. The short head of the biceps receives its innervation from the fifth lumbar and first and second sacral segments through the *common peroneal nerve,* and the long head from the fifth lumbar and first sacral segments through the *tibial nerve.* Semitendinosus is supplied by the fifth lumbar and first and second sacral through the *tibial nerve* and semimembranosus by the fourth and fifth lumbar and first sacral through the *tibial nerve.* Popliteus is supplied by the fifth lumbar and first sacral segments through the *tibial nerve.*

Flexion at the knee is tested while the patient is in the prone position with his leg in partial flexion. His ability to maintain flexion while the examiner attempts to extend the leg will reveal the strength of the hamstrings. The tendons of semimembranosus and semitendinosus (medially) and that of the biceps (laterally) can be seen and felt to contract (Fig. 205). The patient, lying prone, may be asked to maintain his legs in flexion at right angles at the knee; in weakness of the flexors the leg will fall, gradually or rapidly (leg sign of Barré). If flexion at the knee is tested while the patient is lying supine, the simultaneous flexion at the hip may result in a misinterpretation of the strength of the hamstrings. Furthermore, in this latter position the contraction of the muscles cannot be satisfactorily palpated. The function of the sartorius, which is not only a flexor but also a medial rotator of the leg and an abductor, flexor, and lateral rotator of the thigh, may be examined by having the patient attempt to flex his knee against resistance while he is lying supine with the knee moderately flexed and the thigh flexed and rotated laterally. The muscle belly can readily be seen and felt (Fig. 206).

The *quadriceps femoris* is composed of four large muscles, *rectus femoris, vastus lateralis, vastus medialis,* and *vastus intermedius,* which are united into a common tendon inserted into the upper border of the patella. This group of muscles acts as the *extensor* of the leg at the knee; its force is three times that of its antagonists, the hamstrings. The rectus femoris, acting from below, also flexes the thigh at the hip and flexes the trunk forward on the femur. These muscles are innervated by the second, third, and fourth lumbar segments through the *femoral nerve.* The quadriceps is tested when the patient, lying supine, attempts to extend the leg at the knee while the examiner tries to flex it (Fig. 207), or attempts to maintain extension against the examiner's resistance. The contraction of the muscle can be seen and palpated. The examiner may use one arm as a fulcrum, placing it beneath the knee, or he may use one hand to palpate the contraction of the quadriceps. The quadriceps may also be tested with the patient seated. Paralysis prevents the leg from being extended, and when it is passively raised it falls back down. If the quadriceps is weak, the patient will have marked difficulty in rising from a kneeling position and in climbing stairs; he can walk backward, but has difficulty walking forward. In paralysis of the extensors of the leg the oval contour of the thigh, which is normally in a vertical, or upright, position when the patient is

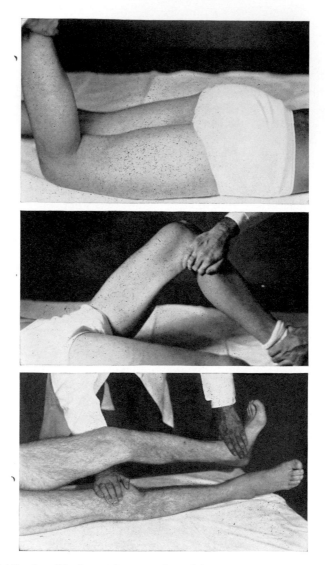

FIG. 205 (*Top*).   Flexion at knee; patient, lying prone, attempts to maintain flexion of leg while examiner endeavors to extend it; tendon of biceps femoris can be palpated on lateral aspect, and tendons of semimembranous and semi-tendinosus medially.

FIG. 206 (*Middle*).   Examination of sartorius; with thigh flexed and rotated laterally and knee moderately flexed, patient is attempting to flex knee further against resistance.

FIG. 207 (*Bottom*).   Extension at knee; patient, lying supine, is attempting to extend leg at knee against resistance; contraction of quadriceps femoris can be seen and palpated.

recumbent, is flattened horizontally. Both the flexors and the extensors of the leg are such powerful muscles that, in the normal individual, it is not possible for the examiner's hand to overcome either flexion or extension at the knee.

Internal and external rotation at the knee are relatively minor movements. *Internal,* or *medial, rotation* is carried out by the semimembranosus, semitendinosus, sartorius, popliteus, and gracilis muscles; *external,* or *lateral, rotation* by the biceps femoris and tensor fasciae latae. These movements may be tested against resistance.

The Ankle Joint: Movements affecting the ankle joint are plantar flexion and dorsiflexion. *Plantar flexion (flexion)* of the foot is carried out principally by the *gastrocnemius, soleus,* and *plantaris* muscles assisted by tibialis posterior, peroneus longus, peroneus brevis, and flexors digitorum longus and hallucis longus. The first three muscles, sometimes known as *triceps surae,* also raise the heel, as in walking, and invert the foot, and the gastrocnemius assists in flexing the leg at the knee. They are innervated by the *tibial division* of the sciatic nerve. The function of these muscles is tested by having the patient attempt to maintain plantar flexion while the examiner offers resistance by means of pressure against the sole of the foot and palpates the contracting gastrocnemius (Fig. 208). They may also be evaluated by having the patient stand on his tiptoes. In weakness or paralysis of the plantar flexors the patient is unable to stand on his toes.

Dorsiflexion (extension) of the foot at the ankle is carried out by the tibialis anterior muscle assisted by peroneus tertius and extensors digitorum longus and hallucis longus. The *tibialis anterior* is supplied by the fourth and fifth lumbar and first sacral segments through the *deep peroneal nerve.* In addition to its action as a dorsiflexor of the foot it is an invertor. When the foot is on the ground it tilts the leg forward, as in walking. It is examined by having the patient dorsiflex his foot while the examiner attempts to press down the toes (Fig. 209). The contracted muscle can be seen and palpated. Dorsiflexion may also be tested by having the patient stand on his heel and raise the ball of the foot and toes. In paralysis of the dorsiflexors there is a "foot drop," and the patient walks with a steppage gait, attempting to raise the depressed toes off the ground by exaggerated flexion at the hip and knee; he is unable to raise the sole of the foot off the ground while standing on his heel.

The Tarsal Joints: Movements at the tarsal joints consist of inversion and eversion. *Inversion,* or *medial deviation* or *elevation of the inner border of the foot,* is carried out by the tibialis posterior assisted by the tibialis anterior, gastrocnemius, soleus, and the flexors digitorum longus and hallucis longus. *Tibialis posterior* is supplied by the fifth lumbar and first sacral segments through the *tibial nerve.* It is also a plantar flexor. Inversion is tested by having the patient attempt to elevate the inner border of the plantar flexed foot against resistance. During this maneuver the tendon of the tibialis posterior can be seen and felt just behind the medial malleolus (Fig. 210).

Eversion, or *lateral deviation* or *elevation of the outer border of the foot,* is carried out by the peronei longus, brevis, and tertius and the extensor digitorum longus. *Peronei longus* and *brevis* are supplied by the fourth and fifth lumbar and first sacral segments through the *superficial peroneal nerve.* They are plantar flexors

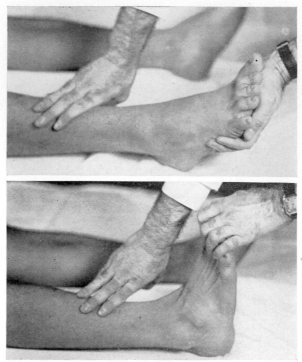

FIG. 208 (*Top*).   Plantar flexion of foot; patient is attempting to plantar flex
foot at ankle joint against resistance; contraction of gastrocnemius and associated muscles can be seen and palpated.
FIG. 209 (*Bottom*).   Dorsiflexion (extension) of foot; patient is attempting
to dorsiflex foot against resistance; contracting tibialis anterior can be seen
and palpated.

as well as evertors. *Peroneus tertius* is supplied by the fourth and fifth lumbar and
first sacral segments through the *deep peroneal nerve*. It is a dorsiflexor as well as
an evertor. To test these muscles the plantar flexed foot is held in a position of
eversion while the examiner attempts to produce inversion; the tendons of the
peronei longus and brevis, which are situated a little above and behind the external
malleolus, can be seen and felt to tighten (Fig. 211).

Muscles of the Foot and Toes: Muscle testing of the foot and toes cannot be
carried out with as much detail as can that of the hand, since the function of the
individual muscles is not so clearly defined. The principal movements are extension
(dorsiflexion) and flexion (plantar flexion). With plantar flexion there is *cupping*
of the sole. Abduction and adduction of the toes are minimal.

The *extensors* of the toes are the *extensors digitorum longus* and *brevis* and the
extensors hallucis longus and *brevis*. These muscles are supplied by the fourth and
fifth lumbar and first sacral segments through the *deep peroneal nerve*. The long
extensors extend the metatarsophalangeal and interphalangeal joints of the toes and
dorsiflex the ankle joint. Extensor digitorum longus is also an evertor. Extensor

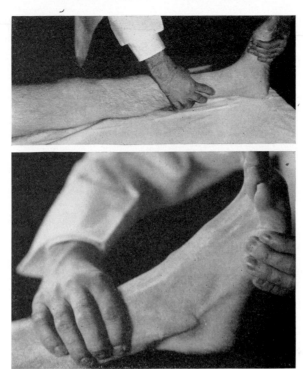

FIG. 210 (*Top*).   Inversion of foot; patient is attempting to raise inner border of foot against resistance; tendon of tibialis posterior can be seen and palpated just behind medial malleolus.

FIG. 211 (*Bottom*).   Eversion of foot; patient is attempting to raise outer border of foot against resistance; tendons of peronei longus and brevis can be seen and palpated just above and behind lateral malleolus.

digitorum brevis, whose most medial and largest belly is the extensor hallucis brevis, aids the long extensor in extending the proximal phalanx of the four medial toes. Dorsiflexion of the toes against resistance may be used as a test for the function of these muscles. The tendons of the long extensors and the belly of the extensor digitorum brevis can be palpated during this maneuver (Fig. 212).

Flexion, or *plantar flexion,* of the toes is carried out by flexors digitorum and hallucis longus, flexors digitorum and hallucis brevis, and certain of the intrinsic muscles of the sole of the foot. *Flexors digitorum longus* and *hallucis longus* are supplied by the fifth lumbar and first sacral segments through the *tibial nerve.* These muscles flex the phalanges of all five toes, acting chiefly at the distal interphalangeal joints. They also plantar flex the ankle joint and invert the foot. *Flexor digitorum brevis,* supplied by the *medial plantar nerve,* acts at the proximal interphalangeal and metatarsophalangeal joints, flexing the middle phalanges of the four lateral toes on the proximal phalanges and the proximal phalanges on the metatarsals. *Flexor hallucis brevis,* also supplied by the medial plantar nerve, acts at the metatarsophalangeal joint and flexes the proximal phalanx of the great toe. In this it is aided

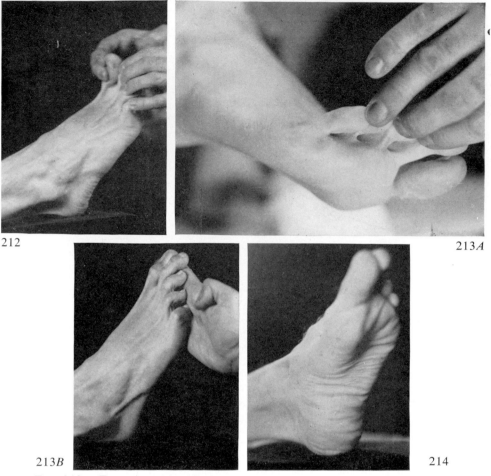

212

213A

213B

214

FIG. 212.   Extension (dorsiflexion) of toes; on attempts to dorsiflex toes against resistance, tendons of extensors digitorum and hallucis longus and belly of extensor digitorum brevis can be seen and palpated.

FIG. 213 *A* and *B*.   Flexion of toes; patient is attempting to flex toes against resistance.

FIG. 214.   Cupping of sole of foot.

by the adductor and abductor hallucis. These muscles are tested by having the patient flex the digits and attempt to maintain flexion against resistance (Fig. 213).

The intrinsic muscles of the sole of the foot, in addition to the short flexors, are as follows: *Quadratus plantae* assists the long flexors in flexing the toes; it is innervated by the first and second sacral segments through the *lateral plantar nerve*. The *abductor hallucis* abducts and flexes the proximal phalanx of the great toe; it is supplied by the *medial plantar nerve*. The *adductor hallucis* adducts and flexes the proximal phalanx of the great toe; it is innervated by the *lateral plantar nerve*. *Abductor digiti quinti* flexes and abducts the proximal phalanx of the little toe, and *flexor digiti quinti brevis* also flexes this phalanx; both are supplied by the *lateral plantar nerve*. The *lumbricales* flex the proximal phalanges of the four lateral toes. The medial one or two lumbricales are supplied by the *medial plantar nerve,* and the lateral two or three by the *lateral plantar nerve*. The *interossei* are innervated by the first and second sacral segments through the *lateral plantar nerve*. They flex the proximal phalanges; the dorsal interossei are abductors of the toes and the plantar interossei, adductors. Any extensor action of the interossei or lumbricales is questionable.

The testing of these muscles individually is a difficult matter. Abduction and adduction are extremely weak movements, and the long and short flexors are so much more powerful in flexion than are the other intrinsic muscles. In fact some of these muscles are more important from a static than an active point of view. Quadratus plantae, adductor hallucis, and flexor digitorum brevis are important in maintaining the longitudinal arches of the foot. The chief function of abductor hallucis is to maintain the medial longitudinal arch, and that of abductor digiti quinti and flexor digiti quinti brevis to maintain the lateral longitudinal arch. These muscles may, however, be tested together in asking the patient to attempt to make a cup of the sole of his foot (Fig. 214).

CONCLUSIONS

To recapitulate, in the testing of motor strength and power all of the important muscles should be tested individually. Movements should be tested at all joints, and evidences of paresis or paralysis noted.

It must be recalled that it is only in lesions of the spinomuscular level, or those of the anterior horn cells or the peripheral nerves, that one finds involvement of individual muscles. The syndromes associated with injuries of the peripheral nerves, plexus involvement, and segmental lesions of the spinal cord are summarized in Part VII. In the presence of dysfunction at the myoneural junction and in the myopathies and myositides the changes are more general. Lesions of the extrapyramidal and pyramidal complexes, whether cerebral in origin or due to interruption of the descending motor pathways, produce loss of strength and power, but under such circumstances the loss is a generalized one and involves either entire extremities or gross movements such as flexion and extension of an entire extremity. Cerebellar involvement is not followed by loss of power, but the resulting ataxia may interfere with voluntary movements. So-called psychomotor involvement may be followed by nonorganic paresis—either of an hysterical type or due to malingering. Under such circumstances the paralysis is often somewhat bizarre and does not follow an organic pattern (Chapter 56).

REFERENCES

Aids to the Investigation of Peripheral Nerve Injuries, Medical Research Council War Memorandum No. 7 (ed. 2). London, His Majesty's Stationery Office, 1943.

CLARKE, H. H. A Manual: Cable-tension Strength Tests. West Springfield, N. H., Stuart E. Murphy, 1953.

DANIELS, LUCILLE, WILLIAMS, MARIAN, and WORTHINGHAM, CATHERINE.   Muscle Testing; Techniques of Manual Examination (ed. 2).   Philadelphia, W. B. Saunders Company, 1956.

ELLWOOD, P. M.   Neurologic examination of the infant.   *Postgrad. Med.* 27:653, 1960.

GROFF, R. A., and HOUTZ, S. J.   Manual of Diagnosis and Management of Peripheral Nerve Injuries.   Philadelphia, J. B. Lippincott Company, 1945.

HAYMAKER, W., and WOODHALL, B.   Peripheral Nerve Injuries: Principles of Diagnosis (ed. 2).   Philadelphia, W. B. Saunders Company, 1953.

HOLLINSHEAD, W. F.   Functional Anatomy of the Limbs and Back.   Philadelphia, W. B. Saunders Company, 1951.

JOHNSON, E. W.   Examination for muscle weakness in infants and small children.   *J.A.M.A.* 168:1306, 1958.

KENDALL, H. O., and KENDALL, F. P.   Muscles: Testing and Function.   Baltimore, The Williams & Wilkins Company, 1949.

KRANZ, L. G.   Kinesiology Laboratory Manual.   St. Louis, The C. V. Mosby Company, 1948.

LOCKHART, R. D.   Living Anatomy: A Photographic Atlas of Muscles in Action and Surface Contours.   London, Faber and Faber, 1948.

LOVETT, R. W., and MARTIN, E. G.   Certain aspects of infantile paralysis, with a description of a method of muscle testing.   *J.A.M.A.* 66:729, 1916.

MAYER, L., and GREENBERG, B. B.   Measurements of the strength of trunk muscles.   *J. Bone & Joint Surg.* 24:842, 1942.

NEWMAN, L. B.   A new device for measuring muscle strength: The myometer.   *Arch. Phys. Med.* 30:234, 1949.

OESTER, Y. T., and MAYER, J. H., JR.   Motor Examination in Peripheral Nerve Injuries.   Springfield, Ill. Charles C Thomas, 1960.

RUSSELL, W. R.   Use of a recording dynamometer in clinical medicine.   *Brit. M. J.* 2:731, 1954.

SCHMIER, A. A.   Research work on a more precise method of determining muscle strength in poliomyelitis patients: A new muscle tester.   *J. Bone & Joint Surg.* 27:316, 1945.

THOMAS, A., CHESNI, Y., and SAINT-ANNE DARGASSIES, S.   The Neurological Examination of the Infant.   London, National Spastics Society, 1960.

TOURTELLOTTE, W. W., HAERER, A. F., SIMPSON, J. F., KUZMA, J. W., and SIKORSKI, J.   Quantitative clinical neurological testing.   *Ann. New York Acad. Sc.* 122:480, 1965.

VIETS, H. R., and SCHWAB, R. S.   Prostigmin in the diagnosis of myasthenia gravis.   *New England J. Med.* 213:1280, 1935.

WAINERDI, H. R.   Simple ergometers for measuring the strength of the hand grasp (grip).   *J.A.M.A.* 144:619, 1950.

WELLS, K. F.   Kinesiology (ed. 2).   Philadelphia, W. B. Saunders Company, 1955.

WESTERBERG, M. R., MAGEE, K. R., and SHIDEMAN, F. E.   Effect of Tensilon in myasthenia gravis.   *Neurology* 3:302, 1953.

CHAPTER 28

MUSCLE TONE

TONE, OR TONUS, has been defined as the tension of muscles when they are relaxed, or as their resistance to passive movement when voluntary control is absent. Muscle itself has such complex functions as extensibility, contractility, elasticity, ductility, and independent irritability. When a muscle fiber contracts it does so maximally or not at all. Even in apparently relaxed muscles there is a constant, slight fixed state of tension by which they are held in a given position, resist changes in their length, prevent undue mobility at joints, assure the retention of posture, and are in readiness either to contract or relax promptly when a significant increase or decrease occurs in the total number of impulses delivered to them. This is necessary to hold the different parts of the skeleton in their proper relationships in the various and frequently changing attitudes and postures of the body, and is greatest in those muscles that maintain the body in an erect position; these are the antigravity muscles, principally the flexors in the upper and the extensors in the lower extremities. Normal muscles, especially those just mentioned, show slight resistance to passive movement in spite of voluntary relaxation.

This state of continuous tension of muscles is dependent upon the integrity of the muscle tissue, the myoneural junction, the peripheral nerves, the alpha and gamma motor neurons and interneurons in the spinal cord, and the central connections. Motor centers in the cerebral cortex and basal ganglia, the facilitatory and inhibitory centers in the midbrain and brain stem reticular formations, the cerebellum, and the vestibular apparatus all supply impulses that influence tone to the motor nuclei in the spinal cord. It has been stated there is a constant discharge of impulses from the anterior horn cells and that this is in part responsible for the comparatively steady contraction of various fibers that go to make up the individual muscles. No action potentials can be obtained by electromyography, however, from normal muscles at rest in well relaxed subjects, in spite of the fact that muscle is normally in a state of slight tension. Action potentials appear only with movement and cease at the end of it.

Tone is a reflex phenomenon, and afferent as well as efferent components in-

497

fluence it. Impulses sent through the gamma efferents stimulate the intrafusal fibers in the muscle spindles which in turn send afferent impulses to the anterior horns of the spinal cord to initiate contraction of muscle by reflex action of the alpha motor neurons. Muscle is flaccid and behaves as noncontractile tissue when deprived of its motor and sensory supply. When a muscle with normal innervation is passively stretched, its fibers actively resist the stretching and enter into an active state of increased and sustained tension. First a lengthening reaction takes place, but proprioceptive impulses carried to the nervous system call forth an increase in tension, and the shortening reaction follows. Thus the "stretch reflex" is evident. This is a reaction evoked by the stimulation of the sensory organs in the muscle; it depends for its development on impulses from tension receptors in the muscle itself. It is present at all times; even in apparently relaxed muscle a slight degree of tension is constantly present as long as the muscle innervation is intact; this is normal tone. If a muscle is stretched beyond its normal limits by gravity, manipulation, stimulation, or disease, additional tension is developed, and a tonic response takes place. A reflex contraction of the antagonistic muscles may block the attempted contraction of the stimulated muscles. Most types of hypertonicity can be abolished by interruption of either the gamma efferent impulses to the intrafusal fibers or the afferent impulses from the muscle spindles. Selective blockade of the gamma efferents may be produced by either intrathecal or epidural injection of novocaine.

An involuntary postural contraction of muscles is necessary for the maintenance of normal positions and attitudes. Tone is the basis or background for posture, and is important in the coordination of movement. Tonic reflexes mediated through the reticular formation, the otolith organs, the vestibular apparatus, and other higher centers are important in maintaining the steady contraction of the antigravity muscles that is necessary to the standing position, as well as in other postural and righting reflexes (Chapter 38). Tone may be influenced by disease at various levels of the nervous system. Interruption of the spinal reflex arc abolishes it, but loss of impulses from supraspinal levels that normally inhibit lower reflex centers usually causes an increase in tone. Imbalance of higher facilitatory and inhibitory centers may either decrease or augment tone, and the same is true, but to a lesser degree, of mental states and volitional factors.

EXAMINATION OF TONE

Tone is difficult to appraise and it cannot be measured quantitatively except as a skilled examiner gives his impression in the light of previous experience. Normal muscle shows some slight resistance to passive movement in spite of voluntary relaxation, and it may be difficult to differentiate between this and slight increase or decrease in tonus. Consequently the evaluation of tone is entirely a matter of judgment and can be learned only by repeated trials. Furthermore, inadequate relaxation or slight resistance to passive movement, on either a conscious or an unconscious basis, may seriously affect tone and may cause misinterpretations. A tense or apprehensive patient may present voluntary or involuntary resistance to passive movement that may simulate an organic increase in tone.

In testing tone one should attempt to secure the complete cooperation of the patient. He should be comfortable and relaxed, and have complete confidence in the examiner. Irrelevant conversation or questioning the patient about unimportant matters during the examination may be of aid in obtaining adequate relaxation. *Observation,* especially of the extremities, is the first test. The character of spontaneous movements and abnormalities of posture or of the position of the extremities may indicate changes in tone. *Palpation* of the muscles, to note their consistency, passive elasticity, firmness, or turgor, may also be valuable, but it should be stated that palpation of the muscle bellies themselves cannot alone be considered to give a reliable indication of tone. An individual with well-developed musculature may have firm muscles in spite of normal tone, or the resting muscles may feel flabby in hypertonic conditions. There may be increased consistency of the muscles in the presence of edema or inflammation, or they may feel firm and rubbery in myositis or the pseudohypertrophy of muscular dystrophy. With spasm secondary to pain there may also be increased turgor. Palpation is most reliable in hyptonicity. Muscle tenderness may also be revealed by palpation (see below). *Percussion,* or stretching the muscle by tapping it, is used in evaluating direct muscular irritability, or idiomuscular contraction (see below).

The most important criterion in the examination of tone is the *resistance of muscles to passive manipulation* when they are relaxed and when voluntary control is absent. In testing tone one examines *passive,* not active, *movement,* and notes the degree of tension present on passive stretching of muscles, as well as the extensibility and range of motion. Changes in tone are more obvious or more readily detected in the muscles of the extremities than in those of the trunk. In testing these the patient is asked to "give the extremity to the examiner," and to relax completely and avoid all tension. The part is moved passively, first slowly and through a complete range of motion, and then at varying speeds. The examiner may shake the forearm to and fro and note the excursions of the patient's voluntarily relaxed hand; he may brace a limb and then suddenly remove the support; he may note the range of movement of a part in response to a slight blow. The resistance to movement and the power to maintain postures against external forces are noted, both on slow and rapid motion and on partial and full range of motion. The distribution of the abnormality in tone, the movements or muscles involved, as well as the type and degree of the change should be recorded. Limitation of range of motion, plasticity, the assuming of new positions, pain on movement, defensive spasm, contractures, fibrotic changes, and ankylosis should be appraised. At times it may be necessary to anesthetize the patient, using general, spinal, or local anesthesia, or to inject drugs such as curare or mephenesin, in order to differentiate between reflex contraction resulting from overactivity of one group of muscles unopposed by weak antagonists and contracture resulting from fibrotic changes in the muscles and tendons.

It is important to bear in mind that tone may be influenced by temperature (cooling increases and heat decreases tone), the speed of passive movement, the presence of synergistic movements, emotional states, and volition. Tone is especially difficult to evaluate in newly born infants, in whom there may be wide variabilities in apparent tonus on different examinations, in either health or disease.

Special methods of examination of tonus are often helpful in the neurologic appraisal. These are most frequently used in evaluation of the rigidity that is a characteristic feature of extrapyramidal diseases, but may also be significant in spasticity and hypotonicity. Some of them are as follows:

The Babinski Tonus Test: The forearms are flexed passively at the elbows while the upper arms are held abducted at the shoulders. With hypotonicity there is exaggerated flexibility and mobility, and the elbows can be bent to an angle that is more acute than normal. With hypertonicity there is reduced flexibility of the forearms against the upper arms, and passive flexion cannot be carried beyond an obtuse angle.

The Head Dropping Test: The patient lies supine, without a pillow; he should be completely relaxed, with his eyes closed and his attention diverted. The examiner places his left hand under the patient's occiput, and with his right hand briskly raises the head and then allows it to drop. Normally the head drops rapidly into the examiner's left hand, but in patients with extrapyramidal rigidity there is delayed, slow, gentle dropping of the head owing to rigidity affecting principally the flexor muscles of the neck. With the nuchal rigidity of meningeal irritation there is resistance to and pain on flexion of the neck.

Pendulousness of the Legs: The patient sits on the edge of a table with his legs hanging freely. The examiner either extends both legs to the same horizontal level and then releases them or gives both legs a brisk push backward. If the patient is completely relaxed and does not voluntarily suppress or increase movement, there will normally be a characteristic swinging of the legs that progressively diminishes in range and usually disappears after six or seven oscillations. In extrapyramidal rigidity there is a decrease in swinging time, but usually no qualitative changes in the response. In spasticity there may be no or slight decrease in time, but there is a qualitative change and the movements are jerky and irregular; the forward movement may be greater and more brisk than the backward one, and the movement may not be limited to the anteroposterior plane, but may assume a zigzag character. In hypotonia the response is increased in range and prolonged beyond the normal. In all the above the abnormality is more apparent if it is a unilateral one.

The Shoulder Shaking Test: The examiner places his hands on the patient's shoulders and shakes them briskly in both a backward and forward and rotatory direction. With extrapyramidal disease there will be decreased range of arm swinging on the affected side, and with hypotonia, especially that associated with cerebellar lesions, the range of swinging will be greater than normal.

The Arm Dropping Test: The patient's arms are briskly raised and then dropped. With increase in tone there is a delay in the downward movement of the arm, while with hypotonicity the dropping is abrupt. A similar maneuver may be carried out, on the recumbent patient, by suddenly lifting and then dropping the extended leg.

Pronation of the Hands: In the presence of hypotonicity, especially that associated with cerebellar lesions or Sydenham's chorea, there is a tendency for the hands to assume a position of pronation; this is apparent with the arms outstretched horizontally, but is exaggerated when they are raised above the head. On forward elevation of the arms there is a characteristic position of the hands, with flexion at the wrists, hyperextension of the proximal and terminal phalanges, and moderate overpronation. When the arms are elevated above the head there is increased pronation of the forearms with internal rotation of the shoulders, and as a result the palms are turned outward. This phenomenon differs from the pronation signs of Strümpell and Babinski in which the response is an abnormal associated movement caused by spasticity of the pronator muscles.

Various mechanical, electronic, and other appliances have been devised for testing tonus; most of these, however, do not measure pure tone, but rather resistance of muscle to stretching, muscle consistency, and an admixture of voluntary motion and the effects of muscle contraction. The electromyogram, when critically evaluated, does give objective evidence in its assessment, but in general careful clinical appraisal is the best criterion of abnormalities in tone.

ABNORMALITIES OF TONE

Abnormalities of tone may occur in the presence of disease of any portion of the motor system. Lesions of the spinomuscular level, either in the anterior horn cell, the peripheral nerve, the myoneural junction, or in the muscle itself may affect tone. Involvement of the extrapyramidal complex, the pyramidal level, the vestibular or midbrain centers, or the psychomotor sphere may be followed by alterations in tone. In addition, it is influenced by interference with the proprioceptive impulses and their pathways of conduction.

Pathologic conditions may cause either a decrease or an increase in tone. Loss or diminution of tone is classified as *hypotonicity,* and pathologic increase, as *hypertonicity*. There are various subdivisions within these groups. Increased tone, in the form of spasm and contracture, may cause limitation of motion and thus simulate paresis.

HYPOTONICITY

Hypotonicity, or flaccidity, is usually the result of *involvement of the spinomuscular level* or of *interference with the proprioceptive pathways*. It is characterized by a decrease in or loss of normal tone. The muscle lies inert and is flaccid and flabby, or soft to palpation. The joints involved offer no resistance to passive flexion or extension, even when such movement is carried out rapidly. The excursion at the joint may be normal, but is usually increased; there is absence of a "checking" action on extremes of passive motion. There is failure of the limb to maintain steadily positions into which it is brought either actively or passively. If the involved extremity is lifted and allowed to drop, it falls with a flail-like attitude. A slight blow causes it to sway through an excessive excursion. The deep reflexes are usually decreased or absent. It must be remembered that flaccid paralysis of muscles may be accompanied by spasm or contracture of their antagonists, which may be misleading to the inexperienced examiner. Abnormalities of joint motility, such as the Ehler-Danlos syndrome in which there is hyperelastic skin with extreme flexibility of joints, are not necessarily accompanied by decrease in muscle tone.

If the *anterior horn cell* or its neuraxis is cut off from the muscle by disease or trauma, the continuous rhythmic impulses that maintain tonus are no longer present, and sustained contraction of muscle is absent. Thus diseases of the *spinal* and *neural* portions of the spinomuscular level cause hypotonicity, or flaccidity, of the muscles involved. Among such lesions are poliomyelitis, progressive spinal muscular atrophy, syringomyelia, and peripheral neuritis. In spinal shock, which follows abrupt transection of the spinal cord, the activity of the anterior horn cells and the spinal reflexes are temporarily suppressed below the level of the lesion, with resulting flaccidity.

Abnormalities of the muscle itself or at the myoneural junction, or of the *muscular* and *neuromuscular* portions of the spinomuscular level, are also accompanied by decrease in tone. Such is the case in the muscular dystrophies, amyotonia congenita, benign congenital hypotonia, many of the myositides, thyrotoxic and carcinomatous myopathy, steroid myopathy, myasthenia gravis, sleep paralysis, and the various types of familial periodic paralysis. Similar decrease in tone may be found in association with certain metabolic or electrolyte disturbances, malnutrition, debilitating disease, specific infectious involvement, or administration of or poisoning by various toxins that affect the function of the myoneural junction (see Chapter 21).

Tone is also decreased when the muscles are deprived of their *proprioceptive impulses,* either by spinal or by neural disease. Thus in tabes dorsalis, in which the proprioceptive pathways are interrupted either in the dorsal root ganglia or in the posterior columns, there is hypotonicity of the muscles with hyperextensibility of the joints. In local anesthesia (peripheral nerve block) and spinal anesthesia (anterior horn cell and nerve root involvement) as well as the deeper stages of general anesthesia (central involvement) there is hypotonicity; sensory as well as motor impulses are interrupted. The association of flaccidity with some lesions of the parietal lobe is probably secondary to disturbances of sensation.

Hypotonicity may occur under other circumstances. It is present with cerebellar disease of various types, but there is no flaccidity of the degree that one finds in disease of the lower motor neurons, and the reflexes are not lost but may be of the pendular variety. There are no pathologic reflexes. Muscle tone is diminished in chorea, akinetic epilepsy, deep sleep, syncope and states of lowered consciousness, and directly after death. In cataplexy, associated with narcolepsy, there are attacks of weakness of the limbs and complete loss of tone, precipitated by emotional stimuli; with narcolepsy there may also be periods of complete paralysis that come on during relaxation or before going to sleep. Immediately following a cerebrovascular lesion of abrupt onset there may be flaccid paralysis of the affected parts; this is sometimes referred to as "cerebral shock." The presence of flaccidity with lesions of the motor cortex (area 4) and its descending pathways in experimental animals and occasionally in clinical states in man, and its relationship to other aspects of motor function, is discussed in Chapter 23. Hypotonicity may also be induced by selective blocking of the gamma efferent fibers and by the administration of mephenesin and other drugs that interrupt internuncial motor neuron discharges.

HYPERTONICITY

Hypertonicity is usually caused by lesions central to the anterior horn cells, or by interruption of impulses from supraspinal regions. It is seen most frequently with dysfunction of the so-called extrapyramidal and pyramidal levels, and is caused by either interruption of impulses that normally inhibit lower centers or imbalance of facilitatory and inhibitory centers, with consequent alteration of the alpha and gamma motor neuron balance. It may also be caused by voluntary or unconscious contraction of muscles, reflex contraction, and muscle disease, and may be present with other disturbances of function. The major types and causes of hypertonocity are discussed below.

Rigidity or *extrapyramidal rigidity* occurs with lesions of the basal ganglia or of some portion of the extrapyramidal level of motor function or its connections with the midbrain and brain stem reticular formations. The various pathophysiologic theories for this increase in tone are discussed in Chapter 22. With rigidity of this type there is a state of fairly steady muscular tension equal in degree in opposing muscle groups. It thus may be seen to involve both flexor and extensor muscles in the extremities, with resistance to passive movement in all directions. The actual degree of such resistance, however, is usually less than that found with spasticity, but it is present throughout the entire range of motion and is continuous from the beginning to the end of the movement. Furthermore, the resistance is present and constant whether the extremity is moved slowly or rapidly. There is a continuous increase in stimulation of both agonists and antagonists, and neither group is ever at complete rest. Electromyographic studies may show a constant slight innervation of the rigid muscles, even when the limb is placed in its most relaxed position. On palpation the muscles may be firm, tense, and prominent. After being moved the part may retain its new position with the same resistance to movement that was noted in the original position (*plasticity*); the extremities may assume awkward postures. This type of hypertonicity is often referred to as waxy resistance, lead-pipe resistance, or cerea flexibilitas. Often the so-called *cogwheel rigidity* is encountered; there is an intermittent yielding of the muscles to stretching, and on passive motion against muscular tension the resistance is interrupted at regular intervals in a jerky fashion, and the muscles seem to give way in a series of steps as if the manipulator were moving a limb attached to a heavy cogwheel or pulling it over a ratchet. This latter phenomenon may be related in part to the tremor that often occurs with rigidity in extrapyramidal disease.

Rigidity of this type is most commonly encountered in Parkinson's disease and postencephalitic parkinsonism (Fig. 142). It appears first in the proximal muscles, spreading later to the distal ones. All muscles may be affected, but there is predominant involvement of those of the neck and trunk and the flexors of the extremities, although the fingers may be extended at the interphalangeal joints. There is associated slowing of the voluntary use of the limbs, in both flexion and extension, but no real paralysis. With repeated active movement there is a gradual decrease in speed and amplitude; this may be brought out by rapid opening and closing of the eyes or mouth, movements of the tongue, or finger-thumb approximation. In addition there is loss of associated movements. Whether the brady-kinesia and loss of associated movements are secondary to the hypertonicity or are of central origin unrelated to the rigidity is still controversial. The rigidity of extrapyramidal disease may be demonstrated by the head dropping, shoulder shaking, and similar tests, as well as by noting slowness of starting and limitation of amplitude of movement, loss of pendulousness of the arms and legs, inability to carry out rapid repeated movements and to maintain two simultaneous voluntary motor activities, and impairment of associated movements, such as swinging of the arms in walking. If the patient, standing upright, is suddenly pushed either backward or forward, he cannot immediately contract the muscles necessary for maintenance of equilibrium, and will fall in the direction he was pushed. The rigidity on one side may be exaggerated by active movement of the contralateral limbs.

Similar rigidity may be encountered in arteriosclerotic encephalopathy, anoxia and carbon monoxide intoxication, poisoning by manganese and other toxins, after the administration of such drugs as reserpine and chlorpromazine, in other extrapyramidal syndromes such as dystonia and athetosis (Chapter 31), and in spasmodic torticollis (Chapter 16). In some of the extrapyramidal disorders, especially athetosis, the *gegenhalten phenomenon* is present. This is the stiffening of a limb in response to contact and as a resistance to changes in position and posture. The rigid type of hypertonicity may be relieved, to some extent at least, by injection of novocaine into the involved muscles, selective blocking of the gamma efferent fibers, introcarotid injection of sodium amobarbital, or the various surgical procedures discussed in Chapter 22.

Spasticity occurs in association with lesions of the so-called pyramidal level of function, and has been ascribed to the loss of, or release from, the normal inhibiting action of the pyramidal cortex on the anterior horn cells (Chapter 23). Experimentally, however, lesions limited to the pyramidal complex may produce flaccidity, and more recent theories of spasticity indicate that it results from an imbalance of the inhibitory and facilitatory centers in the midbrain and brain stem reticular formations, with consequent alteration of the alpha and gamma motor neuron balance. Such increase in tone may be the result of injury to suppressor areas in the cortex or elsewhere, interruption of suppressor impulses to the inhibitory reticular area in the lower brain stem, disease of this area, or enhancement or stimulation of the facilitatory or excitatory reticular areas in the midbrain and brain stem. This leads to facilitatory influx to the spinal cord, conducted by reticulospinal, vestibulospinal, and other pathways and alteration of the balance between the alpha and gamma motor systems. Impairment of the central inhibitory influences that normally reduce spinal stretch reflexes is followed by an exaggerated contraction of muscles subjected to stretching and increased resistance to manipulation. For descriptive purposes, however, the term "pyramidal" will be used for those lesions of the cerebrum and descending pathways that cause spasticity.

Spasticity is a state of sustained increase in tension of a muscle when it is passively lengthened. This tension is caused by an exaggeration of the muscle stretch reflex; there is increased sensitivity to stimulation of proprioceptive receptors within the muscles, and such stimulation causes the shortening reaction to be intensified and the muscular tension to be augmented. This tension may be felt from the beginning of a passive movement and may increase to the extent to which the muscle is lengthened. Passive movement of the extremity may be carried out with comparative freedom if it is done slowly, but on attempts at rapid or forceful movement, tension appears; there is "blocking," with complete limitation of further movement. Passive movement may also be carried out with little resistance through a limited range of motion, but extremes of movement, such as complete flexion or extension, likewise result in "blocking" and limitation of further movement. If the limb is left in the new position, it may be maintained there. There may be an elastic, springlike resistance to stretching at the beginning of movement, especially if the part is moved abruptly or suddenly, following which the muscle resists to a certain point and then suddenly relaxes. This waxing and waning of resistance causes the phenomenon sometimes referred to as "clasp knife" type of resistance, which distinguishes it from rigidity. Occasionally spasticity is so marked that the examiner cannot passively move an extremity, although the patient himself may retain a certain amount of ability to move it. Spastic muscles may be hard and unyielding on palpation, but sometimes they are soft and flabby. The degree of firmness depends not so much on actual amount of spasticity as on the degree of contraction or relaxation at the time of palpation. Completely relaxed spastic muscles show no electrical neuromuscular activity, but minimal stimulation causes an immediate response. Thus far no objective means have been devised for the accurate measuring of spasticity, and clinical evaluation is the most reliable criterion. It must be borne in mind, however, that the range of movement of spastic extremities and the degree of hypertonicity may vary between examinations.

In the presence of spasticity the deep reflexes are exaggerated and pathologic reflexes such as the Babinski and Hoffmann signs can be elicited. Passive dorsiflexion of the ankle, downward movement of the patella, and occasionally even passive extension of the wrist may cause alternate spasm and relaxation of the agonists and antagonists, or clonus. Forced grasping and tonic perseveration of motion may be evident, and there often are abnormal associated movements (Chapter 39). Muscle power is difficult to assess in the presence of spasticity.

Disease syndromes that cause spastic paralysis are often characterized by sustained contraction of specific groups of muscles. In hemiplegia of cerebral origin, for instance, the spasticity is most marked in the flexor muscles of the upper and the extensor muscles of the lower extremity; this causes postural flexion of the arm and extension of the leg, termed the predilection type of paresis (Fig. 152). The arm is adducted and flexed at the shoulder, the forearm is flexed at the elbow, and the wrist and fingers are flexed; there may be forced grasping. The lower extremity is extended at the hip, knee, and ankle, and there is inversion with plantar flexion of the foot; there may be marked spasm of the adductors of the thigh. There is more passive resistance to extension than to flexion in the upper extremities, and to flexion than to extension in the lower extremities. In bilateral cerebral lesions the increased tone of the adductors of the thighs is responsible for the "scissors gait." In relatively complete spinal cord lesions there may be, rather than extension, violent flexor spasms of the lower extremities, reflexes of spinal automatism (Chapter 37) and paraplegia in flexion (Fig. 153). Spasticity is sometimes relieved by selective anterior rhizotomy, peripheral nerve or posterior root section, injection of either alcohol or phenol into the subarachnoid space, or even by removal of part or all of the malfunctioning area of the spinal cord (cordectomy). Neuromuscular blocking agents such as curare, decamethonium,, and succinylcholine, and internuncial blocking agents such as mephenesin, have also proved to be of some therapeutic value.

Muscle spasm of a somewhat different type, usually associated with abnormal posturing, occasionally follows damage to the interneurons in the intermediate gray matter of the spinal cord. The complete isolation of the anterior horn cells causes release of the muscle stretch reflexes, and muscle spasm results from the continual discharge of impulses from these cells.

Catatonic rigidity is similar in many respects to extrapyramidal rigidity and probably is physiologically related. There is a waxy or lead-pipe type of resistance to passive movement, a cerea flexibilitias, but one notes in addition the posturing, bizarre mannerisms, and mental picture of the schizophrenic reaction. It may be possible to mold the extremities into any position, following which they remain in this position indefinitely. Experimental catatonia has been produced in laboratory animals by the use of bulbocapnine, epinephrine, and other drugs, and by the production of chemical, metabolic, and other changes. In *catalepsy* there is total suspension of voluntary motion and the entire body is rigid; this syndrome may be similar, from a physiologic point of view, to catatonic rigidity.

Decerebrate rigidity is characterized by marked rigidity and sustained contraction of all the extensor (antigravity) muscles. The limbs are stiffly extended, the head is erect, and the jaws are closed. The righting reflexes are abolished, tonic neck and labyrinthine reflexes are retained, and tendon and stretch reflexes are exaggerated. This phenomenon results from release of the vestibular nuclei from higher extrapyramidal control, and may follow transection of the brain stem at a level between the superior colliculi (anterior quadrigeminal bodies) and the vestibular nuclei. It is considered further along with the postural and righting reflexes in "The Reflexes," Part V. Generalized rigidity or spasticity with neck retraction, or opisthotonus, may also occur in meningitis, the tonic stage of the convulsive attack, and so-called cerebellar or posterior fossa fits. In all these the hypertonicity and associated symptoms doubtless result from brain stem involvement.

Voluntary rigidity is characterized by a conscious bracing of various muscle groups. This may be done in protecting the body against pathologic change, in response to pain, and in the performance of certain voluntary muscular activities. There is an individual variation in the degree of voluntary rigidity that a patient may present, and it is often difficult to differentiate between factors that are actually volitional and those that are unconscious or involuntary, especially if the hypertonicity is related to excitement, alarm, or fatigue. Tense, apprehensive individuals show a great amount of muscular tension and rigidity at all times, and such persons may have exaggerated deep reflexes. The exaggeration, however, is one of range of response, and the latent period is not shortened. Heavily muscled individuals often relax less well than others, but in such persons the deep reflexes may appear to be diminished and be elicited only on reinforcement. The sudden bracing of muscles in response to shock or in checking a fall may have as its basis both volitional and unconscious factors.

Involuntary rigidity may be similar to the voluntary variety and difficult to differentiate from it. The unconsciously motivated muscle tension of the apprehensive person who shows exaggerated deep reflexes may be wide in distribution and long in duration. It may be precipitated by excitement, alarm, or fatigue. On the other hand, increase of tone of phychogenic origin may be bizarre and simulate any type of hypertonicity. In so-called major hysteria there may be an extreme degree of generalized rigidity with neck retraction and opisthotonus, the body resting with only the head and heels upon the bed (*arc de cercle*); the manifestations may simulate either decerebrate or catatonic rigidity, and may be termed *hysterical rigidity.*

Reflex rigidity, or spasm of skeletal muscle, is a response to sensory irritation, usually to pain. It is a state of sustained involuntary contraction accompanied by muscle shortening and associated with changes in electrical potential. By observation one notes raised, contracted muscles, and on palpation they are found to be firm and resistant. Among the more common examples of reflex spasm of muscles in response to pain are the boardlike abdomen of peritonitis, the rigidity of the neck and back in meningitis, and the localized spasm in the extremities in osteomyelitis. The muscle spasm of arthritis may be of similar origin, as may the spasm that is seen in certain of the myositides and in peripheral vascular lesions such as Volkmann's and other ischemic muscular contractures. Reflex rigidity may result from sensory stimuli other than pain. Cold, for instance, may call forth generalized hypertonicity. Muscle contracture may follow prolonged spasm. In McArdle's disease muscle spasms, painful cramps, and weakness are brought on by exercise and repeated voluntary contractions; these phenomena are hastened and augmented by ischemia. Similar spasms and cramps occur in idiopathic paroxysmal myoglobinuria, where they are followed by paresis or even complete paralysis; during the attacks the affected muscles are edematous, tense, and tender.

In *myotonia,* both the congenital and acquired types, dystrophia myotonica, paramyotonia, and occasionally in myxedema, there is a generalized increase in muscle tone and contraction, more evident on active than on passive movement; tone is usually normal when the muscles are relaxed. There is tonic perserveration of muscular contraction, and relaxation takes place slowly; this may be demonstrated in the hand-grasp test. Sudden movements may be followed by marked spasm and inability to relax; repetition of movements, however, brings about ease of relaxation and a gradual decrease in hypertonicity. Electrical stimulation of muscle causes an exaggerated contraction that relaxes slowly, the so-called myotonic reaction, and percussion myotonia may be elicited by mechanical stimulation. Abrupt tapping of the thenar eminence with the small end of the reflex hammer is followed by opposition of the thumb that persists for several seconds before relaxation begins, and tapping the tongue, deltoid region, or other muscular masses produces a depression or "dimple" that disappears slowly. Excitement, cold, and forced effort aggravate the hypertonia. The muscles may appear hypertrophic, but there is decrease rather than increase in strength, and the reflexes are normal. The hypertonicity of myotonia is probably peripheral in origin, and it has been suggested that either there is hyperexcitability of the motor end plate that leads to abnormal neuromuscular transmission or that the abnormality is in the muscle itself, with some disturbance of electrolyte equilibrium or cell metabolism. Once depolarization has taken place, a repetitively discharging circuit is set up that continues to activate the contraction of myofibrils. Cortisone, corticotropin, quinine, and procaine amide have all been reported to be of some value in reducing the duration of myotonia, although they have little effect on the associated muscle weakness.

Muscular rigidity may also be seen in epilepsy, tetany, and tetanus. In *epilepsy* there may be generalized rigidity during the tonic phase of the fit. Occasionally there are "tonic fits" with no clonic phase. This type of hypertonicity is of central origin; it may result from temporary interruption of the pyramidal or extrapyramidal pathways or from imbalance of inhibitory and facilitatory centers, or it may be related to decerebrate rigidity.

In *tetany* there are tonic muscular spasms and there is hyperirritability of the muscular and nervous systems to mechanical and electrical stimuli leading to localized or generalized hypertonicity. The manifestations may be intermittent or continuous; they involve predominantly the distal limb segments, and are usually bilateral. The spasm may be preceded by feelings of stiffness and pain. In the attacks the fingers are closely approximated and are flexed at the metacarpophalangeal joints and extended at the interphalangeal joints; the thumb is extended and adducted; there is flexion at the wrist with flexion and pronation at the elbow. There is plantar flexion of the toes; the sole of the foot is concave, and the ankle is inverted and may be in plantar flexion or dorsiflexion. The term *carpopedal spasm* is used to include the so-called "obstetrical hand" and the talipes equinovarus deformity. The muscles of the body, head, and face may be involved, and opisthotonus may result. During the attacks the muscles are rigid and painful. Tapping or mechanical irritation (Chvostek's sign) and electrical stimulation (Erb's sign) show the muscles to be overexcitable, and such stimulation reproduces the spasm, as does pressure over the nerves or arteries (Trousseau's sign). Electrical testing shows not only increased irritability but also a shortened chronaxie. The hypertonicity is probably largely of muscular origin. It is related to disturbances of calcium and phosphorus metabolism and to abnormalities in the acid-base equilibrium of the body.

In *tetanus* there is an increase in muscle tone with consequent generalized bodily rigidity. In most instances this first involves the face and jaw muscles, but may affect the abdominal muscles, extremities, and spinal muscles as well, with resulting abdominal rigidity, extensor rigidity, and opisthotonus. Both the prime movers and the antagonists may be hypertonic. Spasm of the muscles of mastication causes *trismus,* and retraction of the angles of the mouth brings about the so-called *risus sardonicus.* Muscle spasm may occur spontaneously, or either voluntary contraction or mechanical, tactile, auditory, visual, or other stimuli may precipitate paroxysms of muscle contraction which increase in intensity and spread to other muscles. Between seizures there is usually some persisting muscular rigidity. Deep and cutaneous reflexes are grossly exaggerated and a light tap upon a tendon may throw the limb into violent spasms. It is believed that the toxin may have a local action on the muscles or motor nerve endings as well as a central action upon the anterior horn cells of the spinal cord. It may be that continuous discharge of affected motor neurons causes a persistent contraction of muscle similar to the sustained contraction of electrically produced tetanus that follows repeated stimulation.

In the so-called *stiff-man syndrome* there are painful tonic muscular spasms and progressive rigidity of the muscles of the trunk, neck, abdomen, back and proximal parts of the extremities. On electromyography there is a constant discharge of normal motor unit potentials simulating what is seen with prolonged volitional contraction of muscles. Pathologically there are nonspecific muscle fiber alterations. The etiology of this syndrome is not known, although it has some clinical resemblance to tetanus. It has been suggested that this rare condition may be a myopathy with some abnormality at the motor end-plate or neuromuscular junction, the result of damage to the interneurons in the gray matter of the spinal cord with an impairment of the inhibitory mechanism of the anterior horn cells, or the result of an as yet undiagnosed metabolic defect.

Focal muscle spasms and *cramps* will be discussed with abnormal movements (Chapter 31).

Related to the inspection, palpation, and passive resistance used in the testing of tone is the observation of the so-called *idiomuscular contraction,* or *myotatic irritability,* which follows percussion or mechanical stimulation of muscle. Muscle tissue has direct or independent irritability, contractility, elasticity, ductility, and extensibility. In normal and normally innervated muscles there is a brief and feeble contraction after it is tapped with a percussion hammer. This response may be so slight in many muscles that it cannot be seen or felt and is observed with difficulty. In certain pathologic states this response is increased. Marked exaggeration of it is known as *myoedema,* in which there is a prolonged, localized contraction of the muscle following mechanical stimulation. One may be able to observe a wave of contraction that radiates along the muscle fibers away from the point of percussion. A small ridge or temporary swelling may be noted at the point of stimulation and this may persist for a few moments; the response differs from percussion myotonia, in which a depression rather than a raised area is seen in the muscle following stimulation. Myotatic irritability is increased in wasting diseases, such as cachexia and emaciation, and in many diseases of the lower motor neuron. It is increased, by both response to minimal stimuli and acceleration of contraction, in progressive spinal muscular atrophy; myoedema, though small in degree, may be present. Mechanical stimulation may bring out fasciculations. In the neuritides the myotatic irritability may be increased, and one may note exaggeration of muscular response to direct stimulation, although the deep reflexes are diminished. In myositis the irritability may be either increased or decreased, and in the dystrophies it is usually diminished. In myotonia there is a persisting contraction following mechanical stimulation of muscle, and in tetany and tetanus there is hyperexcitability to such stimulation.

Muscle tenderness may also be elicited by palpation of the muscles. In the neuritides, especially, squeezing of the muscle masses or the tendons, or even very slight pressure upon them, may cause exquisite pain. Tenderness is also observed in poliomyelitis. It is of diagnostic significance in both, especially if accompanied by paresis, flaccidity, and loss of tendon reflexes. Decrease in tenderness, or rather decrease in deep pain sensation, is noted in tabes dorsalis. Increase in tenderness and loss of deep pain are sensory rather than motor manifestations, but one may appraise them during palpation of the muscles in the examination of muscle tone.

REFERENCES

AGATE, F. J., JR., DOSHAY, L. J., and CURTIS, F. K. Quantitative measurement of therapy in paralysis agitans. *J.A.M.A.* 160:352, 1956.

BRENNAN, J. B. Clinical method of assessing tonus and voluntary movement in hemiplegia. *Brit. M. J.* 1:767, 1959.

BRUMLIK, J., and BOSHES, B. Quantitation of muscle tone in normals and in parkinsonism. *Arch. Neurol.* 4:399, 1961.

COBB, S., and WOLFF, H. G. Muscle tonus: A critical review based on work presented at the International Neurological Congress, Bern, Switzerland, 1931. *Arch. Neurol. & Psychiat.* 28:661, 1932.

DEJONG, H. H. Experimental Catatonia: A General Reaction-Form of the Central Nervous System, and Its Implications for Human Pathology. Baltimore, The Williams & Wilkins Company, 1945.

DE JONG, J. D., and BURNS, B. D. An investigation of Parkinson's disease. *Neurology* 12:402, 1962.

FULTON, J. F. Muscular Contraction and Reflex Control of Movement. Baltimore, The Williams & Wilkins Company, 1926.

HOEFER, P. F. A. Physiological mechanisms in spasticity. *Brit. J. Phys. Med.* 15:88, 1952.

LANDAU, W. M. The essential mechanism in myotonia: An electromyographic study. *Neurology* 2:369, 1952.

LANDAU, W. M., WEAVER, R. A., and HORNBEIN, T. F. Fusiform nerve function in man. *Arch. Neurol.* 3:10, 1960.

LINDSLEY, D. B., SCHREINER, L. H., and MAGOUN, H. W. An electromyographic study of spasticity. *J. Neurophysiol.* 12:197, 1949

MAGOUN, H. W., and RHINES, RUTH. Spasticity: The Stretch Reflex and Extrapyramidal Systems. Springfield, Ill., Charles C Thomas, 1947.

MCKINLEY, J. C., and BERKWITZ, N. J. Quantitative studies on human muscle tonus: I. Description of methods. *Arch. Neurol. & Psychiat.* 19:1036, 1928.

NATHAN, P. W. Intrathecal phenol to relieve spasticity in paraplegia. *Lancet* 2:1099, 1959.

PENRY, J. K., HOEFNAGEL, D., VAN DEN NOORT, S., and DENNY-BROWN, D. Muscle spasm and abnormal postures resulting from damage to interneurones in spinal cord. *Arch. Neurol.* 3:500, 1960.

POLLOCK, L. J., and DAVIS, L. Muscle tone in parkinsonian states. *Arch. Neurol. & Psychiat.* 23:303, 1930.

OLAFSON, R. A., MULDER, D. W., and HOWARD, F. M. "Stiff-man" syndrome. *Mayo Clinic Proc.* 39:131, 1964.

RADEMAKER, G. G. J.   On the lengthening and shortening reactions and their occurrence in man.   *Brain* 70:109, 1947.

RUSHWORTH, G.   Spasticity and rigidity: An experimental study and review.   *J. Neurol., Neurosurg. & Psychiat.* 23:99, 1960.

SHERRINGTON, C. S.   Postural activity of muscle and nerve.   *Brain* 38:191, 1915.

THOMAS, J. E.   Muscle tone, spasticity, rigidity.   *J. Nerv. & Ment. Dis.* 132:505, 1961.

WARTENBERG, R.   Some useful neurological tests.   *J.A.M.A.* 147:1645, 1951.

WEBSTER, D. D.   Dynamic measurement of rigidity, strength, and tremor in Parkinson patients before and after destruction of the mesial globus pallidus.   *Neurology* 10:157, 1960.

WELCH, W. K., and KENNARD, M. A.   Relation of cerebral cortex to spasticity and flaccidity.   *J. Neurophysiol.* 7:255, 1944.

CHAPTER 29

MUSCLE VOLUME AND CONTOUR

THE VOLUME and contour of the individual muscles and the muscle groups give information about the presence of either atrophy or hypertrophy. There is an appreciable individual variation in muscular development, but noteworthy changes in the size and shape of the muscle masses, especially if such changes are circumscribed or asymmetric, may be significant in the examination of the motor system, and on occasion are among the earliest signs of motor dysfunction.

Atrophy may be defined as the wasting or diminution in size of a part. Atrophy of muscles consists of a decrease in their volume or bulk, and is usually accompanied by changes in shape or contour. In the neurologic examination one is specifically concerned with wasting of muscles secondary to nervous system disease, or atrophy of neurogenic origin. Atrophy, however, may also be the result of disease of the muscle itself, resection of its tendon, inactivity, deficient blood supply, inadequate nutrition, endocrine changes, and toxic and infectious factors.

Hypertrophy is an increase in the bulk, or volume, of muscle tissues. It may be the result of excessive use of the muscles, or it may be on a pathologic basis. In myotonia there is what appears to be hypertrophy without actual increase in strength. In some of the myopathies there is pseudohypertrophy due to infiltration of the muscles with fat and connective tissue.

EXAMINATION OF MUSCLE VOLUME AND CONTOUR

Muscle volume and contour are examined and atrophy or hypertrophy appraised by inspection, palpation, and measurement.

By means of *inspection* the general muscular development and the size of the individual muscles and muscle groups are noted, and special attention is paid to abnormalities in volume and contour and to evidences of atrophy and hypertrophy.

Symmetric parts of the two sides of the body should be compared, and the muscular landmarks carefully scrutinized. Any flattening, hollowing, or bulging of the muscle masses should be investigated. The muscles of the face, shoulder and pelvic girdles, and distal parts of the extremities—especially the palmar surfaces of the hands, the thenar and hypothenar eminences, and the interosseous muscles—should be examined specifically. One should also at this time make note of congenital absence of or defects in skeletal muscles.

The muscle masses should also be carefully *palpated,* and their volume, contour, and consistency noted. Normal muscles are semielastic and regain their shape at once when compressed. In myotonia and hypertrophy the muscles are firm and hard; in pseudohypertrophy they appear enlarged but may feel doughy or rubbery on palpation; atrophic or degenerated muscles are soft and pulpy in consistency. Palpation is not a final criterion, however, for degenerated muscles that have undergone fibrous changes may be hard and firm, whereas those that have been overgrown with or replaced by fat may be doughy and rubbery.

In order to determine the degree of atrophy or of hypertrophy, *measurements* may be essential. A pronounced increase or decrease in the size of muscles may be recognized at the first glance, especially when confined to one side of the body or to one extremity or one segment of a limb. If the differences are slight, however, it may be extremely difficult to come to any conclusion from comparison of the corresponding muscles and muscular groups on the two sides of the body by inspection alone, and measurements are necessary. A tapemeasure, calipers, or an oncometer may be used. The size of the individual muscles and the circumference and size of the extremities are measured and compared. Measurements should all be made from fixed points or landmarks, and the sites—such as the distance above or below the olecranon, anterior superior iliac spine, or patella—should be recorded. The extremities should be in identical positions and in equal states of relaxation or contraction, and similar parts of the body should be examined on the two sides. It is often valuable, also, to measure the length of the limbs.

If either atrophy or hypertrophy is present, the distribution should be noted. The changes may be limited to an *individual muscle,* to all the muscles supplied by a *specific nerve,* to those supplied by certain *segments of the spinal cord,* or to *one half of the body,* or they may be *generalized* or *diffuse.* It must be borne in mind, however, that there is a great deal of individual variation in muscular development, in part constitutional and in part due to training, activity, and occupation. Certain individuals have small or poorly developed muscles, whereas others show outstanding muscular development. Individuals who do sedentary work, elderly persons, and those with chronic disease may have small muscles without evidence of wasting or atrophy. Athletes may have substantial muscular development without true hypertrophy. It is also important to remember that in normal individuals there is some difference in the size of the muscle masses and even of the hands and feet on the two sides of the body. In a right-handed person the right side shows better development. The appraisal of bulk and contour should be correlated with the other parts of the motor examination, especially with the evaluations of strength and tone and the electrical tests. In the atrophies associated with arthritis and disuse there may be a pronounced decrease in volume with little change in strength. In the myopathies, on the other hand, there may be little apparent atrophy in spite of a striking loss of power.

If muscular changes in the form of atrophy or hypertrophy are present, and if there is any question regarding etiology, a *muscle biopsy* should be taken. This procedure is usually carried out under local anesthesia. The examiner should be certain that the muscle tissue removed is obtained from the involved area. The tissue is examined for microscopic evidence of pathologic change. One should note the size of the individual muscle fibers, the presence or absence of striations, the character of the sacroplasm, and the appearance and location of the nuclei, and should look for replacement of muscle tissue by connective or fatty tissue, vascular changes, phagocytic or lymphocytic infiltration, and other pathologic alterations. The character of the nerve fibers and motor end-plate may also be observed. Special staining technics are often indicated. The biopsy examination of muscle is valuable in diseases such as myositis, the myopathies, and trichinosis. Examination of the skin and subcutaneous tissues may also give essential information, especially in such conditions as periarteritis nodosa and dermatoneuroangiomyositis.

Electromyography and *electrical testing* of the affected muscles may also aid in the differential diagnosis of muscular atrophy.

ABNORMALITIES OF VOLUME AND CONTOUR

MUSCULAR ATROPHY

Muscular atrophy may be caused by many processes. The most important variety of atrophy is that of neurogenic origin. This latter type must, however, be differentiated from those which are secondary to other etiologic factors. The various types of atrophy are discussed individually.

NEUROGENIC ATROPHY

Under normal circumstances each muscle is being bombarded constantly by a rhythmic volley of motor impulses from the anterior horn cells (Chapter 28). These stimuli are responsible for the trophic state of the muscle. As long as the motor nuclei, their neuraxes, the myoneural junction, and the muscle fibers are in a state of health, the nutrition and tonus of the muscle are maintained. When these impulses no longer reach the muscle, owing to disease of the anterior horn cells or of their neuraxes, certain changes take place. The muscle lies inert and flaccid, and no longer contracts voluntarily or reflexly. There is an alteration in the electrical excitability and in the chemical irritability and constituents. All the affected fibers lose weight and decrease in size, and as a result there is wasting or atrophy of the entire muscle mass. Associated with the loss of substance there may be either a decrease or an increase in connective tissue. There may be fibrotic changes, and the atrophied muscle may be infiltrated by or overgrown with fat. This is *neurogenic atrophy;* the more abrupt or extensive the interruption of nerve supply, the more rapid is the wasting. The atrophy may either precede or follow other evidences of muscular dysfunction, such as paralysis and flaccidity. In rapidly progressing diseases the paralysis and flaccidity precede the atrophy, whereas in degenerative and slowly progressive diseases the atrophy precedes the paralysis and flaccidity. If the pathologic process is confined to the anterior horn cells or the spinal cord, the atrophy is segmental in distribution, whereas involvement of the peripheral nerves is followed by wasting of those muscles supplied by the involved nerves.

Poliomyelitis is characterized by sudden onset and rapid destruction of the anterior horn cells. Atrophy may develop within a short period of time, but it does not appear until after the paralysis. It is segmental in distribution, dependent upon the location of the pathologic process within the spinal cord, and the degree of paralysis and atrophy parallels the severity of the disease. Microscopically there is widespread reduction in size of paralyzed fibers, but there seldom is any increase in fibrous tissue in relation to the atrophy, and when fibrosis is prominent it is probably related to either contracture or overstretching.

Progressive bulbar palsy, progressive spinal muscular atrophy, and *amyotrophic lateral sclerosis* are wasting diseases in which there is a slow but widespread degeneration of the motor nuclei and anterior horn cells, causing a progressive muscular atrophy which may appear before paralysis is evident (Fig. 133). The distribution of the atrophy has been referred to as segmental, but in general the changes are rather diffuse and begin in particular groups of muscles. In progressive bulbar palsy the atrophy is first noted in the muscles supplied by the twelfth, tenth, and seventh cranial nerves; in progressive spinal muscular atrophy of the Aran-Duchenne type it is first seen in the distal musculature—the thenar, hypothenar, and interosseous muscles of the hand, and the small muscles of the foot—and then spreads up the limbs to the proximal parts; in infantile progressive spinal muscular atrophy (Werdnig-Hoffmann paralysis) the atrophy first involves the trunk, pelvic, and shoulder muscles and then spreads toward the periphery. An outstanding manifestation of the above syndromes is the presence of fasciculations in the involved muscles (Chapter 31). Microscopically there is much variation in the size of muscle fibers, with groups of atrophic fibers scattered among normal ones, demonstrating differential atrophy of multiple motor units. In the heredofamilial muscular atrophy described by Kugelberg and Welander principally the proximal muscles are affected; because of this distribution and also because of the slow progression of this disorder, it may be mistaken for muscular dystrophy.

Segmental atrophy may also follow *focal spinal cord lesions* involving the anterior horn cells. The rapidity of the progress depends upon the type of pathologic change. In syringomyelia, where there is a slow degeneration, fasciculations may be seen in the involved muscles.

With isolated *lesions of the peripheral nerves* there is atrophy consequent to interruption of innervation of muscle. The atrophy follows the paralysis, but with traumatic nerve lesions it may develop within a short period of time. It is limited to the muscles supplied by the involved nerve, and the characteristic distribution of paralysis and wasting seen in some of more frequently encountered isolated neuritides may be found in Chapter 44. It has been stated that within a month after denervation there may be a 30 per cent loss of weight of the affected muscle, and a 50 per cent loss in two months; thereafter the atrophy progresses more slowly, and there may be replacement by connective tissue and infiltration by fat.

In *multiple neuritis* and the chronic polyneuritides the atrophy may be more gradual, but is more widespread. The motor changes may vary from slight weakness and wasting to widespread paralysis and atrophy, but are usually greatest in the distal portions of the extremities. The distal atrophy of the peroneal or neural type of muscular atrophy of Charcot-Marie-Tooth (Fig. 134) resembles more closely that of a severe chronic polyneuritis than that of the spinal atrophies; pathologically there is a chronic degeneration of peripheral nerves and nerve roots, although there may be associated changes in the spinal cord as well.

Interruption of the *sensory nerve fibers* alone does not lead to muscular atrophy, although it is possible that some trophic impulses pass to the anterior horn cells by way of the posterior roots, and atrophy may occasionally appear, after some period of time, with destruction of the posterior roots; this is seen in conditions such as tabes dorsalis. It is probable, however, that either interference with autonomic impulses or disuse may be the actual cause of such atrophy. In addition to motor and sensory neurons, however, there are *trophic neurons,* of autonomic origin, which have to do with nutrition and metabolism of muscle and other tissues. In diseases of the lower motor neuron one may find, in addition to muscular atrophy, other "trophic changes" in the skin and subcutaneous tissues, with edema, cyanosis or pallor, coldness, sweating, changes in the hair and nails, alterations in the texture of the skin, osteoporosis of bone, and even ulcerations and decubiti. Interruption of the autonomic fibers may be a factor in muscle atrophy, owing to "trophic dysfunction" as well as to loss of vasomotor control. The changes in the skin, nails, hair, and subcutaneous tissues are the result of interruption of the autonomic pathways, vasomotor paralysis, and destruction of the vasoconstrictor fibers. Interruption of the sensory fibers with loss of pain sensation may predispose to ulcerations following trauma and burns. The complete syndrome of peripheral nerve dysfunction, with paralysis and atrophy, sensory impairment, areflexia, and changes in the skin and other tissues is the result of interruption of motor, sensory, and autonomic fibers. There may be extensive trophic changes with ulcerations at the site of anesthetic areas, decubiti, bone changes, and arthropathies.

It is generally stated that lesions of the upper motor neurons are not followed by atrophy of the paralyzed muscles, although if such lesions are of long duration, and date from birth or early childhood, there may be failure of development of the muscles in the involved portions of the body that may simulate atrophy. If the onset occurs later in life, there may be some generalized loss of muscle volume and secondary wasting because of disuse and also possibly because of spasm or contracture and perverted nutrition of the anterior horn cells from lack of centrifugal stimulation; it is never severe and muscles retain their electrical irritability. Experimentally, however, lesions of the motor cortex (area 4) and the descending pyramidal pathways may be followed by muscular atrophy, and on occasion severe wasting appears with cerebral hemiplegias. The atrophy progresses rapidly if it appears early, and slowly if it appears late. Usually in these cases there are associated trophic and sensory changes, and the wasting may in part be secondary to involvement of the postcentral gyrus or parietal lobe, lesions of which are known to be followed by atrophy of the contralateral portions of the body. The loss of muscle bulk associated with involvement of these latter structures may appear promptly, and the degree depends upon the size and character of the lesion and the extent of the hypotonia and sensory change. The distribution is determined by the localization of the process within the parietal lobe. It is most severe if the motor cortex or pathways are involved along with the sensory areas of the brain.

Congenital hemiatrophy, which may involve the face, or the face and the corresponding half of the body, is characterized by underdevelopment together with progressive atrophy, involving not only the muscles but also the skin, hair, subcutaneous tissues, connective tissue, cartilage, and bone (Fig. 88). It may be the result of autonomic nervous system involvement and/or cerebral pathologic changes. There may be underdevelopment of one half of the body secondary to either lack of development or atrophy of the opposite cerebral hemisphere.

OTHER VARIETIES OF MUSCULAR ATROPHY

Myogenic, or *myopathic, atrophy* is that which arises as a result of disease within the muscles themselves. It may result from the fact that the muscle is no longer able to respond to the impulses sent out from the anterior horn cells, or it may be secondary to specific muscular dysfunction. Atrophy of muscular origin may develop in the myopathies and in the various types of myositis.

Wasting of muscle tissue is an important manifestation of the *dystrophies.* In these conditions atrophy, flaccidity, and weakness may appear simultaneously. The involvement is predominantly of the proximal rather than the distal muscula-- ture, and the shoulder and hip girdles are principally affected (Fig. 135). In the pseudohypertrophic type of Duchenne, which usually has its onset in childhood, the pelvic and shoulder muscles are first weak and atrophic. As the disease progresses there is increasing wasting of all the muscles of the shoulders, upper arms, pelvis, thighs, and chest. There appears to be hypertrophy of the calf muscles; these, however, are not hard and firm but are either soft and doughy or elastic and rubbery on palpation (Fig. 215). The limb-girdle variety, including the scapulo-humeral dystrophy of Erb, affects primarily the shoulder and upper arm muscles; occasionally there is pseudohypertrophy of the deltoid, teres, and spinati muscles. In the facioscapulohumeral type of Landouzy-Dejerine the atrophy predominates in the muscles of the face, shoulder girdles, and arms (Fig. 87). Distal myopathy, affecting the muscles of the hands and feet, is occasionally seen. Other related conditions include amyotonia congenita, benign congenital hypotonia, and congenital nonprogressive myopathy. In dystrophia myotonica the atrophy may be generalized, but is most marked in the facial and sternocleidomastoid muscles. Microscopic examination in the dystrophies reveals marked variation in the size of individual muscle fibers, with some swollen and others atrophic; there is vacuolization and hyaline degeneration of the muscle, and infiltration of connective tissue and fat between the muscle fibers.

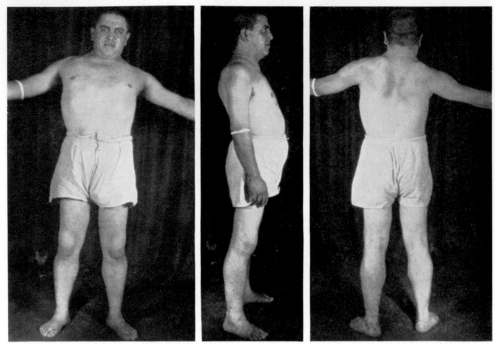

Fig. 215. Pseudohypertrophic muscular dystrophy; shoulder and pelvic girdle muscles are weak and atrophic; marked lordosis; pseudohypertrophy of calf muscles.

In *myositis,* or polymyositis, there is muscular weakness, often symmetric and usually proximal, along with pain, tenderness, atrophy, and increased irritability; there may be flaccid paresis. Microscopically there is a patchy inflammatory reaction with cellular infiltrations, proliferation of sarcolemmal nuclei, and degeneration of muscle fibers. Myositis may be related to dermatomyositis, periarteritis nodosa, or disseminated lupus erythematosus, as a part of a generalized collagen disturbance. Specific varieties of myositis, such as those associated with trichinosis and cysticercosis, may also be encountered.

Atrophy of disuse follows prolonged immobilization of a part of the body. It must be differentiated from neurogenic atrophy. Wasting of this type is characterized by shrinkage of the muscle fibers and reduction in the amount of the sarcoplasm, but there is no loss of striations and no degeneration of the individual muscle fibers or changes in the electrical responses of the muscles. There is no degeneration of the nerves or their endings. The loss of volume may develop almost as rapidly as that which follows absence of stimulation from anterior horn cells. It is brought about by immobilization and the inability of the muscle to respond to stimuli. Changes in lactic acid content, phosphorus and potassium metabolism, and oxygen utilization may also play a part.

Atrophy of disuse may occur in an extremity that has been in a splint or cast, one that cannot be moved due to joint involvement such as arthritis or periarthritis, or one that is paretic following a cerebral lesion. It also develops in tenotomized muscles, in the skeletal muscles of an individual who has been bedfast for any period of time, and in extremities which are not used owing to hysterical paralysis. In this latter condition vasomotor and trophic changes are occasionally seen, contractures may develop, and it may be difficult to differentiate between an organic and a psychogenic lesion.

Arthrogenic atrophy may appear in association with joint disease. In atrophic arthritis (arthritis deformans, or rheumatoid arthritis) the predominant muscular atrophy is in the region of the involved joints; it is usually most marked in the extensor muscles, and in those proximal to the affected joints. It is more severe and rapid in development in acute arthritis. Atrophy of this type may in part be the result of inactivity or disuse, but other suggested causative factors include some reflex influence from the diseased tissues upon the anterior horn cells, possibly secondary to pain and infiltration; involvement of the smaller branches of the motor nerves or of the autonomic nervous system innervation of the atrophic area; muscle spasm; and metabolic changes.

Nutritional atrophy may occur in a variety of circumstances. A normal blood supply is essential to the nutrition and oxygenation of muscles. Interruption of the blood supply may lead to muscle atrophy as well as to alterations in the skin and other trophic changes. If the atrophy is caused by interruption of the continuity of a single artery, the changes are found in the distribution of the occluded vessel. In *Volkmann's ischemic contracture* there is atrophy due to loss of nutrition and oxygenation of a group of muscles; this is usually accompanied by trophic changes in the skin and subcutaneous tissues. Atrophy on a nutritional basis may also occur with cachexia and weight loss. The muscle change is usually generalized. Possibly some vitamin deficiency is the most important factor, although deprivation of oxygen, changes in lactic acid content, disturbances of phosphorus and potassium metabolism, etc., are also significant.

Endocrine dysfunction of various types may lead to atrophy and other changes in muscle. In *chronic thyrotoxic myopathy* there may be weakness, fatigability, and muscular atrophy that may be either localized and diffuse, but the hip and shoulder girdle areas are usually the most severely affected. Coarse fasciculations are often seen in the involved areas. A syndrome of periodic paralysis may also be present with thyrotoxicosis. With *hyperinsulinism* there may be distal muscular atrophy accompanied by paresthesias; this is probably secondary to neuronopathy. With *hyperparathyroidism* there may be symmetric weakness and associated atrophy; mainly the proximal muscles are affected. Muscular weakness and atrophy are also frequent findings in *pituitary cachexia* and in *Addison's disease*. Muscle wasting also occurs with *diabetes*. The most common syndrome is that characterized by distal weakness and atrophy, secondary to a peripheral neuropathy. There are, however, cases with localized, asymmetric atrophy that does not correspond to peripheral nerve distribution; these have been termed diabetic amyotrophy. Patients with diabetes may also develop either localized lipodystrophy or areas of focal muscular atrophy following injections of insulin.

Miscellaneous causes of muscular atrophy may include toxic and infectious factors, amyloidosis, senile atrophy, and trauma. In the amyotrophies associated with carcinoma and the reticuloses the atrophy is not dependent upon cachexia or invasion from the primary tumor. Muscle atrophy may develop in association with the administration of some steroids; this usually is reversible upon withdrawal of the drugs. Occasionally atrophy develops in patients with long-standing myasthenia gravis and periodic paralysis. In localized panatrophy there is wasting of all subcutaneous tissues, and in larger areas the muscles may also be involved; this may be related to either hemiatrophy or scleroderma. In adiposis dolorosa the muscles may be replaced with fat.

MUSCULAR HYPERTROPHY

Hypertrophy of muscles is encountered less frequently than atrophy. Extremely muscular individuals may show pronounced development of certain groups of muscles. This is often found in athletes, smiths, and foundry workers, and may be termed a *functional hypertrophy*. The occupational history may give relevant information. Hypertrophy of the muscles, real or apparent, may be seen in the *myotonias*. Microscopic examination may show an increase in the diameter of all individual muscle fibers. There is, however, a disproportion between muscle bulk and power, and although the muscles appear strong, they may actually be weak. In *dystrophia myotonica* there is myotonia, with or without hypertrophy, but also atrophy, especially of the facial and sternocleidomastoid muscles. In *hypertrophia musculorum vera* there is enlargement of the muscles, usually of the limbs, but any area may be affected. The hypertrophy is progressive, but spontaneous arrest usually occurs. The enlarged muscles may have increased strength, or there may be diminished power and ready fatigue. Electrical reactions are normal. There is no pathologic alteration other than increased size of muscle fibers. In *de Lange's syndrome* there is muscular hypertrophy occurring at birth, with associated extrapyramidal motor disturbances and mental deficiency. Enlarged muscles with reduced strength, fatigability, and slowness of contraction and relaxation may be found in association with *hypothyroidism* and clinical myxedema; in cretinism and infantile hypothyroidism there may be diffuse muscular hypertrophy (the *Debré-Semelaigne syndrome*). In the early stages of *acromegaly* there may be generalized muscular hypertrophy with increased strength, but in later stages these is weakness and amyotrophy. Edema and inflammation of muscles may simulate hypertrophy.

Congenital hemihypertrophy, which may involve the face, or the face and the corresponding half of the body, is more rare than the corresponding hemiatrophy; there are usually other anomalies of development. *Pseudohypertrophy* of certain muscle groups is seen in some of the muscular dystrophies, especially the pseudohypertrophic variety where changes occur principally in the calf muscles (Fig. 215). There is not, however, true hypertrophy, but a degenerative change in the muscles with fatty and connective tissue infiltrations (see above).

REFERENCES

ADAMS, R. D., DENNY-BROWN, D., and PEARSON, C. M.   Diseases of Muscle: A Study in Pathology (ed. 2).   New York, Hoeber Medical Division, Harper & Row, 1962.

AIRD, R. B., and NAFFZIGER, H. C.   The pathology of human striated muscle following denervation.   *J. Neurosurg.* 10:216, 1953.

FENICHEL, G. M., DAROFF, R. B., and GLASER, G. H.   Hemiplegic atrophy: Histological and etiologic considerations.   *Neurology* 14:883, 1964.

GARLAND, H.   Diabetic amyotrophy.   *Brit. M. J.* 2:1287, 1956.

HENSON, R. A., RUSSELL, D. S., and WILKINSON, M.   Carcinomatous neuropathy and myopathy: A clinical and pathological study.   *Brain* 77:82, 1954.

KIRSCHBAUM, W. R.   Histological studies of muscle tissue in neuro-muscular disease.   *J. Neuropath. & Exper. Neurol.* 11:373, 1952.

KUGELBERG, E., and WELANDER, L.   Heredofamilial juvenile muscular atrophy simulating muscular dystrophy.   *Arch. Neurol. & Psychiat.* 75:500, 1956.

MAGEE, K. R., and CRITCHLEY, M.   Gowers' local panatrophy and its relation to certain types of insulin lipodystrophy.   *Neurology* 7:307, 1957.

MAGEE, K. R., and DE JONG, R. N.   Hereditary distal myopathy with onset in infancy.   *Arch. Neurol.* 13:387, 1965.

MULDER, D. W., BASTRON, J. A., and LAMBERT, E. H.   Hyperinsulin neuronopathy.   *Neurology* 6:627, 1956.

RINGNOSE, R. E., JABBOUR, J. T., and KEELE, D. K.   Hemihypertrophy.   *Pediatrics* 36:434, 1965.

SILVERSTEIN, A.   Diagnostic localizing value of muscle atrophy in parietal lobe lesions.   *Neurology* 5:30, 1955.

SUNDERLAND, S., and LAVARACK, J. O.   Changes in human muscle after tenotomy.   *J. Neurol., Neurosurg. & Psychiat.* 22:167, 1959.

WALTON, J. N. (ed.)   Disorders of Voluntary Muscle.   Boston, Little, Brown & Company, 1964.

CHAPTER 30

COORDINATION

ALTHOUGH MOTOR strength and power may be preserved, active movements may be severely affected in conditions in which there is a disturbance of coordination.

In order to carry out any movement, but especially a complex act which involves many muscle groups, it is necessary that the agonists, antagonists, synergists, and muscles of fixation be adequately correlated. The agonists contract to execute the movement; the antagonists relax or modify their tone to facilitate it; the synergists reinforce the movement; the fixating muscles prevent displacements and maintain the appropriate posture of the limb. The individual muscles which enter into the act must be associated in proper and harmonious grouping with synchronous or successive contraction for regulated control of movement. The rate, range, and force of each component part of the act must be regulated. Strength must be steadily maintained. In addition sensory functions, especially proprioceptive ones, must be intact. Coordination may be defined as the normal utilization of motor, sensory, and synergizing factors in the performance of movements. All three are necessarily present in the organization of the perfectly executed act.

The various disturbances of coordination, such as ataxia, dysmetria, asynergy, and dysdiadokokinesia, have been defined and described, along with other disturbances of function and the principal syndromes that occur in cerebellar disease (see pp. 436–442). In this section the tests for coordination and the method of examining correlated motor functions will be presented.

The cerebellum is essential to synergy and is considered to be the center of coordination; the following tests are mainly examinations of cerebellar function. It is important to bear in mind, however, that all of the component levels of the motor system enter into the performance of smooth and accurate muscular activity. Paresis due to involvement of the spinomuscular level may interfere with skill and precision. Diseases of the extrapyramidal system may influence control because of rigidity, akinesia or bradykinesia, lack of spontaneity, and loss of associated movements. A pyramidal lesion may cause jerkiness and clumsiness of movement and loss of control and integration of skilled acts. Psychomotor disturbances often cause difficulty with coordination, and an hysterical or a malingered derangement may simulate a true ataxia. Weakness and abnormalities of tone of any type may interfere with coordination. In the hyperkinesias there may be irregularity in the timing and excursion of successive movements.

Skilled motor activity is dependent upon all levels of motor integration, but the sensory and vestibular systems also play significant roles. *Sensory functions,* especially proprioceptive ones, are essential to the proper correlation of motor acts. Disturbances of the kinesthetic modalities, especially those conveying knowledge of motion, position, and weight, may cause loss of motor control. There may be disturbances of coordination with lesions of the peripheral sensory nerves, dorsal funiculi of the spinal cord, asscending proprioceptive pathways in the brain stem, and parietal lobes of the brain.The *labyrinths* and the *vestibular apparatus* are intimately connected with the cerebellum and are essential to equilibratory control. Diseases of the vestibular apparatus may be difficult to differentiate from disturbances of cerebellar function.

Diseases of other parts of the nervous system may also cause defects of coordination. The connections between the motor cortex and the cerebellum, the cortico-pontocerebellar tracts, are important pathways in motor control, and the motor cortex of one cerebral hemisphere is intimately connected with the opposite cerebellar hemisphere. It may be difficult to differentiate between symptoms caused by a lesion of the motor cortex on one side and those secondary to involvement of the contralateral cerebellar hemisphere. Lesions in the medulla, pons, and midbrain, too, frequently cause disturbances in coordination. In such lesions there may be involvement of the ascending proprioceptive pathways (including the spinocereballar tracts), the vestibular nuclei and their connections, the corticopontocerebellar fibers, or one of more of the cerebellar peduncles. Only in disease of the cerebellum, however, is coordination markedly disturbed in the absence of other changes in motor or sensory function or of other evidences of focal nervous system dysfunction. In the strict sense of the word, the term incoordination may be assumed to signify lack of accuracy of movement which is not secondary to paresis, abnormality of tone, or the presence of involuntary movements.

Disturbances of coordination may differ in degree and type. There is a definite individual variation in motor control, and in disease processes there may be a variation from slight incoordination to severe ataxia. *Agility* is the ability to carry out skilled movements rapidly. *Flexibility,* or *suppleness,* is the ability to move joints with ease through their full range. *Balance* is adequately controlled neuromuscular activity resulting from parallel functions of the motor and kinesthetic systems. Disturbance of any of these may lead to clumsiness or awkwardness of movement. *Equilibratory coordination* is the maintenance of balance, especially in the upright position; *nonequilibratory coordination* is concerned with discrete intentional movements of the extremities, mainly the finer motions. *Static ataxia* is the failure of coordination while in the resting state—the extended but otherwise static extremity cannot be held quietly without swaying or oscillating; *motor,* or *kinetic, ataxia* appears only on movement. The former is the more severe, and if it is present there is also motor ataxia; motor ataxia, however, may be present without static ataxia.

The performance of skilled or complicated acts—those which require higher cerebral control in either the motor or sensory spheres, together with psychic elaboration of the ideational plan before the act is carried out—is considered as an *eupractic function*. The perfect execution of such acts is known as *eupraxia*; a disturbance of the execution of skilled acts is *apraxia*. The eupractic functions and their disturbances will be considered under the cerebral functions (Part VIII).

EXAMINATION OF COORDINATION

Various special examinations may be carried out in the testing of coordination. but oftentimes a careful observation of the patient during the examination as a whole may give much information. He should be watched while he is lying, seated, standing, and walking. He should be observed carefully while carrying out both routine and skilled acts. His performance while dressing and undressing, buttoning and unbuttoning his clothes, and tying his shoe laces should be noted, as should tremors and hyperkinesias. Any disturbance of postural fixation should be described. He may be asked to carry out simple acts such as writing his name, using simple tools, drinking a glass of water, and tracing lines with a light pen while no support is given at the elbow. The general observation of the patient in the above circumstances and while carrying out the above actions may yield as much information concerning coordination as a detailed clinical examination. This is especially true in infants and children, in whom the examination may have to be limited to simple observation of activity during relaxation and at play and by noting the child's ability to reach for and use common toys and objects.

In the detailed testing of coordination one must bear in mind the various portions of the nervous system that may be involved, and their relationship to each other. Tests for coordination may be divided into those concerned with equilibratory and nonequilibratory functions.

EQUILIBRATORY COORDINATION

Equilibratory coordination, or the maintenance of balance and the coordination of the body as a whole, is noted in the examination of station and gait. Only abnormalities characterized by ataxia will be mentioned here; other disturbances are listed elsewhere (Chapter 32). If an abnormality is present while the patient is resting or in a stationary position, it may be considered as a variety of static ataxia; if while the body as a whole is in motion, as motor, or kinetic, ataxia.

The patient may first be observed while he is in the lying or seated position; only very gross disturbances of coordination will be apparent. There may be oscillations or unsteadiness of the body even while lying down. The patient may be unable to fix and coordinate the spinal, trunk, pelvic, and shoulder muscles properly, and may lack the ability to maintain a steady seated position; he may sway or fall if seated without support. There may be nodding movements of the head.

It is in the standing position, however, that moderate disturbances of equilibratory coordination first become apparent. The patient is asked to stand with his feet closely approximated, first with his eyes open, and then closed. The position of the body as a whole and that of his feet, shoulders, and head should be noted, as should tremors, swaying, and lurching. In a sensory type of ataxia, especially if the conduction of the proprioceptive impulses through the spinal cord is impaired, as in tabes dorsalis, the patient may be able to maintain the upright position while the eyes are open, but when the eyes are closed he sways and tends to fall. This is the *positive Romberg sign*. He may attempt to prevent the swaying by placing his feet some distance apart, thus standing with a broad base. In the vermis or midline cerebellar syndrome, which affects principally equilibrium, the patient may have difficulty in standing erect and maintaining a steady position with the eyes either open or closed. He may sway and lurch from side to side or backward and forward, and there may be oscillatory movements of the entire body. He may separate his feet in order to maintain his position. If he falls, it is generally in a backward or forward direction. Even in cerebellar disease, however, the difficulty is somewhat more marked when the eyes are closed. In a unilateral, or hemispheric, cerebellar lesion, or in a unilateral disturbance of vestibular function, the patient will sway or fall toward the involved side. While standing the head may be tilted toward the involved side with the chin rotated toward the sound side, and the shoulder on the involved side is somewhat higher and slightly in front of the normal one.

Various modifications of the postural examination may be carried out. Difficulty with balance may be accentuated if the patient stands with his feet in a tandem relationship—with one heel directly in front of the opposite toes, and especially if he attempts to follow movements with his eyes, not his head. The patient may be given a light push, first toward one side and then toward the other; in a hemispheric lesion he will lose his balance more easily when pushed toward the involved side. He may then be asked to stand on one foot at a time. With hemispheric lesions he may be unable to maintain his equilibrium while standing on the ipsilateral foot, but may stand without difficulty on the contralateral foot. With vermis involvement, diffuse cerebellar disease, and some toxic states, he may move about as though skating or waltzing. In all of these tests sensory can be differentiated from cerebellar ataxia by accentuation of the difficulty when the eyes are closed, and unilateral cerebellar or vestibular disease from vermis involvement by laterality of unsteadiness. In hysteria there may be a false Romberg test; there may be marked unsteadiness, but the swaying is at the hips rather than at the ankles.

Coordination of the body as a whole may also be tested by asking the patient to rise from a lying to a seated position without the use of his hands, and from a seated position to an erect one; to bend forward, flex his trunk and touch the floor with his hands, and then resume the erect position; to bend the head and trunk as far backward as possible, and to bend from side to side. In rising from the supine position he may fail to press down his lower extremities; consequently he will raise his legs, especially the one on the involved side, instead of lifting his trunk forward. In rising from a seated position he may fail to flex his thighs and pull his knees and trunk forward, and accordingly will be unable to secure or maintain balance. In bending forward he may be unable to coordinate the functions of the spinal, pelvic, and lower extremity muscles to maintain balance. In bending backward he may fail to flex his knees to prevent falling. In bending from side to side he may have more difficulty with balance on the involved side, and tend to fall toward that side. If the patient attempts to jump on one foot, while the eyes are either open or closed, unilateral ataxia may be demonstrated.

Gait is tested by having the patient walk forward and backward with the eyes open and closed. Disturbances of function which are moderately evident in the evaluation of station may become more marked in the examination of gait. Any swaying, staggering, or deviation should be noted. With a vermis lesion the patient will exhibit a lurching, staggering, titubating type of gait, both with the eyes open and closed, but without laterality. With sensory ataxia the patient may walk fairly well with his eyes open, as long as he is able to watch the floor and the surrounding environment, but on closing his eyes he sways and staggers. With a hemispheric cerebellar lesion the patient will stagger and deviate toward the involved side.

These abnormalities of gait can be further amplified by certain variations of the test. The patient may be asked to walk along a straight line on the floor, or he may be asked to walk tandem, i.e. by placing one heel directly in front of the opposite toes, both with the eyes open and closed. He is told to walk in a sideward direction and overstep, or cross one foot over the other, in so doing. He is instructed to walk forward and then turn around rapidly, or to walk around a chair, first in a clockwise direction, then counterclockwise. With hemispheric lesions there is a deviation of the body, with a tendency to fall toward the involved side, whereas with vermis lesions the ataxia will be as marked toward one side as the other. The difficulties in gait may be accentuated by asking the patient to walk rapidly or to run, by asking him to arise abruptly from a seated position and walk, or by having him stop abruptly or turn abruptly on command. In the stepping test he is asked to mark time for one minute with his eyes closed; with unilateral cerebellar disease he will gradually rotate the axis of his body toward the involved side. An alternate test is carried out by having the patient walk forward and backward eight steps repeatedly with his eyes closed; with hemispheric lesions there will be a gradual turning toward the affected side ("compass gait"). It must be borne in mind, however, that the above tests may give abnormal responses with disease of the vestibular complex as well as of the cerebellum, and one must elicit additional signs in order to differentiate between the two.

NONEQUILIBRATORY COORDINATION

In testing nonequilibratory coordination we are concerned with the patient's ability to carry out discrete, oftentimes relatively fine, intentional movements with the extremities. Many elements of coordination should be observed. One should note the patient's ability to *control the muscles and movements* that normally act in harmony and to *associate the various components of an act* in their proper synchrony, sequence, and degree, so that the act may be carried out smoothly and accurately; disturbances of these functions cause *dyssynergy*. One should observe his ability to *judge and control the distance, speed, and power* of an act and its component parts; loss of these results in *dysmetria*. The ability to *carry out successive movements* and to stop one act and follow it immediately by its diametric opposite should be appraised; difficulty with these functions causes *dysdiadokokinesia, loss of check movements,* and the *rebound phenomenon.* Finally, one should note the position of the individual parts of the body, especially the extremities, and *posture holding;* defective postural fixation may be diagnostically significant. It must be recalled that in cerebellar disease there are not only the above elements of incoordination, but also hypotonia, asthenia or slowness of movement, and postural deviation, all of which may contribute to the motor disturbance, together with other findings such as dysarthria, nystagmus, tremors of an intention type, usually with an ataxic element, and other abnormal movements (Chapter 24).

In testing coordination of the upper extremities, various routine or special tests may be carried out. It is well to preface these by an inquiry about the patient's handedness, as it goes without saying that right-handed individuals show somewhat more awkwardness in carrying out skilled acts with the left hand. One should also notice the patient's general motor ability and his agility and skill in carrying out various motor acts. Occasionally in toxic and fatigue states and with heavy sedation there may appear to be a clumsiness of motor ability which, while not normal to the individual, is not indicative of focal disease.

The *finger-to-nose test* may be carried out with the patient in the lying, seated, or upright position. He is asked to abduct and extend the arm completely, and then to touch the tip of his index finger to the tip of his nose. The test is performed slowly at first, then rapidly, and with the eyes open, then closed. The examiner may place the outstretched extremity in various positions, and have the test carried out in different planes and from various angles. One should note the smoothness and accuracy with which the act is executed, and look for oscillations, jerkiness, and tremor. An intention tremor may be evident during this test, and often becomes more marked and more coarse and irregular as the finger approaches the nose; a resting tremor may disappear during the test. In sensory ataxia the subject may carry out the act without too much difficulty while the eyes are open, but may be unable to find the nose when the eyes are closed, owing to loss of appreciation of position in space. In cerebellar ataxia the difficulty may vary from slight incoordination with a blundering type of movement to complete inability to execute the act. With dysmetria the patient may stop before he reaches his nose (hypometria), pause and then complete the act slowly and unsteadily (bradyteleokinesia), or either overshoot the mark or bring the finger to the nose with too much speed and force (hypermetria). With dyssynergy the act is not carried out smoothly and harmoniously; there may be irregular stops, accelerations, and deflections, or the act may be decomposed into its constituent parts. If the lesion responsible for the difficulty is confined to one cerebellar hemisphere, the ataxia is limited to that side of the body, or there may be consistent deviation to the ipsilateral side of the nose. If the finger-to-nose test is carried out against slight resistance, the act is reinforced, and slight ataxia becomes more manifest or latent ataxia evident. Such resistance may be applied by having the examiner place his fingers on the volar surface of the patient's forearm and exert slight pressure while the patient moves his arm toward the nose, or by placing a rubber band around the patient's wrist and pulling gently on it during the test. In hysteria there may be bizarre responses of various types; the patient may appear to be unable to touch the finger to the nose, or he may circle it around from one side to the other with widespread, wandering movements, but eventually approximate it to the very tip of the nose.

In the *nose-finger-nose test* the patient touches the tip of his index finger to his nose, then touches the tip of the examiner's finger, and again touches the tip of his own nose. The examiner's finger is moved about during the test, and the patient is asked to touch it when held at different sites as well as to vary the rate of perform- ance; in this way distance, speed, and power are all tested, as well as repetitive movements. The examiner may withdraw his finger slowly, and note the patient's ability to follow it accurately while making repeated efforts to touch it.

In the *finger-to-finger test* the patient is asked to abduct the arms to the hori- zontal, and then bring in the tips of the index fingers through a wide circle to approximate them exactly in the midline. This is done slowly and rapidly and with the eyes first open and then closed. With unilateral cerebellar disease there is deficient abduction; the finger on that side may not reach the midline, and the finger of the normal side crosses the midline to reach it. Also the arm on the affected side may sag and undershoot, so that the finger on that side will be below the one on the normal side.

The usual test for *dysdiadokokinesia* is carried out by having the patient alter- nately pronate and supinate his hands, either outstretched or with the elbows fixed to his sides. The movements are performed as rapidly as possible. Any movement, however, that is concerned with reciprocal innervation and alternate action of agonists and antagonists can be used. The patient may be asked to open and close his fists alternately, flex and extend individual fingers rapidly, approximate the tips of the index finger and thumb, or the tip of the flexed index finger against the interphalangeal joint of the extended thumb (Fisher) repetitively and rapidly, tap on a table with his finger tips, pat his hand rapidly against a table top, pat the palm of one hand alternately with the palm and dorsum of the other, or pat the thighs with the palms and dorsa of the hands alternately. A good test for both dysdia- dokokinesia and rapid skilled movements is carried out by having the patient touch the tip of his thumb with the tip of each finger rapidly and in sequence; he should be instructed to start with the index finger and proceed to the little finger, repeat with the little finger and proceed to the index finger, repeat with the index finger, and thus carry on the test. Coordination, speed of movement, and fatigue can be estimated quantitatively by counting the numbers of times the patient taps a button of a laboratory key counter in a given period of time. Dysdiadokokinesia of the tongue may be tested by having the patient protrude and retract his tongue or move it from side to side as rapidly as possible. In all of these tests the rate, rhythm, accuracy, and smoothness of the movements should be noted. Ataxia may be more obvious with rapid alternating contraction of antagonists. With dysdiadokokinesia one act cannot be followed immediately by its diametric opposite; the contraction of one set of agonists and relaxation of the antagonists cannot be fol- lowed immediately by relaxation of the agonists and contraction of the antagonists. As a consequence, the test is either carried out slowly, with pauses during transition between the opposing motions, or it is done unsteadily and irregularly with loss of rhythm. There may be a rapid fatigability, and the movements may be executed satisfactorily in the beginning, but after a few attempts they become awkward and clumsy; prolonged attempts may lead to confusion and cessation. The two extremities should be examined at the same time, and the normal compared with the abnormal; with unilateral testing the difficulty may not be very marked on either side, but simultaneous testing may cause accentuation of the abnormality on the affected side. In hemispheric disease of the cerebellum there is ipsilateral dysdiadokokinesia. It is important to remember that in normally right-handed individuals skilled movements are not quite as accurate or rapid on the left side. A diagnosis of dysdiadokokinesia cannot be made in the presence of motor paresis, bradykinesia, or gross sensory changes.

The check movements of antagonistic muscles, the ability to contract the antagonists immediately after relaxation of the agonists, and the brake mechanism after the sudden release of a resistance opposing a strong voluntary movement are all evaluated in the *rebound test of Gordon Holmes*. The patient is asked to adduct his arm at the shoulder, flex his forearm at the elbow and supinate it, and clench his fist firmly. The elbow may be supported on a table or it may be held unsupported close to the body. The examiner pulls on the wrist against resistance and then suddenly releases it. In the normal individual the contraction of the biceps and other flexors of the forearm is followed almost immediately by contraction of the triceps, the tendency toward flexion is checked by the rapid action of the antagonists, and the movement of the limb is arrested. In cerebellar disease, on the other hand, when the strongly flexed extremity is suddenly released the individual is unable to stop the contraction of the flexors and follow it immediately by contraction of the triceps. There is loss of the "checking factor." As a consequence the hand flies up to the shoulder or mouth, often with considerable violence. The test may be carried out in other ways. Extension of the forearm against resistance may be tested instead of flexion. Both arms may be outstretched in front of the patient, and the examiner may press either down or up on them against resistance, and then suddenly let go. In this way the rebound phenomenon and loss of checking movements can be compared simultaneously on the two sides.

To test *pointing and past pointing* the patient and examiner are placed opposite each other, either seated or standing, and the outstretched upper extremity of each is held in the horizontal position with the index fingers in contact, or with the patient's index finger placed upon the tip of the examiner's index finger. The patient is then asked to elevate his arm to a vertical position, so that the finger is pointed directly upward, and then return the arm to the horizontal position in such a way that his index finger will again approximate the examiner's. This should be done first with the right arm and then with the left, and should be tried a few times with the eyes open, and then with them closed. Both arms may be tested simultaneously. After the test has been carried out with the patient raising his arm, it may be repeated by having him lower his arm to the vertical position, and then bring it up to the horizontal. It may also be carried out in the horizontal plane (the patient abducts his arm to the horizontal and swings it into the midline) and frontal plane (the patient moves his arm either outward or inward to approximate the examiner's finger). In the normal individual there will be no deviation, but in cerebellar or labyrinthine disease there will be deviation to the involved side, or past pointing, more marked with the eyes closed. The more often the test is repeated, the greater will be the deviation. In vestibular disease there is deviation, or past pointing, of both upper extremities toward the involved side; this is also the side which shows the slow component of the nystagmus. In unilateral cerebellar disease there is past pointing toward the side of the lesion, but only in the ipsilateral arm; there may also be displacement in a downward direction. Furthermore, there is no specific correlation between the direction of the nystagmus and the direction of the past pointing. Vestibular tests may be of further aid in this differentiation.

Position holding in the upper extremities can also be tested, and static ataxia evaluated. The patient is asked to stand with both arms outstretched in front of him at the horizontal level, and to hold them thus, with the eyes first open and then closed. With unilateral cerebellar disease the ipsilateral arm is gradually deviated laterally owing to predominant activity of the abductor muscles. The arm on this side may also be elevated slightly owing to defective grading of movement and overactivity of extensor muscles, or it may be held lower than the normal one, the result of asthenia, hypotonicity, and loss of tonic contraction of the muscles surrounding the joints. Such deviation occurs more promptly and to a greater degree when the eyes are closed; it may be accentuated by having the patient raise his arms to the vertical and then lower them to the horizontal several times. The examiner may tap the patient's outstretched wrists and note either the patient's ability to maintain them in position or the amount of deviation that may occur. Normally there should be sufficient resistance to hold the extremities in their previous position, but with cerebellar disease there may be greater displacement than normal, the arm will swing up and down a few times, and there will be gradual lateral and upward deviation. If the patient tries to hold a joint rigid while the examiner attempts rhythmic alternate movements, there may be instability and rebound owing to imbalance of antagonistic muscles. If support is suddenly withdrawn from braced outstretched arms, the one on the side of a cerebellar lesion will fall through a greater angle and develop irregular movements. There is also a characteristic position of the extended hand in cerebellar disease. The wrist is flexed and arched dorsally, the fingers are hyperextended, and there is a tendency toward overpronation. This position is probably associated with the hypotonia. The hand is similar to that seen in Sydenham's chorea. There may be loss of normal pendular movements of the arms in walking, but in the shoulder-shaking test there is an increase in the range and duration of swinging of the arms, although the movements may be irregular and nonrhythmic.

Other special examinations may be carried out. The patient's judgment of the power and range of movement, as well as accuracy and direction, may be tested by having him make a fist and drive it into the examiner's outstretched palm with as much force as possible. Another test for dysmetria consists in having the patient, with pencil or chalk, draw a straight line, starting and stopping at fixed points. He may have difficulty starting at the correct point and may either stop before he reaches the second point or overshoot the mark. The evaluation of the patient's ability to carry out rapid, skilled, delicate movements with the fingers is often important. His skill in using tools and scissors may be a valuable criterion. He may be asked to thread a needle, pick up pins, put a stylus in a hole, use a pegboard, string beads, pour water from one test tube to another, or draw circles on a board or paper. It is true that many of these acts test other motor functions as well as coordination, but they aid in evaluating the latter. Having the patient grab one thumb with the opposite hand, when the former is held at various levels and positions, tests coordination as well as proprioceptive sensation. With a unilateral cerebellar lesion the patient may underestimate the weight of objects placed in the ipsilateral hand, whereas with an extrapyramidal lesion he may overestimate such weights (Bing).

Tests similar to those used in the upper extremities may be applied to the lower extremities. In the *heel-to-knee-to-toe test* the patient is asked to place the heel of one foot on the opposite knee and then push it along the shin in a straight line to the great toe. If there is dysmetria, he will undershoot or overshoot the mark, and in the presence of dyssynergy the movement may be broken down into its constituent parts and the descent along the shin is jerky and unsteady. Intention tremor and oscillations may be evident. With spinal ataxia the patient may have difficulty in locating the knee with the heel, and may grope around for it; there is difficulty in maintaining the heel on the shin, and it may slide off either laterally or medially during its descent. Similar tests of the lower extremities can be carried out by having the patient place his foot on a chair or some other fixed object, or by asking him to kick the examiner's hand with his foot. The rate, range, and force of movements may be tested by having the patient touch the examiner's finger with his great toe; the finger is moved about during the test, and the patient is asked to touch it at various sites as well as to vary the rate of performance. The patient may be asked to draw a circle or a figure **8** with his foot, either with the foot elevated or on the floor; with ataxia the movement will be unsteady and the figure irregular.

Dysdiadokinesia is tested by alternate dorsiflexion and plantar flexion of the feet or the toes, tapping the floor or some fixed object with the sole of the foot, or tapping the heel of one foot against the shin of the other leg. Rebound is tested by sudden release on the part of the examiner after he has been resisting either flexion or extension at the knee, hip, or ankle.

Position-holding in the lower extremities can be tested in various ways. The patient, lying supine, is asked to raise his legs in the air, one at a time. If there is ataxia the leg cannot be lifted steadily or in a straight line to a vertical position. There may be adduction, abduction, rotation, oscillations, or jerky movements from one position to another. When the limb is again lowered the patient may throw it down heavily and it may not return to its original position, next to its mate, but may be deviated across it or away from it. The seated patient may be asked to extend his thighs and legs without support and attempt to hold them steady; with a unilateral cerebellar lesion there may be oscillations and lateral deviation of the ipsilateral extremity. The patient, lying prone, is asked to flex his legs at the knees and maintain them in the vertical unsupported position; with unilateral cerebellar disease there may be marked oscillations and lateral deviation of the ipsilateral leg. With cerebellar lesions there is increased range and duration of pendulousness of the legs when the extended supported legs are released or given a brisk push.

In both the upper and the lower extremities the patient may be asked to reproduce in one limb the position in which the other has been placed by the examiner. This may be carried out with the tests for position holding. It is in reality, however, a method of evaluating proprioceptive sensibility rather than coordination.

In the differential diagnosis of disturbances of coordination it must be recalled that *sensory ataxia* is always most apparent with the eyes closed. The disability is the result of impairment of proprioceptive sensibility. The patient may be able to carry out simple and complex acts without too much difficulty if vision can be substituted for kinesthetic sensation, but with the eyes closed there is a marked disability. Such disturbances are found predominantly in posterior column disease, and consequently in such disorders as tabes dorsalis and posterolateral sclerosis. There may also be sensory ataxia with disease of the peripheral nerves, interruption of the proprioceptive pathways in the brain stem, and disease of the parietal lobe.

Cerebellar ataxia is present with the eyes open and closed, although the difficulty may be more marked when the eyes are closed. There are the two clearly defined cerebellar syndromes. With the *vermis,* or *midline, syndrome* the outstanding symptoms are those of disturbance of equilibratory coordination, with marked abnormalities of station and gait. In the *hemispheric syndrome* there is non-equilibratory ataxia, with disturbance in coordination of the ipsilateral extremities, the arm more than the leg. These syndromes and the associated disturbances of function in cerebellar disease are discussed in Chapter 24.

Unilateral *vestibular disease* may simulate cerebellar involvement, but there is much more subjective vertigo, and there is postural deviation with kinetic deviation and nystagmus, without a great deal of real dysmetria or dyssynergy. Caloric, rotation, and galvanic tests are of aid in the diagnosis. In disease of the brain stem there may be interruption of the proprioceptive pathways, involvement of the cerebellar peduncles, disturbance of function of the vestibular nuclei and their connections, or dysfunction of other structures, such as the inferior olivary bodies or the red nuclei, which are allied to the cerebellum in function and intimately connected with it. In olivopontocerebellar atrophy there is involvement of the olives, the pons, and the cerebellum. In the posterior inferior cerebellar artery thrombosis the ataxia is in part due to changes in the cerebellum, but also due to involvement of the restiform body. In the acoustic neurinoma, or cerebellopontine angle neoplasm, there is vestibular involvement, but also dysfunction of the cerebellum. In multiple sclerosis and Friedreich's ataxia the symptoms may be those of sensory involvement in the spinal cord and brain stem with cerebellar dysfunction.

Disturbance of function of the contralateral frontal lobe, especially the motor centers, may result in difficulty in coordination which may closely resemble that which follows involvement of the ipsilateral cerebellar hemisphere. In fact, especially in the presence of neoplasms, the differentiation between the two may be extremely difficult. If, however, the lesion is a cerebral one, one should expect to find hyperactivity of the tendon reflexes, increase in tone, and pathologic reflexes in the involved extremities, while in purely cerebellar lesions one would expect hypotonia, diminished or pendular reflexes, and no pathologic reflex responses. Pressure of a cerebellar neoplasm on the brain stem may, however, cause pyramidal tract involvement which may confuse the picture. One would expect more marked papilledema in a cerebellar (posterior fossa) neoplasm than in a cerebral one, but again this finding cannot always be relied upon. It may be necessary to carry out a ventriculogram, or other special procedures, to locate the neoplasm.

REFERENCES

BING, R. Cerebellopallidal anisosthenia. *Neurology* 1:10, 1951.

FISHER, C. M. A simple test of coordination in the fingers. *Neurology* 10:745, 1960; An improved test of motor coordination in the lower limbs. *Ibid.* 11:335, 1961.

KABAT, H. Analysis and therapy of cerebellar ataxia and asynergia. *A. M. A. Arch. Neurol. & Psychiat.* 74:375, 1955.

MEYERS, R. An oculokinetic test of equilibratory co-ordination having differential diagnostic use. *J. Nerv. & Ment. Dis.* 109:226, 1948.

WARTENBERG, R. Cerebellar signs. *J.A.M.A.* 156:102, 1954.

CHAPTER 31

ABNORMAL MOVEMENTS

ABNORMAL MOVEMENTS, or hyperkinesias, may occur in a variety of forms and under many different circumstances. They are for the most part involuntary contractions of the voluntary muscles. They may be of great clinical significance in the diagnosis and localization of disease of the nervous system, and should be carefully observed and described as a part of the examination of the motor system.

Hyperkinesias may involve any portion of the body. They are symptoms and signs of disease, not disease entities. They may be the result of involvement of various parts of the motor system—the motor cortex and its descending pathways, basal ganglia, midbrain and brain stem centers, cerebellum and its connections, spinal cord, peripheral nerves, or the muscles themselves. They may be of organic origin, related to infectious processes, trauma, degenerative disease, inherited defects, anomalies of development, or neoplastic changes, or they may be of psychogenic origin. The character of the movement depends both on the site of the lesion and the type of pathologic change. Lesions at different sites sometimes cause identical movements, but on the other hand unlike pathologic processes which affect one part of the motor system may cause various hyperkinesias.

In the examination of abnormal movements, one should *observe* their clinical appearance and visible manifestations, *analyze* the pattern of the movements, and then *describe* the various components. The following should be carefully noted: the *part of the body involved,* or the exact location of the movements; the *extent* of the hyperkinesia, or its distribution as regards part of a muscle, an entire muscle, movement involving joints, or more complex or composite patterns consisting of a sequence of different movements; the *pattern, rhythmicity, uniformity, multiformity,* and *regularity of recurrence*—there may be a regular or rhythmic recurrence of activity involving the same muscle or groups, or there may be an irregular pattern of constantly changing motion of different parts (chorea); the *course, speed,* and *frequency* of each particular movement; the *amplitude* and *force* of the motor response; the *relationship* to *posture, rest, voluntary activity or exertion, involuntary movement,* and *fatigue;* the *response* to *heat* and *cold;* the *relationship* to *emotional tension* and *excitement;* the *degree* that they are *increased* or *controlled* by *attention;* the *presence* or *absence* of the hyperkinesia during *sleep.* If the movements fit into a definite clinical picture, a specific name should be applied to them, but it is better to describe rather than to attempt to name them. It may on occasion be possible, from their visible characteristics alone, to determine the site of the lesion responsible and the relationship of lesions at various sites to different forms of involuntary movements.

In addition of observation, *palpation* may be used, especially if the movements are very fine ones limited to individual muscles. Various mechanical, electrical, and other means have been used to record the frequency, rhythmicity, and amplitude of the various hyperkinesias, often in an attempt to evaluate the effects of treatment. These include myography, in which the oscillations are transmitted directly to a moving drum or kymograph, electromyography, and other electronic, photoelectric, and electromechanical devices. A cinemotographic record often gives valuable and important information.

The more important of the hyperkinesias are described in detail.

TREMORS

A tremor is a series of involuntary, relatively rhythmic, purposeless, oscillatory movements which results from the alternate contraction of opposing groups of muscles. Tremors may be of small or large excursion, and may involve one or more parts of the body. A *simple tremor* has only one component; it involves only a single group of muscles and its antagonists. A *compound tremor* involves several groups of muscles and is composed of several elements in combination; this results in a series of complex movements, as, for instance, alternate flexion and extension together with alternate pronation and supination. While one is concerned, in the evaluation of tremor, specifically with those muscles having reciprocal innervation, muscles of fixation and synergists also play a part in the movement. Tremors may be apparent on observation during either the resting state or activity, but often are accentuated if the patient is asked to hold his fingers extended and separated and his arms outstretched. Slow movements, writing, and the drawing of circles may also bring them out.

Tremors may be classified in various ways: location, rate, amplitude, rhythmicity, relationship to rest and movement, etiology, and underlying pathogolic change. Also important, however, in their appraisal, are their relationship to fatigue, emotion, attention, self-consciousness, heat, and cold. Tremors may be unilateral or bilateral; they are most commonly seen in the distal parts of the extremities—the fingers or hands—but may also be seen in the arms, feet, legs, tongue, lips, eyelids, jaw, and head. Occasionally they involve the entire body. They may be slow, medium, or rapid in rate. If there are from three to five oscillations per second, the tremor is slow; if there are ten to twenty oscillations per second, it is rapid. Tremors may be coarse, medium, or fine in amplitude. They may be either constant or intermittent and either rhythmic or relatively nonrhythmic; a certain amount of rhythmicity is implied, however, in referring to tremors. Their relationship to either rest or activity may be significant. Resting or static tremors are present mainly during relaxation and disappear with activity; motor or intention tremors appear only or mainly with deliberate, willed movement, and may become more marked toward the termination of such movement; tension or postural tremors become evident during a volitional increase in muscle tonus, as when the limbs are actively maintained in a certain position. Tremors may be present only with emotional tension or fatigue, or they may be accentuated by these factors. Even truly organic tremors are accentuated by emotional excitement, and most normal individuals may develop some tremors with tension, apprehension, cold, and fatigue. Tremors of the shivering type may be brought on by cold, but identical movements can be produced psychogenically. Many tremors fall into more than one group, as far as the above suggestions for classification are concerned, and for that reason it may be best to discuss the more important varieties individually without attempting to place them into definite categories.

There is a *normal* or *physiologic tremor* present during muscular contraction. This may be brought out by placing a limb in a position of postural tension or by performing voluntary movements at the slowest possible rate. This normal tremor varies from eight to twelve oscillations per second, with an average of ten in the young adult; it is somewhat slower in children and in older persons. The frequency for an individual is the same at different sites in the body. The visible tremors of normal persons that are brought out by tension, fatigue, and fright are doubtless accentuations of this physiologic tremor. There have been many theories regarding the source of this tremor. Recent investigators have shown that it persists in the absence of muscle innervation, and therefore have concluded that it does not have neural origin; they have suggested that cardiac and respiratory activity are responsible for it.

Fine tremors are usually *rapid tremors* (ten to twenty oscillations per second). They are usually referred to as *toxic tremors,* and the most typical example is that seen in *hyperthyroidism*. The movements involve principally the fingers and hands. They may be so fine that they are seen with difficulty, but may be brought out by placing a sheet of paper on the outstretched fingers, and the movement of the paper may be apparent even though the fingers are not seen to move. The tremor may be present both at rest and on activity, but it is accentuated by activity as well as by tension and apprehension. Similar tremors are found in association with other toxins such as alcohol, nicotine, caffeine, lead, and mercury, and various drugs such as bromides, barbiturates, chloral, cocaine, adrenaline, amphetamine, and ephedrine. Fine, rapid tremors are also seen in general paresis; here they involve principally the lips and perioral muscles. Fine tremors may be psychogenically initiated in tension and apprehension states, and they may be present in the psychoneuroses. A fine tremor of the closed eyelids (Rosenbach's sign) is seen in hyperthyroidism and in hysteria.

Tremors of medium amplitude and rate are often spoken of as psychogenic. They are seen in anxiety and neurasthenic states, and are precipitated by apprehension, tension, attention, fear, and fatigue, even in the normal individual. The intention tremor of multiple sclerosis and familial tremors are often of medium amplitude.

Coarse tremors occur in a variety of states; they are usually slow. That of Parkinson's disease is one of the most characteristic. Coarse tremors are also seen in Wilson's disease and other extrapyramidal syndromes. Senile familial tremors are coarse in amplitude, and those occurring in general paresis and alcoholism may also be coarse, especially if the movements are diffuse, as they are in delirium tremens. The intention tremor of multiple sclerosis may be coarse and irregular, especially when associated with ataxia. Psychogenic tremors and those associated with diseases of the midbrain and cerebellum may also be coarse and slow.

Resting, static, or nonintention tremors occur more frequently in diseases of the basal ganglia and extrapyramidal structures. The most characteristic tremor of this type is that seen in Parkinson's disease and the parkinsonian syndrome following encephalitis. This is a slow, coarse tremor of the compound type. The rate may vary from two to six oscillations per second, probably averaging at about four to five. The movement in the hand characteristically consists of alternate contractions of agonists and antagonists involving the flexors, extensors, abductors, and adductors of the fingers and thumb, together with motion of the wrist and arm including flexion, extension, pronation, and supination. As a result there is a repetitive movement of the thumb on the first two fingers, together with the motion of the wrist, which produces the so-called pill-rolling or bread-crumbing tremor. This is relatively irregular or nonrhythmic, and is it of the non-intention type; i.e., it is present with inactivity and becomes less marked with activity. It may disappear temporarily while the limb is engaged in some voluntary effort. It is probably incorrect, however, to say that the tremor is present at rest; it is present or most marked when the limb is in an attitude of repose or static posture, and disappears with complete relaxation. It is independent of voluntary movement and may be temporarily suppressed by such movement. Because of the uniformly alternating movements at regular intervals, it is sometimes called an *alternating* tremor. Occasionally the tremor of Parkinson's disease is of both the intention and nonintention types.

The above tremors not only involve the hands, but may also affect the feet, jaw, tongue, lips, and head. They may be unilateral at the onset, but eventually become bilateral in most cases. They disappear during sleep and are aggravated by emotional stimuli, fatigue, and self-consciousness. The associated manifestations of rigidity, loss of associated movement, and bradykinesia may be apparent, but in some patients the tremor is the predominant symptom, whereas in others the rigidity or bradykinesia may be more marked. The postulated relationship of this tremor to disease of the basal ganglia, substantia nigra, and related structures as well as surgical attempts at its relief are discussed in Chapter 22.

As was stated, this type of tremor is seen most characteristically in Parkinson's disease and postencephalitic parkinsonism. It is also present in related extrapyramidal syndromes such as those following carbon monoxide and manganese intoxication and the ingestion of certain drugs, especially the phenothiazines. *Senile tremors* may resemble parkinsonian ones in degree, amplitude, and rate. They, too, are usually present at rest, but may also be increased by activity. They commonly affect the head, jaws, and lips; the movement of the head may be in either an anteroposterior or a lateral direction. The onset occurs much later in life, and there is no associated muscular rigidity or weakness. Some senile tremors are of the familial or essential variety (see below), but late in onset.

Motor, kinetic, or intention tremors are absent while the individual is resting, but appear with activity. As long as the patient is quiet no tremors are apparent, but when voluntary movements are attempted, as when he brings the tip of his finger to his nose, the tremor becomes evident and may be very marked. It increases with continued movement and as the digit approaches the goal (terminal type). This tremor may be of medium amplitude and fairly regular in rhythm, or it may be coarse, jerky, and irregular, especially when associated with ataxia. It is also increased by emotional stimuli and attention. It may involve the extremities, head, or entire body.

This type of tremor is seen most characteristically in *multiple sclerosis,* and it is considered to be quite pathognomonic for this disorder; the tremor may be of either the medium or the coarse type. It is also seen in *Friedreich's* and *Marie's ataxias,* and in other cerebellar syndromes. It is believed to result from involvement of the cerebellar efferent pathways and their connection with the thalamus, and as a consequence usually indicates involvement of the superior cerebellar peduncle (brachium conjunctivum) or the dentothalamic or dentorubrothalamic pathways. If the disease process is in the *cerebellum* itself, the hyperkinetic phenomena are apt to be coarse in amplitude, with involuntary jerking movements that are increased by voluntary effort, although there may also be an oscillation of a more regular, rhythmic type in the absence of active innervation. Not only the extremities but also the head or entire body may be affected. These may in part be manifestations of ataxia, dyssynergy, and loss of the steadying effect which increased tonus of the antagonistic muscles normally affords to voluntary movements. Such hyperkinesias may be termed *ataxic tremors.*

Tension or postural tremors appear with a volitional increase in muscle tonus, as when the limbs are actively maintained in certain postures. Occasionally they are slightly increased by action, but they usually stop with movement. They are usually absent with complete rest, and become marked when the parts are placed in fixed attitudes. They may be brought out by having the arms and hands outstretched, or by stopping the finger-to-nose test a short distance from the nose and holding the finger in that position. They are finer and more rapid than resting tremors, averaging eight to twelve oscillations per second, and less rhythmic. *Familial (benign, essential) tremors* are usually of this type. They are not accompanied by rigidity, weakness, ataxia, or loss of associated movements. They are increased by emotional tension, cold, coffee, tea, and tobacco, and are temporarily decreased by sedatives and alcohol. They may also affect the tongue, head, and larynx. Thalamotomy similar to that used in the treatment of Parkinson's disease has also been employed in selected cases for the relief of incapacitating familial and intention tremors.

The tremor of *Wilson's disease* or *progressive lenticular degeneration* may take various types. There may be a slow, alternating tremor at rest, resembling that of Parkinson's disease, or a tremor that is increased by voluntary action. Most characteristic of the adult variety, however, is a coarse, irregular tremor that may be apparent during movement but is most marked during the maintenance of sustained postural attitudes (static intentional ataxia), and thus is not a true intention tremor. There may be violent up-and-down "flapping" movements of the hands and wrists while they are held outstretched and coarse "wing-beating" movements of the abducted shoulders. In severe cases this may even appear to be present at rest, but the parts are probably not completely relaxed, but under some tension, and the slightest stimulation may elicit the movement. The term *asterixis* (inability to maintain posture) has been proposed for this phenomenon (Adams and Foley). A similar tremor is seen in patients with severe liver disease, and occasionally in those with other conditions, including pulmonary disease.

Psychogenic tremors are often of medium amplitude, but they may be fine or coarse. They may be present at rest but they are usually accentuated by voluntary movement. They may appear when the part is being held still against the force of gravity, as when the arm is outstretched. They result from the contraction of opposing groups of muscles that are in use in the attempt to keep the extremity in a static position. They are precipitated or aggravated by tension, apprehension, attention, fatigue, and cold, and markedly so by emotional stress and strain. They may be brought on by fear, anxiety, or sudden fright, and may involve any part in the body. They may be habitual manifestations. They are seen in hysterical individuals, anxiety states, neurasthenia and other psychoneuroses, and also in almost every person under certain environmental conditions. The tremor of the hand that is accentuated when the individual is being observed closely and the shaking of the knees and tremulousness of the voice that appear when an inexperienced speaker has to address a large audience are common examples of tremors of this type. They may be accentuations of physiologic tremor.

Shivering, or *rigor,* consists of clonic movements of various groups of muscles, principally the masseters but also the muscles of the limbs and trunk. It may be of physiologic or psychologic origin; it is brought out by cold, but also by emotional stimulation. The movements may be inhibited to a certain extent by voluntary contraction of the muscles. Shivering is often accompanied by cutis anserina.

Tremors may occur under a variety of other conditions and may be important manifestations of numerous pathologic processes. Involvement of the *red nucleus* is followed by ataxia and tremor on the opposite side of the body. The tremor is coarse, slow, and rhythmic, and is present at rest; it is accentuated on and aggravated by voluntary movement. In Benedikt's syndrome there are such tremors with ataxia contralateral to the lesion, and an ipsilateral third nerve paralysis. The tremor of *alcoholism* may be of the fine, toxic variety, but it may also be coarse and slow, as in *delirium tremens* where it averages about four per second. The movements may involve the extremities, jaws, lips, face, tongue, or any part of the body. There may be violent tremors of the entire body. In chronic alcoholism one frequently observes a *Quinquaud's sign*. When the patient's fingers, abducted, flexed at the metacarpophalangeal joints, and extended at the interphalangeal joints, are placed vertically in the examiner's hand, at right angles to the palm, a trembling or wormlike sensation is felt, due to the slight shocks from the repeated up and down movements of the individual fingers. Alcoholic tremors may be extremely variable in type and rhythm and may be influenced or aggravated by emotional stimuli.

In *dementia paralytica* there may be tremors of the extremities and characteristically one sees them in the lips (perioral tremors) and tongue. Tremors are often seen in *acute infectious states.* In *spasmus nutans,* which occurs in infants from six months to two years of age, there is a rhythmic nodding or rotatory tremor of the head associated with a fine, rapid, pendular type of nystagmus. If the eyes are closed the tremor may either increase or decrease, and if the movement of the head is controlled the nystagmus usually increases. Tremors and other abnormal muscular movements may be present with disturbances of magnesium, calcium, sodium, and potassium metabolism, following the ingestion of certain drugs, and in various rare diseases, such as kuru, which has been described in New Guinea.

FASCICULATIONS

Fasciculations are fine, rapid, flickering or vermicular twitching movements that appear with contraction of a bundle or fasciculus of muscle fibers. They are usually not extensive enough to cause movement of joints, except occasionally in the digits. They vary in size and intensity. They may be so faint and small that they but slightly ripple the surface of the overlying skin, or they may be coarse enough to be apparent readily. They are often irregular and inconstant, and can be seen in muscles at one time and not at another. At times they are abundant, at others they require a careful search. They are usually present at rest, but they may be brought out, made more rapid, or intensified by light mechanical stimulation of the muscle or by placing it under tension. They are also brought out by fatigue and cold. They may be seen to course backward and forward throughout an entire muscle, without causing it to contract as a whole, or they may occur first in one part of a muscle and then in another. Adequate illumination is necessary in order to visualize them, and they may be seen best with oblique lighting. They may be more difficult to see in women than in men because of the presence of more subcutaneous fat in the former. Occasionally they can be palpated even though invisible to the eye, or they may at times be heard by the use of a stethoscope. Many patients are not aware of the presence of fasciculations, but others may either see or feel them, or both. Electromyography is of aid in their evaluation.

At one time the terms *fibrillation* and *fasciculation* were used synonymously. *Fibrillations,* however, are contractions limited to a single muscle fiber or to a group of fibers smaller than a fasciculus. They are fine, continuous, tremorlike contractions present in denervated muscle. They are too small to be visible through the skin, but occasionally are seen in strong reflected light on the surface of exposed muscle. Electromyographically these are of short duration (less than one or two milliseconds) and low voltage (rarely more than fifty microvolts). *Fasciculations* are contractions of a larger group of fibers, or fasciculus, usually constituting a single motor unit supplied by a single anterior horn cell. Such units may vary in size and may be composed of up to two hundred individual fibers. Fasciculations are thus more gross than fibrillations, and can be seen through the intact skin. They may be from eight to twelve milliseconds in duration, and the discharge is from one-half to one millivolt. They are present in sleep. They are activated by mechanical stimulation of the muscles, but are not affected by emotional or mental activity. They are accompanied by an electrical reaction of degeneration and increased chronaxie. They are exaggerated by the administration of neostigmine, physostigmine, organic phosphates, and acetylcholine, and in fact may be produced in normal individuals by such drugs. They are not abolished by spinal anesthesia or peripheral nerve block. They are completely obliterated by the administration of curare and the injection of local anesthetics directly into the muscle. Quinidine may also abolish fasciculations.

Fasciculations are seen most frequently, and are of most significance, in association with amyotrophy secondary to degeneration of the anterior horn cells of the spinal cord and the motor nuclei of the brain stem, in such conditions as progressive spinal muscular atrophy, progressive bulbar palsy, amyotrophic lateral sclerosis, and syringomyelia, and usually disappear by the time that atrophy is complete. They are rarely seen in the myopathies, disease processes such as poliomyelitis in which there is an abrupt loss of function of the anterior horn cells and their neuraxes, and conditions such as polyneuritis in which the atrophy results from peripheral nerve injury or disease. They are present on occasion, however, in all these conditions, and may be found in poliomyelitis, both in acute stages and in residually paretic muscles following acute poliomyelitis, acute inflammations of the peripheral nerves, compression of the peripheral nerves or nerve roots, myositis, peroneal muscular atrophy (Charcot-Marie-Tooth disease), extramedullary and intramedullary tumors of the spinal cord, toxic states such as thyrotoxic myopathy, uremia, and triorthocresol poisoning, and at times after spinal anesthesia and in completely denervated muscles. Movements similar to fasciculations may be seen as well as tremors with disturbances of magnesium, calcium, sodium, and potassium metabolism affecting the muscle or myoneural junction.

There is some difference of opinion about the exact mechanism and significance of fasciculations. Their mode and site of origin are not definitely known. It was formerly believed that they resulted either from irritation of the anterior horn cells, and were evidences of periodic discharges from these cells that stimulate the muscle fascicles, or from degeneration of these cells with alteration of the rhythmic volley of impulses from them. Failure to abolish fasciculations with interruption of innervation from these cells, however, suggests that some abnormality in the peripheral portion of the neuromuscular unit, probably in the region of the myoneural junction, is responsible. Fibrillations, which make their appearance from five to ten days after denervation of muscle, are evidences of disordered muscle metabolism secondary to loss of trophic influence from the anterior horn cells; there is an abnormal irritability of muscle, probably owing to heightened excitability of the sarcolemma or of rapidly conducting portions of the muscle fibers to traces of free acetylcholine in the tissues. These may originate in the motor end plate of a muscle fiber and extend along the course of the fiber. Fibrillations may be synchronized into fasciculations, or contraction of a group of fibers making up one motor unit, by antidromic impulses from the myoneural junctions. The fasciculations that occur in thyrotoxic myopathy and other toxic states are probably the result of increased concentration of acetylcholine at the myoneural junction or increased sensitivity of the muscle fibers to the transmission of acetylcholine. Those that occur with spinal cord neoplasms, ruptured intervertebral disks, and nerve root or nerve irritation are probably the physiologic equivalent of the contraction of a group of fibers supplied by a single axon. These may indicate either degeneration or irritation anywhere along the course of the lower motor neuron, from the anterior horn cell to the myoneural junction and the muscle. Their presence may be of value in the localization of disease of the spinal cord, nerve roots, or peripheral nerves.

Fasciculations should be searched for carefully, especially in conditions where there is evidence of muscular wasting. They are most significant when present in conditions such as progressive spinal muscular atrophy and amyotrophic lateral sclerosis, and in these indicate progressive degeneration of the anterior horn cells. They may serve as an index to the severity and prognosis of the disease; if they are numerous, the progress of the disease will probably be rapid. They are usually seen first in the shoulder girdles, upper arms, and chest muscles. They may disappear when atrophy is extensive. The presence of fasciculations that is not accompanied by atrophy, however, does not necessarily indicate the presence of a serious disease process. *Spontaneous, benign fasciculations* are not infrequently seen in normal persons, and are especially common in medical students and physicians. These may be present at rest or may be brought out by fatigue and tension states. There is no atrophy or other evidence of muscular or motor dysfunction, and there are no fibrillations by electromyography. It has been suggested that there may be some underlying biochemical or related abnormality at the myoneural junction that is responsible for these benign fasciculations, or they may be similar to the myokymic movements described below.

MYOKYMIC MOVEMENTS

Myokymias, or myokymic movements, are spontaneous, transient or persistent, movements that affect a few muscle bundles within a single muscle but usually are not extensive enough to cause movement at a joint. They are not limited to the muscle fibers or fasciculi, and they are somewhat more coarse, more slow and undulating, and usually more prolonged and widespread than fasciculations. They may be caused by irregular discharges spreading to and through various muscle bundles. There is no associated muscular atrophy. They usually are not affected by motion and position. The electromyogram shows only normal repetitive action potentials. These movements are sometimes referred to as false fasciculations. If they are quivering and flickering in character, they are commonly known as "live flesh."

Myokymic movements may be of physiologic origin. They may occur in normal individuals after strenuous and unaccustomed exercise, in association with unusual fatigue or exhaustion, or as a transitory occurrence in facial muscles, especially the orbicularis oculi. They may appear during an attempt to maintain contraction of weak muscles and disappear when the muscles are relaxed. They may occur with chilling or when going to sleep. They are most often seen, however, in conditions in which there is localized or constitutional weakness or fatigue, such as anemia, debilitating disease, infection, or metabolic disorders. They have been reported in hyperthyroidism and with salt deprivation, uremia, and tetany. They are occasionally familial, and are frequently present in neurasthenic or neurotic individuals, in whom they may appear during emotional stress. The muscular movements that appear in meningitis and dementia paralytica may in part be myokymias. Myokymic movements may be seen, along with fasciculations, in progressive spinal muscular atrophy and the related wasting diseases. Here they probably result from the fatigue that accompanies the weakness and atrophy.

Myokymic movements are occasionally accompanied by cramping and pain; usually there is an associated increase in myotatic irritability. They are not exaggerated following the administration of neostigmine, but are abolished during occlusion of circulation, appearing again about three minutes after the occlusion is removed. The clinical significance of these movements is doubtful, and they are often found in normal persons with no progressive neuromuscular disease. They certainly do not have the prognostic significance of fasciculations. It is believed that they are an expression of differing nutritional influences upon the irritability of either the anterior horn cells or muscle fibers, or they may result from spontaneous impulses arising within the motor nerve fibers. Some chemical process, such as a disturbance of sodium chloride metabolism or a change in the lactic acid content of the muscle or at the myoneural junction, may be responsible. One might raise the question whether so-called benign or spontaneous fasciculations might not more correctly be termed myokymic movements, especially if they are slightly more coarse and irregular than usual fasciculations. Possibly myokymic movements and benign fasciculations represent similar alterations in muscle physiology.

MYOCLONIC MOVEMENTS

The term *myoclonus* has been used for several differing motor phenomena. In general, however, a myoclonic movement may be defined as a disturbance of neuromuscular activity characterized by abrupt, brief, rapid, lightning-like, jerky, arrhythmic, asynergic, involuntary contractions involving portions of muscles, entire muscles, or groups of muscles regardless of their functional association. The movements may be either single or repetitive, and are similar to those which follow stimulation of a muscle. Myoclonias are seen principally in the muscles of the extremities and trunk, but the involvement is often diffuse and widespread, and they may be present in the facial muscles, jaws, tongue, pharynx, and larynx, and may appear symmetrically on the opposite sides of the body. They occur at a rate of ten to fifty per minute, but some varieties are much more rapid. They appear in paroxysms at irregular intervals, during either the resting or active state, but may be activated by emotional, mental, tactile, visual, and auditory stimuli. They may be decreased by voluntary movement and increased during relaxation. They appear during the process of going to sleep, but usually disappear during sleep.

Myoclonic movements, like fasciculations and myokymias, may be too small in degree to cause movement of joints but, on the other hand, they may, if they affect entire muscles or muscle groups, produce clonic movements of the extremities. They may be so violent that they cause an entire limb to be suddenly thrown out, or they may even throw the patient to the ground. There may be successive or simultaneous involvement of many muscles. If the movements are confined to groups of muscle fibers, they may resemble fasciculations, but there is no muscular atrophy and no change in the electrical reaction. Myoclonic movements are not activated by mechanical stimulation or stretching of the muscle and are not affected by neostigmine. Pathologically there has been found hyperplasia of the meso-dermal elements of the endomysium and perimysium. This is, however, probably the result of muscular hyperactivity for a long period of time, rather than a specific change.

There has been some difference of opinion regarding the pathologic process underlying myoclonic movements. It was once felt that the neural discharge which excites the muscular contraction was confined to the lower motor neuron. Their occurrence in association with various degenerative brain diseases, however, sug-gests that in most cases involvement of the cerebral cortex, gray matter, thalamus, substantia nigra, basal ganglia, dentate nucleus, cerebellum, and brain stem, alone or in combination, is responsible for them.

Myoclonic movements may occur in a variety of conditions, and their signifi-cance may vary. They have been observed in acute and chronic encephalitis, meningitis, toxic and postanoxic states, metabolic disorders, degenerative diseases, and vascular and neoplastic conditions; they have been reported with lesions of the peripheral nerves and the gray matter of the spinal cord. They frequently are symptoms of diffuse cerebral degenerative disease, especially in children. They may be of diagnostic significance in the lipidoses, subacute inclusion body encephalitis, the Hallervorden-Spatz and Creutzfeldt-Jakob syndromes, and Wilson's disease. On the other hand, some myoclonias may be benign and without serious significance, whereas others may be psychogenically precipitated. Movements difficult to differ-entiate from myoclonias may be present in hysteria. *Paramyoclonus multiplex of Friedreich* has been described as a disease of adult life coming on after fright, trauma, mental or physical exhaustion, or infection. There are paroxysmal con-tractions of the limb and trunk muscles, occurring at a rate of forty to fifty per minute, which are present at rest, aggravated by emotional stimulation, and dis-appear on voluntary contraction of the muscles and during sleep. The etiology is not known and many authorities question the existence of this syndrome. Singultus, or hiccup, may be due to myoclonic spasm of the diaphragm, but hiccup is usually a reflex response to irritation. Facial spasms and nystagmus have also been said to occur on a myoclonic basis, but other explanations are more sound from a scientific point of view.

Myoclonic movements are frequently encountered in epilepsy. Many epileptic patients have occasionally random myoclonic jerks of the axial or proximal limb musculature; these may appear or increase in frequency immediately prior to a seizure, and occur most frequently in hereditary light-sensitive and reading epilepsy. Massive myoclonic spasms of infancy are characterized by frequent, sudden, violent jerking attacks with flexion of the neck and trunk and adduction or abduction and extension of the arms and legs. The body may bend forward and the child may fall to the floor during the attack. These are often associated with systemic biochemical disorders or degenerative brain disease; the prognosis is poor and there may be intellectual and motor deterioration. In *familial myoclonus epilepsy of Unverricht and Lundborg* myoclonic jerkings are present during and between attacks and become intensified before the fit occurs. They may involve the muscles of the extremities, face, tongue, jaw, and pharynx. There is progressive motor and intellectual deterioration. Because Lafora inclusion bodies have been found throughout the central nervous system, as well as in other organs, in some patients with this syndrome it has been suggested that such cases be called Lafora's disease. In *myoclonic cerebellar dyssynergia* there are myoclonic jerkings and progressive cerebellar degeneration; Hunt attributed the movements to atrophy of the dentate nucleus, but his patients also had involvement of other parts of the nervous system.

While it has been stated that myoclonic movements are arrhythmic and diffuse, the term has also been applied to rhythmic and localized motor phenomena. So-called *palatal* (*palatopharyngolaryngo-oculodiaphragmatic*) *myoclonus* is characterized by involuntary movements of the soft palate and pharynx and sometimes of the larynx, eye muscles, and diaphragm, and occasionally other muscles. It may be unilateral or bilateral. The movements may vary from fifty to two hundred and forty per minute. They are not influenced by drugs or sleep but may be inhibited at first by voluntary effort. The uvula may deviate either upward and downward or to one side; the posterior pharyngeal wall moves laterally, and the larynx moves in an upward and downward direction. If the movements involve the diaphragm or larynx, they may cause a grunting respiratory noise. A clicking sound sometimes accompanies movements of the pharynx. This condition has been associated with lesions of the olivodentorubrometencephalic pathways, and there may be hypertrophy of the inferior olivary nucleus or involvement of the olivocerebellar or the central tegmental tracts, cerebellum, or brain stem. This syndrome most often has its onset in late adult life, and has been reported with vascular, neoplastic, inflammatory, and degenerative lesions. It has also been referred to as palatal nystagmus. Neither myoclonus nor nystagmus is a suitable term, however, as the movement is rhythmic and is actually a tremor. It can be called a myoclonus only if two entirely different motor phenomena are implied by the term.

CHOREIFORM MOVEMENTS

Choreiform movements are described as involuntary, irregular, purposeless, asymmetrical, nonrhythmic hyperkinesias. They are spontaneous in onset and are abrupt, brief, rapid, jerky, unsustained, and explosive in character. The individual movements may be discrete, but they are variable in type and location, so that there may be an irregular pattern of multiform, constantly changing movements of different parts of the body which appear at irregular intervals. There is an interruption of harmonious coordination of prime movers, synergists, and antagonists. The movements are present during the resting state but are brought out or increased by activity and tension. They are aggravated by emotional stress and attention and usually disappear during sleep. At times they appear to be subjectively purposeful, but they are objectively aimless.

Choreiform movements may involve one extremity, one half of the body, or the entire body. They are seen most characteristically in the upper extremities, where they involve principally the distal portions, but may also affect the proximal parts, the lower extremities, the trunk, face, tongue, lips, larynx, and pharynx. There may be repeated twitching and grimacing movements of the face which change constantly in character and location. The patient is frequently unable to hold out his tongue for any length of time, and when asked to protrude it he shoots it out and then jerks it back. The voice may be affected, and there may be abnormal vocalizations, difficulty maintaining phonation, or aphonia. There may be disturbances of chewing and swallowing. The movements of the hands may interfere with dressing and eating. There is a waxing and waning of the grip of the individual fingers when the patient grasps the examiner's hand; this causes the so-called milking grip. Oftentimes the movements may be brought out by asking the patient to carry out two acts at the same time; he can touch his finger to his nose if he does that alone, and he can protrude his tongue alone, but on attempting to do both simultaneously, the jerky movements become noticeable. The hyperkinesias interfere with and distort voluntary movements, and the latter may be sharp, jerky, and unsustained.

In addition to the movements, there is marked hypotonia of the skeletal musculature. As a result there is little force to the spontaneous movements and there is little resistance to passive movement. The outstretched hands are held with hyperextension of the proximal and terminal phalanges, flexion and dorsal arching of the wrist, and moderate overpronation, which is increased when the arms are raised above the head. The fingers are separated and the thumb is abducted and droops downward. In association with the hypotonia there is marked fatigability of the skeletal musculature. There is no paralysis, but the constantly repeated hyperkinesias and their interference with voluntary movement and sustained muscular contraction may cause a marked impairment of motor function. The tendon reflexes are of the pendular or "hung" variety.

The most characteristic choreiform movements are seen in *Sydenham's chorea*. also known as chorea minor, acute infectious chorea, and rheumatic chorea, and known by the laity at St. Vitus' dance. This occurs in childhood and adolescence. The movements may be limited to one extremity or one half of the body, or may be diffuse. In *Huntington's chorea*, or chronic hereditary chorea, the onset is in adult life and there is steady progression. The movements are similar to those of Sydenham's chorea, but are often somewhat slower, less jerky, and more bizarre, widespread, and violent. They may be seemingly purposeful, and the same pattern may be repeated over and over again. Frequently the larger muscle groups and the proximal portions of the extremities are affected, and there may be repeated shrugging of the shoulder girdle or flail-like movements of the arm. Facial grimacing may be more marked, and there may be twisting and lashing movements that lie between those of chorea and athetosis. Movements of the fingers and hands may be accentuated while the patient is walking. This condition is inherited as a mendelian dominant trait. It is always accompanied by progressive intellectual deterioration. Choreiform movements are also seen in chorea gravidarum, senile chorea, chorea associated with hereditary syphilis, encephalitic and arteriosclerotic processes, magnesium deficiency, and other more rare syndromes. Frequently a patient who is recovering from or has recovered from Sydenham's chorea may retain some tics or habit spasms (see below) which may be difficult to differentiate from residual choreic movements.

There is no unanimity of opinion regarding the specific location of the pathologic process responsible for choreiform movements. In Huntington's chorea there is atrophy of the caudate nuclei but there is associated involvement of the putamen and cerebral cortex, with diffuse degenerative changes in the brain. In Sydenham's chorea there are diffuse degenerative and inflammatory lesions that seem to affect mainly the striatum and cortex.

HEMIBALLISMUS

Movements similar to those of chorea are the ballistic movements, seen in *hemiballism,* or *hemiballismus.* These, too, are involuntary, purposeless movements, but are much more rapid and forceful and involve largely the proximal portions of the extremities. They are described as continuous, wild, violent, swinging, twisting, flinging, rolling, throwing, flail-like movements of the extremities. They are usually unilateral, and may involve one entire half of the body, but as a result of their intensity they may cause movement of the entire body. The movements may spare the face and trunk. They are ceaseless during the waking state and disappear only with deep sleep; because of their violence they may lead to exhaustion. Hemiballismus follows an isolated lesion, usually vascular in origin, of the contralateral subthalamic nucleus or its neighboring structures or pathways. The prognosis is usually considered to be very poor, but recoveries have been reported, or as the movements subside they may more closely resemble a hemichorea. Surgical procedures have brought about relief in some cases (Chapter 22).

ATHETOID MOVEMENTS

Athetoid movements, or those of *mobile spasm,* are slower and more sustained than choreiform movements, and their amplitude is somewhat larger. They are involuntary, irregular, coarse, relatively continuous, somewhat rhythmic, writhing or squirming movements. They are described as vermicular, undulating, sinuous, and snakelike. They may involve the extremities, face, neck, and trunk. In the extremities they affect principally the distal portions, the fingers, hands, and toes. The movements are characterized by any combination of flexion, extension, abduction, adduction, pronation, and supination, often alternating and in varying degrees (Fig. 216). Denny-Brown defines athetosis as a fluctuation of posture superimposed upon a persistent attitude; due to the release af two opposing actions, there are "swings" of movement from one to the other, as from hyperextenson of the fingers

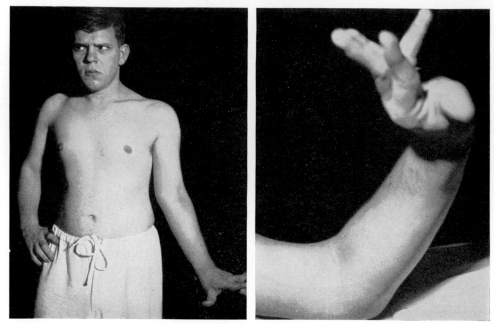

FIG. 216.   Congenital unilateral athetosis.

and wrist and pronation of the forearm to full flexion of the fingers and wrist and supination of the forearm. Facial grimacing, which is slower and more sustained than in chorea, often accompanies the movements of the extremities, and they may be synkinesias affecting other parts of the body. The hyperkinesias may not be constant or continuous, but may recur in series, intensified by voluntary motion or tension. They disappear in sleep. There is usually associated spasticity or hypertonicity of the musculature, with some paresis. Voluntary movements are disturbed and coordinated actions may be impossible.

Athetosis is usually of congenital origin and it may be present in association with varying degrees of congenital spastic paraplegia. It may be either unilateral or bilateral. The predominant pathologic changes are in the caudate and putamen, although there may also be cortical involvement. Double athetosis may be associated with status marmoratus or with brain changes resulting from erythroblastosis fetalis, kernicterus, or infantile encephalitis. Acquired athetosis may follow disease or trauma of later life.

In *pseudoathetosis* there are similar undulating and writhing movements of the extremities, which are more marked when the eyes are closed; there usually is no increase in muscle tone. Movements of this type occur with lesions of the parietal lobe and such conditions as tabes dorsalis, posterolateral sclerosis, and peripheral nerve disease. They are not true hyperkinesias, but are the result of loss of position sense.

Choreo-athetoid movements are those that appear to lie between choreiform and athetoid movements in rate and rhythmicity, and may represent a transitional form.

They probably result from a pathological process similar to that causing athetosis, but slightly at variance in location. They may be present with many disorders, including Wilson's disease, liver disease, and ataxia with oculocutaneous telangiectasia. Athetoid and choreo-athetoid movements have also been relieved in some instances by surgical measures (Chapter 22).

DYSTONIC MOVEMENTS

Dystonic movements, or manifestations of *torsion spasm,* are similar in many respects to those seen in athetosis, but they involve larger portions of the body, with distorted postures of the limbs and trunk resulting from excessive muscular tone in certain muscle groups. The movements are slow, bizarre, and grotesque in type, and they have an undulant, writhing, twisting, and turning character. They may start distally, usually in the foot, with plantar flexion and inversion, and then spread to the opposite side, the upper extremities, and the trunk, face, and tongue. In advanced cases there are writhing movements of the shoulder muscles, hip girdle, and trunk. The patient twists his spine in a peculiar fashion, bringing about marked torsion of the entire vertebral axis with lordosis, scoliosis, and tilting of the shoulders and pelvis. Dysarthria, facial grimacing, and torticollis may be present. The muscles are often in a constant state of hypertonicity, and the muscular contraction itself may cause severe pain. The movements are involuntary but are increased by voluntary activity and emotion. Eventually postures become fixed by contractures and deformities develop. Denny-Brown prefers to use the term dystonia for the postures assumed by the patient, or the fixed or relatively fixed attitude in association with other disorders of movement, rather than for the hyperkinesia itself.

Movements of this type are usually manifestations of *dystonia musculorum deformans,* a rare, heredofamilial disease that is progressive in nature. The condition is associated with pathologic physiology of the extrapyramidal level, principally the caudate and putamen. Dystonic movements and postures, however, may also occur in severe athetosis, status marmoratus, Wilson's disease, Huntington's chorea, tumors, and vascular disease. In *spasmodic torticollis* there are torsion movements of the head and neck and sometimes of the shoulders that resemble those seen in dystonia. In the beginning the twisting and turning may be intermittent, or present only in paroxysms, but later in the course of the syndrome there is persistent contraction of the involved muscles with resulting deviation of the head (Chapter 16).

SPASMS

Spasms are organically precipitated contractions of a single muscle or of a group of muscles, often of all the muscles supplied by a single nerve. Clonic spasms are rapid in onset and brief in duration and may be repetitive; they often result in movement of the affected part, and may resemble the muscular contractions induced by faradic stimulation. Tonic spasms are more prolonged or continuous; they may either cause prolonged alteration of position or limit movement. Spasms that limit movement may be defensive or protective. A painful, tonic, spasmodic muscular contraction is often spoken of as a cramp, or prolonged spasm may cause reflex rigidity or be followed by contracture of muscle.

Spasms are usually of reflex origin and may result from irritation or stimulation at any level from the cortex to the muscle fiber. In most cases, however, they are due to peripheral irritation affecting either muscles or nerves. They may occur in any of the body musculature. They must be differentiated from tics, or habit spasms, which are psychogenic manifestations or conditioned reflexes and are provoked by nonphysiologic stimuli (see below). Unfortunately the two terms are often used interchangeably.

Pain may cause either tonic or clonic spasms of muscles, especially if the painful stimulus is focal or discrete; this may cause defensive spasm and reflex rigidity. Mechanical irritation may cause focal spasm; in pathologic states this may result in myoedema. Associated with the hyperirritability of the nerves and muscles in tetany and tentanus there may be prolonged and characteristic muscle spasm. Muscle spasm and rigidity may also occur in a voluntary basis or in response to fear, excitement, or tension. Most of the above phenomena are considered abnormalities of tone rather than muscle spasms, and are discussed in Chapter 28. Spasms may follow injury or irritation of peripheral nerves, especially during the process of regeneration. They may result from irritation of motor nuclei in the brain stem or spinal cord or from disease processes within these structures. Finally, they may be produced by irritation of cortical centers in the brain or lesions of descending motor pathways. Some of the more common spasms are discussed below.

Facial spasm usually consists of brief, clonic, repeated contractions of the muscles supplied by one of the facial nerves. The movements may involve the frontalis, corrugator, and orbicularis oculi as well as the muscles of the lower portion of the face. The spasm usually follows a peripheral type of facial palsy, and may develop during the course of recovery. The entire nerve or only certain branches may be affected, and there may be repeated contractions of the various muscles supplied by the involved nerve with wrinkling of the forehead, closing of the eye, and retraction of the angle of the mouth. If the spasm affects only the orbicularis oculi, it is termed a blepharospasm. If there is faulty regeneration of the nerve with misdirection of the outgrowth of regenerating fibers, retraction of the mouth may be accompanied by spasm of the orbicularis oculi, or winking may be accompanied by a spasmodic drawing back of the angle of the mouth (Fig. 89, p. 262). If the movements are tonic, there is facial contracture. Reflex spasm may also result from pain in the involved side of the face, irritation of the facial nerve anywhere along its course, irritation of the facial nucleus, or irritation of that portion of the cerebral cortex which controls facial movements (jacksonian manifestations). In the risus sardonicus of tetanus there is a tonic spasm of the facial muscles. Chvostek's sign in tetany is characterized by hyperirritability of the facial nerve and muscles and brief spasm on stimulation of them.

Other spasms have been mentioned with the other motor cranial nerves. Spasm of the eye muscles may be of either peripheral or central origin. Oculogyric crises may be considered as spasms of upward gaze. In trismus there is a spasm of the muscles of mastication. In tic douloureux the facial muscles may go into spasm as a result of sudden, severe pain. Spasm of the larynx, pharynx, esophagus, or cardia may be of reflex origin, associated with organic disease such as rabies or tetany, or of psychogenic origin. Spasm of the sternocleidomastoid, especially if reflex in origin and not persistent, may cause a toricollis. This, however, is more frequently characterized by a dystonic type of movement (see above). Glossospasm, or spasm of the tongue, may be of either reflex or psychogenic origin.

Hiccup, or singultus, is a brief spasm, or reflex contraction, of the diaphragm, usually associated with adduction of the vocal cords and brought about by forcible inspiration of air into the lungs. There is a sudden arrest of inspiration by closure of the glottis; this produces a peculiar respiratory sound. Hiccup may be reflexly excited by stimulation of sensory nerves over a wide area, especially the phrenic or vagus nerves. It may follow irritation of the lower end of the esophagus, gastric distension, irritation of the lungs or pleura, mediastinal or intrathoracic abscesses and tumors, aortic aneurysm, and abdominal irritation or distension. It may also follow central irritation, be associated with changes in the body chemistry (acetonemia or uremia), be a manifestation of encephalitis or other central nervous system disease, or be of psychogenic origin. In intractable cases it may be necessary to perform a phrenicectomy. Spasms may occur in any of the viscera: the stomach, pylorus, small or large intestine, rectum, ureter, bladder, or anal or vesical sphincter. Such spasms may be associated with irritation, pain, inflammation, or other reflex causes. In tabetic crises there is painful spasm of the viscera. Spasm of the bodily musculature, especially if it causes reflex rigidity, may be an important diagnostic criterion in abdominal disease and osteomyelitis. Localized myospasm, or muscular cramps, may occur secondary to vascular insufficiency, fatigue, anoxia, alkalosis, calcium or magnesium deficiency, sodium and potassium imbalance, infection, drug ingestion, and exposure to cold, and in some diseases of muscle, such as McArdle's disease and idiopathic paroxysmal myglobinuria (Chapter 28). Localized spasm may also be of psychogenic origin; such spasm of the posterior cervical muscles may be responsible for the so-called "tension headache."

Focal jacksonian attacks, especially if they are limited to the face, an arm, a leg, or one half of the body, are manifestations of muscle spasm. Here there is involvement of a group of muscles which are synergistic in function. The movements are clonic in nature, and result from stimulation of the contralateral motor cortex. They are *positive* symptoms of overactivity of the nervous system. The positions of predilection in cerebral hemiplegia—flexion in the upper extremity and extension in the lower—may also be considered as manifestations of spasm. Hypertonicity of the muscles, however, with selective preference for certain groups, secondary to removal of cerebral inhibition, adequately explains this phenomenon. Following transection of the spinal cord there may be mass reflex spasms of the lower extremities. They are essentially reflex in nature and are responses to cutaneous and proprioceptive stimuli acting on spinal centers not inhibited by higher levels. They are discussed with the reflexes of spinal automatism (Chapter 37). Spasmodic contractions of the muscles of the extremities following nerve injuries or associated with callus formation and resulting nerve stimulation carry the name of traumatic acrodystonia.

TICS

In contrast to a true spasm, a tic is usually regarded as a habit spasm and is considered to be of psychogenic origin. A tic may be defined as a coordinated, repetitive, seemingly purposive act involving a group of muscles in their normal synergistic relationships. Most tics are conditioned reflexes. They are originally precipitated by some physical or emotional stimulus but are perpetuated as a stereo-typed, recurrent, relatively involuntary movement. Tics, like spasms, consist of brief contractions of whole muscles or groups of muscles, and are always accompanied by motion of the affected part. They appear suddenly and recur at irregular intervals. They may imitate or resemble true spasms, but are often more or less bizarre or complex. They may be faster and sharper than spasms, and are seemingly purposeful. They are not usually confined to a single muscle or group of muscles, and may involve the opposing action of more than one nerve. They are stereotyped in nature and the movements are always reproduced in the same definite pattern. The movements can be controlled to a certain extent by the will. They are often compulsive in nature and they cease during sleep. They are exaggerated by emotional strain and tension; they may become less marked when the patient's attention is diverted. They are often associated with an intolerable mounting tension. Voluntary inhibition causes a state of anxiety that is temporarily relieved by indulgence in the tic.

Tics, or habit spasms, may involve any portion of the body. A blepharospasm, which may originate as a true spasm in association with irritation of the eye, may persist as a tic after the irritating stimulus has been removed. Habit spasms of the face may be difficult to differentiate from true spasms, but they fail to follow the organic distribution of motor stimulation. For instance, instead of raising of the forehead by the action of the frontalis in association with contraction of the orbicularis oculi, there may be lowering of the eyebrow. Other muscles aside from those supplied by the facial nerve may be brought into action. Spasmodic torticollis may originate as a tic or compulsive movement. Rotatory and shrugging movements of the head and shoulders may be tics, and the muscles of the extremities may be involved. Habit spasms of the abdominal muscles and of the diaphragm may resemble a hiccup or may be characterized by sudden jerking movements and cause motion of the body as a whole; they may be accompanied by grunting or barklike respirations. Multiple tics may persist after chorea. Tics are present more often in children than adults. A tiqueur is a person who is subject to one or multiple tics. Gilles de la Tourette's disease, or maladie des tics, is a condition of children characterized by multiple tics, imitative gestures, stereotyped movements, the use of obscene words, and evidences of regressive behavior; usually considered to be nonorganic, some cases have been reported which appear to have an organic basis.

CONVULSIONS, MASS MOVEMENTS, AND HYPERKINESIAS INVOLVING MAJOR PORTIONS OF THE BODY

Convulsive attacks and other involuntary muscular contractions which involve major portions of the body may be regarded as hyperkinesias. Convulsions and the convulsive disorder have been described in detail under the discussion of the neurologic history. It should be repeated that an accurate description of the convulsive attack, should any be seen, is of paramount importance. In the *grand mal seizure* one should note the objective manifestations in the aura, the cry, the tonic and clonic phases of the attack, the postconvulsion manifestations and behavior, etc. Any suggestion of lateralization or localization should be stressed. *Jacksonian,* or *focal* attacks should be described in detail, noting the site of the first hyperkinetic manifestations and the spread of the motor phenomena. One should also attempt to describe, as accurately as possible, *petit mal seizures, psychomotor attacks, akinetic seizures, tonic* (so-called *cerebellar) epilepsy, status epilepticus,* and other equivalents and variants. The diagnosis of the convulsive states is considered more at length in Chapter 55. Fainting, or simple syncope, may be related to epilepsy, and its objective manifestations should be described.

Other generalized disturbances of bodily motility may be seen. Some of these, such as catatonic rigidity, decerebrate rigidity, tetanus, and tetany may be regarded as disturbances of tone rather than hyperkinesias, and are described in the discussion of muscle tone. Decerebrate rigidity and the associated changes in the postural and righting reflexes are also described in Chapter 38. Mass movements which follow transection of the spinal cord are discussed in Chapter 37. In meningitis there may be either spasmodic or persistent generalized rigidity with opisthotonus, emprosthotonus, or pleurothotonus. The diagnostic signs of tetanus and meningitis are also referred to in Part V. Jactitation, the tossing to and fro of a patient who is acutely ill, and carphology, the involuntary picking at the bed clothes by patients in febrile states and conditions of great exhaustion, are indications of grave illness. *Akathasia* is defined as motor restlessness, or the inability to sit still and the irresistible urge to move about. It has been described in Parkinson's disease and postencephalitic states, but also occurs with agitation and after the ingestion of drugs of the phenothiazine group. Children with organic brain damage often are hyperactive, restless, impulsive, and readily distracted.

PSYCHOGENIC HYPERKINESIAS

Psychogenic hyperkinesias, or hysterical movements, are defined as those which do not correspond to any of the above described types; they are bizarre, change in type from time to time, and are influenced by tension and suggestion. There is no adequate collective name for them. Those most frequently seen are the tics, or habit spasms, described above. They may be unconscious and purely involuntary or they may be of compulsive or obsessional origin. Mannerisms are somewhat more complicated and stereotyped and are usually carried out in a more leisurely manner. They may appear only under emotional stress or when the patient is engaged in some particular activity. Occupational spasms, such as writer's cramp and the spasms of the typist's fingers or violinist's shoulder, are characterized by extreme spasm and tension of certain muscle groups that interfere with specific activities and come on only when the attempt is made to carry out these activities.

Many of the abnormal movements that have been described above may occasionally be of psychogenic as well as organic origin, or may be exaggerated by emotion. Convulsions may be precipitated by emotional tension, but attacks which closely resemble grand mal seizures may be seen in hysteria. Generalized hypertonicity which resembles that of tetany and tetanus may also be seen in hysteria. In so-called major hysteria there may be neck retraction and opisthotonus with the *arc de cercle.*

Abnormalities of movement of various types may be encountered in mental disease. There may be either overactivity or underactivity, with psychomotor hyperkinesia, hypokinesia, or akinesia. In *parakinesia,* which is usually of psychogenic origin, there is perversion of motor function which results in strange and unnatural movements. This may cause either distortion of movement, with motor manifestations which resemble those seen in chorea and athetosis, or psychomotor dyspraxia, with difficulty in the performance of skilled acts. In manic states there is motor acceleration with increased activity; in depressed states there is lack of initiative with diminished motor activity; in schizophrenia there may be negativism with bizarre mannerisms and sometimes increase in tone, and in childhood schizophrenia there may be rocking, pushing, and circling movements. Various parakinesias are seen in the organic psychoses, and marked motor overactivity in delirium.

If the hyperkinesia defies classification and is too bizarre to be considered of organic origin, it should be described in detail. The possibility that it may be a hysterical conversion phenomenon should always be borne in mind.

To sum up briefly the hyperkinesias from the point of view of localization, it may be seen that any of the level of the motor system, from the motor cortex to the muscle itself, and also including the so-called psychomotor level, may be involved in their production. Lesions at various sites may be related to different forms of abnormal movement. If one is familiar with the site of the pathologic change which is predominantly responsible for the various types, one may be able to determine the specific localization of the disease process. The lesion itself may not cause the movement, but it may permit intact structures to function in an abnormal manner.

REFERENCES

ADAMS, R. D., and FOLEY, J. M. The disorder of movement in the more common varieties of liver disease. *Electroenceph. & Clin. Neurophysiol.* Supp. III, 1953, p. 51.

AIGER, B. R., and MULDER, D. W. Myoclonus: Clinical significance and an approach to classification. *Arch. Neurol.* 2:600, 1960.

BRUMLIK, J. On the nature of normal tremor. *Neurology* 12:159, 1962.

CARPENTER, M. B. Athetosis and the basal ganglia. *Arch. Neurol. & Psychiat.* 63:875, 1950.

CONN, H. O. Asterixis in non-hepatic disorders. *Am. J. Med.* 29:647, 1960.

COWELL, T. K., MARSDEN, C. D., and OWEN, D. A. L. Objective measurement of parkinsonian tremor. *Lancet* 2:1278, 1965.

CRITCULEY, M. Observations on essential (heredofamilial) tremor. *Brain* 72:113, 1949.

DAVIS, C. H., JR., and KUNKLE, E. C. Benign essential (heredofamilial) tremor. *A.M.A. Arch. Int. Med.* 87:808, 1951

DE JONG, H. H. Clinical and physiological studies on a case of myokymia. *Tr. Am. Neurol. A.* 75:260, 1950.

DE JONG, J. D., and BURNS, B. D. An investigation of Parkinson's disease. *Neurology* 12:402, 1962.

DENNY-BROWN, D. The Basal Ganglia and Their Relation to Disorders of Movement. London, Oxford University Press, 1962.

DENNY-BROWN, D., and PENNYBACKER, J. C. Fibrillation and fasciculation in voluntary muscle. *Brain* 61:311, 1938.

FIELD, J. R., CORBIN, K. B., GOLDSTEIN, N. P., and KLASS, D. W. Gilles de la Tourette's syndrome. *Neurology* 16:453, 1966.

FISCH, S., SINGER, M. M., and DEGRAFF, A. C. A novel method for recording tremor. *Am. J. Med. Sc.* 248:415, 1964.

FORSTER, F. M., BORKOWSKI, W. J., and ALPERS, B. J. Effects of denervation on fasciculations in human muscles: Relations of fibrillations to fasciculations. *Arch. Neurol. & Psychiat.* 56:276, 1946.

FRIEDLANDER, W. J. Characteristics of postural tremor in normal and various abnormal states. *Neurology* 6:716, 1956.

HERZ, E. Dystonia: I. Historical reviews, analysis of dystonic symptoms and physiologic mechanisms involved. *Arch. Neurol. & Psychiat.* 51:305, 1944; II. Clinical classification. *Ibid.* 51:319, 1944.

HODGE, J. R. Akathisia: The syndrome of motor restlessness. *Am. J. Psychiat.* 116:337, 1959.

HUGHES, B. Involuntary movements following stereotactic operations for Parkinsonism with special reference to hemi-chorea (ballismus). *J. Neurol., Neurosurg. & Psychiat.* 28:291, 1965.

HUNT, J. R. Dyssynergia cereballaris myoclonica. *Brain* 44:490, 1921.

KESCHNER, M. "Dyskinesias," in TICE, F., Practice of Medicine. Hagerstown, Md., W. F. Prior Company, Inc., 1942, Vol. 10, pp. 307–443.

MARSHALL, J., and WALSH, E. G. Physiological tremor. *J. Neurol., Neurosurg., & Psychiat.* 19:260, 1956.

MEYERS, R., SWEENEY, D. B., and SCHWIDDE, J. T. Hemiballismus: Aetiology and surgical treatment. *J. Neurol., Neurosurg. & Psychiat,* 13:115, 1950.

NATHANSON, M. Palatal myoclonus: Further clinical and pathophysiological observations. *A.M.A. Arch. Neurol. & Psychiat.* 75:285, 1956.

RIBERA, A. B., and COOPER, I. S. The natural history of dystonia musculorum deformans. *Arch. Ped.* 77:55, 1960.

SCHWAB, R. S., STAFFORD-CLARK, D., and PRICHARD, J. S. The clinical significance of fasciculations in voluntary muscle. *Brit. M. J.* 2:209, 1951.

SCHWARZ, G. A., and YAROFF, M. Lafora's disease: Distinct clinicopathologic form of Unverricht's syndrome. *Arch. Neurol.* 12:172, 1965.

SWANSON, P. D., LUTTRELL, C. N., and MAGLADERY, J. W. Myoclonus: A report of 67 cases and review of the literature. *Medicine* 41:339, 1962.

TOWER, S. S. Persistence of fibrillation in denervated skeletal muscle and its non-occurrence in muscle after tenotomy. *Arch. Neurol. & Psychiat.* 42:219, 1939.

TWITCHELL, T. E. On the motor deficit in congenital bilateral athetosis. *J. Nerv. & Ment. Dis.* 129:105, 1959.

VAN BUSKIRK, C., WOLBARSHT, M. L., and STECHER, K., JR. The non-nervous causes of normal physiologic tremor. *Neurology* 16:217, 1966.

WACHS, H., and BOSHES, B.   Tremor studies in normals and in parkinsonism.   *Arch. Neurol.* 4:66, 1961.

WEBSTER, D. D.   Dynamic measurement of rigidity, strength, and tremor in Parkinson patients before and after destruction of the mesial globus pallidus.   *Neurology* 10:157, 1960.

WHITTIER, J. R.   Ballism and the subthalamic nucleus (nucleus hypothalamicus; corpus Luysi): Review of the literature and study of thirty cases.   *Arch. Nerol. & Psychiat.* 58:672, 1947.

CHAPTER 32

STATION AND GAIT

THE EVALUATION of the patient's station and gait is an essential part of the examination of the motor system, and the appraisal of these functions may yield much relevant information. The patient's position when standing and his mode of locomotion should not, however, be considered sole diagnostic criteria even though they may, at times, be pathognomonic of certain nervous system disorders. They are, nevertheless, important when considered in conjunction with the other neurologic findings.

Reference to the general appearance of the body as a whole was made in "The Physical Examination" (Chapter 3), and the gait has been discussed in some detail in the tests for coordination (see Chapter 30). The postural and righting reflexes are described in Chapter 38. Posture, however, and locomotion merit individual discussion from a diagnostic point of view, and specific disorders of gait are especially significant.

EXAMINATION OF STATION

Posture is an active neuromuscular process which is dependent upon a number of factors and reflex responses. It is a complicated mechanism, especially in the human whose biped gait and erect position over a narrow base require more efficient maintenance and control of equilibrium than is necessary in the lower forms. An involuntary contraction of muscles is necessary for normal positions and attitudes. Tonus, especially of the antigravity muscles, is essential. Centers in the brain stem play a part in controlling the steady contraction of the antigravity muscles which is necessary for the standing position. Righting reflexes and more complex reflexes have as their afferent stimuli proprioceptive impulses from the neck and skeletal muscles as well as labyrinthine and visual impulses. Standing may be considered a postural reflex which is dependent upon reflexes mediated through the medulla and influenced to a marked degree by tonic neck and labyrinthine reflexes. Interference with any of the mechanisms responsible for localized, segmental, or generalized static or postural reflexes will cause an impairment of the act of normal standing. In addition, however, proprioceptive sensations must be mediated from the extrmities and trunk, the skeletal system must be intact, the muscles must be functioning normally, and coordination must be adequate. Posture is affected by disturbances of proprioceptive sensation, derangements of muscle power or tone, abnormalities of vestibular function, and dysfunction of the basal ganglia and cerebellum and their connections.

Station may be defined as the patient's attitude, or manner of standing. His posture and the position of his body as a whole and of its parts are noted, and any abnormality is observed. The attitude and position of the head, the position of the extremities, and any outstanding skeletal anomalies are significant. The healthy individual stands in the erect position with his head up, chest out, and abdomen in. Abnormalities of station may indicate dysfunction of the skeletal and muscular systems as well as nervous system impairment. Skeletal changes such as kyphosis, scoliosis, or lordosis; abnormalities in the position of the head, shoulders, hips, or extremities; and asymmetries, anomalies of development, and abnormalities of contour may give diagnostic information. Poor posture may be an evidence of inadequate muscular development or of organ inferiority. In weakness and in debilitated states the patient may need support to stand erect. If the patient is unable to stand, the position of the body should be noted in the seated or the recumbent position. A tendency to lie on one side, drawing up of the knees, opisthotonus, etc., are all diagnostically significant.

From a neurologic point of view, station is tested by having the patient stand with his feet closely approximated, first with the eyes open and then with the eyes closed. Any unsteadiness, swaying, deviation, or tremor should be noted. Station may be further evaluated by having the patient stand on one foot at a time, on his toes and on his heels, and in a tandem position with one heel in front of the toes of the other foot, with the eyes both open and closed. He may be given a push to see whether he falls to one side, forward, or backward. Additional tests include having him hop on one foot; mark time; rise from a supine or seated position; stoop and resume the erect position; bend forward, backward, and to each side. It is often of value to keep a photographic record of the patient's station and posture.

Certain abnormalities of station are pathognomonic of nervous system dysfunction. In disease of the proprioceptive pathways there is a sensory type of ataxia, and the patient is able to maintain the erect position with the eyes open, but sways or falls when they are closed (positive Romberg sign). He may attempt to compensate for his unsteadiness by placing his feet some distance apart, in order to stand with a broader base. In cerebellar disease there is swaying with the eyes open and closed, and the patient may have to stand with a broad base. With a vermis lesion the patient may sway backward, forward, or to either side. With hemispheric cerebellar disease and unilateral vestibular involvement he falls toward the affected side. In the false Romberg test, seen in hysteria, the patient sways from his hips instead of from his ankles; he may sway through a wide arc and it may seem inevitable that he will fall, but he is usually able to regain his balance and resume the upright position. If he does fall, he does not hurt himself. It may be possible to divert the patient's attention during the Romberg test by having him carry out the finger-to-nose test. In tabes dorsalis or in other syndromes in which there is true sensory ataxia this will be accompanied by increasing unsteadiness; in hysteria the patient may be able to carry out the test without difficulty.

The attitude and station may give specific information in certain disease syndromes. In hemiplegia there is a characteristic deformity with flexion of the upper extremity and extension of the lower extremity. In Parkinson's disease there is stooping with the head and neck bent forward and the arms and knees flexed. In the dystrophies there is a pronounced lordosis. In depressed states there may be a stooped and dejected appearance; in manic states, an erect, domineering position; in schizophrenia the patient may assume bizarre postures which he may hold for long periods of time. Hyperkinesias such as athetoid and choreiform movements may become evident while station is being tested.

EXAMINATION OF GAIT

Gait, or the act of walking or locomotion, is an intricate process which is influenced by a number of bodily mechanisms and is the result of the integrity of many different types of reflexes. As with station, the following are needed: simple reflex mechanisms at the spinal cord level; postural and standing reflexes which hold the body erect by increased tone of the antigravity muscles; neck and labyrinthine reflexes for the proper maintenance of tone; righting reflexes to maintain the position of the head, limbs, and trunk; integration of motor function from the pyramidal cortex; automatic mechanisms mediated by the basal ganglia for posture, tone, associated movements, and synergisms; coordinating functions of the cerebellum; sensory elements, mainly proprioceptive, to inform the individual of the position of the various parts of his body and to give proper spatial orientation.

In walking the weight of the body is supported by one lower extremity while the other executes the movement of progression. The supporting limb is first fully extended, but the heel is lifted as the center of gravity is advanced. The opposite limb begins the movement of progression as soon as the body weight is transferred to the supporting limb. The weight of the body is then supported for a short interval by the heel of the advancing limb, then by the foot until the heel is lifted, and then by the ball of the foot. The normal gait thus represents the heel-toe phase of support and progression. The pelvis rotates slightly to the side of progression. In addition to the movements of the trunk and lower extremities, there are normal associated swinging movements of the upper extremities; as one lower extremity is advanced, the upper extremity of the opposite side advances.

Impairment of the act of walking is found in a wide variety of conditions. Mechanical factors such as diseases of the muscles, bones, tendons, and joints, may be important. Disorders of the nervous system, however, cause the most significant abnormalities in locomotion, and occasionally the appraisal of the gait alone may reveal the presence and diagnosis of nervous system disease to the practiced eye. Disturbances in gait may follow involvement of any portion of the motor system: the motor cortex and its descending pathways, extrapyramidal complex, cerebellum, anterior horn cells, peripheral motor nerves, or muscles, as well as abnormalities of the psychomotor level (hysteria and malingering). Involvement of the vestibular complex, sensory nerves, posterior columns, and afferent cerebellar pathways may also cause changes in gait.

The evaluation of the gait is important, but it must be appraised along with the other findings. The gait, also, is tested with the eyes open and closed, and the patient should not only be asked to walk forward, but also backward, sideward, and around a chair. He may be asked to walk on his toes and on his heels; to follow a line on the floor; to walk on a rail; to walk tandem; i.e., to place one heel directly in front of the toes of the other foot; to walk in a sideward direction and overstep, or cross one foot over the other, in so doing; to walk forward and turn rapidly; to walk forward and backward repeatedly six to eight steps with the eyes closed; to walk slowly, then rapidly, then run; to climb stairs. He may be asked to rise abruptly from a chair, stand erect, walk, stop suddenly, and turn quickly on command (Fournier's test).

In appraising the gait the position of the body as a whole should be noted and also the freedom of movement, position of the extremities, inclination of the pelvis and thighs, supporting and progression movements of the legs and feet, size and speed of the individual steps, swinging of the arms, and associated movements of the eyes, head, and trunk. One should notice whether the patient walks steadily or unsteadily, watches the ground, assumes a broad base, deviates his body, drags his feet, or uses any accessory muscles. At times it may be necessary to observe the gait while the patient is assisted in walking or walks with the aid of a cane, crutches, braces, or other apparatus. Some information regarding the gait may be derived from listening to the patient walk. There is a flopping sound to the gait of a person with a foot drop, a dragging or a scraping in spasticity, and a stamping in ataxia. It may be valuable to note the worn places in the patient's shoes. A cinematographic film often aids in interpretation, and also affords a permanent record. It is necessary to recall that there are marked individual variations in gait: each individual has his own gait, which is so characteristic that he may be recognized by it. There may even be an inheritance of the characteristics of gait, and children may walk like their parents. Persons in certain occupations may develop special types of gaits, and those of the sailor and cowboy are well known.

There are certain mechanical disturbances in gait which may be confused with disorders of neurologic origin. If the skin of the feet is inflamed or irritated by calluses, blisters, or chilblains, or if there are painful hyperesthesias of the feet due to neuritis or vascular disease, there may be an abnormality in gait that is characterized chiefly by a shortened phase of support. Pain caused by relaxation of the metatarsal arches may result in a similar abnormality of gait. Relaxation of the longitudinal arches causes flat feet, often with a peculiar, slapping, everted gait. Infiltrations of the calf or gluteal muscles may cause limping or shuffling on one or both sides as a result of pain. Arthritis may cause difficulties with gait which are secondary to both pain and deformity. Intense pain in the calf muscles interferes with gait in intermittent claudication, usually associated with vascular disease such as thromboangiitis obliterans in the lower extremities. This pain increases as walking is continued and is relieved following a brief period of rest. In pregnancy, ascites, and abdominal tumors there may be a lordosis which resembles that seen in the dystrophies. With dislocation of the hips there may be a waddling element suggestive of the dystrophic gait. Marked stooping in spondylitis rhizomelica may resemble that of parkinsonism. Other skeletal, muscular, and orthopedic dysfunctions may simulate nervous system disease.

There are various abnormalities of gait that are of diagnostic importance in neurologic diseases. Some of them may even be considered as pathognomonic of certain disease processes. The more important and more characteristc of these are described. On occasion two or more of these may be present simultaneously.

THE GAIT OF WEAKNESS

It must be recalled that chronic illness of any duration, and even acute illness of short duration, may be followed by some abnormality in locomotion. This so-called gait of weakness is not characteristic of any specific neurologic disease or of focal nervous system damage, but inasmuch as it may be confused with other gaits, especially the ataxic and astasic-abasic varieties, it should be mentioned. The gait of weakness is seen most frequently in wasting and debilitating diseases of long duration, but it may be present in association with an acute illness of any severity. It may, for instance, be apparent after a short period of confinement to bed or after a brief febrile episode. It is characterized mainly by unsteadiness and the wish for support. The patient staggers and sways from side to side with a suggestion of ataxia (see below). He may appear anxious to lean on chairs for support or to brace himself against a wall. He moves slowly and his knees may tremble. If the difficulty is marked, he may fall.

ATAXIC GAITS

There are two types of ataxic gaits—that resulting from sensory ataxia, and that associated with disease of the coordinating mechanisms.

1. *The Gait of Sensory Ataxia:* This is caused most frequently by interruption of the proprioceptive pathways in the spinal cord. It is most commonly encountered in tabes dorsalis and posterolateral and multiple sclerosis, and is often referred to as the *gait of spinal ataxia.* It may also be seen in conditions such as peripheral neuritis and in brain stem lesions where there is interference with the conduction of kinesthetic sensations. The ataxia is caused by lack of appreciation of the senses of position and motion of the parts of the body, especially of the joints, muscles, and tendons of the feet and legs, and by loss of spatial orientation. The patient is no longer aware of the position of his lower extremities in space, or even of the position of the body as a whole, if visual impulses are not correlated with proprioceptive ones. Locomotion may not be too abnormal when the patient walks with his eyes open, but if there is any marked involvement it will be noted that the gait is irregular and jerky, and that the patient walks with a broad base. He throws out his feet and comes down first on the heel and then on the

toes with a slapping sound, or "double tap." The phase of progression is lengthened as increased time is necessary to execute the muscular movements required to place the feet on the floor. The patient watches his feet and keeps his eyes on the floor while walking. When the eyes are closed the feet seem to shoot out, the staggering and unsteadiness are increased, and he may be unable to walk. The "double tap" mentioned above, by which the hypotonic feet are stamped or brought down noisily in two phases, may be so characteristic of tabes that the trained observer may diagnose the condition by hearing the patient walk.

2. *The Gait of Cerebellar Ataxia:* The gait of cerebellar ataxia is caused by involvement of the coordinating mechanisms in the cerebellum and its connecting systems. It is characterized by ataxia, which is present with the eyes both open and closed, but even here it is increased somewhat when the eyes are closed. With a vermis or midline lesion there is a staggering, unsteady, irregular, lurching, titubating, wide-based gait, and the patient may sway to either side or backward or forward. He is unable to walk tandem or follow a straight line on the floor. Tremors and oscillatory movements of the entire body may be noted. This gait, in an exaggerated degree, is seen also in alcoholic and drug intoxications.

In disease localized to one cerebellar hemisphere or its connections, or in unilateral vestibular disease, there is persistent swaying or deviation toward the involved side. As the patient attempts to walk a straight line or to walk tandem he turns toward the side of the lesion. When walking around a chair, in either a clockwise or a counterclockwise direction, he consistently falls toward the side of the lesion. When walking a few steps backward and forward there may be the "compass" deviation.

SPASTIC GAITS

There are also two types of spastic gaits—that associated with unilateral and that with bilateral involvement of the corticospinal pathways.

1. *The Gait of Spastic Hemiplegia:* The gait of spastic hemiplegia is seen most frequently following a cerebral vascular lesion, but it may be caused by any lesion which interrupts the pyramidal innervation to one half of the body. There is a spastic hemiparesis, contralateral to the lesion, with increased tone, increased reflexes, and a predilection type of deformity. The upper extremity shows marked paresis of extension and is held in flexion and adduction at the shoulder, flexion at the elbow, and flexion at the wrist and interphalangeal joints. The lower extremity shows marked paresis of flexion and is held in extension at the hip and knee, with plantar flexion of the foot and toes (Fig. 152). There is a resulting equinus deformity of the foot, with shortening of the achilles tendon, and the lower extremity on the involved side is functionally slightly longer than that on the normal side. When walking the patient holds his arm tightly to the side, rigid and flexed; he extends it with difficulty, and does not swing it in a normal fashion. He holds his leg stiffly in extension and flexes it with difficulty. Consequently the patient drags or shuffles his foot and scrapes the toes. With each step he may tilt the pelvis upward on the involved side to aid in lifting the toe off the floor, and may swing the entire extremity around in a semicircle from the hip, or

circumduct it. The phase of support is shortened because of weakness and the phase of progression is lengthened owing to spasticity and slowing of movement. The sound produced by the scraping of the toe, as well as the wearing of the shoe at the toe, may be quite characteristic. The patient may be able to turn toward the paralyzed side more easily than toward the normal side. He may walk in a sideward direction toward the paralyzed side without much difficulty, since the opposite, or normal, foot is approximated without scraping. When walking toward the normal side, however, the opposite, or paralyzed, leg is dragged and that foot scrapes as it approaches the normal foot. In patients with a very mild hemiparesis, loss of swinging of the affected arm may be a significant diagnostic finding. Dragging or scraping of the foot may be apparent only with fatigue.

2. *The Gait of Spastic Paraplegia:* The gait of spastic paraplegia is encountered in congenital spastic paraplegia, congenital spastic diplegia, Little's disease, and related conditions. In these there is spastic paresis of both lower extremities, with less marked involvement of the upper extremities. There usually is, in addition to the extensor deformity of the lower limbs with equinus position of the feet and shortening of the achilles tendons, pronounced obturator, or adductor, spasm. As a result the patient walks with a bilateral stiff, shuffling type of gait, dragging his legs and scraping his toes; in addition there is adduction of the thighs, so that the knees may cross, one in front of the other, with each step. This produces the *"scissors" type of gait*. The steps are short and slow; the feet seem to "stick to the floor." Swaying and staggering may suggest an element of ataxia, but usually there is no true loss of coordination. The shuffling, scraping sound, together with worn areas at the toes of the shoes, may be characteristic.

THE SPASTIC-ATAXIC GAIT

In many diffuse diseases of the nervous system, especially in the posterolateral sclerosis of pernicious anemia and in multiple sclerosis, there is involvement of both the pyramidal and the proprioceptive pathways, with a resulting spastic-ataxic gait. The amount of ataxia or of spasticity, or the predominance of one over the other, depends upon the site of the predominant pathologic change. The ataxia may be of either the cerebellar or the spinal type. In pernicious anemia it is predominantly the latter; in multiple sclerosis it may have both sensory and cerebellar origin. In amyotrophic lateral sclerosis there may be a bilateral foot drop as well as spasticity, and this may result in an abnormality in walking which may suggest a spastic-ataxic gait.

THE PARKINSONIAN GAIT

In the various extrapyramidal syndromes, especially Parkinson's disease and postencephalitic parkinsonism, there is an abnormality of gait which is characterized by rigidity, bradykinesia, and loss of associated movements. The gait is slow, rigid, and shuffling; the patient walks with small, mincing steps. There is a characteristic posture with associated bodily deformity. The patient is stooped, with his head and neck forward and his knees flexed; the upper extremities are flexed at shoulders, elbows, and wrists, but the fingers may be extended at the interphalangeal joints (Fig. 142). This stooped position causes a forward shifting of the center of gravity, with a tendency to fall forward when walking (*propulsion*), as well as to increase the speed when walking (*festination*). There is difficulty initiating movements, apparent in getting out of a chair or starting to walk, and in carrying out two actions simultaneously. The patient may move "en bloc" and turn about slowly, making many small steps in order to do so. Loss of associated movements may be apparent by absence of normal arm swinging in walking; this interferes with speed and balance. Tremors may become more marked while walking. In some cases there is profound akinesia, with little ability to move. Occasionally the parkinsonian manifestations are unilateral.

MARCHE À PETITS PAS

In patients with diffuse cerebral disturbances of various types, most commonly of arteriosclerotic origin, there may be an abnormality of gait called marche à petits pas, which bears some resemblance to that seen in Parkinson's disease. Locomotion is slow, and the patient walks with very short, mincing, shuffling, somewhat irregular footsteps. There is often a loss of associated movements. Occasionally there are bizarre manifestations, such as dancing or hopping movements. There may be generalized weakness of the lower extremities or of the entire body, with ease of fatigue.

APRAXIA OF GAIT

Apraxia of gait is the loss of ability to use the lower limbs properly in the act of walking, although there is no demonstrable sensory impairment or motor weakness. It is seen in patients with extensive cerebral lesions, especially of the frontal lobes. The patient cannot carry out purposive movements with the legs and feet, such as making a circle or kicking an imaginary ball. In rising, standing, and walking there is difficulty initiating movements, and the automatic sequence of composite movements is lost. The gait is slow and shuffling, with short steps. The patient may have difficulty lifting his feet from the floor, or he may raise them without advancing them. In addition, there often are perserveration, hypokinesia, rigidity, and stiffening of the limb in response to contact (gegenhalten).

THE STEPPAGE GAIT

The steppage gait appears in association with foot drop and is caused by weakness or paralysis of dorsiflexion of the foot and/or the toes. The patient either drags his foot in walking or, in attempting to compensate for the foot drop, lifts his foot as high as possible to keep the toes from scraping the floor. Thus there is an exaggerated flexion at the hip and the knee; the foot is thrown out and the toe flops down with a characteristic sound before either the heel or the ball of the foot strikes the floor. The phase of support is shortened. The patient is unable to stand on his heel, and when he stands with his foot projecting over the edge of a step, the forefoot drops.

Steppage gait may be unilateral or bilateral, and it may result from any of a number of disorders. Perhaps the most common cause is paresis of the tibialis anterior and/or extensors digitorum and hallucis longus. Lesions of either the common or the deep peroneal nerve, of the fourth lumbar through first sacral spinal segments, or of the cauda equina may cause such paresis. Foot drop and steppage gait may also be present with poliomyelitis, progressive spinal muscular atrophy, amyotrophic lateral sclerosis, the peroneal or Charcot-Marie-Tooth type of musclar atrophy, and multiple neuritis. In many of these conditions the difficulty may be bilateral. If steppage gait is associated with a multiple peripheral neuritis, there is sensory as well as motor involvement, and the gait may be complicated by the presence of pain, dysesthesias, and paresthesias, so that support of the body is distressing. The gait under such circumstances may be one of deliberation and hesitation, with a shortened phase of support and prolonged phase of progression.

THE DYSTROPHIC GAIT

The dystrophic gait is seen in the various myopathies in which there is weakness of the hip girdle muscles. It is most characteristic of muscular dystrophy, but may be present also with myositis and other diseases of the spinomuscular level which affect these muscles. The patient stands and walks with a pronounced lordosis, and in walking there is a marked "waddling" element because of difficulty in fixing the pelvis. The patient walks with a broad base and shows an exaggerated rotation of the pelvis, rolling or throwing his hips from side to side with every step to shift the weight of the body. This compensatory lateral movement of the pelvis is due in a large part to weakness of the gluteal muscles. In addition, the patient has marked difficulty in climbing stairs, and he often needs a hand rail so that he may pull himself up with his hands. He is also unable to get up from a lying or seated position without assisting himself with his hands, "climbing up on himself" by placing his hands first on his knees and then on his hips to brace himself (Fig. 135). A waddling type of gait is also seen in association with dislocation of the hips.

GAITS ASSOCIATED WITH VARIOUS PARESES AND PARALYSES

The most characteristic of these is the steppage gait, mentioned above, but other pareses may cause other anomalies. With paralysis of the gastrocnemius and soleus muscles the patient is unable to stand on his toes, and the heel comes down first in walking. This may cause a shuffling gait that is devoid of spring. With paresis of the hamstring muscles there is weakness of flexion at the knee. With paralysis of the quadriceps femoris muscles, as in a femoral neuritis, there is paralysis of extension at the knee; the patient is unable to extend the leg while seated; he is unable to climb stairs or rise from a kneeling position without bracing the knee, has to walk by holding the knee stiffly, and tends to fall if the knee bends. He has less difficulty walking backward than forward. If the deep peroneal nerve is injured below the point where branches are given off to the tibialis anterior and the extensor digitorum longus, there may be only weakness of dorsiflexion of the great toe. In paralysis of the superficial peroneal nerve there is loss of eversion, and the patient walks on the outer aspect of the foot. Lesions of the sciatic nerve and its larger branches may cause varying types of gait anomalies.

GAITS ASSOCIATED WITH VARIOUS HYPERKINESIAS

In conditions such as Sydenham's chorea, Huntington's chorea, athetosis, dystonia musculorum deformans, etc., the abnormal movements may become more marked while the patient is walking, and the manifestations of the disease more evident. Not only are the hyperkinesias apparent, but also the changes in power, tone, etc., that accompany them. In Sydenham's chorea one may note the jerky, purposeless movements, as well as the hypotonia with the characteristic hypotonic hand. In Huntington's chorea the gait may be grotesque, dancing, and histrionic. In athetosis the distal movements and in dystonia the proximal movements may be marked while walking, and in both there are accompanying grimaces. In postencephalitic states there may be hopping and jumping elements in the gait. The "cock-walk" gait of von Jaksch has been described in chronic manganese intoxication; the feet are held in the talipes equinus or equinovarus positions and the patient walks on the metatarsophalangeal areas of his feet.

GAITS ASSOCIATED WITH PSYCHOSES

In various psychotic processes there are characteristic changes in the gait. The depressed patient is stooped and slowed in walking. The manic patient is overactive and erect. In schizophrenia various abnormalities may be noted, especially if there are catatonic manifestations.

GAITS ASSOCIATED WITH VARIOUS ORGANIC DISEASES

Many other abnormalities of gait may be found in association with muscular, skeletal, and orthopedic abnormalities, with secondary nervous system involvement. These will not be mentioned in detail here, although some of them have significance in the neurologic examination. The gait of sciatic nerve irritation is quite characteristic. The patient may walk with a list to the involved side to prevent stretching of the sciatic nerve; he is bent forward and toward the side of the lesion and drops his pelvis on that side. On other occasions the trunk may be inclined toward the opposite side; a scoliosis may result from attempts to keep the weight on the sound limb, and the pelvis is tilted so that the affected hip is prominent and elevated. There is loss of the normal lumbar lordosis due to involuntary spasm of the low back muscles. The patient walks with small steps; if the pain is severe, he avoids complete extension of the hip and knees and places only the toes on the floor, since dorsiflexion of the foot aggravates the pain. He often uses a cane to keep from bearing weight on the involved leg.

HYSTERICAL GAITS

Individuals with hysteria or other abnormalities in the psychomotor sphere may show various derangements of station and gait. They may be unable either to stand or walk despite the absence of paralysis. Tests for power, tone, and coordination may be normal if carried out while the patient is lying down. The gait is nondescript and bizarre, and may show variations from the normal that do not conform to a specific organic disease pattern. It is often irregular and changeable, with elements of ataxia, spasticity, and other types of abnormality. There are superfluous movements, and often marked swaying from side to side. The patient may appear to be falling, but is usually able to regain his balance without doing so. If he does fall, it is in a theatrical manner without injury to himself. The gait may suggest the presence of a monoplegia, hemiplegia, or paraplegia, yet the limbs can be used in an emergency. It may show skating, hopping, zigzag characteristics; the legs may be thrown out wildly, or there may be a tendency to kneel every few steps. Tremulousness of the extremities or tic-like or compulsive features may be present. Although the patient cannot walk forward, he may be able to walk back-ward or to one side or to run without difficulty (Chapter 56). The term *astasia-abasia* has been given to this type of gait disturbance. These words, however, actually mean "inability to stand and walk," and it is better to use the term *hysterical dysbasia* for the difficulty with gait, and the term *stasibasiphobia* in referring to fear of standing or walking.

REFERENCES

ABD EL NABY, S., and HASSANEIN, M.   Neuropsychiatric manifestations of chronic manganese poisoning.   *J. Neurol., Neurosurg. & Psychiat.* 28:285, 1965.

BRAIN, R.   Posture.   *Brit. M. J.* 1:1489, 1959.

KREMER, M.   Sitting, standing, and walking.   *Brit. M. J.* 2:63, 121, 1958.

MEYER, J. S., and BARRON, D. W.   Apraxia of gait: A clinicophysiological study.   *Brain* 83:261, 1960.

SAUNDERS, J. B. D. M., INMAN, V. T., and EBERHART, H. D.   The major determinants in normal and pathological gait.   *J. Bone & Joint Surg.* 35-A:543, 1953.

THE ELECTRICAL
EXAMINATION

THE CLINICAL EXAMINATION of motor power, tone, muscle volume, coordination, and abnormal movements should, if carried out in detail, provide an adequate, clearcut, objective evaluation of motor functions. On occasion, however, various electrical procedures may be used to supplement the information obtained in the clinical appraisal and to bring out minimal alterations of function. These technics have proved to be of value not only in the investigation and understanding of many neurologic disorders, but also in the diagnosis of certain of them. In the latter field they are concerned primarily with diseases that affect the lower motor neuron, peripheral nerves, neuromuscular junction, and skeletal muscle fibers.

The electrical examination should not be considered a routine feature of neurologic diagnosis, but it is of definite importance under special circumstances where it contributes certain information that cannot be obtained by other means. As a consequence, its uses and interpretation should be known. It is of particular value in the diagnosis and prognosis of peripheral nerve lesions, because electrical evidence of denervation may appear before clinical signs can be recognized, and electrical evidence of reinnervation may precede clinical return of function by several weeks. As a result, various technics of electrical testing may aid in determining the location of the injury, the degree of damage and whether impairment of function is due to division or contusion of the nerve, the presence of degeneration even though anatomic continuity remains intact, and the first signs of nerve regeneration. The electrical examination is also helpful in the diagnosis of disease of anterior horn cells, and may aid in the differentiation of atrophy or paralysis owing to such disease from similar motor dysfunction that may result from disuse, pain, primary muscle disease, or psychogenic factors. It gives information about defects in transmission at the neuromuscular junction and aids in the diagnosis of primary muscle disease and the differentiation of such disease from changes secondary to denervation. It may also be of value in the discrimination between organic and hysterical paralyses.

Three general methods of electrodiagnostic testing are used in the evaluation of neuromuscular disorders. By percutaneous stimulation of nerves and muscles, their response to electrical stimuli is observed and the current used is measured. By electromyography the electrical activity of muscle either at rest or in action is recorded and studied. By the use of both stimulating and recording technics nerve conduction velocity can be determined. All three of these are specialized and somewhat complex procedures, for which specific apparatus is necessary, and should be discussed in great detail if they are to be dealt with adequately. Consequently only the general principles are herein outlined, but the current references are listed.

ELECTRICAL STIMULATION OF NERVES AND MUSCLES

The stimulation procedures are the oldest of the electrodiagnostic tests and are used less frequently today than they once were. Their importance, however, should not be minimized. It has long been known that normal nerves and muscles respond to various types of electrical stimulation in a precise and uniform manner. In certain disease processes there are characteristic changes in these responses. Contraction of a muscle may be induced by percutaneous stimulation through its motor nerve or by direct excitation of the muscle. If a nerve is divided, the distal end loses its power of conduction, and stimulation of the nerve no longer causes contraction of muscle. Muscle, however remains capable of contracting in response to certain types of current if stimulated directly. In general, two types of current, faradic and galvanic, are used in the electrical examination.

Faradic current is an induced, interrupted, rapidly alternating current, produced by means of an induction coil that acts as an interruptor through which a contact is repeatedly made and broken. Such current, in frequencies and strengths usually employed, stimulates only nerves, and muscle contraction is secondary to motor nerve stimulation. The rapidly repeated stimuli to a motor nerve cause a continuous or tetanic contraction of the muscles supplied by the nerve that persists as long as the current flows. Muscles deprived of their nerve supply do not react to ordinary faradic currents. About fifteen days after the division of a motor nerve it can no longer carry a faradic current, and the muscle no longer reacts. Faradic response rarely reappears before the return of voluntary motion.

Galvanic current is a continuous, uninterrupted, or direct current, such as that from a battery. It stimulates both nerves and muscles, and is capable of inducing muscular contraction through either nerve conduction or direct muscle stimulation, although muscles are normally less sensitive than nerves. Under ordinary circumstances, muscular contractions in response to a galvanic current occur only when the current is either applied or interrupted, and polarity is important. The contraction is brief and unsustained. If one starts below the threshold of irritability and gradually increases the current, the first contraction is obtained when the stimulating electrode is the negative pole, or cathode, and on the application (make or closing)

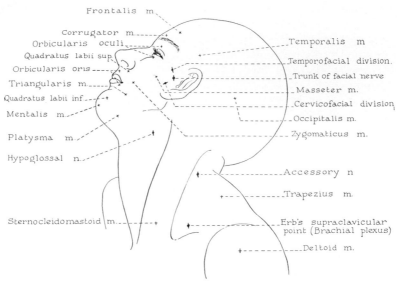

FIG. 217. Nerve and motor points of face and neck. (After Erb.)

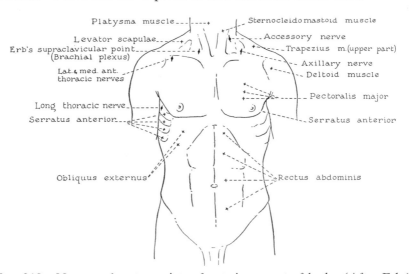

FIG. 218. Nerve and motor points of anterior aspect of body. (After Erb.)

of the circuit, the cathodal closing contraction (CCC). As the current is increased, a response can be obtained at the closing of the current with the positive pole, or anode, the anodal closing contraction (ACC); then at the interruption, or break, of the circuit with the anode, the anodal opening contraction (AOC), and finally at the interruption of the current with the cathode, the cathodal opening contraction (COC). The current is measured in milliamperes. The minimal stimulus of galvanic current necessary to produce a visible contraction of a given muscle is known as the threshold current, or *rheobase*. If a galvanic stimulus is used which is much stronger

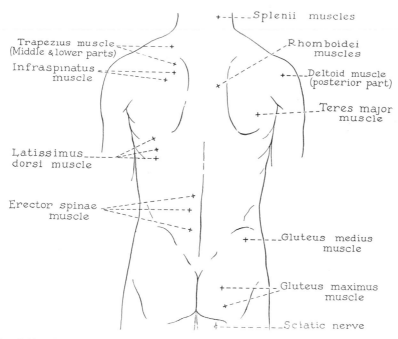

FIG. 219.   Nerve and motor points of posterior aspect of body. (After Erb.)

than that required to cause contraction only on the closing and opening of the circuit, there will be a continuous or tetanic contraction of muscle that persists as long as the current is flowing. This may occur in either normal or denervated muscle, and is known as *galvanic tetanus*.

With lesions of the motor nerves there are certain changes in the responses to galvanic current of the nerves and the muscles they supply. The galvanic irritability of the nerve is diminished or lost. There is persistence of galvanic irritability of the muscles, but there is a change in the amount of current required and the character of the contractions. The irritability of the muscles is sometimes considerably increased; there is a variation in the polar ratio; instead of the normal short, lightning-like contraction there is a slow, long-drawn contraction that passes into a continuous tetanus.

In carrying out the electrical examination, the stimuli are applied to the nerve and the muscle or motor points originally described by Erb (Figs. 217-223). The motor nerves are stimulated where they are near to the surface of the body. The muscle or motor points are the most susceptible or excitable parts of the muscles. They are usually over the area where the motor nerve enters the muscle belly or at the location of the greatest concentration of nerve endings. The stimulating electrade has a key or interruptor by which the examiner can control the circuit; an indifferent electrode is placed at some distant site, usually over the back of the neck or sternum. Occasionally, in bipolar testing, both electrodes are placed on the muscle to be examined. The parts of the body to be tested should be thoroughly

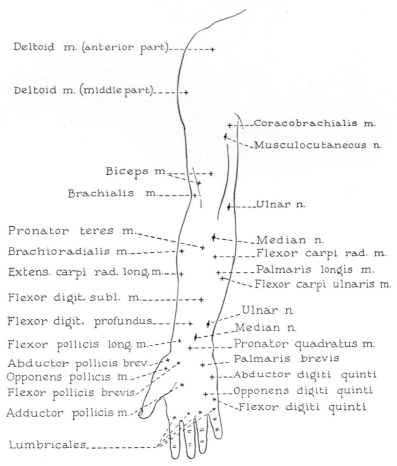

FIG. 220. Nerve and motor points of anterior aspect of upper extremity. (After Erb.)

relaxed. The extremities should be placed in a position favorable for the contraction of the muscles to be stimulated. The examination should be carried out with adequate illumination, so that the slightest response may be seen. Contraction of the muscles may be recognized by direct observation, palpation of the muscle belly or tendon, or movement of the part it supplies. If one applies the stimulus to a nerve, all the muscles supplied by this nerve should contract; if a single motor point is stimulated, a single muscle contracts. Too strong a current, however, may cause a widespread contraction of muscles.

ELECTRICAL TESTING IN PERIPHERAL NERVE LESIONS

Electrical stimulation technics have been used principally in the diagnosis of lesions of the peripheral nerves. In the *reaction of degeneration,* first described by Erb in 1868, there are changes in the character and amount of stimulus necessary

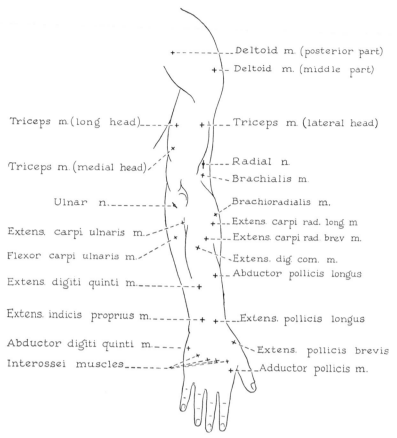

FIG. 221.   Nerve and motor points of posterior aspect of upper extremity. (After Erb.)

to elicit a response, as well as in the type of muscle contraction. In a partial or incomplete lesion of the motor nerve there is an elevation of the threshold to faradic current, but no change in the reaction of either nerve or muscle to galvanic current. Inasmuch as the faradic current ordinarily employed does not act upon muscle directly, there is no response on the part of the muscle to faradic stimulation. If the power of conduction of the nerve is more impaired, there is further decrease in response to faradic current, and an increase occurs in the amount of galvanic current necessary to stimulate both nerve and muscle. Finally the nerve loses its ability to conduct galvanic current, and there is an altered response of muscle itself to such stimulation. There is increased irritability and it reacts to a lesser amount of current than normal, but the type of contraction is changed, and instead of being abrupt and brief it is slow and vermicular in type. In addition there is a reversal of polarity, with the anodal closing contraction occurring before the cathodal closing contraction. In the *complete reaction of degeneration* one finds the following: absence of response, both of nerve and muscle, to faradic stimulation; loss of response on the part of the nerve to galvanic stimulation; an abnormal response on the part of the

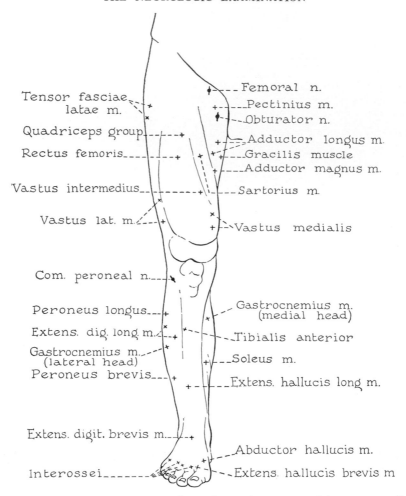

Tensor fasciae
latae m.

Quadriceps group

Rectus femoris

Vastus intermedius

Vastus lat. m.

Com. peroneal n.

Peroneus longus

Extens. dig. long m.

Gastrocnemius m.
(lateral head)

Peroneus brevis

Extens. digit. brevis m.

Interossei

Femoral n.

Pectinius m.

Obturator n.

Adductor longus m.

Gracilis muscle

Adductor magnus m.

Sartorius m.

Vastus medialis

Gastrocnemius m.
(medial head)

Tibialis anterior

Soleus m.

Extens. hallucis long m.

Abductor hallucis m.

Extens. hallucis brevis m

Fig. 222.   Nerve and motor points of anterior aspect of lower extremity.
(After Erb.)

muscle to galvanic stimulation. This latter shows an increased muscle irritability; a change in the muscle response, with a slow, vermicular, long-drawn contraction which passes into a continuous tetanus and lasts for the entire duration of the
current; and a qualitative change in polarity, at times assuming the formula
ACC>CCC>COC>AOC. There are all possible gradations.

In the past the reaction of degeneration was considered one of the more important criteria in the diagnosis and prognosis of peripheral nerve lesions, but interpretation may be difficult and other electrical tests give earlier evidence of both
degeneration and regeneration. As a consequence, it is not used to a very great
extent at the present time. Some of the other stimulation technics used in peripheral
nerve lesions are as follows:

The *galvanic tetanus ratio* is determined by dividing the strength of the galvanic

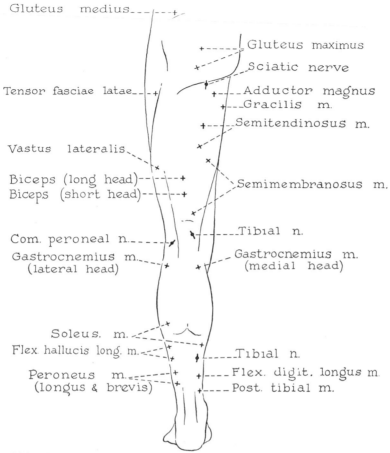

FIG. 223. Nerve and motor points of posterior aspect of lower extremity. (After Erb.)

current required to produce a tetanic response by the minimal strength of the same type of current that is required to produce a simple, perceptible contraction. Early during the process of degeneration both the threshold for galvanic tetanus and the galvanic tetanus ratio are relatively high; there may be an intial rise in both. As degeneration progresses the ratio falls, and at the time of complete denervation the threshold for galvanic tetanus and the ratio are at a minimum. During regeneration, however, there is a marked rise in the threshold and a very high tetanus ratio. This test aids in the determination of neurotization and has been used as a criterion for regeneration.

In order to act as an efficient stimulus to a nerve or a muscle an electrical current must not only be of sufficient strength, but it must act for a minimum period of time, and the duration of the passage of the flow of the current plays an important role. The shorter the duration of the current flow, the greater the strength of current necessary to reach the threshold of excitability. *Chronaxie* is a comparison of the intensity of a current with its time of passage. It is defined as the minimum time required for effective stimulation of a neuromuscular unit by a current that is twice the rheobase. The chronaxie for each muscle and nerve is constant, and that for each muscle and the nerve that supplies it are the same. When a nerve is injured its chronaxie increases, and if the nerve has degenerated it may go as high as one hundred or more times the normal. It decreases during regeneration, and its determination may give important information in evaluating recovery.

The above tests, together with other variations, such as the determination of the strength-duration and strength-frequency curves, have all been used in the diagnosis and prognosis of peripheral nerve lesions. They may give important information in the determination of therapy and in decisions regarding advisability of surgical exploration or repair of injured nerves. They are, however, complicated; special apparatus is needed to carry them out and experience and critical evaluation to interpret them. In general, at the present time, electromyography and conduction velocity determinations have largely replaced stimulation testing in the routine evaluation of peripheral nerve lesions as well as of other disturbances of motor function. They often, however, give essential information.

ELECTRICAL TESTING IN OTHER DISEASES OF THE MOTOR SYSTEM

Electrical testing may be of value in the diagnosis of other abnormalities of the motor system. There are no changes in the electrical reaction in disease of the extrapyramidal, pyramidal, or cerebellar systems, and no changes in hysterical or malingered paralyses. Negative findings under such circumstances may contribute to the differential diagnosis. There may be a moderate diminution in the electrical response in the myopathies, myositis, mild peripheral neuritides, ischemic paralysis, and diseases in which there is atrophy secondary to disuse or joint disease. In these conditions there may be a diminished irritability, with elevation of the threshold to electrical stimulation and a moderate increase in chronaxie. The changes are quantitative rather than qualitative. In amyotonia there may be a decrease in irritability corresponding to the degree of dysfunction; this may progress to absence of response.

The following disease syndromes are characterized by specific changes in the electrical reactions:

In *myotonia congenita* (Thomsen's disease) and *myotonia dystrophica* the threshold for faradic current is normal or slightly increased, but a *persistent,* prolonged, or tonic contraction is obtained, with delayed relaxation. On stimulation with a galvanic current there is a double reaction: stimulation of either the nerve or motor point causes a quick but persistent contraction, whereas stimulation distal to the motor point is followed by a slow, rhythmic, undulatory contraction which proceeds from the cathode to the anode and continues as long as the current is passing through the muscle. The anodal and cathodal closing contractions may become equal. On repeated stimulation the response gradually becomes normal. These changes in the electrical reaction lessen after the administration of quinine, cortisone, and corticotropin.

In *tetany* there is *hyperexcitability,* or increased irritability, of both nerves and muscles. Contractions can be produced with a smaller amount of current than is normally needed (Erb's sign). The hyperexcitability is more accurately measured and is more marked with galvanic than with faradic current. If a strong current is used a tonic or tetanic contraction is obtained, and the muscles go into spasm.

In *myasthenia gravis* there is increased *fatigability* with gradual exhaustion on repeated stimulation, a phenomenon first described by Jolly. A normal response may be obtained with the first few stimuli, but as these are repeated there is a weakening of the muscular response and the contractions gradually become more feeble until, after a number of stimulations, the muscles cease to contract. This change is most easily demonstrated by the use of a faradic, or tetanizing, current. After a period of rest, a normal response can again be obtained. The electrical reactions return to normal after the administration of neostigmine.

In *family periodic paralysis* there is a loss of irritability to both faradic and galvanic stimulation during the period of the paralysis. The muscles may be entirely unresponsive to any type of stimulation for a period of hours. This phenomenon is the so-called *cadaveric response*. There is neither polar change nor reaction of degeneration.

ELECTROMYOGRAPHY

Electromyography is the technic of studying the electrical activity of muscle and of recording the variations of electrical potential that may be present with muscle contraction or in disease states. Needle electrodes are inserted into muscles; either concentric (bipolar electrodes), or monopolar needle electrodes with a skin reference may be used. These pick up the electrical potential, which is transmitted, amplified, and displayed on a cathode ray oscilloscope. The flunctuations in voltage can also be translated to sound waves by connecting the output of the amplifier to a loud speaker. Permanent records can be made by photographing the tracing on the oscilloscope or by storing the sound signal on magnetic tape. Surface electrodes are also used in electromyography, and records may be made by means of an ink-writing oscillograph such as is used in standard electroencephalographic technic. Skin leads, however, give less detailed information and may show the activity of more than one muscle, and ink-writing oscillographs have a limited response to the high frequencies represented in the electrical activity of skeletal muscles. These latter technics, however, may be used in the study of abnormal movements.

Normal muscles at rest show no electrical activity, but with volitional contraction they exhibit a series of action potentials of varied size, frequency, and number. During muscle contraction all the muscle fibers innervated by a single lower motor neuron act together, and their action potentials summate to produce the larger action potential of the motor unit. This is a spikelike diphasic or triphasic wave. The frequency, amplitude, and voltage of these waves vary with the degree of muscular contraction and the number of motor units involved in the contraction. With moderate contraction the motor unit action potentials are recorded with a duration of from five to ten milliseconds, a rate of ten to thirty per second, and an amplitude of up to four millivolts. The pattern of electrical activity varies in muscles depending on their size and the degree of contraction.

Although no electrical activity is detected in normal resting muscle, several types of activity are found in voluntarily relaxed muscles of patients with neuromuscular disease, and changes in activity may accompany electrical stimulation of nerve trunks.

Starting five to ten days after complete interruption of nerve supply to a muscle, spontaneous discharges occur owing to independent, rhythmic contractions of individual muscle fibers. These contractions are fibrillations, and the fibrillation potentials, which are extremely small, are of short duration (less than one or two milliseconds), and low voltage (rarely more than fifty microvolts), and appear at a rate of two to ten per second. These are present in all denervated muscles by three weeks after interruption of nerve supply, and may also be found in any disease that causes degeneration of the lower motor neuron. With incomplete peripheral nerve lesions the electromyogram shows a combination of fibrillation activity with small isolated potentials on voluntary contraction. With complete interruption of nerve supply there are no action potentials on attempted contraction; these changes are limited to the muscles supplied by the affected nerve. With nerve regeneration polyphasic potentials appear and the fibrillations gradually subside. Electromyography shows signs of nerve regeneration much earlier than they are apparent clinically, and probably earlier than electrical stimulation tests. Because of the localization of the electrical changes and the early signs of both denervation and regeneration, the technic is a valuable one in the diagnosis and prognosis of *peripheral nerve lesions*.

Electromyography also gives important information with other neuromuscular disorders. With *anterior horn cell degenerations* (progressive spinal muscular atrophy and amyotrophic lateral sclerosis) there is increased irritability of muscle on insertion of needle electrodes. The fibrillation potentials of denervation are present, but in addition there are fasciculations, or irregular, polyphasic discharges, occurring involuntarily while the muscle is at rest. These are larger than fibrillations, the discharge is from one-half to one millivolt, the duration is from eight to twelve milliseconds, and they occur sporadically at a rate of one to thirty per minute. Isolated motor unit action potentials appear with voluntary contraction; these are reduced in number but increased in amplitude. In *poliomyelitis* there are denervation fibrillations and small isolated action potentials on attempted contraction, but these changes are spotty, corresponding to the affected motor nuclei. Early signs of recovery in poliomyelitis may also be apparent by electromyography.

Various changes during rest and activity are found in diseases of muscle. In the *dystrophies* the action potentials are polyphasic but are shorter and of smaller amplitude than normal. In *myositis* there is marked electrical activity upon insertion of the needle electrodes. Potentials with voluntary contraction are decreased in amplitude and duration and are often polyphasic. There may be fibrillation potentials at rest. In *myasthenia* gravis the action potentials are irregular, with variation in amplitude. Following repeated contraction the potentials decrease in amplitude and frequency and may cease completely. In *myotonia* there is profuse insertion activity and there are prolonged bursts of rapid, high-frequency action potentials with slight contraction or mechanical stimulation. These may continue for a period after relaxation.

Polyphastic discharges, more or less undistinguishable from fasciculations, are found in other conditions. They may occur occasionally in normal persons, in those with myokymia and so-called benign fasciculations, and in patients with certain metabolic disorders. They may occur with degeneration or irritation anywhere along the course of the lower motor neuron, from the anterior horn cell to the myoneural junction and the muscle. The presence of such discharges, along with fibrillation potentials, in individual muscles or in myotomes supplied by specific spinal cord segments or motor nerve roots, is valuable in the diagnosis and localization of focal lesions of the spinal cord, nerve roots, and peripheral nerves, including intramedullary and extramedullary neoplasms, ruptured intervertebral disk syndromes, and compression injuries of the nerve roots or peripheral nerves.

Electromyography is not of much aid in the diagnosis of most upper motor neuron syndromes. There is no electrical activity of completely relaxed spastic muscles, but slight stimulation or minimal contraction causes an immediate response, and groups of large motor units may appear. With rigidity there is slight constant contraction of both prime movers and their antagonists, and there is slight electrical activity at all times; this, too, is markedly increased on stimulation or voluntary activity. Electromyography is helpful in determining the frequency, rhythmicity, and amplitude of certain of the abnormal movements, and thus in the diagnosis and interpretation of them.

NERVE CONDUCTION VELOCITY DETERMINATIONS

Combined stimulation and recording technics are used in nerve conduction velocity tests. For the determination of motor nerve conduction time a maximal electrical stimulus is applied over the main trunk of a motor nerve, and the action potentials of the muscle or muscles supplied by that nerve are recorded on an oscilloscope. The time interval from the stimulus to the motor response may then be determined. In larger nerves the motor trunk may be stimulated at two levels, and the time interval between the stimulus and the onset of the muscle action potential recorded in both instances. If both stimuli are maximal, the difference between the two time intervals gives the conduction time for the propagation of the nerve impulse between the two points stimulated. The nerves most commonly tested are the median, ulnar, peroneal, posterior tibial, and facial. The average conduction times for these nerves have been established, with known variations, depending upon the age of the subject. Under normal circumstances the action potentials from individual muscles show little variation, but with disease of nerves, myoneural junction, or muscle the action potentials may be of lower amplitude and longer duration. With lesions of peripheral nerves, either those of individual nerves or generalized polyneuropathies, there is a slowing of conduction velocity, which finding may aid in differentiating between involvement of the nerves themselves and disease of muscle or anterior horn cells. Velocity studies are often helpful in localizing the site of compression of a peripheral nerve. It is also possible to determine the rate of conduction in sensory nerves by recording nerve potentials through surface electrodes, but the technical difficulties are greater than those in studying motor nerves. Changes in conduction in sensory nerves, however, may aid in the detection of early degrees of peripheral nerve impairment.

No single method of electrodiagnostic testing is universally applicable, and possibly no single method gives complete information on the state of innervation of muscle. Often the results of more than one type of testing may be essential in diagnosing lesions of the peripheral nerves and the motor system. Under all circumstances, however, the results of the electrical tests must be carefully considered in their relationship to the total clinical picture.

OTHER TYPES OF ELECTRICAL EXAMINATIONS

Additional types of electrical examinations have been used in the appraisal of the neurologic case. Some of these are entirely experimental, others are of clinical use but cannot be considered a part of the examination of the motor system.

Electrical examinations have been used extensively in experimental work, such as that of Erlanger and Gasser on the function of individual nerves. These authorities have contributed to the knowledge of the electrophysiology of nerves by means of the cathode ray oscillograph, and have demonstrated that the speed of conduction is correlated with the size of the axon. The greater the diameter of the axon, the greater the speed of conduction. Motor nerves, which are larger than sensory nerves, are stimulated more easily and carry impulses with greater speed. The larger sensory nerves, those which carry proprioceptive and tactile sensations, conduct impulses more rapidly than the smaller ones which carry the impulses mediating pain and temperature sensations.

An electrical dynamometer or electronic myodynemeter may be used in testing muscle strength and power. Electrical stimulation of the brain, spinal cord, or peripheral nerves plays an important part in neurosurgical procedures. The electrical stimulus may be applied directly to the motor cortex in the attempt to localize a lesion responsible for a focal convulsive disorder. In peripheral nerve and plexus surgery electrical stimulation may aid in localization and in the determination of the continuity of peripheral nerves.

Faradic and galvanic currents are sometimes used in the testing of sensation, but the results are difficult to evaluate and contribute less information than other methods. A galvanic current is sometimes used in the appraisal of gustatory sensation. Galvanic stimulation is also important in the examination of the vestibular apparatus. Electromyography of the ocular muscles is sometimes of diagnostic significance. Electronystagmography and electroretinography are used mainly in research, but may have clinical application.

The measurement of the electrical resistance of the skin by means of the dermometer is used in the evaluation of injuries of peripheral nerves. The autonomic component of the peripheral nerve is, however, the important factor, and dermometry is described with the methods of examining the function of the autonomic nervous system.

Electroencephalography is one of the most important of the electrical examinations of the nervous system. It is, however, a special diagnostic procedure which is not described in detail in this volume. Many excellent monographs on the subject are available.

REFERENCES

ARIEFF, A. J., DOBIN, N. B., and TIGAY, E. L. Comprehensive electrodiagnosis. *J.A.MA*. 181: 1140, 1962.

BRAZIER, M. A. B. The Electrical Activity of the Nervous System. New York, The Macmillan Company, 1951.

BUCHTHAL, F., and CLEMMENSEN, S. On the differentiation of muscular atrophy by electromyography. *Acta psychiat. et neurol.* 16:143, 1941.

DENNY-BROWN, D. Interpretation of the electromyogram. *Arch. Neurol. & Psychiat.* 61:99, 1949.

EATON, L. M., and LAMBERT, E. H. Electromyography and electric stimulation of nerves in diseases of motor unit. *J.A.M.A.* 163:1117, 1957.

ERLANGER, J., and GASSER, H. S. Electrical Signs of Nervous Activity. Philadelphia, University of Pennsylvania Press, 1937.

GILLIATT, R. W. Electrodiagnosis and electromyography in clinical practice. *Brit. M. J.* 2:1073, 1962.

HARVEY, A. M., and MASLAND, R. L. A method for the study of neuromuscular transmission in human subjects. *Bull. Johns Hopkins Hosp.* 68:81, 1941

HODES, R., LARRABEE, M. C., and GERMAN, W. The human electromyogram in response to nerve stimulation and the conduction velocity of motor axons. *Arch. Neurol. & Psychiat.* 60:340, 1948.

JOHNSON, E. W., and OLSEN, K. J. Clinical value of motor nerve conduction velocity determination. *J.A.M.A.* 172:2030, 1960.

KUGELBERG, E. Electromyography in muscular disorders: Differentiation between dystrophies and chronic lower motor neurone lesions. *J. Neurol., Neurosurg. & Psychiat.* 12:129, 1949.

LAMBERT, E. H. Neurophysiological techniques useful in the study of neuromuscular disorders. *A. Res. Nerv. & Ment. Dis., Proc.* (1958) 38:247, 1960.

LICHT, S. (ed.) Electrodiagnosis and Electromyography (ed. 2). New Haven, Conn., Elizabeth Licht, Publisher, 1961.

NORRIS, F. H., JR. The EMG: A Guide and Atlas for Practical Electromyography. New York, Grune & Stratton, 1963.

POLLOCK, L. J., GOLSETH, J. G., MAYFIELD, F., ARIEFF, A. J., and OESTER, Y. T. Electrodiagnosis of lesions of peripheral nerves in man. *Arch. Neurol. & Psychiat.* 60:1, 1948.

ROSENTHAL, A. M. Electrodiagnostic testing in neuromuscular disease. *J.A.M.A.* 177:829, 1961.

THOMAS, P. K., SEARS, T. A., and GILLIATT, R. W. The range of conduction velocity in normal motor nerve fibres to the small muscles of the hand and foot. *J. Neurol., Neurosurg. & Psychiat.* 22:175, 1959.

WATKINS, A. L. An evaluation of electrodiagnostic testing. *New England J. Med.* 259:868, 1958.

WEDDELL, G., FEINSTEIN, B., and PATTLE, R. E. The electrical activity of voluntary muscle in man under normal and pathological conditions. *Brain* 67:178, 1944.

PART FIVE

The Reflexes

THE REFLEXES

THE INVESTIGATION of the reflexes is often considered to be the most important part of the neurologic examination. In fact, the cursory appraisal that is carried out by the inexperienced observer or by one not familiar with neurologic technics is frequently limited to an inspection of the pupillary and the biceps, triceps, patellar, and achilles reflexes. It must be stressed, however, that although the examination of the reflexes is essential in the adequate appraisal of a patient with disease of the nervous system, it constitutes only one portion of the neurologic investigation. The reflexes can be evaluated only when considered as a part of the entire picture—the sensory appraisal, the examination of the cranial nerves, the testing of motor functions, and the observation of the other parts of the neurologic routine.

The reflexes are significant for many reasons. In the first place, alterations in their intensity and character may be among the earliest and most delicate indications of disturbance in nervous function. Furthermore, the testing of the reflexes is a more objective procedure than many other parts of the neurologic examination. In the sensory appraisal one relies largely upon the patient's voluntary responses, and the evaluation of muscle strength and tone also necessitates voluntary cooperation. The reflexes, it is true, may be reinforced or decreased voluntarily and in hysterical states, but they are under the control of the will, either consciously or unconsciously, to a lesser extent than many of the other parts of the neurologic examination, and abnormalities of the reflexes are difficult to simulate. They are not as dependent upon the attention, cooperation, or intelligence of the patient, and consequently can be evaluated in confused individuals, those of low intelligence, infants and children, and stuporous and comatose patients, even when other tests cannot be carried out in such persons. The integrity of the motor and sensory systems can sometimes be appraised more adequately by the examination of the reflexes than by the detailed investigation of these systems.

A reflex may be defined as a response to a stimulus. It is an invariable, mechanically determined, adaptive response to the stimulation of a sense organ, which involves the use of a center of adjustment and of the conductors necessary to connect this center with the appropriate receptor and effector apparatus. In other words, it is any action performed involuntarily as the result of an impulse or impression which is transmitted along afferent fibers to a nerve center, reflected to efferent fibers, and thence calls into action certain cells, muscles, or organs. The response may be motor, secretory, or visceral, depending upon the type and intensity of the stimulus, the sensory organ stimulated, and the cells or organs which respond. Although most reflexes are involuntary and relatively independent of consciousness, the subject is usually aware of their presence during or after the response.

An intact sensory system and an intact motor system are needed for a normal reflex response, and knowledge of both sensory and motor functions is necessary to an understanding of reflex action. The *stimulus* is received by the *receptor,* which may be a sensory ending in the skin, mucous membrane, muscle, tendon, periosteum, or, in special types of reflexes, in the retina, cochlea, vestibular apparatus, olfactory mucosa, gustatory bulbs, or lining of the viscera. The stimulation of the receptor initiates an *impulse* which is carried along the *primary conductor,* or the *afferent (sensory) nerve,* whence it is transmitted to the central nervous system. There a synapse takes place with the *intercalated neuron,* which relays the impulse to the *center of adjustment,* the cell body of the *efferent neuron.* The *neuraxis of the efferent neuron,* or the *secondary conductor,* transmits the impulse to the effector, the cell, muscle, or gland which then responds (Fig. 131). A disturbance in function of any of the above parts of the reflex arc—the receptor, sensory nerve, intercalated neuron, motor unit, efferent nerve, or effector apparatus— will cause a break in the reflex arc and loss of the reflex.

Although monosynaptic and polysynaptic reflexes can be differentiated by experimental technics, few of the reflexes that are investigated clinically are as simple as the primitive response to a stimulus described above. All parts of the nervous system are intimately connected, and it is rare for one part to react without affecting or being affected by other parts. Almost immediately upon entering the cerebrospinal axis the afferent nerve divides into ascending and descending branches. These, as collateral fibers, arborize with motor cells at higher and lower levels on the same and the opposite side. Association pathways may carry the impulse to the cerebral cortex for either reflex or voluntary modification of the response. The more complex reflex acts are accomplished through a mechanism which provides for connections between the various segments on the same and opposite sides of the spinal cord, brain stem, and brain. The more complex the reflex, the greater the number of the associated neurons and mechanisms that are utilized.

Innervation of one muscle group is accompanied by inhibition of the antagonist muscle group (*Sherrington's law of reciprocal innervation*); if by reflex action the extensors of a limb are contracted, the flexors are relaxed. The response may be increased gradually to a maximum when the stimulus is prolonged; this is brought about by activation of a progressively larger number of motor neurons and is known as *recruitment.* If the strength of the stimulus is increased, the excitatory process also spreads to a greater number of neurons; this phenomenon is called *irradiation.* Reflexes are under cerebral control, and they may be increased by removal of cerebral inhibitions as well as by overstimulation of the reflex centers.

Reflex activity is essential to the normal functions of the human body. Every striated muscle contracts on direct mechanical, electrical, voluntary, and reflex stimulation. The body and its constituent parts draw away from injurious stimuli— nociceptive reflexes. Reflex activity is important in maintaining the body in its daily environment, in sustaining an upright position, in standing and walking, and in movement of the extremities. It is an integral part of the response to visual, gustatory, olfactory, auditory, and vestibular stimulation. It is essential to metabolism and to the functions of the viscera. All involuntary and many voluntary acts are reflex in nature.

Some hundreds of reflexes have been described. Many of them have no clinical importance, and it is necessary to study only the more essential ones. Reflexes have been named in various ways: some according to the site of elicitation or the part of the body stimulated; some according to the muscles involved or the part of the body that responds; some according to the ensuing movement, the joint upon which it acts, or the nerves involved. Others carry the names of one or more individuals who are said to have first described them. Inasmuch as all the reflexes cannot be tested in the routine neurologic examination, and many have no clinical importance, only the more important ones will be described. The majority of these are muscular responses, and the muscle involved rather than the point of stimulation is the important factor.

When a muscle with normal innervation and with normal tissue is passively stretched, its fibers react by resisting the stretch, and they enter into a state of increased and sustained tension, or contraction. This may be caused by gravity, manipulation, and other factors, but in reflex response this contraction results from stimulation of the sensory organs in the muscle, either directly or indirectly through a stimulus applied to its tendons, the bone to which it is attached, or the overlying skin. Either direct or indirect stimulation of any muscle results first in a lengthening reaction, but then the proprioceptive impulses carried to the nervous system from sensory organs within the muscle itself call forth an increase in tension, and a shortening reaction, or contraction, follows. A sudden stimulus, such as a brief, sharp impact, is followed by an immediate response, with a pull exerted longitudinally through the muscle. Some muscles react more strongly than others. The extensor muscles of the thigh and leg, for instance, which are important in standing and walking, react more promptly and strongly than the flexor muscles. The reflex excitation is damped out rapidly by inhibiting impulses from higher centers; if these inhibiting influences are removed, there is an increase in reflex activity. The stretch reflex occurs in every striated muscle and continues for a period of time even after the nerve supply is gone. In fact there is an increased muscular response to direct stimulation for a short time after the nerve supply has been severed. This phenomenon is known as the idiomuscular response, or myotatic irritability, and the muscular contractions are regarded as pseudoreflexes rather than true reflexes. Myotatic irritability may persist until atrophy has taken place. As a consequence, direct stimulation of muscle tissue has little value in neurologic diagnosis, except to determine myotatic irritability. The reflex responses which have diagnostic value are the indirect ones.

The student should thoroughly understand the important reflexes and why they are tested. He should learn how to obtain them, their relationship to disease symptoms, their significance, and the disease conditions with which they are associated. He should be aware that their presence or absence and the ease with which they are elicited depend on many factors, including the conditions under which they are tested. Furthermore, he should be familiar with the responding muscles and their functions; the innervation, not only of the muscle involved but also of the site of stimulation; the center in the brain, brain stem, or spinal cord that is involved in the reflex activity. In the routine neurologic examination the degree of activity of the reflexes is evaluated by observation and palpation. In carrying out investigative procedures, however, various technics have been employed to quantitate the degree of muscular response and the time consumed for contraction and relaxation. Apparatus used for such measurements include the electromyogram, the kinemometer, and other electronic, electromagnetic, and photoelectric recording devices which register the speed, duration, and pattern of reflexes.

Reflexes may be classified in various ways, and there is necessarily a certain amount of overlapping in the different categories. For the purpose of the present discussion, the following groups are considered: deep (muscle-stretch) reflexes, superficial reflexes, pyramidal tract responses, reflexes of spinal automatism, postural and righting reflexes, associated movements, and miscellaneous neurologic signs, including those of basal ganglion involvement, meningeal irritation, and tetany. Organic, or visceral, reflexes are described in "The Autonomic Nervous System," Part VI. Conditioned, or acquired, reflexes are those in which, as the result of certain experiences, a specific response may be called forth by an indifferent stimulus; they depend upon the integrity of the cerebral cortex, are developed through training and association, and cannot be considered with the other reflexes. At the present time they have little clinical application. Cerebral reflex activities which are concerned with vision, hearing, etc., are discussed with these respective functions. Emotional reflexes, too, involve higher cortical functions; they have little relationship to the neurologic examination.

CHAPTER 34

THE DEEP (MUSCLE-STRETCH) REFLEXES

THE DEEP (MUSCLE-STRETCH) REFLEXES are those which are elicited in response to application of the stimulus to either tendons or periosteum, or occasionally to bones, joints, fascia, or aponeurotic structures. They are often called tendon or periosteal reflexes, and, because the stimulus is mediated through the deeper sense organs such as the neuromuscular and neurotendinous spindles, they may be referred to as proprioceptive reflexes. They are all, however, muscle stretch reflexes and are produced by the indirect stimulation of muscles and the calling forth of a response to a sudden stretch imposed upon them. They are not evoked by direct stimulation of muscle tissues. The term deep reflex is used merely as a classification and not with special implication.

The deep, or muscle-stretch, reflexes are best tested by the use of a rubber percussion hammer, but other objects may also be used. A soft rubber hammer is most desirable, for the pain that may follow a blow with a hard hammer may interfere with the response. The stimulus should be quick and direct, and should be a threshold one, but no greater than necessary. The patient should be comfortable and relaxed. The part of the body to be tested should be in a position for optimum muscular response. Because the amount and briskness of the reaction depends largely upon the state of tone in the muscles, they should usually be in a state of slight tension or contraction. In order to compare the reflexes on the two sides of the body, the position of the extremities should be symmetrical. The reflexes may be examined even though the patient is unconscious. For an accurate determination the examiner should *feel* as well as see the contraction, by placing one hand over the muscle which responds. He should notice both the presence of the reflexes and the degree of activity. The latter is estimated by the *speed and vigor of the response,* the *range of movement,* and the *duration of the contraction.* Reflexes may be classified as absent, sluggish or diminished, normal, exaggerated, and markedly hyperactive. For the purposes of clinical note-taking some neurologists grade them numerically, as follows: O = absent; + = present but diminished; + + = normal; + + + = increased but not necessarily to a pathologic degree; + + + + = markedly hyperactive, often with associated colonus. The response should always be compared on the two sides of the body; unequal reflexes may be as significant as either increased or absent reflexes.

As far as possible the deep reflexes should be named by the muscles involved in the response rather than the site of stimulation or the nerve involved. For the purpose of classification they will be divided as follows: reflexes supplied by the cranial nerves, reflexes of the upper extremities, reflexes of the trunk, and reflexes of the lower extremities.

DEEP REFLEXES INNERVATED BY THE CRANIAL NERVES

These have been discussed in detail under the heading of the respective cranial nerves (Part III).

DEEP REFLEXES OF THE UPPER EXTREMITIES

THE SCAPULOHUMERAL REFLEX

Tapping over the vertebral border of the scapula, either at the tip of its spine or at its base near the inferior angle, is followed by retraction of the scapula. This is done principally through the action of the rhomboidei major and minor, which are innervated by the dorsal scapular nerve (fourth and fifth cervical segments). There may be associated elevation of the scapula and adduction and external rotation of the humerus through the action of the trapezius, latissimus dorsi, infraspinatus, and teres minor.

THE DELTOID REFLEX

Tapping over the insertion of the deltoid muscle at the junction of the upper and middle third of the lateral aspect of the humerus is followed by a contraction of the muscle with resulting abduction of the upper arm. The sensory and motor supply to this reflex are through the axillary nerve (fifth and sixth cervical segments).

THE PECTORALIS REFLEX

With the patient's arm in midposition between abduction and adduction, the examiner places his finger as nearly as possible on the tendon of the pectoralis major muscle near its insertion on the crest of the greater tubercle of the humerus (Fig. 224). Tapping the finger is followed by adduction and slight internal rotation of the arm at the shoulder. The contraction of the muscle may be felt but not seen in the normal individual. This reflex is innervated by the lateral and medial anterior thoracic nerves (fifth cervical through first thoracic segments).

THE LATISSIMUS DORSI REFLEX

With the patient prone and his arm abducted and in slight external rotation, the examiner places his finger on the tendon of the latissimus dorsi near its insertion in the intertubercular groove of the humerus, and taps the finger with a reflex hammer. This is followed by adduction and slight internal rotation of the shoulder. This reflex is innervated by the thoracodorsal (long subscapular) nerve (sixth through eighth cervical segments).

THE CLAVICLE REFLEX

In patients with reflex hyperactivity in the upper extremities, a tap over the lateral aspect of the clavicle is followed by extensive contraction of various muscle groups in the upper limb. There are individual variations, but normally the response should be the same on each side. This is not a specific reflex, but is an indication of the spread of reflex response. It is useful in comparing reflex activity in the upper limbs.

THE BICEPS REFLEX

The arm is held in a relaxed position, with the forearm midway between flexion and extension and in slight pronation. This position is obtained most satisfactorily if the patient's elbow is resting in the examiner's hand. The examiner places his thumb over the biceps tendon and taps the thumb with a reflex hammer (Fig. 225). The outstanding response is a contraction of the biceps muscle with flexion of the forearm on the arm. Inasmuch as the biceps is also a supinator of the forearm, there is often a certain amount of supination. If the reflex is exaggerated, the reflexogenous zone is increased and the reflex may even be obtained by tapping the clavicle. The

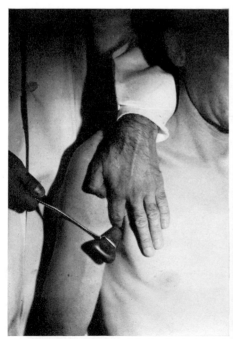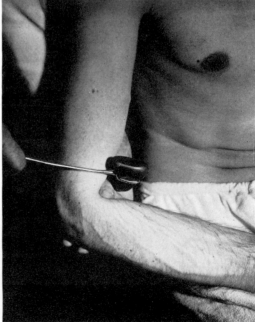

Fig. 224 (*Left*). Method of obtaining pectoralis reflex.
Fig. 225 (*Right*). Method of obtaining biceps reflex.

sensory supply of this reflex is through the midcervical nerves, and the motor supply to the biceps is through the musculocutaneous nerve (fifth and sixth cervical segments). The reflex center is at the fifth and sixth cervical segments.

THE TRICEPS REFLEX

This reflex is elicited by tapping the triceps tendon just above its insertion on the olecranon process of the ulna. The arm is held midway between flexion and extension, and it may be rested on the examiner's hand or on the patient's thigh (Fig. 226). The response is one of contraction of the triceps muscle, with extension of the forearm on the arm. The sensory and motor innervations are through the radial nerve (sixth through eighth cervical segments), and the center is in the lower cervical portion of the spinal cord. The so-called *paradoxic triceps reflex* consists of a flexion of the forearm following stimulation at the olecranon. This response appears when the arc of the triceps reflex is damaged, as in lesions of the seventh and eighth cervical segments; in such cases the stimulus calls forth a flexion response, unopposed by the triceps muscle.

THE BRACHIORADIALIS (RADIAL PERIOSTEAL OR SUPINATOR) REFLEX

If the styloid process of the radius is tapped while the forearm is in semiflexion and semipronation, there will be flexion of the forearm on the arm together with supination (Fig. 227). The latter response is more marked if the forearm has been extended and pronated, but the reflex is much weaker. Sometimes there is associated flexion of the wrist and fingers, with adduction of the forearm. The principal muscle involved is the brachioradialis, and it can be stimulated not only at its tendon of insertion on the lateral aspect of the base of the styloid process of the radius, but also along the lower one-third of the lateral surface of the radius or at its

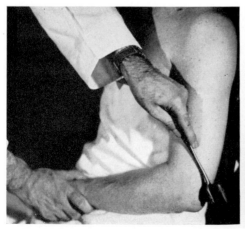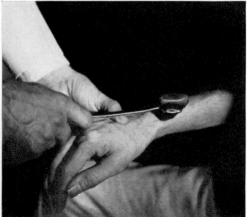

FIG. 226 (*Left*).   Method of obtaining triceps reflex.
FIG. 227 (*Right*).   Method of obtaining brachioradialis reflex.

tendon of origin above the lateral epicondyle of the humerus. The innervation of this reflex is through the radial nerve (fifth and sixth cervical segments). With exaggeration of this reflex there is associated flexion of the hand and fingers. In the presence of pyramidal tract involvement or other conditions causing reflex hyper-activity with, in addition, a lesion of the fifth cervical segment or its neuraxes, there may be contraction of the flexors of the hand and fingers without flexion and supination of the forearm. This is termed *inversion of the radial reflex.*

THE PRONATOR REFLEX

If either the styloid process of the ulna or the postero-inferior surface of the ulna is tapped while the forearm is in semiflexion and the wrist in semipronation, there will be pronation of the forearm, often with adduction of the wrist. There may also be flexion of the wrist and fingers. The same response may be obtained by stimulating the palmar surface of the lower aspect of the radius, causing brief supination which is followed by pronation. The major muscles participating in this response are the pronators teres and quadratus, and the innervation is through the median nerve (sixth cervical through first thoracic segments). This reflex may be exaggerated early in pyramidal lesions.

THE WRIST EXTENSION REFLEX

Tapping of the extensor tendons of the wrist while the forearm is pronated and the wrist is hanging down may be followed by a contraction of the extensor muscles and extension at the wrist. This reflex is supplied by the radial nerve (sixth through eighth cervical segments). Under certain circumstances one may get flexion of the wrist and fingers on tapping the dorsum of the carpometacarpal area. This is known as the *carpometacarpal,* or *carpophalangeal, reflex of von Bechterew,* and it is discussed with the pyramidal tract signs.

THE WRIST FLEXION REFLEX

Tapping the flexor tendons of the wrist on the volar surface of the forearm at or above the transverse carpal ligament when the hand is in supination and the fingers are slightly flexed is followed by a contraction of the flexor muscles of the hand and fingers. This reflex is innervated by the median and perhaps the ulnar nerves (sixth cervical through first thoracic segments). This is also known as the *hand flexor reflex.*

THE THUMB REFLEX

Tapping of the tendon of the flexor pollicis longus muscle just above the tendon of the pronator quadratus is followed by flexion of the distal phalanx of the thumb. This reflex is supplied by the median nerve (sixth cervical through first thoracic segments).

THE FINGER FLEXOR REFLEX

The patients hand is in partial supination, resting on a table or a solid surface, and the fingers are slightly flexed. The examiner places his middle and index fingers on the volar surfaces of the phalanges of the patient's four fingers, and taps his own fingers lightly but briskly with the reflex hammer (Fig. 228). The response is one of flexion of the patient's four fingers and the distal phalanx of the thumb. The reflex may be reinforced by having the patient bend his fingers as the blow is being applied. The nerve supply, as in the wrist flexion reflex, is through the median and ulnar nerves (sixth cervical through first thoracic segments). This reflex is difficult for the inexperienced observer to elicit, but Wartenberg, who has described it, considers it one of the most important reflexes in the upper extremity. Forced grasping, the Hoffmann sign, the "Rossolimo and Mendel-Bechterew of the hand," and other reflexes to be described with the pyramidal tract responses may be pathologic variations of the same response.

Not all of the above deep reflexes can be elicited in the examination of the normal person. The biceps, triceps, and brachioradialis reflexes should be obtained without difficulty in normal individuals, but some of the others may be elicited only to an appreciable extent, and others not at all. If these latter reflexes are conspicuous, one can assume the presence of reflex exaggeration.

DEEP REFLEXES OF THE TRUNK

THE COSTAL PERIOSTEAL REFLEX

Tapping the lower rib margins, the costal cartilages, or the xyphoid process of the sternum with the reflex hammer is followed by contraction of the upper abdominal muscles and slight excursion of the umbilicus toward the site of stimulation. If either the rib margins or costal cartilages are stimulated, there is an oblique deviation of the umbilicus upward and laterally, and if the xyphoid process is

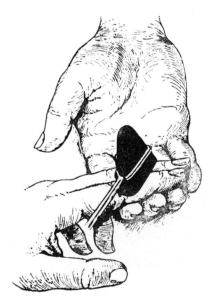

Fig. 228.   Method of obtaining finger flexor reflex. (Wartenberg, R.: *Arch. Neurol. & Psychiat.* 51:113, 1944.)

tapped, there is an upward deviation of the umbilicus. These reflexes are innervated by the upper intercostal nerves (fifth through ninth thoracic segments).

THE ABDOMINAL MUSCLE (DEEP ABDOMINAL) REFLEX

The abdominal muscle reflex is a deep reflex obtained on brisk stretching of the muscles. It may be elicited at many places on the abdominal wall, and there are many methods of testing for it. The examiner may tap the abdominal wall overlying the muscles, but better results are obtained if he stretches the muscles slightly by pressing on them with a tongue blade or ruler, and then taps this briskly with a reflex hammer. He may also use an index finger to press on the muscles, or insert the finger in the umbilicus to effect the same result, and then tap the finger. The response is a prompt contraction of the muscles, and a deviation of the umbilicus toward the site of the stimulus. The reflex is reinforced by slight contraction of the abdominal wall, which may be accomplished by having the patient cough, attempt to raise his head against resistance, or make a slight attempt to rise. The innervation is by the anterior divisions of the fifth through twelfth thoracic nerves (intercostal nerves), as well as the ilioinguinal and iliohypogastric nerves. The abdominal muscle reflex is present to only a minimal extent in normal persons, and is most significant if it is exaggerated or if there is dissociation between the deep and superficial abdominal reflexes.

THE ILIAC REFLEX

Tapping over the iliac crest is followed by contraction of the lower abdominal muscles. This reflex is innervated by the lower intercostal nerves (tenth through twelfth thoracic segments).

THE SYMPHYSIS PUBIS REFLEX

Tapping over the symphysis pubis is followed by a contraction of the abdominal muscles and a downward movement of the umbilicus. The reflex should be tested with the patient recumbent and with his abdominal muscles relaxed and his thighs in slight abduction and internal rotation. If a unilateral stimulus is applied by tapping one and one-half to two centimeters from the midline, there is not only the "upper response" just described, but also a "lower response," or *puboadductor reflex,* with contraction of the adductor muscles of the thigh on the side stimulated, and some flexion of the hip. This latter response is also seen if the reflex is exaggerated. The symphysis pubis reflex is innervated by the lower intercostal, ilioinguinal, and iliohypogastric nerves (eleventh and twelfth thoracic and upper lumbar segments). Both the costal periosteal and symphysis pubis reflexes may be considered as manifestations of the abdominal muscle reflex in which the stimulus is directed toward the site of insertion rather than the muscle itself.

THE BACK REFLEX

With the patient lying prone, the sacral and lumbar areas of the spine are tapped. The reflex response consists of contraction of the erector spinae muscles. The innervation is through the thoracic, lumbar, and sacral nerves.

DEEP REFLEXES OF THE LOWER EXTREMITIES

THE PATELLAR, OR QUADRICEPS, REFLEX

The patellar, or quadriceps, reflex, or the *knee jerk,* is characterized by contraction of the quadriceps femoris muscle, with resulting extension of the leg on the thigh, in response to a stimulus directed toward the patellar tendon. A sharp blow on the tendon draws down the patella and stretches the quadriceps muscle. This is followed by contraction of the muscle. If the reflex irritability is high, the contraction is abrupt and strong and the amplitude of the movement is large. This reflex may be elicited in various manners. It is best tested with the patient seated in a chair with his feet resting on the floor. The examiner places one hand over the quadriceps femoris muscle, so that he can feel the contraction, and with the other hand he taps the patellar tendon, or ligamentum patellae, just below the patella. In this way the examiner can palpate the contraction of the muscle and observe the rapidity and range of response (Fig. 229); he can also compare the responses on the two sides. If the patient is lying in bed, the examiner should partially flex the knee by placing one hand beneath it (Fig. 230); it is advisable to lift both knees, and to have the heels resting lightly on the bed. Many examiners test the patellar reflex by having the patient sit on the edge of a table with his legs hanging over the edge in such a manner that his feet do not touch the floor, or by having the patient sit with one leg crossed over the other and tapping the patellar tendon of the superior leg. In this way the *range* of response can be noted, but inasmuch as it is more important to note the *speed* of response, or the duration of the latent period between the time of the stimulus and the resulting response, as will be discussed below, the better procedure is to palpate the quadriceps. If the patellar reflex is exaggerated, there may be not only extension of the leg, but also adduction of the thigh, which on occasion is bilateral. There may be a bilateral extensor response. Also, if the reflex is exaggerated, the response may be obtained by stimula-

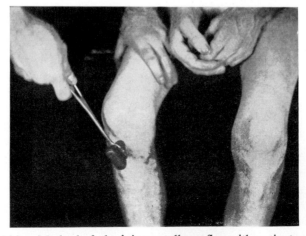

Fig. 229.   Method of obtaining patellar reflex with patient seated.

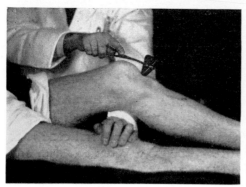 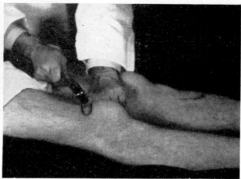

FIG. 230 (*Left*).   Method of obtaining patellar reflex with patient recumbent.
FIG. 231 (*Right*).   Method of obtaining suprapatellar reflex.

tion not only of the ligamentum patellae but also of the tendon of the quadriceps femoris muscle just above the patella, the *suprapatellar,* or *epipatellar, reflex;* the tendon can be tapped directly, or, with the patient recumbent, the examiner can place his index finger on the tendon and tap the finger or push down the tendon. Contraction of the quadriceps causes a brisk upward movement of the tendon, together with extension of the leg (Fig. 231). In marked exaggeration of the patellar reflex one may elicit patellar clonus (see p. 614). Absence of the patellar reflex is known as the *Westphal sign*; this has been described as one of the cardinal signs of tabes dorsalis. The patellar reflex is innervated by the femoral nerve (second through fourth lumbar segments).

THE ADDUCTOR, OR TIBIOADDUCTOR, REFLEX

With the thigh in slight abduction, the medial epicondyle of the femur is tapped in the vicinity of the adductor tubercle, or at times the medial condyle of the tibia is stimulated. The response is a contraction of the adductor muscles of the thigh with inward movement of the extremity. If the reflex is exaggerated, there may be crossed, or bilateral, adduction. The innervation of this reflex is through the obturator nerve (second through fourth lumbar segments). An adductor response can also be obtained, if there is exaggeration of the reflex, by tapping the spinous processes of the sacral or lumbar vertebrae while the patient is in a seated position (the *spinal adductor reflex*) or by tapping the crest or the superior spines of the ilium. The puboadductor reflex is described on page 595.

THE INTERNAL HAMSTRING, SEMITENDINOSUS AND SEMIMEMBRANOSUS, OR POSTERIOR TIBIOFEMORAL REFLEXES

These are elicited by stimulating the tendons of the semitendinosus and semimembranosus muscles just above their insertions on the posterior and medial surfaces and medial condyle of the tibia. This is best done with the patient in the recumbent position with the leg abducted and partially externally rotated, and the knee slightly flexed. The fingers are placed over the lower portions of the muscles and their tendons on the medial aspect of the leg just below the knee, and the fingers are tapped with the reflex hammer. The response is an increased flexion of the leg upon the thigh, with slight internal rotation of the leg. This reflex is supplied through the tibial portion of the sciatic nerve (fourth lumbar through second sacral segments).

THE EXTERNAL HAMSTRING, BICEPS FEMORIS, OR POSTERIOR PERONEOFEMORAL REFLEX

This is elicited by stimulating the tendon of the biceps femoris muscle just above its insertion on the lateral side of the head of the fibula and the lateral condyle of the tibia. With the patient either recumbent or lying on the opposite side, and with the leg in moderate flexion at the knee, the examiner places his fingers over the tendon of the biceps femoris muscle on the lateral aspect of the leg just below the knee, and taps the fingers (Fig. 232). The response consists of a contraction of the muscle with resulting flexion of the leg on the thigh and moderate external rotation of the leg. The reflex may also be elicited by tapping the head of the fibula; this is known as the *fibular reflex*. The nerve supply for the long head of the biceps is the same as that for the posterior tibiofemoral reflex, through the tibial portion of the sciatic nerve, but the short head of the biceps is supplied by the common peroneal portion of the sciatic nerve (fifth lumbar through second or third sacral segments).

THE TENSOR FASCIAE LATAE REFLEX

This reflex is tested by tapping over the tensor fasciae latae muscle at its origin near the anterior superior iliac spine; the patient is in the recumbent position. The response consists of slight abduction of the thigh. This reflex is innervated by the superior gluteal nerve (fourth lumbar through first sacral segments).

THE GLUTEUS REFLEXES

Tapping the lower border of the sacrum or the posterior aspect of the ilium near the origin of the gluteus maximus muscle is followed by a contraction of this muscle, with extension of the thigh. This reflex is best tested with the patient in the recumbent position, but with his weight on the opposite side so that there is moderate flexion of the ipsilateral thigh; it may also be elicited with the patient in the prone position.

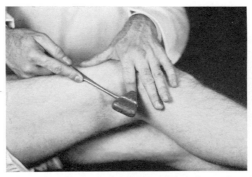

FIG. 232. Method of obtaining biceps femoris reflex.

It is innervated by the inferior gluteal nerve (fifth lumbar through second sacral segments). A gluteus medius reflex may on occasion be elicited by stimulating the anterior portion of the iliac crest near the site of origin of the muscle. The response is one of slight abduction and medial rotation of the thigh. The innervation is the same as that of the tensor fasciae latae reflex (superior gluteal nerve), and the response is almost identical; it may not be possible to differentiate these two reflexes.

THE ACHILLES, OR TRICEPS SURAE, REFLEX

The achilles, or triceps surae reflex, or the *ankle jerk,* is obtained by tapping the achilles tendon just above its insertion on the posterior surface of the calcaneus. This is followed by contraction of the posterior crural muscles, the gastrocnemius, soleus, and plantaris, with resulting plantar flexion of the foot at the ankle. If the patient is seated or is lying in bed, the thigh should be moderately abducted and rotated externally, the knee should be flexed, and the foot should be in moderate inversion; the examiner should place one hand under the foot to produce moderate dorsiflexion at the ankle (Fig. 233). If the reflex is obtained with difficulty, the patient may be asked to press his foot against the examiner's hand in order to tense the tendon. If it cannot be elicited in this manner, the patient should be asked to kneel on his knees on a chair, preferably on a soft surface, while the feet project at right angles; the achilles tendons are percussed while the patient is in this position. (Fig. 234). The reflex may also be obtained while the patient is lying prone with his feet in moderate dorsiflexion. If either of these two latter positions is used, the responses on the two sides may be compared with ease. If the achilles reflex is exaggerated, it may be elicited by tapping the sole of the foot, the *medioplantar reflex,* or by tapping the anterior aspect of the ankle, the *paradoxic ankle reflex.* In more marked exaggeration spontaneous clonus may be obtained when the tendon is tapped. The achilles reflex is innervated by the tibial nerve (fifth lumbar through second sacral segments).

THE EXTENSOR HALLUCIS LONGUS REFLEX

With the patient recumbent, the examiner exerts moderate pressure with his finger on the dorsal surface of the terminal phalanx of the great toe. Tapping the finger is followed by extension of the toe, which may be felt more readily than it is seen. This reflex is innervated by the deep peroneal nerve (fourth lumbar through the first sacral segments). It may be absent with herniation of the nucleus pulposus between the fourth and fifth lumbar bodies.

THE TIBIALIS POSTERIOR REFLEX

Tapping the tendon of the tibialis posterior just above and behind the medial malleolus is followed by inversion of the foot. This reflex is best examined with the patient prone and the foot, in a neutral position or in slight eversion, extended beyond the edge of the bed. The leg should be supported by the examiner and slightly flexed at the knee. This reflex is innervated by the tibial nerve (fifth lumbar

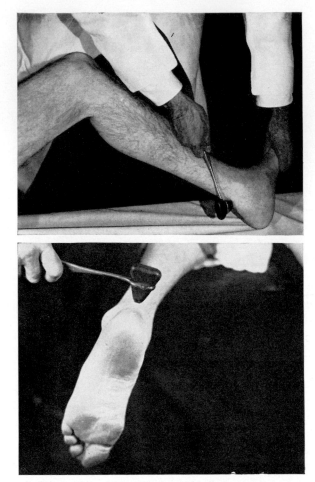

FIG. 233 (*Top*).   Method of obtaining achilles reflex with patient recumbent.
FIG. 234 (*Bottom*).   Method of obtaining achilles reflex with patient kneeling.

through first sacral segments). It may be absent if there is herniation of the nucleus pulposus between the fourth and fifth lumbar vertebral bodies, but it is difficult to obtain in the normal individual, and to be significant its absence must be unilateral.

THE PLANTAR MUSCLE REFLEX

This reflex is described in Chapter 56.

INTERPRETATION OF THE DEEP (MUSCLE-STRETCH) REFLEXES

The above are the most important of the deep, or muscle-stretch (tendon or periosteal), reflexes. All are not of equal significance, however, and all cannot be elicited in the normal individual. The most valuable of them are the biceps, triceps, patellar, and achilles reflexes; under most circumstances one should be able to elicit these in every normal person. It has been determined experimentally, however, that 3 to 4 per cent of individuals with no other evidence of disease of the nervous system may show the absence of one or more of these reflexes, and the statement has even been made that a reflex is occasionally absent in up to 10 per cent. In general, however, if the technic is adequate, the deep reflexes are rarely absent in normal persons.

While the statement has been made that the degree of activity of the deep reflexes depends upon the speed and vigor of reaction, the range of movement, and the duration of the contraction, it is the speed of reaction, or the duration of the latent period between the time of application of the stimulus and the time that the response occurs, that is the essential factor. This latter is the most important criterion in the estimation of reflex activity, and it may be perceived more accurately by palpation than by vision. The adequate evaluation of the reflex response depends upon experience. Each examiner must come to his own conclusions, based upon previous impressions, the type of stimulus used, the intensity of the stimulus, the position of the part at the time the reflex is being tested, the general condition of the patient, the environmental surroundings, etc. The appraisal depends upon the individual interpretation of the examiner. There is no standard, and there is a certain amount of normal variation in reflex activity. What is normal for one individual may be an increased or a decreased response for another. In some persons the reflexes are lively, in others they are sluggish. Under normal circumstances the reflexes should be equal on the two sides—if equal, they are probably not pathologic unless there is either marked diminution or increase of response. It is important to remember that the examination of the deep reflexes is the most objective of reflex determinations.

REINFORCEMENT OF THE REFLEXES

In certain individuals the reflexes may appear to be markedly diminished or even absent, although there is no other evidence of nervous system disease. This is apt to be the case in muscular or athletic individuals with firm, overly developed muscles, or in tense, apprehensive persons who may be bracing their muscles either voluntarily or unconsciously. Under such circumstances it may be necessary to use *reinforcement* in order to elicit the reflexes. Reinforcement may be carried out according to the method of Jendrassik; on testing the patellar reflexes the patient is asked to hook together the flexed fingers of the two hands, placing the palmar surfaces of the fingers of one hand against the palmar surfaces of the fingers of the other, and to attempt to pull them apart at the time the reflex is being stimulated (Fig. 235). He may also be asked to clench his fists, to grasp firmly the arm of the chair or the side of the bed, or to clench one of the hands or the arm of the examiner. In carrying out reinforcement, an attempt is made to divert the patient's attention and thus relax his muscles. This may also be done by having the patient look at the ceiling and cough at the time the reflex is being tested. The examiner can frequently divert the patient's attention merely by talking to him while testing the reflexes, discussing his illness with him, or asking him irrelevant questions. The patient may be asked to take a deep breath, count, read aloud, or repeat verses while the reflexes are being examined. A sudden loud noise, a painful stimulus elsewhere on the body, as the pulling of a hair, or a bright light flashed in the eyes may also be a means of reinforcement. It has been postulated that reflex reinforcement by the Jendrassik and related maneuvers takes place through increased gamma motor (fusiform) activity. It is probable, however, that activation of the alpha motor system plays a major role in such reinforcement.

Increasing the tonus of the antagonistic muscles in an attempt to decrease the tonus of the muscles involved in the response also reinforces the reflexes. This may be done, in testing the patellar reflex, by having the recumbent patient slightly flex his knees and press against the bed with the backs of his heels, thus contracting the hamstring muscles and relaxing the quadriceps. It must be stated, however, that although the muscles should be relaxed, a certain amount of tension is necessary for the reflex response. The overly tense muscle must be relaxed, but there must be some voluntary innervation, and reinforcement may also be accomplished by in- creasing the tension of the muscles being tested. The quadriceps may be tensed by pushing the ball of the foot against the floor or pushing the leg forward against the examiner's hand while the patellar reflex is being elicited, and the gastrocnemius, by pressing the foot against the examiner's hand or against the floor while the achilles reflex is being tested. By these means the amplitude of a reflex may be in-

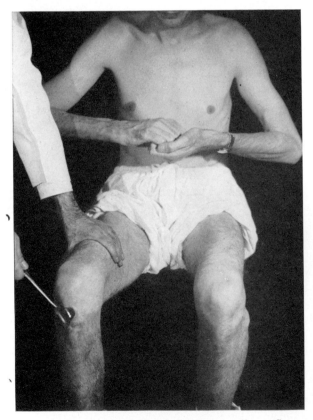

Fig. 235.   Method of reinforcing patellar reflex.

creased or an otherwise latent reflex may be obtained. Reflexes that are normal on reinforcement, even though they cannot be obtained without reinforcement, may be considered normal reflexes.

ABNORMALITIES OF THE DEEP (MUSCLE-STRETCH) REFLEXES

If there is abnormality of the deep, or muscle-stretch, reflexes, the response is manifested by either hypoactivity or hyperactivity. In hypoactivity the response varies from a diminished or a sluggish one to complete absence of the reflexes. In hyperactivity there may be increased speed and vigor of response, exaggeration of the range of movement, decrease in threshold, extension of reflexogenous zone, and prolongation of the muscular contraction. The pathologic conditions in which these various changes occur are discussed below.

DIMINUTION TO ABSENCE OF THE DEEP (MUSCLE-STRETCH) REFLEXES

If there is hypoactivity of the reflexes, there is a sluggish response and/or a diminution in the range of response. An increase in the intensity of the stimulus may be necessary to elicit the reflex, or repeated blows may be necessary, for a single stimulus may be subliminal. Deep reflexes are absent if they are not obtained, even with reinforcement.

Diminution of the reflexes usually results from an interference with the conduction of the impulse through the reflex arc, and absence indicates a *break in the reflex arc*. Such changes may be associated with dysfunction of the receptor, afferent pathway, intercalated neuron, motor unit, efferent pathway, or effector apparatus (Table 7). Interference with the *sensory pathway* may be caused by the following

TABLE 7. REFLEX PATTERNS

	Deep reflexes	Superficial reflexes	Pyramidal tract responses	Reflexes of spinal automatism	Associated movements
Peripheral lesion (peripheral nerve or anterior horn cell)	Decreased to absent	Decreased to absent	Absent	Absent	Normal
Basal ganglion lesion	Normal; occasionally slightly increased or decreased	Normal or slight increase	Absent	Absent	Absence of normal associated movements
Pyramidal tract lesion	Hyperactive (especially in speed of response)	Decreased to absent	Present	Present (associated extrapyramidal involvement)	Presence of pathologic associated movements
Cerebellar lesion	Decreased or pendular	Normal	Absent	Absent	Normal
Psychogenic disorder	Normal or increased (especially in range of response)	Normal or increased	Absent	Absent	Normal

conditions: lesions of the sensory nerves (sensory neuritis), involvement of the posterior roots (radiculitis), affections of the dorsal root ganglia (tabes dorsalis), dysfunction of the posterior columns of the spinal cord (tabes dorsalis, posterolateral sclerosis, etc.). Syringomyelia and other intramedullary lesions may interfere with the function of the *intercalated neuron.* Involvement of the *motor unit and pathway* may be associated with numerous conditions: lesions of the motor nucleus or anterior horn cell (poliomyelitis, progressive spinal muscular atrophy, syringomyelia), affections of the anterior nerve roots and motor nerves (radiculitis, motor neuritis), dysfunction of the myoneural junction (myasthenia gravis, periodic family paralysis). With peripheral nerve lesions the reflexes may not return until there has been recovery of a major portion of motor function. Sometimes there is persisting arflexia following nerve root lesions and peripheral neuropathies, even after complete return of both motor and sensory functions. In myasthenia gravis the reflexes are absent only when there is extensive involvement with failure of muscular contractions, and in familial periodic paralysis they are absent only temporarily. With diseases of the *motor apparatus,* or the muscles, such as the myopathies and myositis, the reflexes may persist until the atrophy or muscular involvement is too extensive to allow a muscular contraction. In pseudohypertrophic muscular dystrophy the proximal reflexes disappear early, but the distal reflexes may persist until later progression of the disease.

The deep reflexes may also be either diminished or absent in various other conditions. Whereas they may be increased in the earlier stages of coma, they are absent in deep coma, narcosis, and deep sedation. They are often absent in deep sleep. They are characteristically lost in nerve block, nerve root block, caudal anesthesia, and spinal anesthesia. They are absent in spinal shock, following a sudden transverse lesion of the spinal cord, but reappear below the level of the lesion after a period of from three to four weeks, and generally become hyperactive (Chapter 37). In fact they may be present in extensive spinal cord lesions in spite of apparent loss of sensation. They are absent in Adie's syndrome (benign areflexia), a symptom complex characterized also by tonic pupils with impaired reaction to light. They are diminished and often lost in asthenic states and severe toxemias. In myxedema there is a prolongation of both the contraction and relaxation times, especially the latter, and the reflex time returns to normal with treatment of the hypothyroid condition. Some observers have stated that careful measurement of reflex time is an accurate test of thyroid function, but others have failed to confirm this, and it must be recalled that slow contraction and relaxation times may also occur with other conditions, including lower motor neuron disease in which there is decreased reflex activity. Delay in relaxation time is also often found in myotonia. In diabetes and neurosyphilis there may be either prolongation of the reflex time or decrease or absence of the reflexes before there are other evidences of nervous system involvement. In porphyria there may be dissociated absence of reflexes; those which remain may be elicited only by a summation of response. They may be either diminished or lost in the presence of increased intracranial pressure, especially in posterior fossa tumors. In exhaustion following extreme exertion they may be diminished or absent.

In paraplegia in flexion it may not be possible to obtain the deep extensor reflexes, even though the neurologic status would suggest that there should be reflex hyperactivity; this is caused by spasm of the antagonist, or flexor muscles, and the flexor reflexes are hyperactive. In severe states of spasticity and rigidity it may not be possible to obtain the deep reflexes. The reflexes may be increased in the early stages of peripheral neuritis, especially if there is pain, owing to the irritability of the afferent nerves, but they disappear after the pathologic changes in the nerves have become more definite. The reflexes may appear to be absent in neurologic disorders in which there is marked spasticity with contractures and in diseases of the joints characterized by inflammation, contractures, and ankylosis. Here their absence is apparent, owing to lack of motility at the joint or pain on moving the joint, rather than real, and careful observation may show that a muscular contraction takes place even though there is no movement at the joint. In parietal lobe lesions there may be an increase in threshold and a slowness of response, but an increased excursion.

HYPERACTIVITY OF THE DEEP (MUSCLE-STRETCH) REFLEXES

Hyperactivity of the deep reflexes is characterized by the following changes: decrease in the reflex threshold, increase in the speed of response (decrease in latent period), exaggeration of vigor and range of movement, prolongation of muscular contraction, extension of the reflexogenous zone (or zone of provocation), and propagation of the reflex response. A minimal stimulus may evoke the reflex, and reflexes which are not normally obtained may be elicited with ease. There may be a wide zone of areas for effective stimulation in neighboring structures, and application of the stimulus to sites at some distance from the usual one may cause the response; the patellar reflex may be elicited by tapping the surface of the tibia or the dorsum of the foot, and the biceps and other arm reflexes by tapping the clavicle. The response may involve adjacent or even contralateral muscles, and the contraction of one muscle may be accompanied by contraction of others; contraction of the biceps or brachioradialis may be accompanied by flexion of the fingers; extension of the leg may be accompanied by adduction of the thigh, or there may be bilateral extension of the legs. One stimulus may be followed by repeated contractions and relaxations, owing to repeated volleys of discharges, so that clonus may be obtained. The deep reflexes are exaggerated in association with an increase in the tone of the contracting muscles.

The deep reflexes are increased with *lesions of the pyramidal system* (using this term in its accepted clinical sense). Spasticity and exaggeration of the deep reflexes have, in the past, been felt to be the result of interruption of impulses from the pyramidal cortex and loss of the inhibiting effect of this portion of the motor system on the anterior horn cells. It is probable, however, that these changes are related more closely to dysfunction of the extrapyramidal, rather than the pyramidal, portion of the motor system, and actually are brought about by imbalance of the facilitatory and inhibitory centers in the midbrain and brain stem reticular formations as well as altered balance between the alpha and gamma motor systems in the spinal cord (Chapter 23). Within the spinal cord those impulses which lead to exaggeration of the stretch reflexes may be carried by the reticulospinal and vestibulospinal rather than corticospinal tracts. From a clinical point of view, however, the term "pyramidal" continues to be used in referring to the site of involvement as well as to the ensuing change in function. A lesion at any level of the pyramidal system, and/or other re- later upper motor neuron components, from the motor cortex to just above the seg- ment of origin of a reflex arc will be accompanied by spasticity and exaggeration of the deep deflexes. Not only are existing reflexes increased in the aspects described above, but latent ones and those which are normally elicited with difficulty may be obtained with ease. In cerebral hemiplegia the position of predilection is that of flexion of the upper extremities, with more marked weakness of the extensors, and of extension in the lower extremities, with more marked weakness of the flexors. Consequently the flexor reflexes are exaggerated to a greater degree in the upper extremities, and the extensor reflexes in the lower. The reflexes may be present in spinal cord lesions in spite of the apparent absence of sensation. If the spasticity is too marked, however, the resulting contractures may inter- fere with the reflex response. This may be the case in paraplegia in flexion, but on the other hand the increased tone of the flexor muscles probably causes absence of the extensor reflexes.

The deep reflexes are also increased in the early stages of coma and anesthesia or narcosis. They are exaggerated in tetany, tetanus, and strychnine poisoning, owing to increased irritability both of the nerves and the muscles. Cold and exer- cise may increase the reflex response, although extreme exercise may be followed by areflexia. The reflexes may be increased in the early stages of a neuritis due to the increased irritability of the nerve fibers, but they disappear after the patho- logic changes have fully developed. The deep reflexes may be increased if the tone of the opposing muscles is diminished; consequently the patellar reflex may be hyperactive if there is palsy of the hamstrings. They are often increased in hyperthyroidism, and the speed of the response is diminished when the thyroid activity is decreased.

Exaggeration of the deep reflexes may also be found in *psychogenic disorders,* such as psychoneurosis and hysteria (Table 7), and also in states of anxiety, fright, and agitation. The reflexes vary in these conditions; they may be nor- mal, they may be diminished due to voluntary or involuntary tension of the an- tagonistic muscles, but they are most frequently increased. The hyperactivity may be marked, but it is an exaggeration not in the speed of the response with de- crease in the latent period, but in the excursion or range of response. The foot may be kicked far into the air and held extended for a time after the patellar tendon is tapped, but the response takes place slowly and relaxation is equally slow. There is often a bilateral response with a jerking of the entire body when the reflexes are tested. There is no increase in the reflexogenous zone in psy- chogenic lesions, and although there may be spurious clonus, there is no real clonus. Furthermore, there are no other signs of organic disease of the pyramidal system.

In lesions of the *extrapyramidal system* there are no consistent changes in the deep reflexes (Table 7). The response depends to a certain extent upon muscular tonicity and the amount of rigidity that is present. Usually the reflexes are slightly exaggerated, owing to increased tension of the muscles, but this is not a consistent finding, and the rigidity may cause retardation or diminution or absence of the reflexes. In diseases of the *cerebellum* the reflexes are often somewhat diminished, perhaps as a part of the hypotonicity and the loss of the reflex contraction of the antagonists (Table 7). Frequently, however, they are of the pendular variety. If the patellar reflex is tested while the foot is hanging free, there may be a series of jerky to-and-fro pendular movements of the foot and leg before the limb finally comes to rest. This increased swinging may also be the result of hyptonia of the extensor and flexor muscles and lack of the restraining influence they normally exert on each other. Normal after-shortening of the flexors is absent. The pendular response may also be observed in chorea, but here more frequently one finds "hung" reflexes; if the patellar tendon is tapped while the foot is hanging free, the leg may be held in extension for a few seconds before relaxing, owing to prolonged contraction of the quadriceps. Furthermore, in chorea the response may not be obtained until the stimulus has been applied a number of times.

REFERENCES

BARRAQUER-BORDAS, L.   On the zone of provocation of the deep muscle reflexes.   *Acta psychiat. et neurol.*   31:227, 1956.

BERGMAN, P. S., HIRSCHBERG, G. G., and NATHANSON, M.   Measurement of quadriceps reflex in spastic paralysis.   *Neurology* 5:542, 1955.

BRONISCH, F. E.   The Clinically Important Reflexes.   New York, Grune & Stratton, Inc., 1952.

CLARE, M. H., and LANDAU, W. M.   Fusiform function. Part V. Reflex reinforcement under fusiform block in normal subjects.   *Arch. Neurol.* 10:123, 1964.

DONAGHY, R. M. P.   The posterior tibial reflex: A reflex of some value in the localization of the protruded intervertebral disc in the lumbar region.   *J. Neurosurg.* 3:457, 1946.

GASSEL, M. M., and DIAMTOPOULOS, E.   The Jendrassik maneuver: II. An analysis of the mechanism.   *Neurology* 14:640, 1964.

HARDIN, W. B., JR., and GAY, A. J.   The phenomenon of benign areflexia.   *Neurology* 15:613, 1965.

LANCE, J. W., and DE GAIL, P.   Spread of phasic muscle reflexes in normal and spastic subjects.   *J. Neurol. Neurosurg. & Psychiat.* 28:328, 1965.

NUTTALL, F. Q., and DOE, R. P.   The achilles reflex in thyroid disorders.   *Ann. Int. Med.* 61:269, 1964.

PAVLOV, I. P.   Conditioned Reflexes: An Investigation of the Physiological Activity of the Cerebral Cortex.   (G. v. Anrep, trans.) London, Oxford University Press, 1927.

PERLSTEIN, M. A.   Deep-tendon reflexes in pseudohypertrophic muscular dystrophy.   *J.A.M.A.* 193:540, 1965.

RANSOME, G. A.   The great-toe jerk.   *Brit. M. J.* 2:548, 1958.

RIVES, K. L., FURTH, E. D., and BECKER, D. V.   Limitations of the ankle jerk test: Intercomparison with other tests of thyroid function.   *Ann. Int. Med.* 62:1139, 1965.

WARTENBERG, R.   The Examination of Reflexes: A Simplification.   Chicago, The Year Book Publishers, Inc., 1945.

CHAPTER 35

THE SUPERFICIAL REFLEXES

THE SUPERFICIAL REFLEXES are those which are elicited in response to the application of a stimulus to either the skin or mucous membrane. Certain of them have been described in association with the individual cranial nerves (Part III). Others with visceral components are discussed in "The Autonomic Nervous System," Part VI. In the present classification will be included only the cutaneous reflexes —those superficial reflexes that may be elicited by stimulation of the skin, usually by a tactile stimulus such as a scratch or an irritation. A painful stimulus such as a prick or a pinch may call forth a defense reaction. These reflexes are not muscle stretch reflexes in the sense of the deep reflexes, but are skin-muscle responses. Inasmuch as the stimulus is a superficial one, they are sometimes known as exteroceptive reflexes, but probably the deep pressure, or proprioceptive, endings are also stimulated. These reflexes respond more slowly to the stimulus than the deep reflexes, their latent period is more prolonged, and they fatigue more easily.

THE PALMAR REFLEX

Gentle stroking of the palm of the hand is followed by a flexion of the fingers or a closing of the hand. The thickness of the skin over the palm interferes with the ease with which this reflex may be obtained, and it is not found to an appreciable extent in normal individuals beyond the first few months of life. It is of significance only in its pathologic state, the grasp, or forced grasping, reflex, which is discussed with the pyramidal tract responses of the upper extremities. The sensory and motor innervation of this reflex is through the median and ulnar nerves (sixth cervical through first thoracic segments).

THE SCAPULAR AND INTERSCAPULAR REFLEXES

These are elicited by scratching or irritating the skin over the scapula or in the interscapular space. There is a contraction of the scapular muscles and a retraction and sometimes an elevation of the scapula. There may be associated adduction and external rotation of the arm. This cutaneous reflex is related to the deep scapulohumeral reflex, and the innervation is similar.

THE SUPERFICIAL ABDOMINAL REFLEXES

Gentle stroking of the abdomen or scratching it with a blunt object is followed by homolateral contraction of the abdominal muscles and retraction or deviation of the linea alba and umbilicus toward the area stimulated. This reflex should be tested with the patient recumbent and the abdominal wall thoroughly relaxed. His arms should be at his sides, and his head should be down to avoid tension of the abdominal musculature. Sometimes the reflex is obtained most satisfactorily at the end of expiration. A blunt point such as a match stick or a wooden applicator is a satisfactory stimulus, although a pinwheel or even a pin, scratching lightly, may be used. If the object is too blunt, there may be no response, and a painful stimulus may call forth a defense reaction. Too firm a stimulus may elicit the abdominal muscle reflex (Chapter 34). The state of tonicity of the recti abdominis muscles and the position of the linea alba and the umbilicus should be noted, and any deviation should be recorded. The abdominal reflexes have been subdivided as follows (Fig. 236): (a) *The epigastric reflex.* A stimulus directed from the tip of the sternum toward the umbilicus, or from the breast or costal margin diagonally toward the umbilicus, is followed by a contraction of the upper abdominal muscles with dimpling and drawing in of these muscles. There usually is no retraction of the umbilicus. This reflex is innervated by the intercostal nerves from the fifth through the seventh thoracic segments. (b) *The upper abdominal, or supraumbilical, reflex.* This is elicited by stimulating the skin of the upper abdominal quadrants, usually in a diagonal fashion, downward and outward from the tip of the sternum, or in a horizontal fashion, starting externally and going medially. There is a contraction of the abdominal musculature and a diagonal deviation of the umbilicus, upward and outward, toward the site of the stimulus. This reflex is innervated by the intercostal nerves from the seventh through the ninth thoracic segments. (c) *The middle abdominal, or umbilical, reflex.* Stimulation of the skin of the abdomen at the level of the umbilicus, either by a horizontal stimulus, starting externally and proceeding medially, or by a vertical stimulus along the lateral abdominal wall at the level of the umbilicus, is followed by a lateral deviation of the linea alba and umbilicus. This reflex is innervated by the intercostal nerves from the ninth through the eleventh thoracic segments. (d) *The lower abdominal, infraumbilical, or suprapubic reflex.* This is elicited by stimulating the skin of the lower abdominal quadrants, either diagonally in an upward and outward direction from the region of the symphysis pubis, or horizontally, starting externally and proceeding medially. There is a contraction of the abdominal muscles and a diagonal deviation of the umbilicus toward the site of stimulation. This reflex is innervated by the lower intercostal and the iliohypogastric and ilioinguinal nerves (eleventh and twelfth thoracic and upper lumbar segments). *Bechterew's hypogastric reflex* consists of a contraction of the lower abdominal muscles in response to stroking the skin on the inner surface of the homolateral thigh.

The above reflexes may be difficult to obtain or evaluate in "ticklish" individuals. They may be absent in acute abdominal conditions (Rosenbach's sign), abdominal

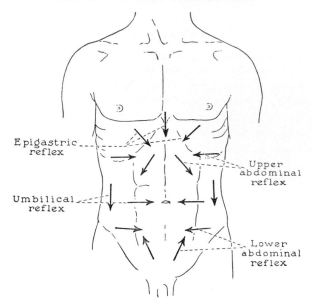

FIG, 236.   Sites of stimulation employed in eliciting the various abdominal reflexes.

or bladder distension, in individuals with relaxed abdominal walls and in women who have borne children. They may be absent on one side owing to the presence of an old abdominal incision. The latency is longer and the response is slower in children and elderly individuals than in young adults. Diminution or absence of the superficial abdominal reflexes is not significant under the above circumstances, but their absence in young individuals, especially muscular males, is definitely pathologic. Dissociation of the reflexes, with absence of superficial abdominals and exaggeration of deep abdominals or of other deep reflexes, is a significant finding (see below). If there is diminution of the reflex response, the reflex may fatigue easily; it may be elicited once or twice and then disappear. If the reflex is diminished or absent, the lower abdominal reflex is usually affected first. In unilateral abdominal paralysis one may get an inversion of the abdominal reflexes with deviation of the umbilicus to the opposite side.

THE CREMASTERIC REFLEX

This is elicited by stroking the skin on the upper, inner aspect of the thigh, from above downward, with a blunt point, or by pricking or pinching the skin in this area. The response consists of a contraction of the cremasteric muscle with homolateral elevation of the testicle. This reflex may be absent in elderly males and in individuals who have a hydrocele or varicocele, or those who have had orchitis or epididymitis. The innervation is through the first and second lumbar segments (ilioinguinal and genitofemoral nerves). This reflex is not to be confused with the *scrotal reflex,* a visceral reflex, which is characterized by a slow, vermicular contraction of the dartos on applying a cold object to it or on stroking the perineum.

THE GLUTEAL REFLEX

A contraction of the gluteal muscles may follow stroking the skin over the buttocks. The gluteus maximus is innervated by the inferior gluteal nerve (fourth lumbar through second sacral segments), and the skin of this area is innervated by the cutaneous branches of the posterior rami of the lumbar and sacral nerves.

THE PLANTAR REFLEX

Stroking the plantar surface of the foot from the heel forward is normally followed by plantar flexion of the foot and toes (Fig. 237). There is some individual variation in the response, with both flexor and extensor components present, and some variability dependent upon the site of maximal stimulation. Stroking of the posterior and lateral portions of the foot is followed by maximal plantar flexion, whereas stimulation of the anterior and medial portions, especially the ball of the great toe, may cause brief extension, more marked in the great toe than the foot. The dominant response, however, except when the ball of the great toe is stimulated, is one of plantar flexion, and with repeated stimulation the normal pattern is one of flexion. This reflex is innervated by the tibial nerve (fourth lumbar through first or second sacral segments). The above predominant flexion response is the normal one after the first year to eighteen months of life but, like the palmar reflex, is of more significance when it is present in its pathologic variation (the Babinski sign, which is described with the pyramidal tract responses of the lower extremities). The normal response may be difficult to obtain in individuals with plantar callosities, and in "ticklish" persons there may be a voluntary withdrawal with flexion of the hip and knee, but in every normal individual there is a certain amount of plantar flexion of the toes on stimulation of the sole of the foot. If the short flexors of the toes are paralyzed, however, one may get an extensor response; this may be termed an inversion of the plantar reflex of peripheral origin. A tonic plantar reflex, characterized by a slow, prolonged contraction, has been described as a sign of frontal lobe and extrapyramidal involvement (Chapter 40).

THE SUPERFICIAL ANAL REFLEX

The anal sphincter reflex is discussed in "The Autonomic Nervous System," Part VI. There is, however, a cutaneous anal reflex that consists of a contraction

FIG. 237.   Method of obtaining plantar reflex.

of the external sphincter in response to stroking or pricking the skin or mucous membrane in the perianal region. This reflex is innervated by the inferior hemorrhoidal nerve (second through fourth or fifth sacral segments).

ABNORMALITIES OF THE SUPERFICIAL REFLEXES

The above superficial reflexes, like the deep reflexes, are either *diminished or absent* in the event of a disturbance of continuity of the reflex arc, in the afferent nerve, motor center, or efferent nerve (Table 7). The superficial reflexes, however, especially the abdominal and cremasteric reflexes, have a special significance when their absence is associated with an exaggeration of the deep reflexes (dissociation of reflexes) or when they are absent in instances where signs of pyramidal tract involvement are elicited. The superficial reflexes have, in addition to a spinal reflex arc, a superimposed cortical pathway. Impulses ascend through the spinal cord and brain stem to the parietal areas of the brain and have connections with the motor centers in the pyramidal or the premotor areas. Efferent impulses then descend either in the pyramidal pathways or in intimate association with them. As a consequence, an interruption of the reflex arc at a higher level, or a lesion anywhere along the pyramidal pathway, will usually cause either diminution or absence of these reflexes. This change is on the side of the body contralateral to the lesion if the lesion is above the pyramidal decussation, and is homolateral if the lesion is below the pyramidal decussation. This dissociation of reflexes, or absence of superficial reflexes in the presence of exaggerated deep reflexes, is a significant finding in pyramidal tract disease. Dissociation of abdominal reflexes alone (diminution of loss of the superficial ones and hyperactivity of the deep ones) may be of diagnostic importance. It must be stated, however, that occasionally with apparent pyramidal tract disease the superficial abdominal reflexes are intact, and such may be the case in congenital spastic paraplegia and even certain transverse lesions of the spinal cord.

The abdominal reflexes are also absent in deep sleep, surgical anesthesia, and coma, and in the presence of violent emotions such as fear. They are absent in newly born infants and appear after about six months to one year, at about the time the plantar response begins to assume the normal pattern; their appearance may be dependent upon the myelinization of the pyramidal pathways, which is not complete at birth. Apparent abdominal reflexes which are elicited in about one third of the infants examined differ from the normal adult response and are characterized by a diffuse reaction, often with associated movement of the legs. It must always be borne in mind that both the abdominal and the cremasteric reflexes may be absent in physiologic states not due to nervous system disease. It has been said that absence of the abdominal reflexes in pathognomonic of multiple sclerosis; this, however, is not a characteristic of the disease itself, but of the spinal cord or pyramidal tract involvement that is so frequently a part of the disorder. Fatigability of the abdominal reflexes may be an early sign in multiple sclerosis and other pyramidal tract disorders.

The superficial reflexes, especially the abdominal reflexes, are occasionally moderately exaggerated in parkinsonism and other extrapyramidal disorders. It has been suggested that this increase results from involvement of a center at the level of the midbrain that normally inhibits the superficial reflexes. The abdominal reflexes may also be increased, often to a marked degree, in tension states and psychoneurosis. On occasion this overactivity is so extreme that the umbilicus is said to "chase the pin" when the stimulating instrument is drawn in a circular manner over the surface of the abdomen. This may have diagnostic significance, for in both pyramidal tract disease and psychogenic states the deep reflexes may be exaggerated, although the type of increase is different; in psychogenic disorders the superficial reflexes may also be increased, whereas they are decreased in pyramidal tract disease. The superficial reflexes are normal with cerebellar lesions.

REFERENCES

ARIEFF, A. J., TIGAY, E. L., and PYZIK, S. W. Superficial and deep reflexes in spinal cord injuries. *Neurology* 8:933, 1958.

GRIMBY, L. Normal plantar response: Integration of flexor and extensor reflex components. *J. Neurol., Neurosurg. & Psychiat.* 26:39, 1963.

KUGELBERG, E., and HAGBARTH, K. E. Spinal mechanism of the abdominal and erector spinae skin reflexes. *Brain* 81:290, 1958.

LEHOCZKY, T., and FODORS, T. Clinical significance of the dissociation of abdominal reflexes. *Neurology* 3:453, 1953.

MADONICK, M. J. Statistical control studies in neurology: 8. The cutaneous abdominal reflex. *Neurology* 7:459, 1957.

MAGLADERY, J. W., TEASDALE, R. D., FRENCH, J. H., and BUSCH, E. S. Cutaneous reflex changes in development and aging. *Arch. Neurol.* 3:1, 1960

CHAPTER 36

PYRAMIDAL TRACT
RESPONSES

WITH DISEASE of the pyramidal system, using the term "pyramidal" in the usually accepted clinical sense (see Chapter 23), certain abnormalities are found in the reflex pattern. This is true whether the disease process is in the motor cortex itself, the projection fibers, or anywhere along the descending tracts. The superficial reflexes are decreased or absent, and the deep reflexes are exaggerated. If the hyperactivity of the latter is sufficiently great or if muscle tonus is markedly increased, there is also a pathologic response in the form of *clonus*—a rhythmic series of involuntary muscular contractions induced by the sudden passive stretching of a muscle or tendon. At times this clonus is spontaneous and will come on at the slightest stimulus; it may be produced merely by placing weight on the toes and actively dorsiflexing the foot at the ankle. On other occasions it may have to be brought on by special maneuvers. Clonus occurs most frequently at the knee, ankle, and wrist, but it may be obtained elsewhere.

Patellar clonus consists of series of rhythmic up-and-down movements of the patella. It follows stretching the quadriceps, and is the result of repeated clonic contractions of this muscle. It may be produced by attempts to elicit the patellar reflex and by downward pressure on the patella in testing the suprapatellar reflex (Fig. 231). It is most easily elicited, however, if the examiner grasps the patella between his index finger and thumb and produces a sudden, sharp, downward displacement of the structure. The leg should be in extension and relaxed as much as possible. *Ankle clonus* consists of a series of rhythmic alternate flexions and extensions of the foot at the ankle; it follows stretching of triceps surae, and is the result of repeated clonic contractions of this muscle. It is sometimes produced by attempts to elicit the achilles reflex, but is easiest to obtain if the examiner supports the leg, preferably with one hand under the knee or the calf, grasps the foot from

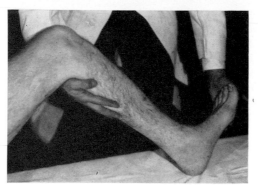

FIG. 238. Method of obtaining ankle clonus.

below with the free hand, and makes a sudden upward dorsiflexion movement and maintains pressure on the sole at the end of the movement (Fig. 238). The leg and foot should be well relaxed, the knee and ankle in moderate flexion, and the foot slightly everted. *Clonus of the wrist* or of the fingers may be produced by a sudden passive extension of the wrist or fingers. *Clonus of the jaw* occurs occasionally.

Varying degrees of clonus may be obtained. Transient, exhaustible, nonsustained, or abortive clonus is significant, although permanent, inexhaustible, sustained clonus is usually an evidence of a more profound disease process. Pseudoclonus, a few movements that subside shortly, and transient clonus, however, are not always indicative of organic disease and may be found in other conditions, either organic or psychogenic, in which there is general hyperactivity of the reflexes. A true clonus must be differentiated from a false or spurious one, which is always indicative of psychogenic disorders. *False clonus* is not only poorly sustained but also irregular in rate and rhythm. At the ankle a true clonus can usually be stopped by a sharp passive plantar flexion of the foot or of the great toe, whereas false clonus is not stopped by such a maneuver.

In addition to the above changes, lesions of the pyramidal system are characterized by the presence of certain *pathologic reflex responses* that are not found in the normal individual. Some of these are actually exaggerations, perversions, or abnormal manifestations of deep and cutaneous reflexes that are normally present; the response may occur on the basis of decrease in threshold, increase in movement, or extension of the zone of provocation. Others are closely allied to postural reflexes and associated movements. Many are probably related to primitive defense reflexes which are normally suppressed by cerebral inhibition but are released when the lower motor neuron is separated from the influence of the higher centers. In most instances they are the result of involvement of the descending extrapyramidal pathways from premotor cortex as well as the descending corticospinal fibers from the motor cortex, but they are generally known as pyramidal tract responses. For the purposes of classification the pyramidal tract responses of the upper and lower extremities are considered separately.

PYRAMIDAL TRACT RESPONSES IN THE UPPER EXTREMITIES

The pyramidal tract responses in the upper extremities are less constant, more difficult to elicit, and less significant diagnostically than those found in the lower extremities. There is a great deal of confusion of names and reflexes, with many variations and modifications of the same response. Those of most frequent occurrence and of most clinical significance follow. These responses occur only with lesions above the fifth or sixth cervical segments of the spinal cord.

THE GRASP, OR FORCED GRASPING, REFLEX

This is a flexor response of the fingers and hand following stimulation of the skin of the palmar surface of the fingers or hand. There are four variations and modifications: (1) If the examiner's fingers are introduced into the patient's hand, especially between the thumb and forefinger, or if the skin of the palm is stimulated gently, there is a slow flexion of the digits. The patient's fingers may close around the examiner's fingers in a gentle grasp that can be relaxed upon command. This is the *simple grasp reflex,* an exaggeration of the normal palmar reflex. (2) If the patient's flexed fingers are gently extended by the fingers of the examiner, they will hook the fingers of the examiner. This is the *"hooking" response.* Inasmuch as stretching of the flexor muscles initiates this effect, it may be considered a pathologic variation of the finger flexor as well as the palmar reflex. (3) If the grasp response as elicited above is marked, the examiner will note that as he tries to withdraw his fingers the rigor of the patient's grasp increases and there is loss of ability to relax it voluntarily or on command. The grip may be so firm that the patient can be lifted from the bed by the examiner. This is known as *tonic perseveration,* or the *forced grasping reflex,* and is a part of the counterholding, or gegenhalten, phenomenon in which muscle contraction develops in response to contact and as a resistance to changes in position and posture. The strength of grasp becomes exaggerated with attempts to withdraw the hand or to extend the fingers passively. (4) The sight of the observer's hand near but not touching the patient's hand, or even a very light touch on the patient's hand between the thumb and forefinger while his eyes are closed, leads him to move his hand in such a way as to facilitate grasping the examiner's fingers, sometimes with a sequence of rhythmic reaching movements. This is termed the *groping response.*

The above responses may be a part of the normal postural or body righting reflexes. They are present in very young infants and disappear at the age of from two to four months. They may be so marked in infants that the child can be suspended by his own grasp. In older individuals these reflexes are inhibited by the action of the pyramidal and premotor cortices and occur only as release phenomena. They may persist in children with birth injuries, developmental disturbances, motor difficulties of crebral origin, and mental deficiency. In adults they may be present in patients with spastic hemiplegia of cerebral origin, but are found more frequently in those with extensive neoplastic or vascular lesions of the frontal lobes or cerebral degenerative processes. These responses are usually contralateral but occasionally ipsilateral, and are believed to indicate predominant involvement of the premotor region, although the pyramidal area is probably affected as well. They may also be present in comatose patients, and have been reported in association with lesions of the posterior fossa, probably secondary to increased intracranial pressure. In experimental neurophysiology forced grasping comes on immediately after the removal of the premotor area, but it does not persist. It becomes permanent after removal of both areas 4 and 6. Whereas the grasping responses are exaggerations of normal reactions and occur as release phenomena, the groping response is a somewhat more complicated reaction that is modified by visual and tactile integrations at the cortical level.

THE HOFFMANN AND TRÖMNER SIGNS AND THE FLEXOR REFLEXES OF THE FINGERS AND HAND

To elicit the *Hoffmann sign* the examiner supports the patient's hand, dorsiflexed at the wrist, so that it is completely relaxed and the fingers are partially flexed. The middle finger is partially extended and either its middle or distal phalanx is grasped firmly between the examiner's index and middle fingers. With a sharp, forcible flick of his thumb, the examiner nips or snaps the nail of the patient's middle finger, causing a forcible increased flexion of this finger followed by sudden release (Fig. 239). If the Hoffmann sign is present, this is followed by flexion and adduction of the thumb and flexion of the index finger, and sometimes flexion of the other fingers as well. The sign is said to be incomplete if only the thumb or only the index finger responds. An alternate method of performing this same test is that described by *Trömner* in which the examiner holds the patient's hand in relaxation by grasping either the proximal or middle phalanx of the partially flexed middle finger between his thumb and index finger. With the middle finger of the other hand he taps the volar surface of the distal phalanx of the middle finger. The response is the same as that in the Hoffmann sign and either manner of testing may be used.

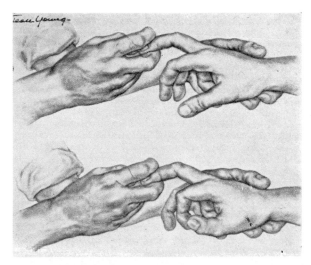

FIG. 239. Method of obtaining the Hoffmann sign. (Echols, D. H.: *J. Nerv. & Ment. Dis.* 84:427, 1936).

Sometimes both are referred to as the Hoffmann test, but they should be differentiated. These signs are variations in the technic of eliciting the *finger flexor reflex* (Fig. 228), and when present indicate hyperactivity of the muscle stretch reflexes. They are often called pyramidal tract signs, and when positive are said to indicate the presence of a lesion of the pyramidal system above the fifth or sixth cervical segment. They are not necessarily pathologic, however, and may be present with increased muscle tonus and generalized reflex hyperactivity associated with psychoneurosis, tetanus, tetany, and tension states. An incomplete Hoffmann sign is encountered fairly frequently in healthy persons. It can be stated, however, that a very active, complete Hoffmann or Trömner sign, especially if unilateral or if associated with other abnormalities of the reflexes or with a history of nervous system disease, is certainly suggestive if not diagnostic of pyramidal tract involvement.

Many other flexor reflexes of the fingers and hand have been described and have been referred to as pyramidal tract responses. Most of these are variations or exaggerations of the finger flexor reflex, which may be barely perceptible in normal persons, or of this response together with the wrist flexion reflex. Some may be related to forced grasping. Probably, like the Hoffmann sign, they show the presence of reflex hyperactivity, but if unilateral or associated with other reflex changes may suggest pyramidal tract involvement. They are not used frequently in the routine examination because many are elicited with difficulty and found only in isolated cases. In the so-called "Rossolimo of the hand," also described by Sterling, Rosner, and others, flexion of the fingers follows either percussion of the palmar aspect of the metacarpophalangeal joints or tapping the volar surface of the patient's finger tips. Flexion of the fingers and hand may follow not only stimulation of the flexor tendons on the volar surface of the forearm, but also percussion of the dorsal aspect of the carpal and metacarpal areas (the *"Mendel-Bechterew of the hand,"* or the *carpometacarpal* or *carpophalangeal reflex of von Bechterew*), or tapping the dorsum of either the hand or the fingers. Flexion of the wrist and fingers appears with an exaggerated brachioradialis reflex, and with inversion of this reflex there is such flexion without flexion and supination of the forearm. The *thumb adductor reflex of Marie-Foix* consists of adduction and flexion of the thumb and sometimes flexion of the adjacent digits and more rarely extension of the little finger in response to either superficial stroking of the palm of the hand in the hypothenar region, or scratching the ulnar side of the palm. The same response is also obtained in the following maneuvers: in the *Foxe reflex* by pinching the hypothenar region; in the *Oppenheim sign* by rubbing the external surface of the forearm; in the *Schaefer sign* by pinching the flexor tendons at the wrist; in the *Gordon flexion sign* by squeezing the muscles of the forearm. The *ulnar adductor reflex of Pool* consists of adduction of the thumb on stimulating any portion of the palm that is innervated by the ulnar nerve.

EXTENSOR REFLEXES OF THE FINGERS AND HAND

Hand flexion may be followed by extension of the fingers and hand, or extension responses may occur instead of flexion. In addition to forced grasping, an extension reaction of the fingers and hand following dorsal stimulation has been described in the newborn. In the *Chaddock wrist* sign either pressure or scratching in the depression at the ulnar side of the tendons of the flexor carpi radialis and palmaris longus muscles at the junction of the forearm and wrist, or pressure on the palmaris longus tendon, is followed by flexion of the wrist and simultaneous extension and separation of the digits. At times the response may follow irritation of almost any part of the skin on the ulnar side of the volar aspect of the forearm, as high as the elbow. In the *Gordon extension sign* extension and occasional fanning of the flexed fingers follow pressure on the radial side of the pisiform bone. In the *extension-adduction reflex of Dagnini* percussion on the radial aspect of the dorsum of the hand is followed by extension and slight adduction of the wrist. In the *Bachtiarow sign* stroking downward along the radius with the thumb and index finger is followed by extension and slight adduction of the thumb. In the *tonic extensor reflex of the digits* described by Vernea and Botez superficial stimulation of the dorsum of the fingers of patients with a grasp reflex is followed by tonic extension of the fingers; this may be followed by the grasp response. These reflexes, too, have been said to indicate lesions of the pyramidal system, but like the flexor reflexes are evidences of reflex hyperactivity and suggest pyramidal tract involvement only if unilateral or associated with other reflex changes.

THE PALMOMENTAL REFLEX OF MARINESCO-RADOVICI

This is manifested by contraction of the ipsilateral mentalis and orbicularis oris muscles in response to stimulation of the thenar area of the hand. There is wrinkling of the skin of the chin and slight retraction and sometimes elevation of the angle of the mouth. The reflex may be elicited by scratching with a blunt point over the thenar eminence from the wrist to the proximal phalanx or in the opposite direction, or by tapping this area. This sign is sometimes present with pyramidal tract disease, but is also found with frontal lobe lesions and diffuse cortical involvement. It is occasionally present in normal persons, especially those who are anxious and apprehensive; it is absent in peripheral facial palsy and may be exaggerated in central facial paresis. If the response is a marked one, there may be wide zones for effective stimulation, including the hypothenar area of the hand. Contraction of the mentalis muscle in response to stroking of the palmar surface of the thumb is known as the *pollicomental reflex*.

THE HAND-MOUTH REFLEX OF BABKIN

Pressure on the palm of the hand in premature and newly-born infants is followed by opening of the mouth, flexion of the neck, and sometimes closing of the eyes and flexion of the forearm. The response is easiest to elicit and most pronounced if the stimulus is bilateral. Except in infants with retarded development this reflex disappears by the third or fourth month of life.

THE KLIPPEL-WEIL SIGN

This sign consists of involuntary flexion, opposition, and adduction of the thumb on passive extension of the fingers when there is some degree of contracture in flexion.

THE LERI SIGN

To test for this sign the examiner holds the patient's supinated and slightly flexed forearm in one hand, and with the other forcibly flexes the patient's fingers and wrist. In normal persons this maneuver is accompanied by contraction of the biceps muscle and flexion of the forearm, and there may also be adduction of the upper arm. This response is absent with lesions of the pyramidal system; this absence is known as the Leri sign. Associated flexion at the elbow may be increased with frontal lobe lesions.

THE MAYER SIGN

The patient's supinated hand is held in the examiner's hand, palm up, with the fingers slightly bent and the thumb in slight flexion and abduction. The examiner places slow but firm pressure on the proximal phalanges of the fingers, especially the third and fourth fingers, flexing them at the metacarpophalangeal joints and pressing them against the palm. In normal persons this is followed by adduction and opposition of the thumb with flexion at the metacarpophalangeal joint and extension at the interphalangeal joint. This response is absent in pyramidal tract lesions, and its absence is known as the Mayer sign. It is occasionally absent in normal individuals, but such absence should be bilateral. It is also absent in hypotonia and peripheral nerve lesions. It is increased in meningitis and may be exaggerated in brain tumors, especially if located in the frontal lobes.

THE BENDING REFLEX

The Mayer and Leri phenomena are probably related to postural reflexes and associated movements. Seyffarth has described a similar phenomenon, which he calls the bending reflex. Forced passive palmar flexion of the wrist is accompanied by flexion of the elbow in normal subjects (the *"bending reflex"*). Attempted passive extension of the elbow during its phase of flexion reinforces the response and causes it to spread to the shoulder muscles. With frontal lobe lesions the associated contraction of the proximal muscles is greatly increased and can be obtained even with passive radial flexion of the wrist.

THE SIGN OF THE FOREARM

Stroking the radial aspect of the semiflexed and semipronated forearm is followed, in the normal individual, by further flexion of the forearm and radial elevation of the hand. In lesions of the pyramidal system there is flexion of the forearm without elevation of the hand, but in psychogenic hyperactivity of the response the elevation of the hand is more marked than the flexion of the forearm.

THE NOCICEPTIVE REFLEXES OF RIDDOCH AND BUZZARD

In pyramidal tract lesions characterized by hemiplegia, painful stimulation by scratching, pricking, or pinching to the ulnar aspect of the palmar surface of the hand or the fingers, the inner surface of the forearm or arm, the walls of the axilla, or the upper part of the chest will result in mass flexion movements of the upper extremity, with abduction and external rotation of the shoulder, and flexion of the elbow, wrist, and finger joints. In quadriplegia, especially if due to a high cervical lesion, the same type of stimulus evokes an extensor response characterized by elevation, retraction, adduction, and internal rotation of the ipsilateral shoulder, extension of the elbow, pronation of the forearm, flexion of the wrist, and hyperextension and adduction of the fingers, with overlapping of the extended fingers and adduction of the thumb in extension. The flexor response is most easily elicited by stimulation of the hand or forearm, whereas the extensor response is most easily initiated by a stimulus to the upper arm or axillary wall. These are considered to be associated postural reactions related to the reflexes of spinal automatism.

Many of the pyramidal tract responses described above are less well defined, less constant, and more difficult to elicit than the pyramidal tract responses in the lower extremity. Some of them, as for instance the grasp reflex, are seen only in instances where the disease process is extensive. Many of them are related to each other and are merely different modes of eliciting the same response. Some may be found in nonorganic as well as in organic lesions. Perhaps the most frequently encountered signs, and the easiest to elicit, are the Hoffmann, the Leri, and the Mayer. The latter two, it must be recalled, are negative signs—that is, they are characterized by the absence of a normal response. The Hoffmann is a positive sign of definite significance, even though it may occur on occasion in the absence of organic disease. The difficulty in eliciting signs of pyramidal tract involvement in the upper extremities is familiar to all neurologists. The signs that are obtained must be evaluated, not on the basis of the individual sign, but as a part of the entire reflex picture.

PYRAMIDAL TRACT RESPONSES IN THE LOWER EXTREMITIES

The pyramidal tract responses in the lower extremities are more constant, more clearly defined, and may be elicited with more ease than those in the upper limbs. As is also the case with the upper extremity reflexes, however, there is a great deal of confusion of names and reflexes, and many of the so-called reflexes are merely variations in the method of eliciting the same response, or modifications of the same reflex. The most important of these responses may be classified as (1) those characterized in the main by dorsiflexion of the toes, and (2) those characterized by plantar flexion of the toes. There are, in addition, a few miscellaneous responses.

PYRAMIDAL RESPONSES CHARACTERIZED IN THE MAIN BY EXTENSION (DORSIFLEXION) OF THE TOES

In the normal individual, stimulation of the plantar surface of the foot is followed by plantar flexion of the toes (Fig. 237). The response is usually a fairly rapid one; the small toes flex more than the great toe; the reaction is more marked on stimulation of the posterior and lateral aspects of the plantar surface. This is the normal plantar reflex, a superficial reflex innervated by the fourth lumbar through the first or second sacral segments by means of the tibial nerve. In disease of the pyramidal system there is an inversion of this reflex, the *Babinski sign*. Stimulation of the plantar surface of the foot, under such circumstances, is followed by dorsiflexion of the toes, especially of the great toe, together with a separation or fanning of the toes (Fig. 240). The two essential manifestations were described separately by Babinski as the *phénomène des orteils* (the dorsiflexion of the toes) and the *signe de l'éventail* (the fanning). In addition, especially if the response is marked, there is dorsiflexion at the ankle, with flexion at the knee and hip, and possibly slight abduction of the thigh. These associated movements are brought about by contraction of the anterior tibial, hamstring, tensor fasciae latae, and related muscles. They are a part of the spinal defense reflex mechanism. The contraction of the tensor fasciae latae is often referred to as *Brissaud's reflex*. The dorsiflexion of the toes may be the only visible effect, but the contraction of the thigh and leg muscles is always present and can be detected by palpation.

The Babinski sign is elicited by stimulating the plantar surface of the foot with a blunt point, preferably a match stick, a tooth pick, wooden applicator, or a broken tongue blade. Some examiners use a finger tip, the thumb nail, or even a pin. The stimulus should be a threshold one, and as light as possible, but if no response is obtained, progressively sharper objects and firmer applications may be used. Both tickling, which may cause voluntary withdrawal, and pain, which may bring about a reversal to flexion as a nociceptive response, should be avoided. The stimulus is directed from the heel forward, usually stopping at the metatarsophalangeal joints, and both the inner and outer aspects of the sole should be tested. If the response is difficult to obtain, it may be elicited more readily by stimulating the lateral aspect of the sole, often continuing along the metatarsal pad from the little to the great toe. The patient should be well relaxed, and it is best to have him lie in the recumbent position with his hips and knees in extension and his heels resting on the bed. If he is seated, the knee should be extended, with the foot held either in the examiner's hand or on his knee. The response may some-

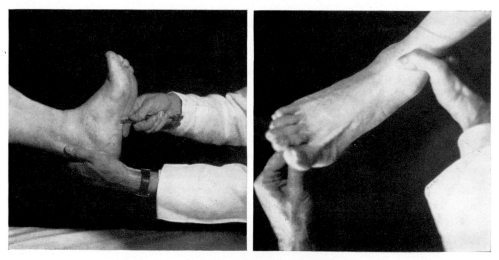

FIG. 240.   Method of obtaining the Babinski sign.

times be reinforced by rotating the patient's head to the opposite side. It may be inhibited when the foot is cold and increased when the foot is warm, although a cold stimulus has been used to evoke the response. It may be abolished by flexion of the knee, and in 50 percent of cases is abolished by placing an Esmarch bandage around the leg.

The characteristic response is one of slow, tonic dorsiflexion of the great toe and the small toes with fanning, or separation, of the toes. Occasionally, however, there is a rapid but brief extension, mainly of the great toe. Other variations include predominant extension at first, which is followed by flexion, or predominant flexion followed by extension. There may be only extension of the great toe, or extension of the great toe with flexion of the small toes. Either dorsiflexion or fanning may occur separately. There may be flexion of the hip and knee with no movement of the toes. The response may depend in part upon the site and intensity of the stimulus. With repeated stimulation to the sole the extensor movement may decrease and then disappear. The phenomenon may also show itself in "formes frustes" which are also significant. For instance, there may be no response whatever to plantar stimulation; this is of consequence if it is known that there is no lower motor neuron lesion to cause paralysis of either extension or flexion, and no lesion of the peripheral sensory nerves. If there is paralysis of the dorsiflexors, there may be no Babinski even though one is expected. These variations and incomplete responses are sometimes referred to as "equivocal Babinski signs." They are all significant, and the examiner should describe the response rather than make an arbitrary statement that the Babinski sign is either present or absent.

The response to plantar stimulation may be difficult to evaluate, especially if the plantar surface of the foot is overly sensitive. Voluntary withdrawal consists of rapid flexion of the ankle, knee, and hip. With plantar hyperesthesia, often present with peripheral neuritis, there may also be a reflex withdrawal that interferes with evaluation of the response. Under such circumstances it may be necessary to hold the foot at the ankle. With thick plantar callosities it may be necessary to intensify the stimulus. In individuals with cavus deformities of the feet and with high arched feet, such as are encountered in Friedreich's ataxia, the response is difficult to evaluate because of the presence of some dorsiflexion of the toes. In instances where the reflex is pronounced there may be either contralateral or bilateral responses, with an increase in the reflexogenous zone (a widening of the receptive field), so that the phenomenon may be obtained by stimulation of other than the usual sites. These alternate sites of stimulation will be mentioned with the other dorsiflexion responses and with the spinal defense reflexes. Occasionally there is a "spontaneous Babinski" following manipulation of the foot; in infants and children it is sometimes brought out by rapid removal of the sock or shoe. In patients with extensive pyramidal tract disease dorsiflexon of the great toe and often of the other toes may follow either passive extension of the knee or passive flexion of the hip and knee, and sometimes the toes are held in a constant position of dorsiflexion and fanning.

False responses, or "pseudo-Babinski signs," may occur in the absence of pyramidal tract disease. The voluntary withdrawal in overly sensitive individuals, the responses in plantar hyperesthesia, and the reactions from too strong a stimulus may give an appearance of a Babinski sign. In athetosis and chorea there may be a false response due to the hyperkinesis. If the short flexors of the toes are paralyzed, there may be an inversion of the plantar reflex of peripheral origin. All these should be borne in mind in describing the response. In most instances, however, there is no contraction of the hamstring muscles in association with the "pseudo-Babinski sign." Also, it has been said that pressure over the base of the great toe will inhibit the withdrawal extensor response, but will not eliminate the extension associated with pyramidal tract disease.

The Babinski phenomenon has been called the most important sign in clinical neurology. It is considered to be one of the most significant indications of disease of the pyramidal system at any level from the motor cortex through the descending corticospinal pathways. It is not obtained following destruction of the pyramidal system in lower primates and there is an altered plantar response with such lesions in intermediate primates, but a positive Babinski response appears with involvement of the pyramidal system in higher forms. Experimental neurophysiology has shown that lesions of the true motor or pyramidal system (area 4 of Brodmann) and its descending pathways are followed by the dorsiflexion response together with the Chaddock sign, whereas lesions of the premotor system (area 6 of Brodmann) and its descending pathways are followed by the fanning response, together with the Hoffmann sign, forced grasping, and the Rossolimo sign. In lesions of both there is a more vigorous extensor response together with fanning. As has been mentioned in the discussion of the pyramidal system, however, for clinical purposes it is best to consider the pyramidal system in the clinically accepted sense, assuming that in most instances of disease of the motor system there is also involvement of the premotor system. The Babinski phenomenon may be an indication of a disturbance, but not necessarily interruption, of the pyramidal pathway. It may be produced following suppression as well as destruction of somatic nerve activity. It is occasionally elicited in persons with no other evidence of pyramidal tract disease and in a small percentage of individuals who show no other evidence of nervous system involvement. It may be the only residual sign of previous disease. If the basal ganglia and the pyramidal tract are both destroyed, there is no Babinski response. In all probability an intact basal ganglion system is essential to its production. It has never been demonstrated unequivocally in lesions of the basal ganglia alone, and its presence in certain extrapyramidal syndromes suggests associated pyramidal tract involvement. Occasionally, however, for reasons not well understood, it may not be possible to elicit the Babinski sign in patients with paraplegia or other diseases affecting the corticospinal pathways, even though other signs of pyramidal tract involvement (spasticity, hyperactive deep reflexes, and clonus) are present. On the other hand, there may be a crossed extensor response or bilateral Babinski responses following unilateral stimulation in some patients with bilateral cerebral or spinal cord disease.

It must be borne in mind, however, that the Babinski phenomenon may at times be found in certain physiologic states and in other conditions in which it is not possible to demonstrate pathologic changes in the pyramidal system. The dorsiflexor reaction is the normal one in the newly born infant, and the response to plantar stimulation gradually assumes its flexor form at from six to eighteen months or two years of age. During the first four to six months of life there is a prompt dorsiflexion of the toes with some adduction of the great toe; this may be accompanied by a mass reaction with dorsiflexion of the ankle and flexion of the knees and hips. Later there is a transitional phase characterized by dorsiflexion of the toes but less flexion of the hips and knees. This is followed in turn by a gradual change, so that by the end of the first year the response is mainly that of adult plantar flexion, and in all normal children the normal reaction should be obtained after eighteen months or two years. The statistics on the frequency with which the Babinski phenomenon is found in infants vary, but perhaps 90 per cent show the response during the first eight weeks, 60 per cent up to six months, 40 per cent up to nine or ten months, and 5 per cent up to the age of two or three years. The development of the normal response probably coincides, as does the appearance of the superficial abdominal reflexes, with the myelinization of the pyramidal pathways, which is incomplete at birth. It has been said that the Babinski response changes into the normal plantar response as the child learns to walk, but since the development of walking depends upon the myelinization of the pyramidal pathways, the latter is probably the important factor.

In individuals with delayed maturation resulting from birth injuries, developmental disturbances, motor difficulties of cerebral origin, and mental deficiency the assumption of the normal plantar response is much delayed, and if there are persisting motor defects the Babinski sign never disappears. Yakovlev has found that prolonged exhaustion or a fourteen-mile march will cause the development of a Babinski response in 7.2 per cent of otherwise normal individuals and in 21.4 per cent of imbeciles. Investigation showed that those who develop a Babinski sign under such circumstances had learned to walk or talk late or were deficient intellectually; many had a history of premature birth or infantile convulsions. In all probability they had a weakness or constitutional inadequacy of the nervous system, especially of the pyramidal centers and pathways, as a result of premature birth, birth injury, or acute disease of the nervous system in early infancy, with a resulting deficiency in myelinization, and it was this, rather than locomotion or exertion *per se* that was responsible for the development of the Babinski sign. The ease with which the response is brought on following exertion is an index of this constitutional inferiority. In a few instances a Babinski phenomenon has been observed in patients whose reactions were brought or reverted to the infantile stage by hypnosis.

The Babinski sign may also be obtained in states of unconsciousness. It is sometimes present in profound sleep; it may be obtained in deep anesthesia, profound narcosis, drug and alcohol intoxication, insulin and hypoglycemic shock, metrazol and electrical shock, coma due to hyperglycemia and uremia, posttraumatic states, and in other conditions where there is complete loss of consciousness. It is found in the postconvulsive state of epilepsy, where it has been used as a criterion of the organicity of the seizure; it is rarely present, however, except during the period of unconsciousness, and is probably a manifestation of the coma or, especially if unilateral, a focal sign pointing to the underlying disease process. In Cheyne-Stokes' respirations the Babinski phenomenon may appear during the period of apnea, whereas in the phase of active respiration the normal plantar reflex is seen. Recovery from deep anesthesia or from coma caused by drug intoxication, such as barbiturate poisoning, is accompanied by the disappearance of the Babinski response, appearance of the superficial reflexes, and gradual return to normal of the deep reflexes. The Babinski sign may be obtained in normal individuals following injection of scopolamine or barbiturates in sufficiently large doses, and a latent Babinski phenomenon may be brought out following the injection of a smaller amount. The injection of physostigmine in physiologic doses may abolish a Babinski response, and a unilateral response is sometimes abolished by simultaneous bilateral stimulation.

There are many other pyramidal tract responses in the lower extremities which are characterized by dorsiflexion of the toes. In fact, there are so many modifications that they cannot all be listed. Some are merely evidences of an increase in the reflexogenous zone, and thus may denote responses from different parts of the receptive field; others, however, are important in that they can be elicited in cases where, for some reason, the plantar surface of the foot cannot be stimulated. The important modifications are listed. The *Oppenheim sign* is elicited by applying heavy pressure with the thumb and index finger to the anterior surface of the tibia, mainly on its medial aspect, and stroking down from the infrapatellar region to the ankle. The response is a slow one and usually occurs toward the end of stimulation. The *Gordon sign* is obtained by squeezing or applying deep pressure to the calf muscles. The *Schaefer sign* is produced by deep pressure on the achilles tendon. The *Chaddock sign* is elicited by stimulating the lateral aspect of the foot with a blunt point; the stimulation is applied under and around the external malleolus in a circular direction. The *Bing sign* is elicited by pricking the dorsum of the foot with a pin. The *Moniz sign* follows forceful passive plantar flexion at the ankle. The *Throckmorton sign* is produced by percussing over the dorsal aspect of the metatarsophalangeal joint of the great toe just medial to the tendon of the extensor hallucis longus muscle. The *Strümpell phenomenon* follows forceful pressure over the anterior tibial region. The *Cornell response* is elicited by scratching the dorsum of the foot along the inner side of the extensor tendon of the great toe. *Gonda* and *Allen* independently described a sign which is elicited by forceful downward stretching or snapping of the distal phalanx of either the second or fourth toe, and *Allen* and *Cleckley* one that is produced by a sharp upward flick of the second toe by pressure applied to the ball of the toe. Gonda has stated that if the response is difficult to obtain, the examiner may flex the toe slowly, press on the nail, and twist the toe and hold it for a few seconds (Fig. 241). Szapiro has described a method of reinforcing the extensor response by adding proprioceptive to exteroceptive stimulation; he presses against the dorsum of the second through fifth toes, causing firm passive palntar flexion, while stimulating the plantar surface of the foot. Similar reinforcement may be brought about by performing two of the above-named procedures simultaneously (i.e., testing for the Oppenheim sign while

Fig. 241.   Method of obtaining the Gonda sign. (Gonda, V. E.: *Arch. Neurol. & Psychiat.* 48:531, 1942.)

stroking the plantar surface of the foot). In all of the above tests, those in which the stimuli are primarily proprioceptive are more apt to be followed by a slow, tonic response, while those that are mainly exteroceptive cause a brief, rapid extension.

These various signs, some of which are elicited by cutaneous stimuli, others by deep pressure, and still others by either passive or active motion, are in all probability incomplete homolateral mass flexion or flexion withdrawal responses, related to the reflexes of spinal automatism (Chapter 37). They are modifications of the Marie-Foix sign, a part of the spinal defense mechanism, which consists of dorsiflexion of the ankle and flexion at the hip and knee in response to squeezing the toes or strongly plantar flexing the toes or the foot. In all the pathologic response is dorsiflexion of the toes, especially of the great toe. Fanning of the toes, if it does occur, is less marked, as is flexion at the hip and knee. The Babinski sign, however, is probably the most delicate, the first to be evident in the presence of disease, and the one that occurs most frequently, but it is occasionally possible to elicit one or more of the others when the Babinski response cannot be obtained. The Chaddock sign is next in frequency. It may be that a more extensive lesion is necessary for the production of the Oppenheim or Gordon sign than for the Babinski or Chaddock. Occasionally it is of value to try two maneuvers simultaneously, such as the Babinski and the Oppenheim or the Babinski and the Gordon, to bring forth a latent dorsiflexion response.

PYRAMIDAL TRACT RESPONSES CHARACTERIZED BY PLANTAR FLEXION OF THE TOES

In the newly born infant there is a *grasp reflex* in the foot as well as in the hand and tonic flexion and adduction of the toes may occur in response to a light pressure on the plantar surface of the foot, especially its distal portion. This disappears by the end of the first year, but it may persist in infants with birth injuries and retarded development. It may be found in adults, along with the hand grasp reflex, in disease of the opposite frontal lobe. A groping response of the foot to visual or light tactile stimulation has also been described.

In addition to the superficial plantar reflex, there is a *plantar muscle reflex* consisting of contraction of the muscles with flexion of the toes on sudden stretching. This response is barely, if at all, perceptible in normal persons, but is present with reflex hyperactivity and, therefore, with pyramidal tract lesions. There is a group of reflexes, often called pyramidal tract signs of the lower extremities, in which the pathologic response is one of plantar flexion of the toes rather than dorsiflexion, in contrast to the Babinski sign. These are probably all manifestations or exaggerations of the plantar muscle reflex, and as such are comparable to the variations of the finger flexor reflex in the upper extremities. They are found in pyramidal tract lesions, but on the other hand their presence may indicate merely a functional hyperactivity of the reflexes. The two to be described first are the most important of the group. The *Rossolimo sign* is elicited by tapping the ball of the foot, percussing the plantar surface of the great toe, tapping or stroking the balls of the toes, or giving a quick, lifting snap to the tips of the toes (Fig. 242). The test should be carried out while the patient is lying in the recumbent position with his leg extended. The *Mendel-Bechterew, or dorsocuboidal, sign* is elicited by tapping or stroking the outer aspect of the dorsum of the foot in the region of the cuboid bone, or over the fourth and fifth metatarsals (Fig. 243). This is also known as the *tarsophalangeal reflex*. Following both of these maneuvers there is slight dorsiflexion of the toes or no movement whatever in the normal individual. There is a quick plantar flexion of the toes, especially of the smaller ones, in the presence of pyramidal tract disease. These signs may occur early in the disease process, and consequently may have marked diagnostic import. They are especially valuable if the Babinski response cannot be obtained owing to paralysis of the dorsiflexors of the toes. They may, however, be elicited in the presence of reflex hyperactivity, which may render them unreliable if found alone. They may be absent in pyramidal tract disease. The Mendel-Bechterew is found less frequently than the Rossolimo and is a less valuable sign. There is some difference of opinion regarding the relative diagnostic value of these signs in contrast to the Babinski sign. Some observers express the belief that the former occur earlier, are more definite and reliable, and consequently are better diagnostic criteria, while others feel that the Babinski is by far the more

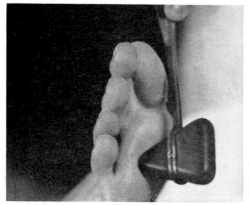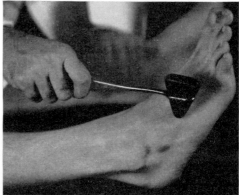

FIG. 242 (*Left*).   Method of obtaining the Rossolimo sign.
FIG. 243 (*Right*).   Method of obtaining the Mendel-Bechterew sign.

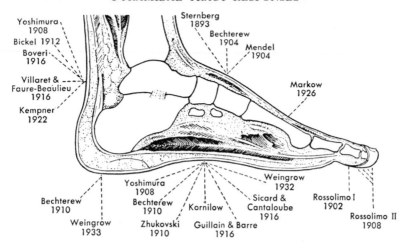

Yoshimura 1908
Bickel 1912
Boveri 1916
Villaret & Faure-Beaulieu 1916
Kempner 1922
Sternberg 1893
Bechterew 1904
Mendel 1904
Markow 1926

Bechterew 1910
Weingrow 1933
Yoshimura 1908
Bechterew 1910
Zhukovski 1910
Kornilow
Guillain & Barre 1916
Weingrow 1932
Sicard & Cantaloube 1916
Rossolimo I 1902
Rossolimo II 1908

FIG. 244.   Plantar muscle reflex; points on surface of foot indicate sites from which a tap with a reflex hammer can produce plantar flexion of toes; names of authors who described these reflexes and dates of publication are shown. (Wartenberg, R.: *Arch. Neurol. & Psychiat.* 52:359, 1944.)

important and reliable. Their relative diagnostic value probably depends largely upon the individual examiner's experience and interpretation. Landau has suggested that there is no real difference in the significance and pathophysiology of the extensor and flexor reflexes, and that the former is actually a hyperactive flexor response in which the extensor hallucis longus is included by irradiation.

Plantar flexion of the toes may also be elicited by application of the stimulus to other portions of the foot or ankle. *Von Bechterew* found that percussion of the middle of the sole or of the heel was followed by a plantar flexion response. In the *medioplantar reflex of Guillain and Barré* and the *heel reflex of Weingrow* there is plantar flexion with fanning of the toes on tapping the midplantar region of the foot or the base of the heel. The *antagonistic anterior tibial reflex of Piotrowski* is characterized by plantar flexion of the ankle and sometimes of the toes when the belly of the anterior tibial muscle is tapped. The *paradoxical ankle reflex of Bing* consists of plantar flexion of the foot on tapping the anterior aspect of the ankle joint. Some of these correspond to the accessory methods of eliciting the achilles reflex, and may indicate a spread of the reflexogenous zone. They are mainly, however, manifestations or exaggerations of the plantar muscle reflex (Fig. 244). They are found in pyramidal tract lesions, but may indicate only reflex hyperactivity. These latter reflexes have less diagnostic value than the Rossolimo and Mendel-Bechterew signs.

MISCELLANEOUS PYRAMIDAL TRACT RESPONSES IN THE LOWER EXTREMITIES

The following miscellaneous responses may on occasion be elicited:

1. *The Adductor Reflex of the Foot:*   Stroking of the inner border of the foot, not the sole, from the great toe to the heel, is followed by a contraction of the

posterior tibial muscle with resulting adduction, inversion, and slight plantar flexion of the foot. This is sometimes known as Hirschberg's sign. It is innervated by the tibial nerve (fourth lumbar through first sacral segments). If the response in contralateral or bilateral it is known as the *Balduzzi sign.*

2. *Von Monakow's Sign:* Stroking of the lateral margin of the foot is followed by eversion and abduction of the foot.

REFERENCES

ADIE, W. J., and CRITCHLEY, M.   Forced grasping and groping.   *Brain* 50:142, 1927.

BRAIN, R., and WILKINSON, M.   Observations on the extensor plantar reflex and its relationship to the functions of the pyramidal tract.   *Brain* 82:297, 1959.

BABINSKI, J.   Sur le réflexe cutané plantaire dans certaines affections organiques du système nerveux central.   *Compt. rend. Soc. de biol.* 3:207, 1896.

BABINSKI, J.   Du phénomène des orteils et de sa valeur sémiologique.   *Semaine méd.* 18:321, 1898.

BABINSKI, J.   De l'abduction des orteils (signe de l'éventail).   *Rev. neurol.* 11:728 and 1205, 1903.

BLAKE, J. R., JR., and KUNKLE, E. C.   The palmomental reflex: A physiological and clinical analysis.   *A. M. A. Arch. Neurol. & Psychiat.* 65:337, 1951.

CHANEY, L. B., and MCGRAW, M. D.   Reflexes and other motor activities in newborn infants.   *Bull. Neurol. Inst., New York* 2:1, 1932.

ECHOLS, D. H.   The Hoffmann sign: Its incidence in University students.   *J. Nerv. & Ment. Dis.* 84:427, 1936.

FRADIS, A., and BOTEZ, M. I.   The groping phenomena of the foot.   *Brain* 81:218, 1958.

FULTON, J. F., and KELLER, A. D.   The Sign of Babinski: A Study of the Evolution of Cortical Dominance in Primates.   Springfield, Ill., Charles C Thomas, 1932.

GRIMBY, L.   Pathological plantar response: Disturbances of the normal integration of flexor and extensor reflex components.   *J. Neurol. Neurosurg. & Psychiat.* 26:314, 1963.

LANDAU, W., and CLARE, M. H.   The plantar reflex in man, with special reference to some conditions where the extensor response is unexpectedly absent.   *Brain* 82:321, 1959.

LASSEK, A. M.   The human pyramidal tract: X. The Babinski sign and destruction of the pyramidal tract.   *Arch. Neurol. & Psychiat.* 52:484, 1944; XI.   Correlation of the Babinski sign and the pyramidal syndrome.   *Ibid.,* 53:375, 1945.

MADONICK, M. J.   Statistical control studies in neurology.   III.   The Hoffmann sign.   *A. M. A. Arch. Neurol. & Psychiat.* 68:109, 1952.

MARGOLIS, L. H., and GRAVES, R. W.   Detection of the latent Babinski sign with scopolamine.   *Arch. Neurol. & Psychiat.* 52:409, 1944.

MCGRAW, M. B.   Development of the plantar response in healthy infants.   *Am. J. Dis. Child.* 61:1215, 1941.

NATHAN, P. W, and SMITH, M. C.   The Babinski response: A review and new observations.   *J. Neurol., Neurosurg. & Psychiat.* 18:250, 1955.

PARMELEE, A. H., JR.   The hand-mouth reflex of Babkin in premature infants.   *Pediatrics* 31:734, 1963.

POLLACK, S. L.   The grasp response in the neonate.   *Arch. Neurol.* 3:574, 1960.

POOL, J. L.   Manual reflex: The ulnar adductor reflex.   *Bull. Neurol. Inst., New York,* 6:372, 1937.

REIS, D. J.   The palmomental reflex.   *Arch. Neurol.* 4:486, 1961.

RIDDOCH, G., and BUZZARD, E. F.   Reflex movements and postural reactions in quadriplegia and hemiplegia, with especial reference to those of the upper limb.   *Brain* 44: 397, 1921.

SEYFFARTH, H.   The reaction to passive straining of joints (bending reflex) in patients with frontal lobe lesions.   *Brain* 76: 457, 1953.

SEYFFARTH, H., and DENNY-BROWN, D.   The grasp reflex and the instinctive grasp reaction.   *Brain* 71:109, 1948.

SZAPIRO, M.   The Babinski sign.   *J. Neurol., Neurosurg. & Psychiat.* 23:262, 1960.

VERNEA, I., and BOTEZ, M. I.   The tonic extensor reflex of the digits.   *Acta neurol. scandinav.* 41:187, 1965.

WALSHE, F. M. R.   The Babinski plantar response, its forms and its physiological and pathological significance.   *Brain* 79:529, 1956.

WARTENBERG, R.   The Babinski reflex after fifty years.   *J.A.M.A.* 135:763, 1947.

YAKOVLEV, P. I., and FARRELL, M. J.   Influence of locomotion on the plantar reflex in normal and in physically and mentally inferior persons: Theoretical and practical implications.   *Arch. Neurol. & Psychiat.* 46:322, 1941.

CHAPTER 37

REFLEXES OF SPINAL AUTOMATISM

THE SPINAL *defense reflexes,* or the *reflexes of spinal automatism,* like the above pyramidal tract signs, become manifest when the inhibiting action of the higher centers has been removed, and thus indicate, in part at least, a release from such inhibition. These reflexes, while present only in pathologic states in human beings and higher animals, are phylogenetically and ontogenetically related to responses seen in lower forms. They are clinical homologues of reflexes seen in "spinal" and decerebrate animals.

The *flexion spinal defense reflex* (Babinski), also known as the *pathologic shortening reflex,* the *reflex of spinal automatism* (Marie), *reflex flexor synergy,* the *withdrawal reflex,* or the *réflexe* or *phénomène des raccourisseurs,* is, in a manner of speaking, an exaggeration of the Babinski phenomenon. As stated above, the Babinksi response consists of dorsiflexion and fanning of the toes together with a certain amount of dorsiflexion at the ankle and flexion of the knee and hip, and possibly abduction of the hip. These latter movements result from contraction of the anterior tibial, hamstring, tensor fasciae latae, iliopsoas, and related muscles. The contraction of the tensor fasciae latae is sometimes referred to as *Brissaud's reflex.* If the Babinski phenomenon is marked, there is a spread of the reflexogenous zone so that the response may be obtained not only by stimulation of the plantar surface of the foot but also by stimulation of the dorsum of the foot and the anterior surface of the tibia, or by a painful stimulus to any part of the foot, toes, or leg. Also, if the response is marked and is due to a spinal lesion that is transverse or partially transverse, it is obtained not only on the side stimulated, but also on the contralateral side.

In normal individuals a painful, or nociceptive, stimulus to the lower portion of the body may be followed by a withdrawal of the legs; this is a quick movement, brief in duration, and while it is characterized by flexion at the hip and knee, there is rarely dorsiflexion at the ankle and there is usually plantar flexion of the toes.

632

With lesions of the spinal cord, especially if they are transverse or nearly transverse, stimulation below the level of the lesion calls forth the *flexion spinal defense reflex*, or *reflex of spinal automatism,* with flexion at the hip and knee, dorsiflexion at the ankle, and usually dorsiflexion of the great toe and dorsiflexion and fanning of the small toes. The response may be bilateral, the crossed flexor reflex. It is pseudo-spontaneous, but is slower and more tonic than the voluntary response. It may be evoked by any type of stimulus, but most frequently by a painful or nociceptive one. Pricking, scratching, or pinching the skin on the dorsal aspect of the foot or ankle, heat or cold, deep pressure, squeezing the toes, or extreme passive plantar flexion of the toes or foot (the *Marie-Foix sign*) may initiate the response. At times it may be brought on by moving the foot, testing the reflexes, touching the skin lightly, or even the weight of the bedclothes. It may be elicited by stimulation of either cutaneous or proprioceptive endings, or by stimuli from the viscera (such as distention of the bladder), at any site below the level of the lesion. The upper border of the reflexogenous zone usually corresponds to the lower limit of the spinal lesion, and thus may be important in localization. At times a stronger or more painful stimulus is needed to elicit the response near the level of the lesion than to obtain it farther down. A painful stimulus above the level of the lesion, however, may cause voluntary movements of the upper part of the body that may be followed by a reflex response of the lower portion; this may constitute a false withdrawal reflex.

The flexion spinal defense reflex appears in patients in whom there has been a partial or a complete isolation of the lower levels from the rest of the central nervous system. It is found most characteristically in association with injuries, compression, and vascular lesions of the spinal cord. It may be regarded as a protective mechanism against noxious stimuli applied to the lower portions of the body. At times patients may mistake the pseudospontaneous movements of the lower limbs in response to minimal stimuli for evidence of return of function and improvement. This reflex may be utilized therapeutically in the rehabilitation of patients with spastic paraplegia.

Various modifications of the flexion spinal defense reflex may be obtained. The most important of these are listed.

THE UNIPHASIC REACTION

In complete transverse lesions of the spinal cord the only response is flexion of the limbs, as described above, with flexion at the hips and knees and dorsiflexion of the ankles and toes. There is never extension. This is termed the *uniphasic motor reaction.* A fixed flexion reflex may result in *paraplegia in flexion* (see below).

THE BIPHASIC REACTION

If the spinal lesion is not a completely transverse one, the flexion response may be transient, and followed by extension. This is the *biphasic motor reaction.* If the lesion is incomplete, one may also get a *paraplegia in extension* with transient flexion reflexes, but a position of extension of the paretic extremities (see below).

THE MASS REFLEX

The flexion spinal defense reflex described above may be accompanied in certain instances by muscular contractions of the abdominal wall, evacuation of the bladder and of the bowels, and by sweating, reflex erythema, and pilomotor responses below the level of the lesion. This is termed the *mass reflex of Riddoch.* It is seen in relatively complete transverse spinal lesions after the period of spinal shock has passed. It is an indication of grave spinal injury. The reflexogenous zone may be extended to the bladder, by distension of which the entire reflex complex may be precipitated. Priapism and even ejaculation may be a part of the response. The mass reflex may at times be utilized in therapy in the re-education of bladder function.

THE CROSSED EXTENSOR REFLEX

The stimulation of the foot or leg on one side may cause flexion of that extremity with an extension response in the other lower extremity. This is the crossed extensor reflex, or *phénomène d'allongement croisé,* sometimes known as *Philippson's reflex,* and is similar to the crossed extensor reflex of the "spinal" animal. It is indicative of a partial or incomplete spinal lesion. Occasionally in premature or newborn infants, strong pressure in the inguinal regions may produce what resembles a crossed extensor reflex, with flexion of the ipsilateral and extension of the contralateral hip and knee.

THE EXTENSOR THRUST

When pressure is applied to the foot of the passively flexed leg, extension may take place. This is known as the *extensor thrust,* or the *stretch reflex.* Similar extension may occur if the leg paralyzed by a spinal lesion is placed in a position of flexion, and the skin in the lumbar or perineal area or the adductor region of the thigh is pinched (*réflexe des allongeurs*). The extension may be followed by flexion. At times alternate extension and flexion occur, producing a stepping movement of the two limbs, or a marching movement. These manifestations occur only in incomplete lesions, and are usually elicited in cases of paraplegia with extensor rigidity.

FLEXION AND EXTENSION DEFENSE REFLEXES IN THE UPPER EXTREMITIES

If the spinal lesion is above the sixth cervical segment of the cord, one may occasionally elicit either flexion or extension defense reflexes in the upper as well as the lower extremities. These have been described under the pyramidal tract responses of the upper extremities as the *nociceptive reflexes of Riddoch and Buzzard.* With pyramidal tract lesions characterized by hemiplegia, painful stimulation by scratching, pricking, or pinching the ulnar aspect of the palmar surface of the fingers or the hand, the inner aspect of the forearm or arm, the axillary walls, or the upper part of the chest will result in a mass flexion response of the upper extremity, with abduction and external rotation of the shoulder, and flexion of the elbow, wrist, and fingers. With quadriplegia due to high cervical lesions, the same type of stimulus is followed not only by flexion of the lower extremities but also by extension of the ipsilateral upper limb with elevation, retraction, adduction, and internal rotation of the shoulder, extension of the elbow, pronation of the forearm, flexion of the wrist, and hyperextension and adduction of the fingers and thumb. The flexor response is most easily elicited if the stimulus is applied to hand or forearm, whereas the extensor response usually follows stimulation of the axilla or upper arm.

SPINAL SHOCK

A transverse, or relatively complete transverse, spinal lesion, if abrupt in onset, is followed immediately not only by complete paralysis and anesthesia below the level of the lesion, but also by complete loss of tone and absence of all reflexes, both deep and superficial. This is *spinal shock,* which is generally transient in duration. The loss of tone and depression of the reflexes are probably the result of a disturbance of the fusiform (gamma efferent) system, which functions to regulate the sensitivity of the muscle stretch receptors. The deep reflexes reappear, but in an exaggerated form, and pathologic responses become manifest as the period of spinal shock subsides. This is usually after an interval of from three weeks to a month. If infection has developed, in the form of a severe urinary tract involvement or infected decubitus ulcerations, the period of spinal shock is prolonged. The later development of an infectious process, especially if it is a severe one with associated septicemia, may be followed by the recurrence of the syndrome of spinal shock. Spinal shock is most frequently encountered in conditions in which the spinal cord lesion has an abrupt onset, as in the traumatic, infectious, or vascular varieties of transverse myelitis, and it is rarely seen in progressive lesions such as tumors of the spinal cord, multiple sclerosis, and posterolateral sclerosis. Spinal shock terminates earlier and the pyramidal tract responses and defense reactions become manifest sooner in incomplete than in complete transverse lesions.

PARAPLEGIA IN FLEXION

In certain cases of transverse involvement of the spinal cord the frequently repeated and easily elicited flexion defense reflexes result in involuntary flexor spasms which occur with increasing frequency. This terminates eventually in a "fixed flexion reflex," with a permanent state of flexion of the hips and knees and dorsiflexion of the ankles and toes. The exaggeration of the flexor reflex holds the limbs in a position of flexion for longer and longer intervals until they can no longer be actively or even passively extended. The legs may be completely flexed, so that the knees press firmly against the abdominal wall. This is termed paraplegia in flexion (Fig. 153). It may be that the slightest stimulus, even the weight of the clothes or bedclothes or the sudden uncovering of the legs, may elicit the flexion response, until finally a permanent flexion occurs. Even after the development of a fixed flexion reflex, any additional stimulus may aggravate the degree of flexion. Secondary contractures may develop at the joints. Paraplegia in flexion is most frequently encountered in traumatic and infectious myelitides and vascular lesions of the spinal cord, but it may develop with extramedullary and intramedullary neoplasms of the spinal cord, multiple sclerosis, posteolateral sclerosis, and other spinal cord affections. Its presence indicates the existence of a relatively complete spinal lesion with interruption of the descending impulses and an approach to a complete separation of the spinal cord below the lesion from the higher levels. This flexion position of the lower extremities is in contradistinction to the extension position that occurs with pyramidal lesions in the cerebum or in the corticospinal pathway above its decussation.

Although it has been said that paraplegia in flexion occurs as a result of release from the inhibiting action of the pyramidal cortex, it never appears in lesions limited to the pyramidal pathways. The patellar and achilles reflexes may be absent and it may not be possible to obtain clonus. The hamstring reflexes, on the other hand, are present and exaggerated. This would suggest that the increase in tone is present only in the flexor muscles, or in the flexor muscles in excess to that in the extensor muscles, in contrast to the usual picture in pyramidal tract disease. It is probable that in addition to the corticospinal pathway, the vestibulospinal and other efferent extrapyramidal pathways are interrupted. The extensor tone from the vestibular centers in the reticular formation is lost, and flexor tone predominates. Scarff and Pool have shown that mass spasms and paraplegia in flexion do not always follow complete transection of the cord, and have suggested that chronic irritation of the cord by scarring of the distal stump may play a part. Paraplegia in flexion has been relieved by freeing the ends of the severed cord from cicatricial tissue and section of the dorsal columns caudal to the lesion, and a spastic paraplegia may be changed to a flaccid one by bilateral interruption of the anterior roots below the level of the lesion, posterior nerve root or peripheral nerve section, injection of either alcohol or phenol into the subarachnoid space, or the administration of certain neuromuscular or internuncial blocking agents. Paraplegia in flexion has also been reported with diffuse cerebral lesions.

PARAPLEGIA IN EXTENSION

Paraplegia with extensor rigidity usually results from supraspinal lesions but may be present with spinal lesions. There is increased tone of both extensor and flexor muscles, but the spasticity predominates in the extensors. As a result there is hyperactivity of the extensor reflexes (patellar and achilles), and clonus may be obtained. There is tonic extensor spasm of the lower limbs, with the legs in adduction and slight internal rotation. This syndrome has been said to be the result of incomplete transection of the spinal cord, with predominant involvement of the pyramidal pathways. It has, however, been observed in patients with complete transverse myelitis. It is probable that neither the reflexes nor the position of the extremities indicate the severity of the lesion. All possible combinations of flexion and extension reflexes may occur in the same patient, and the response may depend less upon the flexor or extensor tone than on the intensity, duration, and site of stimulation. Strong, brief, and distal stimuli are more apt to elicit flexion, and mild, prolonged, and proximal ones, extension. Flexion paraplegia is most frequent with severe and relatively high lesions, but the flexor predominance may change to extensor predominance. It is often possible to avoid the development of paraplegia in flexion with good nursing care, adequate attention to the bladder, and avoidance of excessive stimulation.

REFERENCES

FAY, T.   The use of pathological and unlocking reflexes in the rehabilitation of spastics. *Am. J. Phys. Med.* 33:347, 1954.

FÉNYES, I., GERGELY, C., and TÓTH, S.   Clinical and electromyographic studies of "spinal reflexes" in premature and full-term infants.   *J. Neurol., Neurosurg. & Psychiat.* 23:63, 1960.

GUTTMANN, L.   Studies on reflex activity of the isolated spinal cord in the spinal man. *J. Nerv. & Ment. Dis.* 116:957, 1952.

HEAD, H., and RIDDOCH, G.   The automatic bladder, excessive sweating and some other reflex conditions, in gross injuries of the spinal cord.   *Brain* 40:188, 1917.

MACHT, M. B., and KUHN, R. A.   The occurrence of extensor spasm in patients with complete transection of the spinal cord.   *New England J. Med.* 328:311, 1948.

MARSHALL, J.   Observations on reflex changes in the lower limbs in spastic paraplegia in man.   *Brain* 77: 290, 1954.

POLLOCK, L. J., BOSHES, B., FINKELMAN, I., CHOR, H., and BROWN, M.   Spasticity, pseudospontaneous spasms, and other reflex activities late after injury to the spinal cord.   *A. M. A. Arch. Neurol. & Psychiat.* 66:537, 1951.

SCARFF, J. E., and POOL, J. L.   Factors causing muscle spasm following transection of the cord in man.   *J. Neurosurg.* 3:285, 1946.

WEAVER, R. A., LANDAU, W. M., and HIGGINS, J. F.   Fusiform function: Part II. Evidence of fusiform depression in human spinal shock.   *Arch. Neurol.* 9:127, 1963.

YAKOVLEV, P. I.   Paraplegia in flexion of cerebral origin.   *J. Neuropath. & Exper. Neurol.* 13:267, 1954.

CHAPTER 38

POSTURAL AND RIGHTING REFLEXES

THE POSTURAL AND RIGHTING reflexes constitute a complex group of reactions that probably have more significance in experimental than in clinical neurology. A comprehension of them, however, is important to an understanding of the regulation of posture, the establishment and maintenance of the upright position, and the orientation of the body and its parts in space. They, and abnormalities of them have little application to neurologic diagnosis except in the examination of infants.

Posture is largely reflex in origin (Chapter 32). An involuntary contraction of the muscles is necessary for the maintenance of erect posture and normal positions and attitudes. Tonus, especially of the antigravity muscles, is essential. There are important postural mechanisms in the hindbrain which cause slow and prolonged muscular responses. The vestibular apparatus, especially the lateral (Deiters') vestibular nucleus, maintains a steady contraction of the antigravity muscles and is essential to the erect, or upright, position.

Standing may be considered a postural reflex which is dependent upon stimuli and motor impulses mediated through the medulla but influenced by the cerebral cortex. The essential afferent impulses are largely proprioceptive ones. Any interference with any of the mechanisms responsible for localized, segmental, or generalized static or postural reflexes will cause an interference with the act of normal standing. *The orientation of the head and body in space* and the ability to maintain the head in a definite relationship to the body are faculties possessed by all vertebrates. The decerebrate animal in incapable of righting itself. It cannot resume its normal posture after being placed in an abnormal position. The orientation of the body in space, the orientation of the head in space, the position of the head in relation to the trunk, the appropriate adjustment of the limbs and eyes to the position of the head, the ability to rise from a recumbent position, and the sustained modification of the position of one or more parts of the body involve a series of complex reflex mechanisms. These various functions are called into action by the following afferent impulses: stimuli discharging from receptors situated in the labyrinthine apparatus, principally the utricle, but also the semicircular canals and the saccule if motion is involved; proprioceptive impulses from the deep tissues—the muscles, tendons and joints of the neck, trunk, limbs, and body wall; tactile (exteroceptive) impulses arising in the skin of the body surface and limbs; visual stimuli from the retina. Impulses from these various sources act upon the head, neck, trunk, and extremities. Inasmuch as the integrity of these stimuli is essential to the erect posture and as they aid in righting the head and body, the responses to them are known as *standing and righting reflexes*. The center for simple postural and standing reflexes is probably situated in the brain stem, and that for the more complex standing and righting reflexes in the midbrain. The center for the visual righting reflex is probably in the cerebral cortex, but the eyes, working on the midbrain in coordination with the hindbrain, set up a train of reflex responses which cause a prone animal to look up, sit up, and then to stand in quick, smooth succession, and to maintain its equilibrium and upright position in part by the use of visual stimuli. The communication between the midbrain centers and the vestibular complex—the medial longitudinal fasciculus—is essential to the integrity of the righting reflexes.

Postural reflexes are made up of local static, segmental static, and generalized static reactions. In all of them the responses are tonic ones. *Local static reflexes* are those which are confined to one limb. Either proprioceptive or exteroceptive stimuli may set up a reflex response whereby a previously mobile limb becomes rigid. They may provoke extensor rigidity and convert the limb into a pillar of support. *Segmental static reactions* are those in which a stimulus to one extremity affects the fellow extremity on the opposite side. This may be manifest in the crossed extensor reflex. *General static reactions* have to do with reflexes which arise in one segment but affect muscles innervated by other segments. They may involve the head, the neck, all four extremities, or the entire body. They include righting reactions and statotonic reflexes.

Righting reactions are complex and involve five separate types of reflexes: labyrinthine righting reflexes acting upon the neck muscles, neck righting reflexes acting upon the body, body righting reflexes acting upon the head, body righting reflexes acting upon the body, and optical righting reflexes.

The stimuli which call forth the *labyrinthine righting reflexes* arise in the otoliths of the utricles and to a lesser extent of the saccules; these organs respond to changes of the position of the head in space and have an influence on body tone. The utricles affect or increase the tone of the bodily musculature as a whole bilaterally and that of the neck muscles ipsilaterally. Such changes are results of alterations of the position of the head or the body in space. If the body is tilted, stimuli from the otolith organs act on the neck muscles and the head is rotated in such a manner that it maintains an upright position. If the head is turned, there is increased tone in the neck muscles on the side toward which the face is directed. The response of the labyrinths to movement, especially to rotatory movement and acceleration, is a function of the semicircular canals, and it is discussed with the kinetic labyrinthine reflexes.

The stimuli involved in the *neck righting reflexes* originate in the muscles, tendons, and other deep structures of the neck. These are mediated through the upper two or three cervical nerves and segments, and possibly through the spinal accessory nerve. They act principally on the head, but through the head on the body as a whole. If the head is moved toward one side, the pelvis is tilted slightly toward the opposite side, following which the shoulders and then the hips are turned in the same way that the head is turned.

The stimuli involved in the *body righting reflexes acting upon the head and body* originate in the deeper tissues, principally the skeletal muscles, of the trunk, body wall, and extremities. These proprioceptive impulses are carried to the medulla, probably to centers in the vestibular nuclei.

The *visual,* or *optical, righting reflexes* are probably integrated in the cerebral cortex, but the impulses are mediated to the midbrain and the vestibular centers. When the eyes are turned, the head and body are also turned toward the object on which the attention is directed. Vision does play a large part in posture, but even though vision may be absent there is no impairment of posture or of body righting if the other mechanisms concerned with these functions are intact. On the other hand, in conditions in which there is loss of proprioceptive sensibility, as in tabes dorsalis, this deficiency may be compensated for in part by the use of the eyes.

The *statotonic or attitudinal reflexes* include the tonic labyrinthine and neck reflexes that act upon the limbs and those that act upon the eyes. The former influence the tone of the skeletal muscles and thereby maintain the different parts of the body in an attitude appropriate to a given position of the head. The labyrinthine reflexes influence the tone of the extensor muscles, which is the same (increase or decrease) in all four extremities. The influence of the neck reflexes is usually in an opposite direction in the upper and lower extremities. The centers for these reactions are in the vestibular nuclei and the upper cervical segments of the spinal cord. The tonic labyrinthine and neck reflexes that act upon the eyes result in changes in eye movements in association with changes in the position of the head; the center for these is situated between the vestibular and ocular nuclei.

Kinetic labyrinthine reflexes are those which result from actual movements of the head or body. The afferent impulses concerned with these have their receptors in the labyrinths, especially in the semicircular canals, and the centers are in the vestibular nuclei. They are discussed with the physiology of the labyrinth.

The postural and righting reflexes are difficult to demonstrate clinically, and our knowledge concerning them has come largely from experimental neurology. Certain observers object to any attempt to apply them specifically in the human being because of the difference between the type of response found in the upright organism and that in the quadruped. The postural and righting reflexes, or their homologues, do, however, play an important part in the nervous system function in the human. Righting reflexes can be demonstrated in the very young by movements of the head with passive movements of the body. In the normal individual there is a conjugate deflection of the eyes in association with movement of the head, and a deviation of the arms in the direction of passive rotation of the head.

In certain of the extrapyramidal disturbances the normal reactions to sudden passive tilting of the body are lost along with loss of postural reflexes, and the patient is unable to adjust the body and its parts to changes of position. There may also be gegenhalten, or stiffening of a limb in response to contact and resistance to changes of position and posture.

These reflexes have special importance in understanding pathologic reflex responses such as the grasp reflex and the Babinski sign, attitudinal reactions, reflexes of spinal defense and spinal automatism, supporting and placing and hopping reactions, normal and abnormal associated movements, the Brudzinski sign, and the position of predilection in many nervous system affections. They are characterized by modifications, more or less sustained, of position and tonus, usually of one or more segments of the body, rather than brief muscular contractions. While they do not, in themselves, have a great deal of application to neurologic diagnosis, special modifications of these responses may be seen on occasion, and may constitute valuable diagnostic criteria.

THE MORO REFLEX

This is the body startle reflex. Any sudden stimulus, such as a loud noise, a quick movement directed toward the body, a blow on the bed close to the body, a tap on the abdomen, or a bright light suddenly directed toward the eyes, is followed by abduction and extension of all four extremities and extension of the spine, with extension and fanning of the digits except for flexion of the distal phalanges of the index finger and thumb; this is followed in turn by flexion and adduction of the extremities. This reflex is present during the first three months of life; during the next two months there may be only extension and abduction of the arms and jerking of the knees; then the response gradually disappears, probably with the development of myelinization. Defective children and those with motor difficulties of cerebral origin may show the reflex in a fully developed form for years. The response may be unilateral.

THE LANDAU REFLEX

This may be demonstrated in normal infants during the first one or two years of life. If an infant is held in the examiner's hand in the prone position so that the body is parallel with the floor, there is dorsiflexion of the head with extension of the vertebral column, so that the body assumes an arc with the convexity downward. Passive ventroflexion of the head while the body is in the above position causes flexion of the vertebral column and of the arms and legs, and the body assumes the shape of an arc with the convexity upward. If the child is placed in the recumbent position, there is ventroflexion of the neck, with flexion of the vertebral column, arms and legs. This is probably a combination of otolith and tonic neck reflexes. When the neck is extended by means of the otolith reflexes, the tonic neck reflexes bring the limbs and body into an appropriate position of extension, and when the neck is flexed, the back and limbs are flexed.

TONIC NECK REFLEXES

Magnus and de Kleijn found, in the decorticate animal, that changes in the position of the head relative to the position of the body resulted in reflex modifications of the tonus and posture of the limbs. When the jaw is passively turned toward one side or the head is bent toward one shoulder, there is increased extensor tonus on that side and increased flexor tonus of the opposite side (Fig. 245). The arm on the side toward which the jaw is turned becomes rigid and goes into extension, and the leg may go into extension as well. On the opposite side the arm goes into flexion and the leg may also flex. The flexor tonus is not so great as the extensor tonus, but there is no relaxation of the flexed muscles and the grasp reflex may be elicited on the side of the flexion. The extension is usually accompanied by supination, the flexion by pronation. If the head is anteflexed, the arms flex and the legs go into extension. If the head is dorsiflexed (extended), the arms extend and the legs go into flexion. Pressure over the vertebra prominens results in relaxation of all four limbs. These manifestations are reflex responses to afferent stimuli arising from the neck muscles, but also to labyrinthine stimuli. Similar responses, tonic labyrinthine reflexes, may be obtained by carrying out similar maneuvers after section of the cervical nerve roots. Reflexes of this type are often found in an in-

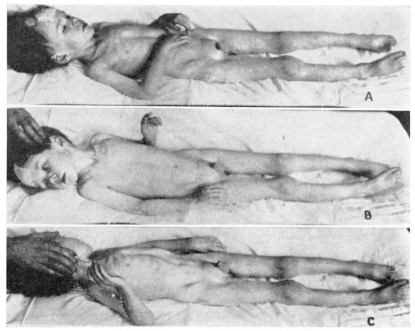

Fig. 245.   Tonic neck reflexes in patient with supracellar cyst; *A*, characteristic attitude of patient, with legs in full extension and arms in semiflexion; *B*, turning of head to right produces increased extensor tonus on that side and flexion of opposite arm; *C*, turning of head to left produces increased extensor tonus on that side and flexion of right arm. (Davis, L. E.: *Arch. Neurol. & Psychiat.* 13:569, 1925.)

complete form in normal infants, but they disappear by the age of four to five months. In pathologic states they may be present in a complete or incomplete form in older children, and they are sometimes found with disease processes of the upper brain stem, usually with fairly diffuse lesions such as basilar meningitis or acute encephelopathy, but occasionally with vascular and neoplastic lesions at the mid-brain level. The patient lies with the arms semiflexed over the chest and the legs in extension, but turning, flexion, or extension of the head causes the responses just described. These reflexes probably indicate a "high" decerebration, or decortication, possibly at the thalamodiencephalic level. They may be present and contribute to the associated movements found in spastic hemiplegia and cerebral diplegia (Chapter 39).

DECEREBRATE RIGIDITY

Sherrington, in 1898, found that prepontine section of the brain stem induced a heightened reflex tonus of the extensor, or antigravity, muscles of the limbs and vertebral columns. This is followed by a state of exaggerated posture character-ized by continuous spasm, sustained contraction, and marked rigidity of the skele-tal muscles, predominantly the extensors. There is opisthotonus, all four limbs are stiffly extended, the head is erect, and the jaws are closed. The arms are in-ternally rotated at the shoulders, extended at the elbows, and hyperpronated, with the fingers extended at the metacarpophalangeal joints and flexed at the inter-phalangeal joints. The legs are extended at the hips, knees, and ankles, and the toes are plantar flexed. The position is an exaggeration or caricature of the normal standing position. The tendon and stretch reflexes are exaggerated, the tonic neck and labyrinthine reflexes are retained, and the righting reflexes are abolished. This phenomenon is known as decerebrate rigidity. The integrity of the vestibular nuclei is essential for the continuance of the picture, and the phenomenon follows transection of the brain stem at any level between the superior colliculi (anterior quadrigeminal bodies) or the decussation of the rubrospinal pathway and the rostral portion of the vestibular nuclei. It is abolished by section of the vestibulo-spinal pathways, and probably results from release of the vestibular nuclei from higher extrapyramidal control. These nuclei must be intact, but isolated from the midbrain. If one half of the brain stem has been severed, the rigidity is homolateral. This suggests that the syndrome must result from interruption of some extra-pyramidal pathways which have already decussated at this level. The intrinsic activity of the vestibular portion of the reticular formation, no longer modified by higher centers, produces a continuous discharge of impulses to the spinal cord. The facilitatory region of the lateral pontine tegmentum is either unchanged or increased in activity, whereas the suppressor region of the medial pontine teg-mentum is depressed. In contrast to the above tonic neck reflexes, which appear following a "high" decerebration, or decortication, this follows a "low" decerebra-tion, but it must be above the level of the vestibular nuclei. The opisthotonus and extreme rigidity that sometimes occur in basilar meningitis, "cerebellar fits," hydrocephalus, and neoplasms and other lesions of the posterior fossa may be clinical manifestations of decerebrate rigidity.

REFERENCES

Byers, R. K.   The functional significance of persistent tonic neck reflexes in fixed brain lesions.   *Tr. Am. Neurol. A.* 78:207, 1953.

Davis, L. E.   Decerebrate rigidity in man.   *Arch. Neurol. & Psychiat.* 13:569, 1925.

Fiorentino, M. R.   Reflex Testing Methods for Evaluating C. N. S.   Development. Springfield, Ill., Charles C Thomas, Publisher, 1963.

Gesell, A., and Ames, L. B.   Tonic-neck reflex and symmetro-tonic behavior.   *J. Pediat.* 36:165, 1950.

Goldstein, K., Landis, C., Hunt, W. A., and Clarke, F. M.   Moro reflex and startle pattern.   *Arch. Neurol. & Psychiat.* 40:322, 1938.

Magnus, R.   Some results of studies in the physiology of posture.   *Lancet* 2:531 and 585, 1926.

Magnus, R., and DeKleijn, A.   Die Abhängigkeit des Tonus der Extremitätenmuskeln von der Kopfstellung.   *Pflüger's Arch. f. d. ges. Physiol.* 145:455, 1912.

Martin, J. P.   Tilting reactions and disorders of the basal ganglia.   *Brain* 88:855, 1965.

McGraw, M. B.   The Moro reflex.   *Am. J. Dis. Child.* 54:240, 1937.

Pollock, L. J. *et al.*   Body reflexes acting on the body in injuries to the spinal cord. *A. M. A. Arch. Neurol. & Psychiat.* 74:527, 1955.

Rademaker, G .G. J.   On the lengthening and shortening reactions and their occurrence in man.   *Brain* 70:109, 1947.

Robertson, R. C. L., and Pollard, C., Jr.   Decerebrate state in children and adolescents.   *J. Neurosurg.* 12:13, 1955.

Sherrington, C. S.   Decerebrate rigidity, and reflex coordination of movements.   *J. Physiol.* 22:319, 1898.

Thomas, A., Chesni, Y., and Saint-Anne Dargassies, S.   The Neuorlogical Examination of the Infant.   London, National Spastics Society, 1960.

CHAPTER 39

ASSOCIATED MOVEMENTS

CERTAIN VOLUNTARY MOVEMENTS have a tendency to be accompanied by other un-intentional, or involuntary responses, the *associated,* or *synkinetic, movements.* These may be defined as automatic movements, or activities, which alter or fix the posture of a part or of parts of the body when some other portion of the body is brought into activity by voluntary effort, or as automatic modifications of the atti-tude of certain parts of the body as a reflex response to the volitional motion of some other portion. These associated movements may be considered, to a certain extent at least, as postural or righting reflexes which have a peculiarly widespread distribution. They may be clinical homologues of movements seen in decerebrate animals. Inasmuch as they are motor responses, in many instances abnormal ones, they might possibly be dealt with in the general discussion of the motor system rather than the reflexes. Their physiologic relationship to various reflex responses and their correlation with various abnormalities in the reflexes are reasons for their inclusion in the present section. The associated movements which accompany or follow voluntary (or involuntary) motion, however, should be differentiated from those alterations in movement which accompany or follow reflex stimulation, and from the defense reflexes and the various reflex synergias, even though it may at times be difficult to distinguish between them.

Associated movements are more complex manifestations of motor function than the simple reflexes, but are more primitive than voluntary movements. They are probably initiated and largely controlled by the extrapyramidal level and its connections, although the pyramidal system does play a part in their occurrence, as may be seen below. Many associated movements are present physiologically; in fact they play a part in all normal motor activity. The physiologic or cooperative functions of the antagonists, synergists, and muscles of fixation in any motor re-sponse may be considered associated movements, as may the successive or syn-chronous activity of the component parts of any coordinated or complex motor act. Generally, however, the term is used for more widespread responses. Among the more common of the *normal associated movements,* which are involuntary

645

accompaniments of all normal voluntary (and involuntary) motor acts, are the following: pendular swinging of the arms when walking; alterations of the muscles of facial expression when talking; facial contortions or grimaces with violent exertion; movements of the head and neck with movements of the eyes; contraction of the frontalis muscle with elevation of the eyes; turning of the eyes, head, or body in response to vestibular or auditory stimulation; normal extension of the wrist with flexion of the fingers; generalized bodily accompaniments of yawning, stretching, coughing, and mental effort. In certain pathologic states these normal associated movements may be diminished or disappear; in others they may be exaggerated, and abnormal associated movements may be present. The normal associated movements are lost in diseases of the extrapyramidal system, especially in the parkinsonian syndrome, where masking of the facial expression and absence of swinging movements of the arms when walking are prominent manifestations. With lesions of the pyramidal system, on the other hand, especially those of cerebral origin, there may be a number of associated movements that are not present in normal persons.

The associated movements which are not usually encountered in the normal individual are discussed herewith.

PHYSIOLOGIC ASSOCIATED MOVEMENTS

In the normal infant there is a certain tendency for movements of one limb to be accompanied by similar involuntary movements of the opposite limb; this disappears as coordination and muscle power are acquired. These movements may persist to a certain extent in children, in whom they may be present only as mirror writing. Similar movements are sometimes observed in adults who are in the process of acquiring new patterns of movement or who are exerting excessive physical or mental effort. If these manifestations persist to any marked degree, they should be considered pathologic. In children they most frequently occur in the form of the transient *mirror movements,* or involuntary imitative movements of the contralateral portions of the body; these usually disappear or become milder at adolescence. They may persist in persons with brain injuries, disturbances of cerebral development, and dysplasias of the upper portion of the spinal cord; under such circumstances there are usually associated abnormalities of motor function, tone, and reflexes, and the movements should be termed pathologic imitative ones. Occasionally persisting mirror movements are familial, and are usually inherited as a simple dominant trait; these are not accompanied by other signs of neurologic involvement.

PATHOLOGIC ASSOCIATED MOVEMENTS

Abnormal, or pathologic, associated movements are usually expressions of activity of paretic groups of muscles which are stimulated by active innervation of other groups. They may be present at all times, be brought out by special examinations, or become evident with physical activity or emotional stress. They are classified as generalized, symmetric, and coordinated associated movements, and are seen predominantly in disease of the pyramidal pathway, mainly in organic hemiplegia. They are automatic, spontaneous, involuntary modifications of the posture of certain parts of the body, usually accompanying vigorous voluntary movements of another part, and occur on the hemiplegic side, probably as a result of the release of the structures which normally modify the postural adjustment of the body. They are slow, forceful accessions of hypertonus in certain muscles of the already spastic parts which lead to the adoption of new postures. They have a longer latent period than primary movements. The greater the spasticity, the greater the extent and duration of the associated movements.

GENERALIZED ASSOCIATED MOVEMENTS

Generalized associated or synkinetic movements are seen in cerebral hemiplegia, where they tend to produce the typical attitude of predilection of the extremities (Fig. 152). The upper limb is held in a position of flexion of the fingers and wrist, flexion and pronation at the elbow, and flexion and adduction at the shoulder; the paralysis of the extensors is more marked than that of the flexors. The lower extremity is held with extension at the hip and knee and plantar flexion at the ankle and toes, and with more marked paralysis of the flexors. These attitudes of predilection are increased with exertion. Straining and attempts to grip with the paretic hand may cause an increase in the spasticity, with increased flexion of the wrist, elbow, and shoulder; this is sometimes accompanied by associated facial movements on the involved side. The new posture may be maintained until the grip is relaxed. Involuntary movements such as yawning, coughing, and stretching may also increase the tonus and cause the affected arm to extend at the elbow, wrist, and fingers, remaining rigidly in this new attitude until the yawn passes off. This response may arouse in the patient or his friends false hope of improvement. Tonic neck reflexes may also influence these generalized associated movements. Turning the head toward the hemiplegic side may cause increased extensor tonus on that side, and turning it to the normal side may be followed by either increased flexor tonus on the paretic side or flexion of the arm and extension of the leg.

SYMMETRIC, IMITATIVE, OR CONTRALATERAL ASSOCIATED MOVEMENTS

Forceful voluntary movements of one limb may be accompanied by identical involuntary movements of its fellow on the opposite side. These are pathologic manifestations or exaggerations of the physiologic associated movements. They are usually identical, imitative phenomena, and are most often present in patients with organic hemiplegia. They are most often seen in the paretic limb when the opposite healthy one is forcibly moved, although occasionally such movements may appear in healthy limb on extreme attempts to move the paretic extremity (especially in extrapyramidal disease). They appear particularly when the patient is exerting himself to carry out a quick or strenuous movement. Thus in squeezing the examiner's hand with the healthy hand the paretic hand is seen to flex, and in smiling there may be an exaggeration of response on the paretic side. Any forceful movement on the normal side may be followed by a similar but slow, tonic duplication of the movement of the paretic side. There may be a spreading of the response, continuing to the above generalized associated movements with assumption of the positions of predilection. The symmetric movements may be influenced by the generalized ones. If the patient clenches his normal hand while his head is straight, flexion of the paretic hand may be accompanied by flexion and adduction of the paretic arm. If the head is turned to the paretic side, flexion may be replaced by extension, and if the head is turned to the normal side, flexion and adduction of the paretic arm may be increased.

COORDINATED ASSOCIATED MOVEMENTS

Involuntary movements of synergistic muscle groups may accompany a voluntary movement of a paretic limb. They are exaggerations or perversions of synergistic and cooperative movements, and may be classified into three groups, as follows: (1) movements, not present normally, which accompany movements of a paretic limb; (2) contralateral coordinated associated movements, and (3) associated movements, normally present, which are abolished in cerebral hemiplegia. These responses are important in the differentiation between organic and hysterical hemiplegia.

Coordinated associated movements which accompany voluntary motion of paretic extremities in patients with cerebral hemiplegia are characterized by a spread of response from one muscle or group of muscles to others. They alter the position of the part and lead to the adoption of new postures. They do not appear in the normal individual or in hysteria.

1. *The Finger Sign, or Interosseous Phenomenon, of Souques:* Active elevation and extension of a paretic arm is followed by involuntary hyperextension and abduction of the fingers.

2. *Wartenberg's Sign:* Active flexion of the terminal phalanges of the four fingers of a paretic hand about a firm object, or against the resistance offered by the examiner's fingers similarly flexed, is followed by adduction, flexion, and opposition of the thumb. In a normal extremity the thumb remains in abduction and extension.

3. *Strümpell's Pronator Sign:* Active flexion of a paretic forearm is followed by pronation and flexion of the hand. If this sign is tested by bringing the hand to the shoulder, the dorsum of the hand strikes the shoulder and the palm is forward. If the forearm is flexed in supination or is passively flexed and supinated by the examiner, it immediately assumes a position of pronation.

4. *Babinski's Pronation Phenomenon:* If the palmar surfaces of the hands are held in approximation with the thumbs upward and then are jarred or shaken, the paretic hand falls into a position of pronation. Pronation also occurs on the paretic side if the arms are actively abducted with the forearm in supination, or if the arms are passively abducted with the forearms in supination and then suddenly released. In the two signs just described, the response is an abnormal associated movement caused by spasticity of the pronator muscles. Similar pronation responses may occur in patients with hypotonicity, and may be seen with cerebellar lesions and in Sydenham's chorea. In the pronation sign described by *Wilson,* which is

present with such hypotonicity, there is pronation of the forearm along with internal rotation at the shoulder when the arm is elevated above the head, and as a result the palm is turned outward.

5. *The Radialis Sign of Strümpell:* Attempts to close the fingers or to make a fist on the paretic side are accompanied by dorsiflexion of the wrist.

6. *Flexion Response of the Forearm:* Flexion of the hips and knees to the squatting position causes increased flexion of the paretic forearm. Flexion of the forearm is also increased by flexion and decreased by extension of the neck.

7. *The Quadrupedal Extensor Reflex:* On leaning forward or bending over, as if to place the hands on the floor, the flexed hemiparetic arm goes into a position of extension.

8. *The Trunk-Thigh Sign of Babinski, or Combined Flexion of the Trunk and Thigh:* The patient, lying recumbent with his legs abducted, attempts to rise to a sitting position while holding his arms crossed in front of his chest. In the normal individual the legs remain motionless and the heels are kept pressed down. In pyramidal hemiplegia there is flexion of the thigh in association with flexion of the trunk; as a result there is an involuntary elevation of the paretic limb, and the heel is raised from the bed (Fig. 246). The toes may spread out in a fanlike fashion. The normal limb is either not elevated or raised slightly but not as high as the paretic limb. In paraplegia both legs are raised. In hysteria the normal leg is elevated, or neither leg is raised. The sign may also be elicited if the patient attempts to sit up from a recumbent position with his legs hanging over the edge of the bed; on doing this the thigh is flexed and the leg extended on the paretic side.

9. *Combined Extension of the Trunk and Thigh:* The patient, seated on the edge of an examining table and holding on to the edge of the table with his hands, is asked to lean backwards as far as his arms will stretch. In the normal individual there is no change in the position of the dependent feet and legs, but in pyramidal paresis there is extension of the thigh and leg with plantar flexion of the foot in association with extension of the trunk.

10. *Combined Flexion of the Thigh and Leg of Neri:* The patient, in a standing position, is asked to flex his hips and lean forward as far as possible. In the normal individual the knees remain in extension, but in a pyramidal paresis there is flexion at the knee (Fig. 247). If the patient, lying recumbent, raises his legs

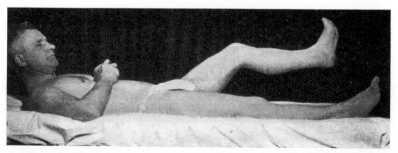

FIG. 246.   The trunk-thigh sign of Babinski in patient with left hemiplegia.

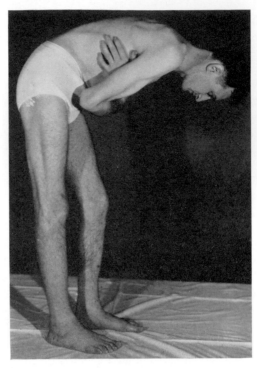

F<small>IG</small>. 247.   Combined flexion of thigh and leg in patient with left hemiplegia.

alternately, the normal leg remains straight but the paretic leg flexes at the knee. This may also be elicited by passively flexing the hip with the leg in extension.

11. *Hoover's Sign:*   When a patient, in a recumbent position, flexes the thigh and lifts one leg, there is a downward movement of the other one. This may be evaluated when the examiner places his hands beneath the patient's heels, or it may be tested quantitatively by placing a manometer bulb or a small scale under the heel. In cerebral hemiplegia and other organic causes for weakness of one lower extremity this downward pressure of the contralateral heel is accentuated when the patient attempts to raise the paretic leg, and is also present, although to a less marked degree, in the paretic leg as the patient raises the normal leg. In hysterical or feigned weakness this phenomenon is absent in the normal leg when the patient seemingly attempts to raise the paretic one, although it may be maintained in the paretic one when he raises the normal leg (a normal associated movement). Increased downward pressure of the contralateral normal leg also occurs when a patient with low-back pain or lumbosacral radiculitis attempts to raise the painful limb.

12. *The Tibialis Sign of Strümpell:*   Sharp, voluntary flexion of the thigh on the abdomen and of the leg on the thigh is followed by involuntary dorsiflexion and inversion of the paretic foot. The patient is unable to flex the hip and knee without dorsiflexing the foot (Fig. 248). This response is accentuated if the movement

is carried out against resistance. In addition to the above movement, there may also be dorsiflexion of the great toe or of all the toes. This sign may also be tested by flexion of the leg on the thigh while the patient is in the prone position (Fig. 249). In the normal individual flexion of the thigh and leg is accompanied by plantar flexion of the foot.

13. *Abduction Response at the Hip Joint:*   If a patient with a pyramidal paresis stands erect and "marks time," there is an abduction movement at the hip joint as the hip and knee on the paretic side are flexed.

14. *The Coughing Sign of Huntington:*   Coughing and straining are followed by flexion at the hip and extension at the knee and consequent elevation of a paretic lower extremity.

15. *The Reinforcement Sign of Babinski:*   When the patient is seated with his legs hanging free from the examining table, forceful pulling of the flexed fingers of one side against those of the other is followed by extension of the leg on the paretic side.

The Klippel-Weil sign, the Marie-Foix phenomenon, and the reflex synergias of Riddoch, Buzzard, and others are sometimes classified as abnormal associated

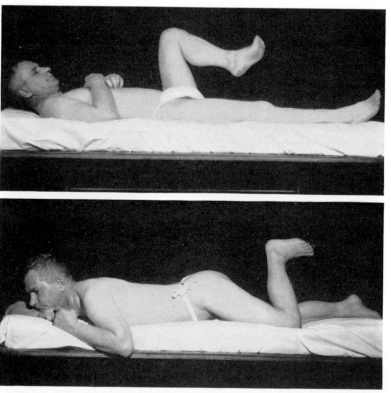

FIG. 248 (*Top*).   The tibialis sign of Strümpell in patient with left hemiplegia.
FIG. 249 (*Bottom*).   The tibialis sign of Strümpell elicited with patient in prone position.

movements. They are related to the spinal automatisms but are also found in patients with cerebral lesions. Inasmuch as they are all characterized by a response to a specific stimulus, they are listed with the pyramidal tract responses rather than with the associated movements.

Coordinated associated movements in which the response is a contralateral one are similar to the symmetric associated movements, but the response is not always an imitative one and may involve muscles other than those used in the primary movement.

1. *Brachioradial Synkinesis:* Extension of the flexed elbow on the normal side, especially if it is extended by the examiner against the patient's resistance, is followed by flexion of the elbow on the paralyzed side.

2. *Associated Contralateral Contraction of the Triceps:* In normal individuals flexion of the biceps muscle in one arm is associated with contraction of the contralateral triceps and extension of the opposite arm. In organic hemiparesis this contralateral extension is present in the normal arm on forceful flexion of the paretic arm, but absent in the paretic arm on flexion of the normal arm.

3. *Sterling's Sign:* Active adduction of the shoulder on the normal side against resistance is accompanied by adduction of the shoulder on the paretic side.

4. *Raimiste's Leg Sign:* If the examiner opposes forceful attempts at abduction or adduction of the leg on the normal side, the paretic leg will carry out a movement identical with that attempted on the normal side. This is evaluated with the patient in the recumbent position and the lower extremities moderately abducted. As the patient attempts to adduct the sound leg against resistance the paretic leg goes into adduction, and the two will be drawn together. As he attempts abduction, the paretic leg also abducts.

Certain *coordinated associated movements which are normally present are abolished in pyramidal lesions.* Some of these are responses to active, or voluntary, movement, whereas others follow passive movement of the parts.

1. *The Platysma Sign of Babinski:* In normal individuals a contraction of the platysma muscle can be seen and palpated when the patient opens his mouth as widely as possible or flexes his chin against his chest. In pyramidal hemiplegia there is failure of the platysma on the paretic side to contract on opening the mouth. If resistance is offered to either opening the mouth or flexion of the chin against the chest, contraction of the platysma will be apparent only on the sound side.

2. *The Phenomenon of Grasset and Gaussel:* The normal individual, when in the recumbent position, can raise either leg separately or can raise them both simultaneously. In pyramidal lesions he may still be able to raise either one separately, but cannot raise them simultaneously. If he first raises the paretic one, it falls back heavily as soon as he attempts to raise the normal one, or if the normal one is passively raised; this is the result of inability to steady the pelvic muscles on the paretic side. On the other hand, if he first raises the normal one and then the paretic leg is passively raised, the sound one remains elevated and is held in place by the fixed pelvic muscles on that side.

3. *The Leri Sign:* This consists of absence of normal flexion at the elbow on passive flexion of the wrist and fingers. It has been listed as one of the pyramidal tract responses of the upper extremities.

4. *The Mayer Sign:* This consists of absence of normal adduction and opposition of the thumb with flexion at the metacarpophalangeal joint and extension at the interphalangeal joint when the fingers are passively flexed. It is also discussed with the pyramidal tract responses of the upper extremities.

5. *The Grip Sign:* With the examiner's fingers inserted into the contracted hand of the patient, grip is relaxed when the hand is passively flexed on the forearm, but is increased as the hand is extended.

The following *changes in motor function,* most of which may be considered abnormalities of the associated movements, are also found in organic hemiplegia and other motor disturbances, principally those of the pyramidal system.

1. *The Babinski Tonus Test:* This is a method of evaluating tone and is described Chapter 28.

2. *The Bechterew Sign:* The arms are flexed at the elbows, passively raised to the level of the shoulder, and then suddenly released. In normal individuals the arm will "hang" in midair for a moment or two and then drop. In pyramidal lesions the arm will "hang" longer and the dropping will be retarded. In flaccid paralyses and psychogenic lesions, on the other hand, the arm will drop precipitously.

3. *Raimiste's Arm Sign:* The patient's elbow is placed on a table and the hand and forearm are held upright by the examiner. When the sound hand is released it remains upright, but when the paretic hand is released it flexes on the forearm to an angle of about 130 degrees. This is a sign of flaccidity rather than spasticity, but may be present immediately after the onset of an organic hemiplegia.

4. *The Pronation Sign of Neri:* With the patient recumbent, his upper extremities are extended and pronated on the examining table. When the forearm is flexed and supinated by the examiner the paretic arm returns to pronation. This is similar in many respects to the Strümpell and Babinski pronator phenomena.

5. *The Leg Sign of Barré:* With the patient prone, the knees are flexed to a right angle and the patient is asked to maintain that position. A normal individual can do so without difficulty. If there is a pyramidal paresis, the leg will fall, slowly or rapidly depending upon the severity of the paralysis, notwithstanding the fact that the posterior thigh muscles may be seen to be contracting more vigorously on the paretic than on the normal side.

6. *Claude's Sign of Reflex Hyperkinesia:* Reflex movemens of either extension or retraction may appear following a painful stimulus to an extremity, even though the part may seem totally paralyzed.

7. *The Leg and Knee Dropping Tests:* With the patient recumbent, the hips and knees are flexed until the posterior angle of the knee joints is about forty-five degrees, and the heels are resting on the table. With a pyramidal lesion the heel will slide downward so that the leg and thigh go into extension and the latter into external rotation and abduction, and the foot assumes a position of plantar flexion and eversion.

REFERENCES

ARIEFF, A. J., TIGAY, E. L., KUNTZ, J. F., and LARMON, W. A. The Hoover sign. *Arch. Neurol.* 5:673, 1961

HAERER, A. F., and CURRIER, R. D. Mirror movements. *Neurology* 16:757, 1966.

HOOVER, C. F. A new sign for the detection of malingering and functional paralysis of the lower extremities. *J.A.M.A.* 51:746, 1908.

LIST, C. F. Peculiar types of reflex-synergias observed in comatose patients. *J. Nerv. & Ment. Dis.* 83:381, 1936.

SAVITSKY, N., and MADONICK, J. M. Statistical control studies in neurology. II. The pronator sign of Wilson. *Arch. Neurol. & Psychiat.* 67:344, 1952.

WARTENBERG, R. Diagnostic Tests in Neurology. Chicago, The Year Book Publishers, Inc., 1953.

CHAPTER 40

MISCELLANEOUS NEURO-
LOGIC SIGNS

MISCELLANEOUS NEUROLOGIC SIGNS, some of them reflexes, some closely related to the defense and postural reflex mechanisms, and others more varied in nature, are elicited in certain diseases of the nervous system. These are herein included with the reflexes, and some of the more important ones are listed.

SIGNS OF BASAL GANGLION, OR EXTRAPYRAMIDAL, INVOLVEMENT

Involvement of the basal ganglia or of the extrapyramidal system is characterized by the following changes: disturbance in tone, usually of a rigid type; derangement of movement, usually hyperkinesia, but occasionally bradykinesia or akinesia; loss of normal associated movements (Chapter 22). Some of the specific methods of investigating and evaluating the hypertonicity and impairment of associated movements are the Babinski tonus, head dropping, pendulousness of the legs, shoulder shaking, arm dropping, and body pushing tests, described in Chapter 28. There is also slowness of starting and inability to carry out rapid movements and loss of ability to maintain two simultaneous voluntary motor activities. There are no very characteristic changes in the reflexes. The deep reflexes may be slightly exaggerated, owing to increased muscular tension, but this is not a consistent finding, and they may be retarded, diminished, or absent. The superficial reflexes may also be slightly exaggerated. There are no pyramidal tract responses unless there is associated pyramidal tract involvement.

Some of the reflexes which are believed to indicate both pyramidal and premotor disease, especially those that are present with diffuse cerebral involvement, may be elicited when there is extrapyramidal dysfunction. These include hyperactivity of the orbicularis oris and oculi (Myerson's sign) reflexes (Chapter 13), and the forced grasping and palmomental reflexes (Chapter 36). In addition, there are a few reflexes, not often elicited, which are said to indicate extrapyramidal involvement.

THE TONIC PLANTAR REFLEX

This reflex is present when stroking of the sole of the foot is followed by slow flexion and adduction of the toes and distal part of the foot that persist for a minute or two. This response has been attributed to prefrontal and extrapyramidal involvement, and may be contralateral, ipsilateral, or bilateral with respect to the lesion.

SÖDERBERGH'S PRESSURE REFLEX

This reflex is present when a slow muscular contraction follows firm stroking of certain bony prominences. If the ulna is stroked in a downward direction, there may be flexion of the three outer fingers, and if the radius is firmly stroked, there may be flexion of the thumb.

THE LITTLE TOE REFLEX OF PUUSEPP

This reflex is characterized by a slow abduction of the little toe in response to light stroking of the outer border of the foot.

THE SCHRIJVER-BERNHARD REFLEX

This reflex is present when percussion of the anterior surface of the leg or tapping the skin over the tibia or anterior leg muscles just below the knee is followed by plantar flexion of the toes. The *Lomadtsé sign,* which consists of plantar flexion of the toes on pressure over the anterior aspect of the tibia, is similar. These are both called *distant toe flexor reflexes.*

SOUQUES' LEG SIGN

When a patient, seated in a chair, is suddenly thrown backward, the legs normally extend to maintain balance. Absence of this extension in an attempt to counteract loss of balance is Souques' leg sign; it is found in advanced striatal disease, and is in reality a loss of associated movements.

SIGNS OF MENINGEAL IRRITATION

Signs of irritation of the meninges are most frequently elicited in association with inflammatory involvement of the meningeal tissues. They may also, however, be secondary to the presence of foreign material in the subarachnoid space, as in subarachnoid hemorrhage, or they may be associated with increased spinal fluid pressure, as in aseptic meningitis and meningismus. The objective manifestations are usually secondary to either displacement of the intraspinal structures or variations in tension on the inflamed and hypersensitive spinal nerve roots (see below). The symptoms and signs of meningeal irritation are varied and depend upon the severity of the process. Among the more common are the following: headache with pain and stiffness of the neck; irritability, hyperesthesia, sensitivity of the skin, photophobia, and hyperacusis; fever, chills, and other manifestations of infection; nausea and vomiting; confusion, delirium, coma, or convulsions; carphology, or involuntary plucking at the bedclothes; paralytic phenomena; a polymorphonuclear leukocytosis and characteristic cerebrospinal fluid changes. In addition there are certain objective diagnostic criteria, known as signs of meningeal irritation. The outstanding of these are listed.

NUCHAL, OR CERVICAL, RIGIDITY

This is probably the most widely recognized and frequently encountered sign of meningeal irritation, and the diagnosis of meningitis is rarely made in its absence. It is characterized by stiffness of the neck and resistance to passive movement, with pain and spasm on attempts at motion. There is resistance to passive flexion, and the chin cannot be placed upon the chest; there may be resistance to hyperextension and to rotatory movements as well. The rigidity may vary from slight resistance to flexion to complete resistance to all movements. It, however, particularly affects the extensor musculature, and flexion may be impossible while hyperextension can be readily carried out; rotatory and lateral movements may also be preserved. If the rigidity of the extensor muscles is marked, there may be *retraction of the neck,* and even the neck and spine, into a position of *opisthotonus.* The only instances in which nuchal rigidity is not found in association with meningitis may be in fulminating or terminal cases or in disease of very young infants. It must be borne in mind that nuchal rigidity may also be a manifestation of cervical arthritis and myositis, cervical adenopathy, retropharyngeal abscess, trauma, caries of the spine, and other disease processes within the neck, and rigidity may also appear in association with severe infections such as pneumonia and typhoid fever.

RESISTANCE OF MOVEMENT OF LEGS AND BACK

The patient lies with his legs drawn up; there is flexion of the thighs on the pelvis and of the legs on the thighs. He resists passive extension of the legs. On rising from a supine to a sitting position he supports himself by placing his hands behind him and pressing them against the bed (Amoss's sign).

KERNIG'S SIGN

Kernig's sign has been described variously and tested for in many different ways. Kernig described it as an involuntary flexion at the knee when the examiner attempts to flex the thigh at the hip while the leg is in extension. It is more commonly elicited, however, by flexing the thigh of the recumbent patient to a right angle, and then attempting to extend the leg on the thigh. This passive extension at the knee is accompanied not only by pain and resistance due to spasm of the hamstring muscles, but also by limitation of extension. Full extension of the leg is impossible if the hip is in flexion (Fig. 250). According to some definitions, the Kernig sign is positive if the leg cannot be extended on the knee to over one and one-half right angles while the hip is flexed. In Lasègue's sign, which is similar, an attempt is made to flex the thigh at the hip while the leg is held in extension. When positive, this sign is also accompanied by pain in the sciatic notch and resistance to movement. Both Kernig's and Lasègue's signs, as well as the nerve-stretching modifications of the latter, are positive in meningitis, probably due to stretching of and tension on the irritated nerve roots and meninges, but both are

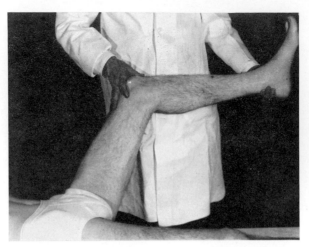

FIG. 250.   Method of eliciting Kernig's sign.

also positive in sciatica and irritation of the lumbosacral nerve roots or plexus due to a ruptured intervertebral disk or other causes. In the latter conditions, however, they are usually unilateral, whereas in meningitis they are bilateral.

BIKELE'S SIGN

This consists of resistance to extension of the elbow when the arm is elevated at the shoulder, and is similar to Kernig's sign in that it is positive on stretching irritated nerve roots. With the patient seated, the forearm is flexed at the elbow and the arm is abducted, elevated, extended, and externally rotated, or is moved upward and backward at the shoulder to a maximal degree. The examiner then attempts passively to extend the forearm at the elbow. The sign is positive if there is resistance to such extension. This sign is also seen in brachial plexus neuritis, and probably more frequently in such involvement of the brachial plexus than in meningitis.

BRUDZINSKI'S NECK SIGN

Passive flexion of the head on the chest is followed by flexion of both thighs and legs, so that both lower extremities may be strongly flexed on the pelvis. The test is carried out by placing one hand under the patient's head and forcibly flexing the neck while placing the other hand on his chest to prevent elevation of the body. Occasionally there is flexion of the arms as well, and there may be fanning of the toes. This sign has been said to represent a tonic neck reflex in a partially decerebrate stage, but, like the other meningeal signs, may be a result of tension on the nerve roots. There may be absence of flexion of the thigh and leg on one side in conditions where meningeal irritation and cerebral hemiplegia are present simultaneously.

BRUDZINSKI'S CONTRALATERAL LEG SIGNS

Passive flexion of one hip, especially if the hip is flexed while the knee is in extension, is accompanied by flexion of the opposite hip and knee. The same result may be obtained by passive extension of the leg on the thigh after the thigh has been flexed to a right angle (Kernig's maneuver). In the *Brudzinski reciprocal contralateral leg sign* one leg and thigh are flexed while the other leg and thigh are extended; when the flexed limb is lowered the contralateral extended one will go into flexion.

BRUDZINSKI'S CHEEK SIGN

Pressure against the cheeks on or just below the zygoma is accompanied by a reflex flexion at the elbows with an upward jerking of the arms.

BRUDZINSKI'S SYMPHYSIS SIGN

Pressure on the symphysis pubis is followed by flexion of both lower extremities.

GUILLAIN'S SIGN

Pinching of the skin over the quadriceps femoris muscle or squeezing the muscle on one side is followed by flexion of the contralateral hip and knee.

EDELMANN'S GREAT TOE PHENOMENON

Flexion of the thigh at the hip while the leg is extended at the knee is followed by dorsiflexion of the great toe. This sign may be present in cerebral edema as well as in meningeal irritation.

Various attempts have been made to explain the above signs. Muscular rigidity, motor irritation, increased intracranial pressure and distention of the meninges, tonic neck reflexes, and crossed reflexes have been suggested as underlying mechanisms. It is probable, however, that in the main the various maneuvers that are carried out produce displacements of the intraspinal structures with changes in tension on the inflamed and hypersensitive spinal nerve roots. O'Connell has recently expressed the belief, based on anatomic observations, that the resulting signs may be postures designed to minimize tension in the inflamed roots, muscle spasms designed to limit movement productive of such tension, or movements designed to produce maximum relaxation in nerve roots rendered tense by some test maneuver.

SIGNS OF TETANY

The clinical manifestations of tetany include spasm and tonic contractions of the skeletal muscles, principally the distal muscles of the extremities. There may be contraction of muscles of the wrist, hands, and fingers, with resulting carpal spasm, the so-called obstetrical or accoucheur's hand, and of those of the foot and toes, causing pedal spasm (Chapter 28). There is hyperirritability of the entire peripheral nervous system, as well as the musculature, to even very slight stimuli. Involvement of the sensory nerves may cause paresthesias of the hands and feet and in the perioral region. There may be irritability of the facial muscles and convulsive phenomena. These changes are related to disturbances of calcium and phosphorus metabolism and to abnormalities in the acid-base equilibrium of the body; these may be verified by various biochemical examinations. There are in tetany, however, certain neurologic signs that may aid the physician in making a diagnosis on the basis of the clinical examination alone. They are all more easily demonstrated if the patient first overbreathes for a few minutes. The more important of these are listed.

CHVOSTEK'S SIGN

Tapping over the point of emergence or division of the facial nerve just anterior to the ear, with either the finger or a percussion hammer, is followed by a spasm or a tetanic, cramp-like contraction of some or all of the muscles supplied by the ipsilateral facial nerve. Sometimes the response may be elicited merely by stroking in front of the ear. It is said that the sign is slight or minimal if there is but a slight twitch of the angle of the mouth or the upper lip; it is of moderate degree if there is movement of the ala nasi and the entire corner of the mouth, and it is maximal if the muscles of the forehead, eyelid, and cheek also contract. This is in reality a trigeminofacial reflex, although the afferent impulse may be a proprioceptive one carried through the facial nerve. When the response is marked, however, the muscles supplied by the trigeminal nerve may also respond. Chvostek's sign is said to be the result of hyperirritability or hyperexcitability of the motor nerves, in this instance of the facial nerve, to mechanical stimulation. It is an important sign in tetany, but is occasionally found in other conditions in which there is increased reflex irritability.

TROUSSEAU'S SIGN

Compression of the arm by squeezing or constricting it with the hand or by means of a tourniquet or sphygmomanometer cuff is followed by carpal spasm of the hand, with resulting accoucheur's hand. There may be a latent period of from one-half to four minutes. Similar pressure over the leg or thigh will be followed by a pedal spasm. It has been suggested that this response may result from pressure on either the nerve trunks or the arteries. It is probable that occlusion of the arteries causes ischemia of the nerve trunks, and this in turn increases the excitability of the nerves. A modification of this is carried out in the *von Bonsdorff technic* in which a pneumatic cuff is placed over the arm and is kept moderately inflated for about ten minutes. It is then removed and the patient is told to hyperventilate. Typical tetanic spasm occurs much earlier in the previously ischemic arm than in the other arm.

ERB'S SIGN

This consists of hyperexcitability of the motor nerves to an electrical current and the appearance of contractions on stimulation with a smaller amount of current than is normally needed. It is more accurately measured and is more marked with galvanic than with faradic current. The cathodal closing contraction may be obtained with a current of less than 5 milliamperes, and sometimes both closing and opening contractions, either cathodal or anodal, may be obtained with a current of less than 5 milliamperes. Chronaxie is shortened. If a strong current is used, a tonic, or tetanic, contraction is obtained, and the muscles go into spasm. The peroneal and ulnar nerves are usually stimulated in the test. There is also increased electrical (and mechanical) irritability of the sensory nerves (*Hoffmann's sign of tetany*), and stimulation of them with a weak galvanic current as well as by pressure may cause paresthesias and pain.

THE POOL-SCHLESINGER SIGNS

Tension on the brachial plexus by forceful abduction and elevation of the arm while the forearm is extended is followed by tetanic spasm of the muscles of the forearm, hand, and fingers. Tension on the sciatic nerve by forceful flexion of thigh on the trunk while the leg is extended is followed by spasm of the muscles of the leg and foot.

SCHULTZE'S SIGN

Mechanical stimulation of the protruded tongue (tapping with a percussion hammer) is followed by a transient depression or dimpling at the site of stimulation. A similar phenomenon may be present in patients with myotonia.

KASHIDA'S THERMIC SIGN

This consists of the development of hyperesthesias and spasms after the application of either hot or cold irritants.

ESCHERICH'S SIGN

There is an increased reaction to stimulation of the oral and lingual mucosa, and contractions of the lips, masseters, and tongue follow percussion of the inner surface of the lips or of the tongue.

HOCHSINGER'S SIGN

Pressure on the inner aspect of the biceps muscle causes spasm and contraction of the hand. It is possible that in carrying out this maneuver one compresses the brachial artery, and this sign may be a variation of Trousseau's sign.

THE PERONEAL SIGN

Tapping over the common peroneal nerve as it winds around the neck of the fibula is followed by dorsiflexion and eversion of the foot (Lust's phenomenon).

REFERENCES

HERMAN, E.   The tonic plantar reflex and its localizing significance.   *J. Nerv. & Ment. Dis.* 116:933, 1952.

HOFFMAN, E.   The Chvostek sign: A clinical study.   *Am. J. Surg.* 96:33, 1958.

KUGELBERG, E.   Neurologic mechanism for certain phenomena in tetany.   *Arch. Neurol. & Psychiat.* 56:507, 1946.

O'CONNELL, J. E. A.   The clinical signs of meningeal irritation.   *Brain* 69:9, 1946.

SIMPSON, J. A.   The neurological manifestations of idiopathic hypoparathyroidism. *Brain* 75:76, 1952.

THORNER, M. W.   Modification of meningeal signs by concomitant hemiparesis.   *Arch. Neurol. & Psychiat.* 59:485, 1948.

TOOMEY, J. A.   Stiff neck and meningeal irritation.   *J.A.M.A.* 127:436, 1945.

WARTENBERG, R.   The signs of Brudzinski and Kernig.   *J. Pediat.* 37:679, 1950.

PART SIX

The Autonomic Nervous System

THE AUTONOMIC
NERVOUS SYSTEM

THE NERVOUS SYSTEM is essential not only in the adjustment of the organism as a whole to its environment, but also in the regulation and coordination of the vital processes. In general, these latter functions are below the conscious level and are not subject to voluntary control. Their nervous integration is accomplished by means of reflex phenomena of varying degrees of complexity. The neurologic regulation of the smooth muscles and glands, which include the blood vessels, viscera, striated musculature of the heart, and endocrine complex, is carried out by a portion of the nervous system which is somewhat distinct, both centrally and peripherally, from that which carries common sensation and supplies striated musculature. The neural components which control the regulation of the vital functions constitute what has been known as the *autonomic, vegetative, sympathetic,* or *involuntary nervous system*. It must be stressed, however, that it is not a separate nervous system. The autonomic and the voluntary nervous systems are two aspects of a single integrated neural mechanism and are closely interrelated both centrally and peripherally. They are interdependent. The central regulatory structures are closely connected, and autonomic fibers are present in every peripheral spinal nerve and in most cranial nerves.

The autonomic nervous system in general is less available for clinical testing and routine examination than the so-called voluntary nervous system, or that part of the neural mechanism which has to do with somatic rather than visceral functions. The intimate correlation, however, between the voluntary and involuntary nervous elements, the interrelations between the conscious and the unconscious, and the presence of many syndromes which are predominantly of autonomic origin make the examination of this portion of the nervous system, inasmuch as it can be carried out, an essential part of the neurologic examination.

CHAPTER 41

ANATOMY AND PHYS-IOLOGY OF THE AUTO-NOMIC NERVOUS SYSTEM

A THOROUGH UNDERSTANDING of the anatomy and physiology of the autonomic nervous system is essential to a comprehension of the reasons for and methods of examining it and also to a clear conception of the clinical syndromes that result from pathologic involvement of its constituent parts. These subjects will be discussed separately for the peripheral autonomic nervous system and the central regulatory structures.

THE PERIPHERAL AUTONOMIC NERVOUS SYSTEM

The autonomic nervous system consists of a series of cerebrospinal nuclei and nerves with widely distributed ganglia and plexuses which subserve the vegetative functions of the body. In its peripheral ramifications the system is characterized by a series of synaptic junctions which are situated outside the central nervous system. From anatomic and physiologic points of view there are two primary divisions, (1) the *parasympathetic,* or *craniosacral,* and (2) the *sympathetic, orthosympathetic,* or *thoracicolumbar.* This subdivision is based upon the point of outflow from the central nervous system, the distribution of peripheral ganglia, the general antagonism in physiologic effects on visceral tissues most of which receive innervation from both divisions, and the response to pharmacologic agents. Each peripheral division of the autonomic nervous system is characterized by a two neuron chain and consists of two histologic elements, the *preganglionic neuron* which terminates in a peripheral ganglion, whence the *postganglionic neuron,* or neuron of the second order, carries impulses to their destinations on the viscera. No impulse goes directly to an organ of termination. Anatomically the two divisions are designated the cranio-

666

sacral and the thoracicolumbar portions, or outflows, but clinically the favored terms are either parasympathetic and sympathetic systems or parasympathetic and sympathetic divisions. The latter nomenclature is used in the present work.

THE ANATOMY OF THE PARASYMPATHETIC DIVISION

The parasympathetic division, or craniosacral or mesencephalic-medullary-sacral outflow, is composed of the visceral efferent fibers of the oculomotor, facial, glossopharyngeal, and vagus nerves, and bulbar portions of the accessory nerve, together with fibers arising in the second, third, fourth, and possibly the fifth sacral segments of the spinal cord. It has also been suggested, but not definitely proved, that there are fibers in the dorsal roots, vasodilator in function, which are related to or have important affinities with the parasympathetic division. The parasympathetic nerves are characterized anatomically by relatively long preganglionic fibers which go to terminal, or peripheral, ganglia near or on the viscera they supply, and by short postganglionic fibers which arise in proximity to or within the viscus innervated. One preganglionic fiber usually synapses with only one postganglionic neuron. The portions of the parasympathetic division are widely separated but, because of these anatomic characteristics, their similarity in function, and their similar pharmacologic responses, they are classified as parts of one system rather than as separate cranial, bulbar, and sacral divisions.

The anatomy of the cranial portions of the parasympathetic division is discussed with the individual cranial nerves (Part III), and is briefly reviewed here. The *tectal,* or *mesencephalic,* portion consists of the parasympathetic nuclei and roots of the *oculomotor nerve.* The nuclear centers are the Edinger-Westphal nuclei, the medial portions of which are sometimes called the anterior median or medial nuclei. Preganglionic fibers course via the inferior division of the third nerve to the ciliary ganglion, and postganglionic fibers are carried by the short ciliary nerves to the ciliary muscle and the sphincter of the pupil. The *bulbar,* or *medullary,* portion consists of the parasympathetic nuclei and roots of the seventh, ninth, tenth, and eleventh cranial nerves. Preganglionic fibers of the *facial nerve* arise in the superior salivatory and related nuclear masses. Some are carried by the chorda tympani and lingual nerve to the submaxillary ganglion and ganglion cells in the hilum of the submaxillary gland, with postganglionic fibers to the submaxillary and sublingual glands and the mucous membrane of the mouth and tongue. Others are carried by the greater superficial petrosal and vidian nerves to the sphenopalatine ganglion, with postganglionic fibers to the lacrimal gland and the mucosa of the nose, orbit, posterior portion of the pharynx and soft palate, and upper portion of the buccal cavity. Preganglionic fibers of the *glossopharyngeal nerve* arise in the inferior salivatory nucleus and are carried through the tympanic and lesser superficial petrosal nerves to the otic ganglion, whence postganglionic fibers go via the auriculotemporal branch of the fifth nerve to the parotid gland, and with the facial nerve to the mucous membrane of the posterior and inferior portions of the pharynx and buccal cavity. Preganglionic fibers of the glossopharyngeal, the bulbar portion of the accessory, and principally of the *vagus nerve* arise in the dorsal efferent nucleus and are carried to ganglia situated near, on, or in the various viscera supplied by these nerves, including the heart, bronchioles, and gastrointestinal tract. The fibers to the heart terminate in the small ganglia of the heart wall, especially the atrium, from which postganglionic fibers are distributed to the musculature. The preganglionic fibers to the esophagus, stomach, small intestine, and greater part of the large intestine terminate in the extensive myenteric (Auerbach) and submucous (Meissner) plexuses, from which postganglionic fibers are distributed to the smooth muscles and glands of these organs. There is also said to be a cranial outflow of the parasympathetic division in the form of fibers to the pituitary stalk which innervate the posterior lobe of the pituitary gland.

The *sacral parasympathetic fibers* arise from cells in the intermediolateral portion of the sacral cord; they are carried through the second, third, and fourth sacral nerves, and possibly through the fifth, and are collected into the nervi erigentes, or pelvic nerves, which proceed to the pelvic plexuses and their branches. Postganglionic fibers may be carried from these plexuses to the pelvic viscera, but most preganglionic fibers continue to small ganglia on or near the viscera, where synapses occur and postganglionic fibers pass into the musculature of the organs. The sacral nerves supply the bladder, descending colon, rectum, anus, and genitalia.

THE ANATOMY OF THE SYMPATHETIC DIVISION

The sympathetic division, or thoracicolumbar outflow, is made up of preganglionic fibers which arise from cells in the intermediolateral columns of the eighth cervical or first thoracic through the first two or three lumbar segments of the spinal cord. These fibers make their exit through the ventral roots of the corresponding segmental nerves (Fig. 251). There is some question whether, in man, the eighth cervical segment and root contribute to the thoracicolumbar division, or whether the uppermost cells lie between the eighth cervical and first thoracic segment and make their exit with the first thoracic nerve root. The termination of the above fibers is threefold: (1) in the paravertebral ganglion chain, (2) in the prevertebral plexuses and collateral ganglia, and (3) occasionally in terminal ganglia. The postganglionic fibers go to the viscera. The sympathetic differs from the parasympathetic division in that the preganglionic fibers are often short and terminate on ganglia some distance from the viscera they supply, and the postganglionic fibers are longer than those of the parasympathetic division. Also, one preganglionic fiber may synapse with many postganglionic neurons.

The *paravertebral, vertebral, or central ganglion chain, or sympathetic ganglionated trunk,* consists of two elongated plexuses, each composed of a series of more or less segmentally arranged ganglia which are bound together by ascending and descending nerve fibers. The preganglionic fibers leave the cord and traverse the ventral spinal root and the mixed spinal nerve to reach the anterior primary ramus. Here they split off from the proximal part of this ramus as finely myelinated fibers (white rami communicantes) and enter the ganglionated chain. They may synapse immediately or may ascend or descend for various extents before they synapse at a higher or lower level. The postganglionic fibers are unmyelinated (gray rami communicantes). On reaching the anterior primary ramus they split into two groups, one extending with the anterior primary ramus, the other joining the posterior

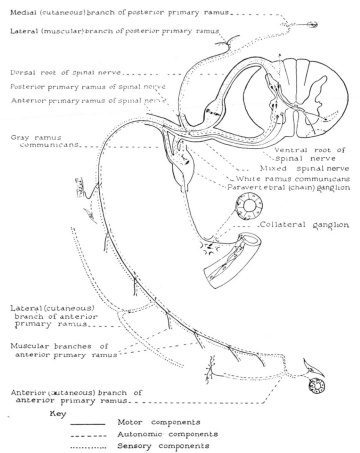

Medial (cutaneous) branch of posterior primary ramus

Lateral (muscular) branch of posterior primary ramus

Dorsal root of spinal nerve

Posterior primary ramus of spinal nerve

Anterior primary ramus of spinal nerve

Gray ramus communicans

Ventral root of spinal nerve

Mixed spinal nerve

White ramus communicans

Paravertebral (chain) ganglion

Collateral ganglion

Lateral (cutaneous) branch of anterior primary ramus

Muscular branches of anterior primary ramus

Anterior (cutaneous) branch of anterior primary ramus

Key

_____ Motor components

- - - - - - Autonomic components

.... Sensory components

FIG. 251. Segmental spinal nerve, showing course of motor, sensory, and preganglionic and postganglionic sympathetic fibers.

primary ramus (Figs. 251 and 252). The sympathetic trunks have from twenty-two to twenty-four ganglia and extend from the level of the second cervical vertebra to the coccyx. There are three cervical, ten to twelve thoracic, four lumbar, and four or five sacral ganglia. The chains usually fuse at the level of the coccyx in an unpaired coccygeal ganglion.

The *cervical portion* of the sympathetic chain consists of the superior, middle, and inferior cervical ganglia. These innervate structures within the head, upper extremities, and thorax. The *superior cervical ganglion,* which is the largest, is opposite the second and third cervical vertebrae and behind the internal carotid artery. It is supplied mainly by the upper four thoracic segments. The *internal carotid nerve,* which is a direct prolongation of this ganglion, contains postganglionic fibers arising therein. It supplies filaments to the internal carotid artery and terminates as the *internal carotid* and *cavernous plexuses.* Anterior branches from the ganglion form plexuses around the middle meningeal and external carotid and

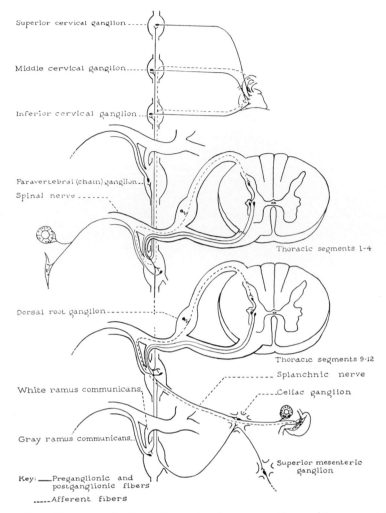

Superior cervical ganglion

Middle cervical ganglion

Inferior cervical ganglion

Paravertebral (chain) ganglion
Spinal nerve

Thoracic segments 1-4

Dorsal root ganglion

Thoracic segments 9-12
Splanchnic nerve
Celiac ganglion

White ramus communicans

Gray ramus communicans

Superior mesenteric ganglion

Key: ——Preganglionic and postganglionic fibers
- - - - Afferent fibers

FIG. 252. The sympathetic outflow, showing connections with paravertebral ganglionic chain, splanchnic nerves, and collateral ganglia.

maxillary arteries. The sympathetic innervation of the ciliary ganglion is carried through the long ciliary nerves from the cavernous plexus. The sphenopalatine ganglion is supplied by the internal carotid plexus through the deep petrosal and vidian nerves. The otic ganglion receives its sympathetic innervation from the plexus around the middle meningeal artery, and the submaxillary ganglion from that around the external maxillary artery. There are further communications from the superior cervical ganglion with the other cranial nerves and the upper four cervical nerves, branches to the pharyngeal plexus, filaments to the carotid sinus and body, and branches to the heart, the *superior cardiac nerves*. The *middle cervical ganglion* communicates with the fifth and sixth cervical nerves and gives off the *middle cardiac nerve* and branches to the thyroid gland. The *inferior cervical ganglion* communicates with the seventh and eighth cervical nerves and gives off the *inferior cardiac nerve* together with nerves to the blood vessels.

The *thoracic portion* of the sympathetic trunk rests against the heads of the ribs and all but the last two ganglia are covered by the costal pleura. Occasionally the first thoracic ganglion is blended with the inferior cervical ganglion to form the *stellate ganglion*. The upper five ganglia send branches to the cardiac and pulmonary plexuses; it may be that much of the sympathetic innervation to the heart is transmitted directly from these ganglia, and not via the cervical sympathetic chain. The *abdominal portion* of the sympathetic trunk is situated in front of the vertebral column along the medial margin of the psoas major muscle, and the *pelvic portion* is in front of the sacrum, medial to the anterior sacral foramina. The fused ganglion in front of the coccyx is known as *ganglion impar*. All these ganglia send gray rami communicantes to the corresponding spinal nerves and many send branches to the various plexuses and collateral ganglia. The postganglionic fibers terminate on blood vessels, sweat glands, and other smooth muscle and glandular structures.

Branches of the lower seven thoracic ganglia unite to form the three splanchnic nerves which penetrate the diaphragm and supply the abdominal and pelvic viscera. These branches are white in color and to a major extent carry preganglionic fibers which pass through the ganglia without synapse and terminate in the prevertebral plexuses or the collateral ganglia. They do, however, contain a few postganglionic fibers which pass through the further plexuses without synapse to reach the viscera. The *greater splanchnic nerve* is formed by branches of the fifth through the ninth or tenth thoracic ganglia; it terminates in the celiac ganglion. The *lesser splanchnic nerve* is formed by branches of the ninth and tenth and sometimes the eleventh thoracic ganglia; it ends in the aorticorenal ganglion. The *lowest splanchnic nerve* arises from the last thoracic ganglion; it ends in the renal plexus.

Within the thoracic, abdominal, and pelvic cavities are aggregations of nerves and ganglia known as the *prevertebral plexuses* and their *collateral ganglia* (Figs. 252 and 253). These are composed of both parasympathetic and sympathetic fibers. The parasympathetic fibers are preganglionic and may synapse in the plexuses or go through without synapse to terminal ganglia. The sympathetic fibers, mainly from the splanchnic nerves, for the most part synapse in the plexuses. From these plexuses, branches are given off to the thoracic, abdominal, and pelvic viscera.

The *cardiac plexus* is situated at the base of the heart and is divided into a superficial part which lies in the concavity of the aortic arch and a deep part between the aortic arch and the trachea. Both are supplied by the cardiac branches of the vagus nerves and the cardiac nerves arising from the cervical sympathetic ganglia; they also receive fibers from the thoracic sympathetic ganglia. Branches go to the anterior and posterior coronary plexuses. The cardiac plexuses also communicate with the anterior and posterior pulmonary and the esophageal plexuses, which are also supplied by the vagus nerve as well as by the thoracic sympathetic ganglia.

The *celiac plexus* is the largest of the three sympathetic plexuses. It is situated in the abdomen at the level of the upper part of the first lumbar vertebra. It lies behind the stomach and omental bursa, in front of the crura of the diaphragm and the abdominal aorta, and between the suprarenal glands. It is composed of the two

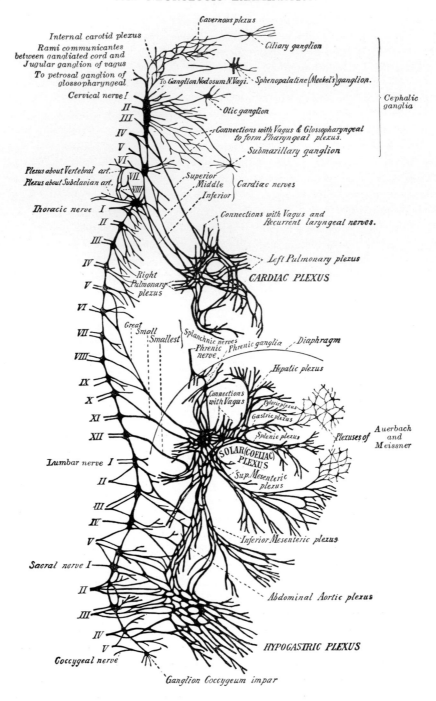

FIG. 253.   The autonomic nervous system, showing communications between parasympathetic and sympathetic divisions, together with main autonomic plexuses. (Morris' Human Anatomy. Philadelphia, Blakiston Company, 1942.)

celiac ganglia which are supplied by the greater splanchnic nerve and filaments from the right vagus, and the *aorticorenal ganglia* which receive the lesser splanchnic nerves. Secondary plexuses arising from or connected with the celiac plexus are the phrenic, hepatic, splenic, superior gastric, suprarenal, renal, spermatic or ovarian, superior mesenteric, inferior mesenteric, colic, sigmoid, superior hemorrhoidal, and abdominal aortic. The superior (anterior) gastric plexus and the hepatic plexus also receive branches from the left vagus nerve. The renal and inferior mesenteric plexuses and their branches are also supplied by the lowest splanchnic nerve. All may receive some innervation from the lumbar sympathetic chain.

The *hypogastric plexus* is situated in front of the last lumbar vertebra and the promontory of the sacrum, between the two common iliac arteries. It is formed by the union of many elements from the aortic plexus and the lumbar sympathetic chain, together with some fibers from the inferior mesenteric plexus. It is divided, below, into the two *pelvic plexuses*. These are formed by fibers from the hypogastric plexus, preganglionic parasympathetic fibers from the second, third, and fourth sacral nerves, and a few filaments from the sacral sympathetic ganglia. Branches are distributed to the pelvic viscera and the internal and external genitalia through the middle hemorrhoidal, vesical, prostatic, vaginal, and uterine plexuses.

THE PHYSIOLOGY OF THE PERIPHERAL AUTONOMIC NERVOUS SYSTEM

The autonomic nervous system governs the activities of cardiac and smooth muscle, including the smooth muscle of the blood vessels, and the functions of sweat, digestive, and other glandular structures, including certain endocrine organs. It is concerned with those processes which normally are beyond voluntary control and for the most part are beneath consciousness. It regulates such important functions as respiration, circulation, digestion, temperature adjustment, and metabolism, all of which are vital to normal existence, and combats forces acting from within or without which would tend to cause changes in the body. Cannon has used the term *homeostasis* for that ability or coordination of the body as a whole to meet changing conditions in its external or internal environment by autonomic adjustments. By homeostasis the constancy of the internal environment of the body and the uniformity and stability of the organism are maintained. During muscular exercise for instance, there is an augmented blood supply with increased metabolism of skeletal muscle, and a shift of blood volume from one part of the body to another; the increased venous return to the heart is accommodated by reflex acceleration of the heart, peripheral vasoconstriction, and a consequent rise in blood pressure which is immediately counteracted by increased activity of the aortic and carotid sinus reflexes. In addition there is bronchiolar dilation to allow for a greater respiratory exchange to meet the oxygen demand, together with cessation of peristalsis, and closing of the sphincters.

The viscera of the body receive a dual autonomic supply; they are innervated by both the parasympathetic and sympathetic divisions. In general these two divisions are antagonistic and reciprocal in their reaction, but there are certain exceptions, and on occasion their functions are correlated rather than antagonistic (Fig. 254).

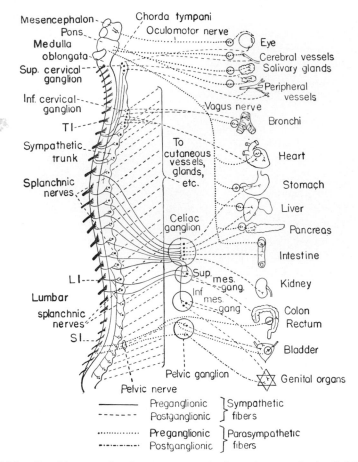

FIG. 254.   Dual innervation by parasympathetic and sympathetic divisions of autonomic nervous system. (Kuntz, A.: A Text-book of Neuro-anatomy. Philadelphia, Lea & Febiger, 1945.)

The functions of the *parasympathetic division* are not as clearly defined as those of the sympathetic division. It supplies only special structures, such as the pupils, salivary glands, heart, lungs, gastrointestinal tract, bladder, and erectile organs. It discharges discretely, i.e. only one outflow or one part of one outflow is active at one time. The structures innervated by the parasympathetic division are partially under the regulation of the motor cortex and may be subject to some degree of voluntary control. In certain parasympathetic functions, as in bladder, rectal, and genital activity, movements of striated musculature are closely correlated with those of smooth muscle. The parasympathetic division is essential to life and the conservation of energy. It controls anabolic, excretory, and reproductive functions, and conserves and restores bodily resources and energy. These latter are termed *trophotrope* activities by Hess.

The *sympathetic division,* on the other hand, supplies all portions of the body. It tends to discharge *en masse.* Its functions are catabolic and directed toward the expenditure of energy. It prepares the organism for either activity or flight, and mobilizes the resources of the body for combat. It acts whenever rapid adjustment to the environment is required. It accelerates the heart, dilates the coronary vessels, increases the arterial blood pressure, empties the blood reservoirs, dilates the bronchi, liberates glucose, and inhibits gastrointestinal activity. It is an emergency protective mechanism which tends to adapt the individual to changes that have taken place in his environment. It temporarily lessens fatigue. It is called into action under emotional stress and causes the individual to react strongly to stimuli of rage and fear. It is not essential to life. Hess uses the term *ergotrope* to describe those activities which enable an organism to display an externally directed behavior.

The functions of the parasympathetic and sympathetic divisions in the innervation of the respective organs and tissues of the body are most easily understood by considering these structures individually and noting the reciprocal or the coordinating action of this dual supply. When both innervate a single organ, the parasympathetic acts largely through the smooth muscle of the organ itself, whereas the sympathetic also acts through the mediums of circulation and vasomotor tone.

THE EYE

The parasympathetic division stimulates the sphincter of the pupil and causes constriction of the pupil, or miosis. It is generally considered that the sympathetic division stimulates the dilator of the pupil and causes mydriasis, but certain observers, principally Langworthy, believe that there is little if any dilator muscle in the iris, and that the pupillary diameter is influenced almost entirely by parasympathetic activity and is dependent upon the contraction and relaxation of the constrictor musculature; the sympathetic influences the size of the pupil only through the medium of the blood vessels of the iris. The parasympathetic also stimulates the ciliary muscle, contraction of the circular fibers of which causes relaxation of the ciliary zonule and decrease in the tension of the lens capsule; this is followed by an increase in the convexity of the lens to adjust the eye for near vision. The sympathetic division supplies the tarsal muscles and the orbital muscle of Müller. The former are smooth muscle sheets in the upper and lower eyelids; that in the upper aids in the elevation of the eyelid. The latter, in the lower forms at least, keeps the globe of the eye forward in the orbit. It is questionable whether the sympathetic causes relaxation of the ciliary muscle for distance vision, but it may aid in flattening the lens by producing contraction of the radial fibers of the ciliary muscle.

Stimulation of the parasympathetic nerves causes miosis and accommodation for near vision, whereas paralysis produces mydriasis and loss of accommodation. Stimulation of the sympathetic nerves causes mydriasis, widening of the palpebral fissure, and tension of the muscle of Müller, sometimes with exophthalmos; paralysis produces miosis, pseudoptosis, and sometimes enophthalmos, along with anhidrosis, and vasodilation, resulting in Horner's syndrome.

THE LACRIMAL AND SALIVARY GLANDS

The parasympathetic division supplies secretory and vasodilator impulses to the lacrimal and salivary glands and to the mucosal glands of the orbit, nose, pharynx, and mouth. The sympathetic division supplies secretory and vasoconstrictor impulses to the salivary glands and vasoconstrictor fibers to the lacrimal glands. Stimulation of the parasympathetic nerves is followed by lacrimation and the formation of a copious amount of thin, watery saliva. Stimulation of the sympathetic nerves is followed by the formation of a scant supply of thick, viscid saliva. Destruction of the parasympathetic nerves causes diminution of lacrimation and salivation, but destruction of the sympathetics causes little change in these functions.

THE SKIN STRUCTURES

The sympathetic division stimulates the arrectores pilorum muscles, and irritation of the sympathetic nerves results in a pilomotor response, or cutis anserina. The sympathetic division also supplies secretory impulses to the sweat glands, and stimulation of the sympathetic fibers results in an excess secretion. Paralysis of the sympathetics results in absence of both pilomotor response and sweating. The parasympathetic division does not supply either the pilomotor muscles or sweat glands. It should be stressed, however, that although the sweat glands are innervated by fibers which belong to the postganglionic sympathetic system, their function is modified by drugs which influence the parasympathetic division. These nerves are, therefore, cholinergic rather than adrenergic.

THE BLOOD VESSELS

The parasympathetic and sympathetic innervation of the various blood vessel systems of the body is not adequately understood. Histologic investigations have demonstrated that the arterioles, capillaries, and veins are supplied by fibers of the sympathetic division which reach the vessels through somatic nerves given off at segmental intervals. There is physiologic evidence that stimulation of these elements causes vasoconstriction, whereas paralysis results in vasodilatation. The sympathetic division probably supplies vasomotor fibers to the entire arterial system with the possible exception of the coronary arteries. This is most marked in the cutaneous, muscular, and splanchnic vessels. Section of the sympathetic trunk, as in Horner's syndrome, causes marked vasodilatation and flushing of the skin and mucous surfaces, and stimulation of the sympathetics causes pallor of the skin and shrinkage of the mucous membranes. The administration of epinephrine or other sympathomimetic drugs in surgical shock results in vasoconstriction and raising of the blood pressure.

Opinion differs concerning the effect of the parasympathetic division on blood vessel caliber; it may either supply general vasomotor impulses, or supply such impulses only to specific structures. Vasodilator fibers carried by the facial and glossopharyngeal nerves innervate the lacrimal, salivary, and associated mucous glands; vasodilator fibers in the sacral nerves supply the helicine arteries. It has been postulated that there may be vasodilator fibers, a part of the parasympathetic division, which reach the peripheral vessels through the dorsal spinal roots, but there is no definite evidence that the peripheral vascular system has reciprocal innervation or has a separate innervation which stimulates vasodilatation. The sympathetics alone may influence the diameter of the vessels through increase and decrease in tone. The dilatation of the vessels which follows stimulation of sensory nerves is probably the result of antidromic efferent conduction through those nerves; such efferent impulses are essential to the axon reflex.

The cerebral and meningeal vessels are constricted by the sympathetic division and possibly dilated by the parasympathetic. Stimulation of the sympathetics, however, causes only partial constriction, or perhaps constriction followed by dilatation. The branches of the external carotid artery may respond differently than the branches of the internal carotid, and in migraine, where there is constriction followed by dilatation of certain arteries, especially the dural and temporal branches of the external carotid artery, this dilatation is not relieved by sympathomimetic drugs but is relieved by ergotamine tartrate.

The helicine arteries are constricted by the sympathetic division and are very definitely dilated by the parasympathetic, stimulation of which results in relaxation of their tonus and engorgement of the corpora cavernosa. Opinion differs on the autonomic regulation of the coronary arteries. It has been stated that the vagus contains vasodilator fibers to these arteries, but it is generally believed that they are dilated by the sympathetic division, possibly by means of a passive rather than an active vasodilatation. Most authorities state that they are constricted by the parasympathetic division.

That the veins as well as the arteries have efferent vasomotor nerves is demonstrated by the therapeutic response to lumbar sympathetic block in the treatment of thrombophlebitis.

THE HEART

Stimulation of the parasympathetic division results in a reduction in heart rate, decreased cardiac output, diminished conduction at the auriculoventricular bundle, and sometimes changes in rhythm such as auriculoventricular block or vagal arrest. In general the parasympathetic inhibits and depresses the activity of the heart, slows the beat, and weakens contraction. Stimulation of the sympathetic division results in acceleration of the cardiac rate, increased output, augmented conduction of the auriculoventricular bundle, and occasionally changes in rhythm characterized by ventricular extrasystoles, paroxysmal tachycardia, or auricular or ventricular fibrillation, together with a secondary rise in blood pressure. Section of the vagus causes tachycardia. Stimulation of the vagus, as in the oculocardiac reflex, causes slowing of the heart rate and may be of therapeutic value in paroxysmal tachycardia.

THE BLOOD PRESSURE

The sympathetic division through its constricting effect on the blood vessels, especially the splanchnic arteries, together with the acceleration of the heart rate, is important in the regulation of blood pressure. The administration of epinephrine or other sympathomimetic drugs, as mentioned above, will raise the blood pressure in surgical shock, and section of the splanchnic nerves and of other portions of the sympathetic complex is useful in the treatment of hypertension (see below). Stimulation of the parasympathetic division may produce some lowering of the blood pressure, possibly partly due to reduction of cardiac rate and output and partly, but questionably, the result of vasodilatation. The drop in blood pressure is much less, however, than the degree of elevation that follows sympathetic stimulation.

THE RESPIRATORY SYSTEM

The bronchial musculature is contracted and the bronchi and bronchioles are constricted by the action of the parasympathetics, which also stimulate the bronchial secretion. The sympathetic division to a lesser extent dilates the bronchi and bronchioles; it probably reduces bronchial secretion by means of vasoconstriction of the arteries supplying the bronchial mucosa, although it may be an inhibitor to the bronchial glands. The symptoms of asthma, the result of bronchial constriction and edema and increased secretion, may be relieved either by drugs which paralyze the parasympathetic or by those which stimulate the sympathetic division.

THE GASTROINTESTINAL SYSTEM

In general the parasympathetic division increases the tone and motility of the gastrointestinal tract, relaxes the sphincters, and causes an increased secretion of the various glandular structures, thus aiding the various functions of the gastrointestinal system, as well as elimination. The sympathetic division, on the other hand, decreases the tone and motility, contracts the sphincters, and may inhibit some of the glandular structures. The supply to the *salivary glands* has already been mentioned. In the *esophagus* the parasympathetic stimulates peristalsis, whereas the sympathetic causes contraction of the cardiac sphincter.

In the *stomach* the parasympathetic division causes increased peristaltic activity and increased secretion of the gastric glands, with, as a rule, relaxation of the pyloric sphincter. The sympathetic causes decrease in motility, contraction of the pyloric sphincter, and possibly inhibition of gastric secretion. It plays a less important role than the parasympathetic in gastric physiology and secretion, but does decrease the vascularity of the stomach wall. Vagotomy, used in the treatment of peptic ulcer, decreases both the tonus and motility of the stomach and the secretion of hydrochloric acid.

In the *intestines* the parasympathetic division also causes an increase in motility, tone, and peristalsis, with, in general, relaxation of the sphincters, including the anal sphincter, and an increase in secretion of the mucosal glands. The sympathetic causes decreased peristalsis, contraction of the sphincters, and possibly inhibition of secretions. The parasympathetic supply to the intestine is carried by the vagus nerve as far as the descending colon, and below this by the sacral nerves. Drugs which stimulate structures innervated by postganglionic cholinergic nerves increase peristalsis, and those which inhibit structures innervated by such nerves decrease it. Defecation is a function of the parasympathetics, and a defecation center has been postulated in the sacral portion of the spinal cord. Some observers believe that the sympathetic division has comparatively little significance in the innervation of the intestine and its sphincters, and it probably is less active than the parasympathetic, but it does play a part. Vagotomy has also been used in the treatment of ulcerative colitis and regional enteritis. The external anal sphincter, which is composed of striated muscle, is innervated by the pudendal, or pudic, nerve from the first through the fourth sacral segments.

The parasympathetic division stimulates bile production in the liver and also contraction of the gall bladder and bile ducts, and the sympathetic may cause relaxation of these structures. The parasympathetic causes increased secretion on the part of both the pancreatic acini and islets, whereas the sympathetic may have no effect on these structures. The parasympathetic division thus not only aids in digestion by stimulation of the external secretion of the pancreas, but it also decreases the glucose content of the blood by production of insulin. The sympathetic, on the other hand, stimulates glycogenolysis in the liver, raises the glucose content of the blood, and may cause glycosuria. The parasympathetic plays no part in these latter functions.

The Ureter and Bladder

The parasympathetic division supplies the bladder through the pelvic nerves from the second, third, and fourth sacral segments, with postganglionic fibers to the musculature, partly from the pelvic and vesical plexuses but mainly from small ganglia in or on the bladder wall (Fig. 255). It increases the tone and motility of the ureter and causes contraction of the detrusor muscle of the bladder with relaxation of the trigone and internal sphincter. It thus promotes micturition and stimulates emptying of the bladder. The sympathetic division also supplies these structures through fibers which issue from the lower thoracic and upper lumbar segments of the spinal cord and terminate in the hypogastric and vesical plexuses, from which postganglionic fibers go to the bladder musculature. It decreases the tone and motility of the urether, relaxes the detrusor, and contracts the trigone and internal sphincter, thereby impeding or inhibiting micturition. Stimulation of the parasympathetics causes micturition, whereas stimulation of the sympathetics causes retention. The activity of the sympathetic, however, is much less marked than is that of the parasympathetic division, and section of the former seems to have little effect on bladder function. Section of the parasympathetic nerves, on the other hand, is followed by bladder paralysis. The smooth muscle of the bladder, however, also has inherent rhythmicity. The voluntary nervous system, through the pudendal, or pudic, nerve from the second through the fourth sacral segments, is motor to the striated musculature of the external sphincter and the accessory muscles of the perineum. It is essential to voluntary initiation and control of micturition. This latter nerve also carries sensation from the bladder, although there is probably an autonomic afferent component as well, carried through both the pelvic and hypogastric nerves.

The Generative Organs

Both the parasympathetic and sympathetic divisions are necessary to sexual activity. Erection depends upon the integrity of the parasympathetic division and is the result of engorgement of the corpora cavernosa by dilatation of the helicine arteries, or possibly by relaxation of their vascular tonus. Tonic contraction of the transverse perineal, bulbocavernosus, and ischiocavernosus muscles also contributes

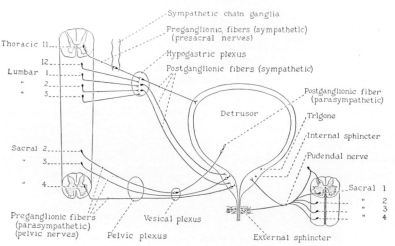

FIG. 255.   Innervation of urinary bladder.

to erection, and maintains erection by interference with the return of the blood. All of these phenomena follow excitation of vasodilator and muscle reflex centers in the sacral portion of the spinal cord (erection center). Engorgement may in part be related also to inhibition of vasoconstrictor centers in the lumbar cord. Stimulation of the sympathetics, on the other hand, causes constriction of the arteries and subsidence of erection. Ejaculation consists of two functions, emission, and ejaculation in the restricted sense. Emission is caused by contraction of the smooth muscle of the internal genitals with delivery of semen to the membranous urethra. This is brought about by stimulation of the sympathetic division which causes a reflex peristalsis of the ampulla of the ductus deferens, seminal vesicles, and ejaculatory ducts, and contraction of the smooth muscle of the prostate. The so-called emission center is said to be located in the lumbar portion of the spinal cord. Ejaculation of the fluid through the urethral canal, or expulsion of the seminal fluid, is carried out by means of the parasympathetic division which stimulates clonic spasms of the ischiocavernosus and bulbocavernosus muscles. The sympathetic division also stimulates contraction of the dartos muscles. A lesion of the parasympathetic causes impotence due to failure of erection and ejaculation, whereas overactivity of the parasympathetic produces priapism. A lesion of the sympathetic division causes impairment of ejaculation, due to failure of the spermatozoa to reach the urethra Overactivity of the sympathetics results in weak erections, ejaculatio precox, and spermatorrhea.

Stimulation of the parasympathetic division causes increased vaginal secretions, erection of the clitoris, and engorgement of the labia minora. The effect of the two divisions on the uterus is variable. The parasympathetic may have little influence, although it may stimulate contraction of the pregnant uterus. The sympathetic causes contraction of the pregnant uterus and may produce either stimulation or inhibition of the nonpregnant uterus. It does stimulate contraction of the fallopian tubes, uterus, and Bartholin's glands at orgasm.

OTHER FUNCTIONS

Stimulation of the sympathetic division causes secretion of epinephrine. This effect may be the result of activity at the postganglionic neuron rather than at the suprarenal medulla itself, and consequently be a cholinergic function, even though a part of the sympathetic physiology. The parasympathetic may inhibit suprarenal secretion. Stimulation of the sympathetic division causes contraction of the splenic capsule and emptying of the blood reservoirs.

THE PHARMACOLOGY OF THE PERIPHERAL AUTONOMIC NERVOUS SYSTEM

Much of our knowledge regarding the physiology of the autonomic nervous system has been acquired from information contributed by the action of various pharmacologic substances upon the individual portions of the system. It is known that certain drugs tend to stimulate either the parasympathetic or sympathetic divisions, whereas other drug depress or inhibit them. These drugs mimic the effects of nerve stimulation and depression. Inasmuch as the two divisions of the system are in many respects antagonistic, drugs which stimulate or depress one part may, indirectly, cause decreased or increased activity of the other. Some of these agents act at the autonomic ganglia and others act directly upon the autonomic effector cells, the smooth muscle or glands. These variabilities in site of action and response are useful not only in understanding the action of the constituent parts, but also in examination and therapy.

Before discussing these various drugs individually, it is necessary to elaborate somewhat on the chemical mediation of nerve impulses. Loewi, in a series of researches begun in 1921, found that on stimulating the vagus a substance was produced or liberated at the myoneural junction which, when applied to another organ, had the same effect as vagus stimulation. This he called vagus-substance or parasympathin. He, Cannon, and others also found that stimulation of sympathetic fibers liberated a substance which had an action similar to that of epinephrine.

The substance liberated by stimulation of the parasympathetic nerves is now known to be *acetylcholine*. It acts as the chemical mediator of the excitatory process initiated by parasympathetic nerve impulses. It is split by the action of cholinesterase, a specific enzyme present in the blood and tissues of the body, to choline and acetic acid. Physostigmine and related drugs inactivate the cholinesterase and prolong and intensify the action of acetylcholine. Acetylcholine has two modes and sites of action: (1) It stimulates the ganglion cells (both parasympathetic and sympathetic) when present in low concentrations, and depresses them when present in high concentrations. In this respect it acts similarly to nicotine, and this is known as its *"nicotinic"* action. It has a like effect on voluntary muscles. (2) It also stimulates the autonomic effector organs (smooth muscle and glands) that are innervated by the parasympathetic nervous system. In this respect it acts similarly to muscarine, and this is known as its *"muscarinic"* action.

The epinephrine-like substance which is produced or released at the myoneural junction by the stimulation of the sympathetic nerves is known as *sympathin*. It is the chemical mediator of the excitatory processes initiated by sympathetic nerve impulses at neuroeffector junctions. It differs, however, from epinephrine in certain respects. Epinephrine has both excitatory and inhibitory effects; sympathin also has both, but they are separable. That released when excitatory responses are stimulated is known as sympathin E, and that which has an inhibitory effect is sympathin I.

Parasympathetic and sympathetic nerve impulses reproduce the peripheral effects of acetylcholine and epinephrine. They are either stimulated or inhibited by the action of drugs. The demonstration that acetylcholine acts as chemical transmitter of impulses for nerves other than postganglionic parasympathetic nerves suggested that it might be better to classify nerves physiologically rather than anatomically. Therefore the term *cholinergic* is used for all nerves that release acetylcholine at their terminals. These include not only all postganglionic parasympathetic nerves but also all autonomic preganglionic fibers, whether parasympathetic or sympathetic, together with the postganglionic sympathetic nerves to sweat glands and certain blood vessels and the somatic nerves to skeletal muscles. The term *adrenergic* is used for those nerves that release sympathin. These include all postganglionic sympathetic fibers except those to the sweat glands and certain vessels (Fig. 256).

The *drugs which act upon the autonomic nervous* system may be classified as those which act at the autonomic ganglia and those which act at the myoneural junction. It must be stressed, however, that all these drugs affect cells and not nerve endings. *Drugs that act upon the cells of the autonomic ganglia* act on both parasympathetic and sympathetic ganglia. Inasmuch as their reaction is related to that of acetylcholine, it is stated that they affect *cells innervated by preganglionic cholinergic nerves* (Table 8). Most of these drugs have a similar action on skeletal muscles.

The principal drug which *stimulates* cells innervated by preganglionic cholinergic nerves is *acetylcholine*. This, in its "nicotinic" action, stimulates all autonomic ganglion cells innervated by preganglionic parasympathetic and sympathetic nerves

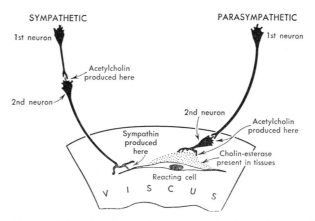

FIG. 256.   The peripheral actions of parasympathetic and sympathetic divisions of autonomic nervous system, showing points at which chemical transmitters are believed to be produced. (Myerson, A.: *J.A.M.A.* 110:101, 1938).

and also cells innervated by all cerebrospinal somatic nerves to skeletal muscle fibers. Other *esters* of *choline,* such as *acetylbetamethylcholine* (Mecholyl), *carbaminoylcholine* (Doryl), and betamethylcholine (Urecholine), have a similar action but are not as readily susceptible to destruction by cholinesterase and therefore are less evanescent in effect; they have a greater "muscarinic" than "nicotinic" action. *Physostigmine (eserine), neostigmine (Prostigmin),* and certain *organic phosphate compounds* may also be considered stimulators of the autonomic ganglion cells; they do not, however, act on the effector organs, but produce cell responses by virtue of their ability to inhibit the cholinesterase from destroying the acetylcholine which is produced at the cholinergic nerve endings. They aid the "muscarinic" action of acetylcholine on smooth muscle, glands, and heart, and its "nicotinic" action on the autonomic ganglia and skeletal muscles. *Nicotine,* in low concentrations, also stimulates ganglion cells. *Edrophonium (Tensilon),* while primarily a curare antagonist at the skeletal myoneural junction, also has actions resembling those of acetylcholine.

Drugs which *depress* or block the action on cells innervated by preganglionic cholinergic nerves are as follows: *Nicotine* in high concentrations prevents the response of ganglion cells to preganglionic nerve stimulation (i.e. it stimulates, then depresses); it blocks the synaptic transmission through autonomic ganglia by acting on ganglion cells to make them unresponsive to acetylcholine. *Acetylcholine,* the *choline esters,* and the *inhibitors of cholinesterase* have a similar effect in high concentrations. *Curare* and the various preparations of *d-tubocurarine* raise the threshold to acetylcholine and prevent ganglion cells and muscles from responding to nerve stimulation, although they have a greater effect on skeletal muscle than on ganglion cells. Their mode of action is similar to that of nicotine. *Erythroidine* has properties similar to those of *d-tubocurarine. Calcium* in high concentrations blocks synaptic transmission to autonomic ganglion cells, whereas a decrease in calcium stimulates the cells so that they are more readily discharged by acetylcholine. Of the methonium compounds, *decamethonium* causes neuromuscular blockade of skeletal muscle, whereas *hexamethonium* and *pentamethonium* cause blockade in autonomic ganglia. *Succinylcholine, gallamine,* and *benzoquinonium* also have a major effect on skeletal muscle. The *tetraethylammonium salts,* especially the bromide and chloride, specifically block the transmission of nerve impulses through autonomic ganglia, both sympathetic and parasympathetic.

The drugs that act upon the autonomic effector cells do not act peripherally on autonomic nerves, but, through performing their function at the myoneural junction, they act directly on the muscle and gland cells (Table 8). These may be divided into those that affect the parasympathetic and those that affect the sympathetic system (Fig. 257).

The Parasympathetic Division

Drugs which act on structures innervated by the postganglionic cholinergic nerves act upon all postganglionic parasympathetic nerves together with postganglionic sympathetic nerves which go to sweat glands and certain blood vessels. Those which act as stimulants are called parasympathomimetic drugs. These include *acetyl-*

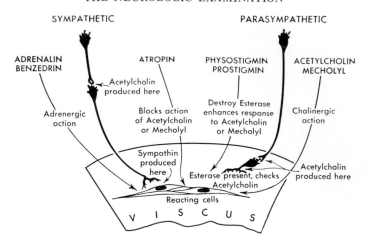

Fig. 257. The peripheral actions of parasympathetic and sympathetic divisions of autonomic nervous system, showing site and mechanism of action of pharmacologic agents. (Myerson, A.: *J.A.M.A.* 110:101, 1938.)

choline and the other *choline esters* mentioned above, *acetylbetamethylcholine, carbaminoylcholine,* and *betamethylcholine,* which have a "muscarinic" action on effector cells. The inhibitors of cholinesterase, *physostigmine, neostigmine, benz-pyrinium,* and the *organic phosphate compounds,* produce similar effects. Other drugs that act directly upon the effector cells in a highly selective manner are *pilocarpine, muscarine,* and *arecoline.* Muscular and glandular responses to these chemicals occur even after complete nerve degeneration. *Potassium* also stimulates structures supplied by cholinergic nerves and enhances the action of acetylcholine.

Drugs that inhibit structures innervated by postganglionic cholinergic nerves are *atropine, scopolamine, hyoscyamine,* and related synthetic drugs such as *homatropine, Novatropin, Syntropan, Trasentine, Eumydrine, Eucatropine, Pavatrine, Banthine, Pro-Banthine,* and others. They do not inhibit the "nicotinic" actions of acetylcholine, but specifically block all "muscarinic" effects, whether they are excitatory or inhibitory in nature. The site of action is directly on the effector cells and not on the nerve endings.

THE SYMPATHETIC DIVISION

Drugs that act on structures innervated by postganglionic adrenergic nerves act upon all postganglionic nerves except those to sweat glands and certain vascular beds. Those that act as stimulants are called sympathomimetic drugs. These include *epinephrine (Adrenalin), levarterenol (1-norepinephrine), ephedrine, amphetamine (Benzedrine),* and many related synthetic drugs. These substances act directly on smooth muscle and gland cells even when the effector organ is denervated. *Cocaine* also possesses sympathomimetic properties and potentiates the action of epinephrine but not of the other sympathomimetic drugs; it may either protect epinephrine and sympathin from oxidative destruction, or increase membrane permeability so that these substances may more readily diffuse into the reacting cells.

Drugs that inhibit structures innervated by adrenergic nerves are *Dibenamine, Dibenzyline,* certain of the *ergot alkaloids, tolazoline, phentolamine,* the *benzodioxanes, yohimbine,* and *azapentine.* The first two have a specific, long-acting adrenergic blocking effect, but the others are less specific and shorter in the duration of their action. They are all more effective in inhibiting responses to circulating sympathomimetic substances than in checking the reaction to stimulation by sympathetic nerve impulses.

There are other drugs which have minor autonomic actions or which act on structures innervated by the autonomic system in a manner similar to that of some of the above drugs. *Histamine* stimulates smooth muscle, regardless of its innervation; it dilates the capillaries and arterioles, stimulates the smooth muscles of the uterus, constricts the bronchioles, and stimulates many glands of external secretion, especially the gastric glands; the antihistamines have an antagonistic action. *Posterior pituitary extract* causes vasoconstriction and contraction of the uterus and of the intestinal musculature. *Morphine* causes contraction of smooth muscles with the exception of those of the blood vessels; it causes constriction of the pupils and of the ureter and bronchial musculature, increased tone but lessened motility of the gastrointestinal tract, and decrease in gastrointestinal secretion. *Strychnine* may stimulate the smooth muscles of the gastrointestinal tract. *Amyl nitrite* and *nitroglycerin* have a relaxing action on the smooth muscle of blood vessels and hollow organs. *Picrotoxin* causes vagal stimulation. *Papaverine* causes relaxation of smooth muscles, including those of the blood vessels, bronchi, gastrointestinal tract, and ureters. *Caffeine* relaxes the smooth muscle of the biliary tract and bronchi. The *barbiturates* decrease gastrointestinal tonus. None of the above drugs, however, should be considered to have any direct or any major effect on the autonomic nervous system, and the action of some of them is central rather than peripheral.

The therapeutic action of the above drugs is well known. The parasympatheticomimetic drugs cause slowing of the heart, increased peristalsis, urgency of urination, pupillary constriction, and increased salivation and lacrimation. Through their action on the sweat glands and cutaneous vessels innervated by the sympathetic division they cause perspiration and increased heat and redness of the skin due to vasodilatation. Those which inhibit the action of the parasympathetics cause pupillary dilatation, tachycardia, diminished salivation, decreased peristalsis, decrease in bronchial secretions, dilatation of the bronchi and bronchioles, and, through their action on the sweat glands and blood vessels, diminished perspiration. The sympathomimetic drugs cause tachycardia, increased blood pressure, pupillary dilatation, pilomotor response, bronchial dilatation, and general vasoconstriction.

THE AFFERENT FUNCTIONS OF THE PERIPHERAL AUTONOMIC NERVOUS SYSTEM

The visceral reflex arc must have its afferent side, and in addition to the efferent nerves supplied by the autonomic nervous system, there are general visceral afferent fibers which are found in many of the cranial nerves and in thoracicolumbar and sacral autonomic nerves. These fibers carry impulses that arise in smooth muscle

TABLE 8.   DRUGS ACTING UPON THE AUTONOMIC NERVOUS SYSTEM

1. DRUGS ACTING UPON THE CELLS OF THE AUTONOMIC GANGLIA (PARASYMPATHETIC AND SYMPATHETIC) AND ON SKELETAL MUSCLES

(These drugs act upon cells innervated by preganglionic cholinergic nerves.)

Stimulants	*Depressants*
Choline esters ("nicotinic" action)	Nicotine (in high concentrations)
Acetylcholine	Choline esters (in high concentrations)
Acetylbetamethylcholine (Methacholine; Mecholyl)	Cholinesterase inhibitors (in high concentrations)
Carbaminoylcholine (Carbachol; Doryl)	Curare
Betamethylcholine (Bethanechol; Urecholine)	*d*-Tubocurarine (Intocostrin; Metubine; Mecostrin)
Cholinesterase inhibitors	Erythroidine
Physostigmine (Eserine)	Calcium
Neostigmine (Prostigmin)	Decamethonium (Syncurine)
Organic phosphate compounds	Hexamethonium (Methium; Bistrium)
Diisopropylfluorophosphate (DFP)	Pentamethonium
Tetraethylpyrophosphate (TEPP)	Succinylcholine
Hexaethyltetrophosphate (HETP)	Gallamine (Flaxedil)
Octamethylpyrophosphoramide (OMPA)	Benzoquinonium (Mytolon)
Nicotine (in low concentrations)	Tetraethylammonium (Etamon)
Edrophonium (Tensilon)	

and glandular structures and conduct sensations of spasm, distention, fullness, pressure, and pain from the viscera.

The afferent fibers which conduct impulses from the viscera to the central nervous system have cell bodies in the cerebrospinal ganglia, as do the somatic afferent fibers. There is some difference of opinion concerning the existence of any anatomic or physiologic differentiation between the visceral and the somatic afferent nerves. The distinction between them may be entirely one of peripheral distribution rather than of fundamental morphologic or functional significance. The controversy is largely one of terminology and classification. Many authorities express the belief that the visceral afferent fibers are not actually a part of the autonomic nervous system, but merely travel with its efferent fibers. The mode of conduction through the spinal cord and the central connections of impulses which conduct visceral sensation differ from those which carry somatic sensation. In spite of the controversy regarding the existence of afferent functions of the autonomic nervous sytem, its sensory connections are important in the meditation of certain types of impulses from the viscera, in the visceral reflexes, and in the syndrome of reflex, or referred, pain.

Primary testing of the sensory functions of the afferent fibers that are carried with the autonomic nerves cannot be executed very effectively, and the types of visceral sensation that can be tested may also be carried by somatic nerves. This problem, the subject of referred pain, and the relief of painful syndromes by sympathectomy are discussed more in detail in Chapter 7.

TABLE 8.   DRUGS ACTING UPON THE AUTONOMIC NERVOUS SYSTEM
(continued)

2. DRUGS ACTING UPON AUTONOMIC EFFECTOR CELLS
(These drugs act directly on muscle or gland cells, not on autonomic nerves.)

a.   *The Parasympathetic Division*

(These drugs act on structures innervated by postganglionic cholinergic nerves, including all postganglionic parasympathetic nerves and certain postganglionic sympathetic nerves to sweat glands and blood vessels.)

Stimulants	*Depressants*
(Parasympthomimetic drugs)	Atropine
Choline esters ("muscarinic" action)	Scopolamine
Acetylcholine	Hyoscyamine
Acetylbetamethylcholine (Methacholine;	Related synthetic drugs
Mecholyl)	Homotropine
Carbaminoylcholine (Carbachol; Doryl)	Novatropin
Betamethylcholine (Bethanecol; Ure-	Syntropan
choline)	Trasentin
Cholinesterase inhibitors	Eumydrine
Physostigmine (Eserine)	Eucatropine
Neostigmine (Prostigmin)	Pavatrine
Benzpyrinium (Stigmonene)	Methantheline (Banthine)
Diisopropylfluorophosphate and congeners	Propantheline (Pro-Banthine)
Cholinergic alkaloids	Oxyphenonium (Antrenyl)
Pilocarpine	Penthienate
Muscarine	Diphenmethanil
Arecoline	Mepiperphenidol
Potassium	Tricyclamol
	Dibutoline
	Dicyclomine
	Aminopentamide
	Cyclopentolate

THE CENTRAL REGULATION OF AUTONOMIC FUNCTION

The peripheral autonomic nervous system is under the control of higher centers at all levels of neural integration. One cannot discuss the anatomy and physiology of the autonomic nervous system and its disturbances of function without consideration of those centers in the cerebral cortex, hypothalamus, midbrain, brain stem, and spinal cord that regulate and influence the function of its peripheral components. The most important of these centers is the hypothalamus.

THE HYPOTHALAMUS

The hypothalamus lies in the ventral portion of the diencephalon just below the thalamus, and in immediate topographic relation with the hypophysis. It forms the greater part of the floor and part of the lateral wall of the third ventricle (Fig. 258).

TABLE 8.   DRUGS ACTING UPON THE AUTONOMIC NERVOUS SYSTEM
(continued)

2.   DRUGS ACTING UPON AUTONOMIC EFFECTOR CELLS (*continued*)

(These drugs act directly on muscle or gland cells, not on autonomic nerves.)

b.   *The Sympathetic Division*

(These drugs act on structures innervated by postganglionic adrenergic nerves, including all postganglionic sympathetic nerves except those to sweat glands and certain vascular beds.)

Stimulants	*Depressants*
(Sympathomimetic drugs)	Dibenamine
Epinephrine (Adrenalin)	Dibenzyline
Levarterenol (Norepinephrine)	Ergot alkaloids
Ephedrine	Ergotamine
Amphetamine (Benzedrine)	Ergotoxine
Related synthetic drugs	Dihydroergotamine
Phenylephrine (Neo-synephrine)	Dihydroergocornine
Hydroxyamphetamine (Paredrine)	Dihydroergocristine
Methoxamine (Vasoxyl)	Dihydroergokryptine
Phenylpropanolamine (Propadrine)	Tolazoline (Priscoline)
Methamphetamine (Desoxyephedrine;	Phentolamine (Regitine)
Methedrine)	Benzodioxanes
Isoproterenol (Isuprel)	Piperoxan (Benodaine)
Methoxyphenamine (Orthoxine)	Prosympal
Naphazoline (Privine)	Yohimbine
Cyclopentamine (Clopane)	Azapentine
Methylhexaneamine (Forthane)	
Tuaminoheptane (Tuamine)	
Phenylpropylmethylamine (Vonedrine)	
Cocaine	

From a strictly anatomic point of view it may be said to include the optic chiasm, neurohypophysis, infundibulum, pars supraoptica, tuber cinereum, and mammillary bodies, but from a physiologic point of view the first three structures are not included. The *pars supraoptica* is situated just above the optic chiasm. The *mammillary bodies* are a pair of small spheric masses of gray matter situated close together in the interpeduncular space rostral to the posterior perforated substance; they form the caudal portion of the hypothalamus. The *tuber cinereum* is an elevated gray area rostral to the mammillary bodies; it forms the rostral part of the hypothalamus. From the under surface of the hypothalamus a hollow, conical process, the *infundibulum,* projects downward and forward and is attached to the posterior lobe of the hypophysis as the stalk of the pituitary gland.

The boundaries of the hypothalamus are not very sharply defined. Anteriorly it passes without specific demarcation into the basal olfactory and preoptic areas, and caudally it is continuous with and merges into the central gray matter and

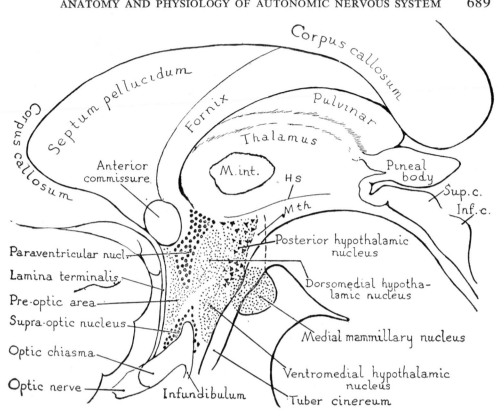

FIG. 258.   Ventricular surface of human diencephalon, showing some of the peripheral nuclear groups of hypothalamus. Symbols used: *Hs,* hypothalamic sulcus; *Inf. c.,* inferior colliculus; *Mth.,* mammillothalamic tract; *Sup. c.,* superior colliculus; *M. int.,* massa intermedia. (Strong, O. S., and Elwyn, A.: Human Neuroanatomy. Baltimore, Williams & Wilkins Company, 1948).

tegmentum of the midbrain. Laterally it is directly continuous with the subthalamic region, but above it is separated from the thalamus proper by the hypothalamic sulcus. The region immediately above and anterior to the optic chiasm and extending to the lamina terminalis and anterior commissure is known as the preoptic area; although this belongs to the endbrain, it is usually considered with the hypothalamic centers. If it is included, one can say that the hypothalamus lies just above and anterior to the optic chiasm, sella turcica, and hypophysis, and between the optic tracts. It extends from the optic chiasm and the lamina terminalis, which marks its boundary from the forebrain, to the caudal tip of the mammillary bodies. The entire area measures only about fourteen by eighteen by twenty millimeters and weighs only four grams.

The hypothalamus is composed of numerous nerve cells which are not uniformly distributed but are arranged into more or less definite nuclear groups (Fig. 259). The entire nerve-complex has been divided into six regions or nuclear groups, which are subdivided as follows: 1. *The preoptic region* lies above and anterior to

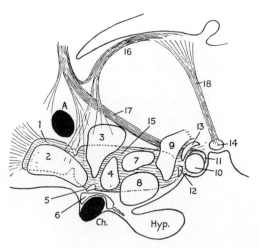

FIG. 259.   The relative position in the sagittal plane of hypothalamic nuclei of a typical mammalian brain, together with their relations to fornix, stria habenularis, and fasciculus retroflexus. Symbols used: *A*, anterior commissure; *Ch.*, optic chiasm; *Hyp.*, hypophysis; *1*, lateral preoptic area (permeated by medial forebrain bundle); *2*, medial preoptic area; *3*, paraventricular nucleus; *4*, anterior hypothalamic area; *5*, suprachiasmatic nucleus; *6*, supraoptic nucleus; *7*, dorsomedial hypothalamic nucleus; *8*, ventromedial hypothalamic nucleus; *9*, posterior hypothalamic area; *10*, medial mammillary nucleus; *11*, lateral mammillary nucleus; *12*, premammillary area; *13*, supramammillary area; *14*, interpeduncular nucleus (a mesencephalic element in which fasciculus retroflexus terminates); *15*, lateral hypothalamic area (permeated by medial forebrain bundle); *16*, stria habenularis; *17*, fornix; *18*, fasciculus retroflexus of Meynert (habenulopeduncular tract). (LeGros Clark, W. E., Beattie, J., Riddoch, G., and Dott, N. M.; The Hypothalamus. London, Oliver and Boyd, Ltd., 1938.)

the optic chiasm and below the anterior commissure. It contains the *medial* and *lateral preoptic areas*. 2. *The anterior group,* or *rostral* or *supraoptic middle region,* lies above the optic chiasm and is continuous anteriorly with the preoptic region. It contains two principal cellular masses. The *supraoptic nucleus* lies immediately above the optic chiasm at the anterior aspect of the optic tract. The *paraventricular nucleus* is a flat plate of cells lying against the ependymal lining of the third ventricle and between the wall of the third ventricle and the column of the fornix; it is situated above the supraoptic nucleus. Other groups of cells in the region are the *nucleus suprachiasmaticus,* the *nucleus supraopticus diffusus,* and the *anterior hypothalamic area*. 3. *The middle group,* or *tuberal* or *infundibular middle region,* occupies the middle portion of the tuber cinereum. It is made up of the *dorsomedial hypothalamic nucleus,* the *ventromedial hypothalamic nucleus,* the *dorsal hypothalamic area,* the *posterior hypothalamic area,* and the *perifornical area*. 4. *The lateral group,* or *region,* occupies the lateral part of the tuber cinereum and includes both the *lateral hypothalamic area* and the *nuclei tuberis laterales*. 5. *The posterior group,* or *caudal* or *mammillary region,* includes the *premammillary area,* the *supra-*

mammilary area, and the *mammilary bodies,* containing the *medial* and *lateral mammillary nuclei* and the *nucleus intercalatus.* The *posterior hypothalamic area* is sometimes placed in this region. 6. *The periventricular region* contains many cellular masses which form the substantia grisea centralis. Included in this area are the *nucleus periventricularis preopticus* and the *nucleus periventricularis arcuatus.*

In spite of its small size, the hypothalamus has extensive and complex fiber connections, some organized into definite bundles or tracts, others diffuse and difficult to trace. There are elaborate intradiencephalic communications. The hypothalamus receives fibers from the secondary olfactory and general sensory tracts, hippocampal and temporal lobe cortex, amygdala, limbic system, basal ganglia, subthalamic-nucleus, thalamus, midbrain reticular formation, and from the frontal cortex either directly or indirectly through the thalamic nuclei. It sends fibers to the anterior thalamic nuclei, posterior lobe of the hypophysis, tegmental nuclei and reticular formation of the midbrain and brain stem, and by means of descending pathways communicates directly or indirectly with the preganglionic autonomic centers of the brain stem and spinal cord. In the midbrain these descending pathways occupy both the central and tegmental portions. In the pons they are concentrated in the tegmental area. In the medulla they are chiefly in the lateral portion of the reticular formation. The descending lateral tectotegmentospinal tract which carries pupillo-dilator fibers and the lateral reticulospinal pathway to the sweat glands of the face are near the periphery; the ventral reticulospinal pathway which innervates the sweat glands and controls vasodilatation and temperature regulation of the body and extremities is more medial. Within the spinal cord the descending autonomic fibers are in the anterolateral fasciculus. They may be widely distributed but are largely in the reticulospinal tracts, chiefly uncrossed but also crossed, with decussation occurring both in the brain stem and at spinal cord levels. Some, especially those subserving bladder control, are in close relation to the pyramidal tracts. Impulses carried through these pathways terminate at appropriate levels in the intermediolateral column of the spinal cord.

The hypothalamus is concerned primarily with the reception of the visceral, or interoceptive, impulses and their correlation and discharge to appropriate visceral efferent centers. It is the region in the brain in which highly organized visceral functions are integrated, and from which the outflow to the respective organs has its origin. It is important in the regulation of the peripheral autonomic nervous system and the various functions necessary for the maintenance of a constant internal environment of the body. This is done largely by means of reflex phenomena which are mediated by the hypothalamus and descend through crossed and uncrossed pathways into the brain stem and spinal cord to activate the cells of the parasympathetic and sympathetic divisions at appropriate levels. The hypothalamus is closely related anatomically and functionally to the hypophysis. These two structures are interdependent; while the latter may have some trophic influence over the former, it is also dependent on it, and intact vascular and/or neural connections between the two are essential for a steady output of corticotropin. Consequently the hypothalamus plays an important in the central regulation of the endocrine glands, including the thyroid, pancreas, adrenals, and gonads. In general it can be stated that all important visceral functions, most of which were once thought to be primarily related to the endocrine system, are under the control of the hypothalamus. These include body temperature regulation, basal metabolism, water and glucose metabolism, fat metabolism, circulation and cardio-vascular regulation including blood pressure adjustment, control of respiration, regulation of bladder functions, influence over sexual activity, and endocrine correlation in general. It has been stated that the hypothalamus is the seat of the emotions; it is probably, however, the motor center for emotional expression, and one of the stations concerned with emotional balance. Primitive pseudo-affective reactions take place when it is released from higher control. It is also important in the control of the sleep cycle, probably through its effect on the cerebral cortex.

Localization of the function within the hypothalamus is not entirely known, experimental work has given some conflicting information. This is easy to understand when one recalls that the entire area weighs only four grams out of a total brain weight of perhaps twelve hundred grams. Much of our knowledge regarding hypothalamic function has been obtained, however, from experimental neurology and neurophysiology. A large accumulation of information has been gathered on the basis of electrical and chemical stimulation of the hypothalamus, while additional data have been obtained from clinical observations of patients with lesions in the hypothalamic area. Definite functions have been attributed to certain regions or nuclear masses as a result of information obtained from either stimulation or destruction. There seems to be a fairly specific topographic orientation for the two divisions of the autonomic nervous system.

The posterior and lateral hypothalamic nuclei (and the ventromedial nucleus) seem to be concerned primarily with sympathoadrenal stimulation and the regulation of sympathetic outflow and vasomotor control. Stimulation of these areas results in an increase of heart rate, decrease in the caliber of the blood vessels, rise in blood pressure, dilatation of the pupils, erection of hair, and increase in rate and amplitude of respirations, with inhibition of secretion and movements of the intestine and bladder. This causes heightened metabolic and somatic activities characteristic of states of emotional stress, combat, or flight. The nuclei of the posterior hypothalamus are also responsible for the massive reaction of "sham rage" which occurs in animals when this region has been released from higher control. Destruction of the posterior nuclei of the hypothalamus and the mammillary bodies produces emotional lethargy, abnormal sleepiness, a reduction in heart rate, and a fall in body temperature and metabolism, owing to reduction of general visceral and somatic activities.

The nuclei of the anterior and medial hypothalamic regions, comprising the anterior and midline hypothalamic nuclei and the tuber cinereum, seem to be concerned with the control of parasympathetic activity. Stimulation of these areas results in increased vagal and sacral autonomic activity with reduction in heart rate, vasodilatation, increased salivation and lacrimation, increased motility and tonus of the intestinal and bladder walls, and increased gastric secretion. Lesions of this region may cause severe gastric disturbances with atony and hemorrhagic erosions of the mucosa of the stomach and intestines.

The relationship of the various nuclear masses to regulation of metabolic functions is clinically important. The supraoptic nuclei are concerned with water metabolism, and destruction of them or of the supraopticohypophysial tract is followed by diabetes insipidus; there is associated degeneration of the nuclei of the posterior lobe of the hypophysis and the nerves in the pituitary stalk. Destruction of the tuber region causes disturbances in carbohydrate and fat metabolism with hyperglycemia and the adiposogenital syndrome. Ablation of the paraventricular nuclei causes hypoglycemia and abnormal sensitivity to insulin. Hyperthermia may result from involvement of the rostral part of the anterior hypothalamic nuclei; this is associated with mechanisms for heat loss, including sweating, vasodilatation, and panting. Hypothermia may follow involvement of the posterior nuclei; this is associated with mechanisms for heat production and conservation, including vasoconstriction, increased visceral and somatic activity, and shivering. Disturbances in sleep regulation and hypersomnia may occur secondary to involvement of the posterior hypothalamic nuclei and mammillary bodies. The medial hypothalamus governs satiety and the lateral portions are responsible for appetite; lesions of the former lead to obesity, and of the latter, failure to eat.

Cells have been described in the supraoptic and paraventricular nuclei which are larger than the other hypothalamic nuclei and have a richer vascular supply. These contain and elaborate a substance which has been called neurosecretory material. There is still controversy about whether portions of the hypothalamus secrete a "neurohormone," and are part of the endocrine system, or whether its influence on the endocrine system is entirely a neural one. It does, however, have a close interrelationship with both the anterior and posterior lobes of the pituitary gland. It stimulates and controls the release of corticotropin, gonadotropins, prolactin, somatotropin, and thyrotropin by the adenohypophysis (anterior lobe), and vasopressin (including antidiuretic hormone) and oxytocin by the neurohypophysis (posterior lobe and infundibulum).

THE CORTEX

The hypothalamus receives communications, either directly or indirectly, from various portions of the cerebral cortex, and experimental and clinical evidence shows that these areas comprise a suprasegmental level for the integration of autonomic functions and the maintenance of a constant internal environment for the body. The term "visceral brain" has been applied to the limbic system. The limbic lobe, or gyrus fornicatus, is composed of the cingulate gyrus, isthmus, hippocampal gyrus, and uncus, but closely related are the subcallosal and retrosplenial gyri, pyriform area, hippocampus, and various subcortical structures including the amyglada and septal nuclei. The insula, medial portion of the temporal lobe, and medial and posterior orbital gyri are also closely allied, although not actually a part of the limbic system. The hypothalamus receives discharges from all these structures, as well as from certain frontal and temporal lobe areas.

Apparently there are no separate cortical centers for parasympathetic and sympathetic control, but the character of the reaction that follows either stimulation or destruction of these areas is dependent upon the general physiologic state of the organism. It has been stated, however, that the orbital gyri may be related to vagal function, whereas various portions on the limbic system may be more closely related to sympathetic function. There is an extensive overlapping between autonomic and somatic motor representation, and the topographic relation between the cortical areas which influence specific autonomic functions and those which regulate corresponding somatic functions is a close one, with interrelations between the two systems. Thus, lacrimation is observed in stimulation of the eye fields and salivation on stimulation of the motor representation of the face and tongue. Pupillary dilation follows stimulation of area $8\alpha\beta\gamma$, and constriction occurs after stimulation of area 19. There is probably correlation between somatic and vegetative functions in both the motor and sensory fields, with the hypothalamus, in part at least, under the control of the cortex.

Experimental investigations indicate that a large variety of autonomic functions are influenced by the cerebral cortex. These are shown more easily by stimulation than by ablation. In addition to lacrimation and salivation, sweating, piloerection, and alterations in cardiovascular, respiratory, gastrointestinal, vesical, and other functions may be demonstrated. The activities of these various systems are partially controlled by the cortex, which acts as a basis for conditioned and visceral reflexes. Subcortical section of the frontal lobes has been shown to interfere with the inhibitory and excitatory autonomic centers in the cortex, and to result in overaction of the autonomic nervous system to direct stimulation.

Some of the more important functions influenced by the cortex are as follows: Gastrointestinal representation is probably largely in the medial aspect of the frontal lobe and in the limbic system. Stimulation results in increased tone and peristalsis of the stomach and intestines, and increased secretion of digestive ferments. Ablation is followed by decrease in motility, which may lead to stasis and intussusception and often to the development of morbid hunger. Olfactory and gustatory hallucinations, smacking or licking of the lips, tasting and swallowing movements, and epigastric sensations follow irritation of the medial aspect of the temporal lobe and the hippocampus and amyglada. Centers regulating both voluntary and autonomic control of the bladder are probably situated in the region of the paracentral lobule and just anterior to it and extend medially and inferiorally into the anterior portion of the cingulate gyrus. Here there is a complicated neurologic mechanism involving somatically innervated sphincters and an autonomically innervated viscus. Stimulation of this area is followed by contraction of the bladder. A lesion of one paracentral lobule brings about transient loss of bladder control, and bilateral lesions are followed by severe disturbances of vesical function. Among the other autonomic phenomena that may be influenced by these various cortical systems are included the following: cardiovascular control, including regulation of blood pressure and heart rate; respiratory rate and rhythm; appetite; vasomotor and temperature regulation. Abnormal affective and emotional responses, fear, and aggressive behavior may be lessened by interrupting the connections between these cortical areas and the thalamus and hypothalamus (Chapter 50).

The anatomic pathways responsible for these reactions are not known. For the most part, perhaps, the impulses are relayed to the hypothalamus, either directly or indirectly through the thalamus, but there may also be projection pathways to the autonomic centers in the brain stem and spinal cord which travel in the lateral columns in close relationship with the pyramidal pathways. The sensory portions of the cerebral cortex play a part in relaying impulses to the motor areas; it is well known that visual, auditory, and other stimuli that call forth emotional responses may cause variations in autonomic activity with changes in circulatory and respiratory function, bladder disturbances, either sweating or anhidrosis, and pupillary dilatation. Although intellectual functions are under the control of the neopallium, affective behavior is under the influence of the limbic system and its connections, and emotional expression is dependent upon the integrating function of this latter portion of the cortex and the hypothalamus. Affective reactions, however, may produce responses of both the autonomic and somatic nervous systems, probably through integration between autonomic centers in the cortex and hypothalamus and motor centers, largely extrapyramidal, in the cortex and basal ganglia.

THE MIDBRAIN AND BRAIN STEM

The autonomic nuclear centers of the oculomotor, facial, glossopharyngeal, and vagus nerves, which are situated in the midbrain and brain stem, have already been mentioned in the discussion of the peripheral autonomic nervous system. There are, however, other autonomic centers, principally of a reflex nature and probably under the influence of the hypothalamus, which are situated in these areas of the nervous system. The most important are as follows: a vasomotor center that exerts an influence in vasodilatation and vasoconstriction and consequently on blood pressure regulation; a center regulating heart rate; and a respiratory reflex center. These are probably situated in the reticular formation of the medulla near the floor of the fourth ventricle and in close association with the dorsal efferent nucleus of the vagus nerve. Inhibitory and facilitatory centers in the midbrain and medulla may enhance inhibitory and facilitatory functions of the hypothalamus. Pressure on the medulla may cause serious disturbances in respiration, heart rate, and blood pressure. Bernard was able to produce glycosuria by a puncture of the floor of the fourth ventricle, but this probably resulted from damage to the descending hypothalamic pathways. Other subsidiary reflex centers influencing pupillary size, gustatory responses, sudomotor activity, piloerection, gastrointestinal function, micturition, and bladder tone may also be located in the brain stem. The descending autonomic pathways in the brain stem and spinal cord and have been discussed.

REFERENCES

ANDREW, J., and NATHAN, P.   Lesions of the anterior frontal lobes and disturbances of micturition and defaecation.   *Brain* 87:233, 1964.

BARD, P.   A diencephalic mechanism for the expression of rage, with special reference to the sympathetic nervous system.   *Am. J. Physiol.* 84:490, 1928.

CANNON, W. B.   Bodily Changes in Pain, Hunger, Fear and Rage (ed. 1).   New York, D. Appleton and Company, 1915.

CROSBY, E. C., and WOODBURNE, R. T.   The comparative anatomy of the preoptic area and the hypothalamus.   *A. Res. Nerv. & Ment. Dis., Proc.* (1939) 20:52, 1940.

DENNY-BROWN, D., and ROBERTSON, E. G. On the physiology of micturition. *Brain* 56:149, 1933.

FIELDS, W. S., GUILLEMIN, R., and CARTON, C. A. (eds.) Hypothalamic-Hypophysial Interrelationships. Springfield, Ill., Charles C Thomas, 1956.

GELLORN, E. Autonomic Regulations: Their Significance for Physiology, Psychology and Neuropsychiatry. New York, Interscience Publishers, Inc., 1943.

GILLILAN, L. A. Clinical Aspects of the Autonomic Nervous System. Boston, Little, Brown and Company, 1954.

GOODMAN, L., and GILMAN, A. The Pharmacological Basis of Therapeutics (ed. 2). New York, The Macmillan Company, 1955.

HARRIS, G. W. Pituitary-hypothalamic mechanisms. *A.M.A. Arch. Neurol. & Psychiat.* 73:124, 1955.

HESS, W. R. Diencephalon: Autonomic and Extrapyramidal Functions. New York, Grune & Stratton, Inc., 1954.

INGRAM, W. R. Nuclear organization and chief connections of the primate hypothalamus. *A. Res. Nerv. & Ment. Dis., Proc.* (1939) 20:195, 1940.

KENNARD, M. A. Focal autonomic representation in the cortex and its relation to sham rage. *J. Neuropath. & Exper. Neurol.* 4:295, 1945.

KUHLENBECK, H. The Human Diencephalon: A Summary of Development, Structure, Function, and Pathology. *Confinia neurol.* Supp. Vol. 14, 1954.

KUNTZ, A. The Autonomic Nervous System (ed. 4). Philadelphia, Lea & Febiger, 1953.

KURU, M. Nervous control of micturition. *Physiol. Rev.* 45:425, 1965.

LANGLEY, J. N. The autonomic nervous system. *Brain* 26:1, 1903.

LANGWORTHY, O. R. General principles of autonomic innervation. *Arch. Neurol. & Psyshiat.* 50:590, 1943.

LEGROS CLARK, W. E., BEATTIE, J., RIDDOCH, G., and DOTT, N. W. The Hypothalamus, London, Oliver and Boyd, 1938.

LIVINGSTON, W. K. Pain Mechanisms: A Physiologic Interpretation of Causalgia and Its Related States. New York, The Macmillan Company, 1943.

LOEWI, O. Uber humorale Übertragbarkeit der Herznervenwirkung. *Arch. f. d. ges. Physiol.* 189:239, 1921.

MacLEAN, P. D. The limbic system and its hippocampal formation. *J. Neurosurg.* 11:29, 1954.

MAGOUN, H. W. Descending connections from the hypothalamus. *A. Res. Nerv. & Ment. Dis., Proc.* (1939) 20:270, 1940.

MILLER, H. R. Central Autonomic Regulations in Health and Disease, with Special Reference to the Hypothalamus. New York, Grune and Stratton, Inc., 1942.

MYERSON, A. Human autonomic pharmacology: XII. Theories and results of autonomic drug administration. *J.A.M.A.* 110:101, 1938.

NATHAN, P. W., and SMITH, M. C. Spinal pathways subserving defaecation and sensation from the lower bowel. *J. Neurol., Neurosurg. & Psychiat.* 16:245, 1953; The centrifugal pathway for micturition within the spinal cord. *Ibid.* 21:177, 1958.

PALUMBO, L. T. Management of Disorders of the Autonomic Nervous System. Chicago, The Year Book Publishers, Inc., 1955.

REICHLIN, S. Neuroendocrinology. *New England J. Med.* 269:1182, 1246, 1296, 1953.

RANSOM, S. W. Some Functions of the Hypathalamus. Baltimore, Williams and Wilkins Company, 1937.

RAY, B. S.   Observations on structure and function of the sympathetic nervous system. *Univ. Michigan Med. Bull.* 21:1, 1955.

RIOCH, D. M., WISLOCKI, G. B., and O'LEARY, J. L.   A précis of preoptic, hypothalamic and hypophysial terminology with atlas.   *A. Res. Nerv. & Ment. Dis., Proc.* (1939) 20:3, 1940.

SELYE, H.   The Stress of Life.   New York, McGraw-Hill Book Company, Inc., 1956.

WHITE, J. C., SMITHWICK, R. H., and SIMEONE, F. A.   The Autonomic Nervous System: Anatomy, Physiology, and Surgical Application (ed. 3).   New York, The Macmillan Company, 1952.

CHAPTER 42

EXAMINATION OF
THE AUTONOMIC
NERVOUS SYSTEM

THE EXAMINATION of the autonomic nervous system gives important information in neurologic disease. Certain of the procedures used are routine ones and should be carried out in every neurologic appraisal, but others are considered special tests which are used only under certain circumstances. The examiner should be familiar with all of the important methods of evaluation of the autonomic nervous system, however, because evidences of dysfunction of this portion of the neurologic complex may be important clues in the diagnosis and localization of disease of the nervous system.

THE GENERAL OBSERVATION OF THE PATIENT

Valuable information about the functional status of the autonomic nervous system may be obtained from the general observation of the patient (Chapter 3). The physique and habitus, body build, state of nutrition, deformities, and abnormalities of configuration are important criteria. The aspects of the physical examination to which special emphasis should be paid are listed.

The Endocrine Status: Evidences of endocrine imbalance, such as dwarfism, giantism, acromegaly, cretinism, and other signs of dysfunction of the pituitary, pineal, thyroid, suprarenal, and sexual glands may be related to disease of the autonomic nervous system. The degree of physical development, including sexual maturity and evidences of senescence, is also important, as well as the estimation of the so-called androgynic index.

The Regulation of Vital Processes: The body temperature as well as the temperature of the extremities and of isolated portions of the body should be noted; there may be either generalized or local changes in temperature regulation and

698

heat production. One should also observe the blood pressure in both arms with the patient recumbent, seated, and standing; the pulse rate and regularity; the respiratory rate and rhythm. Either vertigo or faintness with changes of position may be significant.

The Skin and Mucous Membranes: Important evidences of autonomic dysfunction may be seen in the skin and mucous membranes. If there are changes in color, such as pallor, erythema, flushing, or cyanosis, the examiner should note whether they are localized, limited to the extremities, or generalized. Color changes with alteration of position may be valuable diagnostic criteria. Important variations in texture, consistency, and appearance of the skin include glossiness, hardness, thickening, wasting, scaling, seborrhea, looseness or tightness, oiliness, and moisture or dryness. Urticaria, either generalized or localized edema, angioneurotic edema, hemiedema, trophedema, myxedema, dermatographia, herpetic lesions, vesicles, bullae, perforating ulcers, and decubiti should be noted.

Perspiration: Disease of the autonomic nervous system may be characterized by any of the following: excessive perspiration, decreased perspiration, anhidrosis, and localized changes in sweating.

The Hair and Nails: Hypertrichosis, hypotrichosis, abnormal distribution of hair, localized loss of hair (alopecia), abnormal brittleness, color change, and either localized or premature graying of the hair may be significant. Important abnormalities of the nails include brittleness, striations, fissuring, and cyanosis.

The Extremities: Examination of the extremities is very important in the appraisal of the autonomic nervous system. One should note the development, color, and temperature of the extremities as a whole, the character and pulsation of the arteries, and the influence of changes in position. By these criteria conditions such as erythromelalgia, acrocyanosis, Raynaud's syndrome, and Buerger's disease may be diagnosed.

Salivation and Lacrimation: The secretory responses of the salivary and lacrimal glands to physical and psychic stimulation may give information about autonomic nervous system dysfunction.

Fat Metabolism: Obesity, wasting, lipodystrophy, and adiposis dolorosa are seen in autonomic dysfunction. The localization of wasting and the bodily distribution of the adipose tissue should be noted. Other metabolic disorders must be evaluated by special tests to be described below.

The Bones and Joints: Changes in bone structure and development and arthropathies of various types may result from diseases of the autonomic nervous system.

Evidences of Localized Autonomic Nervous System Involvement: The presence of specific and focal changes, such as Horner's syndrome, gives evidence of focal alteration in the autonomic nervous system.

AUTONOMIC NERVOUS SYSTEM REFLEXES

Many reflexes which are important to the neurologic examination are essentially autonomic nervous system responses. Some of these may be classified as mucous membrane and orificial reflexes, others as true visceral reflexes; all, however, are smooth muscle and glandular responses. Accordingly the reaction is a slower one than that which takes place in striated muscle reflexes. In many instances, however, the smooth muscle response is accompanied by contraction of striated muscle.

The autonomic nervous system reflexes that are functions of various cranial nerves are discussed with the individual nerves ("The Cranial Nerves," Part III). Among these are included the *pupillary, lacrimal, salivary, palatal, pharyngeal, sneeze, sucking, cough, swallowing, vomiting, carotid sinus,* and *oculocardiac reflexes.* In many of these responses other portions of the autonomic nervous system than those innervated by the cranial nerves take part, but the visceral components of the individual nerves play a major function.

There are other reflex responses, largely of autonomic nervous system origin, which should be elicited in the neurologic examination. The most important of these are listed.

The Subcostogastric, or Cutaneogastric, Reflex: Gentle stroking of the skin over the left costal margin is followed by contraction of the gastric musculature. This response may be observed by either palpation or auscultation over the stomach. The reflex is not reliable unless three or four hours have elapsed since the last meal.

The Rectal, or Defecation, Reflex: Either distension of the rectum or stimulation of the rectal mucosa is followed by contraction of the rectal musculature. This reflex is innervated principally by the sacral autonomic fibers (second, third, and fourth sacral segments); it is evaluated in colonmetrography.

The Anal Sphincter Reflex: Contraction of the internal sphincter of the anus may be observed on introduction of the gloved finger into the anus. This reflex is supplied by postganglionic fibers of the sympathetic division through the hypogastric plexus (presacral nerves). If it is lost, the anus does not close immediately after stimulation. The internal anal sphincter reflex should be differentiated from the superficial anal reflex.

The Vesical Reflex: Either distension of the bladder or stimulation of the bladder mucosa is followed by contraction of the detrusor muscle with relaxation of the trigone and internal sphincter. This reflex is supplied largely by the sacral autonomic fibers (second through fourth sacral). The various responses to bladder stimulation and distension are discussed under the subject of cystometry.

The Urethral Sphincter Reflex: This consists of the gripping of a sound as it is introduced into the urethra.

The Scrotal Reflex: Application of a cold object to the scrotum, perineum, or inner thigh or trunk is followed by a slow, vermicular contraction of the dartos musculature. The same response may follow stroking of the skin of the perineum or pricking the perineal region with a pin. The contraction of the dartos does not cause elevation of the testicle, and this reflex should not be confused with the cremasteric reflex.

The Bulbocavernosus Reflex: Stroking, pricking, or pinching the dorsum of the glans penis is followed by contraction of the bulbocavernosus muscle and the constrictor urethrae, which may be palpated when a finger is placed on the perineum behind the scrotum with pressure on either the bulbous or membranous portion of the urethra. There is also a contraction of the external anal sphincter, which may be felt if a gloved finger is placed in the anus. This reflex is supplied by the third and fourth sacral nerves.

The Genital, Sex, Ejaculatory, or Coital Reflex: Stimulation from either the cerebrum or the periphery may be followed by erection of the penis and sometimes by ejaculation. Erection is a function of the sacral autonomic division and is supplied by the second through the fourth sacral nerves, whereas ejaculation is in part a function of the thoracicolumbar autonomic division and is supplied principally by the lumbar nerves. A pathologic exaggeration of this response is seen as a part of the mass reflex, and a spinal defense reflex accompanied by priapism and occasionally by ejaculation may follow stimulation of either the glans penis or the skin of the penis.

The Mass Reflex: This is a variation of the spinal defense reflex and consists of dorsiflexion of the toes and feet and flexion of the knees and hips with, in addition, involuntary micturition and defecation and sweating and vasomotor changes to the level of the lesion. There may be priapism and ejaculation.

Emotional Reflexes: Laughter consists of a deep inspiration followed by a series of short, jerky expirations which may be accompanied by laryngeal sounds. *Weeping* is an analogous phenomenon, accompanied by sobs and usually by lacrimation. Lacrimation may occasionally accompany laughter. Both are elicited by cortical stimuli and by emotions. Laughing may appear as a response to tickling, and weeping as a response to pain. Precipitate, unmotivated, or excessive laughter or weeping may occur in the presence of cerebral lesions which involve either the frontal lobes or the thalamus; this phenomenon is seen principally in the syndrome of pseudbulbar palsy.

Sweating, the pilomotor response, the vasomotor response, and reflex erythema may all be considered reflex phenomena involving a reaction to stimulation of sudorific glands, smooth muscle, or blood vessels. The mode of eliciting these responses is, however, somewhat more complex than that used in testing the simple reflexes, and consequently they are herein considered as individual tests of autonomic function.

SPECIAL TESTS OF AUTONOMIC FUNCTION

In addition to the general observation of the patient and the eliciting of the autonomic nervous system reflexes, there are many special tests and examinations which may have importance in the evaluation of the autonomic nervous system. These are not carried out in every neurologic examination, but the examiner should be familiar with them, for in many instances they are essential to the diagnosis of specific lesions of the individual portions of the autonomic nervous system. Some of the more valuable tests are listed.

SWEATING TESTS

These are important objective tests of autonomic function. The production of sweating, or perspiration, is a function of the sympathetic division of the autonomic nervous system. The efferent neurons are situated in the intermediolateral columns of the thoracic and lumbar portions of the spinal cord; the preganglionic fibers go to the sympathetic chain ganglia, and the postganglionic fibers are carried by the peripheral nerves to the sweat glands. Paradoxically, however, these postganglionic sympathetic nerves are cholinergic rather than adrenergic. Sweating is produced by drugs such as acetylcholine and pilocarpine, which are classed as parasympathomimetic, and is abolished by atropine, scopolamine, and other drugs that inhibit structures innervated by postganglionic cholinergic nerves.

The sweating test is easy to carry out, and the results may be observed over the surface of the entire body. The chronologic appearance of perspiration and quantitative differences may be noted, and photographs may be made at any stage of sweat development. Various methods of color determination of sweating include the following: iodine in oil is painted on the skin and the painted areas are dusted with starch powder, which turns bluish black in the presence of iodine and moisture; the skin is painted with a solution of ferric chloride and then dusted with tannic acid powder, which turn black in the presence of iron and moisture; a saturated alcoholic solution of cobalt chloride, which turns pink when moist, is painted on the skin, or cobalt blue papers are applied to it; absorbent paper impregnated with silver nitrate and potassium chromate are applied to the skin, and the chloride in the sweat reacts with the silver nitrate to form silver chloride; the skin is dusted with quinizarin compound (1, 4-dihydroxyanthraquinone 2, 6-disulfonic acid), which is grayish violet when dry, but becomes a deep purple when moistened. The moisture on the skin may also be evaluated by palpation or measured with a hygrometer or sudorometer, and it is often possible to see the droplets of sweat on the skin, especially on the papillary ridges of the fingers, with the use of the plus-20 lens of the ophthalmoscope.

Various diaphoretic procedures may be used. *Thermoregulatory,* or *"heat"* *sweating* is produced by the use of external heat after the ingestion of hot fluids and acetylsalicylic acid. Large electric bakers or cradles are placed over the patient, the open ends covered with woolen blankets, or an electric heat cabinet may be used. The action is a central one, presumably from the stimulation of the thermoregulatory sweating centers in the hypothalamus, and perspiration is called forth over the entire body (Fig. 260). Since the impulses are carried to the sweat glands via the thoracicolumbar sympathetic fibers and thence via the peripheral nerves, this test is particularly valuable in examining lesions of either of these. *Emotional sweating* is also produced centrally and corresponds to the spontaneous hyperhidrosis of normal and psychoneurotic persons. It may be elicited by emotional stimuli, intellectual strain, or painful cutaneous sensation. Emotional sweating varies in distribution from thermoregulatory sweating, is more localized, and is characterized by more individual variation in response. *Drug sweating* is produced by the subcutaneous injection of twelve to sixteen milligrams of pilocarpine hydrochloride or twelve to twenty-five milligrams of Mecholyl (acetylbetamethylcholine hydrochloride). These drugs act peripherally, stimulating the glands innervated by postganglionic cholinergic fibers. The response to them is more variable than that to heat, and the resulting perspiration may be irregular

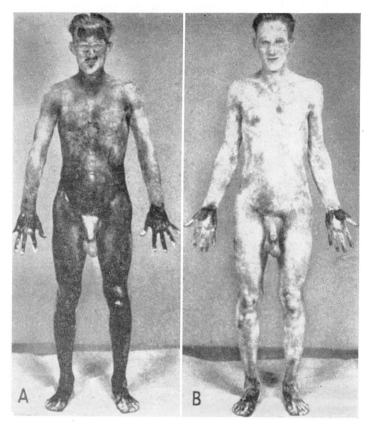

FIG. 260. Areas of sweating in a normal person: *A,* thermoregulatory sweating; *B,* spantaneous ("emotional") sweating. (List, C. F., and Peet, M. M.: *Arch. Neurol. & Psychiat.* 39:1228, 1938.)

and spotty. The reaction may be facilitated by loosely covering the part of the body to be tested with a blanket to inhibit excessive evaporation and loss of body heat. There is an individual variation in the sweating response to drugs. The test is less reliable than the response to heat and has only a limited diagnostic value. *Spinal reflex sweating* is seen only in certain pathologic conditions, such as transverse lesions of the spinal cord, and represents a part of the mass reflex of spinal automatism. It may be elicited by various nociceptive impulses applied below the level of the lesion. *Gustatory sweating* is produced by the introduction of spiced or highly seasoned foods into the mouth. It is valuable only in tests on the face. The response is elicited with difficulty in the normal individual, but is absent in peripheral lesions of the trigeminal nerve. It is exaggerated in certain pathologic conditions, such as the auriculotemporal and chorda tympani syndromes.

The tests for thermoregulatory sweating are the only ones of the above-mentioned procedures that have much application in clinical neurology. They may aid in the diagnosis of intramedullary, partial, and transverse lesions of the spinal cord. A "sweat level," however, is not as accurate as a sensory level in spinal cord localization. They may also give helpful information in the diagnosis of lesions of the lower brain stem, the sympathetic outflow or fiber pathways (Fig. 261), or the peripheral nerves. They may serve as an index of the completeness of nerve section or sympathectomy. Examination of the sweat itself is useful in the diagnosis of cystic fibrosis. An abnormality in the function of the eccrine sweat glands in this disease causes the sweat to contain increased amounts of sodium, chloride, and potassium, and to have increased electrical conductivity.

THE PILOMOTOR RESPONSE

Piloerection is also a function of the sympathetic division of the autonomic nervous system. Stimulation of the sympathetic nerves causes contraction of the arrectores pilorum muscles and erection of the cutaneous hairs, known as cutis anserina or "goose flesh." The response may be elicited with ease, but it is inconstant and transient and cannot be demonstrated adequately in the hands and feet. Piloerection may be provoked by gentle stroking of the skin, tickling, scratching with a pin, faradism, or the application of cold. Ice, cotton soaked in alcohol or

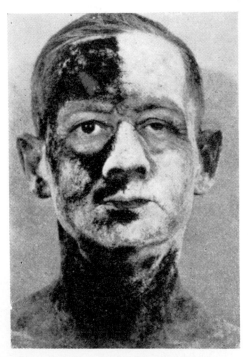

FIG. 261. Changes in sweat secretion in patient with left-sided Horner's syndrome. (List, C. F., and Peet, M. M.: *Arch. Neurol. & Psychiat.* 40:27, 1938.)

ether, or a methyl chloride spray may be used. It is elicited best at the nape of the neck, in the axillae, on the abdominal wall, and at the upper border of the trapezius. The patient should be in a warm room, since cold influences the response. It may be helpful to warm the body before the application of a cold stimulus. It must be borne in mind that emotional stimuli may also provoke piloerection.

The reaction appears slowly, after a latent period of from four to five seconds; it is complete or at its maximum in from seven to ten seconds and lasts from fifteen to twenty seconds. It first occurs at the site of stimulation and then spreads slowly and widely. If a massive stimulus is used, such as chilling the neck with ice, pinching the skin in the cervical region or at the upper border of the trapezius, tickling or scratching the axilla, or applying cold to the axilla or the abdominal wall, there is a descending response which takes about one-half minute to become manifest and lasts for one or two minutes. This is seen best on the trunk and the extensor surfaces of the extremities; symmetrical parts of the body should be observed. If one side of the body is stimulated, the response is ipsilateral, but if the midline is stimulated, it is bilateral.

Piloerection is absent in lesions that involve the descending autonomic pathways in the brain stem and spinal cord, sympathetic trunk, preganglionic and post-ganglionic fibers, and peripheral nerves. It is abolished below transverse spinal lesions, and the descending reaction to a massive stimulus stops at this level. Occasionally, after spinal shock has passed, piloerection is seen as part of the mass reflex of spinal automatism. It must be stated, however, that the pilomotor response has little diagnostic value; it gives only limited and indirect information and is difficult to measure, inconstant, transient, and depends upon a number of factors.

THE VASOMOTOR RESPONSE

This test depends upon the knowledge that vasodilatation causes flushing of the skin and vasoconstriction is followed by pallor. If there is interruption of the sympathetic division of the autonomic system, there is paralysis of vasoconstriction with resulting temporary vasodilatation and flushing. The pallor that follows slight pressure on the skin disappears more quickly in the involved than in the normal areas. The test may be carried out by warming the surface of the body with towels wrung out of very hot water. In transverse spinal lesions there is vasodilatation with flushing, redness, and an increase in skin temperature below the level of the lesion. The vasodilatation will be most marked at the upper level of the vasopara-lytic lesion, and there may be a distinct zone of hyperemia on the skin correspond-ing to the upper limit of the sensory zone of hyperalgesia. The hyperalgesic and hyperemic areas indicate the level of root involvement and the uppermost point of the cord lesion. The warming of the skin may be followed by sudden chilling with application of towels wrung out of ice water; there is a decrease in the vasoconstric-tor response to cold below the level of a spinal lesion.

As is true in the case of the pilomotor response, the vasomotor test depends upon a number of factors and affords only limited and indirect information; it is difficult to evaluate and often is not reliable. More important than the observation of vasodilatation or vasoconstriction, which are not easily measured and may be difficult to interpret, is the quantitative determination of the skin temperature.

REFLEX ERYTHEMA

Stimulation of the skin by stroking it with a blunt point is followed by focal vasodilatation. There is first a local reaction, or the production of a red line along the site of stimulation, which is followed in about one-half minute by a spreading flush, or flare, on each side of the scratch. Depending upon the intensity of the stimulus and individual susceptibility, the site of stimulation becomes elevated, with the development of a welt, or wheal, sometimes with a white line in its center. This response is said to be dependent upon the axon reflex and the liberation of histamine, and is similar to that which follows the intradermal injection of histamine (see below). It disappears after interruption of cutaneous nerves and below transverse spinal cord lesions. It has little diagnostic value.

Exaggeration of reflex erythema is called *dermatographia*; this is present whenever the sympathetic influence is diminished. It is marked in individuals with overactivity of the parasympathetic division, the so-called vagotonics (see below), and in those with labile autonomic nervous systems or with evidence of sympathetic and parasympathetic imbalance. Consequently it is often seen to a marked degree in psychoneurotic persons, in those with other evidences of psychosomatic disease, and in schizophrenia. It may also develop on an allergic basis and as a reaction to chemical and thermal stimuli. It has no diagnostic value other than showing evidence of either autonomic imbalance or hypersensitivity. It may be potentiated by histamine and nicotinic acid esters and can often be relieved by antihistamine and vasoconstrictor drugs.

THE HISTAMINE FLARE

The intradermal injection of 0.1 cc. of a 1:1000 solution of histamine phosphate (0.1 mg.) is followed, in the normal person, by the immediate development of focal erythema and pain at the injection site. This is followed by the appearance of a spreading flush, or flare, which reaches its maximum in about ten minutes, and the development of a wheal at the site of injection. The response is noted at one, five, and ten minutes after the injection and should be compared to that of a similar control injection on another part of the body. The reaction is similar to that which is produced by stroking the skin with a blunt point. An intact arteriolar circulation and an intact axon reflex are necessary for the development of the flare. The histamine flare is of value in the diagnosis of peripheral nerve lesions, but the blood supply as well as the nerve supply must be intact. The reaction is absent with complete section of a peripheral nerve and diminshed with partial section. It is decreased or absent below the level of a transverse spinal lesion. In hysterical anesthesia the reaction is present but painless; in malingering it is present and painful. The response is markedly diminished in children with familial dysautonomia.

SKIN TEMPERATURE STUDIES

The determination of the skin temperature has become a very important part of the examination of the autonomic nervous system. The vasomotor tonus is reflected in the surface temperature of the body, and interruption of the sympathetic division with resulting vasodilatation is followed by a rise in temperature, whereas stimulation of the sympathetics with consequent vasoconstriction is accompanied by a fall in temperature. Quantitative skin temperature determinations can be made and are more accurate and more objective than the observation of flushing and pallor. Not only may one evaluate the continuity of the sympathetic pathways by such determinations made in the resting state, but one may obtain valuable additional information by noting the response to peripheral nerve and sympathetic block, spinal and general anesthesia, warming or cooling in different portions of the body, foreign protein injections, and the use of autonomic blocking drugs. Determinations are made with the use of a differential thermocouple, and the temperature of corresponding areas of the body is compared. Slight differences may be measured, but the results are relative and not absolute, and repeated observations may be necessary. Because the skin temperature is influenced by that of the surrounding environment, studies should be carried out in a room of constant temperature and humidity, and the patient should be placed in the room an hour before testing.

A lesion of the sympathetic division, whether it involves the descending pathways, cells in the intermediolateral columns, preganglionic fibers, sympathetic trunk, postganglionic fibers, or peripheral nerves, is followed by temporary vasodilatation, redness, and increase in skin temperature. The temperature of the involved portion of the body is higher than that of the remainder of the body during the resting state, and in addition it rises more rapidly and to a greater extent when either the body as a whole or an indifferent portion of the body is heated, and decreases more slowly and to a lesser extent when either the body as a whole or an indifferent portion of the body is cooled. This state lasts only a short time. When the walls of the vessels regain tone, they again contract, for when denervated they are hypersensitive to the epinephrine which is normally circulating in the blood. The skin of the involved areas becomes cold and pale, and even cyanotic if the circulation stagnates. The cutaneous vessels fail to respond to stimuli from other parts of the body, and either warming or cooling other parts of the body fails to cause flushing, pallor, sweating, piloerection, or changes in skin temperature in the involved area. This is especially marked in the distal portions of the extremities.

Owing to the wider distribution and extensive overlapping of preganglionic fibers, warmth and redness persist longer and vasomotor disturbances are less marked with interruption of preganglionic than of postganglionic fibers. On the other hand, section of the preganglionic fibers gives more permanent relief in conditions characterized by spasm of cutaneous vessels, since after section of the postganglionic fibers the denervated vessels become more sensitive to circulating epinephrine, and they again contract. If only the sensory nerves are divided, flushing, pallor, and temperature changes occur in the anesthetic areas in response to warming or cooling of other parts of the body. In hemiplegia the state of the cutaneous vessels, and consequently the temperature of the skin, may vary. It may be warmer or cooler than normal, usually the latter, in part owing to inactivity or disuse, but the vasomotor responses are unchanged.

Skin temperature studies are valuable in the diagnosis of lesions of the sympathetic division, the determination of the level of a transverse spinal lesion, the delineation of the extent of a peripheral nerve lesion, the preoperative appraisal of the continuity of sympathetic pathways, and the differential diagnosis of Raynaud's and Buerger's diseases, peripheral arteriosclerosis, and other vascular diseases of the extremities. That is, they aid in the differentiation between circulatory disorders characterized by sympathetic overactivity and vasospasm and those characterized by disease of the vessels themselves or of the vessel walls, with organic obstruction and reduction of the size of their lumens. The various modifications of skin temperature evaluations are listed.

1. *The Resting State:* With lesions of the sympathetic division there is temporary vasodilatation and rise in skin temperature, followed by vasoconstriction and fall in temperature in those areas supplied by the nerves or fibers involved. These may be compared with the corresponding normal areas of the body. With transverse lesions of the spinal cord there is a temporary increase followed by a fall in temperature below the level of the lesion. With vascular disease of the extremities, whether the result of vasospasm or of organic obstruction, the skin temperature is lower than in the corresponding normal extremities.

2. *Diagnostic Novocaine Block of Peripheral Nerves or of Sympathetic Ganglia:* Specific peripheral nerves or sympathetic ganglia are injected with novocaine, and temperature studies of the portion of the body innervated by these nerves and ganglia are made before and after injection. Also the temperature of the portion of the body affected by the injection is compared with corresponding intact areas of the body. The injection blocks the vasomotor fibers, and in the normal individual there is a moderate rise in skin temperature in the involved area of the body. If there has been a previous interruption of the continuity of the sympathetics, there will be no change. If the temperature of the area being tested has been below normal or below that of the corresponding normal portion of the body as a result of sympathetic overactivity or vasospasm, it will promptly return to normal. If it has been decreased as a result of obstruction of the lumens of the peripheral vessels, there will be no change. One must bear in mind, however, that in conditions such as Raynaud's disease there may be an element of obstruction, and in Buerger's disease there may be some spasm. Nevertheless, this procedure is important in the differential diagnosis between these conditions, peripheral arteriosclerosis, and other circulatory disturbances. Diagnostic novocaine block is also used as a preoperative test to determine the degree of vasodilatation that will result from surgery.

3. *Spinal and General Anesthesia:* General anesthesia is followed by a generalized rise in surface temperature and spinal anestheasia by a rise in that portion of the body affected by the anesthetic agent, both the result of sympathetic paralysis. In vasospastic disorders there will be a rise in temperature of the involved

limbs, whereas there will be no change if there is organic obstruction of the vessels.

4. *Heating or Cooling of the Body or Its Parts:* The entire body may be warmed by exposure to higher temperatures by the use of external heat or by foreign protein injection (typhoid vaccine), or it may be cooled by exposure to lower temperatures. More frequently, however, portions of the body are heated or cooled. If one wishes to evaluate temperature changes in the feet, the hands may either be warmed by immersing them in warm water or placing them in a heat cabinet, or cooled by immersing them in cold water. If the hands are to be examined, the feet may be either warmed or cooled. The resulting changes are sometimes said to give the "occlusive index." In the normal individual distant portions of the body respond to warming or cooling indifferent portions. In vasospastic conditions one obtains a normal, though sometimes delayed, response in the involved extremities if the temperature of distant portions of the body is changed, whereas in organic circulatory disturbances there is little or no response. With interruption of the sympathetic pathways, except immediately after such interruption, the cutaneous vessels of the involved areas fail to respond to warming or cooling of other portions of the body, but warming or cooling the involved areas is followed by similar temperature changes elsewhere in the body, probably through the medium of the temperature of the blood acting on higher centers.

5. *Autonomic Blocking Agents:* Various chemical blocking agents may be used in the examination of the autonomic nervous system. The determination of the skin temperature before and after the administration of these drugs gives valuable diagnostic information. The application of these chemicals and their interpretation are discussed with the pharmacologic tests.

DETERMINATION OF SKIN RESISTANCE

Section of a peripheral nerve is followed by a great and permanent increase in the resistance of the portion of skin supplied by that nerve to the passage of a minute, imperceptible current, whereas stimulation of a peripheral nerve is followed by a decrease in skin resistance. The autonomic component of the nerve is the important factor in this resistance, since areas deprived of autonomic supply show a greatly increased resistance even though the other components of the peripheral nerves are intact. The change seems to be correlated with the function of the sweat glands, since the resistance is low if the sweat glands are active and is high if they are inactive, and the results compare closely to those obtained in the sweating test. Vasodilatation may also play a part.

Skin resistance is measured by means of the dermometer. Various types of instruments have been used. That described by Richter consists of a microammeter with a range from 0 to 100 microamperes, a four and one-half volt battery, and a 1000 ohm potential divider. Two electrodes are used; one is attached to the ear lobe and the other to the area of skin to be examined. The current from the battery passes from one electrode to the other, completing a circuit through the body of the patient and the microammeter. The potential divider regulates the amount of current that flows from the battery through the patient's body when the potential is fixed, and the amount of current registered on the ammeter depends upon the resistance of the patient's skin. The response may be registered on an oscillograph and photographed. With these instruments one can outline changes in resistance over the surface of the body without the cooperation of the patient. The procedure is a simple one which can be checked by independent observers.

Skin resistance is increased during sleep, physical inactivity, and absence of emotional excitement. It is high over scar tissues and with lesions of the peripheral nerves and the autonomic nervous system. Skin resistance is decreased by local changes such as abrasions and wounds of the skin, irritation of the skin, muscular effort, and emotional excitement. The dermometer has most value in the neurologic appraisal if it is used in the diagnosis of lesions of the peripheral nerves and the autonomic nervous system. The findings may be compared with those of the motor and sensory examinations, and in peripheral nerve lesions the changes in skin resistance correspond closely with motor and sensory alterations.

By the determination of skin resistance one can localize spinal, nerve root, and peripheral nerve lesions. In nerve lesions one can differentiate between partial and complete involvement and detect early signs of regeneration. Hysteria and malingering can be distinguished from organic disease. The dermometer also provides an objective, practical method to study the autonomic nervous system, to determine the sympathetic components of the peripheral nerves, and to demonstrate changes in function of the autonomic system. By its use the continuity of the sympathetic division may be measured quantitatively. Stimulation of the sympathetic division causes a decrease in resistance, whereas sympathetic depression is followed by increased resistance. Sympathetic dermatomes, which compare closely to sensory dermatomes, may be outlined (Fig. 262). The dermometer may also be used to determine the level of a transverse lesion of the spinal cord, and an increase in skin resistance is found below the level of such a lesion. A transection above the first thoracic segment (or above the thoracicolumbar outflow), however, is followed by increased resistance of the entire body, whereas no increase follows a lesion below the second lumbar segment.

Various modifications of the determination of skin resistance have been carried out in neurologic diagnosis. The *galvanic skin reflex* to light cutaneous stimulation may give an objective differentiation between organic and hysterical anesthesias. There is no change in skin resistance of an intact portion of the body when an anesthetic area is stimulated, but a normal reflex is elicited on stimulation of an area of hysterical anesthesia. Skin potentials have been used to demonstrate visceral pain; there is an increase in the potential of the dermatomes that correspond to a painful organ. The dermometer has also been used to investigate emotional reactions. The decrease in the resistance of the skin following psychic stimuli has been called the *psychogalvanic reflex,* and the instrument used for the determination of this, the psychogalvanometer.

Novocaine Block of Peripheral Nerves and Sympathetic Ganglia

Novocaine block of peripheral nerves, nerve roots, and sympathetic ganglia may be used as a preoperative diagnostic test to determine the value of surgical procedures for the relief of causalgia and other painful disorders of autonomic origin.

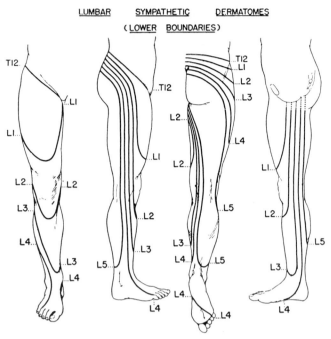

FIG. 262. Four views of lower trunk, thigh, and leg, showing probable boundaries of each of the sympathetic dermatomes from Th 12 to L 5, inclusive, as determined by electrical skin resistance method. (Richter, C. P., and Woodruff, B. G.: *J. Neurophysiol.* 8:323, 1945.)

Novocaine block may also be carried out, in association with skin temperature studies, sweating tests, and dermometry, to determine the continuity of autonomic fibers. It is especially valuable when used with skin temperature studies to detect the amount of vasodilatation that follows interruption of the sympathetic fibers, and aids not only in the differential diagnosis of vascular diseases of the extremities, but also in prognosis.

CAPILLARY MICROSCOPY

By focusing a beam of light on either a fingernail fold or an area of skin on which a drop of cedar oil has been applied, the capillary loops become visible through the lower power objective of the microscope. During vasoconstriction clumps of stagnant erythrocytes can be seen within the capillaries, and during vasodilatation the red blood cells shoot through the vessels so rapidly that they are visible only as a rapid flicker. Furthermore, if there is spasm, changes in the size and shape of the capillary loops may be seen, together with tortuosity and loss of the normal hairpin-shaped forms. These changes may be photographed.

PLETHYSMOGRAPHIC STUDIES

By means of an oscillometer, or plethysmograph, one may measure arteriocapillary tension and determine the expansile pulsation of an extremity at any desired level; thus it may be possible to differentiate between vasospasm and arterial obstruction.

THE COLD PRESSOR TEST

Stimulation of the vasomotor center by cold, with resultant rise in the blood pressure, may be used in the diagnosis of hypertension. The sphygmomanometer cuff is applied to one arm while the other hand and arm are immersed in water of about four degrees Centigrade. Blood pressure readings are taken every thirty to sixty seconds until the highest reading is reached. This is termed the "index of response." The arm and hand are then removed from the cold water and readings are taken every two minutes until the basal level is reached. In the normal individual there is a slight rise in both systolic and diastolic blood pressure, with a fall to normal within three minutes after the stimulus is removed. A response of more than twenty millimeters of mercury, systolic, and more than fifteen millimeters of mercury, diastolic, is considered significant. In hypertension there is a greater and more prolonged rise, with a delayed fall; this effect disappears after the administration of tetraethylammonium chloride, which suggests that the response is a neurogenic one. There is also increased vasopressor reactivity in patients with cerebral arteriosclerosis.

PHARMACOLOGIC TESTS

Although the autonomic nervous system does not lend itself to complete clinical testing in the manner that the voluntary nervous system does, certain information regarding its function may be obtained by inference, especially by noting the effect of drugs that either stimulate or depress its component parts. It may be of diagnostic value to determine the relative irritability of the sympathetic and parasympathetic divisions and to note the effect of both autonomic stimulants and depressants in the relief of symptoms. The injection of 1 mg. of epinephrine causes a more pronounced response in "sympathotonic" than in normal or "vagotonic" persons, and may produce tachycardia, elevation of the blood pressure, hyperpnea, pallor, tremor, restlessness, and feelings of anxiety, and sometimes hyperglycemia and glycosuria. Because the denervated smooth muscle of arterial walls is hypersensitive to epinephrine, injection of this drug may cause striking vasoconstriction after complete degeneration of the sympathetic nerves, especially after a postganglionic operation. The injection of pilocarpine gives little information about parasympathetic overactivity, although sensitive individuals may react with intestinal cramping, perspiration, increased salivation, and muscular fasciculations. The injection of 0.5 to 1.0 mg. of atropine may be followed by a decrease in salivation and perspiration as well as by tachycardia. The response to these drugs is variable, however, and gives little pertinent information about the activity of the autonomic nervous system except for their effect on the relief of clinical symptoms. Atropine, belladonna, methantheline, and related drugs decrease spasm of the stomach and bowel. These same drugs and the sympathomimetic compounds decrease bronchiolar spasm; vasodilatation and edema of the mucosa may be relieved by the sympathomimetic drugs. Physostigmine and prostigmine aid in the control of paralytic ileus. Contractions of the reflex and uninhibted bladder may be lessened by the use of atropine and methantheline, and the atonic bladder and colon may be aided by the use of Mecholyl and prostigmine. Pilocarpine and related drugs are used in the sweating test. Priscoline and phentolamine cause vasodilatation and may relieve the pain of Raynaud's disease and related conditions.

The Funkenstein test has been used as a prognostic criterion and as a guide to the effectiveness of electroshock and other types of therapy in various psychotic states. Blood pressure changes are measured following the intravenous injection of 0.025 mg. of epinephrine and then following the intramuscular injection of 10 mg. of methacholine. It is stated that the prognosis for recovery and for response to electroshock therapy is best in those patients whose systolic blood pressure rises by more than 50 millimeters of mercury following the injection of epinephrine and either rises and remains above or falls and remains below the preinjection level for 25 minutes after the injection of methacholine. Age and other factors influence the response, and the reliability of this test is still not confirmed.

The use of *ergotamine tartrate* in the therapy of *migraine* has led to the development of an important diagnostic test. The subcutaneous or intramuscular injection of 0.5 mg. of this substance early in the course of a migrainous attack relieves the pain in from 80 to 90 percent of patients. This response is believed to be the result of vasoconstricting effect of the drug upon the dilated branches of the external carotid artery. A similar response occurs in patients with a related type of vascular headache which is known by various names, including that of cluster headache; the individual attacks of pain are of such short duration with this headache, however, that it may be difficult to evaluate the effect of ergotamine tartrate. The latter headache may sometimes be precipitated by the subcutaneous injection of 0.5 mg. of histamine phosphate (0.5 cc. of a 1:1000 solution) or other vasodilating agents.

Various autonomic blocking agents or other drugs acting on the autonomic nervous system are of value in the diagnosis of pheochromocytoma. There may be a reduction of an elevated blood pressure after the intravenous administration of phentolamine (Regitine), piperoxan (Benodaine), or Dibenzyline, an immediate but brief rise of the normal resting blood pressure after the injection of tyramine, or a transient fall followed by a rise after the injection of histamine. The diagnosis can also be made by the presence of increased amounts of catecholamines and products of their metabolism in the blood and urine.

Many new drugs which act upon the autonomic nervous system have been synthesized in recent years; these may be used in both diagnosis and treatment. Autonomic blocking agents of various types can be used to differentiate between vasospasm and arterial obstruction, to determine the relative influence of the autonomic nervous system on various visceral symptoms, to prognosticate the effects of therapy, and to treat hypertension and vasospastic disorders. Vasopressor agents can be used in the treatment of shock and hypotensive states. Current research is providing increasing knowledge about these drugs and their effectiveness.

CYSTOMETRY

The cystometric examination is one of the few clinical diagnostic procedures by means of which one can actually test visceral function. Water is introduced into the bladder, and by means of a water manometer and a kymograph the muscle tone and contractions may be estimated and pressure responses carefully determined. Furthermore, interoceptive, or visceral, sensory functions may be tested by noting the reaction to hot and cold water, painful stimulation, and distention. The results are recorded on the cystogram, or cystometrogram. In the normal bladder there are sensations of pain, temperature, and distention. The first desire to void occurs after about 100 to 150 cc. of water have been introduced into the bladder, and the usual capacity, without painful distention, is from 350 to 450 cc. The bladder can accommodate, however, to increased amounts of fluid to the limits of distention. The intravesical pressure varies between one and fifteen centimeters of water. The pressure of the empty bladder is from one to two centimeters, and that of a bladder containing 100 cc. of fluid may not be over six or eight centimeters. In the normal bladder there are no inhibited contractions and no residual urine. The act of micturition is elicited with ease and maintained without straining; it may be initiated and stopped at will. During the later stages of filling small contractions give conscious information that the organ is reaching capacity. There is complete control of the sphincters at all times.

Careful observation of bladder sensation to pain and temperature, of pressures at which the first desire to void and painful distention occur, of the timing and character of the urinary stream, and of bladder capacity and residual provide information about bladder dysfunction that is of value in neurologic diagnosis. Further data may be obtained by electromyography of the bladder wall and monitoring of the activity of the internal and external sphincters. The various types of abnormalities of function are discussed in Chapter 43. Although local disease and psychic factors may also influence the picture, the cystometric and related examinations are important objective means of examining the autonomic nervous system. The information obtained from the cystometrogram may be augmented by adding other technics, such as electromyography of the perineal muscles and sphincters and simultaneous recording of intra-abdominal and intra-vesical pressures.

COLONMETROGRAPHY

Procedures similar to those used in the cystometric examination enable one to evaluate the effect of the autonomic nervous system in the control of function of the gastrointestinal tract, or specifically, the colon. It is also possible to make simultaneous manometric recordings of the contraction and relaxation of the internal and external anal sphincters. These procedures are not used as frequently as cystometry and are somewhat more difficult to appraise, but they may be helpful in neurologic diagnosis.

MISCELLANEOUS TESTS

In disease of the autonomic nervous system, including both the peripheral divisions and the central control in the hypothalamus and cortex, with or without associated endocrine dyscrasia, many other examinations and laboratory procedures, some without definite neurologic significance, may help to ascertain the diagnosis. Among these may be mentioned the following: calorimetric studies for the determination of the heat elimination of an extremity or of the body as a whole; observation of the circulation time and of the response of the blood pressure to injections of Mecholyl (acetylbetamethylcholine), histamine, and Amytal (sodium amobarbital); roentgen determination of the motility of the gastrointestinal tract after the administration of some radiopaque substance such as barium or bismuth; determination of the secretory function of the gastric mucosa before and after the administration of food, histamine, or alcohol; measurement of lacrimal and salivary secretion; observation of the effect of either spinal anesthesia or autonomic blockade in megalocolon; arteriography after the injection of radiopaque substances such as thorium dioxide (Thorotrast), sodium monoiodomethane (Methiodol), and Diodrast; glucose tolerance studies; determination of fluid intake and output and fluid balance; diuretic response to intravenous hypertonic saline solution and to nicotine in the diagnosis of diabetes insipidus; Kepler water test; eosinophile response to the injection of epinephrine, insulin, and corticotropin; blood chemistry studies of various types; assays of estrogen, androgen, and pituitary follicle-stimulating hormone excretion; 17-ketosteroid and 17-hydroxycorticoid determinations and changes in them after the administration of corticotropin; basal metabolic rate, protein-bound iodine, and radioactive iodine uptake determinations.

REFERENCES

ABRAMSON, A. S., ROUSSAN, M. S., and D'ORONZIO, G.   Method for evaluating function of the neurogenic bladder.   *J.A.M.A.* 195:554, 1966

BOYCE, W. H.   Bladder electromyography: A new approach to the diagnosis of urinary bladder dysfunction.   *J. Urol.* 67:650, 1952.

BULLARD, R. W.   Continuous recording of sweat rate by resistance hygrometry.   *J. Appl. Physiol.* 17:735, 1962.

CARDUS, D., QUESADA, E. M., and SCOTT, F. B.   Studies on the dynamics of the bladder. *J. Urol.* 90:425, 1963.

CROSS, R. L., DODDS, M. E., and KNIGHTS, E. M., JR.   The sudomotor test.   *Surgery* 46:1135, 1959.

DARROW, C. W.   Neural mechanisms controlling the palmar galvanic skin reflex and palmar sweating: A consideration of available literature.   *Arch. Neurol. & Psychiat.* 37:641, 1937.

FEINBERG, I.   Current status of the Funkenstein test.   *Arch. Neurol. & Psychiat.* 80:488, 1958.

FUNKENSTEIN, D. H., GREENBLATT, M., and SOLOMON, H. C.   Psychophysiological study of mentally ill patients: I.   The status of the peripheral autonomic nervous system as determined by the reaction to epinephrine and Mecholyl.   *Am. J. Psychiat.* 106:16, 1949; An autonomic nervous system test of prognostic significance in relation to electroshock treatment. *Psychosom. Med.* 14:347, 1952.

GRENELL, R. G., and BURR, H. S.   Surface potentials and peripheral nerve injury: A clinical test.   *Yale J. Biol. & Med.* 18:517, 1946.

GUTTMAN, S. A.   Use of furmethide in testing sweat secretion in man.   *Arch. Neurol. & Psychiat.* 51:568, 1944.

GUTTMANN, L.   Topographic studies of disturbances of sweat secretion after complete lesions of peripheral nerves.   *J. Neurol. & Psychiat.* 3:197, 1940.

HAUPTMANN, A.   Capillaries in the finger nail fold in patients with neurosis, epilepsy and migraine.   *Arch. Neurol. & Psychiat.* 56:631, 1946.

HEUSKIN, J., and BOBON, J.   Un nouveau type de psychogalvanographe à résponse rapide.   *J. belge de neurol. & de psychiat.* 47:22, 1947.

HINES, E. A., JR., and BROWN, G. E.   The cold pressor test for measuring the reactibility of the blood pressure: Data covering 571 normal and hypertensive subjects.   *Am. Heart J.* 11:1, 1936.

JASPER, H. H., and ROBB, P.   Studies of electrical skin resistance in peripheral nerve lesions.   *J. Neurosurg.* 2:261, 1945.

KAHN, E. A.   Direct observation of sweating in peripheral nerve lesions.   *Surg., Gynec. & Obst.* 92:22, 1951.

LAPIDES, J., and BOBBITT, J. M.   Diagnostic value of bulbocavernous reflex.   *J.A.M.A.* 162:971, 1956.

LIST, C. F., and PEET, M. M.   Sweat secretion in man: I.   Sweating responses in normal persons.   *Arch. Neurol. & Psychiat.* 39:1228, 1938.

LOESER, L. H.   Cutaneous histamine reaction as a test of peripheral nerve function.   *J.A.M.A.* 110:2136, 1938.

MINOR, V.   Ein neues Verfahren zu der klinischen Untersuchung der Schweissabsonderung.   *Deutsche Ztschr. f. Nervenh.* 101:302, 1928.

MORRISON, L. M., and SPIEGEL, E. A.   Demonstration of visceral pain by determination of skin potentials.   *Ann. Int. Med.* 22:827, 1945.

NESBIT, R. M., and BAUM, W. C.   Cystometry: Its neurologic diagnostic implication.   *Neurology* 4:190, 1954.

REDLICH, F. C.   Organic and hysterical anesthesia: A method of differential diagnosis with the aid of the galvanic skin reflex.   *Am. J. Psychiat.* 102:318, 1945.

RICHTER, C. P.   Instructions for using the cutaneous resistance recorder, or "Dermometer," on peripheral nerve injuries, sympathectomies, and paravertebral blocks.   *J. Neurosurg.* 3:181, 1946.

RICHTER, C. P., and WOODRUFF, B. G.   Lumbar sympathetic dermatomes in man determined by the electrical skin resistance method.   *J. Neurophysiol.* 8:323, 1945.

SCHUSTER, M. M., et al.   Simultaneous manometric recording of internal and external anal sphincter reflexes.   *Bull. Johns Hopkins Hosp.* 116:79, 1965.

SILVERMAN, J. J., and POWELL, V. E.   A simple technic for outlining the sweat pattern.   *War Med.* 7:178, 1945.

TOLNICK, B., and BECK, W. C.   The histamine flare in the evaluation of peripheral nerve lesions.   *War Med.* 8:386, 1945.

WANG, G. H.   The Neural Control of Sweating.   Madison, University of Wisconsin Press, 1964.

WINKELMANN, R. K., WILHELMJ, C. M., and HORNER, F. A.   Experimental studies on dermographism.   *Arch. Dermat.* 92:436, 1965.

CHAPTER 43

DISORDERS OF THE AUTO-NOMIC NERVOUS SYSTEM

THE DISORDERS of autonomic function are complex, varied, and difficult to classify. It is not the purpose of this volume to give a detailed description of diseases or of the various syndromes and clinical entities that may be encountered, or to give an outline of differential diagnosis. A brief mention, however, of some of the more characteristic disorders of autonomic function will assist in understanding the physiology of the autonomic nervous system, the reasons for carrying out the various diagnostic procedures, and the changes evident in the presence of pathologic processes.

The terms *vagotonia* and *sympathotonia* (Eppinger and Hess) have been used to classify individuals with regard to the preponderant action of either the parasympathetic or sympathetic division. The vagotonic individual is said to be one with overactivity of the parasympathetic division. He is the "cold blooded" type, with contracted pupils, cold and clammy hands and feet, bradycardia, sinus and respiratory arrhythmia, hypotension, hyperperistalsis and spasm of the stomach and intestine, increased salivation and gastric acidity, excessive lacrimation, frequency of urination, hypoglycemia and increased sugar tolerance, and a tendency toward eosinophilia, urticaria, dermatographia, asthma, spastic constipation, mucous colitis, and peptic ulcer. He may be sensitive to pilocarpine, which increases the above manifestations, and atropine, which diminishes them, and have active oculocardiac and carotid sinus reflexes. The "sympathotonic," or "sympathicotonic," individual, on the other hand, is said to be one with overactivity of the sympathetic division. He is the "warm blooded" type, with a warm, rosy skin, hyperhidrosis, tachycardia, hypertension, dilated pupils, widened palpebral fissures, dry mouth, hypotonicity of the gastrointestinal tract, deficient gastric acidity, and hypotonia of the bladder; there may be an increase in the blood glucose with glycosuria. He reacts readily to epinephrine, which increases all of the above manifestations. In hyperthyroidism

717

there is a rather characteristic picture of sympathotonia. It must be stated, however, that very few individuals can be classified specifically as either vagotonic or sympathotonic, but many show evidences of autonomic imbalance. Observations of the above manifestations may, however, throw some light on idiosyncrasy to disease and on the manifestations of the neuroses and the psychosomatic disorders.

DISORDERS OF FUNCTION OF THE PERIPHERAL AUTONOMIC NERVOUS SYSTEM

Lesions of the peripheral portions of the autonomic nervous system are usually manifested by a deficiency or loss of function of one of the divisions of the system, often with an apparent increase in function of the reciprocal division. Occasionally, however, irritation of one division may result in an increased activity of that portion. In general a lesion of the parasympathetic division, the individual fibers of which are supplied to special structures, is manifested by focal changes, whereas a lesion of the sympathetic division causes more generalized changes. With loss of function of the constituent portions of the parasympathetic division there may be mydriasis, paralysis of accommodation, diminution of lacrimal and salivary secretion, cardiac acceleration, bronchial dilatation, gastrointestinal atony with decreased secretion, spasm of the sphincters, bladder atony, and impotence. These symptoms are increased by the administration of atropine and relieved, if paralysis is not complete, by the administration of physostigmine. The sympathomimetic drugs which stimulate the antagonistic sympathetic division, may also increase the symptoms.

A lesion of the sympathetic division may cause vasodilatation, anhidrosis, loss of piloerection, reflex erythema, fall of blood pressure, bradycardia, pupillary constriction, bronchial constriction, and impairment of ejaculation. There is less definite effect on gastrointestinal and bladder functions. These symptoms are increased by further inhibiting the action of the sympathetics or by stimulating the parasympathetics, and relieved, if the paralysis is not complete, by the administration of ephedrine or other sympathomimetic drugs. Such diminution or loss of sympathetic function may be caused by either brain stem or spinal lesions which affect the descending sympathetic pathways, or by involvement of the intermediolateral cell groups, the preganglionic fibers, the sympathetic ganglia, the postganglionic fibers, or the peripheral nerves.

With a transverse spinal cord lesion above the eighth cervical or first thoracic segment there is loss of sympathetic function of the entire body, and if it is complete and interferes with vital functions such as respiration and cardiac function, it is incompatible with life. If partial, it may cause only loss of sweating, piloerection, and vasoconstriction of the face and body. A partial lesion at the eighth cervical and upper thoracic levels, especially if it involves only the intermediolateral cells, may affect only sympathetic fibers to the head and neck, causing anhidrosis, vasodilatation, and a Horner's syndrome. With a transverse spinal lesion at any level of the thoracic or upper lumbar cord there is loss of sympathetic function below the level of the lesion, with anhidrosis, vasodilatation, loss of piloerection, and increase in skin temperature. Later there is vasoconstriction with decrease in temperature; sweating and piloerection may reappear in an exaggerated form as part of the spinal defense reflex. Impairment of bowel, bladder, and sexual functions may also be present, and occasionally such phenomena as orthostatic hypotension or transient hypertension precipitated by bladder or bowel distention. Changes in the body protein and electrolytes, osteoporosis, testicular atrophy, altered excretion of 17-ketosteroids, and even gynecomastia may develop. There are no changes in sympathetic function with lesions below the third lumbar segment, and only the sacral parasympathetic and somatic nerves are affected.

With lesions of the mixed spinal nerves there also are sympathetic changes characterized by loss of sweating, piloerection, and vasoconstriction. With severe involvement there may be extensive alterations in the skin and subcutaneous tissues, described below. In severe neuropathies, such as the so-called visceral neuropathy that may be present with diabetes, there sometimes are more extensive deficits, with a neurogenic bladder, impotence, bowel incontinence or nocturnal diarrhea, and orthostatic hypotension. The sympathetic nerves may be sectioned in the treatment of Raynaud's disease, causalgia, hypertension, and other conditions, and to relieve the pain of angina pectoris, dymenorrhea, and pancreatitis.

The various disorders in function that may follow lesions of the peripheral autonomic nervous system can be comprehended most satisfactorily by listing the tissues, organs, and systems innervated and the dysfunctions that may occur in each. In some of the conditions listed the dysfunction may have a central as well as a peripheral basis, but the peripheral involvement predominates.

THE EYE

A lesion of the Edinger-Westphal and/or the anterior median or medial nucleus of the oculomotor nerve, the preganglionic fibers to the ciliary ganglion, or the postganglionic fibers causes paralysis of the sphincter of the pupil and/or paralysis of accommodation for near vision. Irritation has the opposite effects. Paralysis of the sympathetic fibers to the eye results in miosis, pseudoptosis, and either real or apparent enophthalmos, i.e. a Horner's syndrome; there may be associated anhidrosis of the side of the face and vasodilatation of the face and conjunctiva. This latter complex may follow involvement of the descending autonomic pathways in the brain stem or cervical portion of the spinal cord, the spinal cord at the junction of the eighth cervical and upper thoracic segments, the preganglionic fibers, the cervical sympathetic ganglion chain, or the postganglionic fibers as they follow the carotid artery into the cavernous plexus and thence through the long ciliary nerves. Stimulation of the sympathetic division may cause mydriasis, widening of the palpebral fissure, and exophthalmos. Pupillary changes may also follow cortical stimulation and destruction.

THE LACRIMAL AND SALIVARY GLANDS

A lesion of either the superior or inferior salivary nuclei or their descending fibers or involvement of the submaxillary, sphenopalatine, or otic ganglia or their postganglionic fibers will cause a decrease in the amount of salivation and in the amount of mucous secretion in the nose, mouth, and pharynx, together with a decrease in lacrimation. Stimulation of these structures increases these secretions. Dysfunction of the sympathetic division causes little disturbance in these functions, although its stimulation is followed by the formation of thick, viscid saliva. Salivation is stimulated reflexly by olfactory, gustatory, psychic, and other stimuli mediated through the hypothalamus and/or cortex, and may be inhibited centrally. Lacrimation may be either stimulated or inhibited by central effects. The syndrome of crocodile tears, characterized by lacrimation on taking food into the mouth, is discussed in Chapter 13.

THE SKIN STRUCTURES

The arrectores pilorum muscles, the sweat glands, and probably the vasomotor fibers of the cutaneous blood vessels are innervated entirely by the sympathetic division. Interruption of sympathetic pathways is followed by loss of pilomotor responses, anhidrosis, and vasodilatation. Stimulation has the opposite effect. So-called trophic disorders involving the skin, mucous membranes, hairs, nails, and subcutaneous tissues are frequently encountered in diseases of the sympathetic division and are important in neurologic diagnosis and localization. They are not the result of impairment of innervation to ectodermal tissues alone, but are probably influenced to a great extent by the vasomotor system. In addition to motor and sensory impulses, the peripheral nerves carry autonomic impulses to the parts of the body supplied. These function in vasomotor control and thus in nutrition to the skin, mucous membrane, and underlying tissues; their integrity is essential to the normal physiology and metabolism of these structures, and when their continuity is impaired metabolic changes take place. The resulting abnormalities of function are called "trophic" changes. The more important ones are listed.

With *lesions of the peripheral nerves* there often are pronounced changes in the cutaneous structures and sometimes in the mucous membranes. The skin may become smooth, thin, cold, white, and glossy, with atrophy of the subcutaneous tissues. It may become hard with a leathery appearance, or thick and scaley. Instead of pallor there may be flushing, erythema, cyanosis, or other types of discoloration. Changes in sweat secretion take place, usually in the form of hypohidrosis or anhidrosis, but occasionally, hyperhidrosis. Seborrhea, or oiliness, is sometimes present. Either hypotrichosis or hypertrichosis may occur. The nails become brittle and ridged. These changes are either localized or diffuse.

With *lesions of the dorsal root ganglia,* especially with inflammatory conditions such as herpes zoster, vesicles and bullae develop in the cutaneous distribution of the specific nerve roots. Vesicles may also develop in herpes simplex. With *transverse lesions of the spinal cord* there is anhidrosis with loss of pilo-erection, redness, and hyperthermia below the level of the lesion. Later there is vasoconstriction with hypothermia, cyanosis, and mottling; abnormal sweating and piloerection may reappear as part of the spinal defense reflex.

With *central lesions* such as cerebral hemiplegia the involved extremities may be warmer or colder than normal (often the latter); is followed by disuse cyanosis, edema, and circulatory insufficiency. With cortical involvement there may be an exaggerated pilomotor response on the hemiplegic side. With hypothalamic lesions there may be alopecia areata, vitiligo, and poliosis. In postencephalitic states there may be increased secretion of the sebaceous glands; the skin of the face is greasy and there is marked seborrhea of the face and scalp.

Neurotrophic or *perforating ulcers, decubiti,* and *bed sores* may develop with the various spinal and peripheral nerve lesions, especially if there is interruption of sensory as well as trophic impulses. Pressure over an anesthetic area elicits a flare. If the pressure is not relieved, local anemia occurs and the blood supply to the area is interrupted. This leads to destruction of the deeper layers of the epidermis and the development of vesicles by collection of serum between the papillary layer of the dermis and the epidermis. On further pressure the structures of the dermis are also destroyed with sloughing and the development of an area of necrosis which extends both peripherally and into the deeper structures. Extensive ulcerations may develop owing to the deficient blood supply and the absence of nutrient impulses from the central nervous system; these areas of necrosis, or ulcerations, heal slowly and become infected with ease. They develop at sites of pressure, most frequently over the sacrum, buttocks, trochanters, heels, and malleoli. They are found in transverse myelitides, extensive peripheral nerve lesions, tabes dorsalis, spina bifida, syringomyelia, and myelodysplasia. In tabes dorsalis there may be painless perforating ulcers of the toes and feet (mal perforans), probably the result of dorsal root ganglion involvement. In syringomyelia and myelodysplasia the patient may cut or burn himself without experiencing pain; the resulting lesions heal poorly and become infected easily. Syringomyelia accompanied by painless ulcerations of the fingers is called Morvan's disease; the term main succulente is used if there is edema with lividity and coldness of the hand. Performing ulcers of the mouth and nasal septum may be found in association with syphilis and cranial nerve lesions.

Edema of the skin may occur under a variety of circumstances, often the result of autonomic nervous system involvement. In urticaria there is localized edema with erythema. In angioneurotic edema, or Quincke's disease, there are localized pruritic swellings, single or multiple, that may involve large portions of the body. The manifestations occur in attacks; they may involve the respiratory passages. There is an allergic factor. In hereditary trophedema, or Milroy's disease, there is hereditary swelling of the lower extremities. In myxedema there is a nonpitting edema of the skin. In hemiedema there is swelling of one half of the body. Edema is a frequent manifestation of trophic lesions, and it is found in the paretic extremities in both lower motor neuron, or peripheral, and upper motor neuron, or central, paralysis. Generalized edema, of course is usually the result of cardiac or renal disease. If there is any tendency toward edema, it will develop first in the paretic extremities.

Pigment changes of various types may be noted. Pallor, flushing, and cyanosis have been mentioned. In cases of circulatory insufficiency these vary with change of position. Vitiligo, or leukoderma, is a patchy loss of pigmentation of unknown origin. Vasodilatation and contraction, reflex erythema, and dermatographia contribute to color alterations.

Other varieties of skin changes may be seen in disease of the autonomic nervous system, as well as in clinical entities in which the exact mechanism is not known but an autonomic factor is suspected. Scleroderma is a thickening of the skin with atrophy of the subcutaneous tissues. The skin is hard, shiny, and leathery. There may be anhidrosis and alopecia. This may be generalized or diffuse. Localized scleroderma is known as morphea. Scleroderma may be secondary to Raynaud's disease and syringomyelia, or may occur as a part of hemiatrophy or as a disease entity. It is often a manifestation of the so-called collagen diseases. Either trophic changes or hypertrophy of the skin may occur in leprosy. Dermatographia is discussed in Chapter 42.

THE SWEAT GLANDS

Disorders of sweat secretion vary in type. Generalized *hyperhidrosis* is rare, but may be relieved somewhat by drugs such as atropine and methantheline. Psychoneurotic individuals often have a tendency toward spontaneous hyperhidrosis, which may be localized to the palmar surfaces of the hand and fingers, the plantar surfaces of the feet and toes, the axillae, and the forehead. They may show excessive sweating when under the tension or in cold weather, but the palms and soles may remain relatively dry in warm weather when the entire body is perspiring profusely. Hyperhidrosis is also a symptom of hyperthyroidism and of familial dysautonomia, and either hyperhidrosis or spontaneous sweating occurs with some cerebral lesions. There may be compensatory increase in sweating of other areas of the body after certain segments have been rendered anhidrotic by sympathectomy. Congenital *anhidrosis* is also rare, and is usually associated with congenital absence of sweat glands as a part of hereditary ectodermal dysplasia. Anhidrosis may also occur with familial sensory neuropathy and it may be a manifestation of orthostatic hypotension due to neurologic disease. Progressive anhidrosis due to progressive sudomotor denervation has been reported with Adie's syndrome.

Focal loss of sweating may be associated with lesions of the central autonomic pathways, the intermediolateral cells, the preganglionic or postganglionic sympathetic fibers, or the mixed peripheral nerves; this may be surrounded by a zone of increased sweating. Interruption of the lateral reticulospinal pathway in the brain stem or cervical portion of the spinal cord causes ipsilateral loss of sweating on the face, often a part of Horner's syndrome (Fig. 261). Interruption of the ventral reticulospinal pathway causes ipsilateral loss of thermoregulatory sweating on the body below the lesion; there may be hyperhidrosis at the level of involvement. With transverse myelopathy the sweat response may return below the lesion after the period of spinal shock has passed, and there may be exaggerated spinal reflex sweating as part of the mass reflex of spinal automatism. There may a "sweat level" with thermoregulatory sweating above the lesion and spinal reflex sweating below it. Excessive spinal sweating below a transverse lesion may be relieved by sympathectomy. Abnormal gustatory sweating develops secondary to faulty nerve regeneration in the auriculotemporal and chorda tympani syndromes. Gustatory sweating has also been reported following dorsal sympathectomy.

THE BLOOD VESSELS

In general the blood vessels, except for the coronary arteries, are constricted by the action of the sympathetic division. The parasympathetic division is believed to constrict the coronary vessels, and it does dilate the helicine arteries and some of the arteries supplying specific structures, but is not a general vasodilator. Paralysis of the sympathetic division causes peripheral vasodilatation of the cutaneous vessels. This may not persist, however, since the denervated muscle may become abnormally sensitive to the epinephrine which is normally circulating in the blood, and vasoconstriction may follow. Sympathetic stimulation causes vasospasm.

There is a group of so-called *trophic disorders* in which the pathologic change is primarily in the blood vessels. These conditions, somewhat vague with reference to classification, are also known as the vasomotor neuroses, or angioneuroses. Many of them are disorders of the autonomic nervous system which are manifest chiefly through peripheral vascular involvement; some of them are primary vascular diseases with associated autonomic involvement. All are not primarily lesions of the autonomic system, nor are all true vascular disorders, but in every one there is some evidence, primary or secondary, of involvement of the vasomotor system. Trophic changes do not occur in all. In some there is evidence of vasospasm (Raynaud's disease), in others of vasodilatation (erythromelalgia), and in still others of organic obstruction (arteriosclerosis and Buerger's disease). The more important ones are listed.

1. *Raynaud's disease* is a disorder that is seen principally in young females. It most frequently involves the fingers and hands but may affect the toes, tips of the ears, and nose, spreading to involve larger areas. The manifestations are often symmetrical. There is abnormal sensitivity to cold, and on exposure to cold attacks of "local syncope" are induced. Starting with the digits and spreading proximally, the extremities first become cyanotic and red, and then cold, pale, and numb. After a period of time they again become cyanotic, and then red, hot, and painful. Repeated attacks lead to trophic changes in the digits, ulcerations, scleroderma, and gangrene. Examination shows that the skin temperature is below normal. There is no pallor on elevation or rubor on dependency, but cyanosis and pallor follow exposure to cold. The arterial pulsations are normal.

Raynaud's disease is believed to be a vasomotor neurosis. Cold, emotional stimuli, and other factors cause hyperactivity of the sympathetic division with resulting vasospasm and ischemia. As the disease progresses, changes may appear in the vessel walls. Mecholyl and other parasympathomimetic drugs as well as vasodilator drugs such as tolazoline and phentolamine have been used in the treatment. Protection against cold is important. The best, though not invariable, relief is obtained by preganglionic sympathectomy, with consequent vasodilatation.

A syndrome similar to Raynaud's disease has been described in individuals who work with penumatic drills or riveting hammers. This condition has been known as spastic anemia, "white fingers," pneumatic hammer disease, and traumatic vasospastic disease. The exposure to rapid vibration is believed to be an etiologic factor. In *Raynaud's phenomenon* there are symptoms that are similar to those of Raynaud's disease, but they are less severe, and there is usually a known etiology, such as trauma or collagen disease. It is believed that local sensitization of the vessels to cold is responsible for the symptoms, and there is no evidence of autonomic hyperactivity.

2. *Acrocyanosis* bears some resemblance to Raynaud's disease. The hands and less frequently the feet are persistently cold, blue, and sweaty. Exposure to cold intensifies these changes, which begin at the wrist and proceed distally. There may be some puffiness of the fingers. Pain is not a symptom of consequence, and trophic changes and gangrene never develop. The syndrome is believed to be the result of increased tone of the cutaneous arterioles due to hypersensitivity to cold, with consequent local asphyxia.

3. *Acroparesthesia* is a slowly progressive disorder which is most often found in women of middle age. It is characterized by numbness and crawling and tingling sensations in the extremities, usually the hands, often associated with pain, slight pallor, hyperesthesia, hyperalgesia, and coldness. The symptoms usually occur at night. The syndrome may be due to pressure on the brachial plexus and artery at the thoracic outlet, or even to more distal vascular and nerve compression (carpal tunnel syndrome).

4. *Erythromelalgia,* or Weir Mitchell's disease, is a rare condition of middle life that is characterized by paroxysmal or periodic reddening and severe burning pain and swelling in one or more of the extremities, usually the feet. The attacks, which seldom last more than a few hours, are accompanied by hyperalgesia and sweating of the part. The symptoms are brought on by warmth, excitement, or dependency of the part, and are relieved by rest, cold, or elevation. The skin temperature is elevated; there are no color changes with change of position or exposure to cold. Trophic changes may develop in the skin or nails, but no ulcerations occur. The symptoms are believed to be due to vasodilatation or to be a result of hypersensitivity of the cutaneous pain fibers to warmth and tension.

5. *Buerger's disease,* or thromboangiitis obliterans, is a condition which usually occurs in middle-aged males and most frequently in the lower extremities. One of the early symptoms is intermittent claudication, but later there is pain at rest as well as during exercise. There is either rubor or cyanosis of the extremities on dependency, and pallor on elevation. The arterial pulsations are diminished in one-half the cases, and the skin temperature is low in all. Ulcerations and gangrene may develop. Early in the disease there is hyperactivity of the vasomotor nerves, and at this time vasodilators and even sympathectomy may afford relief. Later there is an organic obstruction of the arteries and to a lesser extent of the veins. The vessels become stiff and hard, the adventitia is thickened, and there is increase in connective tissue in the media, with narrowing of the lumens, a diminution of the blood flow, and a tendency toward thrombosis.

6. *Peripheral arteriosclerosis* usually occurs in the older age group. This may also cause intermittent claudication as an early symptom, probably the result of relative anoxia of the muscles secondary to narrowing of the arteries and deficiency in blood supply. Signs of vascular obstruction occur, with a tendency toward ulcerations and gangrene. There is rubor on dependency with pallor on elevation, but

there are rarely color changes on exposure to cold. The skin temperature is low, arterial pulsations are diminished, and the sclerotic changes in the vessels may be palpated or may be visualized by roentgenography.

7. *Causalgia* is often classed with the vasomotor neuroses. It is occasionally known as reflex sympathetic dystrophy. Following injury or irritation of a peripheral nerve, usually of the median nerve but occasionally of other nerves in the upper extremity or of the sciatic nerve in the lower extremity, a syndrome develops which is characterized by pain and vasomotor and trophic disturbances. The patient complains of a severe, burning pain, first in the distribution of the involved nerve but later radiating peripherally. The pain is made worse by motion, emotional stimuli, exposure to temperature changes, and even by air currents. The injury may have been slight and the pain is out of proportion to the severity of the trauma. There is marked hyperesthesia of the involved extremity. Accompanying the pain are vascular and trophic changes which consist of redness, a glossy skin, coldness, edema, hyperhidrosis, and changes in the hair and nails. There may be either vasoconstriction with lowering of the temperature of the affected part or vasodilatation with elevation of temperature.

The symptoms are doubtless associated, in part at least, with sympathetic dysfunction. The pain may be caused by self-perpetuating activity within the autonomic reflex arcs long after the precipitating process is gone, or it may be brought about by efferent sympathetic discharges from the hypothalamus which cause direct stimulation of afferent fibers near the site of injury. Novocaine injection of the sympathetic ganglia supplying the painful area affords temporary benefit, and in most cases permanent relief follows a complete preganglionic sympathacetomy. A preoperative novocaine block may help to evaluate the results of sympathectomy. The operation is most effective if done early; if the syndrome has been present for a long time, associated psychic changes or secondary hyperirritability of central areas may interfere with the results. Blocking agents and vasodilators such as hexamethonium, Dibenzyline, tolazoline, phentolamine, and tetraethylammonium may also give temporary relief, and some cases have been treated by posterior cordotomy with section of the long intersegmental fibers that lie close to the substantia gelaninosa of Rolando.

8. *Associated posttraumatic manifestations,* sometimes classified as the "minor causalgias" and characterized by local pain and trophic changes in bone, have been variously termed Sudeck's atrophy, traumatic osteoporosis, peripheral trophoneurosis, reflex dystrophy, and chronic traumatic edema. These also may respond to novocaine injection and sympathectomy.

9. *Trench foot,* or immersion foot, follows prolonged soaking in cold water or exposure to cold together with constriction by shoes and other clothing. The toes become white and cold, and sometimes cyanotic and even gangrenous. At the outset the peripheral arteries are contracted, but later they are relaxed, with resulting edema accompanied by paresthesias, pain, and excoriations. The normal vasomotor responses are absent.

Manifestations similar to those of the above-described syndromes may be present with disorders that do not affect primarily the peripheral autonomic nervous system or the blood vessels. These include central lesions such as cerebral hemiplegia, metabolic and hormonal disturbances, blood dyscrasias, the collagen and related disorders, and the effect of drugs or toxin such as ergot. In all of the conditions in which there are symptoms and signs of impaired blood supply to the extremities the degree of impairment may be evaluated by noting color changes and reactive hyperemia with alteration of position and temperature of the part, and by oscillometry, plethysmography, skin temperature studies, and other tests described in Chapter 42.

Migrainous headaches and other types of cephalalgia are in part at least of vascular origin and associated with disturbances of the autonomic supply to the extracranial and intracranial vessels. The pain is believed to be the result of dilatation of certain extracranial and dural arteries, especially the temporal and middle meningeal branches of the external carotid artery, with stimulation of the neighboring neural plexuses. It has been postulated that the preceding prodromal symptoms may be the result of an earlier vasoconstriction, possibly of cerebral arteries. In a large percentage of patients the pain is relieved by the early administration of ergotamine tartrate. In the so-called cluster headache, which may also be relieved by ergotamine tartrate, the attacks of pain are believed to be caused by dilatation of the intracranial arteries at the base of the brain, especially the cerebral and pial branches of the basilar and internal carotid arteries. Other varieties of headache, including those associated with fever, may also result from distension of the intracranial arteries, and still other types may be caused by tension on, displacement or inflammation of, or traction on the arteries of the brain and meninges.

THE HEART

Interruption of the cardioinhibitory fibers which are conducted from the dorsal efferent nucleus through the vagus nerve to the cardiac ganglia on the heart wall causes cardiac acceleration, whereas stimulation of the vagus brings about reduced heart rate, decreased cardiac output, diminished conduction at the auriculoventricular bundle, and sometimes auriculoventricular block or vagal arrest. In a lesion of the vagus nerve both the oculocardiac and carotid sinus reflexes are lost. Stimulation of the sympathetic division produces increased conduction at the auriculoventricular bundle, cardiac acceleration, increased output, and sometimes ventricular extrasystoles, paroxysmal tachycardia, and either auricular or ventricular fibrillation. Injection of epinephrine directly into the heart muscle may be of value in sudden cardiac arrest.

In abnormalities of the autonomic system there may be tachycardia, bradycardia, and abnormalities of rhythm. Bradycardia often has diagnostic value or serious prognostic significance in increased intracranial pressure; it may be the result of hypothalamic involvement, but it more frequently follows pressure on the cardiac center in the medulla as a result of herniation of the medulla into the foramen magnum. Sudden death following spinal puncture may be due to cardiac arrest on such a basis. Paroxysmal tachycardia may be caused by heart disease, or it may occur on a reflex basis or in association with emotional stimuli. It is sometimes stopped by pressure on the eyeballs, by means of the oculocardiac reflex. Heart block is usually a symptom of organic disease of the heart, but in Stokes-Adams attacks there may be cardiac arrest due to stimulation of the inhibitory fibers to the heart. If the carotid sinus reflex is hyperactive, pressure on the neck may bring about slowing or temporary arrest of the heart, fall in blood pressure, and sometimes syncope and convulsions. The so-called vasovagal attacks of Gowers, characterized by palpitation, precordial distress, respiratory arrhythmia, and disturbances in gastrointestinal motility, were once thought to be the result of vagal stimulation. They are now recognized to be psychogenic rather than organic manifestations, and are frequent symptoms in the anxiety psychoneuroses.

The relationship of the autonomic nervous system to the pain of angina pectoris has been the subject of a great deal of discussion. It is believed that the pain is a result of ischemia of the cardiac musculature secondary to spasm of the coronary arteries. The impulses are, however, conducted with the autonomic nerves to the middle and inferior cervical ganglia. This pain has been relieved by either injection or section of the middle and inferior cervical and the upper thoracic sympathetic ganglia. It cannot be stated whether the relief is the result only of interruption of the afferent impulses or of blocking of the motor impulses. The sympathetic division is believed to exert vasodilator rather than vasoconstrictor effects on the coronary vessels, however, so that one may assume that the relief follows interruption of the sensory pathways. Similar results may be obtained by section of the posterior nerve roots. Constriction of the coronary arteries in response to dilatation of the stomach or pain in the abdomen is termed the *viscerocardiac reflex*.

THE BLOOD PRESSURE

The blood pressure is increased by the action of the sympathetic division, which causes constriction of the blood vessels, and it may be slightly decreased by the action of the parasympathetic division. Sympathetic stimulants and vasopressor drugs are used in the treatment of shock and hypotensive states. The height of the blood pressure is regulated largely by the hypothalamus and by tonic activity of the vasomotor center situated in the medulla. The control is not, however, entirely autonomic, since it is also influenced reflexly and by changes in the hydrogen ion concentration of the blood. There are other subsidiary vasomotor centers in the intermediolateral columns of the spinal cord. With focal intracerebral lesions and increased intracranial pressure there may be either a rise or a fall in blood pressure. In paraplegic patients bladder distention may cause hypertension.

Surgery of the sympathetic nervous system, largely section of the splanchnic nerves, was once used quite extensively in the treatment of essential or so-called malignant hypertension. There is still a great deal that is not understood about hypertension and about the physiologic effects of these operative procedures—whether they decrease the blood pressure by vasodilatation of the splanchnic area, elimination of excessive suprarenal secretion, dilatation of the renal vessels, or humoral changes. Furthermore, it is known that hypertension may have either neurogenic or psychogenic origin. These operative procedures, however, were definitely valuable and did contribute one of the major advances to the surgery of the autonomic nervous system, although of late they have largely been supplanted by various types of drug therapy. Among the pharmacologic agents used in the treatment of hypertension are the drugs such as reserpine, which have central action, the vasodilators such as the nitrites, veratrum alkaloids, hydralazine (Apresoline), and Hydergine, and the ganglion blocking agents such as hexamethonium, pentolinium (Ansolysen), chlorisondamine (Ecolid), and mecamylamine (Inversine).

Orthostatic hypotension may have many causes, including adrenal insufficiency, severe neuropathies, tabes dorsalis, and the use of sympatholytic drugs and catecholamine-depleting agents (Chapter 55). Shy and Drager and others have described a progressive disorder affecting both the peripheral autonomic and central nervous system and characterized by orthostatic hypotension, anhidrosis, urinary and fecal incontinence, impotence, ocular palsies, distal wasting and neuropathy, rigidity, and tremor.

THE RESPIRATORY SYSTEM

In bronchial asthma there is constriction of the bronchiolar musculature with swelling of the mucous membrane, increased secretion of thick mucus, and production of eosinophiles. These manifestations may be relieved by the use of atropine and related parasympathetic depressants that decrease both constriction and secretions, by epinephrine and related drugs that decrease secretions by vasoconstriction and may have some bronchial dilator effect, and by the antihistamine drugs. Stimulation of the carotid sinus may cause reflex inhibition of respiration and even apnea.

THE GASTROINTESTINAL SYSTEM

The relationship of the autonomic nervous system to visceral disease of the gastrointestinal tract is varied and complex. Increased tonus and peristalsis as well as increased secretion are usually evidences of parasympathetic overactivity, whereas atonia may be the result of sympathetic overactivity. These manifestations may be symptoms of either organic or psychogenic disorders, and often the two are difficult to differentiate; psychogenic mechanisms may terminate in organic disease.

In cardiospasm there may be spasm of either the esophageal musculature or the cardiac sphincter. The beneficial effect of atropine in certain cases would suggest that, in those cases at least, parasympathetic activity, probably with spasm limited to the esophageal musculature, is the important factor. In peptic ulcer there is increased motility of the gastric musculature and increased secretion of hydrochloric acid. Vagotomy aids in the treatment of peptic ulcers; there is reduction of gastric motility as well as decrease in the volume and acidity of the gastric secretions. In both spastic constipation and mucous colitis there is hyperperistalsis with increased secretion of the intestinal tract. The symptoms may be alleviated by the use of parasympathetic blocking drugs and on occasion by vagotomy. On the other hand paralytic ileus may be relieved by the use of either neostigmine or Mecholyl.

In Hirschsprung's disease, or congenital megalocolon, there is dilatation of the large intestine, once thought to be due to either abnormal activity of the sympathetics or decreased activity of the parasympathetics. It is known, however, that the pathologic segment is not the dilated portion of the colon, but rather a distal narrowed segment in which the myenteric (Auerbach's) plexus is deficient or absent. Lumbar sympathectomy was at one time recommended for the treatment of this disorder, but it is now apparent that successful therapy is possible only by removal of the spastic aganglionic segment. Parasympathetic stimulants such as methacholine and neostigmine may be of some therapeutic value in mild cases.

Intussusception with invagination of one portion of the intestine into another may be caused by increased peristalsis associated with overactivity of the parasympathetics. Congenital hypertrophic pyloric stenosis may be produced by deficient inhibition of the pylorus, either a deficiency of the parasympathetics or an overactivity of the sympathetics. The so-called nervous dyspepsias with hyperacidity, excessive gastric contraction, and pylorospasm may be the result of sympathetic and parasympathetic imbalance.

The stimulus for defecation consists of stretching of the walls of the rectum by the accumulation of fecal material. When this reaches a certain stage, rhythmic contractions develop and the internal sphincter relaxes; the external sphincter, however, which is under voluntary control, may for a while prevent the escape of feces. The parasympathetic plays a larger part than the sympathetic in defecation, and the latter probably acts only to inhibit the movements of the bowel during the accumulation of its contents. Lesions of the spinal cord which involve either the sacral segments or the descending pathways and lesions of either the cauda equina or the pelvic nerves depress the tone and rhythmic contraction of the rectum, with resulting constipation. Defecation may be possible through the action of the levator ani and the abdominal muscles. If the sphincters are toneless, there may be rectal incontinence; the rectal and anal reflexes are lost. In lesions which involve the cerebral centers or descending pathways, or in long-standing disease, the sphincters may regain some tone and reflex activity. These manifestations are better understood in the bladder (see below) than in the rectum, but they are comparable in the two structures.

THE BLADDER

Bladder musculature has tonicity, rhythmicity, and power of accommodation; contractions can be stimulated either reflexly or voluntarily. Vesical function is a complex mechanism which involves both the autonomic and the voluntary nervous systems, and disorders of the bladder function may follow lesions of the paracentral lobule, hypothalamus, descending pathways in the spinal cord, pre- or postganglionic parasympathetic and sympathetic nerves, or pudendal nerve. It is difficult to differentiate between disorders of function that are entirely on an autonomic basis and those with associated voluntary nervous system involvement; these will be considered together. The various disturbances of vesical function may be appraised by the use of cystometry.

The bladder acts as a reflex organ and contracts in response to a stretch reflex. The afferent impulses are carried to the sacral portion of the spinal cord, and stimulation of efferent centers causes contraction of the detrusor muscle and relaxation of the internal sphincter. There is probably a center in the lumbar cord which produces a contraction of the internal sphincter and allows distention of the bladder and retention of urine. In the baby the bladder is purely reflex in function, but with the maturation of the cerebral cortex and the completion of myelinization an inhibitory control is developed over this reflex with voluntary regulation of the external sphincter. For normal micturition it is necessary to have intact parasympathetic arc, sympathetic arc, and spinal pathways, along with normal cerebral inhibition and control of the external sphincter.

Symptoms of bladder dysfunction are often among the earliest manifestations of nervous system disease. Frequency, urgency, precipitate micturition, massive or dribbling incontinence, difficulty in initiating urination, retention, and loss of bladder sensation may occur. The term "neurogenic bladder" has been used for the various types of vesical dysfunction which are caused by lesions of the nervous system. The principal types of neurogenic bladder dysfunction are listed (Fig. 263).

1. *The uninhibited bladder* shows the least variation from the normal. This type of bladder dysfunction is characterized by a more or less infantile type of reaction. There is loss of cortical inhibition to reflex voiding when the bladder is distended. Tone is normal, and the organ contracts in response to the stretch reflex. There is urgency, but there may be no frequency since the bladder capacity is only moderately reduced. Hesitancy may precede urgency. Bladder sensation is usually normal. Several rhythmic uninhibited contractions of the detrusor may take place before bladder capacity is reached and the final emptying contraction occurs. These contractions coincide with the urge to void on the part of the patient, but micturition does not take place until a contraction of sufficient intensity occurs to necessitate emptying the bladder; then the patient urinates precipitously. Up to this point, however, normal voluntary control is possible. There is no residual. This type of bladder dysfunction occurs in mental deficiency, enuresis in adults, early diffuse brain damage, cerebral lesions affecting the dominant hemisphere, hemiplegia, and early multiple and posterolateral sclerosis.

2. *The reflex bladder* results from widespread changes affecting the upper motor neurons, either extensive brain disease or extensive spinal cord involvement above the sacral segments. It occurs in transverse myelitis and advanced multiple and posterolateral sclerosis. There is interference with the descending autonomic fibers which run with the corticospinal pathways, but the spinal reflex arc is intact. The resulting dysfunction is an exaggeration of the reflex bladder of infancy. The organ has small capacity, usually fifty to one hundred cubic centimeters, and tone is increased; sensation is vague and poorly localized. There are rhythmic uninhibited contractions during filling and preceding the emptying contraction, but these are seldom sufficient for emptying. The patient voids by precipitate micturition. There may be a small residual of urine in the bladder after voiding. If the reflex bladder is the result of spinal cord disease such as transverse myelitis, there may also be loss of sensation and external sphincter control, with impairment of ability to initiate micturition. Disturbances of the autonomic nervous system in the nature of abdominal cramps, pilomotor phenomena, flushing, and sweating may, however, give the patient an awareness of the bladder evacuation. The bladder may empty as part of the mass reflex. In the spastic reflex bladder due to cerebral involvement there is no

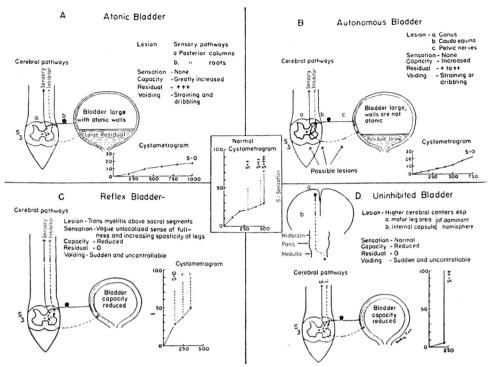

FIG. 263.   Diagram showing the various types of neurogenic vesical dysfunction; classification follows outline given in McLellan's monograph; in the cystometrograms, ordinates represent intravesical pressure in centimeters of water, and abscissae volume of filling in cubic centimeters. (White, J. C., and Smithwick, R. H.: The Autonomic Nervous System, ed. 2. New York, The Macmillan Company, copyright, 1941.)

loss of sensation and there are no associated autonomic phenomena, but micturition is not voluntary and depends upon an uninhibited emptying contraction on the part of the detrusor.

3. *The autonomous bladder* is one without external innervation. It is caused by lesions of the sacral portion of the spinal cord, the conus medullaris or cauda equina, the motor and/or sensory roots of the second, third, and fourth sacral nerves, or the peripheral nerves. There is destruction of the parasympathetic supply. Sensation may be abolished and there is no reflex or voluntary control of the bladder; contractions occur as the result of stimulation of the intrinsic neural plexuses within the bladder wall. There are no sustained contractions of the detrusor as a whole, and no emptying contractions. During filling, however, there are minor inherent contractions of individual muscle groups, and at the height of one of these there may be emptying, which is never complete. There may be a high intravesical pressure, and the amount of residual urine is large, but bladder capacity is not greatly increased. Voiding is usually brought about by increasing the intra-abdom-

inal pressure, and there may be dribbling as a result of the high intravesical pressure. The desire to void is made known by abdominal discomfort.

4. *The atonic (or sensory paralytic) bladder* is found with lesions which involve the posterior roots or posterior root ganglia of the sacral nerves or the posterior columns of the spinal cord. Sensation is absent, and there is no desire to void. There may be distention, dribbling, and difficulty both in initiating micturition and in emptying the bladder. There is a low intravesical pressure and a large capacity, with absence of waves of contraction. Voiding may be brought about by straining, and there is a large amount of residual urine. There is incontinence of an overflow type. This variety of bladder dysfunction is found in tabes dorsalis and with other lesions of the posterior roots or columns.

With spinal cord lesions, especially in those of severe degree and sudden onset, such as traumatic myelopathies, there is first marked retention during the period of spinal shock. Reflex activity is absent; the bladder is atonic and may become markedly distended with overflow incontinence. Later it becomes autonomous in function, due to reflex contraction from the plexuses in the bladder wall. If the patient develops a spastic paraplegia, there will be a reflex bladder of the spinal type with small capacity and precipitate micturition. The paralyzed bladder not infrequently becomes infected, and chronic infection leads to contraction of the viscus and often to continual dribbling. There may be calculus formation.

With cerebral lesions there may be incontinence at the onset of the lesion, due to abolition of inhibitory control, or there may be retention with distention of the bladder and overflow incontinence. The mental apathy associated with frontal lobe lesions may lead to involuntary micturition. Vesical dysfunction may be associated with disease of either the pyramidal or extrapyramidal motor systems. Drugs such as hyoscine and related synthetic compounds used in the treatment of Parkinson's disease occasionally cause retention, especially in elderly patients, and some of the tranquilizing and muscle-relaxing drugs occasionally cause enuresis. Either urinary retention or incontinence may have psychogenic origin. There are many causes, both organic and nonorganic, for nocturnal enuresis in childhood and adolescence.

Local disease in the bladder or the urethra may be manifested by symptoms similar to those associated with neurogenic dysfunction, and often, especially in elderly males with prostatic enlargement, it may be difficult to differentiate between the neurogenic manifestations and those due to local disease. In prostatism, with longstanding obstruction and resulting decompensation of the detrusor, bladder sensation may be decreased, the stream is slow and difficult to initiate, there is a high residual, and the patient voids with straining. It is said that such patients have a hypotonic myogenic variety of vesical dysfunction. A hypertonic myogenic type of dysfunction follows inflammation of the bladder wall; in this there are irritative symptoms, increased sensation, urgency and frequency, and pain on distention.

Surgery of the autonomic nervous system has not contributed significantly to the treatment of neurogenic bladder dysfunction. Blocking or section of the sacral nerves has been used on occasion to relieve retention caused by bladder contraction, and both anterior and posterior rhizotomy have been used to abolish spasm and change a contracted bladder to an autonomous one, with variable results. Electrical stimulation of the bladder wall and the use of an electronic implant have been tried for the treatment of bladder problems associated with spinal cord lesions. Atropine and methantheline (Banthine) may depress the motor impulses and thus give some symptomatic relief in patients with uninhibited and spastic irritable bladders by decreasing frequency and precipitancy, and methacholine, betamethylcholine, and neostigmine may be of some help in controlling the retention of the atonic or autonomous bladder. Imipramine (Tofranil) has been helpful in the treatment of childhood enuresis. Whether its effect results in anticholingeric, stimulant, or antidepressant properties, or from a combination, is uncertain.

GENITAL FUNCTIONS

A lesion of the parasympathetic division causes impotence with failure of erection and ejaculation, whereas stimulation of the parasympathetics may cause priapism. With lesions of the sympathetics, or following the administration of certain adrenergic blocking agents, there may be impairment of ejaculation, because the spermatozoa fail to reach the urethra, although erection and orgasm may be preserved. With sympathetic overactivity there are ejaculatio precox and spermatorrhea, with weakness of erection due to contraction of vasoconstrictor muscles, and hastened flow of spermatozoa due to stimulation of the reflex peristalsis in the seminal vesicles and ducts. Priapism may also result from lesions of the spinal cord above the lumbar level; not only may there be erection, but the coital, or ejaculatory, reflex may be increased to such a degree that the slightest stiumlus to the penis will result in ejaculation. Loss of both libido and potency may follow cerebral lesions and the administration of cerebral depressant and autonomic blocking drugs. Disorders of genital function in the female, as related to the autonomic nervous system, are somewhat less specific. Division of the lumbar sympathetic chains and resection of the superior hypogastric plexus have been carried out for the relief of dysmenorrhea.

DISORDERS OF FUNCTION OF CENTRAL AUTONOMIC REGULATION

The signs and symptoms of disorders of function which involve predominantly the central regulatory centers concerned with the autonomic nervous system are generalized rather than focal. Some of them are referable to specific visceral systems; others are more diffuse. Clinical literature as well as experimental data relating to the hypothalamus and to disorders arising from injury or disease of its parts has increased rapidly during the past few years, and many characteristic syndromes have been described. There may be disturbances of sleep, abnormalities of temperature regulation, changes in carbohydrate and water metabolism, dysfunction of fat metabolism, respiratory anomalies, together with, in many instances, behavioral abnormalities and personality changes. Many of the hypothalamic syndromes which are encountered clinically are residuals of encephalitis or associated with neoplasms. The hypothalamus is, however, under the influence of the cortex, and it may be difficult to distinguish between cortical and diencephalic manifestations. Furthermore, cortical stimulation may be followed by vegetative changes such as the pupillary dilatation and tachycardia that may occur in response to pain and fright. In addition, the close functional relationship between the secondary reflex centers in the midbrain and brain stem and the higher centers may be difficult to differentiate.

Symptoms referable to general vegetative functions and to the various visceral systems constitute some of the more important manifestations of disorders which involve predominantly the cerebral centers of autonomic regulation. Some of the more important of these are listed. Selye has used the term "adaptation syndrome" as the sum of all nonspecific systemic reactions of the body that ensue upon long-continued exposure to stress. When the organism is subjected to sudden or excessive stress there is first the *alarm reaction,* during which the blood pressure and temperature fall and the blood sugar level first rises and then falls. This causes the pituitary and adrenals to secrete an excess of hormones to combat these changes and preserve the welfare of the body, and there is a reversal of the above changes during the *stage of resistance.* If stress is continued too long, the body succumbs to the effects of excesses of these hormones, originally produced for an emergency defense against stress, and the *stage of exhaustion* follows. The hypothalamus, hypophysis, and adrenals are the integrators of the body's defenses against stress, and the symptoms of reaction to stress are essentially those of autonomic imbalance.

DISTURBANCES OF TEMPERATURE REGULATION

Either hypothermia or hyperthermia may result from hypothalamic involvement. Temperature regulation takes place not only through an elevation or a fall in the body temperature, but also by means of the physical concomitants of vasodilatation, vasoconstriction, sweating, and shivering. Hyperthermia may result from involvement of the tuberal region, and especially of the supraoptic nuclei or the rostral portion of the anterior hypothalamic area. It is associated with sweating, vasodilatation, and other mechanisms for heat loss. Hyperthermia is a common symptom with third ventricle tumors, and may follow cerebral trauma or surgery; terminal hyperthermia is a frequent manifestation of cerebral disease. Hypothermia is associated with mechanisms for heat production and conservation, including vasoconstriction, increased visceral and somatic activity, and shivering; it may follow involvement of the posterior hypothalamic area and the mammillary bodies, or of the caudal portion of the lateral hypothalamus. With destruction of the anterior portion of the hypothalamus there is loss of ability to regulate against heat, and with destruction of the posterior portion there is loss of ability to regulate against cold.

DISTURBANCES OF WATER METABOLISM

The hypothalamus is closely related anatomically and physiologically to the posterior lobe of the hypophysis. It is probable that the central nervous system regulates water metabolism through the posterior lobe of the hypophysis. Lesions of the supraoptic nuclei and/or the supraopticohypophysial tract are followed by diabetes insipidus with polydipsia and polyuria (Fig. 264). This involvement is accompanied by degeneration of the nerves in the pituitary stalk and of the nuclei in the posterior lobe of the hypophysis. There is a resulting abnormality of fluid balance, with a marked increase in the fluid intake and output, owing to deficiency of antidiuretic hormone. Diabetes insipidus is a common symptom of tumors in the parasellar region, encephalitis, and meningitis, and may develop following intracranial surgery or cerebral trauma. There may be associated manifestations of hypothalamic dysfunction. The condition should be differentiated from the polyuria caused by diabetes mellitus, psychogenic polydipsia, hypercalcemia, and chronic renal disease. The symptoms may be relieved by the administration of either pitressin or posterior pituitary extract, either by injection or by intranasal insufflation. Diabetes insipidus may be a sequel of encephalitis.

Water intoxication may also be related to hypothalamic dysfunction, and may be caused by either excessive or inappropriate secretion of antidiuretic hormone. Other etiologies include renal insufficiency and sodium depletion, and it is sometimes either iatrogenic or self-induced.

DISTURBANCES OF GLUCOSE METABOLISM

Hyperglycemia with glycosuria, a syndrome resembling diabetes mellitus, may be caused by lesions of the tuber region, whereas hypoglycemia with abnormal sensitivity to insulin may follow lesions of the paraventricular nuclei. Hyperglycemia

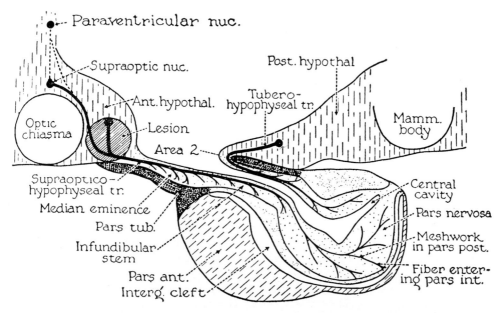

FIG 264. Longitudinal section through cat's hypothalamus and hypophysis, showing supraopticohypophyseal tract whose interruption causes diabetes insipidus. (Fisher, C., Ingram, W. R., and Ranson, S. W.: Diabetes Insipidus and the Neuorhormonal Control of Water Balance. Ann Arbor, Mich., Edwards Brothers Company, 1938.)

has also been reported in association with lesions of the region of the fourth ventricle, but this is probably the result of damage to the descending hypothalamic pathways or of secondary hypothalamic involvement. The hypothalamus has a general regulatory effect over the autonomic nervous system and over the endocrine system. Consequently stimulation of the areas concerned primarily with sympathetic regulation may cause glycogenolysis of the liver with resulting hyperglycemia, and stimulation of those centers concerned primarily with parasympathetic regulation may cause increased formation of insulin with hypoglycemia. Emotional hyperglycemia and glycosuria may be related to hypothalamic activity. Through its central regulatory effect on the hypophysis, thyroid, liver, pancreas, and suprarenal cortex the hypothalamus functions further in the regulation of carbohydrate metabolism. Symmetrical lesions of the lateral nuclei at the level of the tuber nuclei or of the region rostral and lateral to the tuber cinereum in experimental animals have prevented the appearance of hyperglycemia and glycosuria following pancreatectomy. On the other hand, degenerative changes in the paraventricular nuclei have been reported in diabetes mellitus and following pancreatectomy.

DISTURBANCES OF FAT METABOLISM

The Fröhlich, or adiposogenital, syndrome was the first hypothalamic syndrome to be described. This disorder usually occurs in boys and is characterized by disturbances of fat metabolism together with sexual underdevelopment. There is obesity of feminine distribution, often with girdles of fat about the pelvis. Associated manifestations include gynecomastia, underdevelopment of the external genitalia, and retardation of development of the secondary sexual characteristics. There may be underdevelopment of the bony skeleton. This syndrome was originally thought to have pituitary origin, but it is probably caused by a lesion of the nuclei in the middle portion of the tuber region of the hypothalamus. The Laurence-Moon-Biedl syndrome is characterized by obesity, hypogenitalism, mental retardation, polydactylism, and pigmentary degeneration of the retina; it is an inherited condition. The adiposogenital features may be secondary to hypothalamic involvement, and a deficiency of cells in the tuberal nuclei has been noted. In hyperostosis frontalis interna (Morgagni's syndrome) there are endocrine changes and obesity. Other disturbances of fat metabolism which may be secondary to hypothalamic involvement are lipodystrophy and adiposis dolorosa. The former is a generalized or a focal wasting of fatty tissues, especially of the face, upper extremities and upper part of the body, with sparing of the pelvis and lower extremities. The latter, also known as Dercum's disease, is characterized by the presence of large, painful deposits of fat over the shoulders, arms, and legs. Through the endocrine system (see below) the hypothalamus may play a part in the obesity and other disturbances of fat metabolism that occur with disorders of the pituitary and thyroid glands. Extreme wasting may also occur with hypothalamic and endocrine disorders.

DISTURBANCES OF BASAL METABOLISM

Through its effect on temperature regulation and on water, carbohydrate, and fat metabolism, and also through its regulatory effect upon the endocrine glands, the hypothalamus plays a part in the regulation of basal metabolism. Disturbances in the metabolic rate of varying types may be associated with hypothalamic lesions.

DISTURBANCES OF CIRCULATION, CARDIOVASCULAR REGULATION, AND BLOOD PRESSURE EQUILIBRIUM

Through its regulatory effect upon the autonomic nervous system, the hypothalamus plays an important part in the regulation of circulation, heart rate and rhythm, and blood pressure. Stimulation of the posterior and lateral hypothalamic nuclei causes vasoconstriction, an increased heart rate, and a rise in blood pressure, whereas stimulation of the anterior and midline hypothalamic nuclei and the tuber cinereum produces vasodilatation and reduction in heart rate.

The cerebral cortex also has a regulatory effect upon blood pressure and heart rate, and is important in the central control of vasomotor tone. Edema, cyanosis, variations in the caliber of the blood vessels, and temperature changes in the extremities may follow cerebral lesions. In cerebral hemiplegia the temperature of the affected extremities often is first elevated, owing to temporary vasodilatation, and then lowered owing to paralysis of reflex vasodilatation. The edema in cerebral hemiplegia is usually mild and may be associated in part with disuse and dependency. If there is any tendency toward the development of edema, due to cardiac involvement or renal disease, such edema occurs first in the paretic extremities, and the edema that is seen in hemiplegia may on occasion be alleviated by treatment of underlying cardiac or renal disease. It may be that the cerebral lesion merely tends to localize the actual or potential edema to the paretic extremities, but most authorities do believe that in certain instances the circulatory disturbances and edema of the hemiplegic limbs have cerebral origin.

Abnormalities of heart rate and blood pressure also follow lesions of the secondary reflex centers in the medulla. Pressure on the medulla associated with increased intracranial pressure may cause a marked bradycardia and either an elevation or a decline in the blood pressure. This often has serious prognostic significance. So-called essential hypertension may be either hypothalamic or cortical in origin. Emotional hypertension is a reflex response to various affective stimuli; when present over a long period of time, secondary organic changes develop.

Hematopoiesis may also be in part under the influence of the hypothalamus, and polycythemia has been described in association with hypothalamic lesions, especially those involving the hypophysiotuberal region. The presence of an erythrocyte regulatory center in the hypothalamus has been suggested.

DISTURBANCES OF RESPIRATION

Abnormalities of the rate, rhythm, and amplitude of respiration, such as hyperpnea, apnea, Cheyne-Stokes' respirations, Biot's breathing, and air hunger, may be caused by central, probably hypothalamic, involvement. Hiccuping and yawning are often associated with hypothalamic disease. In postencephalitic states there frequently are bizarre abnormalities of breathing, with respiratory tics. Respiration is also influenced by the cortex and is regulated in part by the secondary reflex center in the region of the dorsal efferent nucleus of the vagus nerve. Changes in the electrolyte and carbon dioxide content of the blood may affect this center, and herniation of the medulla into the foramen magnum may cause respiratory arrest by pressure on it.

DISTURBANCES OF GASTROINTESTINAL FUNCTION

The hypothalamus is the center concerned with integration and correlation of visceral impulses. Olfactory, gustatory, and other types of stimuli that come into this region call out various types of visceral responses. Lesions of the hypothalamus and its connections can cause accelerated gastrointestinal motility, increased secretion, hypersalivation, and excessive hunger (bulimia or hyperphagia), or they can cause decreased motility and secretion, dry mouth, and decreased appetite. Bulimia is an important symptom of the Klüver-Bucy and Kleine-Levin syndromes, but it may also be present with other cerebral disorders. Lesions of the anterior and midline nuclei may cause gastric atony, increased gastric secretions, mucosal hemorrhages, and ulcerations, and also ulcerations of the esophagus and intestines and intussusception. Such phenomena may also be associated with cortical lesions, involvement of the medullary centers, and vagal irritation. Projectile vomiting is often associated with increased intracranial pressure, probably the result of pressure on medullary centers. The epigastric aura of epilepsy and the gustatory and olfactory hallucinations and smacking and tasting movements of psychomotor epilepsy are caused by cortical discharges. So-called abdominal epilepsy and migraine may also be caused by cortical discharges.

DISTURBANCES OF BLADDER FUNCTION

Although the hypothalamus undoubtedly plays an important part in bladder function, not much is known concerning the clinical manifestations of vesical disturbances in hypothalamic disease. The relationship of the cerebrum, especially the paracentral lobules, is better known. The types of bladder dysfunction that may follow cerebral lesions are mentioned on page 695.

DISTURBANCES OF THE SLEEP CYCLE

The hypothalamus, especially its posterior portions including the mammillary bodies, are important in the maintenance of the normal sleep rhythm, and lesions of it may cause hypersomnia, inversion of the sleep cycle, and insomnia. Stimulation of the posterior hypothalamus has been reported to cause both hypersomnia and arousal and wakefulness. It is difficult, however, to isolate the part that the hypothalamus plays in the regulation of sleep from that of the closely adjacent and even overlapping ascending reticular activating system and the diffuse thalamocortical projection system (Chapter 51); the hypersomnia and other abnormalities of sleep that have been reported with hypothalamic lesions may not be due to involvement of this structure alone, but also, or instead, due to involvement of the midbrain reticular system, or to interruption of the pathways from the cortex to the hypothalamus or of the mammillary peduncle or the mammillotegmental tract.

Hypersomnia is found in acute encephalitis, posttraumatic states, increased intracranial pressure, Wernicke's syndrome, intoxication by barbiturates and other soporifics, and brain tumors, especially those in the region of the third ventricle. Inversion of the sleep cycle may also occur in encephalitis. *Narcolepsy* may be associated with lesions of the posterior hypothalamus, but in most cases the exact etiology or mechanism is not known. In the *Kleine-Levin* syndrome there are periodic attacks of hypersomnia accompanied by bulimia, irritability, behavioral changes, and unhibited sexuality, usually occurring in young males; a hypothalamic abnormality is suspected, although the basic etiology is unknown. So-called activated or paradoxical sleep (Chapter 55), which is accompanied by rapid eye movements, a low voltage, fast electroencephalographic pattern, dreaming, and motor inhibition, probably has its origin in the reticular formation.

DISTURBANCES OF SEXUAL FUNCTION

Sexual infantilism may occur as an isolated phenomenon or as a part of the Fröhlich syndrome. It is a manifestation of damage to the nuclei in the middle portion of the tuberal region. Sexual precocity has been described as a characteristic symptom of the pineal syndrome; the hypothalamus, however, is the critical site for lesions causing pubertas praecox, and it is probably due to pressure on or involvement of the ventromedial and lateral tuberal nuclei and mammillary bodies. Both sexual infantilism and sexual precocity are described as manifestations of dysfunction of the endocrine glands, especially the pituitary, gonads, and the suprarenal glands; such changes may be secondary to underlying hypothalamic involvement. Increased libido, decreased libido, impotence, amenorrhea, hypermenorrhea, and other manifestations of sexual dysfunction are sometimes partly hypothalamic in origin. The somatic manifestations of the orgasm may be those of hypothalamic stimulation.

DISTURBANCES OF THE EMOTIONS

It has been stated that the hypothalamus is the seat of the emotions and of personality. This assertion cannot be proved, but it is the center which reinforces and coordinates the neural and humoral mechanisms of emotional expression. When the posterior portion of the hypothalamus is released from control by higher centers of the brain, a complex of primitive pseudo-affective reactions take place. This phenomenon can be exhibited in experimental animals by the production of "sham rage" with pupillary dilatation, increased pulse rate and blood pressure, piloerection, and other signs of sympathetic activity. These physical manifestations suggest that an intense emotional reaction is taking place, but there may be merely a motor expression of rage without change in affect. Similar manifestations have been produced by stimulation of the posterior and lateral hypothalamic areas and by bilateral removal of the frontal or temporal lobes. Abnormal affective and emotional reactions, fear, and aggressive behavior, however, may also be lessened by interruption of the connections between various cortical areas in the frontal and limbic lobes and the thalamus and hypothalamus.

In *autonomic,* or *diencephalic, epilepsy* there are paroxysmal attacks characterized by flushing, lacrimation, perspiration, salivation, contraction and dilatation of the pupils, pilomotor disturbances, either chills or hyperthermia, changes in pulse rate and blood pressure, gastrointestinal disturbances, urinary incontinence or frequency, abnormalities of respiration, and occasionally loss of consciousness. These symptoms have been attributed to hypothalamic stimulation. Similar autonomis crises have been described in postencephalitic states.

The physical concomitants of emotion, namely tachycardia, tachypnea, elevation of the blood pressure, perspiration, flushing, piloerection, and various disturbances of gastrointestinal function, are in reality those of hypothalamic function with secondary visceral effects. It has been found that anxiety, resentment, and anger are accompanied by adrenergic changes in the blood, whereas tension and possibly fear are associated with cholinergic changes. In emotional disturbances associated with psychopathologic states these abnormalities of the adrenergic and cholinergic responses are exaggerated. In many of the psychoneuroses the symptoms are largely somatic, or vegetative, in nature, and are similar to the physical symptoms encountered in various emotional states. Those referable to the cardiorespiratory system may be characterized by tachycardia, palpitation, dyspnea, irregular respiration, and pain in the chest. Those referable to the gastrointestinal tract consist of gaseous indigestion, pain, nausea, vomiting, pylorospasm, hyperacidity, spastic constipation, atonic constipation, and diarrhea. Those referable to the genitourinary system may be characterized by frequency, dysuria, impotence, lack of libido, amenorrhea, and frigidity. The symptoms of the anxiety psychoneuroses, namely tension, palpitation, hyperpnea, nausea, frequency, mydriasis, cold hands and feet, dry mouth, and variable blood pressure, are often those of hypothalamic stimulation. All are symptoms of autonomic imbalance, and may be of central origin. Many disease syndromes such as hypertension, coronary disease, hyperthyroidism, peptic ulcer, spastic constipation, ulcerative colitis, migraine, bronchial asthma, and arthritis may have definite psychosomatic correlations, if they are not entirely of psychogenic origin. The hypothalamus certainly plays a large part in their development, either primarily or secondarily, even though its relationship to the disease process and the correlations between the organic process and the psychogenic manifestations are not known. The psychogalvanometer, evaluation of sweating and vasomotor changes, and other tests of autonomic nervous system function may be used in the study of patients with psychosomatic disorders.

There is also evidence which suggests that disturbances of function of the hypothalamus and of the limbic, septal, and related areas of the brain may bear a causal relationship to the development of certain psychiatric syndromes. Lesions of the anterior portion of the hypothalamus tend to produce excitement, whereas posterior lesions may be accompanied by lethargy, indifference, depression, and possibly even catatonic manifestations. Stimulation of the above-mentioned cortical areas, in both experimental animals and man, may cause emotional responses as well as signs of autonomic nervous system activity, and abnormal electrical recordings have been obtained from electrodes implanted in the septal region of schizophrenic patients. Certain drugs and toxins which act upon the hypothalamus and the reticular formation can cause hallucinations and other symptoms of mental disease, whereas other drugs which act upon these same areas can relieve many of the symptoms associated with the psychoses.

Regardless of the actual or proved relationship of the autonomic nervous system, and especially of the hypothalamus and its cortical influences, to the neuroses and psychoses, it must be assumed that it has a close and definite relationship to the emotional state of the individual and its abnormalities. Whether or not one's emotional life is determined by the functional activity and balance of the hypothalamus and the autonomic nervous system, it can be stated without doubt that the physical symptoms which occur in normal and pathologic emotional states are those of autonomic nervous system activity. Changes in personality varying from the organ neuroses and simple depressions to manic states and the major psychoses may be in part related to hypothalamic dysfunction. Interruption of the pathways between the frontal cortex and the thalamus and hypothalamus has been used for the treatment of certain psychotic states.

DISTURBANCES OF ENDOCRINE DYSFUNCTION

The hypothalamus is closely related, both anatomically and functionally, to the hypophysis, or pituitary gland, and it stimulates and controls the release of corticotropin, gonadotropins, prolactin, somatotropin, and thyrotropin by the adenohypophysis and vasopressin (including antidiuretic hormone) and oxytocin by the neurohypophysis. Consequently abnormalities of its function may have a close relationship to the various disturbance of endocrine function.

With disease of the pituitary gland the major symptoms and signs are those of either overactivity or underactivity of the gland itself, but there are often associated hypothalamic disturbances. Either hyperactivity or an eosinophilic adenoma of the anterior lobe causes giantism or acromegaly. With an adenoma of the chromophobe cells there are generalized endocrine changes, with obesity, hypometabolism, and either impotence or decreased sexual appetite in the male and amenorrhea in the female. An adenoma of the basophilic cells causes Cushing's syndrome, with obesity, hypertension, amenorrhea, hypertrichosis, polycythemia, and weakness. Similar symptoms may be present with neoplasms of the adrenal glands, ovaries, and testicles, and with involvement of the paraventricular nuclei of the hypothalamus. Deficiency of the pituitary in a child may cause the Lorain syndrome, or dwarfism. In Simmonds' disease, or pituitary cachexia, atrophy of the pituitary causes symptoms of adrenocortical, gonadal, and thyroid deficiency, with anorexia, weakness, emaciation, loss of sexual functions, and premature aging. In Sheehan's syndrome, or ischemic necrosis of the anterior lobe of the pituitary following childbirth or severe postpartum hemorrhage, the symptoms are similar, but appear more rapidly. Hypophysectomy, or complete ablation of the pituitary, has been carried out in the treatment of severe diabetes mellitus and advanced carcinomatosis.

The hypothalamus, either directly or through the pituitary, may play a part in the development of either hyperthyroidism or hypothyroidism. The nuclei of the tuber region may regulate the internal secretion of the thyroid, adrenal, and other glands. Lesions of the hypothalamus may affect the islet cells of the pancreas, causing either diabetes mellitus or hyperinsulinism with hypoglycemia. The effect on the sexual glands may be direct, rather than through the pituitary, and cause sexual precocity, impotence, amenorrhea, deficient development of primary or secondary sexual characteristics, and sexual infantilism.

MISCELLANEOUS DISTURBANCES OF AUTONOMIC FUNCTION

There are other disturbances of function which seem to be related, in part at least, to abnormalities of the autonomic nervous system. These cannot, however, be attributed specifically to either peripheral or central lesions.

ALLERGIC DISTURBANCES

The predominant manifestations of allergy are vasodilatation and exudation. These occur in individuals of the "exudative diathesis," often those with evidences of some vagal hyperactivity. In the skin manifestations such as urticaria, eczema, and angioneurotic edema there is exudation. In hay fever and allergic rhinitis there is vasodilatation, with hypersecretion of the mucous membranes and lacrimal glands. In asthma there is spasm of the bronchial musculature together with vasodilatation and exudation of the mucosa. In migraine there is vasodilatation. Many of these manifestations are relieved by the use of parasympathetic depressants, sympathomimetic drugs, and antihistamine compounds. There is also a close relationship between anaphylaxis and the autonomic nervous system.

TROPHIC DISORDERS

In addition to trophic disorders which involve the skin and blood vessels there are trophic disturbances of autonomic origin which affect the bones, joints, and muscles. They are usually associated with lesions of the motor or sensory nerves or both, but involvement of the autonomic, or trophic fibers is responsible for the pathologic changes.

Trophic changes involving the bones and joints are seen most frequently in tabes dorsalis, but they may also occur in syringomyelia, spinal cord tumors, and other spinal lesions, and they have been described in diabetic neuropathy and in other types of peripheral neuropathy. There is first an osteoporosis accompanied by an abnormal brittleness of the bones which may lead to spontaneous fracture, but the most characteristic changes are those in the joints. There are secretory disturbances of the synovia with swelling of the joints, destruction of joint surfaces and ligaments, atrophy of cartilage or bone, and often painless intra-articular fractures and dislocations; this is known as the Charcot arthropathy. With posttraumatic and other peripheral nerve lesions there may be osteoporosis (Sudeck's atrophy or reflex sympathetic dystrophy). Effusions into the joints, known as acute intermittent articular hydrops, may be a manifestation of angioneurotic edema. Osteoporosis, osteomalacia, and osteitis fibrosa cystica may occur with parathyroid dysfunction.

Primary atrophy of the muscle is a result of disease of the voluntary motor system. In disease of the autonomic nervous system, however, there may be muscle atrophy associated with trophic changes in the skin and subcutaneous tissues. In

Volkmann's contracture, or ischemic paralysis, there is muscle atrophy due to loss of nutrition and decreased oxygenation of the muscles, and this may be accompanied by changes in the skin and subcutaneous tissues, with cyanosis, coldness, edema, fibrous change in the subcutaneous tissues, etc. Later there is fibrous transformation of the muscles and tendons, with resulting deformities. These changes are out of proportion to the involvement of the motor and sensory nerves.

Either *hemiatrophy* or *hemihypertrophy* may involve one half of the face or one half of the face and body. There is atrophy of the skin, subcutaneous tissues, muscles, and bones. There may be alopecia and scleroderma in the atrophic areas.

OTHER DISTURBANCES

Familial dysautonomia, or the *Riley-Day* syndrome, is a rare congenital disease of infancy characterized by peripheral vascular disturbances, excessive perspiration, deficient lacrimation, postural hypotension, erratic temperature control, areflexia, relative indifference to pain, defective taste discrimination, poor coordination, an exaggerated hypertensive response to norepinephrine and increased response to methacholine, and emotional lability. Changes in the peripheral autonomic nervous system have been reported.

Cerebral lesions, especially those of the frontal lobes and/or hypothalamus, may cause various disturbances of *electrolyte metabolism,* usually with hypernatremia and hyperchloremia.

Swift's disease, acrodynia, erythredema, or pink disease is often considered to be a disorder of the autonomic nervous system. It is characterized by loss of weight, anorexia, motor weakness, dysesthesias, tachycardia, hypertension, erythema and cyanosis of the extremities, hyperhidrosis, insomnia and inversion of the sleep cycle, psychic disturbances, and trophic changes with stomatitis and loss of hair, nails, and teeth. Its etiology and its relationship to the autonomic nervous system are not known.

Tabetic crises consist of painful spasms of the viscera. They most frequently involve the stomach but may involve the intestines, bladder, larynx, and vagina. They may be initiated through overactivity of the autonomic nervous system.

REFERENCES

ANDERSON, E., and HAYMAKER, W. "Disorders of the Hypothalamus and Pituitary Gland," in Baker, A. B. (ed.), Clinical Neurology (ed. 2). New York, Hoeber Medical Division, Harper & Row, 1962, vol. 3, pp. 1338–1405.

BROUWER, B. Positive and negative aspects of hypothalamic disorders. *J. Neurol., Neurosurg. & Psychiat.* 13:16, 1950.

CALDWELL, K. P. S., FLACK, F. C., and BROAD, A. F. Urinary incontinence following spinal injury treated by electronic implant. *Lancet* 1:846, 1965.

CUSHING, H. Papers Relating to the Pituitary Body, Hypothalamus and Parasympathetic Nervous System. Springfield, Ill., Charles C Thomas, 1932.

DAVISON, C., and DEMUTH, E. L. Disturbances in sleep mechanism: A clinicopathologic study. I. Lesions at the cortical level. *Arch. Neurol. & Psychiat.* 53:399, 1945; II. Lesions at the corticodiencephalic level. *Ibid.,* 54:241, 1945; III. Lesions at the diencephalic level (hypothalamus). *Ibid.,* 55:111, 1946; IV. Lesions at the mesencephalometencephalic level. *Ibid.*, 55:126, 1946; V. Anatomic and neurophysiologic considerations. *Ibid.*, 55:364, 1946.

DRAGSTEDT, L. R.   Vagotomy for gastroduodenal ulcer.   *Ann. Surg.* 122:973, 1945.

ECHLIN, F., OWENS, F. M., JR., and WELLS, W. L.   Observations on "major" and "minor" causalgia.   *Arch. Neurol. & Psychiat.* 62:183, 1949.

EPPINGER, H., and HESS, L.   Vagotonia: A Clinical Study in Vegetative Neurology. (W. K. Kraus and S. E. Jelliffe, trans.)   New York, The Nervous and Mental Disease Publishing Company, 1917.

FISHER, C., INGRAM, W. R., and RANSON, S. W.   Diabetes Insipidus and the Neuro-hormonal Control of Water Balance: A Contribution to the Structure and Function of the Hypothalamico-hypophyseal System.   Ann Arbor, Michigan, Edwards Brothers Company, 1938.

FULTON, J. F.   The limbic system: A study of the visceral brain in primates and man. *Yale J. Biol. & Med.* 26:107, 1953.

GARLAND, H., SUMNER, D., and FORMAN, R. P.   The Kleine-Levin syndrome.   *Neurology* 15:1161, 1965.

GELLHORN, E.   Analysis of autonomic hypothalamic functions in the intact organism. *Neurology* 6:335, 1956.

GREEN, J. D.   "Neural pathways to the hypophysis," in FIELDS, W. S., GUILLEMIN, R., and CARTON, C. A. (eds.) *Hypothalamic-Hypophysial Interrelationships.* Springfield, Ill., Charles C Thomas, 1956.

HARRIS, M. A.   The hypothalamus and endocrine glands.   *Brit. M. Bull.* 6:345, 1950.

HEATH, R. G.   (ed.) Studies in Schizophrenia: A Multidisciplinary Approach to Mind-Brain Relationships.   Cambridge, Mass., Harvard University Press, 1954.

LUHAN, J. A.   Hemiedema in cases of hemiplegia.   *Arch. Neurol. & Psychiat.* 36:42, 1936.

MacLEAN, P. D.   The limbic system ("visceral brain") and emotional behavior. *A. M. A. Arch. Neurol. & Psychiat.* 73:130, 1955.

MAJOR, S.   Schizophrenia: A diencephalic syndrome.   *Psychiatric Quart.* 23:83, 1949.

MASSERMAN, J. H.,The hypothalamus in psychiatry.   *Am. J. Psychiat.* 98:633, 1942.

MAYFIELD, F. H.   Causalgia.   Springfield, Ill., Charles C Thomas, 1951.

McLELLAN, F. C.   The Neurogenic Bladder.   Springfield, Ill., Charles C Thomas, 1939.

MORGAN, L. O.   Cell changes in the hypothalamus in the major psychoses.   *A. Res. Nerv. & Ment. Dis., Proc.* (1939) 20:753, 1940.

PAPEZ, J. W.   A proposed mechanism of emotion.   *Arch. Neurol. & Psychiat.* 38:725, 1937.

PENFIELD, W. G.   Diencephalic autonomic epilepsy.   *A. Res. Nerv. & Ment. Dis., Proc.* (1928) 9:645, 1930.

POLLOCK, L. J., *et al.*   Defects in regulatory mechanisms of autonomic function in injuries to spinal cord.   *J. Neurophysiol.* 14:85, 1951.

POUSSAINT, A. F., and DITMAN, K. S.   A controlled study of imipramine (Tofranil) in the treatment of childhood enuresis.   *J. Pediat.* 67:283, 1965.

RILEY, C. M.   Familial autonomic dysfunction. *J.A.M.A.* 149:1532, 1952.

ROSS, A. T.   Progressive selective sudomotor denervation: A case with coexisting Adie's syndrome.   *Neurology* 8:809, 1958.

SEDDON, H.   Volkmann's ischaemia.   *Brit. M. J.* 1:1587, 1964.

SELYE, H.   The general adaptation syndrome and the diseases of adaptation.   *J. Clin. Endocrinology* 6:117, 1946.

SHY, G. M., and DRAGER, G. A.   A neurological syndrome associated with orthostatic hypotension. *Arch. Neurol.* 2:511, 1960.

SINGER, H. D.   Psychosis and the central autonomic nervous system. *J.A.M.A.* 110:2048, 1938; *Arch. Neurol. & Psychiat.* 42:562, 1938.

SOLITAIRE, G. B., and COHEN, G. S.   Peripheral autonomic nervous system lesions in congenital familial dysautonomia (Riley-Day syndrome). *Neurology* 15:321, 1965.

SWENSON, O., RHEINLANDER, H. F., and DIAMOND, I.   Hirschsprung's diseases: A new concept of the etiology: Operative results in thirty-four patients. *New England J. Med.* 241:551, 1949.

WECHSLER, I. A.   Clinical hypothalamic syndromes: Anatomicophysiological correlations. *J. Nerv. & Ment. Dis.* 117:492, 1953; Hypothalamic syndromes. *Brit. M. J.* 2:375, 1956.

PART SEVEN

Diagnosis and Localization of Disease of the Peripheral Nerves, Nerve Roots, and Spinal Cord

DIAGNOSIS AND LOCALIZATION OF DISEASE OF THE PERIPHERAL NERVES, NERVE ROOTS, AND SPINAL CORD

To MAKE an accurate neurologic diagnosis one must not only establish the presence of a lesion, but also, if possible, localize the lesion accurately in either the central or the peripheral nervous system. Following this, one should attempt to determine the nature and etiology of the process. Disorders of the nervous system may affect either its peripheral portions, the individual nerves and the nerve roots, or its central portions, the cerebrospinal axis, including the spinal cord, brain stem, midbrain, cerebellum, and cerebrum. Neurologic localization depends upon the determination of the exact site or sites of involvement of the nervous system.

To localize a lesion of the peripheral nerves one must know the anatomy and physiology of the nerves. Accurate delineation of the site of involvement depends upon specific sensory, motor, trophic, vasomotor, and reflex changes. This is also true of the nerve roots and of the larger nerve trunks in the major plexuses. To localize a lesion within the spinal cord one must be familiar not only with the cross-sectional anatomy of the cord, the cellular distribution in the gray matter, and the principal ascending and descending fiber pathways in the white matter, but also with the details of the longitudinal anatomy and the segmental supply of the sensory, motor, and autonomic functions.

CHAPTER 44

DISEASE OF THE PERIPHERAL NERVES

ANATOMY AND PHYSIOLOGY OF THE PERIPHERAL NERVES

A TYPICAL PERIPHERAL nerve has mixed functions. That is, it conducts sensory, motor, and autonomic impulses. The anatomic, physiologic, and clinical characteristics of the cranial nerves are discussed individually ("The Cranial Nerves," Part III). Those of the peripheral spinal, or segmental, nerves are considered in the present part.

The *motor components* of the peripheral nerves arise in the anterior horn cells of the spinal cord and course in the converging filaments of the ventral spinal root. They are ultimately distributed to striated muscles. The *sensory components* arise in the various receptors, or end organs; they have their cell bodies in the dorsal root ganglia and enter the spinal cord through the dorsal spinal roots. The ventral and dorsal roots unite to form the mixed spinal nerve. After this has passed through the intervertebral foramen it divides into anterior and posterior primary rami. These rami subdivide to supply muscular and sensory structures (Fig. 251). The *autonomic components* of the twelve thoracic and upper two or three lumbar segments of the spinal cord (sympathetic division) arise from cells in the intermediolateral column. They make their exit with the ventral roots of the corresponding segmental nerves and traverse the mixed spinal nerve to reach the anterior primary ramus. Here they split off from the proximal part of this ramus as finely myelinated fibers (white rami communicantes) and enter the ganglionated sympathetic chain. The postganglionic fibers are unmyelinated (gray rami communicantes); on reaching the anterior primary ramus they split into two groups, one going with the anterior and the other with the posterior primary ramus. Other autonomic fibers, both those of the parasympathetic division and those from the prevertebral plexuses and collateral ganglia, join the mixed nerves peripherally, although fibers of the sacral portion of the parasympathetic division enter the mixed nerves with the ventral roots.

The posterior primary rami are smaller than the anterior primary rami. They supply the dorsal structures of the body, including the skin of the posterior surfaces and the longitudinal muscles associated with the axial skeleton. The anterior primary rami, which are larger, are really the continuations of the mixed nerves. They supply the ventral and lateral muscles and the skin of the ventrolateral aspects of the body. In the region of the extremities they form the plexuses which innervate the limbs. The anterior primary rami of the thoracic segments of the spinal cord are continued as the intercostal nerves. The lack of correspondence between the spinal segments and their emerging fibers and the spinous processes of the vertebrae is discussed elsewhere (see p. 78 and Fig. 16).

Disease of the peripheral nerves is characterized by diminution or loss of certain functions and/or perversion of function. These changes are secondary to either impairment or interruption of the conduction of impulses through the nerves, or to irritation.

Diminution or loss of function may involve interference with both efferent and afferent impulses. *Interference with conduction of efferent impulses* causes motor and autonomic changes. *Motor changes* are characterized by paresis or paralysis of certain muscles or muscle groups. This paresis is focal, often complete for the muscles involved, and is hypotonic, or flaccid, in character. It may be accompanied or followed by atrophy and altered electrical responses. *Interference with conduction of autonomic impulses* results in sudomotor, pilomotor, and vasomotor paralysis, with dryness of the skin, vasodilatation, and loss of piloerection. Later there may be cyanosis, edema, secretory and temperature disturbances, and "trophic" changes in the skin, subcutaneous tissues, hair, and nails, and sometimes in the blood vessels, bones, and joints. Involvement of either parasympathetic or sympathetic fibers which mediate specific visceral and other impulses may cause widespread disturbances of autonomic function (Part VI). *Interference with conduction of afferent impulses* produces impairment or loss of pain, temperature, tactile, pressure, and proprioceptive sensibility. Interference with the conduction of either efferent or afferent impulses may cause loss of reflexes.

Perversions of function may also involve either efferent or afferent impulses They may be caused by irritation, incomplete loss of conduction, or partial assumption of function by intact elements. *Perversions of function of efferent motor impulses* may produce muscular twitchings (fasciculations), muscle spasm, or reflex rigidity. *Abnormal function of efferent autonomic impulses* causes alterations of sweating, vasomotor changes, glossy skin, and edema. *Disturbances of function of the afferent fibers* produce spontaneous pain, paresthesias, phantom sensations, or abnormal responses to heat and cold.

Injuries to nerves may vary in degree and extent, and are classified variously. Using the histologic classification of Seddon, a complete division of a peripheral nerve is known as *neurotmesis*. There is interruption of continuity of all essential structures, with complete loss of conduction of both efferent and afferent impulses. This leads to complete and permanent degeneration of the nerve. In *axonotmesis* there is loss of function of the axons, or nerve fibers, with resulting peripheral degeneration of the conducting structures of the nerve, but the supporting tissues, the epineurium and endoneurium, are preserved. Spontaneous recovery may occur, and during regeneration the nerve fibers follow their original channels. In *neurapraxia* there is a transient block or interruption of continuity, due to compression or blows by blunt instruments. There is a minimal lesion which does not produce complete paralysis and is not accompanied by peripheral degeneration, although there may be some loss of myelin; recovery is rapid and complete. Sunderland, on the other hand, uses a classification based on both histologic and physiologic changes. He lists five degrees of injury dependent upon the alterations of the axon, axonal sheath, funiculus, and epineurium. With first degree injury conduction is blocked but the continuity of all components is preserved, so that function is rapidly and completely restored. With second degree injury the axon degenerates below the site of injury but the rest of the nerve is intact; the axon can regenerate in its original endoneurial tube, and there is complete restoration of the original pattern of innervation. With third degree injury both the axon and the continuity of the endoneurial tube are destroyed, and the chances of cross-shunting of regenerating axons is introduced. With fourth degree injury there is complete disorganization of the internal structure of the nerve with preservation of its continuity; the regenerating fibers may become lost or terminate blindly. With fifth degree injuries there is complete severance of nerves.

Most or all peripheral nerves of any size are myelinated. When such a nerve is cut or severed from its cell body, certain changes take place, and there is *Wallerian degeneration* distal to the point of transection. The myelin sheath swells, retracts, becomes fragmented, and breaks down into lipoid materal. The neurofibrillae of the axon become swollen and fragmented. The neurilemmal cells of Schwann multiply; the sheath hypertrophies and fills up the space formerly occupied by the myelin, and its cells assume phagocytic activity. Within one to three months the fibers and myelin have completely disappeared, and the motor end plates have degenerated. The neurilemmal sheath and the connective tissue septa of the nerve are left. The proximal segment of the nerve degenerates for only a short distance. If the injury is close to the cell body, the latter may undergo chromatolysis. *Regeneration,* if it takes place, proceeds distally from the central stump, and the growing fibers penetrate the scar tissue and enter the empty sheath. Functional maturation of the axonal pathway (myelinization and restoration of fiber diameter) proceeds more slowly than regrowth of the axis fibers. Regeneration is facilitated by suturing the nerve. The rate of growth varies with different nerves, and atrophy of muscle has an adverse effect on restoration of function. Regeneration does not take place within the central nervous system. If tissue is interposed and there is some obstruction to regeneration, or if the nerve has been completely severed, a neuroma may develop at the distal end of the proximal segment.

Nerves may be injured by trauma to the neuron or its neuraxis, pressure, chemical or toxic influences, interruption of blood supply, infectious processes, or deficiency in substances normally required for nerve metabolism. There is a difference in the diameter of the various nerve fibers, and this is accompanied by a variability in the rate of conduction of impulses and refractory period and by a difference in vulnerability to different types of injury. The largest, or "A," fibers carry motor, proprioceptive, pressure, and tactile impulses. These are the most susceptible to pressure and anoxia. The smaller "B" fibers carry localized, "first," or fast pain impulses, as well as thermal sensibility. The smallest, or "C," fibers are mainly unmyelinated and carry less well localized, "second," or slow pain, together with vasomotor impulses. Cocaine, which blocks the conduction of the smaller fibers first, causes loss of sensation in the order of slow pain, cold, warmth, fast pain, touch, and position. Autonomic functions disappear before motor functions. Pressure, which blocks the conduction of the large fibers first, causes loss of motor power, then diminution in sensation in the order of position, vibration, pressure, touch, fast pain, cold, warmth, and slow pain, followed by vasomotor paralysis.

The diagnosis and localization of peripheral nerve lesions depends upon the recognition and delineation of changes in function. Diminution or loss of function produces changes which are more outstanding and more apparent objectively than perversion of function. To determine the presence and ascertain the site of involvement of peripheral nerves, one must utilize those portions of the neurologic examination which have already been described. It is important to recognize the specific nerve or nerves involved, to estimate the degree of damage, and to determine whether the dysfunction is progressing or lessening, and whether spontaneous recovery may be expected or surgical treatment is required. It is necessary to be familiar with peripheral nerve, plexus, and nerve root supply to the individual muscles and to cutaneous areas in order to differentiate between peripheral nerve, plexus, radicular, and spinal cord lesions.

The *sensory examination* must be done carefully and completely (Part II, "The Sensory System"), and the examiner should be familiar with the cutaneous distribution of the more important peripheral nerves (Fig. 11, pp. 71–72). There may be loss or diminution of all types of sensation. The exteroceptive sensations are more important than the proprioceptive ones, especially in lesions restricted to the smaller nerves or to the individual branches of the larger nerves, but with extensive involvement the proprioceptive changes are also significant. There may be areas of anesthesia, hypesthesia, or hyperesthesia corresponding to the sensory distribution of the nerves involved. One must, however, bear in mind the individual variation in areas supplied by the peripheral nerves (Fig. 12), and the algesic overlap (Fig. 13). Occasionally there is spread of sensory loss beyond the field of the injured nerve. With incomplete and irritative lesions there may be either paresthesias or pain. The latter may be dull, sharp, steady, or intermittent, but is often stabbing or lancinating in character. Pain and numbness may be present simultaneously. The nerves themselves may be hyperalgesic and sensitive, or tender to pressure, and the associated muscles and tendons may show tenderness to pressure. Tender areas along the course of affected nerves are called *Valleix's points*. Pain in the distribution of a single nerve group of nerves may be relieved by section of the nerves involved or by injection of novocaine or alcohol; to prevent regeneration the nerve should be sectioned central to the dorsal root ganglion.

The *motor examination* is directed especially toward the recognition of loss or impairment of function of specific muscles or muscle groups (Part IV, "The Motor System"). The examiner should be familiar with the nerve supply of the individual muscles (Tables 3 to 6, pp. 454–484), and should test the muscles for active motor power. In addition it is important to note tone, volume and contour, hyperkinetic phenomena, contractures, and abnormalities of position. Electrodiagnostic procedures, including the electromyogram and nerve conduction velocity determinations, are often of extreme importance.

The examination of the *autonomic nervous system* may include such investigations as sweating tests and vasomotor and skin temperature studies. The determination of skin resistance gives information about the continuity of the sympathetic component of the peripheral nerves. The histamine flare is disturbed in nerve lesions, and its presence aids in the diagnosis of such lesions as well as in the differentiation between organic and psychogenic changes. Novocaine block and autonomic nervous system injections also have diagnostic value. Trophic changes such as dryness and abnormalities of texture of the skin, cyanosis, hyperhidrosis, hypertrichosis, loss of hair, brittle nails, ulcerations, slow healing, and edema should always be looked for (Part VI).

The deep and superficial *reflexes* must be tested (Part V), as well as certain autonomic nervous system reflexes. Palpation of the involved nerves is an important part of the examination. The size, tenderness, and consistency should be noted, and abnormalities of contour, irritability, thickening or hypertrophy, and evidences of infiltration looked for. There may be pain on passive stretching of the nerves. In the hypertrophic neuritis of Dejerine and Sottas there is hyperplasia of the involved nerves; neuromas and neurofibromas are often palpable. Tenderness of the muscles and tendons may be associated with nerve tenderness. Occasionally both muscle and nerve biopsies give pertinent information. In peripheral involvement of the cranial nerves special methods of examination are carried out (Part III).

Syndromes of interruption, compression, contusion, concussion, and irritation of the peripheral nerves are described. In *complete interruption of the continuity* of a nerve there is an immediate, complete paralysis of all muscles supplied by it. This is followed by progressive loss of tone, with atrophy and a loss of electrical reactions. Spasm and overactivity of the antagonistic muscles may cause contractures. There is also an immediate, complete anesthesia, with absence of pain on pressure applied to the nerve distal to the lesion. Autonomic functions disappear. Reflexes, both deep and superficial, are lost if either the afferent or efferent portion of the arc is carried by the involved nerve, but muscular irritability may be increased. There usually is no pain. With *partial interruption* there usually is clinical evidence of complete loss of function for a period of time after the injury, following which the intact fibers resume normal conduction of impulses. The injured fibers may not regain their functions, and irritative phenomena and trophic changes frequently appear. The objective findings vary according to the degree and site of injury; motor, sensory, or autonomic changes may predominate.

In the *syndrome of compression* there may be either complete or incomplete paralysis, with variable sensory changes. Tone is preserved, atrophy and reflex changes may or may not be present, and there is a partial reaction of degeneration.

Pain may be present or absent. If the compression is abrupt but is relieved, there will be progressive recovery of function. On the other hand, compression by callus formation or scar tissue and entrapment at a point where a nerve goes through a fibrous or osseofibrous tunnel or changes its course over a fibrous or muscular band may cause progressive impairment leading to complete loss of function. In *contusion* there is rupture of the fibers within a nerve trunk, with or without hemorrhage. Mild contusions are manifested by incomplete loss of function with progressive recovery; severe ones may cause complete loss of function. *Concussion* is a term used to signify a temporary derangement of nerve function, partial or complete, without detectable histologic changes.

In the *syndrome of irritation* there are variable motor and sensory changes accompanied by pain and hyperesthesia. Tone is preserved, idiomuscular reflexes are increased, and trophic changes may be pronounced. Irritation is usually associated with partial injury, compression, or contusion. Syndromes of irritation are most frequently encountered in median, tibial, and sciatic nerves. The pain varies in intensity and degree; either heat or cold may increase it.

In *regeneration* the autonomic fibers are restored first, as shown by improvement in the color and texture of the skin. There may be return of sensory function before motor regeneration. It is said that protopathic sensations, those mediating gross or poorly localized pain and pressure, return first, whereas the epicritic qualities of tactile discrimination and localization, focal pain sensation, and joint sensibility return later. This point of view is not universally accepted, and the initial return of sensation may be the result of sensory overlap from ingrowth of fibers from adjacent uninjured nerves. There may be faulty localization of sensory stimuli during regeneration. The muscles first become painful to pressure, then atrophy is arrested and tone is restored, and finally motor power returns. Those muscles nearest the site of injury or of repair recover first. Galvanic reactions are an important index of regeneration; faradic reactions return late; chronaxie shortens progressively. A careful evaluation of sensory, motor, and autonomic changes may give valuable information about regeneration. Certain of the electrical procedures that have been described may give the earliest clue. *Tinel's sign,* a tingling of the distal portion of a limb on pressure or percussion over the site of a divided nerve, is also an early sign. It is elicited most satisfactorily by means of gentle taps with a single finger. The most peripheral point at which this tingling is elicited may be taken roughly as the site to which the fibers have regenerated. Tinel's sign is believed to indicate the presence of young axis cylinders in the process of regeneration. It is considered by many authorities, however, to have doubtful significance; it is often absent, and is sometimes present in spite of complete division of a nerve. Absence of Tinel's sign probably has no diagnostic value; if the sign is present, and if it is found to be advancing peripherally from a nerve lesion, one may assume that regeneration is taking place.

The rate of nerve regeneration is a somewhat disputed subject. It is usually stated that peripheral nerves regenerate at a speed of approximately one millimeter a day, or about one inch a month. The rate is probably not dependent upon fiber size, but on the type and severity of the injury. Neurotization, or nerve growth, proceeds more rapidly than maturation, or return of function. Regeneration is probably more rapid after simple axonal disruption (axonotmesis) than after complete interruption followed by nerve suture, but under both circumstances the regenerating fibers advance at a progressively diminishing rate. Sunderland found that in the early stages functional maturation may proceed as much as three millimeters a day; the rate gradually slows until it reaches a value of approximately one-half millimeter a day during the terminal stages of recovery, with an average, over-all rate of about one millimeter per day.

It may not be possible to tell at the outset, or on the basis of a single examination, whether there has been compression, physiologic interruption without loss of continuity, contusion, partial interruption (second to fourth degree injury), or anatomic severance of a nerve. It is often difficult to decide, without repeated examinations, whether degeneration or regeneration is taking place. It is much easier to recognize what nerve or nerves are affected than to ascertain how severely a nerve is injured, whether it will recover spontaneously, or whether an anatomic interruption exists which requires surgical treatment. The sparing of some of the muscles supplied by the involved nerve indicates an incomplete lesion, but this does not imply the possibility of recovery. On the other hand, a complete loss of function due to pressure or contusion may be followed by rapid, complete recovery.

LESIONS OF THE PERIPHERAL NERVES

The term *neuritis* is used to denote damage to peripheral nerves regardless of etiology, although many authorities prefer the term *neuropathy* if the damage is not of infectious origin. Involvement of a single peripheral nerve is referred to as *mononeuritis* (or *mononeuropathy*); such focal lesions usually have mechanical origin. Nerves may be injured by direct trauma such as bullet, cutting, stab, or crushing wounds; severance or tear by fractures, dislocations, or birth injuries; damage during surgical operations; rupture by either blunt or sharp objects, or injections of drugs or other substances. They may be injured indirectly by crushing by a cast or crutch, entrapment, compression by callus formation or scar tissue, pressure by tumors and abscesses, malposition of part of the body during sleep or anesthesia, sudden stretching of an extremity, dislocation of a major joint, or a combination of pressure and stretching in certain positions and occupations. Compression, if sufficient in degree and duration, may lead to degeneration as a result of ischemia; so-called tourniquet paralysis may be caused by either mechanical pressure or ischemia. Stretching of a nerve beyond the limit of physiologic elasticity causes damage to the epineural vessels with focal ischemic changes in the nerve fibers. More extensive stretching causes rupture of the perineurium, herniation of the endoneurium, and necrosis of the nerve fibers. Tumors of peripheral nerves (neuromas, neurofibromas, fibroblastomas, neurofibrosarcomas) may interrupt the continuity of the nerves. The history may help to determine the etiology of an isolated nerve lesion.

Peripheral nerve involvement is most frequently seen in the extremities, and one should be familiar with the sensory distribution, motor supply, and reflex innervation of the major nerves. It is important to bear in mind that the various toxic, infectious, metabolic, deficiency, and vascular disturbances that may cause polyneuritis (see below) may render individual nerves more susceptible to damage by such things as pressure and stretching. The peripheral nerve lesions encountered following coma and carbon monoxide intoxication may be caused by anoxia super-imposed on pressure and vascular insufficiency, and chronic alcoholism and mal-nutrition may be contributing factors in neuropathies following coma or apparently caused by compression. Trauma of various types, however, is the precipitating cause of most mononeuritis. The major manifestations encountered with involvement of those nerves that are especially vulnerable to mechanical injury are presented in the following discussion.

THE RADIAL (MUSCULOSPIRAL) NERVE

This nerve is the largest branch of the brachial plexus and is a continuation of its posterior cord. It is derived from the fifth cervical through the eighth cervical or the first thoracic segments. After separating from the other nerves of the plexus, it winds about the humerus in the musculospiral groove. In the antecubital fossa it divides into its terminal (deep and superficial) branches. It supplies the triceps; the anconeus which functions with the triceps; the brachioradialis; the extensors carpi radialis longus, carpi radialis brevis, carpi ulnaris, digitorum communis, digiti quinti proprius, and indicis proprius; the long and short extensors and the long abductor of the thumb, and the supinator brevis (Table 4, p. 457). It transmits sensory im-pulses from the dorsal aspect of the lower forearm, wrist, hand, and radial fingers (excluding the middle and distal phalanges), and from the radial aspect of the thenar eminence. Radial nerve paralysis is the most frequently encountered of all peripheral nerve palsies. The nerve may be affected anywhere along its course. It is commonly injured by pressure in the axilla by a crutch, the back of a chair, or dis-location of the shoulder. It may be involved in fractures of the humerus or radius, or perforating wounds. It may be compressed by callus formation after fracture of the humerus or by pressure just above the wrist, or its branches may be com-pressed (Fig. 265). Radial nerve paralysis is a frequent manifestation of lead neuropathy.

The outstanding manifestation of a radial nerve paralysis is the loss of extension and abduction of the wrist, fingers, and thumb, with, as a result, a characteristic wrist drop. The flexors of the fingers are not impaired, but there is weakness of grip because the patient cannot completely flex his fingers with the wrist in flexion, owing to weakness of the synergists. Extension of the interphalangeal joints is pre-served. In the characteristic syndrome the forearm is pronated; the thumb is ad-ducted, flexed, and opposed, and the wrist and fingers are flexed (Fig. 180, p. 470). This deformity is best seen if the forearm is flexed at the elbow. If the lesion is above the nerve supply to the brachioradialis, this muscle is also affected, and there is weakness of flexion of the semipronated forearm, but only slightly impaired supination. In a lesion still higher, there is also involvement of the triceps, so that there is paralysis of all the extensors of the forearm, wrist, and fingers. The sensory manifestations of a radial paralysis are variable and often minimal, due to over-lapping of cutaneous nerves (Fig. 12, p. 73). The anesthetic area is usually limited to the dorsum of the thumb, although it may involve the dorsum of the radial half or two-thirds of the hand, the first interosseous space and the index finger, and the dorsum of the adjacent proximal phalanges. Trophic changes are minimal. The

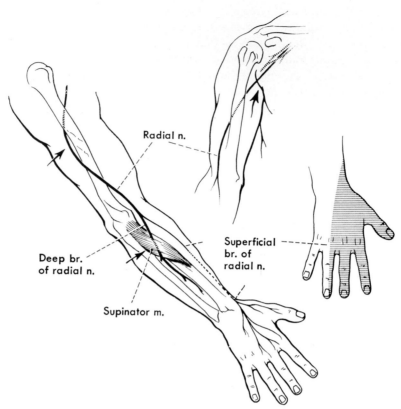

Radial n.

Deep br.
of radial n.

Superficial
br. of
radial n.

Supinator m.

FIG. 265. Common sites for injury to radial nerve. (Mulder, D. W.,
Calverly, J. R., and Miller, H. M.: *M. Clin. North America* 44:898, 1960.)

triceps and brachioradialis reflexes may be lost. The function of the brachioradialis
is usually spared in plumbism.

Entrapment of the deep radial (posterior interosseous) nerve or compression
by a tumor where it passes through the supinator muscle just below the elbow may
cause progressive paralysis and atrophy of the extensor muscles of the wrist and
fingers, without sensory change; there is usually pain and tenderness in the region
of the elbow. Neuropathy of the superficial radial nerve will cause pain and
alterations of sensation in its distribution; it may be injured with cuts or other
types of trauma at the wrist, or it may be compressed by stenosing tenosynovitis
of the de Quervain type.

THE MEDIAN NERVE

This nerve arises from two roots, one from the medial and one from the lateral
cord of the brachial plexus. Its fibers are derived from the sixth or fifth and sixth
cervical through the first thoracic segments. Its motor fibers supply the pronators
teres and quadratus, flexor carpi radialis, flexor digitorum sublimis, the radial half
of the flexor digitorum profundus, palmaris longus, flexor pollicis longus, flexor

pollicis brevis (lateral head), abductor pollicis brevis, opponens pollicis, and the two or three radial lumbricales (Table 4, p. 457). It transmits sensory impulses from the radial half of the palm of the hand, the palmar surfaces of the thumb and the index and middle fingers, the palmar aspect of the radial half of the ring finger, and the dorsal aspect of the middle and distal phalanges of the index and middle fingers and radial half of the ring finger. The median nerve is well protected by soft tissues, and accordingly is injured less frequently than either the radial or the ulnar nerve. It may, however, be involved in dislocations of the shoulder, injuries of the elbow joint, fractures of the humerus or radius, perforating wounds of the arm or the palmar surface of the wrist, pressure on the arm or forearm, or compression in the forearm or at the wrist (Fig. 266).

The outstanding motor manifestations in a median nerve lesion are paralysis of flexion of the wrist as well as the thumb and radial fingers, loss of grip, loss of pronation, and inability to oppose or approximate the thumb and finger tips. Although flexion at the wrist is impaired and flexion of the distal phalanges of the index and middle fingers is markedly impaired, the proximal phalanges can still be flexed. Loss of ability to flex the distal phalanx of the index finger is a pathognomonic sign. The wrist is supinated and drawn to the ulnar side; the thumb lies ad-

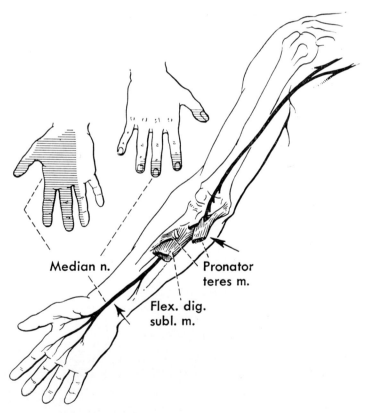

Median n.

Pronator
teres m.

Flex. dig.
subl. m.

FIG. 266. Common sites for injury to median nerve. (Mulder, D. W., Calverly, J. R., and Miller, H. M.: *M. Clin. North America* 44:898, 1960.)

ducted and extended and it cannot be either opposed to the tip of the little finger or abducted at right angles to the palm (palmar abduction), and the terminal phalanx cannot be flexed (Fig. 267). Many of the lost movements, except for flexion of the distal phalanx of the index finger and movements of the thumb, can be substituted by muscles supplied by the ulnar nerve. There is no substitution for palmar abduction, and comparison of this movement on the two sides, while the finger tips are held together at an angle of ninety degrees, is an important test of median nerve function. If the lesion is in the upper part of the forearm or higher, the pronators are paralyzed and the arm is in supination; there may be some weakness of abduction of the wrist. If it is low down, only the muscles of the thumb may be affected. Owing to the atrophy of the thenar and other muscles and the resulting deformity, a median nerve paralysis is said to result in a simian hand, or "monkey paw." The sensory changes involve the radial side of the palm of the hand, including the inner aspect of the thumb, the index and middle fingers, and the radial half of the ring finger (Fig. 13, p. 74). They are less complete on the dorsum of the hand than on the palmar surface, and usually involve only the distal (or middle and distal) phalanges of the index and middle fingers, and sometimes part of the thumb and radial half of the ring finger. There are no significant reflex changes. Median nerve paralysis is often accompanied by vasomotor and trophic changes and by intractable, burning pain known as *causalgia,* especially if the lesion is an incomplete one. The skin may be flushed, cyanotic, and either wet or dry; the nails are brittle or striated, and there may be changes in hair growth (see p. 725).

FIG. 267. Motor changes in lesion of median nerve, showing loss of flexion and opposition of thumb and of flexion of the distal phalanges of the radial fingers.

Compression of the median nerve as it passes between the two heads of the pronator teres muscle, just below the elbow, often referred to as the *pronator syndrome,* affects both motor and sensory components of the nerve. More common is the *carpal tunnel syndrome,* caused by compression of the nerve as it passes under the transverse carpal ligament at the wrist (Fig. 268). Weakness is most pronounced in the abductor pollicis brevis, causing loss of palmar abduction of the thumb, although the opponens and short flexor may also be affected. There is thenar atrophy, often with paresthesias affecting the distal palmar surfaces of the fingers, and burning pain and numbness, although objective sensory changes may be absent. The carpal tunnel syndrome has also been called median thenar neuritis and partial thenar atrophy. It may be caused by synovitis, tumor, trauma, thickened ligaments, or rheumatoid or gouty arthritis, or may be associated with systemic disease such as myxedema. It occurs in women more frequently than men, is often bilateral, and is probably the most common cause of so-called acroparesthesias. Most cases may be relieved by section of the transverse carpal ligament or removal of a neuroma or ganglion that is compressing the nerve.

THE ULNAR NERVE

This nerve is derived from the medial cord of the brachial plexus and receives its supply from the eighth or seventh and eighth cervical through first thoracic segments. It innervates the flexor carpi ulnaris, ulnar half of the flexor digitorum profundus, adductor pollicis, medial head of the flexor pollicis brevis, palmaris brevis, interossei, ulnar lumbricales, and the muscles of the hypothenar eminence—the abductor, opponens, and flexor digiti quinti brevis (Table 4, p. 458). It supplies sensation to the dorsal and palmar aspects of the ulnar side of the hand, including the little finger and the ulnar half of the ring finger. The ulnar nerve may be affected by either acute or minor but repeated trauma at the elbow or wrist or by perforating

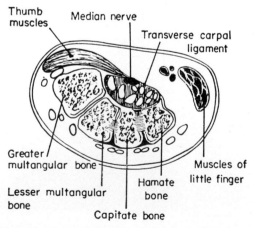

FIG. 268. Cross section at wrist showing relationship of median nerve to transverse carpal ligament.

wounds along its course. An ulnar nerve paralysis may be a late sequel of fractures or dislocations of the elbow; the symptoms develop after the nerve has been damaged by callus formation and fibrous adhesions.

In an ulnar nerve involvement flexion and adduction of the wrist and fingers are impaired, and the hand is turned radialward. Extension of the distal phalanges and flexion of the proximal ones, especially of the two ulnar fingers, is lost; adduction and abduction of the fingers are impaired, and adduction of the thumb and abduction and opposition of the little finger are lost. The *signe de journal* (see p. 762) is present. The grip, especially that of the two ulnar fingers, is weak. There is atrophy of the hypothenar eminence and to a lesser extent of the thenar eminence, the palm is hollowed out, and the interosseous spaces are deeply grooved. There is hyperextension of the fingers at the metacarpophalangeal joints and flexion at the inter-

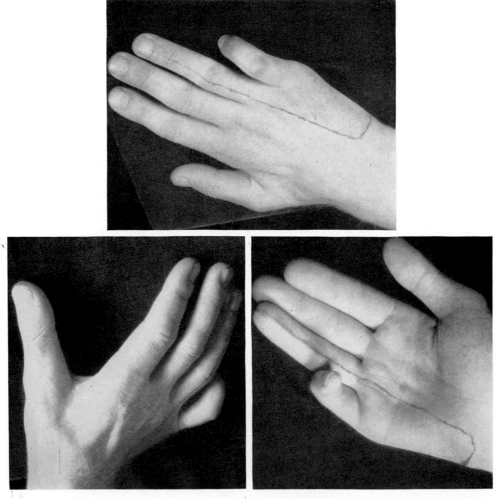

FIG. 269.   Motor and sensory changes in lesion of ulnar nerve.

phalangeal joints, especially those of the two ulnar fingers. The resulting deformity of the hand is spoken of as *main en griffe,* or claw hand (Fig. 269). Although the abductor of the little finger is paralyzed, this finger may assume a position of abduction when the fingers are extended, owing to action of extensor muscles. Sensory changes are found on the little finger and the ulnar half of the ring finger (Fig. 13). There are no important reflex abnormalities, and usually no trophic changes. The claw deformity is less marked with a lesion above the elbow, since with paralysis of the flexor digitorum profundus there is less flexion of the distal phalanges. With paralysis of the deep palmar branch of the ulnar nerve, usually caused by prolonged pressure on the hypothenar eminence, there are weakness and atrophy affecting the adductor pollicis and interossei more than the hypothenar muscles, without sensory change. Combined median and ulnar paralyses are not rare, and with them there is a complete claw hand (Fig. 270). A Volkmann's ischemic contracture of the forearm may simulate a combined median and ulnar paralysis (Fig. 271). Similar deformities may be seen in Charcot-Marie-Tooth disease, progressive spinal muscular atrophy, and amyotrophic lateral sclerosis.

THE AXILLARY NERVE

The axillary, or circumflex, nerve is derived from the fifth and sixth cervical segments through the posterior cord of the brachial plexus and winds around the

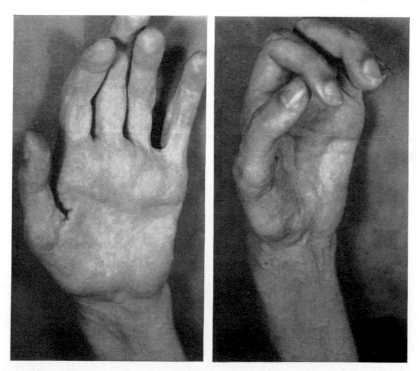

FIG. 270. Motor changes and deformity seen in combined lesion of median and ulnar nerves.

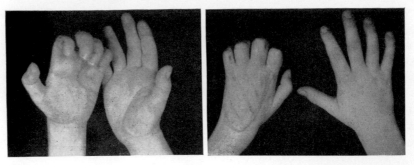

Fig. 271. Motor and sensory changes in left hand in a case of Volkmann's ischemic contracture.

neck of the humerus. It supplies the deltoid and teres minor muscles, and transmits sensation from the surface of the upper and outer aspects of the arm. It may be injured by pressure in the axilla, fracture or dislocation of the head of the humerus, perforating wounds, or direct blows against the shoulder; it is commonly affected by the neuritis which follows serum injections. In an axillary nerve lesion there is paralysis of abduction and weakness of external rotation of the arm; the patient is unable to raise his arm to the horizontal plane. There also is some weakness of flexion, extension, and internal rotation. These is anesthesia involving a small area on the upper third of the outer surface of the arm.

THE MUSCULOCUTANEOUS NERVE

This nerve is derived from the fifth, sixth, and seventh cervical segments through the lateral cord of the brachial plexus. It innervates the biceps, brachialis, and coracobrachialis muscles, and transmits sensation from the lateral aspect of the forearm, from the elbow to the thenar eminence. It is not frequently injured. In a musculocutaneous lesion there is weakness of flexion of the forearm if the latter is in supination, and marked weakness of supination. The semipronated forearm can still be flexed by the brachioradialis. There is a relatively small area of anesthesia on the lateral surface of the forearm. The biceps reflex is lost.

THE LONG THORACIC NERVE

This nerve is derived from the fifth through the seventh or eighth cervical segments. It supplies the serratus anterior muscle. It may be injured by continued muscular effort with the arm above the shoulder, by pressure from carrying heavy objects on the shoulder, or by supraclavicular or axillary wounds. Involvement of this nerve causes paralysis of the serratus anterior muscle, with resulting winging of the scapula (Fig. 167, p. 460).

THE PHRENIC NERVE

This is one of the major motor nerves of the cervical plexus and is the principal respiratory nerve of the body. It is derived from the third through the fifth cervical segments. It is mainly motor, innervating the diaphragm, but it also carries sensory filaments from the diaphragm, pericardium, parts of the costal and mediastinal pleura, and the extrapleural and extraperitoneal connective tissues. It may be injured by neoplasms or penetrating wounds. In the past it was sectioned to produce unilateral diaphragmatic paralysis in the surgical treatment of pulmonary tuberculosis. Unilateral paralysis of the diaphragm causes few or no symptoms; the liver and spleen may be elevated on the affected side, the excursion of the costal margins is slightly increased, Litten's sign is absent, and fluoroscopic examination shows relative immobility of one half of the diaphragm. With bilateral paralysis there is dyspnea on the slightest exertion, with a scaphoid abdomen which does not protrude on expiration, absence of Litten's sign, increased excursion of the costal margins, retraction of the epigastrium on inspiration, and overactivity of the accessory respiratory muscles, and difficulty coughing or sneezing.

THE FEMORAL NERVE

The femoral nerve is the largest branch of the lumbar plexus. It arises from the posterior divisions of the anterior primary rami of the second, third, and fourth lumbar segments. It supplies the iliacus, pectineus, sartorius, and quadriceps femoris muscles (Table 6, p. 483). Through its sensory branches, the *intermediate* (*anterior*) and *medial cutaneous nerves* and the *saphenous nerve,* it transmits sensation from the anterior and medial aspects of the thigh and the medial (or anteromedial) aspect of the leg to the ankle. The femoral nerve may be involved in pelvic tumors, psoas abscesses, fractures of the pelvis and upper femur, pressure, aneurysms of the femoral artery, and bullet or stab wounds; it is commonly affected in diabetic neuritis, and may be injured during labor or abdominal or pelvic surgery (Fig. 272). With injury to this nerve there is complete loss of extension of the leg at the knee and there may be weakness of flexion of the hip. Walking forward and climbing stairs is done with difficulty, although the patient may walk backward with ease. It is necessary to walk with the leg stiff, and if the knee bends the patient may fall. Injury to the posterior divisions of the anterior primary rami of the second to fourth lumbar segments within the pelvis or abdomen will also affect the function of the psoas major, with loss of flexion of the thigh. With lesions of the femoral nerve the patellar reflex is lost and there is anesthesia of the anterior and medial aspects of the thigh and the medial aspect of the leg. The *saphenous nerve,* which supplies the skin over the medial, or anteromedial aspect of the leg, may be injured during operations on varicose veins or by trauma to or operations on the knee.

THE OBTURATOR NERVE

This nerve arises from the lumbar plexus by fusion of the anterior divisions of the anterior primary rami of the second through the fourth lumbar segments. It supplies the adductor muscles of the thigh and gracilis and obturator externus, and transmits sensation from a small area on the medial aspect of the thigh. Injuries to this nerve are rare, but when they occur there is weakness of adduction and external

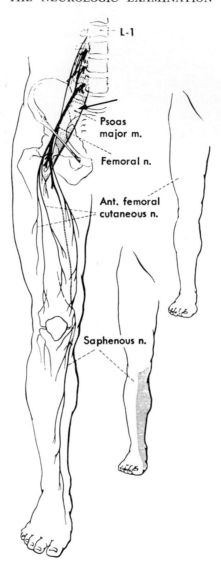

FIG. 272.   Common sites for injury to femoral nerve. (Calverly, J. R., and Mulder, D. W.: *Neurology* 10:963, 1960.)

rotation of the thigh, with a small area of anesthesia over the inner surface of the thigh. In the Howship-Romberg syndrome, caused by pressure on the obturator nerve by an obturator hernia, there is pain on the medial aspect of the thigh and knee.

THE LATERAL FEMORAL CUTANEOUS NERVE

This nerve is supplied by the posterior divisions of the anterior primary rami of the second and third lumbar segments. It is entirely afferent and transmits sensation from the skin of the anterolateral aspect of the thigh. Involvement of this nerve, usually where it passes under or through the inguinal ligament just medial to the anterior superior iliac spine or pierces the fascia lata, is followed by hypesthesia, sometimes with painful paresthesias, in its cutaneous distribution. The underlying etiology of this syndrome, known as *meralgia paresthetica,* is probably some anatomic variant in the course of the nerve, but the precipitating causes are increased intra-abdominal pressure, pregnancy, obesity, trauma, pressure by a belt or truss, occupational postures requiring prolonged hip flexion, debilitating disease, or toxins, infections, and other causes of peripheral neuritis.

THE COMMON PERONEAL NERVE

The common peroneal nerve is formed by a fusion of the upper four posterior divisions of the sacral plexus (fourth lumbar through second sacral segments). It innervates the short head of the biceps femoris muscle and divides to form the *superficial* and *deep peroneal nerves.* Through the *lateral sural cutaneous nerve* it transmits sensation from the lateral and posterolateral aspects of the upper portion of the leg. The *peroneal anastomotic branch* joins the medial sural cutaneous branch of the tibial nerve to form the *sural nerve;* this transmits sensation from the posterolateral aspects of the leg and ankle and the lateral aspects of the heel and foot.

The *superficial peroneal nerve* is supplied by the fourth and fifth lumbar and first one or two sacral segments of the spinal cord. It innervates the peronei longus and brevis and transmits sensation from the skin on the anterolateral aspect of the leg and ankle and the dorsum of the foot. After interruption of this nerve the foot can no longer be everted. Dorsiflexion is possible, but during the process the foot becomes inverted. The sensory changes follow the cutaneous distribution of the nerve. The *deep peroneal nerve* has the same general segmental supply. It innervates the tibialis anterior, peroneus tertius, and extensors hallucis longus and brevis and digitorum longus and brevis (Table 6, p. 484). It also transmits sensation from the skin in the region of the first interosseous space. In a lesion of this nerve there is loss of dorsiflexion of the foot and toes, with a characteristic foot drop and resulting steppage gait. The patient is unable to stand on his heel and raise the sole of the foot; he attempts to raise the depressed toes off the ground by exaggerated flexion at the hip and knee; the sensory changes are characteristic. Either the superficial or deep peroneal nerve may be injured by trauma, stretching, or other causes. The common peroneal nerve is very vulnerable to injury, especially where it winds around the neck of the fibula. It may be affected by penetrating wounds, pressure subsequent to fracture of the head of the fibula, compression from a tightly applied plaster cast, or even pressure from sitting with the legs crossed or from kneeling or assuming bizarre postures in certain occupations (Fig. 273). Recent loss of weight may increase the susceptibility of the nerve to damage from pressure, as may alcoholism, diabetes, malnutrition, and other causes of peripheral neuritis. The nerve is commonly involved in lead neuropathy. If the common peroneal nerve is injured, the sensory and motor changes correspond to the distributions of both the superficial and deep peroneal branches; the sensory functions of the lateral sural cutaneous and sural nerves may or may

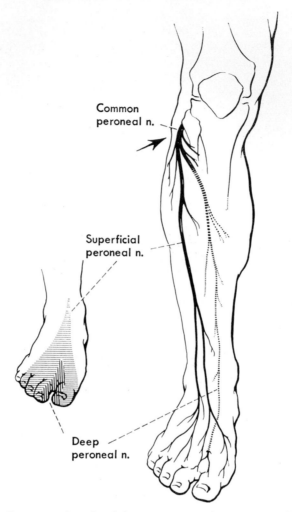

FIG. 273. Common sites for injury to peroneal nerve. (Mulder, D. W., Calverly, J. R., and Miller, H. M.: *M. Clin. North America* 44:898, 1960.)

not be affected, but the innervation to the biceps femoris is usually spared. A foot drop associated with a peroneal palsy should be differentiated from the deformity of the foot seen in Friedreich's ataxia (Fig. 274), as well as from that which occurs in the Charcot-Marie-Tooth variety of muscular atrophy (Fig. 134, p. 384).

THE TIBIAL NERVE

The tibial nerve is the larger of the two terminal branches of the sciatic nerve. It is formed by a fusion of all five of the anterior divisions of the sacral plexus (fourth lumbar through second or third sacral segments). It innervates the long head of the biceps femoris, and the semimembranosus, semitendinosus, gastrocnemius,

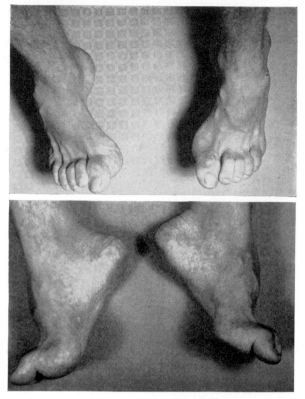

FIG. 274.   Deformity of feet in Friedreich's ataxia.

popliteus, soleus, plantaris, tibialis posterior, and flexors digitorum and hallucis longus muscles and, through the *medial* and *lateral plantar nerves,* the plantar flexors of the toes and the small muscles of the foot. Through the *sural nerve,* formed by a junction of the *medial sural cutaneous nerve* (tibial) and the *anastomotic branch of the common peroneal,* it transmits sensation from the posterolateral aspects of the leg and ankle and the lateral aspects of the heel and foot. *Calcaneal nerves* supply the posterior and medial aspects and plantar surface of the heel, and the *medial* and *lateral plantar nerves,* the plantar surface of the foot. If the tibial nerve is injured, there is loss of the functions of these muscles, with anesthesia over the plantar and lateral aspects of the foot, the heel, and the posterolateral aspects of the leg and ankle. The patient is unable to either plantar flex or invert the foot, or to flex, adduct, or abduct the toes. He cannot stand on his toes. Trophic changes and causalgic pain may be present. The achilles reflex is lost. Injuries to this nerve are relatively infrequent because of its deep location and protected course, but it may be involved in lesions in or below the popliteal space. Compression of the nerve as it passes behind the medial malleolus and deep to the flexor retinaculum may cause burning pain and sensory loss of the toes and sole of the foot and paresis or paralysis of the small muscles of the foot; this has been called the *tarsal tunnel syndrome.*

THE SCIATIC NERVE

The common peroneal and tibial nerves are fused within the pelvis to form the sciatic nerve, the largest nerve in the body. Rami from the tibial trunk supply the semimembranosus and semitendinosus muscles and the long head of the biceps; a branch also goes to the adductor magnus. Rami from the common peroneal trunk go to the short head of the biceps. Serious injury to the main trunk of the sciatic nerve results in loss of function of both the common peroneal and tibial nerves. This is uncommon, but if it occurs there is complete paralysis of all of the muscles of the foot and anesthesia of the foot and all but the anteromedial aspect of the leg. Flexion at the knee is also greatly impaired, the only muscles participating in this movement being the sartorius and gracilis. Ability to flex and extend the ankle and toe joints and the powers of inversion and eversion of the foot are lost. The patient cannot stand on either his heel or toes. Trophic disturbances and causalgic pain are frequent. The sciatic nerve may be injured in pelvic fractures, dislocations of the hip, tumors, stab or gunshot wounds, dystocia, traction in breech presentations, or intragluteal injections into the nerve. Specific syndromes of sciatic irritation and dysfunction are discussed in Chapter 48.

LESIONS OF OTHER PERIPHERAL NERVES

Peripheral nerves other than those mentioned above may occasionally be implicated in isolated neuritides. Brief mention may be made of some of the less common syndromes of peripheral nerve involvement.

The *iliohypogastric nerve* arises from the first lumbar nerve. It is mainly a sensory nerve, but sends a few filaments to the transversus abdominis and the obliquus internus abdominis, and sometimes to the obliquus externus abdominis. The lateral cutaneous branch is distributed to the skin of the gluteal region, behind the lateral cutaneous branch of the twelfth thoracic nerve; the anterior cutaneous branch transmits impulses from the skin of the hypogastric region, just above the symphysis pubis. With a lesion of this nerve there may be pain or sensory changes in these areas.

The *ilioinguinal nerve* is also a branch of the first lumbar nerve. Like the iliohypogastric nerve, it is mainly sensory but supplies a few filaments to the transverus abdominis and obliquus internus abdominis and occasionally to the obliquus externus abdominis. It transmits sensation from the skin of the upper and medial part of the thigh, as well as from the upper part of the root of the penis and the scrotum in the male, and the mons pubis and the labium majus in the female. There is pain along with loss of sensation in these areas with lesions of the ilioinguinal nerve.

The *genitofemoral nerve* arises from the first and second lumbar nerves. Its *external spermatic branch* supplies the cremaster muscle and transmits sensation from a portion of the skin of the scrotum, and its *lumboinguinal branch* transmits sensation from a small area on the anterior surface of the upper part of the thigh.

The *superior gluteal nerve* arises from the posterior divisions of the fourth and fifth lumbar and first sacral nerves. It innervates the gluteus medius, gluteus minimus, and tensor fasciae latae muscles. The *inferior gluteal nerve* arises from posterior divisions of the fifth lumbar and the first and second sacral nerves, and innervates the gluteus maximus. With a lesion of the former nerve, occasionally damaged by intragluteal injections, there is weakness of abduction and internal rotation of the thigh; with a lesion of the latter there is impairment of extension of the thigh.

The *posterior femoral cutaneous nerve* is supplied by the posterior divisions of the first and second sacral nerves and the anterior divisions of the second and third sacral. It transmits sensation from the posterior aspect of the thigh and upper leg. Its *gluteal branches* supply the skin of the lower gluteal region; the *perineal branches* are distributed to the upper and medial aspect of the thigh; the *inferior pudendal branch* supplies the skin of the perineal region together with scrotum in the male and the labium majus in the female.

The *pudendal nerve* arises from the anterior divisions of the second, third, and fourth sacral nerves. Its branches are as follows: The *inferior hemorrhoidal nerve* is distributed to the external anal sphincter and to the skin and mucosa about the anus. The *perineal nerve* divides into *muscular* and *posterior scrotal* (*or labial*) *branches;* the former supply the bulbocavernosus, ischiocavernosus, and other perineal muscles, together with the external vesical sphincter; the latter transmit sensation from the scrotum in the male and the labium majus in the female. The *dorsal nerve of the penis* (*or clitoris*) supplies the corpus cavernosum and the skin and mucous membrane of the dorsum of the penis (or clitoris), including the glans. The pudendal nerve also transmits sensation from the bladder. Isolated lesions of these individual nerves are rare.

POLYNEURITIS, OR MULTIPLE PERIPHERAL NEURITIS

Among the numerous causes for polyneuritis are the following: exposure to or ingestion of toxic substances, both organic and nonorganic; deficiency states, especially deficient intake or absorption of the vitamin B complex (thiamin, niacin, pyridoxine, and cyanocobalamin); infections (diphtheria, leprosy, and probably viral and nonspecific systemic infections); metabolic disorders (diabetes, hyperinsulinism, porphyria, electrolyte and acid-base disturbances); collagen diseases (periarteritis nodosa and disseminated lupus erythermatosus), vascular insufficiency and ischemia; allergy (serum neuritis and possibly postinfectious neuritis); genetic disorders (Charcot-Marie-Tooth disease, hypertrophic interstitial neuritis, hereditary ataxic polyneuropathy, hereditary sensory neuropathy); neoplastic infiltrations (carcinoma, leukemia, Hodgkin's disease), and other causes that are difficult to classify, such as that for the noninfiltrating neuritis associated with carcinomatosis and the neuritides associated with amyloidosis, sarcoidosis, myeloma, and for those developing with exposure to cold and after irradiation. Under many circumstances more than one etiologic factor may be implicated.

Polyneuritis most frequently involves the nerves to the extremities. Although specific nerves are affected, there may be a generalized diminution of function of many without a clear-cut loss of conduction of any individual nerve. As a result, the changes may be diffuse and widespread rather than focal. The sensory disturbances may be characterized by pain, paresthesias, hypesthesia, or anesthesia. The impairment of sensation is often confined to the distal portion of the extremities; there is a peripheral blunting of sensation for the entire part, without a well-delineated border. This may simulate a glove or stocking distribution, but the gradual change and the presence of tenderness and hyperpathia in the hypesthetic zone is important in diagnosis. There may be profound impairment of proprioceptive sensations. The motor changes may vary from slight weakness to extensive paralysis with atrophy and deformities, and are also most marked in the distal portions of the extremities. Electrical testing shows decrease in the conduction velocities of both motor and sensory nerves. Autonomic changes may be absent or minimal, but occasionally they are profound, and may even be responsible for bladder, bowel, and related dysfunctions (Chapter 43). The peripheral nerves and the muscles and tendons may be tender to pressure, and there is often cutaneous hyperesthesia and hypersensitivity, especially of the soles of the feet, in spite of an elevated sensory threshold. In hypertrophic interstitial polyneuritis and leprosy, and sometimes in amyloid neuritis, the affected nerves are thickened and palpable. Mononeuritis multiplex consists of dysfunction of more than one peripheral nerve, but the diffuse changes encountered in most cases of polyneuritis are absent. Nutritional and other factors responsible for a polyneuritis may contribute to a mononeuritis caused by trauma or pressure.

NEURALGIA

The term neuralgia is used for that syndrome which is characterized by pain in the distribution of certain nerves in the absence of objective signs of dysfunction. There are no motor, sensory, or reflex changes, and there are said to be no pathologic changes of nerve structure. Neuralgias may be reflex phenomena, secondary to some irritation or toxic or infectious factor. Occasionally a detailed examination may show some minimal evidence of nerve dysfunction. Trigeminal, glossopharyngeal, and sphenopalatine neuralgia are discussed elsewhere. Brachial, occipital, cervical, intercostal, crurai, obturator, sciatic, and other neuralgic syndromes have been described.

REFERENCES

Aids to the Investigation of Peripheral Nerve Injuries, Medical Research Council War Memorandum No. 7 (ed. 2). London, His Majesty's Stationery Office, 1943.

BRAIN, W. R., WRIGHT, A. D., and WILKINSON, M. Spontaneous compression of both median nerves in the carpal tunnel. *Lancet* 1:277, 1947.

CLIFTON, E. E. Unusual innervation of the intrinsic muscles of the hand by median and ulnar nerve. *Surgery* 23:12, 1948.

Committee on Rating of Mental and Physical Impairment: The peripheral spinal nerves. *J.A.M.A.* 189:128, 1964.

FAVILL, J. Outline of the Spinal Nerves. Springfield, Ill., Charles C Thomas, 1946.

GHENT, W. R. Further studies on meralgia paresthetica. *Can. M.A.J.* 85:871, 1961.

GROFF, R. A., and HOUTZ, S. J. Manual of Diagnosis and Management of Peripheral Nerve Injuries. Philadelphia, J. B. Lippincott Company, 1945.

GUTMANN, E., GUTMANN, L., MEDAWAR, P. B., and YOUNG, J. Z. Rate of regeneration of nerve. *J. Exper. Biol.* 19:14, 1942.

HAYMAKER, W., and WOODHALL, B. Peripheral Nerve Injuries: Principles of Diagnosis (ed. 2). Philadelphia, W. B. Saunders Company, 1953.

HENDERSON, W. R. Clinical assessment of peripheral nerve injuries: Tinel's test. *Lancet* 2:801, 1948.

HOLMES, W., and YOUNG, J. Z. Nerve regeneration after immediate and delayed suture. *J. Anat.* 77:63, 1942.

KANTARJIAN, A. D., and DE JONG, R. N. Familial primary amyloidosis with nervous system involvement. *Neurology* 3:399, 1953.

KEEGAN, J. A., and HOLYOKE, E. A. Meralgia paresthetica: Anatomical and surgical study. *J. Neurosurg.* 19:341, 1962.

KELLY, M. Spread of sensory and motor loss after nerve injury. *Neurology* 2:36, 1952.

KOPELL, H. P., and THOMPSON, W. A. L. Peripheral Entrapment Neuropathies. Baltimore, The Williams & Wilkins Company, 1963.

LAM, S. J. A. A tarsal-tunnel syndrome. *Lancet* 2:1354, 1962.

LYONS, W. R., and WOODHALL, B. Atlas of Peripheral Nerve Injuries. Philadelphia, W. B. Saunders Company, 1949.

MAGEE, K. R. Neuritis of deep palmar branch of ulnar nerve. *A.M.A. Arch. Neurol. & Psychiat.* 73:200, 1953.

MULDER, D. W. Diagnosis and management of mononeuropathies. *Postgrad. Med.* 36:321, 1964.

NACHMANSOHN, D. Basic aspects of nerve activity explained by biochemical analysis. *J.A.M.A.* 179:639, 1962.

OESTER, Y. T., and MAYER, J. H. Motor Examination of Peripheral Nerve Injuries. Springfield, Ill., Charles C Thomas, 1960.

OLSEN, C. W. Lesions of peripheral nerves developing during coma. *J.A.M.A.* 160:39, 1956.

POLLOCK, L. J., and DAVIS, L. Peripheral Nerve Injuries. New York, Paul B. Hoeber, Inc., 1933.

SEDDON, H. J. (ed.) Peripheral Nerve Injuries. London, Her Majesty's Stationery Office, 1954.

SEDDON, H. J., MEDAWAR, P B., and SMITH, H. Rate of regeneration of peripheral nerves in man. *J. Physiol.* 102:191, 1943.

SIMPSON, J. A. Biology and disease of peripheral nerves. *Brit. M. J.* 2:709, 1964.

SUNDERLAND, S. Rate of regeneration in human peripheral nerves: Analysis of the interval between injury and the onset of recovery. *Arch. Neurol. & Psychiat.* 58:251, 1947; A Classification of peripheral nerve injuries producing loss of function. *Brain* 74:491, 1951.

TINEL, J. Nerve Wounds: Symptomatology of Peripheral Nerve Lesions Caused by War Wounds. (Fred Rothwell, trans.) New York, William Wood & Company, 1917.

WARTENBERG, R. Neuritis, Sensory Neuritis, Neuralgia: A Clinical Study with Review of the Literature. New York, Oxford University Press, 1958.

WOLTMAN, H. W., KERNOHAN, J. W., and GOLDSTEIN, N. P. "Diseases of the Peripheral Nerves," in Baker, A. B. (ed.) Clinical Neurology (ed. 2). New York, Hoeber Medical Division, Harper & Row, 1962, vol. 4, pp. 1811–1896.

CHAPTER 45

DISEASE OF THE NERVE ROOTS

THE SUBJECTIVE and objective manifestations of nerve root involvement are similar to those of peripheral nerve involvement, but the distribution of the changes is somewhat different. The sensory manifestations, both the perversions of function such as pain and paresthesia and the areas of anesthesia, hypesthesia, and hyperesthesia, are confined to dermatomes, or those cutaneous areas supplied by specific cord segments, dorsal roots, or ganglia (Fig. 14, p. 75). Owing to the overlap of sensory supply by the nerve roots, it may not be possible to map out an area of sensory loss in a lesion involving only one nerve root. The motor changes are also dependent upon the radicular or segmental innervation of the muscles, rather than their peripheral nerve supply (Tables 3 to 6, pp. 454–484), and are found in the myotomes, or those groups of muscles supplied by specific spinal segments and their ventral roots. Owing to the fact that most muscles are supplied by more than one segment of the spinal cord, and thus by more than one nerve root, there may be no discernible motor change in instances where there is involvement of but one nerve root.

The pain and hyperesthesia of nerve root origin are termed *radicular* in distribution. If the pain is bilateral and symmetrical, involving the trunk, it is called a *girdle pain*. Radicular pain is often increased by movement and by actions such as coughing, sneezing, and straining, which either increase the intraspinal pressure or cause stretching of the nerve roots. It is often lancinating in character and usually intermittent, but occasionally constant. Pain of nerve root origin may be relieved by section of the nerve roots central to the dorsal root ganglia, spinal anesthesia, intraspinal injection of alcohol, and caudal analgesia.

Radicular involvement may be caused by many processes. These include extramedullary spinal lesions such as pachymeningitis, extradural abscesses, extramedullary tumors, and ruptured intervertebral disks; compression of the spinal column with pressure on the nerve roots by neoplasms, trauma, or infectious processes affecting the vertebrae; inflammatory processes involving the dorsal root ganglia and nerve roots (radiculitis). Occasionally muscle spasm alone causes nerve root compression. Those syndromes which are related to pathologic changes of the spinal cord are discussed in Chapter 47; those localized to the cervical and brachial nerves, in Chapter 46; and those involving the lumbar and sacral nerves, in Chapter 48.

In *herpes zoster,* a viral infection affecting predominantly the dorsal root ganglia, there is a severe, burning pain in the distribution of one or more dermatomes. This is followed shortly by the development of vesicles in the cutaneous distribution of the involved root and ganglion (Fig. 275). A residual pain, referred to as a post-herpetic neuralgia, may remain after the disappearance of the vesicles. There may be hyperpathia in the involved area in spite of hypesthesia. Motor involvement is rare. Symptomatic herpes zoster may accompany systemic infections or leukemic or neoplastic infiltrations or inflammatory involvement of the vertebrae or nerve roots. With *tabes dorsalis* there are inflammatory and degenerative changes in the dorsal roots and ganglia and in the posterior funiculi of the spinal cord. There may be radicular pains, sometimes in a "girdle" distribution. Sensory changes are characterized by loss of proprioceptive sensation and a delayed cutaneous pain response, and autonomic changes are common. There is loss of reflexes with hypotonia, but no actual loss of motor power. In *polyradiculoneuritis (Guillain-Barré syndrome)* there are motor, sensory, and reflex changes similar to those found in polyneuritis,

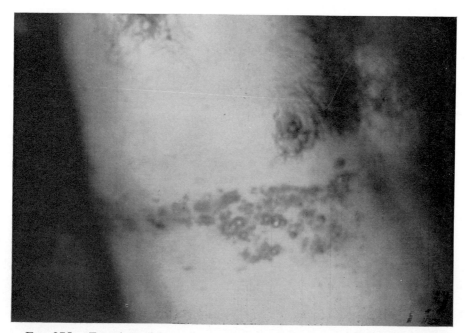

Fig. 275. Eruption of herpes zoster in distribution of right sixth thoracic nerve root.

but the involvement is more extensive. The high protein content of the cerebrospinal fluid gives evidence of change within the subarachnoid space, and microscopic examinations reveal involvement of the nerve roots and dorsal root ganglia, with an ascending, or axonal, degeneration of the anterior horn cells. In *hereditary sensory neuropathy* there are profound sensory disturbances, both superficial and deep, with areflexia and trophic disturbances, but little motor dysfunction; the primary pathologic changes are in the dorsal root ganglia. In *hereditary ataxic polyneuropathy* (Refsum's syndrome) there are visual and auditory symptoms, electrocardiographic abnormalities, and elevation of the protein content of the cerebrospinal fluid, in addition to ataxia and peripheral nerve manifestations. There is thickening with infiltration of the peripheral nerves, but the nerve roots are also affected and there is axonal degeneration within the central nervous system.

REFERENCES

DeJong, R. N. The Guillain-Barré syndrome: Polyradiculoneuritis with albuminocytologic dissociation. *Arch. Neurol. & Psychiat.* 44:1044, 1940.

Denny-Brown, D. Hereditary sensory radicular neuropathy. *J. Neurol., Neurosurg. & Psychiat.* 14:237, 1951.

Keegan, J. J. Relations of nerve roots to abnormalities of lumbar and cervical portions of the spine. *Arch. Surg.* 55:246, 1947.

Refsum, S. Heredopathia atactica polyneuritiformis. *Acta psychiat. et. neurol. scandinav.* Suppl. 38, 1946.

CHAPTER 46

DISEASE OF THE NERVE PLEXUSES

INVOLVEMENT of the major nerve plexuses, such as the cervical, brachial, and lumbosacral plexuses, may produce changes in sensory and motor functions which differ somewhat in distribution from those caused by peripheral nerve involvement, and also from those associated with radicular lesions.

THE CERVICAL PLEXUS

The cervical plexus is formed by the anterior primary rami of the upper four cervical nerves. There are connections with the superior cervical sympathetic ganglion and the spinal accessory and hypoglossal nerves. The plexus is situated on the side of the neck, behind the sternocleidomastoid and in front of the levator scapulae and scalenus medius muscles. The cutaneous branches supply the skin on the lateral occipital portion of the scalp, the greater part of the auricle, the angle of the jaw, the neck, and the supraclavicular region and upper thorax through the lesser and greater occipital, great auricular, cutaneous cervical, and supraclavicular nerves (Fig. 74). Muscular branches supply the scalenus medius and levator scapulae, diaphragm, many of the vertebral muscles, and in part the sternocleidomastoid, trapezius, and infrahyoid muscles. There are communications with the tongue musculature and the suprahyoid muscles. Injuries to the cervical plexus are infrequent, but any of the individual nerves may be damaged by penetrating wounds, operative trauma, or disease of or trauma to the cervical vertebrae. Division of cutaneous branches is apparent from sensory changes; irritation of them may cause cervico-occipital neuralgia or headache. Interruption of motor branches causes weakness, paralysis, and atrophy of specific muscles; irritation may cause spasm of the neck or diaphragm. Rigidity of the neck in meningitis and diseases of the cervical vertebrae and muscles may be a protective reflex mechanism. The method of exam-

777

ing the various muscles supplied by the cervical plexus and the changes resulting from weakness and paralysis are described in "The Motor System" (Part IV) and under the discussion of the eleventh and twelfth cranial nerves.

THE BRACHIAL PLEXUS

Lesions of the brachial plexus cause motor and sensory syndromes involving the muscles of the upper extremities which differ somewhat from those which follow lesions of the individual nerves. The brachial plexus is formed by the anterior primary rami of the four lower cervical nerves and the greater part of the first thoracic (Fig. 276). The fifth and sixth cervical rami unite to form the *upper trunk;* the seventh cervical forms the *middle trunk,* and the eighth cervical and first thoracic form the *lower trunk.* The trunks are situated in the supraclavicular fossa just distal to the scalenus anterior muscle. Each of the trunks divides into an *anterior* and a *posterior division,* from which the three cords are derived. The *lateral cord* is formed by the anterior divisions of the upper and middle trunks (anterior primary divisions of the fifth, sixth, and seventh cervical nerves); the *medial cord* is formed by the anterior division of the lower trunk (eighth cervical and first thoracic nerves); the *posterior cord* is formed by the posterior divisions of all of these trunks and nerves. The divisions are situated deep to the middle third of the clavicle and extend just beyond the lateral border of the first rib. The cords are in the axilla. The lower trunk is immediately behind the subclavian artery, and all three cords approximate the axillary artery.

The fifth cervical ramus, with the fourth, gives off the dorsal scapular nerve to the rhomboids and in part to the levator scapulae; the fifth through the seventh or eighth cervical rami give off the long thoracic nerve to the serratus anterior; the fifth cervical ramus also sends a twig to the phrenic nerve, and the fifth through the eighth cervical rami, branches to the scaleni and longus colli muscles. The *upper trunk* gives off the suprascapular nerve to the supraspinatus and infraspinatus muscles, and the nerve to the subclavius. From the *lateral cord* issues the lateral anterior thoracic nerve to the pectoralis major; from the *medial cord* arise the medial anterior thoracic nerve to the pectoralis major and minor and the medial antibrachial and brachial cutaneous nerves; from the *posterior cord* originate the subscapular nerves to the subscapularis and teres major and the thoracodorsal nerve to the latissimus dorsi. The terminal branches of the posterior cord are the axillary and radial nerves; the terminal branches of the lateral cord are the musculocutaneous nerve and the lateral component of the median nerve; the terminal branches of the medial cord are the ulnar nerve and the medial component of the median nerve. There may be marked anatomic variation of the brachial plexus. In the "prefixed" plexus a large component of the fourth cervical nerve may be included, and less of the first thoracic; in the "postfixed" plexus there are no components of the fourth cervical, but the entire first thoracic and even a part of the second thoracic may be included.

The upper arm type of brachial plexus palsy (*Erb's palsy,* or *Duchenne-Erb paralysis*) follows injury to the fifth and sixth cervical roots, the upper trunk, or

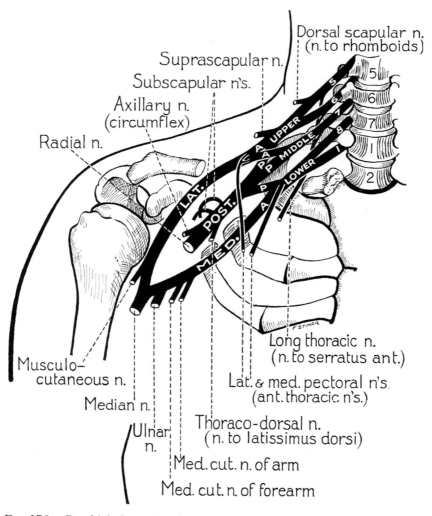

Dorsal scapular n.
(n. to rhomboids)

Suprascapular n.

Subscapular n's.

Axillary n.
(circumflex)

Radial n.

Long thoracic n.
(n. to serratus ant.)

Musculo-
cutaneous n.

Median n.

Lat. & med. pectoral n's.
(ant. thoracic n's.)

Ulnar
n.

Thoraco-dorsal n.
(n. to latissimus dorsi)

Med. cut. n. of arm

Med. cut. n. of forearm

FIG. 276. Brachial plexus showing its various constituents and their relationships to structures in region of upper chest, axilla, and shoulder. (Figs. 276,
277, and 278 from Haymaker, W., and Woodhall, B.: Peripheral Nerve
Injuries. Philadelphia, W. B. Saunders Company, 1945.)

sometimes the upper and middle trunks. It may be caused by traction on the head
or shoulder, blows or falls against the head or shoulder, stab wounds, or obstetric
injury, especially in the delivery of the aftercoming head in breech presentation.
There is paralysis of the deltoid, biceps, brachialis, brachioradialis, and sometimes
the supraspinatus, infraspinatus, and rhomboid muscles. The arm hangs limp at
the side of the body, in adduction and internal rotation, and the forearm is in extension, pronation, and medial rotation. The patient is unable to abduct or externally rotate the arm or to flex or supinate the forearm. The biceps reflex is lost.
There is little sensory change due to overlapping of the peripheral nerve distribu-

tions, but there may be partial anesthesia of the outer aspect of the arm, forearm, and hand (fifth and sixth cervical segments). The *lower arm type of brachial plexus palsy* (*Dejerine-Klumpke syndrome*) follows injury to the eighth cervical and first thoracic roots, lower trunk, or medial cord. It may be associated with tumors or other pathologic changes of the apex of the lung, fracture of the clavicle, cervical rib, aneurysm of the arch of the aorta, fracture or dislocation of the head of the humerus, sudden upward pull on the arm, or other injuries from below. Traction on the arm or shoulder or hyperabduction with or without dislocation of the shoulder may also cause the syndrome. There is paralysis of the muscles supplied by the ulnar and to a lesser extent of those supplied by the median nerve, with sensory changes in the distribution of these nerves, or along the inner border of the arm, forearm, and hand (eighth cervical and first thoracic segments). There is loss of flexion of the wrist and fingers, and weakness of the small muscles of the hand and of grip. Edema and trophic changes, and a Horner's syndrome, may be present. Paralysis of the flexors of the wrist and fingers results in a claw hand. A *middle arm type of brachial plexus palsy* has been described, but is rare; there is weakness of the extensors of the forearm, wrist, and fingers, and there may be sensory changes corresponding to the distribution of the radial nerve.

In *lesions of the posterior cord of the brachial plexus* there is involvement of the muscles supplied by the axillary and radial nerves, and to a lesser extent of those supplied by the subscapular and thoracodorsal nerves, with loss of abduction and rotation at the shoulder, extension of the forearm, extension of the wrist and fingers, and supination; there may be paralysis of the thumb muscles. The triceps and brachioradialis reflexes are lost. There is anesthesia in the distribution of the axillary and radial nerves. *Lesions of the lateral cord* cause paralysis of the biceps, brachialis, and coracobrachialis muscles, and of all supplied by the median nerve except the intrinsic muscles of the hand. *Lesions of the medial cord* cause paralysis of the muscles supplied by the ulnar nerve and of the small muscles of the hand supplied by the median nerve. Infraclavicular lesions cause involvement of the cords of the brachial plexus; fractures and dislocations of the humerus are often responsible. In *total brachial plexus palsy* there is a flaccid paralysis of the entire arm, the only remaining movement being weak adduction. The hand, forearm, and arm are totally anesthetic except for a small area near the axilla that is supplied by the intercostobrachial nerve. There may be trophic changes and a Horner's syndrome. Due to individual variations in the brachial plexus, together with variability in types of injury, there are many incomplete syndromes and a wide range of resulting symptoms.

A number of syndromes have been described in which the symptoms and signs are the result of abnormal compression of the brachial plexus or its constituents and/or the subclavian or axillary vessels in the thoracic outlet (or inlet). These may be referred to as *cervicobrachial neurovascular compression syndromes*. The most characteristic of these is the *scalenus syndrome,* in which a cervical rib, a hypertrophied scalenus anterior muscle, or both may exert pressure on the nerve trunks of the brachial plexus and compress the subclavian artery and vein. Two varieties have been described: the superior type, with pressure on the upper trunk of the brachial plexus by the tendons of origin of the scalenus anterior, and the lower type, which is more frequent, with compression of the lower trunk by the tendons of insertion of the muscle. The outstanding symptom is pain in the outer and anterior shoulder region which radiates into the supravlavicular area and into the arm and hand, either the ulnar or radial side or both. It may radiate to the neck, scapula, shoulder, or thoracic wall. The pain often is worse at night, and is increased by recumbency, turning the head toward the unaffected side, downward traction on the arm and shoulder, retraction of the shoulder, and pressure on the scalenus muscle, which is tender and painful to palpation (especially at its site of insertion on the first rib). It may be relieved by abduction of the arm. Paresthesias, especially of the thumb and fingers, are common, but objective sensory changes may be minimal. Motor alterations, too, may not be marked; if present they consist of weakness of the hand and finger muscles. Occasionally there is atrophy of the interossei and the thenar and hypothenar muscles. The alterations, both sensory and motor, are most marked in the areas and muscles supplied by the ulnar nerve, but those innervated by the median and even the radial nerve may also be affected. Vascular and autonomic changes include either pallor or cyanosis, subjective coldness and decreased skin temperature, alterations in sweating, edema of the arm and hand, and sometimes even thrombosis of digital arteries and gangrene of the affected fingers. There may be associated aneurysm of the subclavian artery. The radial pulse may be either diminished or obliterated by various maneuvers and diagnostic procedures described below, and the brachial blood pressure may be lower on the affected side. Section of the hypertrophied scalenus anterior muscle or its fibrous connections usually causes relief of the symptoms, even when there is a cervical rib or a long transverse process of the lowest cervical vertebra.

Other neurovascular compression phenomena which cause somewhat similar symptoms and signs are as follows: In the *costoclavicular syndrome* there is a narrowed space between the clavicle and first rib, with pressure on the brachial plexus and subclavian artery and/or vein as they pass through this aperture; this is accentuated by depression or retraction of the shoulder. The symptoms may be relieved by resection of the first rib. In the *subcoracoid-pectoralis minor* (or *hyperabduction*) *syndrome* hyperabduction of the arm causes pressure on the stretched vascular structures as they pass posterior to the pectoralis minor muscle and under the subcoracoid process. The symptoms have been relieved by resection of the pectoralis minor tendon. Other anomalies in the muscular or skeletal development of the thoracic outlet or the shoulder girdle, as well as sequelae of trauma, may cause similar symptoms. Pain, paresthesias, and motor changes in the hands which resemble those described above may also be caused by involvement of the cervical portion of the spinal cord and its emerging nerve roots (as in cervical spondylosis) and by the carpal tunnel syndrome.

Similar symptoms may be associated with other conditions. In *paralytic brachial neuritis* (neuralgic amyotrophy) there is sudden onset of pain in the region of the shoulder, followed by extensive paralysis with resulting atrophy of muscles supplied by certain branches of the brachial plexus, as well as sensory changes, but usually no vascular symptoms. Occasionally a brachial plexus neuritis develops

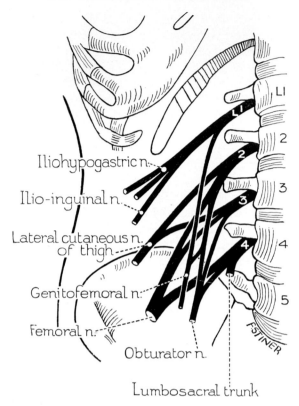

Iliohypogastric n.

Ilio-inguinal n.

Lateral cutaneous n. of thigh

Genitofemoral n.

Femoral n.

Obturator n.

Lumbosacral trunk

L1
2
3
4
5

FIG. 277.   Constituents of lumbar plexus.

following the injection of foreign proteins, especially tetanus antitoxin. In *brachial plexus neuralgia* there may be pain without objective sensory or motor changes; this may have obscure etiology or reflex origin associated with arthritic changes, periarthritis, myositis, or bursitis. If these are present, there may be localized tenderness and limitation of motion at the shoulder joint. *Lesions of the lung apex,* especially superior pulmonary sulcus tumors, may cause symptoms resembling the lower type of compression, or those of a lower arm type of brachial plexus palsy; there is often a Horner's syndrome. Subacromial bursitis, arthritis of the cervical spine, abnormal first rib, cervicodorsal scoliosis, postural defects, ruptured supraspinatous tendon, spinal cord tumors, herniated intervertebral disks, arthritis or periarthritis of the shoulder, fibrositis, myositis, synovitis, and Raynaud's disease should also be considered in the differential diagnosis of the scalenus syndrome. In the so-called *shoulder-hand syndrome* there may be pain, atrophy, autonomic changes, and osteoporosis of the hand associated with pain and disuse of the shoulder. This may occur secondary to such variable factors as disease in the region of the shoulder joint, disuse following fracture or paralysis, pressure on the cervical nerve roots or brachial plexus, and myocardial infarction.

Tumors of the cervical portion of the spinal cord, especially extramedullary ones, and *herniated intervertebral disks* in the cervical region may cause pain, motor changes, and sensory abnormalities in the distribution of the brachial plexus, usually without vasomotor dysfunction. The pain may be increased on coughing or straining. Because of the limited space between the spinal cord and the vertebral bodies and the fixed position of the cord, midline protrusions of the intervertebral disks produce symptoms which resemble those of spinal cord tumors, with segmental sensory changes and compression of the ascending and descending pathways that may result in a spastic paraplegia. Lateral protrusions cause monoradicular syndromes; these occur most frequently between the fifth and sixth and the sixth and seventh cervical vertebrae, with pressure on the sixth and seventh cervical roots, respectively. Radicular pain, tenderness, stiffness of the neck, alterations in the reflexes, objective and subjective changes in sensation in the distribution of the involved roots, and weakness, atrophy, and fasciculations of the muscles in the involved myotomes are the principal manifestations. With compression of the sixth cervical root the pain is mainly on the radial side of the forearm, with paresthesias of the thumb and index finger and weakness of the biceps, brachioradialis, and wrist extensor muscles. With involvement of the seventh cervical root the pain is on either the dorsal or volar aspect of the forearm, with paresthesias of the thumb and index finger, and predominant weakness of the triceps. With involvement of the eighth cervical root the pain is in the ulnar aspect of the forearm, with paresthesias of the ring and little fingers and weakness of the small muscles of the hand. The pain of cervical nerve root irritation may simulate that of coronary artery disease. Spasm of the scalenus anterior muscle may also occur, and division of the muscle may relieve the symptoms in some cases. A syndrome of unilateral ventral pressure, with cord compression but without radicular symptoms, has also been described. Similar syndromes may also occur in cervical spondylosis, in which there is both foraminal narrowing and cord compression, and in various traumatic states and developmental anomalies. Roentgenography, myelography, and electromyography may be necessary in order to differentiate the various syndromes. Diskography has also been done, but it has not been widely accepted, and some of the early proponents have abandoned it. On occasion angiography may aid in the diagnosis of the neurovascular syndromes. Inasmuch as some of the above-mentioned conditions are characterized predominantly by spinal cord rather than nerve root or plexus involvement, they will be considered more in detail in Chapter 47.

Special diagnostic procedures may be of aid in the clinical differentiation of certain of the above syndromes. In the *Adson test* the patient is asked to inspire, hold his breath, and hyperextend his neck. Then the head is turned as far as possible, first toward one side and then the other. With the scalenus syndrome there may be accentuation of the pain and weakening or obliteration of the radial pulse, accompanied by a drop in blood pressure, when the head is turned toward the unaffected (or sometimes the affected) side. The pulse may disappear on both sides with turning of the head in either direction, but there is a longer lag in its return on the affected side. During the maneuver a bruit may develop that is heard best in the supraclavicular space. In the *Allen test,* also positive with the scalenus syndrome, the pulse is diminished on the affected side when the arm is elevated to ninety degrees and rotated externally with the elbow at a right angle, and the head turned forcibly to the nonaffected side. In the *hyperabduction test* the arm is passively hyperabducted and may also be placed in a position of posterior extension. In most normal subjects there is a decrease or weakening of the radial pulse with such a maneuver, but in the hyperabduction syndrome it is obliterated with greater ease than is normal. In the *shoulder bracing test* the shoulder is passively retracted and depressed; with the costoclavicular syndrome the radial pulse on the affected side is decreased more readily than in the normal subject. *Forced depression or downward traction of the arm and shoulder* causes increased pain in the presence of a scalenus syndrome, and there is tenderness and pain on pressure over the scalenus anterior muscle. In the *foraminal compression test* the neck is hyperextended and flexed laterally toward the affected side, following which downward pressure is applied to the top of the head. With a laterally herniated intervertebral disk or extramedullary mass the radicular pain is produced or aggravated. Similarly this radicular pain may be relieved by the *neck traction test,* in which the examiner, grasping both sides of the patient's head, exerts strong upward

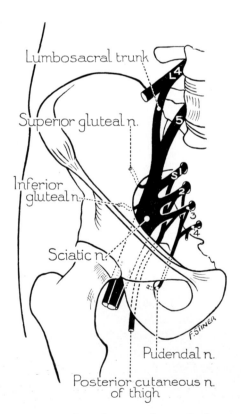

Fig. 278.   Constituents of sacral plexus.

traction. It must be stressed that these various maneuvers may aid in diagnosis, but are not as reliable as a detailed history and thorough neurologic examination.

THE LUMBAR PLEXUS

The lumbar plexus is formed by the anterior primary rami of the first three lumbar nerves and a part of the fourth, and it may receive a contribution from the twelfth thoracic nerve (Fig. 277). It gives off the iliohypogastric, ilioinguinal, genitofemoral, lateral femoral cutaneous, obturator, accessory obturator, and femoral nerves, together with the nerves to the psoas muscles and the lumbrosacral trunk to the sacral plexus. There are also collaterals from the first through the fourth lumbar rami to the quadratus lumborum and intertransversarii. The plexus is situated in the substance of the psoas major muscle, in front of the transverse processes of the lumbar vertebrae. Injuries to the lumbar plexus are relatively uncommon, but they may occur in association with fractures or dislocations of the vertebrae, penetrating wounds, Pott's disease, psoas abscesses, or pressure from pelvic tumors. Infectious processes or metastatic infiltrations may also affect it. One observes more frequently, however, either radicular symptoms resulting from involvement of the individual rami, or lesions of the constituent nerves. Pain or sensory changes in the distribution of these nerves has localizing value.

THE SACRAL PLEXUS

The sacral plexus shows a great deal of variability. It is formed by the anterior primary rami of the fourth lumbar through the third sacral segments (Fig. 278). It lies against the piriformis muscle on the posterior wall of the pelvis. From it are given off various cutaneous branches together with the superior and inferior gluteal nerves, the nerves to the quadratus femoris, obturator internus, and piriformis, and the sciatic nerve. Injuries to the sacral plexus are uncommon, but lesions of the roots or of the primary rami are followed by disabilities of segmental distribution. The individual nerves are frequently involved in lesions of the cauda equina. The various syndromes associated with dysfunction of the sacral plexus will be discussed in Chapter 48. The *pudendal and coccygeal plexuses* and their branches are rarely involved in specific injuries. The principal manifestations are those of dysfunction of the vesical and anal sphincters and of the genitalia, together with sensory changes. These are discussed in part under the autonomic nervous system and will be dealt with further under lesions of the cauda equina and conus medullaris.

REFERENCES

ADSON, A. W., and COFFEY, J. R. Cervical rib: a method of anterior approach for relief of symptoms by division of the scalenus anticus. *Ann. Surg.* 85:839, 1927.

CLOWARD, R. B. Cervical diskography. *Am. J. Roentgenol.* 79:563, 1958.

DEJONG, R. N. Syndrome of involvement of the posterior cord of the brachial plexus. *Arch. Neurol. & Psychiat.* 49:860, 1943.

FALCONER, M. A., and WEDDELL, S. Costoclavicular compression of subclavian artery and vein: Relation to scalenus anticus syndrome. *Lancet* 2:539, 1943.

HOLT, E. P., JR.   Fallacy of cervical discography.   *J.A.M.A.* 188:799, 1964.

MAGEE, K. R., and DE JONG, R. N.   Paralytic brachial neuritis.   *J.A.M.A.* 174:1258, 1960.

MICHELSEN, J. J., and MIXTER, W. J.   Pain and disability of shoulder and arm due to herniation of nucleus pulposus of cervical intervertebral disks.   *New England J. Med.* 231:279, 1944.

NAFFZIGER, H. C., and GRANT, W. T.   Neuritis of the brachial plexus mechanical in origin: The scalenus syndrome.   *Surg., Gynec. & Obst.* 67:722, 1938.

SPURLING, R. G.   Lesions of the Cervical Intervertebral Disc.   Springfield, Ill., Charles C Thomas, 1956.

STEINBROCKER, O., SPITZER, N., and FRIEDMAN, H. H.   The shoulder-hand syndrome in reflex dystrophy of the upper extremity.   *Ann. Int. Med.* 29:22, 1948.

WALSHE, F. M. R.   "Nervous and vascular pressure syndromes of the thoracic inlet and cervico-axillary canal," in FEILING, A. (ed.),   *Modern Trends in Neurology.*   New York, Paul B. Hoeber, Inc., 1951, p. 542.

WRIGHT, I. S.   The neuromuscular syndrome produced by hyperabduction of the arms.   *Am. Heart J.* 29:1, 1945.

YOSS, R. E., CORBIN, K. B., MACCARTY, C. S., and LOVE, J. G.   Significance of symptoms and signs in localization of involved root in cervical disk protrusion.   *Neurology* 7:673, 1957.

CHAPTER 47

DISEASE OF THE SPINAL CORD

ANATOMY

THE SPINAL CORD is an elongated, nearly cylindrical portion of the nervous system which is continuous with the medulla above and ends in a conical extremity, the conus medullaris (Fig. 279). It is situated within the vertebral canal. From the apex of the conus medullaris a delicate filament, the filum terminale, descends to the periosteum of the posterior surface of the first segment of the coccyx. The spinal cord is slightly flattened in an anteroposterior direction. An anterior median fissure and a posterior median sulcus divide it into two symmetrical halves. The posterior nerve roots enter the posterolateral sulcus, and the anterior nerve roots make their exit at the anterolateral sulcus. The parenchyma of the spinal cord consists of a butterfly or H-shaped core of gray matter, containing nerve cells, which is surrounded by tracts of longitudinally arranged nerve processes, mainly myelinated, which carry ascending and descending impulses. Within the center of the gray matter and running throughout the entire length of the cord is a minute central canal surrounded by a single layer of ependymal cells.

The cellular elements in the gray matter are arranged in functional groups (Fig. 280). Those in the *anterior horn* supply motor impulses to striated muscles. The cells in the medial portion of the anterior horn (nuclei dorsomedialis and ventromedialis) supply trunk muscles. The central cells in the cervical region supply the diaphragm and the muscles innervated by the spinal accessory nerve (nuclei phrenicus and accessorius), whereas those in the sacral region supply the perineal muscles (nucleus centralis). The lateral cells, present only in the cervical and lumbosacral enlargements, supply the extremities (nuclei ventrolateralis, dorsolateralis, and retrodorsolateralis). The cells in the *lateral horn* belong to the autonomic nervous system; the intermediolateral cells in the thoracic and upper

787

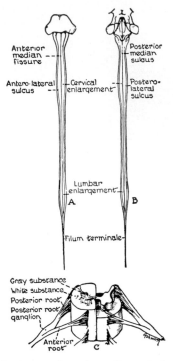

FIG. 279.   Spinal cord; *A,* anterior view; *B,* posterior view; *C,* segment of spinal cord with anterior and posterior nerve roots attached. (Larsell, O.: Anatomy of the Nervous System. New York, D. Appleton-Century Company, 1939.)

lumbar segments supply preganglionic nerves of the sympathetic division, and the lateral cells in the sacral area supply preganglionic parasympathetic fibers. The cells in the *dorsal portion* of the gray matter are nuclei of termination of afferent neurons. The stellate cells (substantia gelatinosa of Rolando) and dorsal funicular cells (nucleus proprius dorsalis) are present throughout the entire extent of the cord, and receive exteroceptive impulses; nucleus dorsalis of Clarke is present from the eighth cervical through the third lumbar segment; it receives proprioceptive impulses and gives rise to the dorsal spinocerebellar tract.

The fiber pathways in the white matter are in part crossed and in part uncrossed (Fig. 280). Afferent impulses enter the fasciculus dorsolateralis (Lissauer). The descending pathways carry impulses from higher centers; these terminate in spinal cord nuclei on which they have regulatory and inhibitory functions. The ascending pathways carry sensory impulses of various types from the extremities, trunk, or neck to higher centers. The principal tracts in the dorsal funiculus are the fasciculi gracilis and cuneatus which carry uncrossed proprioceptive and tactile impulses to the respective nuclei in the medulla, and thence, after decussation, to the thalamus. Ascending pathways in the lateral and ventral areas are the lateral and ventral spinothalamic tracts, both of which carry crossed exteroceptive impulses, together

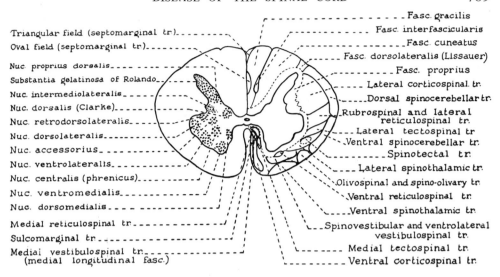

Triangular field (septomarginal tr.)
Oval field (septomarginal tr.)
Nuc. proprius dorsalis
Substantia gelatinosa of Rolando
Nuc. intermediolateralis
Nuc. dorsalis (Clarke)
Nuc. retrodorsolateralis
Nuc. dorsolateralis
Nuc. accessorius
Nuc. ventrolateralis
Nuc. centralis (phrenicus)
Nuc. ventromedialis
Nuc. dorsomedialis
Medial reticulospinal tr.
Sulcomarginal tr.
Medial vestibulospinal tr.
(medial longitudinal fasc.)

Fasc. gracilis
Fasc. interfascicularis
Fasc. cuneatus
Fasc. dorsolateralis (Lissauer)
Fasc. proprius
Lateral corticospinal. tr.
Dorsal spinocerebellar tr.
Rubrospinal and lateral reticulospinal tr.
Lateral tectospinal tr
Ventral spinocerebellar tr.
Spinotectal tr.
Lateral spinothalamic tr.
Olivospinal and spino-olivary tr.
Ventral reticulospinal tr.
Ventral spinothalamic tr.
Spinovestibular and ventrolateral vestibulospinal tr.
Medial tectospinal tr.
Ventral corticospinal tr.

FIG. 280. Cross section of spinal cord, showing arrangement of cellular groups in gray matter and fiber pathways in white matter.

with the dorsal and ventral spinocerebellar, spino-olivary, spinotectal, and spino-vestibular tracts. Descending pathways are the lateral corticospinal (crossed pyramidal), ventral corticospinal (uncrossed pyramidal), rubrospinal, olivospinal, vestibulospinal, tectospinal, and reticulospinal tracts. There are other less well defined tracts which may be important avenues of conduction, as well as inter-segmental, intrasegmental, and association pathways. Recent work has shown that there is a certain amount of intermingling of fibers wtihin the various tracts, and that it is not possible to outline or delineate the individual pathways as distinctly as has been done in the past.

The spinal cord extends from the foramen magnum, or the level of the upper border of the atlas, to the level between the first and second lumbar vertebrae. It is surrounded by pia mater, arachnoid, and dura mater. The pia mater is a delicate membrane which closely invests the spinal cord. The arachnoid is a trans-parent membrane which is close to the inner surface of the dura, but fine strands extend to the pia. The dura mater is a strong, fibrous membrane, penetrated by the nerve roots, which forms a firm tubular sheath. It is separated from the wall of the vertebral canal by the epidural space which contains areolar tissue and a plexus of veins. The subdural space is a potential space containing a small amount of fluid. The subarachnoid space, which extends to about the level of the second sacral vertebra, is a well-defined cavity containing cerebrospinal fluid. The dentate ligament extends along the lateral surface of the spinal cord, between the anterior and posterior nerve roots, from the pia to the dura mater. It suspends the spinal cord in the vertebral canal. The spinal nerves, with their dorsal and ventral roots, are segmentally arranged in thirty-one pairs. There are eight pairs of cervical nerves, twelve thoracic, five lumbar, five sacral, and one coccygeal. Situated on each dorsal root is the dorsal root ganglion. The spinal cord is greater in width and diameter in the cervical and lumbosacral regions, the site of nuclear centers which supply the extremities.

During the process of maturation the vertebral column elongates more than the spinal cord, and in the adult the spinal cord is shorter than the vertebral column and the spinal nerves course downward before making their exits through the intervertebral foramina. Those which originate in the lower part of the spinal cord become more and more oblique in their downward descent. The lumbar and sacral nerves descend almost vertically to reach their points of exit; these are designated the cauda equina. Consequent to this developmental change, there is discrepancy between the segments of the spinal cord and the level of the spinous processes of the vertebrae. In the upper cervical area the cord level is about one segment higher than the corresponding spinous process; in the lower cervical and thoracic areas there is a difference of about two segments, whereas in the lumbar region there is a difference of almost three segments (Fig. 16).

BLOOD SUPPLY

There is some individual variation in the blood supply of the spinal cord. The *anterior spinal* (or *anterior median spinal*) *artery* is formed by the union of the arterial branches which pass caudally from each vertebral artery and unite in the midline near the foramen magnum. It descends the entire length of the spinal cord, taking a somewhat undulating course, and lies in or near the anterior median fissure. Below the fourth or fifth cervical segment the anterior spinal artery is fed or reinforced by unpaired anterior medullary arteries which arise from the lateral spinal arteries. These latter vessels enter the vertebral canal through the intervertebral foramina, and in the cervical region are branches of the ascending cervical artery; in the thorax, of the intercostals; in the abdomen, of the lumbar, iliolumber, and lateral sacral arteries. They pierce the dural sheaths of the spinal roots and split into anterior and posterior radicular branches (Fig. 281). The radicular arteries are asymmetric and sometimes absent. The largest medullary artery, often called the great radicular, or anterior medullary, artery of Adamkiewicz, supplies the lumbar enlargement, usually on the left side. The blood supply to any given level of the spinal cord is proportional to its cross-sectional area of gray matter, and the caliber of the anterior spinal artery is largest at the level of the lumbar and cervical enlargements.

The so-called *posterior spinal arteries* are really plexiform channels rather than distinct single vessels. They lie near the posterolateral sulci and the entrance of the rootlets of the posterior nerves. They also arise from the vertebral arteries, and posterior medullary arteries join them at irregular intervals. Central arteries, branches of the anterior spinal, supply the anterior and central portions of the cord, and branches of the anterior and posterior spinal arteries form a peripheral anastomosis, the arterial vasocorona, which supplies the periphery of the cord, including the lateral and ventral funiculi. This anastomosis is least efficient in the region of the lateral columns. Within the substance of the cord the posterior spinal arteries supply the posterior horns and most of the dorsal funiculi, whereas the

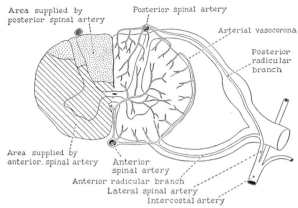

Area supplied by posterior spinal artery
Posterior spinal artery
Arterial vasocorona
Posterior radicular branch
Area supplied by anterior spinal artery
Anterior spinal artery
Anterior radicular branch
Lateral spinal artery
Intercostal artery

Fig. 281. Arterial supply of spinal cord.

anterior spinal artery supplies most of the remainder of the cord. Certain boundary zones between ascending and descending sources of blood supply are sites of least adequate circulation in the spinal cord. The fourth thoracic segment is one such site, and this is especially vulnerable to vascular occlusion and ischemic necrosis.

The venous drainage of the spinal cord courses from the capillary plexuses to peripheral venous plexuses that correspond somewhat to the arterial supply. The major portion of the venous drainage takes place through the intervertebral foramina into veins in the thoracic, abdominal, and pelvic cavities, but the spinovertebral venous plexus also continues upward into the intracranial cavity and venous sinuses; this may be a means of transport of tumor cells and other emboli to the brain.

PHYSIOLOGY

The spinal cord is essential to the regulation and administration of various motor, sensory, and autonomic activities of the body. By means of its segmentally arranged spinal nerves and its nuclear centers, it receives impulses at various levels and carries them to motor cells in the same or adjoining segments for distribution to appropriate muscles. Thus it provides for reflex action and governs motor activity. By means of its descending pathways from higher centers, it regulates and inhibits spinal cord reflexes and motor activity. Through its ascending pathways, it conducts impulses from the extremities, trunk, and neck to higher centers and to consciousness. It also has a regulatory and administrative action over various visceral activities. In disease of the spinal cord any or all of these functions may be affected, and it is often possible to localize spinal cord lesions in both the transverse and the longitudinal planes. The resulting symptoms depend upon the location and the extent of damage to various functional elements, and often upon the type of damage and the rapidity with which the lesion develops.

Lesions of the spinal cord are characterized by sensory, motor, and autonomic changes. If there is involvement of the posterior roots or of the sensory cells in the posterior horns of the gray matter, there are segmental sensory changes; there may be either loss of certain or all varieties of sensation in the dermatomes supplied by the involved segments, or irritative phenomena such as pain and paresthesias. If there is involvement of the ascending pathways, there is loss of sensation, principally the pain, temperature, and proprioceptive modalities, below the lesion; there is often a dissociation of sensation, with loss of some varieties, but sparing of others. If there is involvement of the anterior horn cells or of the anterior roots, there is a lower motor neuron paralysis in the myotomes supplied by the involved segments, occasionally with either fasciculations or muscle spasm. If there is involvement of the descending motor pathways, either corticospinal, extrapyramidal, or vestibulospinal, there are changes in motor power and tone below the level of the lesion. If there is involvement of the intermediolateral cell group of the gray matter, the neuraxes of these cells, or the descending autonomic pathways, there are changes in autonomic function. Alterations of the reflexes, ataxia, disturbances of gait, dysfunction of the sphincters, and other abnormalities of function are all secondary to either isolated or combined motor, sensory, or autonomic involvement.

In order to localize spinal cord disease in the transverse plane, one must be familiar with the anatomy and function of the cell groups within the gray matter, the dorsal and ventral roots, and the principal afferent and efferent paths in the dorsal, lateral, and ventral columns. In order to localize disease in the vertical, or longitudinal, direction, one must be familiar with the segmental sensory, motor, reflex, and autonomic supply, and the relationship between the spinal cord segments and the vertebral bodies and spinous processes.

The *motor deficits* resulting from spinal cord diseases depend upon the site and extent of the lesion (Tables 3 to 6). There is usually a flaccid paralysis of those muscles supplied by the affected segment, and a flaccid paresis that later becomes spastic below the level of the lesion. The first through the fourth cervical segments innervate muscles which control movements of the head and neck. A lesion of the upper two or three cervical segments is usually rapidly fatal, owing to proximity to the important vasomotor and respiratory centers in the medulla; there may be hyperpyrexia. Involvement above the fourth cervical segment causes respiratory difficulty due to diaphragmatic paralysis; the patient is able to breathe with only the accessory muscles of respiration. With a lesion at the fourth cervical segment respiration is possible through the function of the diaphragm and the accessory muscles of respiration, but there is paralysis of all four extremities. The fourth or fifth cervical through the first or second thoracic segments control movements of the upper extremities. Involvement of the fifth or fifth and sixth cervical segments causes a syndrome resembling the upper arm type of brachial plexus palsy; there is paralysis of the rhomboid, supraspinatus, infraspinatus, teres major and minor, deltoid, biceps, and brachioradialis muscles, with loss of the biceps and brachioradialis reflexes and sometimes inversion of the radial reflex. The arms are adducted and may be in a position of internal rotation. With a lesion of the sixth cervical segment the biceps is predominantly affected, and the deltoid and triceps may both be intact. A lesion of the seventh cervical segment causes paralysis of the triceps and the extensors of the wrist and fingers; there is either loss of the triceps reflex or a paradoxic reflex with flexion instead of extension of the forearm. The patient holds his upper arm in abduction and his forearm in flexion, and there is usually flexion of the wrist and fingers. This position, if unilateral, is referred to as Jolly's sign; if bilateral it is spoken of as either Bradborn's or Thorborn's sign. Involvement of the eighth cervical and first thoracic segments causes a syndrome which resembles the lower arm type of brachial plexus palsy; there may be an atrophic paralysis of the flexors of the wrist and fingers and the small muscles of the hand; the arm reflexes are preserved, but the wrist and finger flexion reflexes are affected.

The thoracic segments control movements of the trunk, thorax, and abdomen. Involvement of the midthoracic segments causes atrophic paralysis of the intercostal muscles; the abdominal reflexes are affected, and Beevor's sign may be present. The segments from the first lumbar through the third sacral control movements of the lower extremities. A lesion of the first two or three lumbar segments causes paralysis of flexion and adduction of the thigh and of extension of the leg; the patellar reflex is lost. With a lesion of the fifth lumbar and first sacral segments there is loss of extension of the hip, with paralysis of plantar flexion and dorsiflexion of the foot, paralysis of flexion of the knee, and loss of the plantar and achilles reflexes. Involvement of the second sacral segment causes paralysis of the small muscles of the foot. The lower sacral segments innervate the bladder, rectum, anus, and genitalia. A lesion of the third and fourth sacral segments causes paralysis of the rectum and bladder, impairment of erection, and loss of the anal and bulbocavernous reflexes. In all of the above motor syndromes, a focal lesion which involves only the anterior horn cells will cause a flaccid loss of power, with consequent atrophy, limited to the involved myotomes. A lesion which involves the descending motor pathways will cause either a pyramidal or an extrapyramidal paralysis below the level of the lesion. If both the anterior horn cells and the descending tracts are affected, there will be a segmental flaccid paralysis together with an upper motor neuron paresis below the level of the lesion.

The *sensory changes* associated with spinal cord lesions are usually segmental, or dermatome, in distribution (Fig. 14). There may be either loss or diminution of one or more modality, or perversions in the form of either pain or parethesias. The areas of diminution or loss, and the paresthesias as well, may involve the entire body below the level of the lesion, whereas the pain is usually segmental and affects only the dermatome supplied by the level of the lesion. The sensory loss is usually of the dissociated variety, with impairment of certain modalities and sparing of others. Pain, temperature, and proprioceptive sensations are predominantly involved. There may be hyperesthesia at the level of the lesion, with increased irritability even though the threshold may be raised. The level for pain and temperature sensations is the most specific, and it may be difficult to delineate a definite level for either tactile or proprioceptive sensations. With cervical lesions, however, there may be marked proprioceptive loss as well as stereoanesthesia of the upper extremities (Chapter 8). *Lhermitte's sign,* the development of sudden, electric-like shocks spreading down the body on flexion of the neck, occurs in focal traumatic and neoplastic lesions at the cervical level, but also in multiple sclerosis and spinal cord degenerations.

The *autonomic nervous system* changes may vary. A lesion at the eighth cervical and first thoracic segments may cause a Horner's syndrome, but a Horner's syndrome may also follow a lesion of the descending autonomic pathways above this level. Transverse spinal lesions are followed, early in their course, by loss of sweating, vasodilatation, loss of piloerection, increase in skin resistance, and increase in skin temperature below the level of the lesion. Later there is vasoconstriction with decrease in temperature, and there may be an increase in sweating and piloerection. Interruption of the descending pathways causes disturbances of bladder, rectal, and sexual functions. A lesion at the eighth cervical or first thoracic segment, above the thoracicolumbar outflow, may cause a disturbance of the sympathetic innervation of the entire body. A lesion of the thoracic or upper lumbar portions of the spinal cord will cause a loss of sympathetic function that corresponds roughly to the motor and sensory level; one below the third lumbar segment causes no disturbance in sympathetic function. A focal lesion at the first through the third lumbar segments causes impairment of ejaculation; a lesion of the third and fourth sacral segments causes an autonomous bladder and loss of erection.

Special diagnostic tests may aid in the evaluation of disease of the spinal cord. The presence of either local tenderness or muscular rigidity may signify the level of the pathologic process. Electromyography assists in the localization of lesions if either the anterior horn cells or motor roots are involved. Dermometry and other tests of autonomic function may also aid in localization (Chapter 42). In many cases roentgenographic examinations, spinal puncture, and myelography are necessary for the accurate diagnosis and specific localization of spinal cord lesions. On occasion additional procedures such as diskography and intraosseous vertebral venography have been done.

LESIONS OF THE SPINAL CORD

There are many varieties of spinal cord lesions. *Transverse syndromes* are characterized by complete interruption of the continuity of the spinal cord; there is loss of all motor, sensory, and autonomic function below the level of involvement. *Incomplete transverse lesions* are followed by loss of function of certain portions of the cord; there may be dysfunction of one half, one quarter, or a certain portion or segment of the cord. *Syndromes of the gray matter* show segmental loss of function of certain cell groups. Disease of the ventral gray matter is followed by a segmental flaccid paralysis (anterior poliomyelitis, progressive spinal muscular atrophy); disease of the dorsal gray matter, by segmental sensory changes; disease of the gray commissure, by dissociation of sensation (syringomyelia). *Syndromes of the white matter* cause interference with the ascending and descending pathways. In disease of the dorsal funiculi there is interference with the ascending proprioceptive impulses (tabes dorsalis), and in disease of the lateral columns, the lateral corticospinal, lateral spinothalamic, or other tracts may be affected. *System disease* is characterized by dysfunction of anatomically and functionally related systems of cells or fibers (primary lateral sclerosis, posterolateral sclerosis, and amyotrophic lateral sclerosis). *Disseminated disease* is manifested by patchy involvement, with many lesions of a focal nature. *Diffuse disease* shows widespread involvement, but some cells or fibers may be affected more than others.

A detailed history will usually give much pertinent information that is necessary to determine the etiology of spinal cord disease. Traumatic lesions are usually abrupt in onset. Compression of the spinal cord by extradural neoplasms, caries or other degenerative changes within the vertebral column, and focal infections of the meninges may cause a gradual onset of symptoms. Most intradural neoplasms are characterized by a progressive increase in manifestations of dysfunction, but occasionally the first symptoms come on precipitously. Vascular lesions, except for those associated with disseminated and diffuse involvement, and inflammatory myelitides appear abruptly. Most degenerative conditions are manifested by a slow and gradual progression of symptoms, although in some conditions, such as multiple sclerosis, there may be periods of remission with exacerbations.

COMPLETE TRANSECTION

Complete transection of the spinal cord, whether of traumatic, neoplastic, vascular, or other origin, causes isolation of the segments below the level of the lesion. The upper portions of the cerebrospinal axis function normally, but motor, sensory, and autonomic functions are lost distal to the lesion. The term *transverse myelitis* is often used for syndromes which result in complete transection, even though the process may not be inflammatory in origin; in most cases the term transverse myelopathy is more appropriate.

If a transverse lesion is abrupt in onset, the state of *spinal shock* or *diaschisis* occurs. There is flaccid paralysis together with loss of all types of sensation, absence of autonomic function, and areflexia below the level of the lesion. Spinal shock usually lasts for about three or four weeks, after which the reflexes gradually return and become exaggerated, pathologic reflexes appear, muscle tone becomes increased, and the nature of the bladder and rectal dysfunction becomes altered. Sensation does not return. If infection supervenes, however, in the form of a severe urinary tract involvement or infected decubiti, the period of spinal shock is prolonged.

In transverse myelopathy there is a general loss of all types of sensation below the uppermost level of the lesion, and the lowest level of preserved sensation corresponds to the dermatome supplied by the lowest intact segment. This is most apparent and most clearly delineated in the exteroceptive sensations, especially the superficial pain and temperature modalities. There is loss of these sensations below the level of the lesion, or within one or two segments of the level of the lesion. It must be borne in mind, however, that there is some discrepancy between the spinal cord segments and the corresponding vertebral spinous processes. There may be hyperesthesia at the level of the lesion. The level for tactile sensation is seldom clearly delineated; proprioceptive sensations are also lost, but it is difficult to demonstrate a specific level for these.

After the initial period of flaccidity, the musculature below the level of the lesion becomes spastic, or sometimes spastic and rigid. There is increased tone with increased resistance to passive movement. The deep reflexes return and then become hyperactive. The superficial reflexes do not return. Pyramidal tract responses may appear, but they do not do so as characteristically in complete as in incomplete transverse syndromes. There may be an exaggeration of sweating and piloerection below the level of the lesion, with changes in skin temperature and cutaneous vascular function. The bladder, first atonic and distended, with retention and overflow incontinence, becomes small and contracted; the patient develops a reflex type of neurogenic dysfunction. There may be priapism. With the development of the above changes, reflexes of spinal automatism appear. These may be elicited by nociceptive stimuli up to the level of the lesion. They are usually of the uniphasic, or flexor, variety, and frequently are accompanied by the mass response with urination, defecation, and sweating below the level of the lesion.

The position of predilection in complete transverse lesions is one of flexion of the lower extremities. The paralysis and sensory loss are symmetrical and total; voluntary power does not return; vasomotor and sphincter disturbances are evident; pyramidal tract responses usually are minimal, but defense responses are definite; there is a marked tendency toward the development of decubiti. Inasmuch as the response is mainly one of flexion, the extensor reflexes may be difficult to elicit. With transverse lesions of long duration there may be metabolic alterations including increased excretion of proteins, fall in serum protein, increase of potassium and decrease of sodium and chlorides in the blood and tissue fluids, hypercalcuria, osteoporosis, testicular atrophy, gynecomastia, altered urinary excretion of 17-ketosteroids, and orthostatic hypotension. The hypertonicity of transverse spinal lesions is sometimes relieved by selective anterior rhizotomy, peripheral nerve section (obturator and others), posterior root section, selective cordectomy, or injection of alcohol into the subarachnoid space. Regeneration resulting from growth of neural elements within the spinal cord has been reported in experimental animals, but no functional regeneration has been observed in man following complete transverse lesions. With incomplete transection, however, or gradual compression of the cord, there may be recovery of function.

INCOMPLETE TRANSECTION

If the spinal cord is only partially divided, the resulting signs and symptoms will depend upon the pathways and cellular structures involved. If there is a sudden onset, there may also be a period of spinal shock, but after recovery from this there is evidence of retention of function of some portions of the cord. The disturbance of superficial pain and temperature sensations depends upon the extent of the damage to the lateral spinothalamic tracts. Inasmuch as the impulses from the lower portions of the body are in the dorsolateral aspects of these tracts, and those from the upper portions of the body are ventral and medial, the sensory level depends upon the site of damage in the transverse plane. If only the lateral portion of one tract is affected, the level for loss of these sensations may be some distance distal to the lesion; it is always contralateral to the side of the cord involvement. Because tactile impulses are conducted to consciousness through both ipsilateral and contralateral pathways, there may be no demonstrable level for loss of such sensations. Proprioceptive sensations are lost on the side of the lesion; those from the lower portion of the body are medial, and an interruption of the lateral part of the tract may not affect them. The extent of motor change, autonomic nervous system dysfunction, and reflex disturbance depends upon the site and extent of the damage. In a partial lesion the motor changes are usually asymmetric and incomplete, and there is some return of voluntary power. The lower extremities may be in a position of extension if the vestibulospinal pathways are intact. The vasomotor changes are variable, but there is lesser tendency toward the development of decubiti than in complete lesions. The bladder may be overactive with a reduced capacity and precipitate micturition. There may be spinal defense reflexes, or reflexes of spinal automatism, but these are usually of the biphasic type with flexion followed by extension, or there may be a crossed extensor reflex or an extensor thrust. The tendon reflexes are markedly hyperactive, especially the extensor responses. Babinski reflexes and other pyramidal tract responses are obtained.

Hemisection of the spinal cord causes the *Brown-Séquard syndrome*. The essential findings, below the level of the lesion, are as follows: ipsilateral spastic paresis with increased reflexes and pyramidal tract responses; ipsilateral loss of proprioceptive sensation with sensory ataxia; contralateral loss of pain and temperature sensations extending to one or two segments below the level of the lesion. There may be little or no objective evidence of change in tactile sensation. The following additional neurologic changes may also be present: ipsilateral vasomotor paralysis below the level of the lesion; ipsilateral segmental flaccid paralysis in the myotome supplied by the level of the lesion; ipsilateral segmental loss of all sensation with vasomotor paralysis in the dermatome supplied by the level of the lesion; hyperesthesia instead of anesthesia in the dermatome supplied by the level of the lesion; a zone of hyperesthesia above the anesthetic area, both ipsilaterally and contralaterally; bilateral anesthesia, hyperesthesia, or radicular pain in the distribution of the affected segments. A quadrantic lesion of the spinal cord which involves the dorsal quadrant causes ipsilateral loss of proprioceptive sensation and pyramidal paresis below the level of the lesion. Involvement of the ventral quadrant causes an ipsilateral segmental flaccid paralysis, due to involvement of the anterior horn cells, together with a contralateral loss of pain and temperature sensations below the level of the lesion.

TRAUMATIC LESIONS

Traumatic lesions of the spinal cord are usually abrupt in onset. They are most frequently associated with vertebral injuries such as fractures or dislocations of the vertebral column, or with gunshot, stab, or perforating wounds. The violence may be either direct or indirect. The regions of greatest mobility are most susceptible to trauma, and the fifth through seventh cervical, twelfth thoracic, and first lumbar levels are most often affected. Either physiologic interruption, usually temporary, or anatomic interruption of the cord, usually permanent, can occur without bony lesions. Birth injuries of the spinal cord usually follow difficult breech deliveries. The impairment of spinal cord function following trauma may be caused by actual damage to the cord (see below), compression or mechanical blockage, interference with blood supply, herniation of intervertebral disks, or extramedullary or intramedullary hemorrhages, or combinations of these. Anterior, posterior, or central injuries may occur. Spinal shock appears immediately if the lesion is a severe or extensive one. Roentgen studies may aid in diagnosis and localization.

Syndromes of spinal cord concussion, contusion, laceration, and compression have been described. *Concussion of the spinal cord* is said to follow indirect violence to the cord without fracture or dislocation. There is an immediate but transitory loss of sensory and motor function. It is said that there are no structural alterations, but there may be edema and mild fiber and intracellular changes of a reversible nature. Traction and compression of the peripheral nerves and nerve roots may cause some of the symptoms. If paralysis lasts longer than ten to fourteen days, it is believed that the damage is more serious in type. In *contusion of the spinal cord* there are petechial hemorrhages into the cord, especially the gray matter, which cause focal disturbances of function. Recovery of function may or may not be complete. *Lacerations of the spinal cord* cause more severe disturbances of function than contusions. In actual *compression of the spinal cord* there is pressure on the structure with either partial or complete loss of function. The symptoms in all of these syndromes depend upon the location and the severity of the damage to the spinal cord. There may be manifestations of either complete or incomplete transection. Radicular pain, rigidity of the muscles supplied by the affected nerve roots, localized tenderness and rigidity of the spine, and motor, sensory, and autonomic nervous system changes may be found.

The syndrome of *acute central cervical spinal cord injury* usually follows severe hyperextension of the neck. There may be a dislocation of the vertebral bodies at the fifth and sixth cervical levels. There is more impairment of motor power, with varying degrees of sensory loss, in the upper than the lower extremities, and with recovery sensation and motor power return first in the legs, then in the upper arms, and finally in the hands. The central involvement of the cord is probably a result of vascular insufficiency. With acute anterior spinal cord injuries the clinical picture resembles that of thrombosis of the anterior spinal artery, and either lacerations of the cord or interruption of blood supply, or both, may be responsible. In the more common so-called *whiplash* or *flexion-extension injury* of the neck the pain and other symptoms are more often the result of damage to the soft tissues (muscles and ligaments) and stretching of nerves and nerve roots, than of actual trauma to the spinal cord itself. The symptoms and disability, however, do depend, at least in part, upon the type and severity of the injury, and there may be structural damage to the vertebral column with foraminal encroachment, compression of the vertebral artery, interverebral disk herniation, and even spinal cord involvement in some cases.

NEOPLASMS

Neoplasms within the spinal canal may be either extradural or intradural in site. Intradural tumors may be either extramedullary or intramedullary. Tumors may be classified further according to their horizontal location and vertical level within the spinal canal. The onset of symptoms and signs in spinal cord neoplasms is usually a slow and progressive one, but on occasion the first manifestations appear precipitously. Pain and paresthesias are often symptoms of consequence, but motor, reflex, and vegetative changes are also important.

Extradural tumors may be either primary or metastatic in origin. There may be involvement of the vertebral bodies or extradural space by such neoplasms as carcinoma, sarcoma, lymphosarcoma, and multiple myeloma, with pressure on the spinal cord. *Intradural* but *extramedullary neoplasms* usually arise from the meninges, nerve roots, connective tissue, and blood vessels. These include meningiomas, neurofibromas, lipomas, dermoids, and hemangiomas, as well as metastatic tumors. In both groups the early manifestations are caused by compression and later there is interference with blood supply. The essential symptoms and signs are listed in Table 9. Spontaneous pain is an early and prominent symptom; it may be radicular in distribution, and sharp and lancinating in character. It is often increased by movement and by increasing either the intracranial or intraspinal pressure. A history of prodromal root pains is sometimes obtained. The motor and sensory changes may be slow in onset because of progressive loss of function of ascending and descending pathways. They often assume a Brown-Séquard distribution, with segmental alterations at the level of the tumor. There is contralateral loss of pain and temperature modalities, with ipsilateral loss of proprioceptive sensations. Inasmuch as the lateral portions of the lateral spinothalamic tract are primarily involved, the sensory loss may be more profound in the distal portions of the body; the defect in pain and temperature sensations may be prominent in the sacral areas. If there is anteroposterior pressure on the spinal cord, the proprioceptive sensations are severely affected. The motor changes are usually of a spastic type with little atrophy, but there may be segmental lower motor neuron involvement at the level of the lesion. There may be irritative motor phenomena with spasm and defense reflexes. Hyperactive deep reflexes and pyramidal tract responses are noteworthy and occur early. Trophic changes are not marked unless there is extensive spinal cord involvement. Changes in the content and pressure relationships of the spinal fluid occur early.

Intramedullary neoplasms are usually glial, ependymal cell, or vascular in origin. They frequently start in the gray matter of the cord, in the vicinity of the central canal, and extend into the white matter (Table 9). Spontaneous pain, if it occurs, is burning in type and poorly localized. Radicular pain is rare. The sensory changes are dissociated in type; there is segmental loss of pain and temperature sensations with little involvement of tactile or proprioceptive modalities. If the process extends to involve the lateral spinothalamic tract, it affects first the inner fibers, or those which have come from dermatomes just slightly below the level of the lesion. There may be "spotty" changes in sensation. The motor signs are those of lower motor neuron involvement, and there may be focal but often widespread paralysis with atrophy and fasciculations. Pyramidal paresis appears late and is minimal. Increase in the deep reflexes and pyramidal tract responses appear late. Trophic changes may be marked. Alterations in the content and pressure relationships of the spinal fluid occur later than in extramedullary neoplasms, and are less definite.

TABLE 9. DIFFERENTIATION BETWEEN EXTRAMEDULLARY AND
INTRAMEDULLARY TUMORS OF THE SPINAL CORD

	Extramedullary tumors	*Intramedullary tumors*
Spontaneous pain	Radicular in type and distribution; an early and important symptom	Burning in type; poorly localized
Sensory changes	Contralateral loss of pain and temperature; ipsilateral loss of proprioceptive; (Brown-Séquard type)	Dissociation of sensation; "spotty" changes
Changes in pain and temperature sensations in saddle area	More marked than at level of lesion	Less marked than at level of lesion
Lower motor neuron involvement	Segmental	Marked and widespread, with atrophy and fasciculations
Pyramidal paresis	Prominent	Late and minimal
Deep reflexes	Increased early and to a marked degree	Changes are minimal and occur late
Pyramidal tract responses	Early	Late
Trophic changes	Usually not marked	Marked
Spinal subarachnoid block and changes in spinal fluid	Early and marked	Late and less marked

The symptoms and signs of an intramedullary tumor may closely resemble those of syringomyelia.

The diagnosis and localization of spinal cord neoplasms can often be confirmed by spinal puncture, roentgen studies, and myelography. If there is a space-occuing lesion within the vertebral canal, there is often either partial or complete block to the flow of cerebrospinal fluid. There may be increased protein, sometimes with a yellowish discoloration of the fluid. Roentgen studies may show evidence of erosion of the vertebral processes, narrowing or separation of the pedicles, or even collapse of the bodies. The clinical manifestations associated with the tumor are sometimes increased following spinal puncture, especially if there had been a partial or complete block and the hydrodynamics were altered by removal of some of the fluid. Spinal fluid and roentgen changes are more marked in extradural and extramedullary than in intramedullary tumors.

Herniated intervertebral disks which press on the spinal cord, nerve roots, or nerve fibers, may give the symptoms of an extramedullary tumor. This is especially true when they occur in the cervical and thoracic regions of the cord. The more commonly encountered ruptured intervertebral disks in the lumbar and lumbosacral regions are considered with the syndromes of low-back pain (Chapter 48).

Neoplasms and lesions of other types in the region of the conus medullaris and the cauda equina may present some diagnostic difficulties. In lesions of the conus there is symmetric involvement, suggestive of an intramedullary lesion. In lesions of the cauda equina the manifestations are more asymmetric and are suggestive of nerve root involvement (Table 10).

TABLE 10. DIFFERENTIATION BETWEEN LESIONS OF THE CONUS MEDULLARIS AND CAUDA EQUINA

	Conus medullaris	*Cauda equina*
Spontaneous pain	Not common or severe; bilateral and symmetric; in perineum or thighs	May be most prominent symptom; severe; radicular in type; may be unilateral or asymmetric; in perineum, thighs and legs, back, or bladder; distribution of sacral nerves
Sensory changes	Saddle distribution; bilateral, usually symmetric; dissociation of sensation	Saddle distribution; may be unilateral and asymmetric; all forms affected; no dissociation of sensation
Motor changes	Symmetric; not marked; fasciculations may be present	Asymmetric; more marked; may be atrophy; usually no fasciculations
Reflex changes	Only achilles reflex absent	Patellar and achilles reflexes may be absent
Bladder and rectal symptoms	Involvement early and marked	Involvement occurs late and is less marked
Trophic changes	Decubiti common	Decubiti less marked
Sexual functions	Erection and ejaculation impaired	Involvement less marked
Onset	Sudden and bilateral	Gradual and unilateral

VASCULAR LESIONS

Vascular lesions affect the spinal cord less frequently than the brain or brain stem. However, thrombosis, embolism, hemorrhage, and arteriosclerotic changes may occur.

Thrombosis of the anterior spinal artery causes ischemic necrosis and myelomalacia in the area of distribution of this vessel. It may occur at any level, but is most common in the boundary zones between ascending and descending sources of blood supply, especially in midthoracic areas. The onset is usually abrupt, with or without pain. There is a partial transverse myelopathy affecting predominantly the anterior horns and the ventral and lateral funiculi, with a flaccid paralysis at the level of the lesion and a spastic paresis below. Bowel and bladder functions are usually lost, but proprioceptive sensations are spared. The thrombosis is usually secondary to atherosclerosis of the anterior spinal artery, but it may also develop in association with either a dissecting aneurysm of the aorta or thrombosis of an aortic aneurysm, and it has been reported following aortography. The cord dysfunction caused by neoplasms, herniated disks, and inflammatory involvement of the meninges may be the result of compression of the anterior spinal artery. Thrombosis of the anterior spinal artery within the cranium is discussed in Chapter 18.

Meningeal hemorrhage, if subarachnoid, gives symptoms of subarachnoid hemorrhage; if either subdural or extradural, it may cause focal manifestations. The term *hematorachis* is used for any hemorrhage into the spinal canal, it is usually traumatic in origin. *Intraspinal hemorrhage* produces focal manifestations. *Hematomyelia* may follow trauma to the spinal column or acute inflammation of the spinal cord; it may be associated with purpura or hemophilia. The lesion is usually in the vicinity of the spinal canal, and the symptoms are similar to those of syringomyelia. Angiomas, hemagiomas, arteriovenous malformations, and varices of the meninges and spinal cord may cause focal symptoms which come on either abruptly or gradually, but there are also recurrent episodes of meningeal bleeding. *Arteriosclerotic changes, anemia,* and *hyperemia* may cause focal, disseminated or diffuse involvement. Progressive degenerative changes of the spinal cord with symptoms suggestive of posterolateral sclerosis may have an arteriosclerotic basis. Symptoms similar to those of vascular occlusion occur in caisson disease, sometimes causing a transverse myelitis. In addition there are muscular cramps, paresthesias, vertigo, staggering, and nausea.

INFLAMMATORY LESIONS

The term myelitis is used to indicate inflammatory disease of the spinal cord. It is also used, however, for lesions which are not obviously inflammatory or are of unknown etiology; for these the term myelopathy would be more appropriate. *Inflammatory transverse myelitis* may be suppurative in type, secondary to meningitis, adjacent infections (such as osteomyelitis or caries of the vertebrae), or infections elsewhere in the body (pneumonia or septicemia), or it may be of viral or suspected viral origin. Tuberculous, syphilitic, rickettsial, mycotic, and parasitic forms also occur. Occasionally there is a sudden onset of transverse involvement, which may or may not follow symptoms of systemic infection and may or may not be accompanied by a pleocytosis in the cerebrospinal fluid. The source of the infection may not be determined, and the prognosis is unpredictable at the onset. Myelitis may develop on the basis of demyelination, as in certain cases of multiple sclerosis, and in neuromyelitis optica and postvaccinal and postinfectious myelopathies. It may also occur with collagen disease and the use of intrathecal anesthetics and drugs, following radiation and electrical injuries, in association with visceral carcinoma, and as the so-called acute or subacute necrotic myelopathy, which may be of vascular origin.

In *Landry's paralysis,* or *acute ascending paralysis,* there is an ascending motor deficit, usually with sensory changes which are less marked. This syndrome may be caused by an actual inflammatory disease of the spinal cord, predominantly the anterior horn regions, or it may be associated with a polyradiculoneuritis. In *anterior poliomyelitis* the inflammatory process is limited largely to the anterior horn cells, and there is a focal flaccid paralysis, segmental in distribution, with resulting atrophy. There is loss of both motor power and reflex action in the segments involved by the area of inflammation, often with associated vasomotor involvement, but no sensory changes. A meningeal reaction, with a pleocytosis in the cerebrospinal fluid, accompanies the process. *Herpes zoster* is discussed with lesions of the nerve roots (Chapter 45). *Syphilitic myelitis* may cause manifestations of primary lateral sclerosis or of amyotrophic lateral sclerosis.

Meningeal inflammation may be accompanied by spinal cord involvement in the absence of transverse myelitis; *adhesive spinal arachnoiditis* usually causes both localized and disseminated changes. *Cervical hypertrophic pachymeningitis* produces focal manifestations suggestive of an extradural neoplasm; there may be associated pain and muscle spasm, sensory changes, and spinal subarachnoid block. A *spinal epidural abscess* may present symptoms of a focal, space-occupying, extramedullary lesion; there are usually associated signs of infection. While Pott's disease may cause cord symptoms, they are more often those of compression than of infection. Infections of the intervertebral disks cause pain and signs of systemic infection, but rarely cause spinal cord involvement. With all of the above extramedullary inflammation, signs of spinal cord disease, if they occur, may be the result of interference with blood supply rather than of extension of the infectious process.

DEGENERATIVE PROCESSES AND SYSTEMIC DISEASES

So-called degenerative processes and systemic diseases of the spinal cord of unknown etiology may take various forms. The manifestations may be diffuse, disseminated, or systemic.

In *progressive spinal muscular atrophy,* sometimes known as chronic anterior poliomyelitis, there is atrophy with paresis and fasciculations secondary to degenerative changes in the anterior horn cells. In *amyotrophic lateral sclerosis* there are the above changes, together with evidence of pyramidal tract and bulbar involvement.

In *tabes dorsalis* the principal manifestations are loss of proprioceptive sensations and sensory ataxia secondary to involvement of the posterior funiculus. Associated involvement of the dorsal roots and dorsal root ganglia causes radicular pain, girdle sensations, decreased reflexes, loss of deep pain, and a delayed pain reaction. It may be that the pathologic process starts in the dorsal roots and progresses to the posterior funiculi. Other important changes include vesical dysfunction of an atonic type, rectal incontinence, impotence, and trophic disturbances in the form of perforating ulcers and a Charcot type of arthropathy.

Primary lateral sclerosis has been described as a disease entity, but it may be the earliest manifestation of amyotrophic lateral sclerosis, posterolateral sclerosis, or multiple sclerosis. Erb's spastic paraplegia may be a manifestation of central nervous system syphilis. In lateral sclerosis there are bilateral pyramidal pareses with hyperreflexia, pyramidal tract responses, and loss of superficial reflexes, but no sensory manifestations. The syndrome of primary lateral sclerosis may also be associated with anterior spinal cord compression; the larger fibers, which mediate motor impulses, are affected earlier by pressure than the smaller fibers, which transmit pain and temperature sensations.

Posterolateral sclerosis is characterized by pathologic changes which involve predominantly the lateral column (pyramidal pathway) and the posterior funiculus. The clinical manifestations include pyramidal paresis with hyperreflexia and pyramidal tract responses, loss of proprioceptive sensation with sensory ataxia, and vegetative manifestations with bladder and rectal involvement and impotence. Posterolateral sclerosis is most frequently associated with pernicious anemia, but it may appear in certain deficiency states, pellagra, diabetes mellitus, senility, and arteriosclerosis, and may occur as a disease *sui generis*.

In *Friedreich's ataxia* there is involvement of the posterior columns and the spinocerebellar tracts; there is often associated affection of the lateral columns and of the cerebellum. The ataxia is both spinal and cerebellar in type. Nystagmus is marked. The patellar reflexes are absent owing to interference with tone, but the Babinski response is usually present.

Syringomyelia is a disease in which the pathologic changes consist of gliosis, fibrosis, necrosis, and cavitation in the central portion of the spinal cord; the process often extends into the medulla as well (syringobulbia). Many etiologies have been suggested, but the condition is probably of developmental origin. Anomalies of or interference with the intramedullary blood supply lead to vascular insufficiency of the affected areas. The patients often have other associated malformations and disturbances of development. On occasion the syrinx may be associated with an intramedullary neoplasm. Those cases in which localized cavitation of the cord develops secondary to trauma, compression, extramedullary vascular lesions, and meningeal inflammation can usually be differentiated pathologically from true syringomyelia. The degeneration usually occurs in the cervical enlargement; it starts in the region of the central canal and extends peripherally in an irregular fashion. The canal itself is not always involved in the process. Owing to interference with the decussating sensory fibers, the first manifestation is often a loss of pain and temperature sensations in the dermatomes supplied by the involved segments, with relative sparing of tactile sensation. As the process extends there is involvement of the anterior horn cells with focal paresis, atrophy, and fasciculations, and affection of the cells of the intermediolateral column with focal vegetative changes. Later there is pressure on the fiber pathways with a pyramidal paresis and interruption of the ascending lateral spinothalamic tract. There may be extensive trophic changes in the skin and subcutaneous tissues, with indolent ulcers and infected whitlows. There may be painless ulcerations of the fingers (Morvan's disease) and edema and lividity of the hands (main succulente), as well as Charcot joints. The manifestations of syringomyelia resemble those of hematomyelia and intramedullarly neoplasms. In syringomyelia, however, spontaneous pain and evidence of spinal fluid block are rarely encountered.

Multiple sclerosis is characterized by disseminated lesions of the central nervous system. These are found in the spinal cord, where they affect largely the white matter, and also in the brain stem, cerebellum, cerebrum, and optic nerves. There may be fluctuation of symptoms, with remissions and exacerbations. Spinal cord involvement frequently causes a spastic paresis, hyperactive deep reflexes, loss of superficial reflexes, pyramidal tract responses, interference with proprioceptive sensations, and sensory ataxia. Disturbances of exteroceptive sensation are not common. In *neuromyelitis optica* there is, in addition to an acute optic neuritis, a rapidly progressing myelopathy, often with pain and paresthesias.

It is well known that certain alterations of the spinal cord take place with the aging process. There is gliosis with demyelination of fasciculus gracilis as well as atrophy of ganglion cells. These changes, along with ischemia secondary to arteriosclerosis, may cause proprioceptive defects and progressive weakness of the lower extremities.

DEVELOPMENTAL DISTURBANCES AND CONGENITAL DEFECTS

Developmental disturbances of various types may cause abnormalities of spinal cord function. These include, among others, heterotopias, spina bifida, agenesis, meningocele, myelocele, myelomeningocele, and myelodysplasias of various types and in various sites. Spina bifida, which is most frequent in the lumbosacral area, may cause a cauda equina syndrome with a flaccid paralysis of the lower extremities, sensory changes in the saddle or perianal area, loss of bowel or bladder control, and trophic involvement. Developmental disturbances in the region of the atlas and axis are discussed in Chapter 18.

OTHER CAUSES OF SPINAL CORD DISEASE

Structural and other abnormalities of the vertebral column, especially those in the cervical region, may cause spinal cord and nerve root compression and thus bring about alterations of function. Osteomyelitis, syphilitic osteitis, Paget's disease, Pott's disease, and severe osteoporosis may result in vertebral compression with consequent pressure on the spinal cord. There may be erosion of the vertebral bodies by a dissecting aortic aneurysm. Scoliosis of varying etiologies may cause spinal cord symptoms. Absence of one or more of the cervical vertebrae (Klippel-Feil syndrome) may cause disturbances of function; this may be associated with the Sprengel deformity, and the wasting of the shoulder girdle muscles may simulate poliomyelitis. Rupture and protrusion of intervertebral disks at various levels may cause spinal cord symptoms, as may spondylosis and spondylitis of various etiologies. This is especially true in the cervical region, where spondylitis, usually either posttraumatic or degenerative, causes pressure on the emerging nerve roots as well as on the spinal cord with resulting pain, weakness, and sensory changes in the radicular distribution and a significant and progressive myelopathy. Occasionally pressure on the vertebral arteries causes symptoms of vertebrobasilar insufficiency with transient attacks of vertigo and weakness.

The injection of foreign substances into the subarachnoid space, which may be done for either diagnostic or therapeutic purposes, may on occasion cause dysfunction of nerve roots, an aseptic meningitis that may be followed by a progressive or constricting arachnoiditis, or an actual myelitis. Fortunately these complications are rare, but the fact that they may occur should be a deterrent to the use of intrathecal injections except when specifically indicated. Excessive doses of either radium or roentgen rays over the spinal cord may cause a radiation myelopathy, with necrosis of the parenchyma in the affected areas and thickening and proliferation of the blood vessels; the damage to the nervous tissue may not become evident until six months or more after the therapy.

REFERENCES

AUSTIN, GEORGE (ed.)   The Spinal Cord: Basic Aspects and Surgical Considerations. Springfield, Ill., Charles C Thomas, 1961.

BAILEY, A. A.   Changes with age in the spinal cord.   *A. M. A. Arch. Neurol. & Psychiat.* 70:299, 1953.

BATSON, O. V.   The function of the vertebral veins and their role in the spread of metastases.   *Ann. Surg.* 112:138, 1940.

BRAIN, W. R., NORTHFIELD, D., and WILKINSON, M.   The neurological manifestations of cervical spondylosis.   *Brain* 75:187, 1952.

BROCK, S. (ed.)   Injuries of the Brain and Spinal Cord and Their Coverings (ed. 4). New York, Springer Publishing Co., Inc., 1960.

CADWALADER, W. B.   Diseases of the Spinal Cord.   Baltimore, The Williams & Wilkins Company, 1932.

CREED, R. S., DENNY-BROWN, D., ECCLES, J. C., LIDDELL, E. G. T., and SHERRINGTON, C. S.   Reflex Activity of the Spinal Cord.   Oxford, The Clarendon Press, 1932.

ELSBERG, C. A.   Tumors of the Spinal Cord.   New York, Paul B. Hoeber, Inc., 1925.

GILLILAN, L. A.   The arterial blood supply of the human spinal cord.   *J. Comp. Neurol.* 110:75, 1958.

ITABASHI, H. H., BEBIN, J., and DE JONG, R. N.   Postirradiation cervical myelopathy. *Neurology* 7:844, 1957.

KAHN, E. A.   Role of the dentate ligaments in spinal cord compression and the syndrome of lateral sclerosis.   *J. Neurosurg.* 4:191, 1947.

NETSKY, M. G.   Syringomyelia: A clinicopathologic study.   *Arch. Neurol. & Psychiat.* 70:741, 1953.

PERESE, D. M., and FRACASSO, J. E.   Anatomical considerations in surgery of the spinal cord: A study of vessels and measurements of the cord.   *J. Neurosurg.* 16:314, 1959.

POSER, C. M.   The Relationship between Syringomyelia and Neoplasms.   Springfield, Ill., Charles C Thomas, 1956.

SCHNEIDER, R. C.   The syndrome of acute anterior spinal cord injury.   *J. Neurosurg.* 12:95, 1955.

SCHNEIDER, R. C., CHERRY, G., and PANTEK, H.   The syndrome of acute central cervical spinal cord injury.   *J. Neurosurg.* 11:546, 1954.

STEEGMANN, A. T.   Syndrome of the anterior spinal artery.   *Neurology* 2:15, 1952.

SUH, T. H., and ALEXANDER, L.   Vascular system of the human spinal cord.   *Arch. Neurol. & Psychiat.* 41:659, 1939.

TARLOV, I. M.   Spinal Cord Compression: Mechanism of Paralysis and Treatment. Springfield, Ill., Charles C Thomas, 1957.

TUREEN, L. L.   Circulation of the spinal cord and the effect of vascular occlusion. *A. Res. Nerv. & Ment. Dis., Proc.* (1937) 18:394, 1938.

CHAPTER 48

LESIONS CAUSING LOW BACK PAIN WITH LUMBO- SACRAL RADIATION

THE DIAGNOSIS of lesions that cause low back pain, pain of lumbosacral radiation, or both is one of the distressing problems of neurology. Such pain must always be regarded as a symptom, not a disease, and every attempt should be made to determine its etiology. Possible causes to be considered are the following: involvement of skeletal, muscular, and related structures; pelvic or abdominal disease, postural abnormalities; psychogenic factors. Among the frequent and important causes of such pain, however, are the neurogenic ones, and they must be carefully diagnosed before adequate treatment can be undertaken. The character and localization of the pain must be determined, and the examiner must decide whether the neurogenic difficulties are primary, or whether they are secondary to skeletal muscular, or other disease.

The history is extremely important (Chapter 2), especially if there is a relationship to trauma or infection, or if there have been previous episodes or recurring manifestations. One must take into consideration the character of the pain and its exact distribution and areas of radiation, the presence of paresthesias and other subjective sensory changes, and the history of motor disturbances such as weakness and atrophy. Associated symptoms such as bowel and bladder disturbances or rectal or genital anesthesia, may be important. The relationship of the pain to position and exercise may give relevant information. The pain of a ruptured intervertebral disk, for instance, may be more severe when the patient is seated than when he is standing, but it is usually increased by activity and by bending or stooping, especially when the legs are extended at the knees; it is characteristically intensified by coughing, straining, and sneezing. The pain of a spinal cord tumor

807

may also be aggravated by increasing the intracranial or intraspinal pressure, but it is often more severe when the patient is lying down than when he is seated.

A complete examination of the back is essential (Chapter 3). Abnormalities of posture, deformities, tenderness, and muscle spasm are important. With pain of sciatic or lumbosacral radiation there may be loss of the normal lumbar lordosis due to involuntary spasm of the back muscles. In addition there often is a lumbar scoliosis, with a compensatory thoracic scoliosis. Most commonly the list of the body is away from the painful side, and the pelvis is tilted so that the affected hip is prominent and elevated. The patient attempts to keep his weight on the sound limb. The list and scoliosis may, however, alternate, or be toward the painful side, and the patient's body is bent forward and toward that side to avoid stretching the involved nerve. With very severe sciatic pain the patient will usually avoid complete extension at the hip and knee, and frequently places only the toes on the floor, since dorsiflexion of the foot aggravates the pain. He may walk with small steps and keep his leg semiflexed at the knee. In bending forward he flexes his knee to avoid stretching the sciatic nerve *(Neri's sign)*. In sitting he keeps the affected leg flexed at the knee and rests his weight on the opposite buttock. He may rise from a seated position by supporting himself on the unaffected side and placing one hand on his back while he bends the affected leg *(Minor's sign)*. Areas of maximal tenderness in the lumbosacral region should be determined, especially in those instances in which either manipulation or percussion of the spinous processes or pressure just lateral to them reproduces or accentuates the pain. A sharp blow with a percussion hammer, on or just lateral to the spinous processes while the patient is bending forward, may bring out the pain. The distribution of the muscle spasm may give objective information about the radiation of the pain, and not only the back muscles, but also the hamstrings and gastrocnemius may be in spasm. On the other hand, the achilles or posterior tibial tendon may have decreased resistance to palpation on the affected side; palpation is carried out while the patient is standing with his weight supported equally on both feet. Flexion, extension, and lateral deviation of the spine are limited; the pain is usually accentuated with passive rotary extension of the lumbar spine toward the affected side while the patient is standing erect. Manipulation of the spine may be painful, and there may be localized tenderness at the sciatic notch and along the course of the sciatic nerve.

Roentgenologic examinations should always be carried out; pelvic and rectal examinations are necessary, chiefly to exclude neoplasms originating outside the spine. Electromyography may aid in localization. Spinal puncture and myelography are important diagnostic measures, and on occasion diskography is used.

The neurologic examination must be carefully executed. Sensory changes are important and should be thoroughly evaluated. Either hypesthesia or hyperesthesia and hyperalgesia may be present. One should differentiate peripheral nerve and segmental changes. The exact localization of a ruptured intervertebral disk may be pend upon the delineation of segmental changes in sensation. The motor examination should be complete, and one should carefully test motor power in the individual muscles and look for atrophy and fasciculations as well as muscle spasm. Reflex changes are also important diagnostic criteria. There may be dysfunction of the sacral portion of the parasympathetic division, but there is no outflow of pre-ganglionic sympathetic fibers in the spinal roots below the second (or third) lumbar root level.

A number of special diagnostic procedures should be carried out in the examination of the patient who is suffering from pain in the low back with lumbosacral radiation. Some of these are of special interest to the orthopedist, but those which are essential to the neurologic examination are listed.

THE LASÈGUE SIGN

Flexion of the thigh at the hip while the leg is extended at the knee causes stretching of the sciatic nerve. Such stretching may be done as an active process if the patient stoops while his legs are extended at the knees, but it is done as a diagnostic neurologic test by passively flexing the hip of the supine patient while holding the leg in extension at the knee (Fig. 282). This maneuver may be carried out without the patient experiencing radiating pain if there is disease of the hip joint, but with either disease or irritation of the sciatic nerve, or of the nerve roots which enter into it, there is pain in the sciatic notch accompanied by pain and hypersensitivity along the course of distribution of the sciatic nerve. This is the *positive Lasègue sign*. The procedure is similar to that used in eliciting the Kernig sign, but in the latter the thigh is flexed at the hip, and then an attempt is made to extend the leg at the knee. Both, when positive, indicate the presence of irritation of the meninges or of the lower lumbosacral nerve roots. The Lasègue maneuver is sometimes called the *straight-leg-raising test;* the examiner should note both the angle of flexion of the hip at which pain occurs and the amount and site of the pain experienced by the patient. The pain may be felt as a tight sensation or actual pain in the lumbar or sacral region, gluteal region, or posterior aspect of the thigh, or sometimes in the opposite limb. The test is most positive if the maneuver reproduces the patient's subjective pain. There may even be numbness and par-

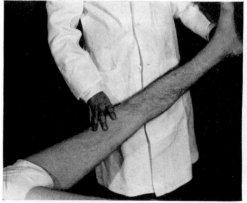 

Fig. 282 (*Left*).   Method of eliciting the Lasègue sign.
Fig. 283 (*Right*).   Accentuating the Lasègue sign by dorsiflexion either of foot or great toe (nerve-stretching test).

esthesiasis in the distribution of the affected nerve roots. It has been stated that pain produced by flexion of less than 40 degrees is indicative of movement of an affected nerve root against a protruded disk; if pain does not occur until flexion has been carried to 70 or 80 degrees, one may assume that there is an abnormally sensitive nerve root, but not necessarily a demonstrable lesion of the root or protruded disk (Charnley). Evidences of sciatic nerve or nerve root irritation can also be elicited by examining the patient while he is seated, with thighs at a right angle with the hips. The leg is then passively extended at the knee until pain is produced. It is generally believed, however, that the supine is preferable to the seated position for carrying out these maneuvers.

To test for the *buckling sign* (Michelle) the straght-leg test is carried out as described above, by passively flexing the hip while the knee is extended until the knee begins to flex or buckle. This is an involutary reaction which signifies a release from the sciatic nerve tension which is producing the pain.

Various modifications of the Lasègue test give additional information. The pain may be more severe, or elicited sooner, if the test is carried out with the thigh and leg in a position of adduction and internal rotation (*Bonnet's phenomenon*). Dorsiflexion of the foot (*Bragard's sign*) or of the great toe (*Sicard's sign*) while carrying out the examination increases the stretching of the tibial portion of the sciatic nerve and aggravates the pain (Fig. 283). The examiner may flex the hip until the first manifestations of pain are noted, and then flex either the toe or foot. In mild cases, no pain may be present with the usual Lasègue maneuver, but dorsiflexion of the foot or toe, after the hip is completely flexed, may cause pain. Sometimes the pain is brought on while the patient is supine with his thighs and legs extended, merely by dorsiflexion of the foot or great toe. This later aggravation of pain by passive dorsiflexion of the foot is sometimes called *Gower's sign*. Similar tests have also been described by Viner and Purves-Stewart. All the modifications of the Lasègue maneuver in which either the foot or the great toe is dorsiflexed may be called *nerve stretching tests;* the term *Spurling's sign* is also used. A similar modification may be carried out by flexing the thigh to an angle just short of that necessary to cause pain, following which the neck is flexed; this may produce the same exacerbation of pain that would be brought about by further flexion of the hip. Occasionally the pain may be brought on merely by passive flexion of the neck when the patient is recumbent with both the hips and knees extended.

NERVE PRESSURE SIGNS

Tension on the sciatic nerve is increased when the tibial nerve is pressed in the popliteal space. The Lasègue maneuver is carried out to the angle where pain is first noted, and then the knee is flexed about 20 degrees. Following this the hip is further flexed to a degree just short of that causing pain, and firm pressure is applied in the popliteal space over the tibial nerve; when the test is positive, this causes sharp pain in the lumbar region, affected buttock, or along the course of the sciatic nerve. This test may also be carried out with the patient seated on a table. The affected leg is extended passively at the knee to the point at which pain is reproduced. It is then flexed slightly, and pressure is applied in the popliteal space, which, in cases of sciatic nerve or nerve root irritation, will cause pain (Deyerle and May) (Fig. 284).

O'CONNELL'S TEST

In carrying out this test, the Lasègue maneuver is first carried out on the sound limb, and the angle of flexion and site of pain are recorded; the pain may be on the opposite side (Fajersztajn's sign). Then this test is carried out on the affected limb, and the angle and site of pain again noted. Then both thighs are flexed simultaneously while extension is maintained at the knee. The angle of flexion permitted may be greater than that allowed when the affected limb is flexed alone, or when either is flexed separately. Finally, having flexed both thighs to an angle just short of that which produces pain, the sound limb is lowered to the bed; this may result in a marked exacerbation of pain, sometimes associated with paresthesias.

THE VIETS AND NAFFZIGER TESTS

Increase of the intracranial or intraspinal pressure causes exaggeration of radicular pain in patients with space-consuming lesions pressing on the nerve roots. The pressure may be increased temporarily by coughing, sneezing, and straining, and by digital compression of the jugular veins (Viets). Pressure should be maintained

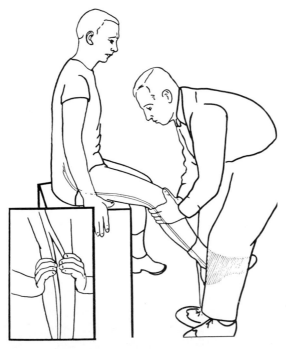

FIG. 284. Sciatic tension test; with sciatic nerve or nerve root irritation, pressure over tibial nerve in popliteal space causes pain in back and/or leg. (Deyerle, W. M., and May, V. R., Jr.,: *South. M. J.* 49:999, 1956.)

until the patient complains of a feeling of fullness in the head, and the test should not be considered to be negative until venous return has been impeded for at least two minutes. Jugular compression can also be carried out with a sphygmomanometer cuff, maintaining a pressure of 40 mm. of mercury for ten minutes (Naffziger). The patient may be in either the recumbent or upright position. In a patient with a ruptured intervertebral disk there will be radicular pain in the distribution of the affected nerve roots following jugular compression. The pain is similar to that which follows coughing and straining, and the Viets and Naffziger tests are rarely positive in patients who do not have aggravation of pain when coughing and straining. Occasionally the pain may be noticed on the release of the pressure. A similar aggravation of the pain may sometimes be brought about merely by having the patient perform the Valsalva maneuver.

PATRICK'S SIGN

This sign consists of pain in the hip when the heel or the external malleolus of the painful extremity is placed upon the opposite knee and the thigh is pressed downward. The pain thus occurs on simultaneous flexion, abduction, external rotation, and extension of the involved hip. When the maneuver is carried out it may be noted that the knee on the affected side is kept elevated and cannot be pressed toward the bed. The Patrick sign is positive in hip joint disease, but is usually absent in sciatic nerve involvement.

ELY'S SIGN

This sign is probably indicative of contracture of the fascia lata. With the patient prone on the examining table, the examiner flexes the leg upon the thigh, bringing the heel toward the buttock. With a positive test, the pelvis rises from the table during such flexion and the thigh is abducted.

OBER'S SIGN

The patient lies on one side, with the thigh and leg of that side in flexion; the examiner abducts and extends the opposite thigh and then suddenly releases it. If the thigh fails to drop promptly, there is contracture of the tensor fasciae latae on that side.

CAUSES OF LOW BACK PAIN WITH LUMBOSACRAL RADIATION

Low back pain with lumbosacral radiation may be due to a multiplicity of causes, and these should all be considered in arriving at a diagnosis. Involvement of the skeletal, muscular, and related structures which may cause pressure on and irritation of the lumbosacral plexus or its branches include the following: acute trauma with fractures or subluxations of the spine, fractures of the hip or pelvis, ligamentous or tendinous tears or strains, repeated mechanical strain, acute or chronic arthritis, congenital anomalies of the spine, spondylolisthesis, spondylolysis, sacralization of the fifth lumbar vertebra, bony spurs (osteosclerosis) of the lumbar spine, reduction of the lumbosacral joint space, disease of the sacroiliac area, diseases of the hip joint, narrowing of the intervertebral foramina, osteitis deformans, osteomyelitis, myositis, fibrositis, bursitis, irritation of the piriformis muscle, abnormally increased tension of the fascia lata, chronic postural anomalies, and hypertrophy of the ligamentum flavum. Intrapelvic and intra-abdominal causes include neoplastic or inflammatory involvement of the pelvic and abdominal viscera, endometriosis, aortic obstruction or aneurysm, and malposition during pregnancy. Spinal conditions include tumors of the vertebrae or spinal cord, tumors and inflammations of the cauda equina, meningitis, pachymeningitis, arachnoiditis, hemangiomas, arachnoid and extradural cysts, nerve root cysts, and ruptured intervertebral disks. The sciatica nerve or its root may be affected by a primary neuritis, perineuritis, radiculitis, the presence of a neuroma or neurinoma, or by trauma to the nerve itself or injection into it. Psychalgias and psychogenic etiologies must also be considered, especially in the presence of camptocormia and coccygodynia.

The most common cause of low back pain with lumbosacral radiation is the ruptured intervertebral disk. There may be either extrusion of a portion of the annulus fibrosus or rupture of the annulus with herniation of the nucleus pulposus (Fig. 285). The protrusion may be either posterolateral or midline. In most cases there is a history of trauma which was followed by the onset of low back pain with radiation down one leg. The herniated, or protruded, nucleus pulposus presses upon the roots of the lumbosacral plexus and causes the symptoms (Fig. 286). The radiation of the pain and the localization of the symptoms is dependent upon the degree and site of the herniation. Such herniation is most apt to occur in the lumbar region, although it may occur in the cervical and thoracic areas also. In the lumbar spine the herniation most frequently occurs between the

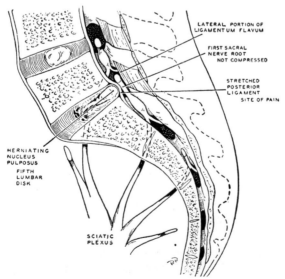

FIG. 285.   Early herniation of nucleus pulposus into spinal canal. (Keegan, J. J.: *J.A.M.A.* 126:868, 1944.)

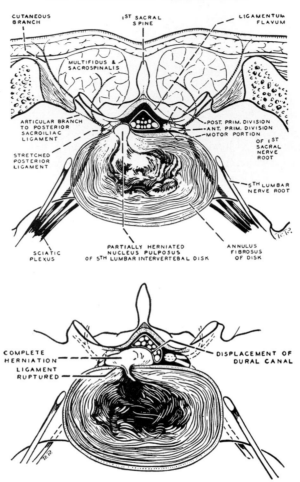

FIG. 286.   *Above:* Partial herniation of nucleus pulposus of intervertebral disk with rupture of annulus fibrosus, stretching of posterior longitudinal ligament, and compression of a single nerve root. *Below:* Complete herniation of nucleus pulposus with rupture of posterior longitudinal ligament. (Keegan, J. J.: *J.A.M.A.* 126:868, 1944.)

fourth and fifth lumbar vertebrae, with pressure on the fifth lumbar nerve root, or between the fifth lumbar and first sacral bodies, with pressure on the first sacral root (Table 11).

Pain in the back with radiation down the posterior aspect of the thigh and the posterior or lateral aspect of the leg, to the heel or foot, is the most common symptom of a ruptured intervertebral disk. The pain is aggravated by coughing and straining and by bending either forward or to the affected side; it may be relieved by standing upright. Associated with the pain may be paresthesias, together with motor changes. In order to make an unequivocal diagnosis of a ruptured intervertebral disk, certain objective sensory, motor, and reflex changes should be pres-

TABLE 11. DIFFERENTIATION BETWEEN FOURTH LUMBAR
AND FIFTH LUMBAR HERNIATIONS

	Fourth lumbar herniation	Fifth lumbar herniation
Site of lesion	Between fourth and fifth lumbar bodies	Between fifth lumbar and first sacral bodies
Nerve root affected	Fifth lumbar	First sacral
Radiation of pain and paresthesias (including site of pain experienced on eliciting the Lasègue sign)	Lateral aspect of thigh, anterolateral aspect of leg, dorsal aspect of foot, occasionally affecting great toe	Posterior aspect of thigh, posterolateral aspect of leg, and lateral aspect of foot, including the heel and one or two outer toes
Superficial sensory changes	Hypesthesia or anesthesia, occasionally hyperesthesia, in the above-mentioned distribution, especially distally (fifth lumbar dermatome)	Hypesthesia or anesthesia, occasionally hyperesthesia, in the above-mentioned distribution, especially distally (first sacral dermatome)
Vibratory sensory changes	Loss or impairment over medial malleolus and medial aspect of foot and toes	Loss or impairment over lateral malleolus and lateral aspect of foot and toes
Motor changes	Paresis of extensor hallucis longus and occasionally of extensor digitorum brevis and tibialis anterior; atrophy of anterior calf muscles	Paresis of plantar flexors of foot (triceps surae); atrophy of posterior calf muscles
Reflex change	Tibialis posterior reflex may be absent	Diminished or absent achilles reflex
Accentuation of pain	Pressure or percussion at the fourth lumbar interspace causes radiation of pain	Pressure or percussion at the lumbosacral interspace causes radiation of pain

ent. The sensory disturbances consist of either hypesthesia or hyperesthesia and hyperalgesia, most frequently in the distribution of the fifth lumbar or first sacral segments. Occasionally there are more diffuse sensory changes, even with saddle anesthesia. Alterations in vibratory sensation are sometimes found. There may be referred hyperalgesia and muscle spasm when the skin of the back or loin on the affected side is stimulated. The motor abnormalities may not be marked if only one nerve root is affected, since most muscles are supplied by more than one such root. There may, however, be weakness of the extensor hallucis longus, extensor digitorum brevis, tibialis anterior, or gastrocnemius muscles. The two sides should always be compared. In addition to weakness there may be atrophy and/or fasciculations. The most common reflex change is the loss of the achilles reflex, but occasionally the tibialis posterior reflex is absent. Autonomic nervous system disturbances such as bladder and bowel dysfunction are less common. Bilateral involvement is not encountered unless there are bilateral herniations or a large ruptured disk in the midline. Under such circumstances the first through the lower sacral roots may be affected, and the clinical picture resembles that found with a lesion of the cauda equina. The sensory changes include the saddle and genital areas as well as the posterior aspects of the thighs and legs, there may be weakness of the triceps surae muscles bilaterally, one or both achilles reflexes may be absent, and there may be sphincter disturbances and impotence.

In most patients with low back and lumbosacral radiation pain due to ruptured intervertebral disks the Lasègue and associated signs of sciatic and nerve root irritation are positive. Roentgenograms often show evidence of reduction of the joint space between the fourth and fifth lumbar vertebral bodies or at the lumbosacral level, or other abnormalities. There may be electromyographic changes in those muscles supplied by the affected nerve roots. A spinal puncture may show the presence of increased protein. Myelography is usually positive; it may on occasion give misleading information, but is important in differentiating between a ruptured intervertebral disk and tumors of the spinal cord and cauda equina. Occasionally such procedures as diskography and intraosseous vertebral venography are used for diagnosis, although neither of these procedures is widely accepted.

REFERENCES

AIRD, R. B., and NAFFZIGER, H. C. Prolonged jugular compression: A new diagnostic test of neurological value. *Tr. Am. Neurol. A.* 66:45, 1940.

ALPERS, B. J. The neurological aspects of sciatica. *M. Clin. North America* 37:503, 1953.

BRADFORD, F. K., and SPURLING, R. G. The Intervertebral Disc: With Special Reference to Rupture of the Annulus Fibrosus with Herniation of the Nucleus Pulposus (ed. 2). Springfield, Ill., Charles C Thomas, 1945.

CHARNLEY, J. Orthopaedic signs in the diagnosis of disc protrusion. *Lancet,* 1:186, 1951.

DEYERLE, W. M., and MAY, V. R., JR. Sciatic tension test. *South. M. J.* 49:999, 1956.

DIMITRIJEVIC, D. T. Lasègue sign. *Neurology* 2:453, 1952.

FALCONER, M. A., GLASGOW, G. L., and COLE, D. S. Sensory disturbances occurring in sciatica due to intervertebral disc protrusions: Some observations on the fifth lumbar and first sacral dermatomes. *J. Neurol., Neurosurg. & Psychiat.* 10:72, 1947.

FALCONER, M. A., McGEORGE, M., and BEGG, A. C. Observations on the cause and mechanism of symptom-production in sciatica and low-back pain. *J. Neurol., Neurosurg., & Psychiat.* 11:13, 1948.

KEEGAN, J. J. Diagnosis of herniation of lumbar intervertebral disks by neurologic signs. *J.A.M.A.* 126:868, 1944.

LEWIN, P. Backache and Sciatic Neuritis: Back Injuries, Deformities, Diseases, Disabilities, with Notes on the Pelvis, Neck, and Brachial Neuritis. Philadelphia, Lea & Febiger, 1943.

LINDBLOM, K. Technique and results of diagnostic disc puncture and injection (discography) in the lumbar region. *Acta orthop. scandinav.* 20:315, 1951.

LOVE, J. G.   The differential diagnosis of intraspinal tumors and protruded intervertebral disks and their surgical treatment.   *J. Neurosurg.* 1:275, 1944.

MICHELE, A. A.   Determinations of sciatic nerve tension.   *Postgrad. Med.* 28:488, 1960.

MIXTER, W. J., and BARR, J. S.   Rupture of the intervertebral disc with involvement of
the spinal cord.   *New England J. Med.* 211:210, 1934.

O'CONNELL, J. E. A.   Sciatica and the mechanism of the production of the clinical
syndrome in protrusions of the lumbar intervertebral discs.   *Brit. J. Surg.* 30:315,
1943.

SCOBINGER, R. A., KRUEGER, E. G., and SOBEL, G. L.   Comparison of intraosseous
venography and pantopaque myelography in the diagnosis of surgical conditions of
the lumbar spine and nerve roots.   *Radiology* 77:376, 1961.

SHERBOK, B. C.   A maneuver of help in the diagnosis of ruptured disk.   *Arch. Surg.*
76:986, 1958.

SJÖQVIST, O.   Mechanism of origin of Lasègue's sign.   *Acta psychiat. et neurol.* (supp.)
46:290, 1947.

VIETS, H. R.   Two new signs suggestive of cauda equina tumor: Root pain on jugular
compression and the shifting of the lipiodol shadow on change of posture.   *New
England J. Med.* 198:671, 1928.

WARTENBERG, R.   Lasègue sign and Kernig sign.   *A. M. A. Arch. Neurol. & Psychiat.*
66:58, 1951.

ZERVOPOULOS, G.   Diagnosis and localization of herniated intervertebral disks.   *Neurology* 6:754, 1956.

PART EIGHT

Diagnosis and Localization of Intracranial Disease

DIAGNOSIS AND LOCALI-
ZATION OF INTRACRANIAL
DISEASE

THE RECOGNITION and accurate localization of intracranial disease is one of the most important, and at the same time one of the most difficult, problems in neurologic diagnosis. It is essential not only to establish the presence of a lesion, but also to localize it accurately and to determine its nature and etiology. It is only after one accumulates all of the pertinent information that he can consider the treatment and the prognosis.

The history is of utmost consequence in the diagnosis of intracranial lesions (see Chapter 2). In some diseases causing neurologic symptoms there may be no objective manifestations at any time, and in others, such as those causing periodic convulsions, there may be none between attacks.. In these, the diagnosis may have to be made on the basis of the history alone. Furthermore, the mode of onset, duration of symptoms, progression or regression of manifestations, and response to therapy may give pertinent clues to diagnosis. Vascular lesions are usually abrupt in onset, although occasionally intermittent or progressive. The onset of symptoms in intracranial neoplasms is usually progressive, and sometimes insidious; occasionally however, the first manifestations appear precipitously. Degenerative diseases are usually slowly and gradually progressive, but in some, such as multiple sclerosis, there may be intermittent and remittent features. In posttraumatic states the history is usually self-revealing; in disturbances of development and hereditary affections the manifestations can often be traced back to birth or the postnatal period; in infectious and toxic conditions one should be able to elicit systemic as well as nervous system changes, and in occupational and nutritional disorders, a history of exposure, physical or mental strain, or inadequate diet.

In cerebral disease even more than in involvement of other portions of the nervous system one must evaluate meticulously the often conflicting information that may be presented by those symptoms and signs which are the result, variously, of *destruction, release, irritation,* and *partial assumption of function by healthy tissues*. There may be either *neural shock,* or *diaschiasis,* a temporary more or less complete depression of function of nervous structures following an acute, catastrophic lesion, or a transient decrease of function in the areas surrounding a contusion, hemorrhage, or infarct due to reversible ischemia, edema, or compression by the injured tissues. Furthermore, one must differentiate between the following: *positive symptoms,* which may be due to either release or irritation; *negative symptoms,* which follow loss of function of certain parts; *primary symptoms,* correlated directly with either focal structural disease or local disorders of function; *secondary (indirect) manifestations,* which occur as a result of overactivity of certain nervous mechanisms, due to release from inhibition normally executed by the injured areas, alteration of function of the physiologic mechanisms of the parts damaged, or reorganization of function of uninjured structures. There may be symptoms of both irritation and destruction, such as recurrent jacksonian attacks which are followed by a transitory localized paralysis (Todd's paralysis). In addition, edema, pressure from tumors and other expanding lesions, and interference with the circulation of the blood or flow of the cerebrospinal fluid may cause dysfunction of distant parts of the brain or brain stem, and produce symptoms and signs, known as *false localizing signs,* which may suggest involvement of the opposite hemisphere or of other areas of the nervous system which are not affected by the primary process.

Localized lesions are limited to one region, and may affect all of the tissues regardless of their structures and functions. In diffuse disease the damage of the functional elements is usually incomplete, and certain structures suffer more than others. In system disease only anatomically and functionally related systems of cells or fibers are involved. When a lesion develops rapidly, negative symptoms are always greater and more widespread immediately after the onset; there may be recovery of function. Slowly progressive lesions, on the other hand, cause less severe disturbances of function in relation to their extent and severity. In all diseases of the nervous system, but especially in cerebral disorders, those most recently acquired, highly specialized, and most complex functions are the first to be affected, and the last and least complete to return during the recovery process.

The localization and diagnosis of disease of certain intracranial constituents are discussed elsewhere. The infratentorial structures (those below the tentorium cerebelli) are the cerebellum, midbrain, pons, and medulla. The functions of the cerebellum and the disturbances of function that result from disease are discussed in "The Motor System," Part IV. Localization of disease of the midbrain, pons, and medulla is dependent upon a knowledge of the functions and distribution of the third through the twelfth cranial nerves as well as of the motor and sensory pathways which traverse these structures. The more important clinical conditions that may affect the midbrain and pons are discussed with the individual cranial nerves which have their nuclei of origin and termination within these structures; clinical involvement of the medulla is discussed in Chapter 18. The functions and disorders of some of the supratentorial structures are also discussed individually. The basal ganglia are dealt with in Chapter 22, and the hypothalamus, in "The Autonomic Nervous System," Part VI. In the present section clinical cerebral localization will be considered with respect to the cerebral cortex and certain noncortical areas of the cerebrum, namely the thalamus, corpus callosum, and internal capsule.

CHAPTER 49

GROSS AND MICROSCOPIC ANATOMY OF THE CERE-BRAL HEMISPHERES

In the diagnosis and localization of intracranial lesions it is necessary to have a general knowledge of cerebral anatomy and function. The brain, the seat of the higher sensory, motor, and intellectual functions, is composed of two hemispheres which are incompletely separated from each other by the median longitudinal fissure (Fig. 287). At the bottom of this fissure lies a broad band of commissural fibers, the corpus callosum, which forms the chief bond of union between the hemispheres. Areas within the individual hemispheres communicate by means of association fibers, and the cerebrum is connected with lower centers by means of projection pathways. The brain is covered by a layer of gray matter, the cerebral cortex. Underneath is the white matter which consists of the association, commissural, and projection fibers. At the base of each hemisphere are several gray masses, or nuclei, including the basal ganglia and the diencephalon, which consists of the thalamus, metathalamus, epithalamus, subthalamus, and hypothalamus. The cortex of the cerebrum with its underlying white matter is known as the pallium, or cerebral mantle, and in the human this is tremendously expanded and forms by far the larger part of the hemispheres. The more primitive portions of the pallium are the paleopallium in the pyriform lobe area and the archipallium in the hippocampal formation; these constitute the rhinencephalon (allocortex) which is connected structurally and functionally with the limbic lobe. The phylogenetically more recently acquired neopallium (isocortex) is highly developed only in mammals, and in humans constitutes the major portion of the cerebrum.

Each cerebral hemisphere is transversed by fissures and sulci (Figs. 288 and 289). The more important fissures divide the hemispheres into lobes, and these in turn are subdivided by the sulci into gyri, or convolutions. This separation of the

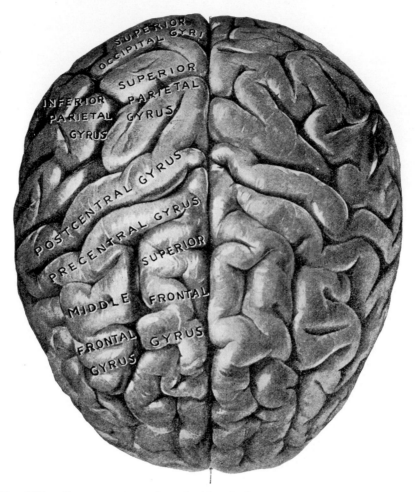

Fig. 287.   Gross structure of cerebral hemispheres as seen from above. (Figs. 287, 288, and 289 from Tilney, F.: The Brain from Ape to Man. New York, Paul B. Hoeber, Inc., 1928.)

parts of the brain has practical significance for anatomic purposes, but the divisions are arbitrary morphologic ones, and the individual lobes are not necessarily functional units. The classification of the various areas of the brain by physiologic and histologic criteria is discussed later.

On the lateral surface of the brain are two large fissures, the *lateral,* or *sylvian,* and the *central,* or *rolandic.* The former begins on the basal surface of the brain and extends lateralward, posteriorly, and superiorly. The latter runs obliquely, nearly reaching the sylvian fissure; it makes an angle of seventy degrees with the dorsal surface of the brain, and its peak is just behind the middle of the dorsal border of the hemisphere. The *frontal lobe,* which constitutes the anterior one third of each hemisphere in man, extends, on the lateral surface of the brain, from the

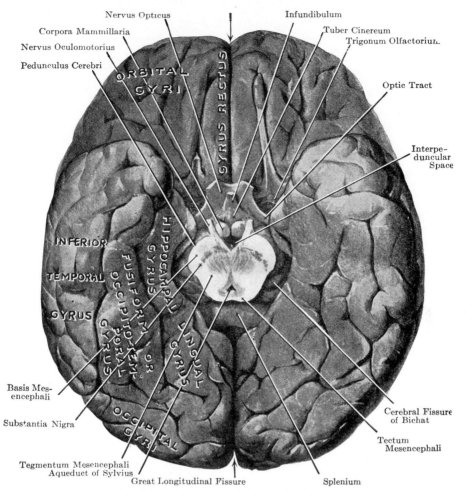

FIG. 288.   Base of human brain.

frontal pole to the rolandic fissure, and lies above, or rostral to, the sylvian fissure (Fig 289). One the medial surface of the brain it extends to the sulcus cinguli. It is made up of four principal gyri (Fig. 290). The precentral gyrus, also known as the anterior central or posterior frontal gyrus, is situated between the central and precentral fissures. The superior frontal gyrus is located rostral to the superior frontal sulcus; the middle frontal gyrus, between the superior and the inferior frontal sulci; the inferior frontal gyrus, beneath the inferior frontal sulcus. The middle frontal sulcus runs through the middle frontal gyrus. The portion of the precentral gyrus which lies on the medial aspect of the brain above the sulcus cinguli is known as the paracentral lobule. Two divisions of the sylvian fissure, the anterior horizontal ramus which runs anteriorly and the anterior ascending ramus which extends dorsally, divide the inferior frontal gyrus into the pars orbitalis which lies

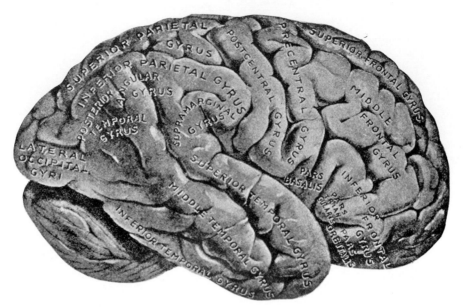

FIG. 289.   Lateral view of right cerebral hemisphere.

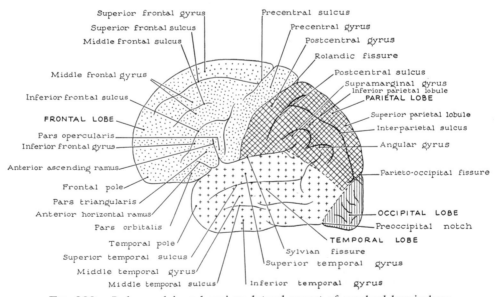

FIG. 290.   Lobes, sulci, and gyri on lateral aspect of cerebral hemisphere.

below the anterior horizontal ramus, the pars triangularis which is between the two rami, and the pars opercularis which lies between the anterior ascending ramus and the rolandic fissure.

The *parietal lobe* extends from the central sulcus to an imaginary line drawn between the parieto-occipital fissure and the preoccipital notch, and lies above the lateral fissure and an imaginary line connecting that fissure with the middle of the preceding line. It consists of five principal gyri. The superior parietal lobule lies above the interparietal sulcus; the postcentral (posterior central or anterior parietal) gyrus lies between the rolandic fissure and the postcentral sulcus; the inferior parietal lobule is situated beneath the interparietal sulcus; the supramarginal gyrus curves around the upturned end of the sylvian fissure; the angular gyrus is similarly related to the terminal ascending portion of the superior temporal sulcus.

The *temporal lobe* lies beneath the sylvian fissure and extends to the arbitrary limits of the parietal and occipital lobes; the tongue-shaped anterior projection terminates in the temporal pole, and the ventral surface lies on the floor of the middle cranial fossa. It contains three definite sulci, the superior, middle, and inferior temporal, dorsal to each of which is a gyrus bearing a similar name. The superior temporal gyrus, bordering on the lateral fissure, is marked in its posterior aspect by the presence of horizontal convolutions, the transverse temporal gyri, sometimes known as Heschl's convolutions. The inferior temporal sulcus is located on the basal portion of the lobe, and between it and the collateral fissure lies the fusiform gyrus. The insula, or island of Reil, may be considered as a lobe that lies buried at the depth of the lateral fissure. It is surrounded by the limiting, or circular, sulcus. Those portions of the frontal, parietal, and temporal lobes which overlie the insula are known as the frontal, parietal, and temporal opercula.

The *occipital lobe* occupies only a small part of the dorsolateral surface of the hemisphere, that area lying behind the line drawn between the parieto-occipital fissure and the preoccipital notch, but it occupies a large triangular field between the parietal and temporal lobes on the medial aspect of the brain. The medial surface is traversed by the calcarine fissure, and the portion of the occipital lobe above this fissure is the cuneus, whereas that below is the lingual gyrus (Fig. 291).

On the medial surface of the brain are the sulcus of the corpus callosum and the sulcus cinguli, between which lies the gyrus cinguli. The hippocampal gyrus is situated between the hippocampal fissure and the collateral fissure with its anterior projection, the rhinal fissure; its rostral extremity bends around the hippocampal fissure to form the uncus. It is connected with the gyrus cinguli by the isthmus, and the term gyrus fornicatus, or limbic lobe, is used to include the gyrus cinguli, isthmus, hippocampal gyrus, and certain subcortical structures including the amygdala and septal nuclei. These are usually considered parts of the rhinencephalon, but from a clinical point of view the hippocampal gyrus and uncus are sometimes assigned to the temporal lobe and the gyrus cinguli is divided between the parietal and frontal lobes.

The cerebral cortex is a laminated structure composed largely of cellular matter which dips into the fissures and sulci and covers the gyri and convolutions. It is

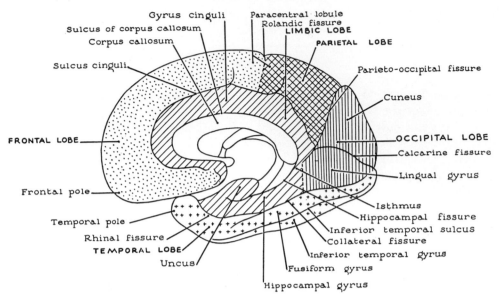

FIG. 291.   Lobes, sulci, and gyri on medial aspect of cerebral hemisphere.

said that about one third of the cortex is on the exposed surfaces of the brain and the remaining two thirds dips into the fissures and sulci. It has been estimated that in addition to nerve fibers, neuroglia, and blood vessels, there are cell bodies of nearly fourteen billion neurons in the cortex (Economo). The structure varies in thickness from 4.5 mm. in the precentral gyrus to 1.25 mm. near the occipital pole. The size and types of cells found in the cortex vary at different depths from the surface and in different portions of the brain, but in general they are arranged in fairly definite layers (Fig. 292), separated by myelinated bands. Cajal described eight layers, but the usually accepted classification of the lamination is that of Brodmann, which is as follows:

I. *Lamina zonalis,* or the *molecular,* or *plexiform layer,* is the most superficial. It is covered by the pia and forms a dense tangential fiber network composed of the terminal dendrites of the deeper cells. The ganglion cells are small and few in number.

II. *Lamina granularis externa,* or the *layer of small pyramidal cells,* consists of many small, closely packed pyramidal cells.

III. *Lamina pyramidalis,* or the *superficial layer of medium-sized and large pyramidal cells,* may be divided into two substrata, the more superficial containing the medium-sized and the deeper one the large pyramidal cells.

IV. *Lamina granularis interna,* or the *layer of small stellate cells,* is characterized by the presence of a large number of small multipolar cells with short axons, among which are some small pyramidal cells.

V. *Lamina ganglionaris,* or the *deep layer of medium-sized and large pyramidal cells,* contains the largest cells of the cortex. In the motor region these are known

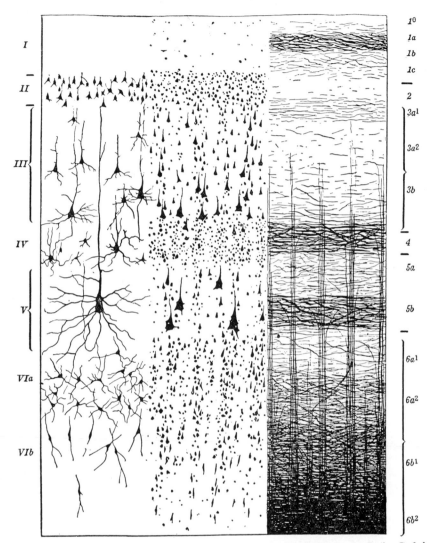

FIG. 292. Cell layers and fiber arrangements of cerebral cortex. *Left,* Golgi stain; *middle,* Nissl stain; *right,* Weigert stain. I, lamina zonalis; II, lamina granularis externa; III, lamina pyramidalis; IV, lamina granularis interna; V, lamina ganglionaris; VI*a* and VI*b,* lamina multiformis; 3*a*[1], band of Bechterew; 4, outer band of Baillarger; 5*b,* inner band of Baillarger. (Brodmann.)

as the giant pyramidal cells of Betz, and these, along with other neurons, give origin to the fibers of the corticospinal tract.

VI. *Lamina multiformis,* or the *layer of polymorphic cells,* contains irregular fusiform and angular cells, the axons of which enter the subjacent white matter.

Although the cortex of the entire brain can be divided into the above six lamina, the histologic features vary from place to place, and this variation is probably responsible for differences in function. Individual areas present their characteristic appearances in thickness of cortex as a whole, thickness and arrangement of specific cellular layers, cell structure, number of afferent and efferent myelinated fibers, and number and position of white striae. The differences in cellular structure have been spoken of as the *cytoarchitectonic*, and those of the fibrillary structure as the *myeloarchitectonic*, features of the cortex.

Histologic surveys based on the differences in the arrangements and the types of cells and the pattern of myelinated fibers have furnished several fundamentally similar cortical maps in which a number of areas of slightly different structure have been described. These individual segments, the total of which has been variously estimated, have been grouped into regions which compare roughly to the boundaries imposed by the fissures and sulci. Flechsig, in 1876, outlined thirty-six

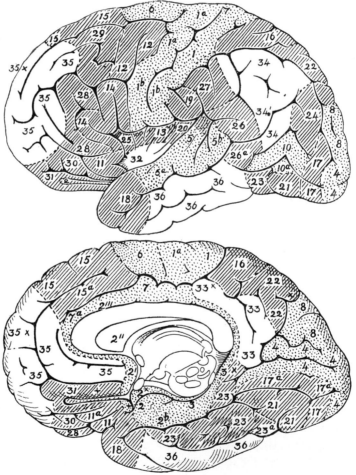

Fig. 293. Cortical areas as determined by the myelogenetic method. (Flechsig.)

areas of the cortex on the basis of the differences in the time of myelinization of the nerve fibers (Fig. 293). Campbell's publication in 1905, based on work done in 1903, divided the human cortex into some twenty regions and described the cellular and fibrillary lamination of each (Fig. 294). Elliot Smith, in 1907, identified twenty-eight to thirty areas on the basis of gross examination; he noted the relative thickness of the gray and white matter, texture, and color in each region. Brodmann, in 1909, carried out more detailed observations and differentiated forty-seven different fields by means of a histologic survey of the cortex using the Nissl method (Fig. 295). C. and O. Vogt, in 1919, described over two hundred areas; their work was based upon the differences in the pattern of the myelinated fibers. In 1925 von Economo and Koskinas reduced all cortical variations to five fundamental types, but divided the cortex as a whole into one hundred and seven different

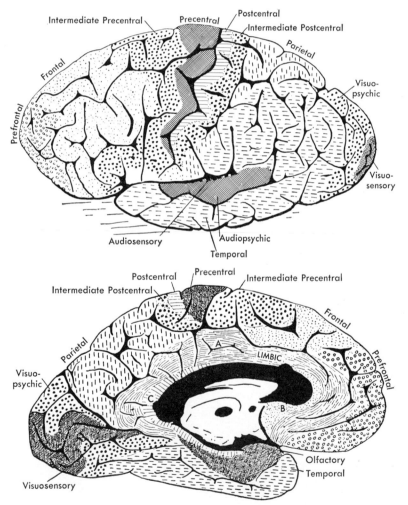

FIG. 294.   Areas of cerebral cortex as outlined by Campbell. (Campbell.)

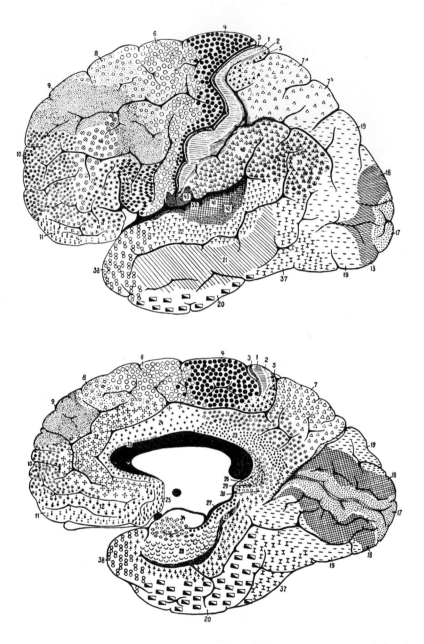

FIG. 295. Areas of cerebral cortex, each of which possesses a distinctive structure. (Nielsen, J. M.: A Textbook of Clinical Neurology, ed. 2. New York, Paul B. Hoeber, Inc., 1946.) (After Brodmann.)

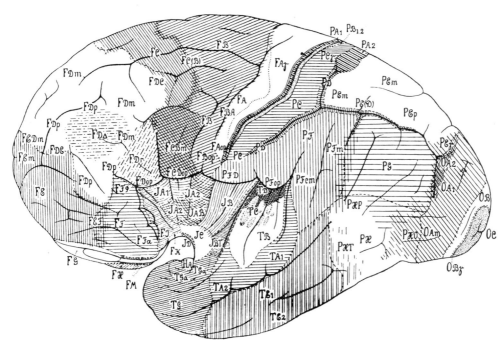

FIG. 296. Cytoarchitectural map of cerebral cortex as outlined by von Economo; frontal and parietal lobes have been pushed aside to show the insula. (von Economo.)

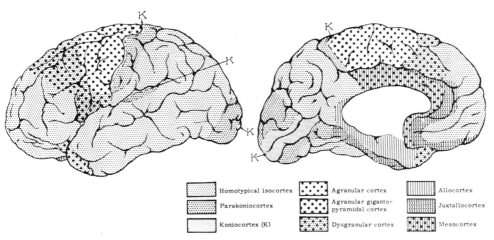

▨ Homotypical isocortex		⦂ Agranular cortex		▥ Allocortex	
▨ Parakoniocortex		❋ Agranular giganto-pyramidal cortex		▥ Juxtallocortex	
▨ Koniocortex (K)		❋ Dysgranular cortex		▦ Mesocortex	

FIG. 297. Black-and-white supplement for color map of Bailey and von Bonin. (Chusid, J. G.: *Neurology* 14:134, 1964.)

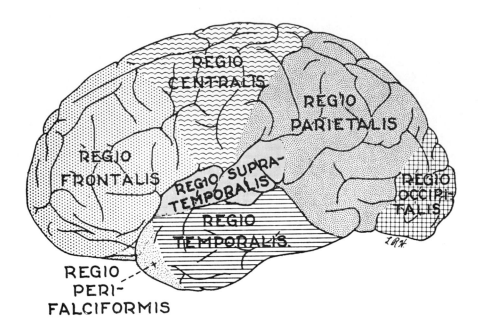

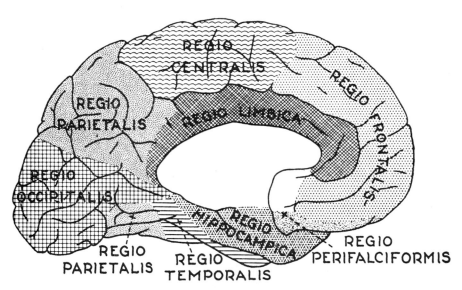

Fig. 298.   Sectoral map of the cerebral cortex based on distribution of the thalamocortical radiations. (Bailey, P., and von Bonin, G.: The Isocortex of Man. Urbana, Ill., University of Illinois Press, 1951.)

areas (Fig. 296); their work was based fundamentally on the work of Brodmann.

The classification of the brain into areas dependent upon histologic structure has attained greater value in functional localization than the division based on lobes and fissures. The granular cells, which make up the bulk of the second and fourth layers, are concerned with reception of impulses, and hence these layers are the largest in the sensory areas. The pyramidal cells, on the other hand, are efferent in function, and are largest and most numerous in the motor areas, which regions also possess the thickest cortex. It has become obvious, however, that although the above-described classifications are important from a topographic point of view, they cannot be correlated completely with the intrinsic functions of the individual regions. Neurophysiologic research and functional localization by Dusser de Barrenne, McCulloch, Bailey, von Bonin, and others, using strychninization and observation of electrical activity (physiologic neuronography) to investigate the arrangement of associational and commissural systems within the hemispheres, have shown that the histologic areas must be considered as somewhat arbitrary and artificial from a functional point of view. Furthermore, there are gradations of function, and limits between various zones cannot always be outlined specifically. Bailey and von Bonin prefer to use colors to identify the various cortical areas, and thus to demonstrate the existence of transitional zones. Chusid has made a black-and-white supplement for their color map (Fig. 297). Bailey and von Bonin have also designated the division of the cortex into sectors, or those regions of the brain which have afferent connections with a particular thalamic nucleus (Chapter 51). In their tentative map they divide the cortex into frontal, central, parietal, occipital, supratemporal, temporal, perifalciform, limbic, and hippocampal sectors (Fig. 298). They state that the boundaries are only roughly approximate, and that the density of radiation is not uniform throughout the various regions. They do express the belief, nevertheless, that such a subdivision promises to be a more useful guide to further studies than the cytoarchitectural maps previously utilized. In spite of the fact, however, that by histologic examination many areas of the cortex cannot be distinguished from each other, the major zones described by the various anatomists are probably correct with respect to extent and boundaries, bearing in mind individual variations. Consequently, for both descriptive purposes and classification the numerical designations of Brodmann or modifications of them remain generally accepted.

REFERENCES

BAILEY, P., and VON BONIN, G.   The Isocortex of Man.   Urbana, Ill., The University of Illinois Press, 1951.

VON BONIN, G.   Essay on the Cerebral Cortex.   Springfield, Ill., Charles C Thomas, 1950.

VON BONIN, G. (ed.)   Some Papers on the Cerebral Cortex.   Springfield, Ill., Charles C Thomas, 1960.

BRODMANN, K.   Vergleichende Lokalisationlehre der Grosshirnrinde in ihren Prinzipien dargestellt auf Grund des Zellenbaues.   Leipzig, J. A. Barth, 1909.

CAJAL, S. RAMON y.   Studies on the Cerebral Cortex (Limbic Structures). (L. M. Kraft, trans.)   Chicago, The Year Book Publishers, Inc., 1955.

CAMPBELL, A. W.   Histological Studies in the Localisation of Cerebral Function. Cambridge, Cambridge University Press, 1905.

CHUSID, J. G.   Black-and-white supplement for the color brain map of Bailey and von Bonin.   *Neurology* 14:154, 1964.

VON ECONOMO, C., and KOSKINAS, G. N.   Die Cytoarchitektonik der Hirnrinde des erwachsenen Menschen.   Berlin, J. Springer, 1925.

FLECHSIG, P.   Die Leitungsbahnen in Gehirn und Rückenmark des Menschen auf Grund entwickelungsgeschichtlicher Untersuchungen.   Leipzig, Wilhelm Engelmann, 1876.

HINES, M.   Cyto-architecture of the cerebral cortex in man.   *A. Res. Nerv. & Ment. Disc., Proc.* (1932) 13:26, 1934.

LeGros CLARK, W. E.   A note on cortical cyto-architectonics.   *Brain* 75:96, 1952.

PENFIELD, W., and RASMUSSEN, T.   The Cerebral Cortex of Man: A Clinical Study of Localization of Function.   New York, The Macmillan Company, 1950.

POYNTER, F. N. L. (ed.)   The History and Philosophy of Knowledge of the Brain and Its Functions.   Springfield, Ill., Charles C Thomas, 1958.

SHOLL, D. A.   The Organization of the Cerebral Cortex.   London, Methuen & Co., Ltd., 1956.

CHAPTER 50

FUNCTIONS AND DIS-
ORDERS OF FUNCTION OF
THE CEREBRAL CORTEX

THE FIRST CRUDE conceptions of the localization of cerebral functions were introduced by Gall and Spurzheim between 1800 and 1825; they also, however,
attempted to correlate variations in function with the shape of the brain and skull,
and thus introduced the pseudoscience of phrenology. Flourens (1823) found that
he could destroy large areas of the brain without causing symptoms; he expressed
the belief that the cerebrum functions as a single unit and denied the existence
of localized action. Broca in 1861, demonstrated that destruction of the left third
frontal convolution resulted in the loss of the ability to speak, and Fritsch and
Hitzig, in 1870, showed that galvanic stimulation to the region of the central sulcus
of the exposed brain of a dog was followed by movements on the opposite side of
the body. Three years later Ferrier, using a faradic stimulus, described constant
focal responses in the contralateral extremities on stimulating fixed points of the
brain in cats, dogs, rabbits, and other animals, and the next year he carried out
similar studies outlining in great detail the motor cortex of monkeys; he also produced paralysis by ablation of the excitable region. His work was followed by that
of Horsley (1884), Sherrington, and others. It is of interest that the prediction by
Hughlings Jackson of the presence of an area in the cerebral cortex which governed
isolated movements was made during the period 1864–1870 on the basis of the
study of focal epilepsy, and that it preceded the above experimental demonstrations. In fact, Jackson was the first to point out that there is such a thing as the
motor cortex. The human cortex was first stimulated by Roberts Bartholow in

837

Cincinnati in 1874; in a 30-year-old patient whose skull was eroded by an epithelioma of the scalp, needle electrodes plunged through the dura and into the cortex were stimulated by a faradic current, and motor and sensory responses were observed in the arms and legs.

The above observations, confirmed and amplified by many observers, have proved definitely that certain areas of the cerebral cortex possess specific functions. Physiologic studies both on animals and man, pathologic observations on the operating and autopsy tables, and careful clinical observations in focal lesions have all shown that certain areas of the cortex influence the activity of subcortical and spinal centers. It is possible by careful histologic study to correlate these areas with regions which have characteristic cell and fiber lamination. Clinical manifestations of disease in specific areas can make themselves known in widely differing manners.

Irritation, or *excitation,* of a center of brain function causes an *overresponse* of this focus; the symptoms are those of *stimulation* of the area. *Destruction* of a focus causes either a *deficiency* or a *loss of function* of the center, with resulting *paralytic* manifestations. *Symptoms of release* appear when the inhibiting effect of a higher center is removed. *Signs of compensation* are manifest when other structures or areas take over or assume the activity of the diseased parts.

One must recall, in considering localization in the brain, that a "center" is not necessarily the focus which has sole control of a specific activity or one which has only one function, and that it can never function as an isolated unit. A "center" is merely the seat of greatest intensity of a function, and other contiguous or even far distant foci may control the same action to a certain extent. The "center" under consideration may also influence the function of distant areas as well as govern its own specific activity. In addition, there are many regions of the brain which do not respond to stimulation, and disease of them has been thought to cause no symptoms or signs. These were once spoken of as "silent areas," but clinical and physiologic studies have demonstrated the functional significance of most or all of these regions. One must also bear in mind the concept of *cerebral dominance* in the diagnosis of lesions of the cerebral cortex. In lower animals both hemispheres have equal influence. A particular attribute of human brain, however, is the dominance of one hemisphere over the other in the control of certain functions, especially language, gnosis (the interpretation of sensory stimuli), and praxis (the performance of complex motor acts). The dominant hemisphere is usually the left one in right-handed individuals. It is the hemisphere which is contralateral to the hand, the foot, and the eye which the person uses by preference. Handedness and dominance are believed to be inherited.

Certain recent studies have denied the concept of localization in the cerebral cortex, and have stated that those functions hitherto believed to originate from particular parts of the brain depend upon the changing state of activity of the entire nervous system. Both clinically and physiologically, however, there is definite evidence for cortical localization, and those areas of the brain whose functions have been verified are discussed in the following section. The physiology of the projection areas has been studied more adequately than that of the association areas.

THE FRONTAL LOBES

THE MOTOR AREA

The posterior portion of the frontal lobe is designated the motor projection area, or the true motor area. This region coincides with the area gigantopyramidalis, or area 4 of Brodmann (Fig. 295) and contains the giant pyramidal cells of Betz in layer V; at this site the gray matter is of maximum thickness. The cortex is the agranular type, with prominent pyramidal cells but no internal granular and a thin external granular layer. The Betz cells are extremely large, and those in the lower limb area may measure sixty by twenty-five micra. Bucy, von Bonin, and others distinguish between area 4γ, the gigantopyramidal cortex, and area 4a which is similar in structure but lacks the Betz cells (Fig. 299). This latter area covers most of the exposed surface of the precentral convolution at the level of the middle and inferior frontal gyri; it is similar in structure to area 6 (see below) and is found only in the human brain. Area 4γ is situated mainly within the central fissure and is the only constituent of the motor cortex which extends to the medial surface of the brain. In man the motor area starts in the depths of the central sulcus and occupies the anterior wall of the sulcus and the adjacent part of the precentral, or posterior frontal, gyrus, together with that part of the paracentral lobule which lies rostral to the continuation of the central sulcus on the medial aspect of the hemisphere. It is narrow at its lower extremity, almost coming to a point just above the sylvian fissure, and is much wider rostrally.

The motor area gives rise to impulses that initiate volitional movements on the opposite side of the body. It is subdivided into centers; each of these controls muscles that govern movements of individual parts of the opposite half of the body. These are represented in inverted order. The center for the pharynx and larynx is lowest, just above the sylvian fissure, and above that, in ascending order, those for the palate, mandible, tongue, lips, mouth, face, eyelids, forehead, neck, thumb, individual fingers, hand, wrist, forearm, arm, shoulder, upper thorax, diaphragm, lower thorax, abdominal muscles, thigh, leg, foot, toes, bladder, rectum, and

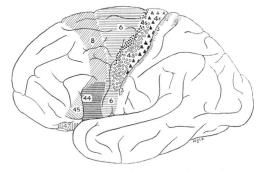

FIG. 299.   Precentral motor cortex of man, as drawn by von Bonin. (Bucy, P. C., ed.: The Precentral Motor Cortex. Urbana, University of Illinois Press, 1944.)

genitalia. In the human the centers for the lower extremities as well as for those organs innervated by sacral nerves are situated on the medial aspect of the hemisphere. The areas for the tongue, face, and digits are especially large, and each finger is represented individually (Fig. 148). This is probably the result, not of the size of the part, but of the number and complexity of movements executed by it. It must again be stressed that there is a certain amount of overlapping of the various centers, and that although the center which governs the movements of an individual portion of the body is predominantly located at one site, impulses from adjoining areas may also affect such movements. This multiplicity and wide extent of representation, as well as the existence of supplementary and secondary motor areas, may account for recovery of function of individual parts of the body following focal lesions.

The motor area gives rise to the corticobulbar and corticospinal pathways, and the axons of the pyramidal cells, together with axons of other cells, constitute the pyramidal tracts which descend through the corona radiata, the genu and anterior two thirds of the posterior limb of the internal capsule, and the cerebral peduncle. The corticobulbar fibers terminate in the pons and medulla, but the corticospinal fibers continue their descent. At the pyramidal decussation, in the lower medulla, the majority of them (80 to 85 per cent) cross and descend in the lateral corticospinal pathways, while a few descend uncrossed in the ventral corticospinal pathways (Fig. 150). The cells of the motor area undergo chromatolysis when the pyramidal tracts are sectioned, and the tracts degenerate when the motor cortex is destroyed.

THE PREMOTOR AREA

Situated just anterior to the motor area, principally in its rostral portions, is the premotor area. This corresponds to area 6 of Brodmann (Fig. 295) and is similar to area 4γ except for the absence of the giant pyramidal cells in layer V. The cells of layer V are, however, pyramidal in shape and obviously motor in type; those in both layers III and V are arranged in a columnar pattern. The boundaries of the premotor area are somewhat less definite and distinct than those of the motor area, but it roughly parallels the latter and extends with it onto the medial surface of the hemisphere to the sulcus cinguli. The premotor area also exerts motor control over the opposite half of the body, and the localization within it parallels that in the motor region.

The portion of transitional cortex between areas 4 and 6 has been termed area 4s (Fig. 299). Some investigators have stated that stimulation of this region causes suppression of activity of other cortical centers, especially area 4, with resulting muscular relaxation and loss of motor function, whereas ablation is followed by spasticity, hyperreflexia, and loss of fine movements. Other investigators, however, have questioned either the anatomic or physiologic existence of such a suppression area.

The details of the functions of the motor and premotor areas, including the results of stimulation and ablation and the various concepts of pyramidal function and its disorders, are discussed in Chapter 23. The principal manifestation of a

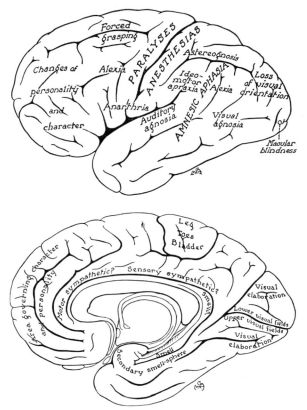

Fig. 300. Scheme of cerebral hemisphere: *Top,* diagram of lateral surface of left hemisphere indicating the various symptoms which result from injury to certain zones; *Bottom,* medial surface of right hemisphere, showing functions disturbed by injuries in various regions. (Bailey, P.: Intracranial Tumors, ed. 2. Springfield, Ill., Charles C Thomas, 1948.)

destructive lesion is paresis or paralysis of the opposite side of the body (Fig. 300). This paralysis affects predominantly the distal parts, and fine, skilled volitional movements are entirely abolished. It has generally been accepted by clinicians that the paralysis that follows lesions of the motor (and/or premotor) neurons or their neuraxes is a spastic one (although it may flaccid at the onset), and is accompanied by exaggeration of the deep reflexes as well as by certain pathologic reflex responses. Because the larynx, pharynx, palate, upper face, trunk muscles, diaphragm, rectum, and bladder are bilaterally innervated, the functions of these structures are little affected with unilateral lesions. Irritation of the motor (and/or premotor) cortex causes motor responses of the corresponding contralateral portion of the body. Such irritation caused by a neoplasm or scar may result in focal or jacksonian convulsive manifestations. Stimulation experimentally or as a diagnostic procedure causes discrete motor responses.

The motor and premotor areas also have connections with other important nervous structures. Frontopontine fibers, which make up an important part of the corticopontocerebellar tract, arise from the middle frontal convolution, anterior to areas 6 and 8. The impulses are carried to the pons, and after a synapse are relayed through the middle cerebellar peduncle (brachium pontis) into the contralateral cerebellar hemisphere. Loss of function of these fibers causes ataxia. At times it is difficult to differentiate between ataxia due to frontal lesions and that due to cerebellar involvement, but involvement of the frontal cortex or of the frontopontine fibers is followed by contralateral ataxia, whereas a lesion of the cerebellar hemisphere causes ipsilateral ataxia. The premotor area, and, to a lesser extent, the motor area have intimate connections with the basal ganglia. Certain of the hyperkinesias have been treated by surgical removal of either area 6, area 4, or both. Focal epilepsy is sometimes alleviated by surgical excision of either meningocerebral cicatrices or foci of circumscribed atrophy in the motor areas.

THE FRONTAL MOTOR EYE FIELD

Area 8, which lies just anterior to area 6, is called the frontal motor eye field (Fig. 299). It is the center for volitional control of conjugate ocular movements. Stimulation of this region, especially of area $8\alpha\beta\gamma$ of Vogt, causes strong, rapid conjugate deviation of the eyes to the opposite side, which may be accompanied by conjugate movement of the head and rotation of the trunk. If the lower portion of this area is stimulated, the eyes are deviated upward and laterally, and if the upper portion is irritated, they are moved downward and laterally. There may be associated opening of the eyelids and dilatation of the pupils. Ablation of area $8\alpha\beta\gamma$ is followed by paresis of conjugate gaze to the opposite side and transient visual hemiagnosia; the eyes are turned toward the injured side. Area 8 (or 8s) also functions as a suppressor region with many of the same functions as area 4s. According to many anatomists, the frontal eye field extends into both area 6 and area 9.

THE MOTOR SPEECH AREAS

The lower portion of the motor and premotor regions is known as Broca's area, or the motor speech center. The limits of this center have not been definitely established, but it is probably located in the region about the base of the precentral sulcus in the inferior frontal convolution. It is situated in the left cerebral hemisphere in right-handed individuals, and in the right hemisphere in left-handed persons. Area 44 of Brodmann is the principal site; this corresponds to pars opercularis of the inferior frontal gyrus (Fig. 290), but area 45 in pars triangularis, area 47 in pars orbitalis, and area 46 above area 45, are also important. Possibly this region does not have the specific and localized functional characteristics that were once ascribed to it, and it may act only in association with the contiguous portions of the temporal and parietal lobes and the underlying insula. Stimulation of it, however, has been followed by outbursts of logorrhea, or occasionally by slowed speech, and destructive lesions produce an oral expressive type of aphasia.

THE FRONTAL ASSOCIATION AREAS

The portions of the frontal lobe which lie anterior to areas 6 and 8 and the motor speech centers are areas 9, 10, 11, 12, 32, and others. They are connected with the somesthetic, visual, auditory, and other sensory areas by association fibers, and with the thalamus and hypothalamus by projection fibers. They are often called the prefrontal areas, but inasmuch as they are frontal and not actually prefrontal, the term frontal association areas is a better one. From the point of view of cellular structure this region is strikingly different from areas 4 and 6. The cortex is thin and is particularly rich in granular cells, and the pyramidal cells in layer V are reduced in both size and number. These areas of the brain are the most conspicuously developed in man, and they have long been considered the seat of the higher intellectual functions, including memory, judgment, reasoning power, and the various perceptual, associative, and executive functions of the mind. Experimental studies, however, have given little information regarding their functions. They are inexcitable to all forms of stimulation, and unilateral ablation in lower forms causes no obvious disturbance. Bilateral removal is followed by restlessness, distractibility, failure of recent memory, and loss of ability to utilize past experiences. Although the animals are less able to perform complex tasks, they lose their anxiety over failure and are placid in their reactions. Most information concerning the functions of the frontal association areas has come from clinical observation of patients with degenerations, injuries, or tumors of the frontal lobes, and from examinations performed on those who have been subjected to surgery in these regions.

The "case of the crowbar skull" is the first reported instance of an injury to the frontal lobes which was followed by personality changes. A man, aged 25 years, was injured in a powder explosion in 1848, and a tamping iron was forced into the left frontal pole of the brain, making its exit from the skull just to the right of the coronal suture. He died thirteen years later after having traveled extensively and having been, for a period of time, in Barnum's exhibit. He was said to have been irreverent, profane, impatient of restraint, and unable to hold a job. He was "a child in his intellectual capacities with the general passions of a strong man." Rynlander has described thirty-two patients in whom part of one frontal lobe was removed in the treatment of either tumor or abscess. In the majority of cases about two-thirds of the lobe was removed. In about one-half of the patients there was some bilateral involvement. The outstanding symptoms were diminished inhibition of affective response, euphoria, restlessness, loss of initiative, and disturbances of intellectual faculties characterized by loss of attention, slowing of intellectual processes, loss of memory for details, and difficulty with associations. About one fifth of the patients showed significant personality changes along with a marked increase in weight and appetite. In most instances the mental symptoms and alterations in personality were not severe enough to destroy the patient's ability to lead a normal social existence, but they did interfere with intellectual work. Many cases of unilateral frontal lobectomy have been reported in which there were almost no discernible alterations. In some, on the other hand, slight changes in personality and minimal loss of initiative and impairment of abstract thinking have been described. These symptoms are more marked if the left frontal lobe is removed in a right-handed individual.

Some studies have been made on patients who have had both frontal lobes removed in the excision of large tumors. Brickner reported in detail on a 40-year-old stockbroker who underwent a bilateral frontal lobectomy for the removal of a meningioma. The excision was carried back as far as the premotor regions, and areas 9, 10, 11, 12, 45, 46, 47, and parts of 8, 32, and 44 were extirpated, slightly more on the right than the left. Psychologic observations, reported six and eight years after the operation, revealed the following changes: slowing and stereotypy of mental activity; limitation in the capacity to associate and synthesize, with distractibility and impairment of selection, retention, and learning; loss of judgment, initiative, and the ability to reason abstractly; defective emotional restraint, with euphoria, boasting, hostility, temper outbursts, and lack of sexual inhibitions. On the Stanford-Binet test he earned an intelligence quotient of 94, although his mental age was only nine years on the Pintner-Paterson scale. He lacked appreciation of the gravity of his situation and had learned nothing since his operation. In contrast to this report, Ackerly and Spurling found only moderate emotional changes and no permanent defect in the intellectual status of a patient who had had the entire right prefrontal area removed, even though there had been a previous partial destruction of the left prefrontal area.

An appraisal of the functions of the frontal association areas may be made by a review of the alterations in these functions which take place in the various degenerative and atrophic lesions of the frontal lobe. In dementia paralytica, senile dementia, Alzheimer's disease, and Pick's disease the earliest change is often a loss of memory, especially of recent memory or of retention and immediate recall. This may be followed by an impairment of judgment, especially in social and ethical situations. Absence of the restraint imposed by the inhibitions which have been acquired in training may lead to an increase in natural appetites, carelessness of habits of dress and personal hygiene, and loss of shame, often with sexual promiscuity. There may be loss of ability to carry out business affairs. The ability to perceive abstract relationships is impaired early, and the patient may be able to carry out simple, well-organized actions, but incapable of dealing with new problems, even though they may be within the scope and range usually handled by a person of his age and education. Tasks attempted are solved in a roundabout manner, and those requiring him to break away from old mental habits and adapt to unfamiliar situations are the most difficult to perform. The power of attention is less, and distractibility may be marked; initiative, ambition, and decision may be impaired. There is difficulty in comprehension with loss of association, especially in acquiring and synthesizing new material. The time and rate of intellectual reactions are prolonged, and the patient fatigues rapidly. Emotional lability may be outstanding, with vacillating moods and outbursts of crying, rage, or laughter, even though the patient had formerly shown even temperament and steady habits. There may be marked irritability. Although the mood is often one of euphoria with an increased sense of well-being, facetiousness, levity, and senseless joking and punning (witzelsucht),

there may be apathy, indifference, and torpor. The patient may fail to link immediate impressions with past experiences, and this may lead to confusion and disorientation. There is progressive dementia as the deterioration increases.

Similar symptoms may be encountered in patients with neoplasms of the frontal
lobe. In neoplasms, however, either witzelsucht and euphoria or indifference and
apathy are early manifestations, and may be evident before memory loss and difficulties with judgment become apparent. Often, however, there are other signs of
intracranial disease. Pressure on the motor areas may cause pareses, focal or
generalized convulsive manifestations, frontal ataxia, or forced grasping; pressure
on either the olfactory or visual pathways may produce either anosmia or visual
defects; increase in intracranial pressure may be evident by the presence of headaches, papilledema, and slow pulse. Injury to the frontal lobes causes more severe
disturbance in children than adults.

In conclusion it may be said that the frontal association areas govern the higher
intellectual development of man. They are concerned with memory, judgment, association, reasoning, mental synthesis, abstract thinking, and restraint over emotional impulses. In loss of function of these areas there is impairment of higher
control, with intellectual deterioration and change in character and personality.
The more automatic functions of intelligence, such as remote memory and the
ability to perform learned acts, may persist. Biologic intelligence is affected more
than psychometric intelligence. The final picture may depend to a large extent
upon the previous personality pattern of the individual.

Although it is known that impairment of the above functions occurs in lesions of
the anterior portion of the frontal lobes, further localization is not possible. There
is no definite focus whose removal leads to dementia, and massive lesions of the
frontal lobes, especially if unilateral, may cause few symptoms, particularly if the
involvement is in the nondominant hemisphere. Some psychologic studies have
seemed to indicate that disturbance of such functions as retention and learning are
dependent upon the size of a lesion, whereas impairment of intellectual ability is
more dependent upon the site of the lesion, and is more marked with left-sided
involvement. The original concept of Hughlings Jackson that the brain functions
as a whole intellectually and emotionally may account for the fact that extensive
lesions in the frontal lobes may be necessary before impairment is obvious. This
theory is stressed by those who state that there is no representation of function
in the cerebrum, and express the belief that the cortex merely selects, abstracts,
and integrates patterns of nervous activity and that differences in intellectual ability
are dependent upon the amount of activity of the brain rather than the function
of individual cellular components. It is almost universally accepted, however, that
the disturbances of the mental, intellectual, and emotional processes described
above are symptoms of dysfunction of the frontal association areas, although it
is not possible to state whether they are the result of *irritation* or of *destruction*
or of both, but they are probably caused by both. In cases of brain tumor, however,
where there may be marked change in personality and memory, the removal of an
entire frontal lobe may to all appearances return the patient to normal; in such
instances the symptoms are undoubtedly those of irritation. Following hemispherec-

tomies carried out in patients with infantile hemiplegia and associated convulsions, behavioral and mental symptoms have improved without increasing the motor deficit. In the progressive dementias, on the other hand, and in observations such as those of Brickner, the symptoms, which are identical with those sometimes relieved by operation, are without doubt the result of deficiency or destruction.

The observation that lesions of the frontal lobes may decrease emotional and affective responses and relieve anxiety, apprehension, and nervous tension led to the operation of *prefrontal leukotomy,* or *lobotomy,* for the relief of mental symptoms. This procedure, first carried out in Portugal by Moniz in 1936, was done rather extensively over a period of years, both in this country and abroad, in the treatment of patients with manic-depressive psychosis, involutional depressions, schizophrenia, obsessive-compulsive states, anxiety reactions, and hysteria, and to decrease the reaction to intractable pain of organic disease. It has largely been discontinued, however, although it is still used occasionally for the last-named purpose. The operation consisted of cutting the white matter in the plane of the coronal suture in each frontal lobe, and apparently the association fibers which connect the prefrontal areas with the subcortical gray masses, especially the thalamus and hypothalamus, were sectioned. There was loss of nervous tension, anxiety, depression, obsessive tendencies, and awareness of or concern over pain, but there might also be emotional flattening, inertia, loss of judgment, and indifference. Intelligence as such was said to be intact in most cases, but application of the intelligence was impaired. Modifications of the technic, also largely discontinued, consisted of bilateral cortical excision, especially of areas 9 and 10 (*topectomy* or *gyrectomy*), undercutting of areas 9 and 10 by an orbital approach (*transorbital leukotomy*), and direct attack of dorsomedial nuclei of the thalamus (*thalamotomy*).

THE PARIETAL LOBES

The postcentral region is composed of areas 3, 1, and 2; it occupies all but the lowest part of the postcentral gyrus and is continued over the superomedial border into the adjoining part of the paracentral lobule. In the depth of the central fissure area 3 joins area 4. In the postcentral area there is a typical sensory type of cortex with all six layers well developed. The anterior parts are very thin and are characterized by the density of the granular layer and the presence of granular cells which have replaced other nuclei in the outer pyramidal layer. The largest nuclei are found in the inner layer of the large pyramidal cells; they are smaller than the giant cells of Betz and occur discretely rather than in clusters. In the posterior parts the large pyramidal cells are reduced both in size and number, and the granular layer is wider but is not so densely packed with cells.

Area 5a, or the preparietal area, is situated in the upper part of the parietal lobe, just posterior to area 2. It contains large deep pyramidal cells, some as great as the smaller Betz cells in area 4. Area 5b, the superior parietal area, occupies a large part of the superior parietal lobule in man and extends over the medial surface of the hemisphere to include the precuneus. Area 7, the inferior parietal area, constitutes the major portion of the inferior parietal lobule; it includes the supra-marginal and angular gyri, which are sometimes separately designated as areas 40 and 39, respectively. In areas 5b, 7, 39, and 40 there are no large pyramidal cells in layer V; the granular layers are of great depth and density.

The postcentral region is the *somesthetic sensory,* or *sensory receptive, area.* It receives enormous projections from nuclei ventralis posterolateralis and postero-medialis of the lateral nuclear mass of the thalamus. These relay impulses from the spinothalamic tracts, medial lemniscus, and secondary trigeminal tracts, and course through the posterior limb of the internal capsule. The various regions of the body are represented in specific portions of the postcentral gyrus, and the pattern roughly parallels the motor localization on the opposite anterior lip of the central fissure, although it is not as definite or as well defined. The distal portions of the extremi-ties are widely represented. Cutaneous sensations for the face and body may have bilateral representation, but those for the extremities, as well as deep sensations, have only contralateral representation. The somesthetic area may extend posteriorly into areas 5 and 7, and even rostrally into the precentral gyrus (areas 4 and 6). The superior and inferior parietal lobules (areas 5 and 7), constitute the *psycho-sensory* or *sensory association area.* This has connections with the postcentral gyrus by means of association pathways, and receives fibers from nuclei lateralis dorsalis and posterior of the thalamus. There is no definite localization of function in the parietal lobe posterior to the postcentral gyrus, although localization is more acute near to this gyrus than distant from it.

The functions of the parietal lobe are essentially those of reception, corre-lation, analysis, synthesis, integration, interpretation, and elaboration of the primary sensory impulses that are received from the thalamus. The somesthetic area is the initial reception center for afferent impulses, especially for tactile, pressure, and position sensations. It is necessary for the discrimination of the finer, more critical grades of sensation and recognition of intensity. Stimulation of this area by either artificial excitation or disease process produces paresthesias on the opposite side of the body. There are tactile and pressure sensations, with numb-ness, tingling, senses of constriction and of movement, and occasional thermal sensa-tions, but rarely pain. Such sensations may precede jacksonian convulsions as an aura of the seizure, or may accompany the convulsion, and the spread of the stimulus follows the same general pattern as in the motor area. On stimulation of the postcentral gyrus in experimental animals there is evidence of bilateral paresthesias. Destructive lesions are followed by a raising of the sensory threshold on the opposite side of the body, but both exteroceptive and proprioceptive sensa-tions are perceived, and there is never a complete anesthesia. Also, since localization is rather diffuse, it is necessary to have a larger lesion to produce hypesthesia than to cause paralysis. The sensory association areas are essential for synthesis and interpretation of impulses, appreciation of similarities and differences, interpre-tation of spatial relationships and two-dimensional qualities, evaluation of vari-ations in form and weight, and localization of sensation. Irritation of these areas is followed by minimal symptoms such as vague paresthesias or hyperesthesias on the opposite side of the body; destructive lesions produce a complex of symptoms affecting mainly the gnostic aspects of sensation. Simple appreciation of the stimulation of primary sensory endings remains, but perceptual functions are lost. There is impairment of those aspects of sensation that involve interpretation of stimuli, analysis, and synthesis of individual modalities, correlation and elaboration of impulses, integration into concrete concepts, and calling out of engrams to aid in association and identification. Attempts have been made to associate these various functions with individual portions of the parietal lobe, but such localization has never been confirmed.

The clinical manifestations of parietal lobe lesions are described in Chapter 8. The extremities, especially their distal parts, are more affected than the trunk and face, and the midline is spared on the latter areas. The threshold for superficial pain may be raised slightly; there is loss of discrimination for temperature, especially in the intermediate ranges; light touch is little disturbed, but tactile discrimination and localization may be profoundly affected. Joint position, passive movement, and spatial orientation are impaired, and as a result there may be sensory ataxia and pseudoathetoid movements. There is loss of stereognostic sense, appreciation of similarities and differences in size and weight, localization of stimulation, recognition of textures, identification of figures written on the skin, and two-point discrimination. The period of time required for sensory adaptation is prolonged, and occasionally allachesthesia is experienced. Sensory *inattention* or *extinction* on the affected side of the body is often an early and important finding; with simultaneous stimulation of identical areas on the two sides of the body, the stimulus is not perceived on the side opposite the affected parietal lobe, even though sensation on that side may be normal to routine testing.

Lesions of the parietal lobe, predominantly the subordinate one, may also cause defects of orientation of the opposite side of the body in space, identification of portions of the body, and awareness of disease. *Autotopagnosia* or *somatotopagnosia* is the loss of power to orient the body or the relation of its individual parts; there may be loss of identification of one limb or one part of the body. *Amorphosynthesis* is the lack of recognition of the opposite side of the body and of space. *Anosognosia,* the ignorance of the existence of disease, is used specifically to imply the lack of awareness of hemiplegia or a feeling of depersonalization toward or loss of perception of paralyzed parts of the body. The patient may deny the existence of paresis and believe that he is able to use the affected extremities in a normal manner. Along with this there may be unilateral neglect of the involved portion of the body. The posterior and inferior portions of the parietal lobe, especially the angular and supramarginal gyri and the areas in close proximity to the occipital and temporal lobes, are associated in function with the visual and auditory systems. The optic radiations course through a portion of the parietal lobe to reach the visual cortex, and a deeply placed lesion of the lobe may cause either an inferior quadrantic or a hemianopic defect in the visual fields. Stimulation of the angular gyrus causes contralateral deviation of the eyes. These same portions of the parietal lobe of the dominant hemisphere are important in relation to language and related functions, and lesions in these areas may be responsible for various types of receptive aphasia, agnosia, and apraxia of a sensory type; these are discussed in Chapter 53.

Occasionally parietal lesions result in contralateral muscular atrophy, with quantitative diminution in response to both faradic and galvanic stimulation, flaccidity, either absence or increase of deep reflexes, and trophic changes which consist of smooth, shiny skin, decrease in temperature, dry, brittle hair and nails, and edema. There may be hypotonia and slowness of movement of the opposite side of the body, especially of the proximal muscles, with ataxia and pseudoathetoid groping movements secondary to the sensory disturbances. Focal motor seizures and partial or pseudoparalysis involving the contralateral portions of the body may also occur in parietal lesions; these may be caused by interruption of communications with areas 6 and 4, or may denote that the parietal lobe also possesses some motor functions.

Spastic hemiparesis has been relieved by section of the parietal cortex. The pain of a phantom limb has also been relieved by removal of the cortical sensory representation of the part.

THE OCCIPITAL LOBES

The occipital lobe is more nearly a structural and functional entity than any of the other cerebral lobes. All of its functions are concerned either directly or indirectly with vision. It is composed of areas 17, 18, and 19 of Brodmann.

The *visual receptive area* (area 17) is located on the lips of the calcarine fissure and adjacent portions of the cuneus and lingual gyrus, and extends around the occipital pole to occupy a portion of the lateral surface of the hemisphere (Fig. 295). The cortex is granular in type. It is extremely thin, but layer IV is relatively thick and is subdivided by a light band into three sublayers. The middle sublayer is occupied by the greatly thickened outer band of Baillarger, here known as the band of Gennari, which is visible to the naked eye in sections of the fresh cortex and has given the region the name *area striata*. The optic radiations, or the geniculocalcarine tract, pass from the lateral geniculate body to the striate cortex on the upper and lower lips of the calcarine fissure. These fibers convey impulses from the ipsilateral half of each retina; those from the lower half terminate on the lower lip of the fissure, and those from the upper half, on the upper lip. The macular fibers occupy the posterior portion of the region, in a wedge-shaped area, apex anterior; they have a wide cortical distribution. Impulses from the paracentral and peripheral retinal areas are represented more anteriorly in serial concentric zones (Fig. 24). The striate area is the receiving center for visual impressions; color, size, form, motion, illumination, and transparency are perceived and determined here. The recognition and identification of objects, however, requires the associated function of the adjoining visuopsychic areas. Stimulation, or irritation, of the calcarine cortex produces unformed visual hallucinations, such as scotomas and flashes of light, in the corresponding fields of vision. Destructive lesions result in defects in the visual fields supplied by the affected areas. Destruction of both striate regions causes total blindness.

The *parastriate,* or *parareceptive, region,* area 18, receives and interprets impulses from area 17; it is essential for the recognition and identification of objects. It is said that engrams for the memory of inanimate objects are stored in the lateral and inferior part, and those for animate objects and the body itself in the upper part (Nielsen). The *peristriate,* or *perireceptive* or *preoccipital region,* area 19, has connections with areas 17 and 18 and with other portions of the cortex. It functions in more complex visual recognition and perception, revisualization, visual association, and spatial orientation. These regions are classed together as the *visuopsychic areas;* the cortex is thicker than in the striate region, and there is an increase in the size and number of cells in layer III, but almost complete absence of large cells in layer V. Stimulation of them causes formed visual hallucinations and destruction is followed by difficulty with fixation and with maintaining visual attention, loss of stereoscopic vision, impairment of visual memory, difficulty with accurate localization and discernment of objects, and disturbances in the spatial orientation of the visual image, especially for distance, in the homonymous field There is loss of ability to discriminate with respect to size, shape, and color. There may be errors in the patient's ability to localize either himself or stationary or moving objects in space, with a loss of visual perception of spatial relationships, and there may be distortion of objects, or metamorphopsia. In bilateral lesions there may be marked loss of visual orientation with anosognosia, or denial of blindness (Anton's symptom), due to interruption of the pathways between striate cortex and other centers. Visual aphasias are discussed in Chapter 53.

Areas 18 and 19, especially the latter, also contain the cortical centers for optically induced eye movements and optic fixation reflexes, in contrast to the volitional center in the frontal lobe. Corticofugal fibers pass through the optic radiations to the superior colliculus (anterior quadrigeminal body) and tegmentum of the midbrain, and thence through the medial longitudinal fasciculus to the nuclei of the ocular nerves. There are also association pathways from the occipital to the frontal cortical areas, with radiation of impulses to the frontal cortex before they descend in the internal capsule. Stimulation causes a slow, forced, conjugate deviation of the eyes to the opposite side and pupillary constriction; ablation is followed by loss of following and reflex ocular movements and of optic fixation releases. Although voluntary control is maintained, there may be difficulty in focusing the eyes.

THE TEMPORAL LOBES

The *auditory receptive region* (areas 41 and 42) is located in the transverse temporal gyri (Heschl's convolutions) which lie on the dorsal surface of the posterior part of the superior temporal convolution, partially buried in the floor of the lateral sulcus. Area 41 occupies the middle of the anterior transverse gyrus and a portion of the posterior, and it is surrounded by area 42, which extends on the lateral surface of the middle region of the superior temporal convolution. Area 41 is composed of granular cortex similar to that in the parietal and occipital receptive regions; area 42 has a number of large pyramidal cells in layer III. The auditory radiations pass from the medial geniculate body to the auditory receptive region (Fig. 91). Hearing is bilaterally represented in the temporal lobes, although a greater number of impulses may be received from the contralateral ear. There is no conclusive localization of the various auditory impulses in the temporal lobe, although it has been stated that high-pitched tones are received in the more medial and posterior portions, whereas low tones are received more laterally and anteriorly. From the above cortical centers connections are made with adjacent areas in the superior temporal convolution where sound, word, and memory patterns are stored. In this region auditory impressions are differentiated and interpreted as words. It is believed that the superior temporal convolution may also receive vestibular impulses, but the exact localization of cortical centers for these impulses is not known. It has also been said that the middle and inferior portions of the temporal lobe receive olfactory and gustatory impulses; these latter functions, however, are discussed with the olfactory centers.

Stimulation of the superior temporal convolution produces vague auditory hallucinations in the form of tinnitus and sensations of roaring and buzzing, and stimulation of adjacent areas causes vertigo and a sensation of falling. Strychninization of the temporal lobes is followed by vertigo which is sufficient in degree to cause convulsions; this phenomenon is abolished by section of the eighth nerves. Unilateral destruction of the transverse temporal gyri never causes deafness (because there is bilateral representation of hearing) although there may be an impairment of the localization of sounds on the opposite side, especially in regard to the distance from which the sounds are coming; furthermore, there may be a bilateral dulling of auditory acuity with a perceptible difference in the intensity of sounds and impairment in the recognition of musical notes. Unilateral destructive lesions of the superior temporal convolution may, in addition, cause difficulty with equilibrium and a sensation of unsteadiness and falling to the opposite side. Bilateral destruction of the temporal lobes may cause deafness. A destructive lesion in the region of the anterior transverse temporal gyrus or the adjacent posterior and lateral portion of the superior temporal convolution (Wernicke's area) on the left side in right-handed persons will cause a loss of ability to understand or comprehend spoken words. The auditory receptive aphasias are discussed in Chapter 53.

The functions of the remainder of the temporal lobes have been less specifically defined in the past, and those areas other than the ones dealing with the auditory and vestibular systems have often been referred to as "silent" ones. Experimental and recent clinical studies, however, have demonstrated important functions and have shown the relationship of the temporal lobes to various clinical syndromes and disease processes. Certain regions are related to the visual system, and stimulation of the middle temporal convolution (area 21) causes contralateral deviation of the eyes, often accompanied by similar deviation of the trunk and adversive and synergic movements of the opposite arm and leg. The optic radiations pass through the temporal lobe and curve around the descending horn of the lateral ventricle; encroachment on them may cause either a superior quadrantic or a hemianopic defect in the visual fields. Irritation of these fibers or of certain portions of the temporal cortex may cause visual hallucinations that are better formed and organized than the hallucinations associated with occipital lobe lesions. The posterior portions of the middle and inferior temporal convolutions communicate with the cerebellum through the temporopontocerebellar pathways, and unilateral destruction of these regions may cause contralateral ataxia. Ablation of major portions of one temporal lobe, especially the anterior region, causes few or no symptoms in experimental animals, but Klüver and Bucy have demonstrated that bilateral ablation produces a characteristic syndrome. This consists of psychic blindness or visual agnosia, loss of fear and rage reactions, increased sexual activity, bulimia, hypermetamorphosis (excessive tendency to attend and react to every visual stimulus), and a severe memory defect. These manifestations occur only if the uncus and hippocampus are included in the ablation. From an anatomic and physiologic point of view these latter regions on the medial aspect of the lobe, along with the amygdaloid complex, belong to the limbic lobe (see below), but they are considered parts of the temporal lobe by most clinicians.

Penfield and his associates have demonstrated that stimulation of the temporal lobe cortex in epileptic patients gives rise to illusions of perception, hallucinations, and automatisms. Furthermore, they were able to elicit psychic responses on stimulation of the lateral and superior surfaces, and to produce "memories," or instances in which the patient would seem to relive earlier experiences. Consequently Penfield has stated that the temporal lobe is utilized in the interpretation of current experiences and in the recall of memories. On the basis of these observations, the demonstration by Gibbs and others that the electroencephalographic discharge of so-called psychomotor epilepsy consists of a spike potential in one or both of the anterior temporal regions, and detailed anatomic and pathologic studies as well as experimental investigations, the relationship of the temporal lobe and contiguous structures to a specific type of epileptic syndrome, is now well accepted. Jackson, in 1873 and subsequent years, described seizures characterized by olfactory and visual hallucinations, dreamy states and reminiscenses, automatisms, and gastric and autonomic symptoms, and observed that they were associated with lesions of the medial aspect of the temporal lobe. He referred to these as the "uncinate group of fits," but clinicians in general have used the term *uncinate* only for those with olfactory hallucinations, and until recently the psychic and other manifestations were not ascribed to focal dysfunction of the temporal lobe.

At the present time the term "psychomotor" and "temporal lobe" are used almost synonymously for those seizures that include some or all of the following: automatisms consisting of brief or prolonged inappropriate but seemingly purposeful automatic movements; disordered consciousness, usually with amnesia for the period of abnormal behavior; perceptual illusions and hallucinations that may be visual, auditory, olfactory, or gustatory; motor accompaniments of the olfactory and gustatory hallucinations (chewing, tasting, and swallowing movements); disorders of recognition and recall, often with reminiscences, dreamy states, and phenomena such as déjà vu and déjà pensée in which the patient experiences either visual manifestations or thoughts that seem strangely familiar to him and that he feels he has lived through or observed previously; psychic manifestations such as anxiety, fear, rage, obsessive thoughts, compulsive speech or actions, or feelings of unreality. These phenomena have been found to be associated with abnormal discharges and/or pathologic lesions of the anterior and medial portions of the temporal lobes, including the hippocampal gyrus, uncus, amygdaloid complex, and buried hippocampus, or the subcortical connections of these structures, many of which actually belong to the limbic or olfactory systems (see below). Relay of impulses to the hypothalamus, thalamus, or mesencephalic reticular formation may also be of importance. In certain cases of psychomotor epilepsy there may be associated involvement of the insula, posterior orbital surface of the frontal lobe, basal ganglia, or contiguous structures. Experience has shown, however, that removal of a portion of the abnormally discharging temporal lobe has been effective therapy in certain cases of psychomotor epilepsy. In rare instance bilateral lobectomy has been attempted, but a syndrome similar to that described by Klüver and Bucy in animals has been reported in humans subjected to such bilateral ablations.

Disease of the temporal lobes may also be manifested by symptoms other than the phenomena described above. Major convulsions occur frequently with neoplasms and similar lesions. A tumor of the superior aspect of the temporal lobe may press upon the lower frontal and parietal areas and cause either motor and sensory changes in the face and arm or focal convulsions. Neoplasms of the temporal lobes are second only to those of the frontal lobes in the frequency with which they are accompanied by mental symptoms, among which are the following: psychic manifestations varying from vague personality changes to frank behavioral disturbances; emotional abnormalities such as anxiety, depression, fear, and anger; paranoid syndromes; intellectual impairment, including memory defects (usually for recent memory), learning and cognitive disabilities, slowing of cerebration, and apathy. These are most apt to occur with diffuse and rapidly growing lesions, especially if the dominant hemisphere is affected. A neoplasm of the mesial aspect may press on the midbrain and cause dilatation of the ipsilateral pupil, a third nerve palsy, or even decerebrate fits. There have been reports of ablation of the amygdaloid complex for the suppression of auditory hallucinations in psychotic states and for the treatment of behavioral disorders.

THE LIMBIC LOBES

The hippocampal gyrus, uncus, isthmus, and gyrus cinguli are grouped together as the limbic lobe. Closely related are the subcallosal and retrosplenial gyri, pyriform area, hippocampus, and various subcortical structures including the amygdala and septal nuclei. Certain of these are often included in the temporal lobe, but anatomically and physiologically they are placed in the limbic system, or "visceral brain." The insula and the medial and the posterior orbital gyri of the frontal lobe are closely allied, although not actually a part of the limbic system. Phylogenetically the majority of these structures are a part of the rhinencephalon, which constitutes the major portion of the cerebral hemisphere in lower forms, and are related to the olfactory and gustatory systems, which are so important in these forms. In the human, however, the development of the neopallium greatly overshadows the olfactory and gustatory portions of the brain, and the connections of the latter are largely subcortical and with the thalamic and hypothalamic centers. The gyrus cinguli may be more closely related in function to the frontal and the parietal lobes, but the hippocampal gyrus and uncus, even though allied anatomically to the temporal lobe, are undoubtedly in part olfactory and gustatory in function, and the fibers of the lateral olfactory stria terminate in them. Irritation, or stimulation, of these produces either olfactory or gustatory hallucinations. These are often very disagreeable and described with difficulty. The hallucinations may be accompanied by smacking or licking of the lips, tasting movements of the tongue, swallowing, and salivation, and constitute an important part of the psychomotor seizure. Destruction of these areas is not followed by loss of smell or taste, owing to bilateral connections.

It is generally conceded by anatomists and physiologists that smell and taste are functionally related, and that the central connections dealing with gustatory sensations are correlated with those for olfactory sensations, not only in the uncus and hippocampal gyrus, but also in the thalamus and hypothalamus. Börnstein and other clinicians, however, do not believe that these two sensory modalities are related, and express the belief that gustatory is more closely allied to tactile sensation and that the cortical center for taste is not in the hippocampal gyrus and uncus, but rather in the parietal cortex. It has been stated that area 43, or the pararolandic operculum, which overlies the lower aspects of the parietal and frontal lobes, has both sensory and motor functions concerned with taste. The posterior portion of this area, which overlies the locus for somatic sensation from the tongue, may be the cortical center for gustatory sensation, and the anterior portion has been called the site for the control of movements necessary for tasting and swallowing. Stimulation of area 43 may be followed by smacking, tasting, and swallowing movements, and by gustatory hallucinations.

The limbic lobe and related structures have rich connections with the hypothalamus and thalamus, and play an important part in the central regulation of the autonomic nervous system (Chapter 41) as well as of visceral and sexual functions and the autonomic aspects involved in emotional expression. In addition to the oral and alimentary reactions mentioned above, stimulation of certain of the areas may cause genital and sexual responses and manifestations of rage, fear, and defense. Abnormal affective and emotional responses, fear, and aggressive behavior may be lessened by interruption of the connections between these cortical areas and the thalamus and hypothalamus. Bilateral or even unilateral lesions or resection of the hippocampus and hippocampal gyrus are followed by marked impairment of recent memory. Bilateral lesions of the cingulate gyrus (area 24) cause apathy, akinesia, and mutism. It is probable that many of the manifestations of psychomotor epilepsy are the result of involvement of the limbic lobe structures rather than the temporal lobe. The relationship of the various structures included in the "visceral brain" to emotional and mental disease is assuming increasing importance (Chapter 43).

OTHER CORTICAL AREAS

Only those regions of the cerebral cortex whose functions have been either demonstrated experimentally or observed clinically have been discussed; these are principally the projection areas. Cytoarchitectural studies show that there are many other distinct regions that may be significant clinically, but the functions of these areas are either less well defined or unknown. In view of the lack of definite knowledge of their functions, however, they need not be considered from a clinical point of view.

REFERENCES

ACKERLEY, S.   Instinctive, emotional and mental changes following prefrontal lobe extirpation.   *Am. J. Psychiat.* 92:717, 1935.

BAILEY, P.   Concerning the functions of the cerebral cortex.   *J. Nerv. & Ment. Dis.* 110:369, 1949.

BARTHOLOW, R.   Experimental investigation into the functions of the human brain. *Am. J. M. Sc.* 67:305, 1874.

BELL, E., JR., and KARNOSH, L. J.   Cerebral hemispherectomy: Report of a case ten years after operation.   *J. Neurosurg.* 6:285, 1949.

BRICKNER, R. M.   The Intellectual Functions of the Frontal Lobes: A Study Based upon Observation of a Man after Partial Bilateral Frontal Lobectomy.   New York, The Macmillan Company, 1936.

BRODAL, A.   The hippocampus and the sense of smell: A review.   *Brain* 70:179, 1947.

BUCY, P. C. (ed.).   The Precentral Motor Cortex.   Illinois Monographs in the Medical Sciences, Urbana, Ill.   University of Illinois Press, 1944.

CRITCHLEY, M.   The Parietal Lobes.   London, Edward Arnold & Co., 1953.

DEJONG, R. N.   "Psychomotor" or "temporal lobe epilepsy": A review of the developmental of our present concepts.   *Neurology* 7:1, 1957.

DENNY-BROWN, D., and BANKER, B. Q.   Amorphosynthesis from left parietal lesion. *A. M. A. Arch. Neurol. & Psychiat.* 71:302, 1954.

FERRIER, D.   The Function of the Brain.   New York, G. P. Putnam's Sons, 1886.

FLUORENS, P.   Recherches physiques sur les propriétés et les fonctions du système nerveux dans les animaux vertébrés.   *Arch. gén. méd.* 2:321, 1823.

FOERSTER, O.   The motor cortex in man in the light of Hughlings Jackson's doctrines. *Brain* 59:135, 1936.

FREEMAN, W., and WATTS, J. W.   Psychosurgery in the Treatment of Mental Disorders and Intractable Pain (ed. 2).   Springfield, Ill., Charles C Thomas, 1950.

FRENCH, J. D.   Brain physiology and modern medicine.   *Postgrad. Med.* 27:559, 1960.

FRITSCH, G., and HITZIG, E.   Ueber die Elektrische Erregbarkeit des Grosshirns.   *Arch. f. Anat., Physiol. u. wissench. Med.* 37:300, 1870.

FULTON, J. F.   Functional Localization in Relation to Frontal Lobotomy.   New York, Oxford University Press, 1949.

GIBBS, E. L., GIBBS, F. A., and FUSTER, B.   Psychomotor epilepsy.   *Arch. Neurol. & Psychiat.* 60:331, 1948.

GOLDSTEIN, K.   The mental changes due to frontal lobe damage.   *J. Physiol.* 17:187, 1944.

GOODDY, W.   Cerebral representation.   *Brain* 79:167, 1956.

HALSTEAD, W. B.   Brain and Intelligence: A Quantitative Study of the Frontal Lobes. Chicago, University of Chicago Press, 1947.

HARLOW, J. M.   Passage of an iron rod through the head.   *Boston Med. & Surg. J.* 39:389, 1848.

HEATH, R. G., MONROE, R. R., and WICKLE, W. A.   Stimulation of the amygdaloid nucleus in a schizophrenic patient.   *Am. J. Psychiat.* 111:862, 1955.

HEBB, D. O.   Man's frontal lobes: A critical review.   *Arch. Neurol. & Psychiat.* 54:10, 1945.

JACKSON, J. H.   Selected Writings of J. Hughlings Jackson.   (James Taylor, ed.), London, Hodder and Stoughton, 1931.

JACOBSEN, C. F.   Studies of Cerebral Function in Primates.   Comparative Psychology Monographs, Baltimore, Johns Hopkins Press, Vol. 13, No. 63, 1936.

KLÜVER, H., and BUCY, P. C.   "Psychic blindness" and other symptoms following bilateral temporal lobectomy in rhesus monkeys.   *Am. J. Physiol.* 119:352, 1937.

KRYNAUW, R. A.   Infantile hemiplegia treated by removing one cerebral hemisphere. *J. Neurol., Neurosurg. & Psychiat.* 13:243, 1950.

MACLEAN, P. D.   The limbic system ("visceral brain") and emotional behavior.   *Arch Neurol. & Psychiat.* 73:130, 1955; New findings relevant to the evolution of psychosexual functions in the brain.   *J. Nerv. & Ment. Dis.* 135:289, 1962.

McCULLOCH, W. S.   The functional organization of the cerebral cortex.   *Physiol. Rev.* 24:390, 1944.

McFIE, J., and PIERCY, M. F.   Intellectual impairment with localized cerebral lesions. *Brain* 75:292, 1952.

METTLER, F. A., POOL, J. L., HEATH, R. G., LANDIS, C., *et al.*   Selective Partial Ablation of the Frontal Cortex.   New York, Paul B. Hoeber, Inc., 1949.

MEYER, A., BECK, E., and McLARDY, T.   Prefrontal leucotomy: A neuro-anatomical report.   *Brain* 70:18, 1947.

VON MONAKOW, C.   Die Lokalisation in Grosshirn und der Abbau der Function der kortikale Herde.   Wiesbaden, J. F. Bergmann, 1914.

MONIZ, E.   Tentatives opératoires dans le traitement de certaines psychoses.   Paris, Mason & Cie, 1936.

MULDER, D. W., and DALY, D.   Psychiatric symptoms associated with lesions of temporal lobe.   *J.A.M.A.* 150:173, 1952.

NARABAYASHI, H., *et al.*   Stereotaxic amygdalotomy for behaviour disorder.   *Arch. Neurol.* 9:1, 1963.

PAPEZ, J. W.   A proposed mechanism of emotion.   *Arch. Neurol. & Psychiat.* 38:725, 1937.

PENFIELD, W., and JASPER, H.   Epilepsy and the Functional Anatomy of the Human Brain.   Boston, Little, Brown & Co., 1954.

POOL, J. L., and RANSOHOFF, J.   Autonomic effects on stimulating rostral portions of cingulate gyri in man.   *J. Neurophysiol.* 12:385, 1949.

RINKEL, M., GREENBLATT, M., COON, G. P., and SOLOMON, H. C.   Relation of the frontal lobe to the autonomic nervous system in man.   *Arch. Neurol. & Psychiat.* 58:570, 1947.

RYLANDER, G.   Personality analysis before and after frontal lobotomy.   *A. Res. Nerv. & Ment. Dis., Proc.* (1947) 27:691, 1948.

SCOVILLE, W. B., and MILNER, B.   Loss of recent memory after bilateral hippocampal lesions.   *J. Neurol., Neurosurg. & Psychiat.* 20:11, 1957.

SPIEGEL, E. A., and WYCIS, H. T.   Stereoencephalotomy: Thalamotomy and Related Procedures.   New York, Grune & Stratton, Inc., 1952.

SYMONDS, C.   Disease of mind and disorder of the brain.   *Brit. M. J.* 2:1, 1960.

TERZIAN, H., and ORE, G. D.   Syndrome of Klüver and Bucy reproduced in man by bilateral removal of the temporal lobes.   *Neurology* 5:373, 1955.

WARD, A. A., JR.   The anterior cingulate gyrus and personality.   *A. Res. Nerv. & Ment. Dis., Proc.* (1947) 27:488, 1948.

WILLIAMS, J. M., and FREEMAN, W.   Amygdaloidectomy for the suppression of auditory hallucinations.   *Med. Ann. District of Columbia* 20:192, 1951.

WOODBURNE, R. T.   Certain phylogenetic anatomical relations of localizing significance for the mammalian central nervous system.   *J. Comp. Neurol.* 71:215, 1939.

CHAPTER 51

FUNCTIONS AND DISOR-
DERS OF FUNCTION OF
CERTAIN NONCORTICAL
AREAS OF THE CEREBRUM

THE DIAGNOSIS and localization of intracranial disease are dependent to a large extent upon evidences of disturbance of function of the cerebral cortex and the white matter underlying it. There are structures deeper in the cerebrum, however, whose functions are also of clinical importance. Some of these, such as the basal ganglia and related nuclear centers, are discussed elsewhere (Chapter 22) and will not be dealt with here. Others lack clinical significance. Evidences of involvement of the following structures and complexes, however, may give important diagnostic and localizing information.

THE THALAMUS

The thalamus is one of the major constituents of the diencephalon. It is a large ovoid structure which is placed medially in the cerebrum. Its dorsal aspect forms the floor of the lateral ventricle, and it is bounded medially by the third ventricle and laterally by the internal capsule and basal ganglia; ventrally it is continuous with the subthalamus. Its nuclear centers have been classified and named variously, but in general the terminology of Walker is followed at the present time (Fig. 301). The nuclei of the thalamus are classed morphologically into specific groups.

The *anterior nuclear group* occupies the anterior part of the thalamus and projects

857

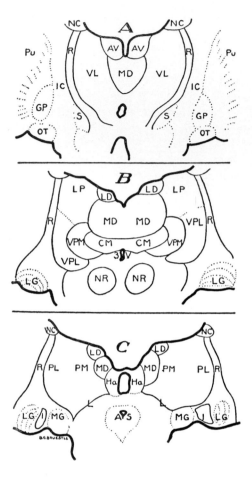

FIG. 301.   Cross section of chimpanzee thalamus, showing principal nuclear masses at three levels. (Walker, A. E., in Fulton, J. F.: Physiology of the Nervous System. New York, Oxford University Press, 1938.) *A,* anterior thalamus; *B,* midthalamus; *C,* posterior thalamus. AS, aqueduct of Sylvius; AV, nucleus anteroventralis (anterior nuclear group); CM, nucleus centrum medianum (medial nuclear group); GP, globus pallidus; HA, habenula; I, inferior nuclear group of pulvinar; IC, internal capsule; L, nucleus limitans (posterior nuclear group); LD, nucleus lateralis dorsalis (later portion of lateral nuclear mass); LG, lateral geniculate body; LP, nucleus lateralis posterior (lateral portion of lateral nuclear mass); MD, nucleus medialis dorsalis (medial nuclear group); MG, medial geniculate body; NC, caudate nucleus; NR, red nucleus; PL, lateral nuclear group of pulvinar; PM, medial nuclear group of pulvinar; Pu, putamen; OT, optic tract; R, nucleus reticularis (lateral nuclear mass); S, subthalamic nucleus; VL, nucleus ventralis lateralis (ventral portion of lateral nuclear mass); VPM, nucleus ventralis postomedialis (ventral portion of lateral nuclear mass); VPL, nucleus ventralis posterolateralis (ventral portion of lateral nuclear mass); 3v, third ventricle.

into the lateral ventricle. It consists of the nuclei anterodorsalis, anteroventralis, and anteromedialis, whose connections are largely with the cingulate cortex and the hypothalamus. The *nuclei of the midline* are clusters of cells which lie close to the wall of the third ventricle and in the massa intermedia. They are connected chiefly with the hypothalamus, for visceral functions, but are poorly developed in man. The *medial nuclei* lie between the nuclei of the midline and the internal medullary lamina. Their most important representative is the *nucleus medialis dorsalis,* or the *dorsomedial nucleus,* which has connections with other thalamic nuclei, the preoptic and hypothalamic regions, the parolfactory area, the striatum and globus pallidus, the amygdaloid complex, and areas 8, 9, 10, 11, 12, 44, 45, 46, and 47 of the frontal cortex and possibly areas 40 and 42 on the temporal operculum. The anterior, midline, and medial nuclei are centers for the correlation of interoceptive impulses, including olfactovisceral, general visceral, and probably gustatory impulses, with exteroceptive and equilibratory sensations. They are closely related to the hypothalamus and periventricular gray matter. The connections of the medial nuclei with the frontal cortex is thought to have great significance in the anatomic basis for behavior and personality.

The major component of the group of *intralaminar nuclei* is the *nucleus centromedianus,* which has connections with the caudate, putamen, and globus pallidus. The *nucleus reticularis* has been regarded as one of the regions of termination for ascending multisynaptic pathways and as a relay center in an activating system to the cortex.

The *ventral nuclear group* lies between the internal medullary lamina and the internal capsule, anterior to the pulvinar. Its most rostral portion is the *nucleus ventralis anterior* which receives fibers from globus pallidus and the caudate nucleus and sends other fibers to globus pallidus, caudate, and putamen, and possibly to the premotor cortex. Behind it lies the *nucleus ventralis lateralis* which receives dentatothalamic and rubrothalamic fibers from the brachium conjunctivum and red nucleus, as well as fibers from the frontal cortex; it sends impulses to the motor and premotor cortex of the frontal lobe. It is a relay station from the cerebellum and red nucleus to the cerebral motor centers. The posterior part of the ventral division is the *nucleus ventralis posterior,* the largest cell mass in the ventral nuclear group. It is divided into four parts, the nuclei ventralis posteromedialis, posterolateralis, posteroinferior, and intermedius, but the first two are the most important. Within the *nucleus ventralis posteromedialis* terminate the fibers of the secondary trigeminal tracts, and within the *nucleus ventralis posterolateralis* terminate the fibers of the spinothalamic tracts and the medial lemniscus. By means of thalamocortical fibers arising in these centers, impulses are relayed to the somethetic sensory cortex in the postcentral gyrus. Within the thalamus the receptive area for the face is located medially and caudally, that for the leg laterally and rostally, and that for the arm in an intermediate position. These respective areas are connected with corresponding regions of the sensory cortex by specific portions of the thalamic radiations. Impulses from the upper areas of the body (medial part of the thalamus) go to the inferior portions of the postcentral gyrus; those from the lower regions of the body (lateral part of the thalamus), to the superior sensory centers; those from the intermediate regions of the body and parts of the thalamus, to the middle portion of the sensory cortex.

The *lateral nuclear group* consists of the *pulvinar* and the *nuclei lateralis dorsalis* and *posterior*. The latter receive fibers from other thalamic nuclei and communicate with the cortex of the posterior parts of the parietal lobe. The pulvinar is a large mass which forms the caudal extremity of the thalamus. Fibers reach it from other thalamic nuclei and possibly from the geniculate bodies, and it has connections with the peristriate area and the posterior parts of the parietal lobes. It was once thought to receive fibers from the optic tracts. These nuclei are closely interrelated with the cerebral cortex, particularly with the parietal area, and are believed to integrate and reinforce cortical discharges.

The *lateral* and *medial geniculate bodies* are thalamic nuclei that have been displaced downward so that they lie lateral to the upper end of the mesencephalon under cover of the pulvinar. The portion of the thalamus in which they are situated is sometimes referred to as the metathalamus. The lateral geniculate bodies receive the fibers of the optic tracts, and after a synapse relay the impulses to the striate cortex through the geniculocalcarine pathways. There is a specific anatomic relationship between the various portions of the retinae, localization in the geniculate bodies, and the site of termination of the impulses in the occipital cortex (Fig. 24). The medial geniculate bodies receive impulses from the cochlear nuclei by way of the lateral lemnisci and send them via the thalamotemporal radiations to the auditory areas in the superior temporal convolutions (Fig. 91).

The thalamus may also be subdivided into the *dorsal thalamus* and the *ventral thalamus*. The former, which includes the constituents described above, is a receptive center for impulses, in most cases after synapse in lower regions, and transmits them to the corpus striatum, cortex, or lower efferent centers. The ventral thalamus, or subthalamus, is on the efferent side of the arc; it conducts impulses received from the dorsal thalamus, the motor cortex, and the lenticular nucleus to lower efferent centers in the midbrain, pons, medulla, and spinal cord. It is an upward prolongation of the tegmental region of the midbrain and forms a zone of transition between the tegmentum and the thalamus. It occupies a triangular area between the dorsal thalamus above, the internal capsule and cerebral peduncle laterally, and the hypothalamus medially. The *epithalamus,* above the thalamus, includes the habenular nuclei and their connections, and the stria medullaris, epiphysis, and posterior commissure; it is an olfactosomatic correlation center for conscious and reflex response to olfactory stimulation, and also has endocrine functions. The hypothalamus, below the thalamus, is discussed elsewhere ("The Autonomic Nervous System," Part VI).

The thalamus is connected with the cerebral cortex by the thalamic peduncles. The *anterior thalamic peduncle* consists of frontothalamic, thalamofrontal, striothalamic, and thalamostriatal fibers which run in the anterior limb of the internal capsule. The thalamocortical fibers are believed to allow certain emotional impulses and "feeling tones" to reach the cortex. The *superior thalamic peduncle* consists of thalamoparietal fibers which transmit sensation from the thalamus to the cortex; these fibers run in the posterior limb of the internal capsule. The *posterior thalamic peduncle* contains the optic radiations from the lateral geniculate body to the occipital cortex, and the *inferior thalamic peduncle* carries auditory radiations from the medial geniculate body to the temporal cortex.

The thalamus has various functions. It is the principal relay center in the forebrain. It receives pain and temperature impulses from the spinothalamic and dorsal secondary ascending trigeminal pathways, tactile and proprioceptive sensations from the medial lemniscus and ventral secondary ascending trigeminal tract, cerebellar projections from the brachium conjunctivum, afferent fibers from the optic and auditory systems, and also olfactory and gustatory impulses. After an interruption these are forwarded to cortical levels. It is also a complex integrating organ. Impulses are not passed through it without change, but they are associated and synthesized; it is connected with the cerebral association areas and not only projects to but also receives fibers from the cortex. There is probably some awareness of sensation in the thalamus, with a crude, uncritical form of consciousness, and the organ may be the primary receptive area, or end station, in the quantitative appreciation of pain, heat, cold, and heavy contact. It is more important, however, in the affective rather than the discriminative aspects of sensation.

Lesions of the thalamus may be followed by a definite complex of symptoms. The *thalamic syndrome* of Dejerine and Roussy occurs as a result of damage which predominates in the nucleus ventralis posterolateralis or, possibly, interrupts the pathways from the thalamus to the cortex. It is usually caused by a vascular lesion, most frequently either rupture or occlusion of one of the thalamo-geniculate branches of the posterior cerebral artery. There is a characteristic group of symptoms. There is diminution of sensation on the opposite half of the body without complete anesthesia. The limbs and trunk are affected more than the face, which may be spared. There is usually a permanent disturbance of deep sensibility—postural sense, appreciation of passive movement, heavy contact, and deep pressure. The defect may range from a slight to a profound one. Cutaneous sensations are also impaired, but the change may be a transient one. The threshold for tactile, pain, and temperature sensations is raised, but pain sense exhibits a specific alteration. All stimuli, when effective, excite unpleasant sensations, and even the lightest stimulus may evoke a disagreeable, burning, agonizing type of pain response in the affected parts of the body. Light touch, extremes of hot and cold, roughness, tickling, and even the pressure of clothing or bed clothes may excite marked discomfort. Various visceral and affective states as well as auditory and visual impulses may cause the response. As a result the patient may complain of an intractable pain which is not relieved by ordinary analgesics. Owing to the presence of this hyperpathia, or hyperaffectivity, in spite of the raised sensory threshold, the term *anesthesia dolorosa* has been associated with this symptom-complex. The thalamic overaction is the result of either irritation of the thalamus or release from higher cortical control. Every stimulus acting on the thalamus produces an excessive effect on the abnormal half of the body, especially as far as the affective element, the pleasant or unpleasant character in its appreciation, is concerned. Occasionally pleasurable stimulation, such as that produced when a warm hand is applied to the skin on the affected side, may be markedly accentuated. In addition to the above sensory changes, the thalamic syndrome may also include, on the opposite side of the body, a transient or permanent hemiparesis, a hemiataxia with choreiform or choreo-athetoid movements due to involvement of the cerebellorubrothalamic connections, a mimetic type of facial paresis with weakness present on emotional but not on voluntary contraction, and a quadrantic or hemianopic field defect. There may be increased emotional lability, with easily precipitated laughter and crying.

Prolonged psychic disturbances, including confusion, amnesia, and confabulation, have been reported following thalamectomy and thalamolysis performed for the treatment of hyperkinetic and other disorders, and pathologic alterations of the thalamus have been described in association with some psychiatric illnesses. Penfield and his associations have included the thalamus, especially the intralaminar and reticular nuclei, along with the reticular formation of the midbrain and brain stem, the tegmentum of the midbrain, and the basal diencephalic area in the so-called centrencephalic integrating system in which certain "deep level" epileptic seizures, including petit mal and some generalized attacks, originate. Epileptic discharges arising in this complex appear simultaneously in both cerebral hemispheres, and the electroencephalographic abnormality which accompanies them is bilaterally synchronous. If such a system does exist, however, it is probably more caudally placed, mainly in the reticular formation (see below), and epilepsy does not arise in the diencephalon, although this portion of the brain may be involved in the propagation of generalized seizures.

The clinical manifestations of lesions of other portions of the thalamus are poorly understood. Involvement of the anterior part causes few sensory changes. Unmotivated laughter and crying, which may occur without associated affective changes, are thought to be caused by lesions of the anterior thalamic peduncle. Both severe dementia and choreo-athetoid movements have been reported with symmetrical degeneration of the thalamus affecting principally the anterior, medial, and lateral nuclei, and it has been suggested that affection of the thalamus may be a major feature of many psychoses and degenerative diseases. The relief of mental and emotional symptoms that follows prefrontal lobotomy may be the result of interruption of the pathways between the frontal regions and the thalamus, and similar relief of symptoms and also amelioration of hyperkinetic phenomena have been reported following the placing of circumscribed lesions in the thalamus. The dorsomedial nucleus has been destroyed by stereotaxic surgery in the treatment of psychotic states and personality disorders and for the relief of intractable pain; lesions have also been placed in the nuclei ventralis posteromedialis and posterolateralis for the control of intractable pain; destructive lesions have been made in the nucleus ventralis lateralis and other thalamic nuclei for the relief of the tremor and rigidity of Parkinson's disease and in the treatment of other dyskinetic states. Only the latter of these therapeutic endeavors, using chemical injections, electrocoagulation, electrolysis, ultrasound, radiofrequency, and cryosurgery, has been very widely used.

THE CORPUS CALLOSUM

The corpus callosum is the largest of the commissural systems of the brain. It consists of a broad band of white fibers located at the bottom of the median longitudinal fissure, and connects the neopallium of the two hemispheres. It is composed of a major portion, or body, an anterior genu ending in the rostrum, and a thickened posterior termination, or splenium. Fibers connecting the anterior portions of the frontal lobes, including the speech areas, course through the anterior third; the body carries fibers from the posterior portions of the frontal lobes and from the parietal lobes; the splenium contains fibers from the temporal and occipital lobes.

The corpus callosum is believed to facilitate the cooperation of the two cerebral hemispheres, especially in man, in whom one hemisphere is dominant. Its clinical significance, however, is not well understood, for its absence may cause no symptoms. Furthermore, it may be difficult to differentiate between signs caused by disease of the corpus callosum and those resulting from disease of contiguous parts. The statement has been made many times in the past that lesions of the middle third of this structure cause apraxia, or the inability to carry out skilled movements, and that involvement of the anterior third causes both apraxia and aphasia (Chapter 53). With acute lesions there may be emotional excitement, confusion, and irritability, followed by apathy, drowsiness, personality changes, and either hemiplegia or paraplegia, and later by stupor and coma. While certain of these symptoms may result from disease of the corpus callosum itself, others may be due to involvement of neighboring areas, including the corona radiata and the cingulate gyri. The corpus callosum has been sectioned in an attempt to relieve convulsive attacks, principally to stop the spread of the epileptogenic discharge from one hemisphere to the other. The results have not been convincing but, it is interesting to state, few clinical symptoms have resulted from section of this commissure.

Various clinical syndromes of involvement of the corpus callosum have been described. Agenesis is most frequently discovered only by autopsy or pneumoencephalography. There is usually mental deficiency and there may be hemiplegia, paraplegia, and convulsions. These symptoms are usually associated with additional congenital malformations of the brain. Primary degeneration of the corpus callosum, Marchiafava-Bignami disease, is a rare condition probably due to a combination of chronic alcoholism and undernutrition. There are organic mental symptoms, convulsions, and motor disabilities. With tumors of the corpus callosum mental symptoms are prominent; they consist of apathy, drowsiness, loss of memory, difficulty in concentration, personality changes, and other manifestations suggestive of frontal lobe involvement. There is also double hemiplegia associated with other motor changes. Apraxia is present in only a small proportion of cases. Thrombosis of the anterior cerebral artery causes softening of a large portion of the commissure; it has been said that there is always motor apraxia on the left, regardless of the side of the lesion, but observations have shown that this is not always the case. In all of these conditions, the diagnosis of involvement of the corpus callosum is dependent upon the presence of signs referable to disease of neighboring parts of the brain.

THE INTERNAL CAPSULE

The cerebral hemisphere is connected with the brain stem and spinal cord by an extensive system of projection fibers, some of which are efferent, others afferent.

These fibers either arise from or terminate in the entire extent of the cortex, and within the white substance of the hemisphere they appear as a radiating structure, the *corona radiata.* They converge into a broad band, the *internal capsule,* which connects the cortex with the underlying structures. This tract is composed of all of the fibers, both efferent and afferent, which communicate with the cerebral cortex; a large part of the capsule is composed of the thalamic radiations, and the rest consists of efferent fibers to lower structures. Below the level of the thalamus the descending systems make up the cerebral peduncle of the midbrain.

The internal capsule separates the lentiform nucleus, which is lateral to it, from the caudate nucleus anteromedially and the thalamus posteromedially. Between the caudate and the thalamus it bends sharply at the genu. In horizontal section the internal capsule is seen to be composed of three parts (Fig. 149). The frontal portion is the shorter *anterior limb,* or lenticulocaudate division, which extends rostrally and laterally between the lentiform and caudate nuclei. The junctional zone is the *genu,* or geniculate portion, which forms an obtuse angle between the two limbs. The longer *posterior limb,* or lenticulothalamic portion, extends laterally and posteriorly between the lentiform nucleus and the thalamus; its caudal extremity is divided into a *retrolenticular* portion, which projects behind the lentiform nucleus to reach the occipital cortex, and a *sublenticular portion,* which passes below the posterior part of this nucleus to reach the temporal lobe.

The *anterior limb of the internal capsule* is composed of the *frontopontine tract* and the *anterior thalamic radiations.* The former, which carries the corticopontocerebellar impulses from the frontal region, conveys fibers which arise in the premotor region of the frontal cortex, probably from the middle frontal convolution anterior to areas 6 and 8, to the homolateral pontine nuclei; after a synapse, the impulse is transmitted through the brachium pontis to the opposite cerebellar hemisphere. The anterior thalamic radiations, or anterior thalamic peduncle, carries the following: thalamofrontal fibers from the nucleus ventralis lateralis to the motor and premotor cortex, from the anterior nuclear group of the thalamus to the cingulate gyrus and inferior region of the frontal cortex, and from nucleus medialis dorsalis to the frontal association areas; frontothalamic fibers from the motor and premotor regions to the lateral nuclear mass, especially nucleus ventralis lateralis, as well as from the frontal association areas to nucleus medialis dorsalis; thalamostriatal and striothalamic fibers. Projections from areas 4s, 8, 9, and possibly other regions of the frontal cortex to the caudate nucleus may also be carried through the anterior limb.

The *corticobulbar tracts* are situated at the *genu of the internal capsule;* they carry impulses from the lower portion of precentral (and premotor) cortex to the motor nuclei of the cranial nerves. The fibers to the eye muscles and face are placed most anteriorly, and those to the mouth and tongue extend a short distance into the posterior limb. The corticobulbar impulses pass largely but not entirely to contralateral nuclei.

The *posterior limb of the internal capsule* has many important constituents. The *corticospinal* and *corticorubral tracts* are situated in the anterior half or two thirds of the lenticulothalamic portion. The corticospinal pathway carries impulses from the upper portion and the paracentral region of the precentral (and premotor) cortex to the motor nuclei of the spinal cord, predominantly those on the opposite side. The fibers destined for the arm are more anterior than those for the leg. It is important from both anatomic and clinical points of view that the pyramidal pathway, which includes both the corticobulbar and corticospinal tracts, is situated in a small area of the internal capsule, occupying the genu, the anterior portion of the posterior limb, and perhaps a very small portion of the anterior limb. The arrangement of the fibers differs somewhat from the order of cortical representation (Fig. 146), and in the internal capsule the fibers to the eyes and face are placed most anteriorly, followed, in a backward direction, by those to the mouth, tongue, shoulder arm, forearm, hand, fingers, thumb, trunk, hip, leg, ankle, and toes. The corticorubral tract, which is lateral to the corticospinal pathway, carries impulses from the frontal cortex, probably mainly area 4, to the ipsilateral red nucleus, as well as rubrocortical fibers from the red nucleus to the cortex. Corticonigral and corticosubthalamic impulses may accompany the corticorubral tract. Fibers from the frontal cortex, areas 4 and 6, to the caudate nucleus, putamen, and globus pallidus are carried as collaterals of the corticospinal neurons.

The *thalamic radiations* which compose the superior thalamic peduncle make up a large portion of the posterior limb of the internal capsule. These consist of thalamocortical fibers from the nuclei ventralis posteromedialis and posterolateralis to the somesthetic sensory cortex in the postcentral gyrus, as well as those from nuclei lateralis dorsalis and posterior to the posterior parts of the parietal lobe. It may be that some thalamofrontal fibers from nucleus ventralis lateralis to the motor and premotor cortex are also carried with these thalamic radiations, as well as thalamolenticular, thalamostriatal, lenticulothalamic, and striothalamic impulses. The *temporopontine* and *occipitopontine fibers* which carry corticopontocerebellar impulses from association areas in the middle and inferior temporal convolutions and also from the anterior portion of the occipital lobe (or lower parietal region) to the homolateral pontine nuclei, and thence to the contralateral cerebellar hemisphere, also course through the posterior limb of the internal capsule, as do the optic and auditory radiations.

The *optic radiations,* or the posterior thalamic peduncle, make up most of the retrolenticular portion of the posterior limb. They constitute the geniculocalcarine tract and carry impulses from the lateral geniculate body, and possibly the pulvinar, to the striate cortex. Corticofugal fibers from the areas 18 and 19, especially the latter, to the superior colliculus (anterior quadrigeminal body), and thence through the medial longitudinal fasciculus to the nuclei of the ocular nerves, pass with the optic radiations, as do communications between the pulvinar and the peristriate area. The occipitopontine fibers are also in the retrolenticular division.

The *auditory radiations,* or the inferior thalamic peduncle, make up the major portion of the sublenticular division of the posterior limb. They carry impulses from the medial geniculate body to the auditory areas in the transverse temporal convolutions, through the thalamotemporal radiations. There may also be some impulses which pass in the opposite direction. The temporopontine fibers are also in the sublenticular division, as are some of the thalamostriatal, striothalamic, thalamopallidal, and pallidothalamic fibers.

The internal capsule is of great clinical importance. Fiber pathways that communicate with various areas of the brain converge here and are concentrated in a small area. In the second place, the blood supply of the region is such that hemorrhages and vascular occlusions frequently affect the structure. Owing to the close crowding of the fibers in the internal capsule, a small lesion may cause a profound contralateral hemiplegia; this is especially true of involvement at or just posterior to the genu. Posterior lesions are also accompanied by sensory changes and hemianopic defects. Involvement of the anterior limb of the internal capsule causes symptoms of thalamic release with unmotivated laughter and crying. Owing to the proximity of the internal capsule to the basal ganglia and the thalamus, lesions of the capsule may also affect these structures.

THE RETICULAR FORMATION

Groups of cells situated in the reticular formation of the midbrain, pons, and medulla and in the thalamus (especially the intralaminar and reticular nuclei) and contiguous areas perform many functions that are widespread in their pattern of effects. Collectively, these are known as the reticular formation, the reticular activating system, or the ascending and descending multisynaptic projection system. Into this complex come collaterals of the long ascending sensory paths as well as motor collaterals from the descending pyramidal tract and extrapyramidal pathways. In addition there are connections with the cerebellum and the various cranial nerve nuclei. Intimate synaptic relations connect all these fiber systems, and projections are sent out in both rostral and caudal directions. The actions of this complex in the facilitation or suppression of motor activity and the part it plays in the regulation of tone, reflex response, and movement are discussed in Chapter 22. It has similar influences on sensory conduction, which it may either inhibit or enhance.

The reticular activating system also plays an important part in regulating the awareness to sensation, arousal to wakefulness, and alerting to attention, as well as in the control of neuroendocrine functions. It participates in determining not only the level but also the content of consciousness. Consequently it may have influence in the control of emotional states and behavior. It may correspond closely to the so-called centrencephalic integrating system in which certain "deep-level" epileptic seizures are said to originate. The syndromes of akinetic mutism (Chapter 55) may result from involvement of the reticular activating system. Many of the drugs that inhibit or enhance motor or sensory responses, affect consciousness and behavior, and control certain varieties of epileptic attacks, have their sites of action in this small area of the brain. Current investigations on the reticular formation are demonstrating the widespread influence it has in the activation and regulation of nervous system functions.

REFERENCES

AKELAITIS, A. J. E.   Psychobiological studies following section of the corpus callosum. *Am. J. Psychiat.* 97:1147, 1941.

COOPER, I. S.   Clinical and physiological implications of thalamic surgery for disorders of sensory communication.   *J. Neurol. Sc.* 2:493, 1965.

DEJERINE, J., and ROUSSY, G.   La syndrome thalamique.   *Rev. neurol.* 14:521, 1906.

DELAFRESNAYE, J. F. (ed.).   Brain Mechanisms and Consciousness.   Springfield, Ill., Charles C Thomas, 1954.

ETTLINGER, E. G. (ed.)   Functions of the Corpus Callosum.   Ciba Foundation Study Group No. 20, Boston, Little, Brown & Company, 1965.

FRENCH, J. D.   The reticular formation.   *J. Neurosurg.* 15:97, 1958.

HESS, W. R.   Physiologie du thalamus.   *Internat. Neurol. Cong., Rapports* 4:53, 1949.

JASPER, H. H., PROCTOR, L. D., KNIGHTON, R. S., NOSHAY, W. C., and COSTELLO, R. T.   The Reticular Formation of the Brain.   Boston, Little, Brown & Company, 1958.

KUHLENBECK, H.   The Human Diencephalon: A Summary of Development, Structure, Function and Pathology.   *Confinia neurol.* Suppl. Vol. 14, 1954.

MAGOUN, H. W.   The ascending reticular activating system.   *A. Res. Nerv. & Ment. Dis., Proc.* 30:480, 1950.

MARK, V. H., and HACKETT, T. P.   Surgical aspects of thalamotomy in the human.   *Trans. Am. Neurol. A.* 84:92, 1959.

PAPEZ, J. W., and BATEMAN, J. F.   Cytologic changes in cells of thalamic nuclei in senile, paranoid and manic psychoses: The significance of the dorsal thalamus in psychoses.   *J. Nerv. & Ment Dis.* 112:401, 1950.

PENFIELD, W., and JASPER, H.   Epilepsy and the Functional Anatomy of the Human Brain.   Boston, Little, Brown & Company, 1954.

ROSE, J. E., and WOOLSEY, C. N.   Organization of the mammalian thalamus and its relationships to the cerebral cortex.   *Electroencephalog. & Clin. Neurophysiol.* 1:391, 1949.

SPIEGEL, E. A., WYCIS, H. T., and FREED, H.   Stereoencephalotomy: Thalamotomy and related procedures.   *J.A.M.A.* 148:446, 1952.

VAN WAGENEN, W. P., and HERREN, R. Y.   Surgical division of the commissural pathways in the corpus callosum.   *Arch. Neurol. & Psychiat.* 44:740, 1940.

WALKER, A. E.   The Primate Thalamus.   Chicago, University of Chicago Press, 1938.

WATKINS, E. S., and OPPENHEIMER, D. R.   Mental disturbances after thalamolysis.   *J. Neuro., Neurosurg. & Psychiat.* 25:243, 1962.

WILLIAMS, D.   The thalamus and epilepsy.   *Brain* 88:530, 1965.

CHAPTER 52

THE BLOOD SUPPLY OF THE BRAIN, INCLUDING THE VASCULAR SYNDROMES

THE CEREBRAL ARTERIES

THE BRAIN RECEIVES its blood supply from the vertebral and internal carotid arteries. Although these vessels communicate with each other, in general the branches derived from the vertebral arteries supply the caudal half of the brain including the hind brain, midbrain, thalamus, occiptal lobes, inferior portion of the temporal lobes, and most of the thalamus, whereas branches of the internal carotid arteries supply the basal ganglia, frontal and parietal lobes, lateral portion of the temporal lobes, and most of the internal capsule. Branches of these arteries and communications between them and their branches make up the *arterial circle of Willis* at the base of the brain (Fig. 302). *Central arteries* arise from the circle of Willis and the proximal portions of the principal cerebral arteries and dip perpendicularly into the brain substance; they are terminal branches and do not anastomose with each other, and hence occlusion of one of these vessels produces softening of the area deprived of its blood supply. *Cortical branches* arise from distal portions of the arteries and enter the pia mater where they form a superficial plexus of more or less freely anastomosing vessels, and from these plexuses smaller terminal branches enter the brain substance at right angles. Owing to the anastomosis of the larger cortical arteries, occlusion of one of them may be compensated to a variable extent by blood supply from neighboring branches.

The two *vertebral arteries* enter the cranial cavity through the foramen magnum and run rostrally along the ventral surface of the medulla. They unite at the

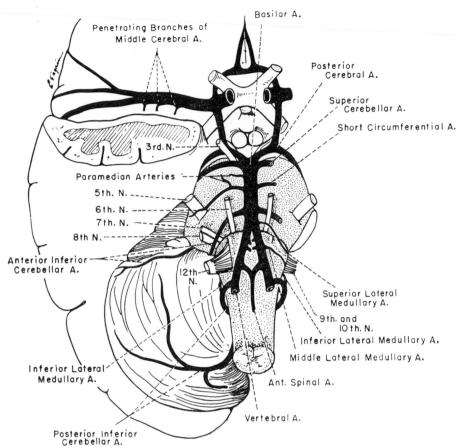

FIG. 302.   Diagram showing circle of Willis and principal vessels of brain stem. (Fisher, C. M., in Fields, W. S. (ed.): Pathogenesis and Treatment of Cerebrovascular Disease, Springfield, Ill., Charles C Thomas, 1961.)

lower border of the pons to form the basilar artery. Two important branches of the vertebral artery are the posterior inferior cerebellar artery, which winds around the medulla to the inferior surface of the cerebellum, and the anterior spinal artery. The posterior spinal and the medullary arteries are smaller branches. The *basilar artery* is formed by the junction of the two vertebral arteries at the lower border of the pons and ends at the upper border of the pons by dividing into the two posterior cerebral arteries. Branches of the basilar are the two anterior inferior cerebellar arteries, the two internal auditory arteries, several pontine branches, and the two superior cerebellar arteries.

The *posterior cerebral arteries* are formed by the bifurcation of the basilar artery. Each one is directed backward and laterally around the cerebral peduncle, where it is close to the upper border of the pons, parallel to the superior cerebellar artery, and in front of the oculomotor nerve. After receiving the posterior communicating branch from the internal carotid artery, it is continued along the medial

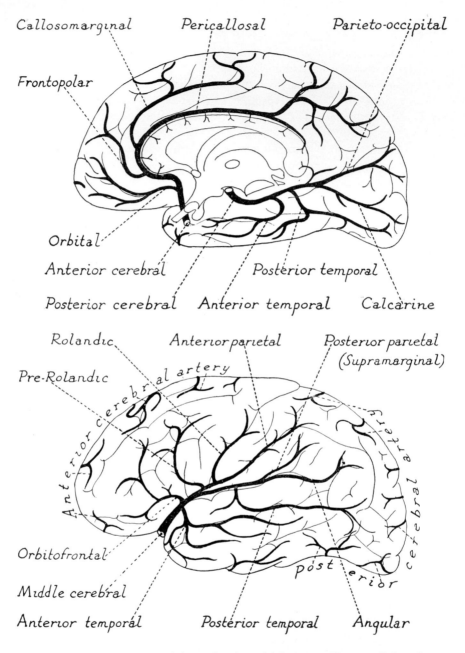

Callosomarginal   Pericallosal   Parieto-occipital

Frontopolar

Orbital

Anterior cerebral   Posterior temporal

Posterior cerebral   Anterior temporal   Calcarine

Rolandic   Anterior parietal   Posterior parietal (Supramarginal)

Pre-Rolandic

Anterior cerebral artery

Orbitofrontal

Middle cerebral

Anterior temporal   Posterior temporal   Angular

FIG. 303.   Scheme of arterial supply of cerebral cortex: *Top*, medial surface; *Bottom*, lateral surface. (Strong, O. S., and Elwyn, Adolph: Human Neuroanatomy. Baltimore, Williams & Wilkins Company, 1948.)

surface of the corresponding cerebral hemisphere, beneath the splenium of the corpus callosum, to reach the medial and inferior surfaces of the temporal lobe and the medial surface of the occipital lobe (Fig. 303), where it divides into its four cortical branches. The *anterior temporal artery* supplies the uncus and the anterior parts of the inferior temporal, fusiform, and hippocampal gyri, exclusive of the temporal pole which is supplied by the middle cerebral artery. The *posterior temporal artery* supplies the rest of the fusiform and inferior temporal gyri. The *calcarine artery* supplies the lingual gyrus and the inferior half of the cuneus, and the *parieto-occipital,* or *posterior occipital, artery* supplies the upper part of the cuneus, with branches to the splenium of the corpus callosum. Thus the cortical branches of the posterior cerebral artery carry blood to the medial surface of the occipital lobe, which includes all of the visual receptive area, the medial and inferior surfaces of the temporal lobe, and the splenium of the corpus callosum. Their terminal branches wind around the borders of the hemisphere and supply a small portion of the lateral surfaces of the temporal and occipital lobes and even a small part of the superior parietal lobule; they anastomose with branches of the middle and anterior cerebral arteries.

The deep branches of the posterior cerebral artery are the following: the *posterior choroidal arteries,* of which there are usually two, encircle the cerebral peduncle and give off branches to the midbrain, tela choroidea and choroid plexus of the third ventricle, and the superomedial surface of the thalamus; the *postero-medial arteries,* derived from the posterior communicating artery as well as the posterior cerebral, supply the hypophysis, infundibulum, tuberal and mammillary regions of the hypothalamus, walls of the third ventricle, medial and anteromedial portions of the thalamus, subthalamic structures, tegmentum of the midbrain, red nucleus, and medial portion of the cerebral peduncle; the *posterolateral,* or *thalamogeniculate* arteries, supply the caudal half of the thalamus, the posterior portion of the internal capsule, the superior cerebellar peduncle, the superior colliculus, and the geniculate bodies.

The *internal carotid* artery arises in the neck as one of the terminal branches of the common carotid. It passes through the carotid canal in the petrous portion of the temporal bone and enters the cranial cavity through the foramen lacerum. It makes a series of turns within the cavernous sinus, and just before leaving this structure gives off the *ophthalmic artery*. It reaches the brain lateral to the optic chiasm and near the medial side of the temporal pole and the medial and lower extremity of the lateral cerebral fissure. Here it divides into its two terminal branches, the anterior and middle cerebral arteries. Before dividing, however, it gives off the posterior communicating artery which connects the internal carotid and posterior cerebral arteries, and the anterior choroidal artery which runs backward to reach the choroid plexus of the lateral ventricle.

The *anterior cerebral artery,* the smaller of the two terminal branches of the internal carotid artery, crosses the anterior perforated space above the optic nerve and runs forward and medially to the median longitudinal fissure; just in front of the optic chiasm it is joined with the opposite anterior cerebral artery by the *anterior communicating artery*. It then goes forward and rostrally within the inter-

hemispheric fissure, where it lies on the medial surface of the hemisphere close
to the corpus callosum. It curves around the genu of this body and turns backward, continuing along the upper surface of the corpus callosum to the posterior
parietal region. Along this course the artery gives off four cortical branches. The
orbital artery arises where the main trunk turns upward, and it spreads out over
the orbital surface of the frontal lobe, supplying the olfactory lobe, gyrus rectus,
and medial and inferior portions of the orbital gyri. The *frontopolar artery* supplies the medial surface of the prefrontal region as far forward as the frontal pole.
The *callosomarginal artery* arises opposite the genu of the corpus callosum and
courses backward in the cingulate sulcus; it gives off an *anterior internal frontal
branch* about the middle of the superior frontal gyrus, a *middle internal frontal
branch* at the posterior extremity of the superior frontal gyrus, and a terminal
posterior internal frontal branch in the region of the paracentral lobule. The *pericallosal artery* continues backward over the body and posterior part of the corpus
callosum to anastomose with branches of the posterior cerebral artery. Numerous
small branches of both the anterior cerebral and pericallosal arteries penetrate
the corpus callosum. Thus the cortical branches of the anterior cerebral artery
supply the medial and orbital surfaces of the frontal lobe, the medial surface of
the parietal lobe as far as the parieto-occipital fissure, the cingulate gyrus, and
the genu and anterior four-fifths of the corpus callosum; these areas include the
motor and somesthetic centers in the paracentral lobule. Their terminal branches,
like those of the posterior cerebral artery, wind around the border of the hemisphere to supply a small portion of the lateral surface, in this case, of the frontal
and parietal lobes.

The largest of the deep, or central, branches of the anterior cerebral artery is
the *recurrent artery of Heubner,* or the medial striate artery. It takes a recurrent
course, and after giving a few branches to the orbital cortex, passes through the
anterior perforated space to join the deep branches of the middle cerebral artery.
It supplies the lower part of the head of the caudate nucleus, the lower part of the
frontal pole of the putamen, the frontal pole of globus pallidus, the adjacent frontal
half of the anterior limb of the internal capsule, and the anterior portions of the
external capsule and lateral ventricle. The *anteromedial group* of central arteries
arise from the anterior cerebral and anterior communicating arteries and supply
the anterior hypothalamus including the preoptic and suprachiasmatic regions,
the genu of the corpus callosum, the septum pellucidum, the anterior pillars of the
fornix, and part of the anterior commissure.

The *middle cerebral artery* is the largest of the cerebral arteries. It runs first
laterally and then laterally, posteriorly, and upward in the sylvian, or lateral,
fissure, over the surface of the insula and between the frontal and temporal lobes.
It gives off many cortical branches which supply the lateral surface of the brain.
The *anterior temporal artery* curves out of the lateral fissure and runs backward
over the temporal lobe; it supplies the temporal pole and the anterior third of the
superior and middle temporal gyri. The *orbitofrontal artery* supplies the lateral
part of the orbital surface of the frontal lobe, the lateral surface of the orbital

gyri, and the lateral surface of the inferior frontal convolution. The *prerolandic artery* runs for a short distance in the central fissure and then curves over the precentral gyrus to enter the precentral fissure; it supplies the lower and anterior portions of the precentral gyrus and the posterior portions of the middle and inferior frontal convolutions. The *rolandic artery* runs over the opercular part of the postcentral gyrus and then enters the central fissure; it supplies the posterior portion of the precentral gyrus and the anterior part of the postcentral gyrus. The *anterior parietal artery* curves over the opercular portion of the parietal lobe and reaches the interparietal fissure; it supplies the posterior border of the postcentral gyrus and the anterior parts of the others parietal convolutions. The *posterior temporal artery* descends from the lateral fissure and supplies the posterior two-thirds of the superior and middle temporal convolutions. The *posterior parietal (supramarginal) artery* arises near the end of the lateral fissure and supplies the supramarginal gyrus and the posterior part of the inferior parietal lobule. The middle cerebral artery terminates as the *angular artery,* which supplies the angular gyrus and the adjoining parts of the parietal lobe. Near their extremities these branches anastomose with branches of the anterior and posterior cerebral arteries which project onto the lateral surface of the hemispheres. Thus the cortical branches of the middle cerebral artery supply the lateral surfaces of the frontal and parietal lobes, and the lateral and upper surface of the temporal lobe, the insula, and the lateral part of the orbital gyri. These areas include the middle and inferior frontal convolutions, the lateral parts of the premotor and precentral regions, the postcentral gyrus, the superior and inferior parietal lobules, the angular and supramarginal gyri, the superior and middle temporal convolutions including the temporal pole, and the preoccipital region. Situated in these areas are the language centers, the auditory receptive area, and the major portion of the motor and somesthetic cortex.

The deep, or central, branches of the middle cerebral artery arise from the proximal part of the vessel. They constitute the *anterolateral group,* or *lateral and medial striate arteries,* which pierce the anterior perforated substance and supply the whole of the putamen except for its anterior pole, the upper part of the head and the whole of the body of the caudate nucleus, the lateral part of globus pallidus, and the posterior part of the anterior limb, the genu, and the anterior third of the posterior limb of the internal capsule. The thalamus is nowhere supplied by branches of the middle cerebral artery, although such vessels have been described by some authors (lenticulo-optic). Under most circumstances it is not possible to distinguish among the striate arteries any individual branch such as the lenticulo-striate artery, although Charcot and others expressed the belief that there was such a vessel, the largest of the group, which they termed the "artery of cerebral hemorrhage" because they believed that it was frequently affected in apoplexy.

The *anterior choroidal artery* arises from the internal carotid artery just before its bifurcation. It passes backward along the optic tract and around the cerebral peduncle as far as the lateral geniculate body, where its main branches turn to enter the inferior horn of the lateral ventricle; it supplies the choroid plexus of the lateral ventricle. In its course it gives branches to the optic tract, hippocampus, tail of the caudate nucleus, medial and intermediate portions of the globus pallidus, posterior two-thirds of the posterior limb of the internal capsule, middle third of the cerebral peduncle, and outer part of the lateral geniculate body. The retro-lenticular and sublenticular portions of the internal capsule are also supplied by this artery. Branches of the *posterior communicating artery* enter the base of the brain between the infundibulum and the optic tract and supply the genu and anterior one-third of the posterior limb of the internal capsule, the anterior one-third of the thalamus, and the walls of the third ventricle.

Studies of the circle of Willis have shown that it is subject to wide variations in configuration and that anomalous formations are frequent. There may be hypoplasia of one or more of the components, which may have a string-like caliber, or there may be duplication or triplication of vessels, absent vessels, or persisting embryonic origin of certain of the constituents (Fig. 304). Alpers and associates have shown that the circle is actually normal in only 52.3 per cent of individuals without evidence of nervous system disease, and Riggs and Rupp have demonstrated anomalous formations in 79 per cent of adults with clinical manifestations of neural dysfunction.

Clinical and investigative studies have thrown new light upon the cerebral circulation. Angiography has given much important information about the distribution of the major cerebral arteries and their communications, and has demonstrated the effects on cerebral circulation of obstruction of them. Investigations of cerebral blood flow by means of various physiologic technics have revealed the relationship of cerebral circulation to such factors as arterial blood pressure, venous pressure, cerebrovascular resistance, oxygen and carbon dioxide tension, and intracranial cerebrospinal fluid pressure. Such technics also show the effects on cerebral circulation and oxygen consumption of autonomic nervous system stimulation and depression, various drugs and metabolites, and disease processes of either the vessels or the blood itself. It is probable that the circle of Willis is a potential but not an actual anastomotic structure in the normal state, and there is little or no interchange of blood in the distribution of the major cerebral arteries. In disease states, however, this anastomotic circle allows blood to be supplied to areas that would otherwise be deprived of their blood supply. The susceptibility to disease is often determined to a major extent by individual variations in the circle of Willis.

THE CEREBRAL VEINS AND THE VENOUS SINUSES

The *cerebral veins* do not parallel the cerebral arteries; they possess no valves, and their walls, owing to the absence of muscular tissue, are extremely thin. They may be divided into an external, superficial, or cortical group, and an internal, deep, or central group (Fig. 305). Studies of the venous phase of angiography as well as the injection of contrast material into the venous sinuses have both aided in diagnosis of intracranial disease and broadened our knowledge of the distribution of venous channels.

The external veins arise from the cortex and medullary substance of the hemi-

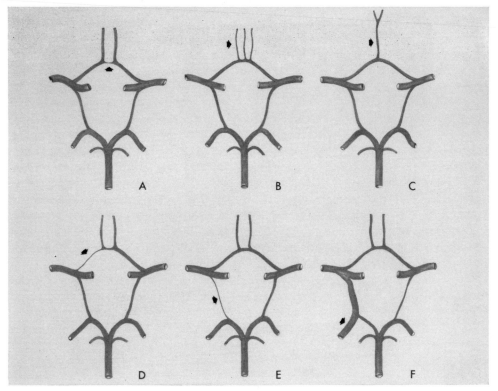

Fig. 304.   Variations in the circle of Willis; *A,* hypoplasia of anterior communicating artery; *B,* anomalous anterior cerebral arteries; *C,* fusion of anterior cerebral arteries; *D,* and *E,* hypoplasia of branches of internal carotid
artery; *F,* posterior cerebral from internal carotid artery. (After Alpers,
B. J., Berry, R. G., and Paddison, R. M.: *Arch. Neurol. & Psychiat.* 81:409,
1959.)

sphere; they anastomose freely and form a network of large trunks in the pia
mater. The *superior cerebral veins,* eight to twelve in number, drain the superior,
lateral, and medial surfaces of the hemispheres above the sylvian and callosomarginal fissures. Most of them are lodged in the sulci between the gyri, although
some of the larger trunks run across the convexity of the gyri. They pierce the
arachnoid membrane and the inner layer of the dura mater, and after a short intradural course terminate in the superior sagittal sinus or its venous lacunae. The
arrangement on the two sides is asymmetrical, and a separation into anterior and
posterior groups is usually evident. The *anterior veins* drain the upper parts of the
frontal lobe and enter the sinus at right angles to its lateral wall. The *posterior
veins,* which are larger, drain the parietal region and are directed forward before
entering the sinus; some from the convex surface of the occipital lobe may terminate
in the transverse sinus.

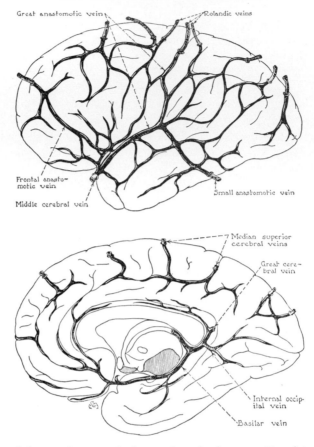

FIG. 305.   Scheme of venous drainage of cerebral cortex: *Top,* lateral surface; *Bottom,* medial surface. (Bailey, P.: Intracranial Tumors, ed. 2. Springfield, Ill., Charles C Thomas, 1948.)

The *inferior cerebral veins* are small and drain the basal surfaces of the hemispheres and the lower portion of the lateral surfaces. Those on the orbital surface of the hemisphere enter the superior veins and thus reach the superior longitudinal sinus, whereas those of the temporal lobe anastomose with the middle cerebral veins and enter the cavernous, sphenoparietal, transverse, and superior petrosal sinuses. The *middle cerebral vein* courses through the lateral fissure and drains the insula and the opercular region; it terminates in either the cavernous or sphenoparietal sinus, or occasionally in the transverse or superior petrosal sinus. It is connected with the superior sagittal sinus by the great anastomotic vein of Trolard, and with the transverse sinus by the small, or posterior, anastomotic vein of Labbé.

The *deep cerebral veins* drain the interior of the hemispheres. The *choroidal vein* runs the entire length of the choroidal plexus and receives branches from the hippocampus, fornix, and corpus callosum. The *terminal vein* commences in the groove between the caudate nucleus and thalamus and receives many tributaries from these structures as well as from the internal capsule. Near the interventricular foramen the terminal and choroidal veins fuse to form the *internal cerebral vein*. The *basal vein* (*of Rosenthal*) is formed at the anterior perforated space by the union of a small anterior cerebral vein which accompanies the anterior cerebral artery, the deep middle cerebral vein, and the inferior striate vein; it passes backward around the cerebral peduncle to end in the internal cerebral vein, and receives tributaries from the cingulate gyrus, anterior part of the corpus callosum, orbital surface of the frontal lobe, olfactory groove, optic chiasm, hypophysis, cerebral peduncle, interpeduncular fossa, inferior horn of the lateral ventricle, hippocampal gyrus, and midbrain. The *internal occipital vein* also enters the internal cerebral vein.

The *great cerebral vein of Galen* is formed just behind the pineal body by the union of the two internal cerebral veins. It is a short median trunk which curves backward and upward around the splenium of the corpus callosum and ends in the anterior extremity of the straight sinus.

The venous sinuses of the dura mater are channels which are situated between the two layers of the dura; the cerebral veins terminate in them (Fig. 306). The *superior sagittal* (or *longitudinal*) *sinus* occupies the convex, or attached, margin of the falx cerebri from the foramen caecum backward to the region of the internal occipital protuberance, where it is continued as one of the transverse sinuses. In its middle portion it gives off a number of lateral diverticula, or venous lacunae, into which protrude the arachnoid granulations, or pacchionian bodies. It receives the superior cerebral veins, veins from the diploë and dura mater, and, in the parietal region, emissary veins from the pericranium. In early childhood it receives branches from the nasal veins. The *inferior sagittal* (or *longitudinal*) *sinus* is situated in the posterior half or two-thirds of the free margin of the falx cerebri and receives veins from the falx and from the medial surfaces of the hemispheres. It terminates in the *straight sinus,* which is situated at the junction of the falx cerebri and tentorium cerebelli and runs backward to end in the transverse sinus opposite to the one in which the superior sagittal sinus ends. It receives, in addition to the inferior sagittal sinus, the great cerebral vein of Galen and the superior cerebellar veins.

The *transverse* (*lateral*) *sinuses* begin in the region of the internal occipital protuberance as continuations of the superior sagittal and straight sinuses, and pass laterally and forward in the attached margin of the tentorium cerebelli to the petrous portion of the temporal bone. They then pass downward and medially to reach the internal jugular foramen where they end in the internal jugular veins. Those portions which occupy the groove on the mastoid part of the temporal bone are sometimes called the *sigmoid sinuses*. The transverse sinuses receive blood from the superior petrosal sinuses, inferior cerebral and inferior cerebellar veins, and emissary and diploic veins. The *occipital sinus* commences at the margin of the foramen magnum and courses through the lower attached margin of the falx cerebri to the transverse sinus. The place of union of the superior sagittal, straight, transverse, and occipital sinuses is the *confluence of sinuses,* or *torcular Herophili.*

The *cavernous sinuses* are placed on each side of the body of the sphenoid bone, lateral to the sella turcica, and extend from the superior orbital fissure to

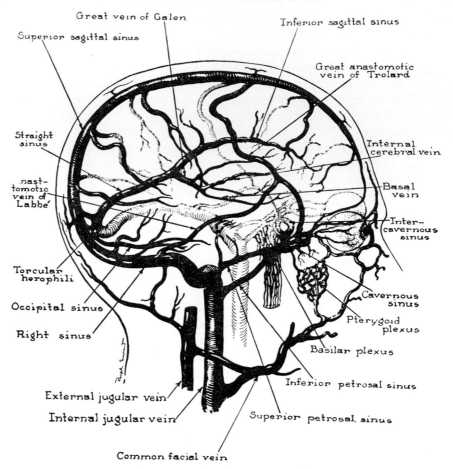

FIG. 306. Venous drainage of brain, showing dural sinuses and their principal connections with extracranial veins. (Sweet, R., in Shenkin, H. A., Harmel, M. H., and Kety, S. S.: *Arch. Neurol. & Psychiat.* 60:240, 1948.)

the petrous portion of the temporal bone. They open behind into the petrosal sinuses. The internal carotid artery and the carotid plexus are on the medial wall of the sinus, and lateral to them are the abducens, oculomotor, and trochlear nerves, and the ophthalmic and maxillary divisions of the trigeminal nerve (Fig. 51). The cavernous sinuses receive the ophthalmic veins, some of the cerebral veins, and the small *sphenoparietal sinus* which courses under the surface of the small wing of the sphenoid bone. The two sinuses communicate with each other by the anterior and posterior intercavernous sinuses.

The *superior petrosal sinus* connects the cavernous with the transverse sinus and receives cerebellar and inferior cerebral veins and veins from the tympanic cavity. The *inferior petrosal sinus* connects the cavernous sinus with the internal jugular vein and receives the internal auditory veins and veins from the cerebellum and medulla. The *basilar plexus* consists of several interlacing venous channels between the layers of the dura mater on the basilar part of the occipital bone; it connects the two inferior petrosal sinuses and communicates with the vertebral venous plexuses. *Emissary veins* pass through apertures in the cranial wall and establish communications between the sinuses inside the skull and veins external to it. *Diploic veins* occupy channels in the diploë of the cranial bones and communicate with the sinuses of the dura mater, veins of the pericranium, and meningeal veins.

SYNDROMES OF CEREBROVASCULAR DISEASE

The clinical concepts of vascular disease of the brain have undergone some major changes in recent years. It was long believed that most cases, if not all, of such disease of arterial origin were the result of either occlusion or rupture of the major cerebral arteries or their terminal branches. It is now known, however, that either stenosis or occlusion of extracerebral and even extracranial arteries is responsible for a large percentage of instances of so-called cerebrovascular disease. The affected vessels may be in the neck and even in the thorax, and include the internal carotid, common carotid, and vertebral arteries, and even the site of origin of these vessels from the subclavian artery, innominate artery (brachio-cephalic trunk), or arch of the aorta. Furthermore, all instances of cerebrovascular disease are no longer classified as either hemorrhage, thrombosis, or embolism. A large percentage consist of brief spells of vascular insufficiency in the distribution of either the carotid or the vertebrobasilar system, with episodes of transient focal cerebral ischemia without infarct formation.

Most instances of vascular insufficiency and occlusion are secondary to athero-sclerotic involvement of the affected arteries. There is thickening of the intima of the larger arteries, an accumulation of lipids (especially cholesterol) in the intimal cells, the formation of atherosclerotic plaques, and consequent decrease in the caliber of the vessels, especially at the site of bifurcations, branchings, and curves (Fig. 307). As the atherosclerotic plaque thickens, the vascular lumen narrows and blood flow diminishes. With a sudden drop in the systemic blood pressure, as may occur with hemorrhage elsewhere in the body, or with shock, the vessel may be temporarily occluded, and symptoms may occur due to decrease in blood supply to the terminal branches of the affected artery; if the pressure is not restored promptly, permanent changes may occur. Of more serious consequence is the formation of a thrombus at the site of a plaque, with resulting complete occlusion of the vessel. On occasion processes such as arteriolar sclerosis, senile arterioscler-osis, hypertension, thromboangiitis obliterans, syphilitic endarteritis, and other processes may also contribute to vascular occlusions.

The nerve cells of the brain are highly sensitive to variations in blood and oxygen supply. The cerebral circulation, through the communications of the circle of Willis and the anastomoses of the cortical branches, is designed to maintain as constant a supply of both blood and oxygen as possible, and to provide adequate collateral circulation in case of local damage. The failure of anastomosis of the central branches makes the deep parts of the brain more vulnerable to vascular

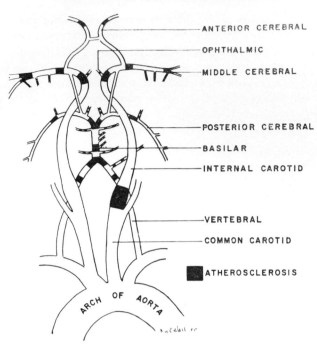

FIG. 307. Diagram of cerebral circulation showing sites of predilection for atherosclerosis and occlusion. (Fisher, C. M., in Fields, W. S. (ed.): Pathogenesis and Treatment of Cerebrovascular Disease, Springfield, Ill., Charles C Thomas, 1961.)

disease. Intermittent cerebrovascular insufficiency, usually due to involvement of the extracerebral vessels, causes transient ischemic attacks, with symptoms referable to the areas supplied by the terminal branches of the affected arteries. These may progress in severity, with decreasing return of function after each episode. Complete ischemia is followed in a relatively short period of time by irreversible changes that lead in necrosis and scarring. Focal cerebral damage of vascular origin is, in most cases, the result of either hemorrhage or infarct formation. Hemorrhage results from rupture of one of the intracerebral vessels, and may be secondary to hypertension, aneurysmal dilatation, vascular anomaly, blood dyscrasia, or other causes. An infarct results from interruption of blood supply; this may be due to either thrombus formation, with obliteration of the vessel lumen, or embolism, with obstruction by lodging of a foreign particle in a vessel which is too small to permit its passage. The onset of symptoms with all of these is usually abrupt—the so-called "stroke"—although the symptoms of thrombosis occasionally appear more gradually than those of either hemorrhage or embolism. The possible development of unilateral cerebral edema in association with vascular occlusion may suggest the presence of a neoplasm. Cerebral arteries are occasionally compressed by neoplasms or by sudden increase in intracranial pressure.

Owing to the fact that specific areas of the brain are supplied by individual arteries, occlusion or rupture of such vessels produces disturbances of function of these regions with characteristic signs and symptoms of disease. By appraisal of these signs and symptoms one may be able to localize the disease process and identify the affected vessel. It must be borne in mind, however, that there is a certain amount of variability in the vascular supply of the brain, and that anomalies of the cerebral vessels are frequently encountered. Furthermore, the symptoms of vascular disease may be influenced by the richness of anastomosis of cerebral vessels, the ability of healthy parts of the brain to assume the functions of destroyed areas, and the dominance of certain cerebral centers over others. In some patients who have extensive vascular disease, especially of the extracranial arteries, but have been without symptoms because the blood supply to the brain is still adequate, the occlusion of a vessel may result in symptoms and signs referable not only to the distribution of the recently thrombosed artery but also to areas whose circulation had previously been impaired. Angiography is often of value in the diagnosis and localization of cerebrovascular disease. It may be of aid in the differentiation between extracranial and intracranial disease (which in many cases is difficult), in the exact localization of the vascular obstruction, in the assessment of the extent of the vascular disease, and in the evaluation of the possibility of surgical and other means of therapy.

A discussion of the vascular supply to the various areas of the brain and of the syndromes of occlusion and rupture of the more important arteries is given below. Syndromes of insufficiency, occlusion, and rupture of the vertebral and basilar arteries and their branches are described in Chapter 18, as well as in the discussion of involvement of the ocular, trigeminal, and facial nerves. The areas of distribution of each of the cerebral arteries has been described in detail. To aid in visualization of vascular disease, however, the various areas of the brain and the arteries which supply them are listed. The *cerebral cortex* receives blood from the anterior, middle, and posterior cerebral arteries. The anterior cerebral artery supplies the medial surfaces and upper portions of the convexities of the frontal and parietal lobes, and the cortex of the cingulate gyrus; this includes the motor and somesthetic cortex for the lower extremity. The middle cerebral artery supplies the cortex of most of the convexity of the brain—the lateral aspects of the frontal and parietal lobes, the upper portion of the temporal lobe including the temporal pole, and the insula; it is distributed to the motor and somesthetic areas for the face and upper extremity, the motor speech area, the auditory receptive region, and important association foci. The posterior cerebral artery supplies the medial and inferior parts of the temporal lobe, exclusive of the temporal pole, and the medial aspect of the occipital lobe, including the visual receptive area. The *caudate* and *putamen* are supplied mainly by striate branches of the middle cerebral arteries, but their anterior extremities receive blood from the anterior cerebral. The medial and intermediate segments of the *globus pallidus* are supplied by the anterior choroidal artery, but the lateral segment receives blood from both the striate branches of the middle cerebral and anterior choroidal artery. The *thalamus* is supplied by the deep branches of the posterior cerebral and posterior communicating arteries, and by the anterior choroidal artery. The anterior *hypothalamus* is supplied by the branches of the anterior cerebral artery, and the posterior hypothalamus and *subthalamus* by branches of the posterior communicating and posterior cerebral arteries. The anterior part of the anterior limb of the *internal capsule* is supplied by the anterior cerebral artery; the posterior part of the anterior limb, the genu, and the anterior part of the posterior limb receive their blood supply from the middle cerebral and posterior communicating arteries; the posterior portion of the posterior limb is supplied by the anterior choroidal artery and the deep branches of the posterior cerebral artery. The genu may receive a few small filaments directly from the internal carotid artery.

Occlusion or rupture of the *anterior cerebral artery,* before the origin of the recurrent branch, results in a severe contralateral hemiplegia of the spastic type, the leg being affected more than the arm or face. There may be mental symptoms in the nature of memory loss, sluggishness, emotional liability, confusion, and disorientation, and at times actual dementia. If the lesion is left-sided, there is some expressive aphasia which may be temporary, and there is apraxia on the right which may be masked by the paresis. If the lesion is right-sided, there is left-sided apraxia which, again, may be masked. It is stated that there may be a left-sided apraxia with a right-sided hemiplegia in lesions of the left anterior cerebral artery. There often is sensory impairment of the lower extremity. There may be psychic symptoms in the nature of peculiar sucking and chewing movements and catatonic manifestations, and transient incontinence, forced grasping, and groping. Dandy has postulated a "center for consciousness" in the distribution of the anterior cerebral artery, with loss of consciousness following interruption of the continuity of this vessel at the genu of the corpus callosum, either on the right or bilaterally; he associated the loss of consciousness with necrosis of the anterior portion of the corpus striatum.

If the anterior cerebral artery is occluded after the origin of the recurrent artery, the hemiplegia will predominate in the leg, which is often flaccid. There will be sensory changes, as above, and the apraxia may be present in the left arm, regardless of the side affected by the paralysis. The mental changes, aphasia, and forced grasping are as above. If only the artery of Heubner is occluded, there will be paresis of the face, tongue, and shoulder on the opposite side, due to softening of the anterior part of the internal capsule, and there may be rigidity and hyperkinesis, due to striatal involvement. If only the callosal branches are involved, there may be apraxia and mental changes, without paresis. If only the paracentral lobule is affected, there may be paralysis and sensory changes of the leg with sparing of the arm. Bilateral involvement of the anterior cerebral arteries may cause the syndrome of pseudobulbar palsy. Rupture of the anterior communicating artery causes symptoms of subarachnoid hemorrhage.

Symptoms resulting from occlusion or rupture of the *posterior cerebral artery* include hemiplegia, hemianesthesia, hemianopia, receptive aphasia with alexia predominating, hyperkinetic phenomena, asynergia, and third nerve paralysis; there may be temporary bilateral blindness. Due to abundant anastomoses, however, involvement of the entire area is rare, and the peduncular region in particular escapes. Occlusion near the origin of the artery causes a hemianesthesia of the thalamic type, and the hemiparesis is mild but is accompanied by some asynergy due to involvement of the superior cerebellar peduncle. Of the cortical branches, the calcarine is most often affected; there is resulting hemianopia, with or without alexia, depending on the hemisphere affected.

Occlusion or rupture of the entire *middle cerebral artery* produces such widespread softening of one hemisphere that profound coma takes place at once, with complete hemiplegia, hemianesthesia, and hemianopia, and with aphasia if the lesion is in the dominant hemisphere; death usually follows. If the perforating branches alone are involved, the syndrome of capsular hemiplegia occurs, with hemiparesis affecting especially the face and upper extremity, often accompanied by sensory loss. Extreme rigidity and contractures may develop. If the trunk of the artery is affected after the origin of the perforating branches, or if the cortical branches are involved, there may be localized pareses and sensory changes, aphasia of varying types, astereognosis, apraxia, or a hemianopic defect, depending on the site of the occlusion. Involvement of the orbitofrontal artery on the left causes expressive aphasia; of the prerolandic artery, paresis of the opposite side of the face and tongue; of the rolandic artery, both paresis and hypesthesia of the opposite face and arm; of the anterior parietal artery, contralateral astereognosis; of the posterior temporal artery on the left, auditory receptive aphasia; of the supramarginal and angular arteries, hemianopia or, if on the left, visual receptive aphasia and apraxia. Two or more branches may be occluded simultaneously.

Occlusion of the *internal carotid artery,* if it occurs suddenly, is followed in most instances by a severe contralateral hemiplegia and hemianesthesia, often with ipsilateral blindness due to occlusion of the ophthalmic artery. If the dominant hemisphere is affected, there is complete aphasia. Pathologically there is softening of the entire hemisphere with the exception of the thalamus, inferior portion of the temporal lobe, and medial portion of the occipital lobe. Convulsions may occur at the onset. If the occlusion takes place gradually, and if the circulation of the circle of Willis is adequate, there may be very few symptoms. Since the introduction of angiography it has become apparent that occlusion of the internal carotid artery occurs much more frequently than was realized in the past, and usually takes place in the neck just above the bifurcation of the common cartoid or at the level of the carotid sinus. With atherosclerotic involvement of this vessel there may be transient, recurring symptoms of cerebrovascular insufficiency, or if the occlusion is gradual in onset there may be premonitory manifestations consisting of contralateral hemiparesis or monoplegia, parethesias, or visual field defects, along with aphasia and ipsilateral monocular blindness. There may be secondary embolic phenomena. Occasionally it is necessary to occlude the internal cartoid artery to stop hemorrhage or to excise aneurysms. If the vessel can be occluded gradually there may be no untoward symptoms. Atherosclerosis, stenosis, and occlusion of the internal carotid in the neck or of its origin in the mediastinum may be treated surgically by thromboendarterectomy and reconstruction of the vessel wall.

Occlusion or rupture of the *anterior choroidal artery* is followed by hemiplegia and sensory defects, affecting principally the leg, and either a quadrantic or hemianopic field defect opposite to the side of the lesion, together with added signs resulting from involvement of the basal ganglia, hippocampus, thalamus, and mesencephalon. Cooper has recommended ligation of this artery for the treatment of Parkinson's disease, but his results have not been confirmed.

Aneurysmic dilation of the arteries which make up the circle of Willis, especially the communicating branches, may cause localized compression of the cranial nerves. The third nerve and the visual pathway (optic nerve, chiasm, or tract) are affected most frequently. When the aneurysm is located on that portion of the internal carotid artery which lies within the cavernous sinus, the third, fourth, and sixth nerves and the ophthalmic division of the fifth may be involved. Rupture of such aneurysms causes spontaneous subarachnoid hemorrhage. This appears suddenly, often after strenuous exertion. There may be loss of consciousness and generalized convulsions at the outset. The symptoms are largely those of meningeal irritation with intense nuchal or occipital headache, stiff neck, and photophobia, but there may also be manifestations of focal nervous system dysfunction and signs of increased intracranial pressure. The spinal fluid is under increased pressure and contains blood; within a short time the supernatant fluid becomes xanthochromic. Arteriovenous aneurysms within the cavernous sinus may cause proptosis, chemosis, dilatation of the conjunctival vessels, engorgement of the retinal veins, papilledema, and cranial nerve involvement, together with a pulsating exophthalmos. A bruit can often be heard over the eye or forehead. The pulsation of the eye can be abolished by compression of the ipsilateral common cartoid artery.

SYNDROMES OF OCCLUSION OF THE CEREBRAL VEINS AND VENOUS SINUSES

Syndromes of occlusion of the cerebral veins and of the venous sinuses occur less frequently than those of occlusion of the cerebral arteries, but the sinuses are affected more often than the veins. There is a great deal of evidence at the present time, however, that structural changes in the veins may be responsible for many of the manifestations that have been attributed in the past to pathologic alterations of the arteries. Thrombosis of the cerebral veins or venous sinuses is usually secondary to trauma, infection, cachexia, or blood dyscrasia, and occurs most often in infants and children.

Occlusion of the superior cerebral veins may cause either motor or sensory changes on the opposite side of the body, depending upon whether the anterior or posterior group is affected. Occlusion of either the middle cerebral or small anastomotic vein may cause weakness of the facial muscles; if the occlusion is on the left, there may be aphasia. Obliteration of the internal occipital vein produces hemianopia. Occlusion of the great cerebral vein of Galen may cause coma, hyperpyrexia, tachycardia, contraction of the pupils, either convulsions or tonic fits, decerebrate rigidity, and papilledema.

Occlusion of the *superior sagittal sinus* in young children is followed by generalized convulsions, spastic paralysis, and distention of the veins of the scalp and nose. In adults disease of this sinus is followed by spastic paralysis and cortical sensory changes, with more marked involvement of the lower than the upper extremities. There may be jacksonian convulsions, loss of sphincter control, nausea and vomiting, delirium, apathy, stupor, papilledema, and edema and dilatation of the veins of the scalp, eyelids, and forehead. Thrombosis of the *straight sinus* causes decerebrate rigidity and other manifestations similar to those of occlusion of the great vein of Galen.

The *transverse sinus* may be occluded or thrombosed in disease of either the middle ear or mastoid; the thrombus extends into the jugular bulb and vein. In addition to symptoms of septicemia, there may be headache, nausea and vomiting, tenderness and induration of the jugular vein on the involved side, edema and distention of the veins of the neck and mastoid area, meningeal signs, and papilledema most marked ipsilaterally, together with auditory and vestibular involvement, and sometimes dyspnea, dysphagia, and bradycardia due to vagus involvement. The Queckenstedt maneuver on the affected side fails to cause a rise in spinal fluid pressure. In Crowe's test for lateral sinus thrombosis there is failure of dilatation of the retinal veins on ipsilateral jugular compression.

Thrombosis of the *cavernous sinus* may complicate infections of the orbit, nose, paranasal sinuses, or contiguous areas of the face on the involved side. In addition to manifestations of septicemia there is pain in the eyes and forehead, with ipsilateral proptosis, chemosis, edema of the eyelid and conjunctiva, papilledema, dilatation of the retinal veins, retinal hemorrhages, and involvement of the third, fourth, and sixth nerves and the ophthalmic division of the trigeminal nerve. The process may extend to the opposite side.

Thrombosis of the dural sinuses may be a cause of brain swelling of unknown etiology, or so-called pseudotumor cerebri. The process may have its origin in the transverse sinus of one side and extend to either the superior sagittal or straight sinus and cause intracranial hypertension through interference with absorption of cerebrospinal fluid.

REFERENCES

ALEXANDER, L. The vascular supply of the striopallidum. *A. Res. Nerv. & Ment. Dis., Proc.* (1940) 21:77, 1942.

ALPERS, B. J., BERRY, R. G., and PADDISON, R. M. Anatomic studies of the circle of Willis in normal brain. *Arch. Neurol. & Psychiat.* 81:409, 1959.

ARING, C. D. Vascular diseases of the nervous system. *Brain* 68:28, 1945.

CARPENTER, M. B., NOBACK, C. R., and MOSS, M. L. The anterior choroidal artery: Its origin, course, distribution, and variations. *A. M. A. Arch. Neurol. & Psychiat.* 71:714, 1954.

COOPER, I. S. Surgical occlusion of the anterior choroidal artery in parkinsonism. *Surg., Gynec. & Obst.* 99:207, 1954.

CORDAY, E., ROTHENBERG, S. F., and PUTNAM, T. J. Cerebral vascular insufficiency: An explanation of some types of localized cerebral encephalopathy. *A. M. A. Arch. Neurol. & Psychiat.* 69:551, 1953.

CRITCHLEY, M. The anterior cerebral artery and its syndromes. *Brain* 53:120, 1930.

DANDY, W. E.   Intracranial Arterial Aneurysms.   Ithaca, N. Y., Comstock Publishing Company, 1944.

DAVISON, C., GOODHART, S. P., and NEEDLES, W.   Cerebral localization in cerebrovascular disease.   *Arch. Neurol. & Psychiat.* 30:749, 1933.

FIELDS, W. S. (ed.)   Pathogenesis and Treatment of Cerebrovascular Disease.   Springfield, Ill., Charles C Thomas, 1961.

FISHER, M.   Occlusion of the internal carotid artery.   *A. M. A. Arch. Neurol. & Psychiat.* 65:346, 1951.

GILLILAN, L. A.   General principles of the arterial blood vessel patterns to the brain.   *Tr. Am. Neurol. A.* 82:65, 1957.

KAPLAN, H. A., BROWDER, J., and RABINER, A. M.   The transcerebral venous system: An anatomical study.   *Am. Neurol. A.* 81:97, 1956.

KENDALL, D.   Thrombosis of intracranial veins.   *Brain* 71:386, 1948.

KETY, S. S.   Circulation and metabolism of the human brain in health and disease.   *Am. J. Med.* 8:205, 1950.

McHENRY, L. C.   Cerebral blood flow.   *New England J. Med.* 274:82, 1966.

MEYER, J. S., and DENNY-BROWN, D.   The cerebral collateral circulation.   *Neurology* 7:447, 1957.

MURPHY, J. P.   Cerebrovascular Disease.   Chicago, The Year Book Publishers, Inc., 1954.

OLIVECRONA, H., and RIIVES, J.   Arteriovenous aneurysms of the brain: Their diagnosis and treatment.   *Arch. Neurol. & Psychiat.* 59:567, 1948.

RAY, B. S., and DUNBAR, H. S.   Thrombosis of the dural venous sinuses as a cause of "pseudotumor cerebri."   *Ann. Surg.* 134:376, 1951.

RIGGS, H. E., and RUPP, C.   Variation in form of circle of Willis.   *Arch. Neurol.* 8:8, 1963.

ROGERS, L.   The function of the circulus arteriosus of Willis.   *Brain* 70:171, 1947.

SCHMIDT, C. F.   The Cerebral Circulation in Health and Disease.   Springfield, Ill., Charles C Thomas, 1950.

SHENKIN, H. A., HARMEL, M. H., and KETY, S. S.   Dynamic anatomy of the cerebral circulation.   *Arch. Neurol. & Psychiat.* 60:240, 1948.

SYMONDS, C.   Otitic hydrocephalus.   *Neurology* 6:681, 1956.

TOOMEY, J. A., and HOLT, H. B.   Thrombosis of the dural sinuses.   *Am. J. Dis. Child.* 77:285, 1949.

VANDER EECKEN, H. M., FISHER, M., and ADAMS, R. D.   The arterial anastomoses of the human brain and their importance in the delimitation of human brain infarction.   *J. Neuropath. & Exper. Neurol.* 11:91, 1952.

WOLF, B. S., NEWMAN, C. M., and SCHLESINGER, B.   The diagnostic value of the deep cerebral veins in cerebral angiography.   *Radiology* 64:161, 1955.

WRIGHT, I. S., and LUCKEY, E. H. (eds.)   Cerebral Vascular Diseases.   New York, Grune & Stratton, 1955.

CHAPTER 53

APHASIA, AGNOSIA, AND APRAXIA: EXAMINATION OF LANGUAGE AND RELATED FUNCTIONS

LANGUAGE IS DEFINED as audible, articulate human speech which is produced by the action of the tongue and adjacent vocal cords, and *speech* as utterance of vocal sounds which convey ideas, or the faculty of expressing thoughts by words (articulate sounds which symbolize and communicate ideas). Speech is more than a motor activity; it is the mechanism by which one gives external expression to internal symbolization, or thinking. Language and speech are considered to be attributes of the human race—qualities which have developed through an evolutionary process. Thoughts and ideas, however, are expressed not only in speech, by auditory symbols, but also in writing, by graphic symbols, and in gestures and pantomime, by motor symbols. Consequently language may be regarded as any means of expressing or communicating feeling or thought, usually by spoken words, but also by writing and gestures. Furthermore, such expression, to be accurate and comprehensible, requires not only the motor acts necessary for execution, but also the reception and interpretation of these acts when they are carried out by others, along with the retention, recall, and visualization of the symbols. Speech is as dependent upon the interpretation of the auditory and visual images which reach consciousness and the association of these images with the motor centers which control expression as upon the motor elements of such expression.

An extremely important part of cerebral, or cortical, function is concerned with the ability of the individual to express himself by speech, writing, and gestures; to comprehend spoken and written words and gestures; to recognize the significance of various sensory stimuli; and to carry out purposive or complex movements.

A detailed discussion of these subjects would of necessity be too comprehensive for a book of this size, and would merit a complete monograph. The importance of these functions in neurologic diagnosis, however, warrants a general review of them, together with an outline of the examination of language and related functions.

The word aphasia has been used as a general term to include all disturbances of language which are caused by lesions of the brain but are not the result of faulty innervation of the speech muscles, involvement of the organs of articulation themselves, or general mental or intellectual deficiency. It may include those varieties of agnosia, or failure to recognize the importance of sensory stimuli, and of apraxia, or loss of ability to carry out purposive acts, which have to do with language. Furthermore, because of close association of language with other forms of symbolic interpretation and expression, it is pertinent to discuss all varieties of agnosia and apraxia along with a consideration of aphasia.

Gall is accredited with one of the earliest descriptions of disturbances of language function. Lordat, in 1823, expressed the opinion that "alalia" was due to asynergy of the muscles used for speech. Bouillaud, in 1825, first noted that the ability to form words could be lost even though the words were retained in memory and the motor functions for carrying out speech were intact; he believed that the faculty of language was situated in the frontal lobes. Dax, in 1836, made the statement that word memory is a function of the left cerebral hemisphere. Broca, in 1861, noted loss of speech associated with a lesion of the inferior frontal convolution on the left; due to the fact that the loss of speech was not the result of paralysis of the speech organs, the defect was called aphemia. Trousseau, in 1862, first used the term aphasia. Wyllie, in 1866, and Bastian, in 1869, observed that patients with motor aphasia might have difficulty in the comprehension of spoken words, and Wernicke, in 1874, described sensory aphasia, or loss of comprehension of words, due to abolition of sound images (word deafness), in a lesion of the left superior temporal gyrus. Later he noted that a lesion somewhat posterior to the superior temporal gyrus, in the region of the angular gyrus, was followed by inability to comprehend written words (alexia, or word blindness).

The history of the development of the concepts of speech functions is a complex one. On the basis of the above observations Bastian, Broadbent, Wernicke, and others attempted to make an anatomic classification of the aphasias and to map out the various language centers and their connections. Aphasias were classified as motor, with lesions in the lower precentral region, and sensory, with lesions in the superior temporal, angular, or supramarginal gyri, and were subdivided into cortical, subcortical, and transcortical groups. In the former only specific centers were affected; in the subcortical groups, the deeper structures below the center; in the transcortical group, the association pathways between the various centers.

Other investigators, however, made functional, or physiologic, classifications. Hughlings Jackson stressed the complexity of language disorders, and pointed out the difference between propositional and emotional speech. Starr, in 1889, stated that he had failed to find any cases which substantiated Broca's viewpoint. Marie, in 1906, expressed the belief that every true aphasia involves defects in general intelligence as well as in special language functions and in comprehension of spoken words as well as in speech. He examined the brains of Broca's first two patients and stated that his observations did not afford support for the conclusions Broca had drawn from them; he concluded that the third frontal convolution plays no special role in speech. Since Marie's time the investigators of aphasia have fallen into two general groups: those who continue to stress an anatomic basis and those who use a psychologic approach. The latter believe that language must be considered as a coherent whole and that one must analyze not only the speech disturbance but also the psychologic changes that appear with cerebral lesions. Pick made noteworthy contributions in an attempt to search for the psychologic explanation for disturbed language and thinking. Goldstein investigated the mental state of the aphastic patient and the relation of language to thought. He considered speech part of a pattern, or gestalt. In aphasia there is inability to perceive the entire pattern; only parts of the whole are perceived and their correct relationship to each other is not recognized. There is distortion in the relationship between the immediate reaction, or figure, and the peripheral field of activity, or background. Head considered aphasia to be a disorder of symbolic formulation and expression, or a complexity of language disintegration. On the basis of his analysis of cases he described the following four varieties: *Verbal aphasia* consists of a difficulty in the formulation of words, with, as a result, a restricted vocabulary. *Syntactical aphasia* is characterized by loss of ability to arrange syllables or words in proper sequence (jargon aphasia). *Nominal aphasia* consists of defective use of words, or inability to name objects, colors, etc.; there is loss of memory for words. *Semantic aphasia* is characterized by the lack of recognition of the full symbolic significance of words and phrases.

It is not possible to separate definitely the anatomic and the physiologic substrata of aphasia. It may be, as Freud has stated, that the so-called speech centers are only cornerstones of a larger cortical area in the dominant hemisphere concerned with speech, or, as Symonds has postulated, that circuits are affected more than centers. Even Head has said, "The form assumed by an aphasia may differ with the site of the lesion. The deeper it extends from the surface into the substance of the brain, the more definite and permanent will be the disorders of speech." Later investigators, including Wilson and Weisenburg, and current ones, such as Bay, Brain, Critchley, and Russell, have correlated and combined the anatomic, physiologic, and psychologic features of language disorders, and have called attention to the interdependence of speech, language, thought, memory, gestures, and behavior.

For a rational understanding and a practical and comprehensive classification of aphasia and the related disorders, it seems that the definition and classification of Weisenburg are acceptable, broadening the scope of both somewhat in order to include the agnosias and apraxias in the classification. *Aphasia,* then, may be defined as a defect in (dysphasia) or loss of the power of expression by speech, writing, or gestures, or a defect or loss in the ability to comprehend spoken or written language or to interpret gestures. *Expressive aphasias* may be considered varieties of apraxia, which is defined as the loss of power to execute purposive movements or complex acts in the absence of paralysis of the motor apparatus for carrying out the acts; in most instances there is perfect comprehension of the meaning and ultimate intention of the acts. *Receptive varieties of aphasia* may be considered manifestations of *agnosia,* or loss of power to recognize the importance of sensory stimuli in the absence of sensory defects which would explain the difficulty in comprehension. Many of the apraxias and agnosias are evidences of disturbances of a lower functional level than the aphasias, but it is felt that one is justified in including all of them with the aphasias, inasmuch as even those which are disorders of the non-language field involve intelligent thought.

Before considering the examination of the aphasic patient, it is well to recall that there are three cortical levels as far as the reception of impulses is concerned. The first is the level of *"arrival,"* a function of the primary cortical reception areas; at this level one perceives, or sees and hears, without further differentiation of the impulses. The second level is that of *"knowing,"* or gnostic function, which is concerned with the recognition of impulses, formulation of engrams for recall of stimuli, and revisualization. The third level, the one of greatest importance in aphasia, is that which has to do with recognition of symbols in the form of words, or the higher elaboration and association of learned symbols as a function of *language.* There are also three levels of speech function, and in aphasic defects the most automatic of these is least frequently affected, and the least automatic is most often involved. The most automatic is the *emotional level,* and the patient may be able to respond to a painful stimulus with the word "ouch" or to give vent to an expletive under emotional strain, even though the other functions of speech are entirely absent. The next is the *propositional level,* or that concerned with casual, automatic speech; the patient may be able to answer questions with words such as "yes" and "no" even though the other elements of speech are impaired. The highest level is the *volitional,* or *intellectualized,* which is the first to be affected and the last to return; the patient is unable to repeat words said by the examiner or to make statements which require thought and concentration. It is of interest that in return of speech during recovery from aphasia, those languages which were learned earliest in life or learned most thoroughly are the first to come into use.

THE EXAMINATION OF THE PATIENT WITH APHASIA, AGNOSIA, AND APRAXIA

The testing of language and related functions in the patient who shows evidence of aphasia, agnosia, or apraxia should be carried out after the rest of the neurologic examination has been completed. Careful appraisal, however, during the taking of the history as well as throughout the routine examination may give valuable information regarding both expressive and receptive defects.

The history is extremely important in the evaluation of the aphasic patient. It should include not only detailed information about the patient's present and past illnesses (Chapter 2), but also data relative to his cultural background, education, and training. The examiner should determine the patient's native tongue, the order in which he has learned other languages, and his fluency in all languages he has known. He should inquire about school attainment, grade reached, and age at completion of formal education. Other important elements in the history include some knowledge of the patient's linguistic and reading habits, speech defects and handicaps, mathematical ability, and occupational pursuits. It is important to know not only the patient's dominance of hand, eye, and foot in writing and other acts, but also whether this dominance (especially handedness) is native to him or the result of training. A family history of either left-handedness or ambidexterity as well as of speech handicaps may give relevant information.

Before attempting to evaluate disturbances in language function, the examiner must appraise the patient's vocabulary, intellectual capacity, emotional equilibrium, sensorium, orientation, attention, memory, retention, and recall (Chapter 4). It is needless to state that it is not possible to evaluate disturbances of language function in patients who are confused, semistuporous, or markedly agitated or depressed. Furthermore, fright and other emotional states as well as the conversion mechanisms of hysteria may produce defects in both expression and reception which may simulate those seen in organic disease. The general neurologic findings, including especially sensory changes, motor difficulties, visual and auditory defects, and disturbances in the function of the bulbar muscles, may contribute essential information.

It is not possible, in testing aphasia, agnosia, and apraxia, to separate completely receptive and expressive factors; it is necessary for the patient to comprehend visual and auditory impulses if he is to understand commands, but responses to such commands are performed by expressive faculties. All tests should be carried out in a quiet environment with minimal distractions; fatigue and irritation should be avoided as far as possible. If fatigue becomes apparent, or if the findings are equivocal, it may be necessary to repeat the examination on other occasions. The examiner should attempt to evaluate the various components individually, and then record the results. At the completion of the examination he can synthesize the findings and appraise the patient's performance as a whole. The outline which follows contains the essential points to be noted in the examination.

1. SPEECH

In testing speech or the formulation and expression of ideas and feelings by means of spoken words, phrases, or more complex statements, we take note of spontaneous, automatic, emotional, propositional, and volitional varieties, as well as abstract speech.

a. *Spontaneous Speech:*   The patient's use of words in giving his history and relating his symptoms should be closely observed. An appraisal of his spontaneous and unrehearsed narration may be one of the most important parts of the speech investigation, and it is often valuable to make verbatim recordings. The examiner should note pronunciation, enunciation, formation not only of words but also of sentences, fluency, cadence, rhythm, prosody, elision of syllables or words, omission or transposition of words, misuse of words, circumlocutions, repetition, perseveration, paraphasic defects, and suggestions of jargon aphasia. He should observe the patient's ability to talk, form simple words, and utter less familiar words and those of several syllables. He should also note the extent of the patient's vocabulary as well as his ability to formulate grammatical sentences and to express himself and his ideas accurately in speech. Any slight deviation from the normal should be appraised. Among the abnormalities in spontaneous speech, the following give clues suggestive of a defect and have diagnostic significance: slight errors in word formation with omission or substitution of letters, such as the use of "inconscious" for "unconscious," or "thumbness" for "numbness"; misplacement not only of letters, but also of syllables and words; the use of unusual synonyms or circumlocutions in order to avoid the use of a word that the patient is unable to recall; discrepancies in the implication of words; omissions of words; hesitations and inappropriate pauses; perseveration; verbal stereotypy; neologisms; agrammatism; jargon or gibberish; the use of pantomime or gesture to compensate for defects in oral expression. In severe aphasia the patient may be unable to utter a single word; in other cases there may be recurring utterance of syllables, a specific word, "yes" or "no" or both, a phrase, or a fragment of meaningless jargon.

b. *Automatic Speech:*   Series of words which were well learned in early life may be retained even when spontaneous speech is lost; these may be considered a part of automatic speech. The patient is asked to repeat the alphabet, count, list the days of the week or months of the year, spell simple words, and repeat the Lord's prayer and simple poems and nursery rhymes.

c. *Emotional Speech:*   Emotional speech is important, and the patient may be unable to speak consecutively while he retains the ability to express himself by the use of expletives, swearing, or other emotional ejaculations.

d. *Propositional Speech:*   The relevancy of responses to questions gives information about propositional speech. If there is a profound aphasia, the examiner may ask questions whose answers require but single words, especially in either the affirmative or the negative.

e. *Volitional Speech:*   Volitional, or intellectualized, speech, is apparent in the patient's spontaneous utterances, but some of these may be reflex or semi-automatic. Volitional speech is further tested by having the patient speak from dictation and repeat simple sounds, words, short phrases, and sentences spoken by the examiner. These should contain all of the English sounds and include digit and letter sequences, nonsense syllables, disconnected words, short phrases and sentences, and short stories.

f. *Functional and Abstract Speech:*   Functional speech is tested by having the patient spell complex words and define simple words and objects. Abstract language is evaluated by noting the patient's ability to define or interpret proverbs.

g. *Singing:*   Musical speech or singing should be tested, and the patient may retain his ability to sing, even though he is unable to talk. Retention of a melody may aid in the recall of words that the patient associates with it.

h. *Recall of Words and Naming of Objects:*   The patient should be asked to recall words and use them as names. He may first be asked to name colors and simple objects such as a key, pencil, coin, book, watch, or parts of the body. He may then be asked to name more complex and less common objects, such as the intricate parts of a watch or the individual structures in the eye. Finally he may be asked to name and describe what he sees in pictures. If the patient is unable to recall words or names, he may be asked to select the correct name out of a group of words suggested to him (reinforcing expression by either auditory or visual symbols), or to tell the number of letters or syllables in the word he wishes to speak (Lichtheim test).

2. WRITING

Writing as well as speech should be considered in the evaluation of the patient's ability to formulate ideas and express himself.

a. *Spontaneous Writing:* Spontaneous writing may be tested by having the patient write, in both print and script, whatever comes into his mind; this may include his name and address or short sentences. A letter recently written by the patient, if one is available, may give pertinent information about his ability to express himself and his thoughts in writing. One should note, as in the evaluation of spontaneous speech, slight errors such as the omission or substitution of letters, misspelling, or elision of syllables or words. The presence of mirror writing may also give diagnostic information.

b. *Automatic or Semi-automatic Writing:* The patient is asked specifically to write his name and address, spell simple words, and write the days of the week or the months of the year.

c. *Propositional Writing:* The examiner requests the patient to reply in writing to various questions.

d. *Volitional Writing:* Volitional writing is tested in a variety of ways. The patient may be asked to write, in both print and script, letters, words, and sentences that are dictated to him. This involves not only volitional writing, but also the ability of the patient to translate auditory into visual symbols, and is reliable only when comprehension of speech is not seriously defective. The patient may be asked to copy, in both print and script, printed and written material. This tests not only volitional writing, but, in addition, the ability to comprehend visual symbols and to translate one visual symbol into another, and is reliable only when visual receptive functions are intact.

e. *Recall of Words and Naming of Objects:* As is done with speech, the patient is asked to recall words and to name objects by having him write down names and colors of simple and complex objects.

3. COMPREHENSION OF SPOKEN LANGUAGE

The patient's responses to verbal requests and commands and everyday questions and comments give information about his ability to understand articulate speech, or spoken language, but for an adequate evaluation specific tests may be arranged in the order of increasing complexity. It should be noted whether the patient has more difficulty with polysyllabic words and long sentences than with simple words and short sentences, and whether he recognizes concepts as well as words. He is first asked to point to objects which have been named for him. He is then given simple commands in the form of short sentences, such as "Place your finger on your nose," "Close your eyes," "Show your teeth," "Turn out the light," and "Open the door." The commands are then made somewhat more complex, such as "Place your right hand on top of your head," "Put your left index finger on your right ear," "Turn to page 87 in the book." Compound sentences and double or complex commands may finally be employed, as "Put out your hands and close your eyes," "Place one hand on your head, turn around, and sit down," "Take that coin from the table and give it to me," or "Place one coin on the table, give me the second, and keep the third in your hand." In the Marie paper test the patient is told, "Here is a piece of paper; tear it in four parts and place one on the table, give one to me, and keep two for yourself." In the token test he is given a group of tokens of different shapes and colors and is asked to pick out individual ones and rearrange them in patterns of increasing complexity. Auditory comprehension can be further tested by making definite statements which are either true or false, and asking the patient to indicate the answer by saying "Yes" or "No" or by making the appropriate gesture. Both comprehension and retention are evaluated by telling a short story and then asking questions about it that can be answered similarly. It is important, also, to observe whether the patient comprehends what he himself says.

4. COMPREHENSION OF WRITTEN LANGUAGE

The patient's ability to understand written language is evaluated by having him demonstrate his skill in *reading*. Again the tests are arranged in order of increasing difficulty, commencing with numbers and letters, then passing to words, both short and complex, and proceeding to phrases and simple and complicated sentences. His ability to read both printed material and script should be noted. The patient may first be given cards bearing the names of simple objects, such as a key or a pencil, which are placed on a table before him; he should point to the objects when he reads their names. The examiner should also call out the names of the objects, and the patient should point to the card bearing the appropriate name. He may then be given simple written commands, and finally more complex commands, such as "Place your hand on your head," then "Place your right index finger on your left eye," inscribed in block letters or easily legible script. Later he is asked to read, both aloud and silently, simple printed material and then sentences of increasing complexity, and to explain the meaning of what he has read. One notes the ability to recognize and comprehend the meaning of letters and syllables and the significance of simple sentences that are either true or false, and then more complex written material. If he is unable to express himself sufficiently to explain what he has read, he may be interrogated about it with questions that can be answered with "Yes," "No," or gestures. When the patient reads aloud and then explains what he has read, oral expression is tested as well as reading; the patient may be able to understand what he has read silently, even though he cannot read aloud or translate the visual symbols into oral ones. It is also important to observe whether the patient is able to read what he himself has written.

5. EXPRESSION BY GESTURES AND THE COMPREHENSION OF GESTURES AND SYMBOLS

In patients who are unable to express themselves by either speech or writing, it is important to note their ability to express themselves by gestures, and, likewise, in those unable to comprehend spoken or written language, one may test compre-hension of the meaning of pantomime, gestures, and symbols. A patient who is unable to make his desires known in other ways may indicate his responses and his desires by shaking or nodding his head, shrugging his shoulders, or showing visible emotional reactions; even though unable to comprehend spoken or written words, he may recognize threatening gestures. A patient who is unable to understand either oral or written commands may imitate the actions of the examiner in placing his finger to his nose or putting out his tongue. Expression and comprehension of symbols may be examined specifically by having the patient write mathematical figures and musical symbols and state the significance of each as well as of certain signs, such as the Red Cross or the caduceus, and letters and abbreviations, such as Y.M.C.A. He may also be asked to interpret the meaning and significance of pic-tures.

6. DRAWING

The patient's ability to express himself in drawing is tested by having him draw first simple objects such as a square, circle, triangle, or Greek cross, and then more complex pictures such as a man, house, daisy, or map. He should also be asked to trace, copy, reproduce figures immediately after presentation, and draw from a model.

7. CALCULATION

The patient's arithmetical ability is examined first by having him do simple computations involving addition, subtraction, multiplication, and division, and then by having him solve simple and more complex problems, both orally and on paper.

8. GNOSTIC FUNCTIONS

The recognition of sensory stimuli other than those which are specifically involved in language functions should also be noted. In vision this includes the appre-ciation of such concepts as color, form, and direction, as well as perception of space, identification of geometric figures and pictures, recognition of fingers and parts of the body, comprehension of laterality, and identification of both inanimate and animate objects. It is important to determine whether the patient recognizes objects even if he is unable to name them; he may recall the name on hearing it said even though he cannot state it spontaneously. He should be asked not only to name colors (an expressive function), but also to match them (a gnostic process). In Poppelreuter's visual searching test objects are placed to each side of the fixation point and the patient is asked to indicate their presence when they are named. With extinction, inattention, or disregard for one field of vision, the patient will fail to see the objects on that side. In the auditory field one notes the patient's ability to recog-nize inarticulate sounds, tone, and music; he should be asked to identify such sounds as the ringing of a bell, clinking of coins, jingling of keys, and crumpling of paper, and to recognize simple musical melodies. In the tactile field one notes his recogni-tion of objects by feeling of them, comprehension of block letters and figures, and identification of parts of the body from tactile stimulation. The routine tests for cortical sensory functions are described in "The Sensory System," Part II. In testing for the syndrome of finger agnosia the patient should be asked to point to individual fingers and parts of his body when his eyes are both opened and closed and to name and select fingers and parts of the body, both his own and the examiner's, when looking at them, when the examiner points to them, and when they are touched (with eyes both opened and closed). He should also be asked to indicate laterality, both on his own and the examiner's body; testing of agraphia and acalculia are mentioned elsewhere. Examination for comprehension of symbols is discussed above.

9. PERFORMANCE OF PURPOSIVE ACTS

Eupractic functions and disturbances of such functions may be tested by having the patient carry out various purposive acts. Muscular weakness and incoordination must, of course, be differentiated from loss of ability to formulate motor plans and carry out skilled movements, and spontaneous and more or less reflex or automatic acts must be distinguished from volitional ones. It is important to determine whether the patient recognizes the nature and understands the use of common objects, and whether he is able to use them in a normal manner. The execution of spontaneous, requested, and imitative (mimicking the examiner) movements is observed, and the ability to carry out movements with each hand individually and both hands together is noted. The patient may first be asked to stand, walk, sit down, protrude his tongue, and carry out simple acts with his hands and feet, such as making a fist, separating his fingers, and stamping his foot; then to perform movements directed to parts of his own body, such as placing one hand on top of the head, touching his nose with his finger, and placing one heel on the opposite knee. It is noted whether there is either weakness or ataxia, and whether the movements are performed skillfully, or in a crude manner; dexterity for fine movements is important. He is then asked to carry out various symbolic actions which involve pantomime and gesture, such as throwing a kiss, waving good-bye, shaking hands, greeting a friend, beckoning, threatening, giving a military salute, and pretending to play the piano. Finally he is told to demonstrate the use of simple objects, such as a key, comb, fountain pen, scissors, hammer, screwdriver, and toothbrush, both by pantomime and with the utilization of the objects. He may be asked to wind a watch, dress himself, button his clothes, strike a match and light a cigarette, stamp a letter, tie a knot, drink a glass of water, or even to play a musical instrument. In testing for constructional apraxia the patient is asked to draw figures and pictures and to copy designs made by the examiner, to form geometric figures with matches and toothpicks and more complex three-dimensional structures with blocks, and again to copy designs made by the examiner.

10. SIMULTANEOUS TESTING OF GNOSTIC AND EUPRACTIC FUNCTIONS

In many of the tests mentioned above both receptive and expressive elements and gnostic and eupractic functions are evaluated simultaneously. These combined functions may be tested in other ways. One may determine whether the patient is able not only to recognize objects, but also to name them, tell their use, and then use them, and whether he is able to understand what he has said and written. If a patient is asked to set a clock both on command and by duplication of the setting of another clock, auditory and visual receptive functions as well as the ability to carry out purposive acts are evaluated, and if he is asked to tell the time and to write it down, expression by both speech and writing are tested. The use of simple games and puzzles, including checkers, chess, and cards, may give information. The patient may be able to play some games more or less automatically, yet be unable to explain what he is doing or to follow commands. Chesher has outlined a simple and brief routine that may be used in the examination of an aphasic wherein both expressive and receptive functions are tested together. The patient is given a few simple objects, such as a key, pencil, penny, match box, pair of scissors, and comb. He is then asked the following: (1) Name the objects. (2) Repeat single words (say names after the examiner). (3) Comprehend spoken words (point to the objects as their names are called). (4) Read printed words giving the names of the objects. (5) Comprehend printed words (point to object on reading its name). (6) Write the names of the objects. (7) Write the names from dictation. (8) Copy the names. (9) Spell the names aloud. To this may be added tests for gnostic and eupractic functions by asking the patient to identify the objects by feeling them and by having him demonstrate their use. Another simultaneous test for both auditory and visual comprehension and motor execution may be carried out by giving the patient four coins of different denominations and having him stand in front of four numbered bowls. He is then asked to place the coins in the respective bowls on both oral and written commands.

11. REVISUALIZATION

The patient's ability to revisualize may be appraised by asking him to tell the color of various objects with which he is familiar, and to describe the physical characteristics of friends and both describe and draw the plan of his home. Recall of auditory stimuli is tested by asking the patient to tell poems or sing songs, and recall of both auditory and visual stimuli, by having him spell aloud words given by the examiner.

12. ADDITIONAL METHODS OF TESTING

Intelligence tests, both of the language and nonlanguage varieties, vocabulary tests, word association tests, performance tests, sentence completion tests, form boards, imitation and sorting tests, digit-symbol substitution tests, drawing and picture completion and reconstruction exercises, and other special methods of examination, including the Bender visual-motor gestalt test, the Kohs block design exercises, and examination with the use of the tachistoscope have paramount value in the final evaluation of the aphasic patient. Many of these tests are mentioned in Chapter 4. Technics using test boards, cards, and specialized equipment, such as the Halstead-Wepman aphasia screening test and Reitan's modification of it, the Wepman-Jones test, Eisenson's test, the Minnesota test for the differential diagnosis of aphasia, and Schuell's short examination for aphasia are used by many clinicians and speech pathologists.

CLASSIFICATION OF THE APHASIAS, AGNOSIAS, AND APRAXIAS, AND THEIR VALUE IN CEREBRAL LOCALIZATION

The diagnosis and classification of the aphasias and related disorders is a complex problem. They may occur in varying degrees and incomplete stages, and they are frequently mixed in type. Furthermore, owing to the complexity of the language process and the extent to which it has permeated all thinking functions, there is often an extensive and complicated alteration of both speech and comprehension. Consequently, there have been many attempts at classification, from both anatomic and physiologic points of view. The strictly anatomic classification does not apply in all instances, for a small lesion may be followed by conspicuous impairment of both expression and comprehension, whereas an extensive lesion sometimes causes but an isolated defect. On the other hand, a classification that stresses only function may also be unsatisfactory, for every motor act has a sensory element, and sensory functions can be revealed only by motor expression. It is believed, however, that the classification of Weisenburg, although it is essentially a functional one, is the most practicable, especially if the examiner correlates function with anatomic knowledge. In this classification the aphasias are designated as *predominantly expressive, predominantly receptive, expressive-receptive,* and *amnesic varieties.* Expressive aphasia is in reality an apraxia of the muscles of speech or writing, and all motor apraxias may be considered defects in self-expression. The receptive aphasias, on the other hand, are actually visual and auditory agnosias, and all agnosias involve failure to interpret stimuli and are disabilities in the receptive fields. Most disorders of speech are complex and involve both reception and expression, although one may be affected more than the other.

In spite of the statements of Head and others that language must be considered a coherent whole, a function of the entire brain, clinical studies and surgical and autopsy confirmations have shown that the aphasias and related defects have localizing significance. Furthermore, even though one uses a functional classification, he can usually correlate the disturbance of physiology with anatomic localization. In a large majority of cases the lesions that causes an aphasia, and some of the agnosias and apraxias as well, is located in the dominant hemisphere. This is especially true of right-handed persons, in 95 per cent or more of whom the lesion causing an aphasia is in the left hemisphere. Cerebral dominance for language is not so definite in left-handed individuals, who make up from 5 to 10 per cent of the population. Some of these may have bilateral speech representation, but it is usually unilateral and most often on the left. In slightly more than 50 per cent of sinistrals the lesion that causes an aphasia is in the left hemisphere; the speech defect that follows a lesion of the right hemisphere is often less severe and more transient. Apparent inconsistencies between handedness and the side of the lesion responsible for an aphasia may be the result of many factors. Handedness is usually inherited, but many native sinistrals have been trained to use only the right hand; left-handedness occasionally is the result of disease of the motor areas of the left hemisphere in early life; injuries and amputations in childhood may bring about change in handedness and possibly also in dominance for speech; many ambidextrous persons are shifted sinistrals. The presence of an aphasia may not only lateralize a lesion, but also further localize it. Aphasias of the expressive type are in most instances the result of a lesion anterior to the rolandic fissure, and those of the receptive variety are usually caused by disturbances posterior to this fissure, in the temporal and parietal regions (Fig. 308).

EXPRESSIVE APHASIA

Weisenburg found, in a study of 60 aphasic patients, that 43.3 per cent showed a disability of language function that was characterized predominantly by a defect or loss in the power of expression by speech, writing, or gestures. This may vary from complete inability to utter a single word to loss of ability to express thoughts or feelings adequately. These are all, in reality, varieties of apraxia.

Oral expressive aphasia, or "aphemia," corresponds to the motor aphasia of Broca, or, to a lesser extent, to the verbal aphasia of Head. In the absence of any loss of function of the organs of articulation, the patient is unable to form words and to combine or integrate the movements of the organs of articulation which are necessary for speech. He knows what he wishes to say, but is unable to say it; he is unable to talk, repeat, or read aloud. He is able to hear and understand spoken language, and to read and comprehend written language, but is unable to repeat what he hears or reads. He can identify objects, but cannot name them. The patient may be able to write and draw, although in most circumstances the lesion which causes the aphasia also causes paralysis of the right hand. There may be loss of expression by recently acquired languages, but preservation of languages

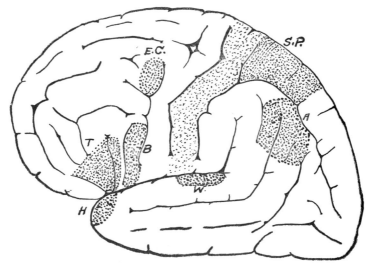

FIG. 308. Centers important in language. *A,* angular gyrus; *B,* Broca's convolution; *E.C.,* Exner's writing center; *H,* Henschen's music center; *S.P.,* superior parietal lobule, which with the lightly stippled postcentral gyrus is important in tactile recognition; *T,* pars triangularis (of importance in singing); *W.* Wernicke's area. (Nielsen, J. M.: Agnosia, Apraxia, Aphasia, ed. 2. New York, Paul B. Hoeber, Inc., 1946).

learned early in life, and there may be loss of volitional and propositional speech, but preservation of automatic and emotional speech. In mild cases (dysphasia) there may be only slight errors in word formation, occasional circumlocutions, or reduction of vocabulary. In others perseveration, palilalia, or the recurring utterance of syllables, words, or phrases may be evident. Dysarthria is sometimes present in aphasic patients, and may be the result of apraxia of the tongue and facial muscles.

It is important to differentiate between expressive aphasia (aphemia, or loss of speech) and the various disorders of articulation. *Dysarthria* is the imperfect utterance of sounds or words; symbolic formulation of words is normal and phonation is preserved, but disease of the nerves to the organs of articulation or of the central regulation of the nerves interferes with clear enunciation. *Anarthria* is the total loss of ability to articulate; it is caused by more extensive dysfunction of the nerves or their regulatory centers. *Dysphonia* and *aphonia* are disorders of function of the larynx in which phonation is lost even though articulation may be preserved; the dysfunction may be caused by either disease of the larynx or hysteria. *Dyslalia* is a disturbance of utterance in which there is no organic neurologic defect, but there is damage to the articulatory apparatus on a structural basis.

Although it has often been stated that oral expressive aphasia is usually caused by a lesion in the lower motor region of the dominant hemisphere, principally that about the base of the precentral sulcus in the posterior part of the inferior frontal convolution (Broca's area) and the adjoining gyri (areas 44, 45, 46, and 47 of Brodmann), such accurate localization is seldom possible. Conrad has shown that lesions in many widespread areas, mainly just in front of or along the rolandic fissure, may cause motor aphasia (Fig. 309). Penfield and Roberts state that Broca's area, or the frontal cortex in its immediate vicinity, is important in speech and it should be carefully avoided during surgery, but they feel that most persisting aphasias follow extensive lesions of the left hemisphere, including, in most cases, the posterior temporoparietal region. They have produced transient dysphasias with limited excisions of many areas in the dominant hemisphere. It may be that the aphasia which follows a lesion of a specific cortical area may not be the result of specific loss of function of this region, but rather a disturbance of the connections between this region and other portions of the brain, especially those having to do with the recognition and interpretation of spoken and written words.

Loss of expression by writing is sometimes referred to as *agraphia;* it is characterized by inability to formulate words in either script or printing in the absence of paralysis of the arm or hand. It usually accompanies oral expressive aphasia, and may indicate the presence of a somewhat larger lesion which involves also the hand area ("Exner's writing center" in the middle frontal convolution, Fig. 308). There may, however, be loss of ability to write, even though speech is retained. The defect is essentially an apraxia of the right hand. In place of agraphia there may be contraction of words, elision of letters or syllables, errors in transposition of words, or mirror writing. In dissociated dysgraphia there may be difficulty in writing spontaneously or to dictation, but retention of the ability to copy written or printed material. Agraphia may also follow a posterior lesion and may be a part of the Gerstmann syndrome.

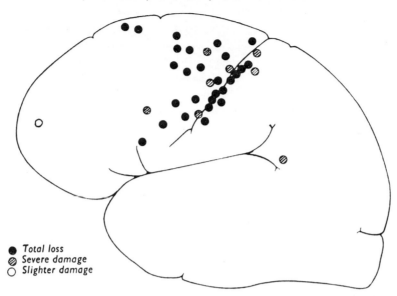

● Total loss
◍ Severe damage
○ Slighter damage

FIG. 309. Sites of lesions causing expressive aphasia, showing degree of speech disturbance at onset. (Conrad, K.: *Brain,* 77:491, 1954.)

Loss of expression by gestures may be an important part of an aphasic defect. Speech and writing are both means of self-expression by use of symbols, one by spoken words, the other by written ones. There are, however, additional types of expression that involve different symbols, such as gestures, mimicry, and pantomime. In a severe, or global, aphasia the patient may be unable to nod his head to signify "yes" or to shake his head to indicate "no." He may have lost the ability to use his hands in talking, shrug his shoulders, and express himself by other gestures and movements. The term *asymbolia* is sometimes used for the loss of ability of expression by symbols, and *amimia* for a defect in expression by gestures and mimicry. Kennedy and Wolf have described the case of an artist who lost her skill in drawing following a depressed fracture of the left frontoparietal area, in the absence of difficulty with speech, reading, or writing.

Motor, or *kinetic, apraxia* is the loss of ability to carry out purposeful acts in the absence of paralysis. Most of the expressive aphasias which have been mentioned above are actually varieties of motor apraxia, and in reality all motor acts are means by which the individual expresses himself, although eupraxia is not a function of language. The apraxias are discussed separately.

RECEPTIVE APHASIA

The predominantly receptive aphasias are characterized by a defect or loss of ability to comprehend spoken or written language or to interpret gestures. They are varieties of agnosia. Weisenburg found that 28.3 per cent of his aphasic patients had a defect which was predominantly receptive in type.

Visual receptive aphasia is also known as visual sensory aphasia and visual agnosia. In its pure form it is characterized by loss of ability to comprehend the meaning or significance of printed or written words in the absence of actual loss of vision; this is known as *alexia,* or word blindness. Actually, however, there are many varieties of disturbances of visual reception in addition to true word blindness.

Area 17 of Brodmann, or the striate cortex, is the site of the primary reception, or *arrival,* of the visual impulses. A lesion here causes loss of perception, or blindness, which is restricted in extent to the visual field affected. Area 18 is concerned with *gnostic functions,* or the recognition of the stimulus. A lesion here causes a *visual agnosia for objects;* the patient sees the objects but cannot identify them and reacts to them as a blind person would; he may retain the ability to distinguish them in other ways, as by touch. This syndrome is designated psychic blindness, or mind blindness. There may be either loss of recognition of the object with retention of color vision, or loss of color perception (*color agnosia,* or achromatopsia); there is also impairment of interpretation of form and shape. Occasionally there is visual agnosia which is limited to nonidentification of the human face, and a type characterized by loss of ability to interpret pictures and gestures.

Area 19 is important in *revisualization, activation of engrams,* and *space perception.* Lesions in this region cause a visual agnosia which is characterized by loss of ability to revisualize, or to describe an object after it has been seen, although the object may be identified when the patient sees it; there is loss of memory for objects and persons. There is also loss of ability to localize and to perceive distance, space relationships, and motion (*visual spatial agnosia*); there may be disorganization of spatial judgment and visual disorientation in which the patient cannot find his way in familiar surroundings. Occasionally there is unilateral or bilateral neglect of external space. The patient may be able to perceive parts but not the whole of a pattern, and may have difficulty with constructional tasks, copying, and drawing. In the *Charcot-Wilbrand syndrome* there is visual agnosia together with loss of revisualization; the patient cannot draw from memory.

The region of the angular gyrus (area 39 of Brodmann) and the adjacent cortex in the dominant hemisphere have been said to be essential for the recognition and interpretation of symbols in the form of letters and words, and the association of learned symbols as a *function of language.* A lesion of this region, or of the connections between the striate cortex and it, causes *alexia,* or *visual receptive aphasia.* There is loss of power of recognition, interpretation, and recall of the visual symbols of language; written and printed words have no meaning, although the patient may talk without difficulty and understand what is said to him. There may be impairment of recognition of letters and syllables as well as of words. Occasionally the patient with alexia may be able to read by kinesthetic sense, and can recognize embossed letters by feeling them even though he cannot identify them when he sees them. In congenital or developmental dyslexia there may be a severe reading disability, often with difficulty in writing as well. This occurs most often in boys and it may be inherited.

Impulses from the striate cortex go to both angular gyri, but they go only to the dominant hemisphere for recognition of language symbols. Consequently a unilateral lesion of either area 18 or 19 causes agnosia of objects, color, form, space perception, or motion, or loss of revisualization in the opposite, sometimes hemianopic, visual field, whereas a lesion of the major angular gyrus causes alexia. In bilateral lesions there may be *anosognosia,* or denial of blindness, owing either to involvement of the striate cortex itself or interruption of fibers from it to other cortical areas.

Auditory receptive aphasia is also known as auditory sensory aphasia and auditory agnosia. In its pure form it is characterized by loss of ability to comprehend the significance of spoken words in the absence of deafness (word deafness).

The three cortical levels for the reception and interpretation of the auditory impulses are not as clearly defined as those for the reception and interpretation of visual impulses. Areas 41 and 42, located in the transverse temporal gyri (Heschl's convolutions) on the dorsal surface of the posterior portion of the superior temporal convolution are probably the centers for both primary reception and recognition of auditory impulses. Certain authorities, however, designate the medial geniculate bodies as the primary receptive areas, and Heschl's convolutions as the centers for recognition; others state that areas 41 and 42 are the receptive regions, and that the adjacent paratransverse portions of the superior temporal convolutions function in the recognition of sounds. Lesions of areas 41 and 42, or the regions immediately surrounding them, may cause a general auditory agnosia in which the patient loses his ability to recognize or interpret and his memory for ordinary sounds, such as the ringing of a bell. This is psychic deafness; there may be loss of "reauditorization" of sounds. Due to the fact that auditory impulses pass to both temporal lobes and there is little unilateral cerebral dominance for ordinary sounds, there is never any very marked disability, either deafness or complete auditory agnosia, with unilateral temporal lobe lesions.

Wernicke's area, which occupies a crescentic zone in the posterior third of the superior temporal convolution of the dominant hemisphere, just lateral to the transverse temporal gyri of Heschl, has been said to be the center for the recognition, interpretation, and recall of word symbols and their association as a function of language. A lesion of this side causes an *auditory receptive aphasia,* auditory verbal agnosia, or word deafness. There is loss of ability to comprehend the significance of or recall the meaning of spoken words, although the patient can still hear and can recognize voices, but not the words which they utter; he cannot repeat what he hears. He can read without difficulty, and may be able to speak normally, but the loss of ability to comprehend the significance of spoken words includes those spoken by the patient himself as well as by others, so that there is usually a syntactical defect, or inability to arrange words in proper sequence, accompanied by the employment of incorrect or unintelligible words, unconventional and gibberish sounds, and senseless combinations. The patient is not aware of his errors in speaking. The resulting misuse of words and defect of sequence is termed agrammatism, *paraphasia,* or *jargon aphasia.* He may be able to repeat what others have said even though he does not understand the meaning. Word deafness occasionally is congenital.

Receptive aphasia for gestures is usually a part of an extensive aphasic or agnostic defect. It may be referred to as either *asymbolia* or *amimia,* the inability to comprehend the meaning of acts, symbols, gestures, or pantomime.

Ideational, or *sensory, apraxia* is discussed with the apraxias.

EXPRESSIVE-RECEPTIVE APHASIA

Weisenburg stated that the major percentage of aphasic patients showed difficulty in language function affecting predominantly either expression or interpretation, and found what he termed mixed defects in only one fifth of the patients he examined. It is probable, however, that a much larger percentage show some evidence of difficulty in both fields, and it may be impossible to distinguish between the defects or to determine which process is affected most seriously. For this reason specific localization of the lesions which cause aphasia cannot always be made. Oral expressive aphasia occurs with a lesion of the frontal lobe, but on the other hand the paraphasia that occurs with a receptive defect in the temporal region may cause similar changes in speech. Agraphia is usually caused by frontal involvement, but it may also be associated with posterior lesions. Alexia is most frequently caused either by defects in the connections between the occipital cortex and the lower parietal regions or by involvement of the angular gyrus, but it may also occur with frontal lesions. Expressive-receptive aphasias may, like the other types, vary in degree of involvement, just as they may vary in the amount that the individual language functions are affected. The mixed defect in which there is complete or almost complete loss of both expression and perception of language is termed a *global* or *total aphasia,* or sometimes central aphasia.

Attempts have been made to correlate both mixed and global aphasias with isolated lesions of the brain, although under most circumstances defects in both the expressive and receptive fields are the result of either extensive cortical lesions or subcortical damage with interruption of the association pathways. Involvement in the region of the so-called quadrilateral space of Marie, which is situated between the cortex externally and the internal capsule medially and within the limits of the insula anteriorly and posteriorly, may cause interruption of the association fibers which course through the external capsule to connect Broca's area with the other language centers; there may be a mixed aphasia characterized by agraphia and paraphasia or by alexia and oral expressive aphasia. Mixed aphasia, often temporary, may also occur in lesions of the internal capsule as a result of interruption of the association bundles which pass just above and below the lentiform nucleus and connect the frontal, temporal, parietal, and occipital regions. Penfield and Roberts have stated that the posterior temporoparietal region is the most important area of the brain as far as speech is concerned.

Idiokinetic apraxia results from interruption of the impulses between the site of comprehension and that of execution of the act. Amimia and asymbolia may be either expressive (loss of ability to perform gestures or pantomime), or receptive (loss of comprehension of such acts).

AMNESIC APHASIA

Amnesic aphasia has been defined by Weisenburg as a difficulty in evoking the names for objects, conditions, or qualities, with serious limitations in speaking and writing. This type of aphasia corresponds to the nominal variety of Head, or *anomia.* The disability is said to be different from that of the typical expressive disorder; speech is correctly articulated, but is hesitant and fragmentary owing to difficulty in the recall of certain names and words. Comprehension of spoken and written language is relatively satisfactory, but nonlanguage performances are generally superior to language performances. The patient, however, has a fairly accurate understanding of a concept even when he cannot produce the name as a symbol for it, and he can almost always recognize the correct word and select it from a number suggested to him.

Amnesic aphasia is said to be relatively rare, and Weisenburg found it in only 8.3 per cent of his patients. Nielsen, however, considers it to be more important. He has postulated the presence of a language formulation center in the posterior temporal region between Wernicke's area and the angular gyrus (the upper parts of areas 22 and 37) where engrams are stored for both visual and auditory memory of words, and has expressed the belief that a lesion here, or interruption of the association pathways, causes amnesic aphasia. This latter variety of aphasia, however, is extremely difficult to differentiate from the oral expressive type, and it must be concluded that amnesic aphasia, if it does exist as an entity, is probably caused by a diffuse rather than a focal lesion. Semantic aphasia, in which there is a quantitative reduction in the capacity for comprehension of speech, with lack of recognition of the full significance of words and phrases, may be related to amnesic aphasia. It is rarely associated with focal lesions, and is found in toxic, senile, and fatigue states.

Aphasia may be the result of a wide variety of cerebral lesions. Those of vascular origin constitute the most common cause, followed by neoplasms and trauma. Congenital aphasia does occur, but is extremely rare. The prognosis for recovery is good with acquired aphasia that develops in childhood, although there may be some impairment of intellectual development due to involvement of the dominant hemisphere. The prognosis for recovery is usually also good with aphasia in ambidextrous persons as well as in left-handed individuals, regardless of whether the responsible lesion is in the left or the right hemisphere. The relationship between aphasia and intelligence is a controversial subject, inasmuch as psychometric testing is difficult if either the expressive or receptive aspects of language function are much impaired. In testing dysphasic or mildly aphasic individuals, however, and those with lesions of the left cerebral hemisphere without clinical evidence of speech impairment, there is often some evidence of difficulty with verbal tests and conceptual thinking, whereas in persons with lesions of the right hemisphere there is difficulty with the performance tests and especially with visuospatial functions.

AGNOSIA

Agnosias of all types are characterized by loss of ability to comprehend the meaning or to recognize the importance of various types of stimulation; these are actually receptive defects. Gnosis is the higher synthesis of sensory impulses, with resulting appreciation and perception of the stimuli. Auditory and visual agnosias in which there is loss of recognition of symbols which have to do with language are essentially aphasias, but other receptive defects in the nonlanguage field also have diagnostic importance.

There are varieties of agnosia in which the receptive defect involves cutaneous and postural stimuli. *Astereognosis,* or *tactile agnosia,* is the loss of power to perceive the shape and nature of an object and the inability to identify it by superficial contact alone, in the absence of any demonstrable sensory defect. Although the term tactile agnosia is used, there is a defect in the higher correlation of proprioceptive sensations as well. Astereognosis follows lesions of the parietal lobe, principally in the cortex of the posterior portions and the superior parietal lobule, although occasionally in the thalamic radiations. There is no cerebral dominance in the interpretation of cutaneous and proprioceptive stimuli, and the defect is always contralateral to the lesion. Some observers use the term astereognosis for minor defects in which the patitent is unable to recognize form, and tactile agnosia for more profound difficulties which are characterized by loss of ability to identify objects.

Anosognosia is defined as the ignorance of the existence of disease, and the term has been used specifically to imply the imperception of hemiplegia, or a feeling of depersonalization toward or loss of perception of paralyzed parts of the body. It may vary from a mere imperception of weakness, in which the patient may believe that he can move his paretic limbs in a normal manner, to a lack of concern for or even denial of existence of the hemiparesis. The defect usually follows a lesion of the inferior parietal region in the vicinity of the supramarginal gyrus in the hemisphere that is contralateral to the paralysis, and it almost invariably occurs with a lesion of the nondominant hemisphere, although there have been reports of similar disturbances with involvement of the dominant half of the brain. A lesion of the thalamic radiations may possibly cause the same syndrome. Associated with anosognosia there may be loss of awareness of one half of the body, a feeling of absence of the paralyzed extremities, or unilateral neglect (motor, sensory, and visual) of one side of the body. There may also be anosognosia for blindness and deafness. The term anosognosia has also been used to indicate denial of illness in general and of events in the patient's recent experience, often with associated disorientation and confabulation; this has usually been reported with diffuse cerebral disease (Weinstein and Kahn).

In *autotopagnosia,* or *somatotopagnosia,* there is loss of power to identify or orient the body or the relation of its individual parts—a defect in body scheme appreciation. The patient may have complete loss of personal identification of and amnesia for one limb or one half of the body. He may drop his hand from a table onto his lap and believe that some object has fallen, or he may feel an arm next to his body and be unaware that it is his own. He may be unable to point out the paretic extremities or to distinguish laterality. Lack of awareness of one half of the body has been referred to as *agnosia of the body half.* Autotopagnosia occurs with lesions of either the thalamoparietal pathways or the cortex bordering on the interparietal sulcus, especially near the angular gyrus. Like anosognosia, it usually occurs with lesions of the nondominant hemisphere, but has been reported also with involvement of the left parietal lobe. Denny-Brown and Banker have reported what they term amorphosynthesis, a disorder of recognition of the opposite side of the body and of spatial relationships, with a lesion of the left parietal lobe. Most disturbances with visuospatial relations, however, including visuospatial neglect, occur with right hemisphere lesions.

In the syndrome of *finger agnosia of Gerstmann* there is loss of ability to recognize, name, or select individual fingers, either when the patient is looking at them or when the examiner points to them. This may apply to both the patient's and the examiner's fingers. Associated with this are disorientation of right and left (confusion of laterality), agraphia, and acalculia. This has been said to result from a lesion of the angular gyrus, or of that portion of the parietal lobe between the angular gyrus and the occipital region, in the dominant hemisphere. Partial syndromes, however, and various combinations of its component parts, may occur with focal lesions of other areas in the dominant hemisphere or even with diffuse involvement.

Prosopagnosia, or *agnosia for faces,* is a perceptual defect of a specific nature and usually follows a lesion of the posterior portion of the minor hemisphere. There may be associated phenomena, including defects in the contralateral visual field, constructional apraxia, visuospatial defects, and disturbances of the body scheme. *Apractic agnosia,* usually associated with involvement of the parieto-occipital region of the nondominant hemisphere, is a combination of agnostic and apractic defects. In addition to body scheme disturbances of the anosognostic type, there are constructional disabilities, apraxia for dressing, and difficulties with spatial orientation. Those agnosias which are largely visual are discussed under visual receptive aphasia and in Chapter 10.

APRAXIA

Apraxia is a defect in the ability to carry out purposive, useful, or skilled acts, especially if complicated; there is loss of capacity to use objects correctly. Apraxia may be defined as the inability to move a certain part of the body in accordance with a proposed purpose, the motility of the part being otherwise preserved. Sometimes the term mind blindness is used as a synonym. Purposive acts are built up by the synthesis of simple individual movements. The performance of complex and skilled motor activity requires intact motor strength and power, normal coordination, and adequate tonus and sensation. In addition, however, the psychic elaboration of an ideational plan must be present before any skilled act can be carried out. The perfect performance of motor activity is known as eupraxia, and loss of such performance is apraxia, which, of course, cannot be diagnosed if there is paresis or paralysis, ataxia, rigidity, akinesia, hyperkinesia, or sensory loss. One must also exclude, in the diagnosis of apraxia, difficulties due to loss of comprehension, dementia, and auditory and visual defects. Oral expressive asphasia and other varieties of expressive aphasia are in reality apractic defects.

Kinetic, or *motor, apraxia* is the simplest of the apraxias. It usually affects only one limb, principally an upper extremity, although it may be more extensive and include the throat and head region, and it may be bilateral. There is no motor weakness and the extremity can be used for unconscious and associated movements, but not for deliberate, purposeful acts. The patient may be able to carry out activities in which he uses the limb as a whole, but he cannot execute fine motor acts with the individual fingers. He cannot perform movements which he has learned, acquired, and brought to perfection. There is a loss of dexterity which resembles ataxia, and all skilled movements, even those of a simple pattern, are carried out in crude, garbled, unsteady manner; learned acts are performed clumsily, as though for the first time. The difficulty is equally pronounced whether the act is spontaneous, requested, or imitative. The patient is unable to utilize objects whose use he understands, even though he can see and recognize the objects, name them, and tell their use.

Kinetic apraxia may be interpreted as an expressive defect. It is in most instances caused by a lesion of the cell groups in the precentral or premotor cortex (areas 4 or 6) which are essential for executing the movement, or of their descending neuraxes. The apraxia is usually contralateral to the lesion. If the lesion is on the right, the apraxia is on the left; if the lesion is on the left, the apraxia may be on the right, or in cases of outstanding cerebral dominance, it may be bilateral. There may be apraxia of the left upper extremity in right-handed persons in association with a cortical lesion which causes paralysis of the right upper extremity, although in many instances damage to both hemispheres is necessary for bilateral apraxia. Kinetic apraxia has also been reported with lesions of the anterior portion of the corpus callosum (Chapter 51). It occurs on the left in right-handed persons with pronounced dominance of the left hemisphere, and is said to result from interruption of the commissural fibers which convey the dominating influence to the right side of the brain. Section of the corpus callosum has been carried out in humans, however, without causing apraxia. This absence of apraxia has been explained on the basis of either representation of eupractic functions in both hemispheres or ability to utilize other subcortical pathways. Apraxia of gait (Chapter 32) is probably a kinetic apraxia. There is loss of ability to use the lower limbs properly in walking, although there is no demonstrable motor weakness or sensory impairment. In addition there often are perseveration, hypokinesia, rigidity, and gegenhalten. This occurs with extensive cerebral lesions, usually of the frontal lobes.

Idiokinetic, or *ideomotor* or *"classic,"* *apraxia* is caused by an interruption of the pathways between the center for formulation of an act and that for execution of the act; there is a break in the continuity of the association fibers between the site where the ideational plan is elaborated and the center which governs the motor mechanism. The idea is correctly formulated, but the plan fails to reach motor expression. The patient can carry out simple movements and spontaneous and automatic acts, but he cannot execute either complex voluntary or imitative movements if they require a sequence of muscular activities, or if he has to plan the act before performing it. The patient may be able to perform the constituent parts of an act, but he is unable to synthesize the correct combination of single muscular responses necessary for the execution of a complex movement. He may know what he wishes to do and be able to describe the act, but he is unable to execute the act when he wants to or on command. The patient may wind his watch, button his clothes, or comb his hair normally when such acts are carried out automatically, yet he is unable to do these things on request. When asked to throw a kiss he may place the back of his hand to his mouth and may perform sucking rather than kissing movements with his lips. He may be unable to handle objects such as a hammer or screwdriver, although he can explain their use. The movements in idiokinetic apraxia, like those of kinetic apraxia, may be crude and incoordinated and resemble the motor responses in ataxia and athetosis. The predominance of an apractic element in certain cases of oral expressive aphasia may be demonstrated by noting the patient's inability to protrude his tongue or wet his lips on command. although he can carry out these acts unconsciously and can use these portions of the speech apparatus normally for other purposes and in forming those words that he is able to utter. Loss of ability to sing or to play musical instruments may constitute a musical apraxia.

Idiokinetic apraxia is often bilateral and affects the extremities of both sides equally. It has been ascribed to lesions of the supramarginal gyrus, the motor and premotor areas, and the body of the corpus callosum. The first-named site is probably the most important, and frontal lesions are believed to produce predominantly kinetic varieties. A cortical or subcortical lesion of the right supramarginal gyrus (area 40) may cause idiokinetic apraxia limited to the left side, but a cortical or subcortical lesion of the left supramarginal gyrus produces bilateral apraxia. A lesion of the corpus callosum may cause apraxia on the left in right-handed individuals, owing to interruption of the commissural pathways.

Ideational, or *sensory, apraxia* is characterized by loss of ability to formulate the ideational plan which is necessary for executing the several components of a complex act. It is true mind blindness. Kinesthetic memory and the appreciation of the nature of the act are defective, and as a result the motor mechanism which is essential for its execution cannot be produced. The general conception of the act is incorrect or imperfect. Simple and isolated movements are normal, and the component parts may be executed properly, but they cannot be synthesized into a purposeful plan, and may be performed in the wrong order or in faulty combinations. Consequently, there is a distortion of the entire performance, with incorrect adjustment in space and time of the individual elements. The confusion and disturbance of motor activity resemble those seen in extreme absent-mindedness. In attempting to light a cigarette the patient may strike the match on the wrong side of the box, or he may place the match in his mouth and attempt to strike the cigarette.

Ideational apraxia is actually a variety of agnosia, and it is almost always bilateral. It has been ascribed to focal lesions of the posterior part of the left parietal lobe, the left supramarginal gyrus, and the corpus callosum, but in most instances it is the result of diffuse rather than localized cerebral involvement. It occurs most frequently in toxic states and in diffuse cerebral degenerations such as dementia paralytica, arteriosclerotic encephalopathy, presenile and senile phychoses, etc. It is sometimes found in psychoneuroses, functional psychoses, fatigue states, and extreme absent-mindedness. If the manifestations are unilateral they are probably symptoms of tactile agnosia rather than of ideational apraxia.

The so-called *constructional apraxia of Kleist* is characterized by loss of visual guidance, impairment of the visual image, and disturbance of revisualization. The patient is unable to guide his movements by vision or by visual memory. He cannot write when his eyes are open, but may be able to write either automatically or by kinesthetic memory when his eyes are closed. He cannot guide his hand in constructing small geometric figures and in building forms with blocks. In drawing the figure of a man he may place the eyes outside of the head. This variety of apraxia is probably caused by interruption of the pathways between the occipital and parietal regions of the brain, usually in the vicinity of the angular gyrus. It may occur with lesions of either hemisphere, but is more frequent and severe if they are right-sided. *Apraxia for dressing* may also be a specific type of loss of purposive movement, although it is probably a blend of apraxia and agnosia. The lesion responsible is in the parieto-occipital region, usually on the right side. This is combined with constructional, anosognostic, and visual difficulties in the syndrome of apractic agnosia.

RÉSUMÉ

Aphasia, agnosia, and apraxia are important in the diagnosis and localization of intracranial disease, although it is not always safe to localize a lesion by the presence of these difficulties alone. There is still a difference of opinion regarding anatomic features, pathologic physiology, and classification into definite categories. Furthermore, it is not always possible to differentiate the individual types, distinguish between expressive and receptive defects, separate apractic and agnostic elements, and localize specifically the lesion that is causing the difficulty. Aphasia, agnosia, and apraxia must be regarded as general terms, but individual varieties may indicate the presence of focal involvement of the nervous system. Certain conclusions that aid in diagnosis may be drawn from the following paragraphs.

As was stated above, in a large majority of cases the lesion which causes aphasia is situated in the dominant, or major, cerebral hemisphere. Unilateral dominance is more marked for language than for nonlanguage functions, and it does not play as great a part in the agnosias and apraxias which are not related to language disabilities. The minor hemisphere is thought to assume some of the functions of the dominant one in the control of speech, but this occurs to a variable degree in different individuals. It does so with great facility in some instances, with difficulty in others, and not at all in some. This bilaterality of speech functions, or compensatory action of the opposite hemisphere, is important both in the development of and the recovery from aphasia.

Various centers have been described which are important in the regulation of language function. These are widely separated in the cortex of the dominant cerebral hemisphere (Fig. 308). These centers are not areas which have an isolated function, but they are regions which are more important than the surrounding portions of the cortex in the performance of certain activities. Furthermore, they can never function alone, but only in cooperation with each other and with other parts of the brain. It is not possible, in most instances, to state whether the process that causes an aphasic defect is cortical, subcortical, or transcortical. A small, localized lesion may on occasion result in a widespread loss of the various elements of speech function, whereas destruction of a large area may cause impairment of only one phase of either expression or interpretation. Even though there may be complete loss of volitional and propositional speech, due to a lesion of the dominant hemisphere, expletive and emotional speech may be retained, possibly as a function of the opposite hemisphere.

The centers which have to do with motor activity and with the expressive elements of language are situated in the motor region of the brain, anterior to the rolandic fissure. Many cases of purely oral expressive aphasia have been observed in which the lesion was localized to Broca's area, and cases of expressive aphasia involving writing and drawing in which the lesions were situated just above this site. Similar disabilities, however, have been found occasionally in patients with lesions in the temporal and parietal lobes. The centers which have to do with interpretation and with the receptive elements of language are situated posterior to the rolandic fissure, in the temporal, parietal, and occipital lobes. Many cases of visual receptive aphasia have been studied in which the lesion was localized to the region of the angular gyrus, and of auditory receptive aphasia with the lesion restricted to the superior temporal convolution. Abnormalities of comprehension of written and spoken language, difficult to differentiate from visual and auditory receptive aphasia, may, however, be caused by more anterior lesions.

The agnosias, other than those concerned with vision and audition, are somewhat less well localized; they are mainly the result of parietal lobe lesions, and the symptoms are contralateral to the side of cerebral involvement. Syndromes characterized by disturbance of the body scheme of an anosognostic type, however, are usually the result of lesions of the nondominant parietal area, although the syndrome of finger agnosia usually occurs with involvement of the parieto-occipital region of the dominant side. The localization of the apraxias is not as specific as that of the aphasias, but it may also be said that the motor apraxias are the result of lesions anterior to the rolandic fissure, whereas sensory apraxias follow involvement posterior to this fissure. Kinetic apraxia is usually associated with a lesion of the precentral gyrus, idiokinetic apraxia with one of the parietal lobe, especially the supramarginal gyrus, and ideational apraxia with diffuse brain involvement. The relationship of the corpus callosum to the apraxias is still disputed, and there is a possibility that any one of the varieties may be caused by a callosal lesion. Cerebral dominance probably plays a major part only in idiokinetic apraxia, although kinetic apraxia of the left upper extremity has been reported in right-handed individuals with cortical lesions which cause paralysis of the right upper extremity. There is a possibility that some instances of ideational apraxia, which is essentially an agnosia, may follow lesions of the left parietal lobe, especially the supramarginal gyrus.

A careful and detailed examination is indicated whenever the presence of aphasia, agnosia, or apraxia is suspected. It is important to bear in mind that nonorganic lesions may produce symptoms which resemble those of aphasia. Fatigue states and conversion processes may cause language defects which simulate aphasia, and the disorganized speech which is apparent in many of the functional psychoses is often difficult to differentiate from a specific disability of language function. In diffuse organic brain disease, too, there may be difficulties with speech and paraphasic defects that resemble those encountered in some aphasias; in both functional and organic psychoses, however, there usually are associated changes in behavior, orientation, and mood. On the other hand, a patient with either an expressive or receptive aphasia may be thought to be psychotic because of his irrelevant and disorganized speech. A definite diagnosis of aphasia, agnosia, or apraxia is not always possible in the presence of confusion, lowered consciousness, dementia, or amentia. On the whole, however, unless the involvement is extensive or there are multiple cerebral lesions, there need be no definite or permanent impairment of higher intellectual functions, memory, or judgment in the aphasic patient, even though a superficial appraisal may suggest the presence of marked intellectual deterioration. The apraxias, especially the ideational varieties which are usually the result of diffuse lesions, are often accompanied by intellectual impairment.

In the study of the aphasic, the apractic, and the agnostic patient neurology meets psychiatry, physiology may be taken over by psychology, and clinical evaluation and judgment are extremely important.

REFERENCES

AKELAITIS, A. J. A study of gnosis, praxis and language following section of the corpus callosum and anterior commissure. *J. Neurosurg.* 1:94, 1944.

ALAJOUANINE, T. Verbal realization in aphasia. *Brain* 79:1, 1956.

ALAJOUANINE, T., and LHERMITTE, F. Acquired aphasia in children. *Brain* 88:653, 1965.

BAY, E. Aphasia and non-verbal disorders of language. *Brain* 85:411, 1962.

BENTON, A. L. Right-Left Discrimination and Finger Localization: Development and Pathology. New York, Paul B. Hoeber, Inc., 1959.

BENTON, A. L., and FOGEL, M. L. Three-dimensional constructional praxis: A clinical test. *Arch. Neurol.* 7:347, 1962.

BRAIN, R. Speech Disorders: Aphasia, Apraxia, Agnosia. Washington, Butterworth's, 1961; The Neurology of Language. *Brain* 84:145, 1961.

BROWN, J. R., and SIMONSON, J. A clinical study of 100 aphasic patients: I. Observations on lateralization and localization of lesions. *Neurology* 7:777, 1957.

CHESHER, E. C. Aphasia: I. Technique of clinical examinations. *Bull. Neurol. Inst. New York* 6:134, 1937.

CONRAD, K. New problems of aphasia. *Brain* 77:491, 1954.

CRITCHLEY, M. The Parietal Lobes. London, Edward Arnold & Co., 1953; Developmental Dyslexia. London, William Heinemann Medical Books, Ltd., 1964; The problem of visual agnosia. *J. Neurol. Sci.* 1:274, 1964.

DENNY-BROWN, D. The nature of apraxia. *J. Nerv. & Ment. Dis.* 126:9, 1958.

DENNY-BROWN, D., and BANKER, B. Q. Amorphosynthesis from left parietal lesion. *Arch. Neurol. & Psychiat.* 71:302, 1954.

DE RENZI, E., and VIGNOLO, L. A. The token test: A sensitive test to detect receptive disturbances in aphasics. *Brain* 85:665, 1962.

DE REUCK, A. V. S., and O'CONNOR, W. (eds.) Ciba Foundation Symposium: Disorders of Language. Boston, Little, Brown & Company, 1964.

EISENSON, J Examining for Aphasia (ed. 2). New York, The Psychological Corporation, 1954.

ETTLINGER, G., JACKSON, C. V., and ZANGWILL, O. L. Cerebral dominance in sinistrals. *Brain* 79:569, 1956.

FREUD, S. On Aphasia: A Critical Study. New York, International Universities Press, 1953.

GESCHWIND, N. Disconnexion syndromes in animals and man. *Brain* 88:237, 585, 1965.

GERSTMANN, J. Fingeragnosie: Eine umschreibene Störung der Orientierung am eigenen Körper. *Wein. klin. Wchnschr.* 37:1010, 1924. Some notes on the Gerstmann syndrome. *Neurology* 7:866, 1957.

GOLDSTEIN, K. Language and Language Disturbances. New York, Grune & Stratton, Inc., 1948.

GOODGLASS, H., and QUADFASEL, F. A. Language laterality in left-handed aphasics. *Brain* 77:521, 1954.

GRANICH, L. Aphasia: A Guide to Retraining. New York, Grune & Stratton, Inc., 1947.

HALSTEAD, W. C., and WEPMAN, J. M. The Halstead-Wepman aphasia screening test. *J. Speech & Hearing Disorders* 14:9, 1949.

HEAD, H. Aphasia and Kindred Disorders of Speech. Cambridge, The University Press, 1926.

HECAEN, H., and DE AJURIAGUERRA, J. Left Handedness: Manual Superiority and Cerebral Dominance. New York, Grune & Stratton, 1964.

HECAEN, H., and ANGELERGUES, R. Agnosia for faces (prosopagnosia). *Arch. Neurol.* 7:92, 1962.

HEIMBURGER, R. F., DE MYER, W., and REITAN, R. M. Implications of Gerstmann's syndrome. *J. Neurol., Neurosurg. & Psychiat.* 27:52, 1964.

HEIMBURGER, R. F., and REITAN, R. M. Easily administered written test for lateralizing brain lesions. *J. Neurosurg.* 18:301, 1961.

KENNEDY, F., and WOLF, A. The relationship of intellect to speech defect in aphasic patients, with illustrative cases. *J. Nerv. & Ment. Dis.* 84:125 and 293, 1936.

McFIE, J., PIERCY, M. F., and ZANGWILL, O. L. Visual-spatial agnosia associated with lesions of the right cerebral hemisphere. *Brain* 73:167, 1950.

MONRAD-KROHN, G. H. The prosodic quality of speech and its disorders. *Acta psychiat. et neurol.* 22: 255, 1947.

MOUNTCASTLE, V. B. (ed). Interhemispheric Relations annd Cerebral Dominance. Baltimore, The Johns Hopkins Press, 1962.

NIELSEN, J. M. Agnosia, Apraxia, Aphasia: Their Value in Cerebral Localization (ed. 2). New York, Paul B. Hoeber, Inc., 1946.

ORTON, S. T. Some studies in the language function. *A. Res. Nerv. & Ment. Dis., Proc.* (1932) 13:614, 1934.

PENFIELD, W., and ROBERTS, L. Speech and Brain Mechanisms. Princeton, N. J., Princeton University Press, 1959.

PIERCY, M., and SMYTH, V. O. G. Right hemisphere dominance for certain non-verbal skills. *Brain* 85:775, 1962.

REINHOLD, M. An analysis of agnosia. *Neurology* 4:128, 1954.

RIESE, W. The early history of aphasia. *Bull. Hist. Med.* 21:322, 1947.

RUSSELL, W. R. Some anatomical aspects of aphasia. *Lancet* 1:1173, 1963.

RUSSELL, W. R., and ESPIR, M. E. L. Traumatic Aphasia: A Study of Aphasia in War Wounds of the Brain. London, Oxford University Press, 1961.

SCHUELL, H. M. Minnesota Test for Differential Diagnosis of Aphasia, Research Edition. Minneapolis, University of Minnesota Press, 1955; A short examination for aphasia. *Neurology* 7:625, 1957.

SCHUELL, H., JENKINS, J. J., and JIMENEZ-PABON, E. Aphasia in Adults: Diagnosis, Prognosis, and Treatment. New York, Hoeber Medical Division, Harper & Row, 1964.

SUBIRANA, A. The prognosis in aphasia in relation to cerebral dominance and handedness. *Brain* 81:415, 1958.

SYMONDS, C. Aphasia. *J. Neurol., Neurosurg. & Psychiat.* 16:1, 1953.

WEINSTEIN, E. A., and KAHN, R. L. The syndrome of anosognosia. *Arch. Neurol. & Psychiat.* 64:772, 1950.

WEISENBURG, T. H., and McBRIDE, K. E. Aphasia: A Clinical and Psychological Study. New York, The Commonwealth Fund; London, Oxford University Press, 1935.

WEPMAN, J. M., and JONES, L. V. Studies in Aphasia: An Approach to Testing. Chicago, Education-Industry Service, 1961.

WILSON, S. A. K. Aphasia. London, Kegan Paul, Trench, Trubner & Co., Ltd., 1926.

ZANGWILL, O. L. Cerebral Dominance and Its Relation to Psychological Function. Springfield, Ill., Charles C Thomas, 1960.

CHAPTER 54

DIFFERENTIAL DIAGNOSIS OF INTRACRANIAL DISEASE

THE DIFFERENTIAL DIAGNOSIS of intracranial disease is dependent upon a thorough knowledge of the anatomy and physiology of the cerebrum, including both the cortical and subcortical structures and the blood supply of each, together with a familiarity with the changes in function that may be brought about by various pathologic processes. One must not only establish the presence and localization of an intracranial lesion, but also determine its nature and etiology, before treatment can be suggested and prognosis can be evaluated.

Disease of the brain, like disease of other portions of the body, may be caused by neoplasms, vascular damage, infection, trauma, toxic substances, metabolic changes, degenerative processes, and disturbances of development. These various pathologic processes may cause not only focal damage, with resulting evidences of disturbed function of one or more areas, but also disturbances of function of neighboring or adjacent areas by edema and pressure. In addition, certain types of intracranial disease may produce increased intracranial pressure; subjectively this may be manifested by the presence of headaches of increasing severity, nausea, vertigo, vomiting (often projectile in type), visual loss, and drowsiness; and objectively by papilledema, ocular palsies, and slowing of the pulse rate. If there is a marked increase in intracranial pressure there may be elevation (or occasionally decline) in the blood pressure, slowing of the respiratory rate, apathy, stupor, generalized convulsions, and coma. In children there may be a "cracked-pot" resonance, enlargement of the head, or separation of the sutures. Pressure by the edematous brain in the region of either the incisura of the tentorum cerebelli or the foramen magnum may cause signs of false localization.

The first procedures to be carried out in the differential diagnosis of intracranial disease are those which are essential to the diagnosis of any neurologic condition. The examiner should obtain a detailed history, and follow this by physical and mental examinations and a careful neurologic appraisal. The history may give significant information. With cerebrovascular disease there is often a sudden onset of symptoms which is followed by either complete or incomplete recovery or death; occasionally the symptoms are transitory, or there may be recurring small episodes with gradual increase in severity. With trauma and acute infections, as with acute cerebrovascular disease, the onset is sudden, followed by variable degrees of recovery or death; with some infections, however, there may be prodromata and a progressive course. With neoplasms and degenerative diseases the symptoms and signs are usually progressive in character, although occasionally the onset is abrupt. In multiple sclerosis there may be remissions followed by exacerbations of increasing severity. The importance of the history in the differential diagnosis in such conditions as headaches and convulsive disorders is stressed in Chapter 2.

Under most circumstances it is necessary to resort to auxiliary diagnostic measures. *Roentgen studies* are essential in cases of trauma and are often of aid in the diagnosis of neoplasms. Increased intracranial pressure may be manifested by increased convolutional markings and erosion of the clinoid processes or of the sella turcica; in children there may be enlargement of the head and separation of the sutures. Localized neoplastic processes may cause focal areas of erosion, unusual vascular markings, areas of osseous proliferation or hyperostosis, or intrasellar erosion. Intracranial calcifications may be seen in oligodendrogliomas, astrocytomas (rarely), aneurysms, angiomas, hematomas, chronic abscesses, tuberculomas, craniopharyngiomas, and some parasitic diseases. Displacement, or shift, of the calcified pineal gland to one side, or in an anterior, posterior, upward, or downward direction, is one of the most valuable localizing signs. A *spinal puncture* is often essential to the diagnosis of intracranial disease, but it should not be carried out unless there is a definite indication for the procedure, and until after the examiner has determined that there are no contraindications.

Ancillary diagnostic procedures often add information that is important to the understanding of the disease process and to diagnosis and differential diagnosis as well as to localization. *Electroencephalography* has become a routine procedure, in most clinics, for the evaluation of cerebral disease. So-called contrast studies, *pneumoencephalography, ventriculography,* and *angiography,* may be essential to the accurate localization of brain lesions; the two former procedures may also be of help in the diagnosis of hydrocephalus and cerebral atrophy, and the latter gives relevant information in the interpretation of both extracranial and intracranial vascular disease.

Brain scanning following the intravenous injection of *radioactive isotopes* may be of outstanding value in the diagnosis and localization of both primary and metastatic neoplasms, especially those in the cerebral hemispheres; the amount of uptake may be either proportional to the degree of malignancy of the tumor or related to its vascularity. Other lesions, including abscesses, hemorrhagic infarctions, hematomas, arteriovenous malformations, and contusions may also be identified. Various substances and isotopes have been used, including radioiodinated human serum albumin (I^{131}), radioarsenic (A^{74} or As^{72}) in either nonorganic or organic arsenical preparations, Cu^{64}, F^{18}, chlormerodrin tagged with either Hg^{203} or Hg^{197}, and technetium^{99m} (Fig. 310).

Echoencephalography, or the use of ultrasonic scanning for intracranial localization, has been used mainly to measure the position of midline structures. Two-dimensional echoencephalography, or ultrasonic B-scanning, gives additional information of a localizing nature. *Palencephalography,* a technic for the recording of infrasonic vibrations believed to originate from the propagation of the pulse waves of intracranial arteries, may prove to be of value in detecting changes in the vascularity of the brain and in localizing intracranial lesions. *Rheoencephalography* is the study of the electrical impedance of cranial tissues to a high frequency alternating current; it is of aid in evaluating changes in cerebral circulation. The intra-carotid injection of the sodium amobarbital (Amytal) has been used to determine the lateralization of speech dominance. Cerebral biopsy may be used to distinguish various types of cerebral degeneration and also for the diagnosis of neoplasms.

The differential diagnosis of the various causes of headaches alone constitutes one of the most important problems in the identification of intracranial disease. A headache, it must be recognized, is a symptom and not a disease, and it is always essential to determine the cause of the symptom. Individuals react differently to headaches, and some have a special susceptibility to them. Many etiologies and mechanisms have to be considered, some of the more important of which are distension or dilatation of extracranial or intracranial arteries, contraction or irritation of the muscles and fasciae in the cervical and suboccipital regions, irritation of the pain-afferent cervical and cranial nerves or neuralgias of these nerves, inflammation or irritation of the basal meninges, focal intracranial disease, disease of other structures in the region of the head and neck (eyes, ears, nose, paranasal sinuses, throat, teeth, cervical spine), systemic disease (infections, allergy, anemia or polycythemia, endogenous or exogenous toxins), and psychogenic or conversion

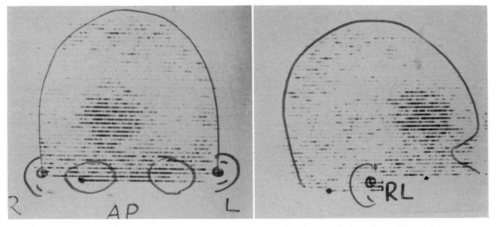

Fig. 310.   Mercury^{197} scan of a right frontal astrocytoma. (Courtesy of Dr. H. J. Cohn.)

mechanisms. For the accurate diagnosis of the cause of a headache, especially if it is of a chronic or recurring type, one needs not only a detailed history and thorough physical and neurologic examinations, but also, in some cases, examinations of the eyes, ears, paranasal sinuses and teeth, allergic investigations, psychologic studies, roentgenologic and cerebrospinal fluid examinations, and, on occasion, certain of the ancillary procedures listed above.

INTRACRANIAL NEOPLASMS

The term intracranial neoplasm is used to designate all tumors which involve the structures within the skull; it includes intrinsic neoplasms of the brain substance, meninges, cranial nerves, and pituitary and pineal glands, as well as metastatic tumors which affect these structures and neoplasms of the skull which invade the intracranial space. The symptoms and signs of such tumors depend upon their location, expansile nature, and pathologic peculiarities, as well as upon their tendency to cause increase in intracranial pressure. Their prognosis depends upon their pathologic characteristics, location, accessibility to surgery, and response to radiation therapy, as well as upon the extent of involvement of important intracranial structures and the stage at which diagnosis is made; early diagnosis is, of course, important. Their onset is usually insidious but occasionally, as in the case of the glioblastoma multiforme, abrupt.

Focal manifestations of intracranial tumors include irritative phenomena such as jacksonian or generalized convulsive seizures, and symptoms of destruction such as progressive paralysis. They may cause motor, sensory, auditory, visual, olfactory, gustatory, mental, endocrine, or hypothalamic disturbances, as well as cranial nerve dysfunctions. Tumors arising in "silent areas" may reach considerable size before they become apparent. The majority of the intracranial tumors in adults (except for acoustic neurinomas) arise above the tentorium cerebelli, whereas the majority of tumors in children (except for craniopharyngiomas) arise below the tentorium. The expansile nature of neoplasms, as well as their tendency to block the circulation of the cerebrospinal fluid and interfere with its absorption, causes symptoms and signs of increased intracranial pressure.

Important early symptoms and signs of intracranial neoplasms include the following: enlargement of the head in infancy; vomiting without apparent cause in childhood; headaches, progressive paralysis, and either focal or generalized convulsions which have their onset in adult life; failing vision in all age groups; mental and personality changes. The presence of minimal but early neurologic signs is important in diagnosis. These include slight changes in the visual fields, reflex inequality, minor cranial nerve palsies, and early manifestations of papilledema. The later signs of marked increase in intracranial pressure are listed above.

Approximately 50 per cent of all intracranial neoplasms belong to the *glioma group*. These neoplasms, which are primary tumors of the brain substance, have been subdivided variously by neuropathologists and neurosurgeons, and their nomenclature is still disputed. They arise in various regions of the brain and are composed of cells of neuroectodermal origin, some of which are glial, others neuronal.

The individual tumors of this group are characterized by excessive proliferation of either embryonic cells or adult supporting or neuronal cells, or a mixture of the two. All are malignant, but some more so than others. They are usually classified according to their histogenesis, which gives some information regarding both growth history and degree of malignancy. Correlation of the histopathology, clinical manifestations, and usual localization of each has made it possible to learn much about their course and prognosis. The scheme of Bailey which shows the growth history of the various descendants of the cells of the primitive medullary epithelium (Fig. 311) and the neoplasms that may arise from these developing cells (Fig. 312) is generally used in classification, although some pathologists prefer the more simplified scheme of Kernohan.

The *astrocytoma* is one of the most common intracerebral neoplasms, and constitutes about one third of the gliomas. It is intermediate in rapidity of growth and degree of malignancy. Astrocytomas have been classified microscopically as fibrillary and protoplasmic; they are found predominantly in the cerebral hemispheres of adults and the cerebellar hemispheres of children. *Astroblastomas* are composed

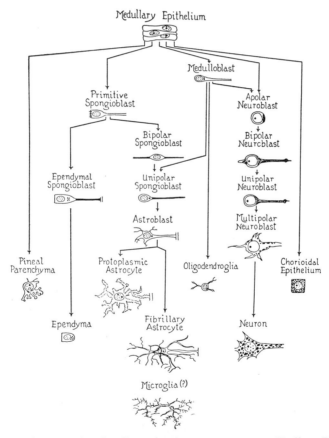

FIG. 311.   Histogenesis of cell types of nervous system. (Bailey, P.: Intracranial Tumors, ed. 2. Springfield, Ill., Charles C Thomas, 1948.)

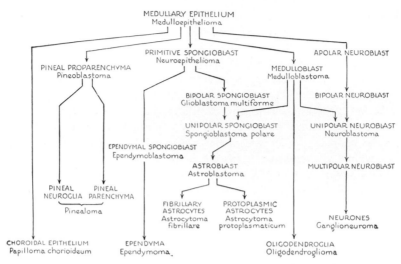

FIG. 312. Embryologic development of cell types of central nervous system and related tumors which contain predominantly the individual varieties of cells. (After Bailey, from Davis, L.: The Principles of Neurological Surgery, ed. 3. Philadelphia, Lea & Febiger, 1946.)

of more primitive and rapidly growing cells, and consequently are somewhat more malignant; they occur principally in the cerebral hemispheres. The *glioblastoma multiforme* (sometimes known as spongioblastoma multiforme) is one of the most malignant neoplasms of the brain; it also constitutes about one third of the glioma group. Tumors of this type are composed of primitive, rapidly growing cells; they often have a dramatic and sudden onset within the white matter of the cerebral hemispheres, and the symptoms may progress rapidly to a fatal termination. *Oligodendrogliomas* grow more slowly and are less malignant; owing to the fact that these tumors often contain areas of calcification, they are sometimes diagnosed and localized by roentgenography. The *spongioblastoma polare* is less malignant than the glioblastoma multiforme, but as it usually occurs in portions of the nervous system which are relatively inaccessible to surgery, its prognosis is poor. In children these tumors are frequently present in the region of the optic nerves and chiasm and in the pons and midbrain, and in adults in the region of the brain stem, the corpus callosum, and the under surface of the cerebral hemispheres. *Medulloblastomas* are relatively malignant tumors which sometimes metastasize; they show a predilection for the region of the roof plate of the fourth ventricle in children, and cause the midline cerebellar syndrome (Chapter 24). Medulloblastomas make up about 15 per cent of the gliomas.

Other tumors of the glioma group include the following: ependymomas. pinealomas, ganglioneuromas, neuroblastomas, medulloepitheliomas, neuroepitheliomas, and papillomas of the choroid plexus. *Ependymomas,* like medulloblastomas. have a predilection for the roof plate of the fourth ventricle and may cause midline cerebellar syndromes, although they also originate in the cerebrum, brain stem, and spinal cord. *Pinealomas,* which usually arise in the region of the pineal gland, are often classed with the gliomas; they are relatively rare, usually occur in males between the ages of fifteen and twenty-five years, and often press upon the superior colliculi and give rise to the pineal, or Parinaud's, syndrome with paresis of upward gaze and disturbance of pupillary response (often an Argyll Robertson pupil). Pinealomas also cause vegetative symptoms because of pressure on the hypothalamus, and signs of rapidly increasing intracranial pressure due to early obstruction of the sylvian aqueduct. Pubertas precox, which has often been described in association with pinealomas, is probably the result of pressure on the ventromedial and lateral tuberal nuclei and the mammillary bodies.

The *meningiomas* are relatively benign tumors which make up about 16 per cent of all intracranial neoplasms. They are probably of connective tissue (mesodermic) rather than neuroectodermic origin, and invade the brain tissue by pressure rather than infiltration. Accordingly their prognosis is better than that for tumors of the glioma group, although the technical aspects of surgical removal may be difficult because of vascularity, great size, and tendency to involve the major dural sinuses. The clinical course is usually a long one, so that the tumor may have attained great size before it is recognized. Meningiomas usually arise from the arachnoid, and there may be some relationship between these tumors and the arachnoid granulations. The bones of the skull in juxtaposition to them may show either erosion or thickening with localized hyperostosis. There are various classifications of meningiomas, including mesenchymatous, angioblastic, meningotheliomatous, psammomatous, osteoblastic, fibroblastic, melanoblastic, lipomatous, and sarcomatous. Irrespective of their exact histologic origin, architecture, and cell type, however, they produce characteristic syndromes which are dependent upon the sites of development and which may be classified regionally. They are usually supratentorial.

Olfactory groove meningiomas arise from the cribriform plate area of the ethmoid bone and produce a clinical syndrome which is characterized by bilateral anosmia, often with optic atrophy on one side and papilledema on the other (Chapter 9). *Sphenoidal ridge meningiomas* may grow either forward under the frontal lobe to the orbital plate or backward into the middle fossa; they produce unilateral proptosis, papilledema, and anosmia, and often cause temporal lobe manifestations with a hemianopic visual field defect and uncinate attacks. *Parasagittal meningiomas* arise from the wall of the superior longitudinal sinus and may be attached to the falx cerebri as well; they are manifested clinically by a progressive spastic paresis of one or both lower extremities, with, in addition, jacksonian convulsive seizures which originate in one or both feet. *Meningiomas which arise in the foramina of the individual cranial nerves* affect most frequently the eighth, second, and fifth nerves. A meningioma in the region of the eighth cranial nerve may cause a syndrome which cannot be distinguished from that of the acoustic neurinoma. Tumors which arise from the arachnoid sheath of the optic nerve, even in the orbit itself, produce a unilateral, painless exophthalmos with primary optic atrophy. Meningiomas which arise in association with the trigeminal nerve may involve the gasserian ganglion and cause pain and sensory change in the distribution of the individual divisions of the nerve, and often motor changes as well. *Meningiomas of the tuberculum sellae* may cause a syndrome which simulates that of either a pituitary adenoma or a craniopharyngeal duct tumor, with bitemporal hemianopia, bilateral optic atrophy, and endocrine changes. *Meningiomas en plaque* consist of sheet-like proliferations which are usually found at the base of the brain.

Acoustic neurinomas constitute from 5 to 10 per cent of all intracranial tumors. They arise from the perineurium of the eighth cranial nerve near to or within the internal acoustic meatus and cause the characteristic cerebellopontine angle syndrome. Tinnitus and progressive deafness are usually the first symptoms, and may be present for a long period of time before other manifestations are noted. Other symptoms include numbness and/or pain of the ipsilateral side of the face (trigeminal nerve involvement), a peripheral facial palsy (seventh nerve), attacks of vertigo (vestibular portion of acoustic nerve), ipsilateral cerebellar signs (involvement of either cerebellum or cerebellar peduncles), and an ipsilateral sixth nerve palsy. There may be dysphagia and dysarthria (affection of bulbar nerves). Following these manifestations there are signs of increased intracranial pressure with headaches, papilledema, and vomiting. The fully developed syndrome consists of the following from an objective point of view: nerve deafness with absence of labyrinthine response on the affected side; ipsilateral facial palsy, cerebellar signs; loss of the corneal reflex; and roentgen evidence of erosion of the internal acoustic meatus. The tumor has been variously described as a neuroma, neurinoma, neurofibroma, and perineural fibroblastoma. Many patients show evidences of Recklinghausen's disease with multiple neurofibromas, pigmented moles, and *café-au-lait* spots. These tumors are usually encapsulated and are relatively benign. The prognosis is good if the diagnosis is made early, but surgical removal is difficult in late stages.

Blood vessel tumors include *angiomas, hemangiomas,* and *hemangioblastomas.* Angiomas of the cerebral hemispheres may be accompanied by unilateral facial nevi in the distribution of the ophthalmic or maxillary distribution of the trigeminal nerve (Sturge-Weber syndrome, Parkes-Weber-Dimitri disease, or encephalotrigeminal angiomatosis). Angiomas of the retina (von Hippel's disease) may be accompanied by hemangioblastomas of the cerebellum (Lindau's disease). Angiomas may be diagnosed by roentgenography if there is calcification of the vessels; in Sturge-Weber syndrome there are calcium deposits within the cerebral cortex.

Tumors of the hypophysis may be of various types. They frequently impinge on the optic chiasm and cause bitemporal hemianopia and bilateral optic atrophy as well as signs of endocrine dysfunction. Adenomas commonly affect the anterior lobe. With *chomophobe adenomas,* which are the most frequent, there are signs of "hypopituitarism," with amenorrhea in the female and loss of potency and libido in the male; in both sexes there are other endocrine changes, with loss of body hair, alterations in the skin, and obesity. *Acidophilic (eosinophilic) adenomas* produce the syndrome of acromegaly, with increase in the size of the skull, jaw, and hands, and a generalized osseous overgrowth which results in gigantism; these changes are also accompanied by amenorrhea and loss of potency. With *basophilic adenomas* there are manifestations of the so-called Cushing syndrome, with obesity, hypertension, cyanosis, hypertrichosis, and striae. Both the chromophobe and acidophilic adenomas are characterized by a cellular proliferation and an increase in the size of the gland. Since the hypophysis is confined by a capsule of dura mater and the bony structure of the sella turcica, these tumors immediately meet with resistance to their growth. The walls of the sella turcica become eroded and thinned by constant pressure, and the sella becomes greatly enlarged. The capsule of dura mater become distended, and as the tumor bulges upward it produces pressure on the optic chiasm, at first from below and behind, so that the characteristic bitemporal, upper quadrantic visual field defect is produced. Later, there is a bitemporal hemianopia, and finally, complete blindness, often with optic atrophy; occasionally there are homonymous defects. The intrasellar erosion may be diagnosed by roentgenography.

Craniopharyngiomas include those tumors which have also been known as hypophyseal duct tumors, suprasellar or epithelial cysts, Rathke's pouch neoplasms, and adamantinomas. They are of congenital origin and arise from cell rests in the region of the sella turcica; they become manifest most frequently in childhood or young adult life. There are signs of hypophyseal dysfunction, often with a so-called Fröhlich's syndrome, together with those of pressure on the optic nerves or chiasm, stimulation or paralysis of important hypothalamic structures, and hydrocephalus due to obstruction of the foramen of Monro. In the majority of cases calcification within the tumor and changes in the sella turcica can be demonstrated by roentgenography. Other *congenital tumors* include dermoid cysts, colloid cysts, teratomas, cholesteatomas, chordomas, chondromas, and hamartomas. These may be intracerebral, subpial, or intradural in location, and may arise in any of the cranial fossae.

Metastatic tumors, which constitute from 10 to 20 per cent of all intracranial tumors, are encountered with increasing frequency. They may be single or multiple. Primary bronchogenic carcinomas are especially apt to metastasize to the brain, but carcinomas of the breast, gastrointestinal tract, thyroid, prostate, or other organs, as well as hypernephromas and sarcomas may also invade the brain. Melanosarcomas often cause diffuse meningeal and cerebral symptoms. Carcinoma of the nasopharynx or neck may invade the cranial cavity by direct extension and erosion; diffuse cranial nerve palsies may be the earliest symptoms. Meningeal carcinomatosis may give a clinical picture resembling a chronic meningitis.

Granulomas of various types, including gummas, tuberculomas, and granulomas associated with schistosomiasis japonica, actinomycosis, cysticercosis, and echinococcosis may give manifestations of cerebral tumor. *Tumors of the bones of the skull,* such as osteomas and myelomas, as well as Paget's disease (osteitis deformans) may also invade the intracranial structures.

VASCULAR DISEASE

Vascular disease of the brain accounts for the majority of cases of organic nervous system disease encountered in the general practice of medicine. The more common syndromes of cerebrovascular disease, both intracranial and extracranial, are discussed in Chapter 52.

Intracerebral hemorrhage, once regarded as the most common cerebrovascular syndrome, usually has an abrupt onset and a grave prognosis. It is most often a disease of hypertensive individuals and has its onset during periods of unusual physical exertion or emotional stress; it most commonly affects the deep, or striate, branches of the middle cerebral artery. There may be premonitory symptoms characterized by occipital or nuchal headache, vertigo, syncope, epistaxis, or transient motor or sensory symptoms. There is then a sudden appearance of hemiplegia, often with coma, shock, drop in blood pressure, stertorous breathing, and feeble pulse. Intracerebral hemorrhage may also occur in association with congenital anomalies of the blood vessels, trauma (delayed posttraumatic intracerebral hemorrhage, or spätapoplexie), and blood dyscrasias (leukemia, purpura, hemophilia, and polycythemia). It may be that, regardless of etiology, the hemorrhage is largely venous rather that arterial in origin.

With *cerebral thrombosis,* also, the onset may be sudden, but is often more gradual than in cerebral hemorrhage, and there is less apt to be coma or shock. Inasmuch as smaller or terminal vessels may be affected, the symptoms are often focal in character. *Cerebral embolism* is always secondary to disease elsewhere in the body. The most frequent causes are vegetative heart disease (usually with auricular fibrillation), subacute bacterial endocarditis, and pulmonary neoplasms and abscesses. Air and fat emboli are relatively rare. Occasionally an intracerebral hematoma secondary to a hemorrhage or unilateral cerebral edema in association with an infarct may suggest the presence of a neoplasm.

Either stenosis or occlusion of the extracranial arteries is responsible for a large percentage of instances of so-called cerebrovascular disease. Brief periods of vascular insufficiency, in the distribution of either the carotid or the vertebrobasilar system, cause episodes of transient cerebral ischemia without infarct formation. These may increase in severity and cause progressive neurologic dysfunction; complete occlusion may finally take place.

Diffuse cerebrovascular disease may cause a slowly progressive impairment of brain function, often with diffuse involvement. Cerebral arteriosclerosis, hypertensive encephalopathy, syphilitic endarteritis, and progressive occlusion of the internal carotid arteries, as well as systemic diseases such as diabetes mellitus which are accompanied by vascular changes, may cause evidences of diffuse brain damage. There are multiple focal areas of softening with nerve cell degeneration, glial infiltration, and focal atrophy, scarring and cystic degeneration. The onset is usually insidious and gradually progressive, although there may be transient intermittent or recurring apoplectic attacks of varying severity which are followed by recovery but leave some residual localized symptoms. There may be impairment of circulation in certain regions before the vessels are completely occluded. The most common syndrome is that of progressive mental and intellectual deterioration, largely manifested by changes in frontal lobe function. There may also be vertigo, transient periods of loss of consciousness, temporary sensory and motor changes, convulsions, and, especially in hypertensive encephalopathy, headaches. In the so-called hypertensive crisis there may be premonitory signs of headache, irritability, fatigue, and lowered consciousness which are followed by the sudden onset of severe headache, drowsiness, vomiting, convulsions, and coma. There is marked edema of the brain, with focal areas of destruction, either miliary or extensive. In Binswanger's disease, or progressive subcortical encephalopathy, there are multiple small areas of arteriosclerotic infarction in the white matter of the brain, with sparing of the cortex. Repeated cerebrovascular accidents, affecting first one hemisphere and then the other, may give rise to the syndrome of pseudobulbar palsy.

Syndromes of cerebral anemia and hyperemia have also been described. The former is characterized by vertigo and syncope; the latter, which may be caused by hypertension, venous obstruction, or polycythemia, is manifested by headache, severe dizziness, focal signs, convulsions, and coma. Leukemia, the lymphomas, and Hodgkin's disease may also affect the nervous system.

Spontaneous subarachnoid hemorrhage is usually the result of the rupture of a congenital aneurysm of one of the branches of the arterial circle of Willis, although it may be caused by trauma, bleeding from a cerebral neoplasm (especially one impinging on the meninges or the ventricles), rupture of a vascular anomaly or a mycotic or syphilitic aneurysm, arteriosclerotic or hypertensive arteriopathy, blood dyscrasia, or massive intracerebral or intraventricular hemorrhage. The onset is usually precipitous, often in association with strenuous exertion or emotional stress, and the patient notices a sudden, severe nuchal or occipital headache which may be accompanied by convulsions or loss of consciousness. Vertigo, vomiting, lethargy, and bradycardia are commonly observed. The principal signs are those of meningeal irritation, with stiff neck, Kernig and Brudzinski signs, and photophobia; there may be focal neurologic changes, ocular palsies, papilledema, and retinal hemorrhages. The diagnosis is confirmed by finding either hemorrhagic or xanthochromic cerebrospinal fluid. Intracerebral *angiomas* and *arteriovenous anomalies* may cause convulsions, localized headaches, and focal neurologic signs. They occasionally rupture and cause subarachnoid bleeding; this is the most common cause of recurrent subarachnoid hemorrhage in children.

Subdural hematomas and *hydromas* are almost invariably posttraumatic in origin; they are either immediate or delayed, although there is usually a symptom-free period between the time of the injury and that of development of symptoms. There are signs of increasing intracranial pressure together with those of focal cerebral involvement. Diagnosis is confirmed by trephination. *Extradural bleeding* is also posttraumatic in origin; there is usually loss of consciousness followed by a brief lucid interval, and then deepening stupor accompanied by signs of increasing intracranial pressure. There is often a dilated pupil which may react neither to light nor in accommodation on the side of the hemorrhage, with a contralateral hemiplegia. There may be a fracture line in the region of the middle meningeal artery. Disease of the cerebral veins and venous sinuses are discussed in Chapter 52.

INTRACRANIAL INFECTIONS

Intracranial infections may cause either diffuse or focal involvement, and the infectious process may affect the meninges, the brain tissue, or both. The more severe clinical manifestations of the meningitides are usually those of a meningoencephalitis, and some of the diagnostic criteria in the encephalitides are the result of associated meningeal involvement.

MENINGITIS

Infectious involvement of the pachymeninges is rare, and such involvement usually follows either osteomyelitis of the skull associated with disease of the paranasal sinuses or the mastoid air cells, or trauma with extension to the large dural sinuses. There is formation of purulent material in the extradural and subdural spaces, often with direct extension to the large dural sinuses. The process may spread through the arachnoid to produce a leptomeningitis. There are signs of systemic infection (fever, leukocytosis, etc.), together with those of increased intracranial pressure, and there may be focal cerebral manifestations which appear as a result of thrombosis of the dural sinuses and interference with the venous drainage of the brain. The cerebrospinal fluid is under increased pressure and shows changes which are characteristic of an aseptic meningeal reaction.

Leptomeningitis is caused by a variety of pathogenic micro-organisms. *Purulent, or suppurative, meningitis* is acute in onset, and is most frequently due to invasion of the meninges by an organism of the coccus group. The meningococcic, pneumococcic, streptococcic, staphylococcic, and gonococcic varieties are the most important, although *Hemophilus influenzae* may also cause a purulent meningitis. The organisms may gain access to the meninges by any of the following mechanisms: by continuity along the nerve sheaths and cerebrospinal fluid pathways to the subarachnoid space; by direct extension from the nasal passages through the cribriform plate of the ethmoid bone (rhinogenous meningitis); by contiguity from infections of the paranasal sinuses, mastoid cells, and bones of the skull, with production of localized external pachymeningitis, internal pachymeningitis, and then leptomeningitis (rhinogenous and otogenous meningitis); as a consequence of a penetrating injury or compound fracture of the skull (traumatic meningitis); through the blood stream by metastasis from infections elsewhere in the body, or as a result of systemic infections. The onset is sudden, with headache, stiff neck, signs of infection (fever and leukocytosis), and sometimes coma and/or convulsions. There may be irritability, restlessness, photophobia, ocular palsies, and dissociation of extraocular movements, as well as objective manifestations of meningeal irritation with nuchal rigidity and Kernig and Brudzinski signs. The outstanding cerebrospinal fluid changes consist of a polymorphonuclear pleocytosis, increase in protein, decrease in glucose and chlorides, and changes in the colloidal gold curve. Often the causative organism can be demonstrated by direct smear culture.

The *subacute (nonsuppurative) meningitides* are somewhat more gradual in onset than the purulent types, but the clinical manifestations are similar. In *tuberculous meningitis* the pleocytosis is less marked than that seen in the acute varieties, and there are both lymphocytes and polymorphonuclear cells, but predominantly the former; the changes in the chemistry of the cerebrospinal fluid are similar. In a fairly large percentage of cases the causative organism cannot be demonstrated by direct stain, but in almost every instance it can be obtained by either culture or guinea pig inoculation. In the meningitis caused by *Cryptococcus neoformans* (Torula histolytica), the most common form of fungal infection of the nervous system, the onset of symptoms is less abrupt than in tuberculous meningitis, but the cerebrospinal fluid picture is similar; the diagnosis is made by finding the organisms in the fluid, preferably by staining them with India ink, or by culturing them on Sabouraud's medium.

There are many meningitides in which the cerebrospinal fluid response is predominantly a lymphocytic one, with from 25 to 50 cells to 200 or sometimes more. There are few other changes in the cerebrospinal fluid, and the course is often benign. These are often called instances of aseptic meningitis because no organism is found in the fluid on direct examination or by the usual culture methods. Many of them, however, are of viral origin, and in some of them the virus has been isolated from the fluid by special technics; in others it has been found in the feces or in nasal and pharyngeal washings, or the diagnosis has been confirmed by neutralization or complement-fixation tests, usually done on blood serum. Among the most common viral etiologies are the virus of lymphocytic choriomeningitis, the Coxsackie, ECHO, and Giles viruses, and the viruses of mumps, herpes zoster, and herpes simplex. Poliomyelitis virus and those responsible for the arthropod-borne encephalitides may cause a similar meningeal response.

It is important to bear in mind that signs of meningeal irritation, often with a definite meningitis, may occur in association with systemic diseases of various types. There are moderate meningeal signs in tabes dorsalis and dementia paralytica, and occasionally there is an acute syphilitic meningitis with a marked lymphocytic pleocytosis and other signs of meningeal involvement. Brucellosis, typhoid fever, malaria, subacute bacterial endocarditis, and other systemic infections may be complicated by meningeal involvement and signs, as well as by encephalitic manifestations (see below). With brain abscesses, especially if near either the surface of the brain or the ventricles, there may be definite meningeal signs and cerebrospinal fluid alterations.

Carcinomatous meningitis is being recognized with increasing frequency. Because of the lymphocytic reaction in the cerebrospinal fluid, along with increase in the protein content and decrease in glucose, the illness may be mistaken for a subacute infectious meningitis. With careful staining of the cells, however, and histologic study of the stained sediment, it may be found that some of the cells which were thought to be lymphocytes are, in reality, cancer cells (Chapter 59). A similar meningeal reaction may occur in association with leukemia and lymphoma. A subacute meningeal reaction may occur in *sarcoidosis*; there may be associated cranial nerve palsies, optic neuritis, and encephalitic manifestations. Acute meningeal symptoms may also be present with infectious mononucleosis; there may, in addition, be encephalitic, myelitic, and neuritic involvement. Recurring meningitis may be secondary to traumatic cerebrospinal fluid rhinorrhea. A benign recurrent meningitis for which no etiology has been found is known as *Mollaret's meningitis*.

In both true *aseptic meningitis* and *meningismus* there may be objective manifestations which suggest invasion of the meninges. The former occurs when there is a pyogenic infection near the meninges which has not yet invaded them, or as a reaction on the part of the meninges to the introduction of foreign substances such as drugs, air, contrast media, etc. There is an increase in the spinal fluid pressure and protein content, often with a marked pleocytosis, but the fluid is sterile. The syndrome is the result of increased permeability of the perineural and perivenous lymph spaces. Occasionally it is the precursor or first stage of purulent meningitis. Meningismus is a reaction to a systemic infection or febrile illness, usually in children. The spinal fluid pressure is increased, but the fluid itself is normal. *Cystic, adhesive,* or *optochiasmatic arachnoiditis* is a focal involvement of the meninges in the region of the optic chiasm; there may be papilledema, loss of vision, ocular palsies, and exophthalmos. In the syndrome referred to as benign intracranial hypertension, brain swelling of unknown cause, pseudotumor cerebri, and otitic hydrocephalus, there is increase in spinal fluid pressure leading to papilledema, but no pleocytosis; this is sometimes secondary to thrombosis of the dural sinuses, but other cases seem to be associated with generalized infections, trauma, or metabolic disturbances.

ENCEPHALITIS

Encephalitis, or inflammation of the brain, may be the result of the response of the cerebral tissues to a wide variety of infections, and sometimes to toxins as well. Some of these clinical and pathologic syndromes are better termed encephalopathies; the diagnosis of encephalitis is usually restricted to those diseases in which there is a diffuse, nonpurulent cerebral inflammation which affects principally the gray matter. Following the first World War there was a wide-spread epidemic of encephalitis lethargica, or von Economo's encephalitis, which was characterized in its acute stages by lethargy or other disturbances in the sleep cycle, ocular palsies, fever, headache, confusion and disorientation, either stupor or hyperexcitability, and occasionally hyperkinetic phenomena. There were mild meningeal signs with a moderate pleocytosis. The disease was accompanied by a high mortality, and many patients who seemed to have recovered later developed other signs of nervous system damage. In children these sequelae took the form of personality or behavior disorders, and in the adult, parkinsonian manifestations, oculogyric crises and other ocular disturbances, and hypothalamic changes. The disease is rarely, if ever, diagnosed today. A viral etiology was suspected, but no causal agent was ever isolated.

Encephalitides which are somewhat similar to the von Economo variety, but are caused by specific filtrable viruses which have been identified, occur in all parts of the world. These include St. Louis encephalitis and eastern and western (equine) encephalitis in the United States, Russian spring-summer encephalitis, Japanese B encephalitis, Australian X disease, and many others, including similar diseases in domestic and other animals. The clinical picture varies, depending upon the specific virus involved, the part of the nervous system maximally affected, the age of the patient (the symptoms are more severe in infants and aged persons), and other factors. There may or may not be residuals and sequelae. In most of these the neurotropic virus is arthropod-borne, and is transferred to man by mosquitoes and ticks, usually from a reservoir of infection in certain wild and domestic animals and birds. The diagnosis can be confirmed (usually retrospectively) by complement-fixation and neutralization tests. Poliomyelitis and rabies also cause an encephalitis which affects principally the gray matter; in the former, however, the involvement is predominantly in the anterior horn cells of the spinal cord, and in the latter, in the brain stem, rather than in the midbrain, basal ganglia, hypothalamus, or cortex. Polioencephalitis superior and inferior are mentioned elsewhere.

Inclusion body encephalitis (Dawson), also known as subacute sclerosing leukoencephalitis, is a rare disease of childhood and adolescence characterized by increasing dementia, ataxia, and myoclonic movements. The course is progressive, and death usually occurs in a period of weeks or months. There may be a slight pleocytosis in the cerebrospinal fluid, but there is often a first-zone colloidal gold curve, even though the protein content may be normal. A viral etiology is suspected because of the presence of inclusion bodies, similar to those of herpes simplex encephalitis, within the nuclei of neurons and oligodendroglia. *Cytomegalic inclusion-body disease* may be a cause of stillbirth or neonatal death. There is involvement of the brain and also of the kidneys, liver, and other organs, probably from an infection acquired *in utero*. Hydrocephalus, microcephaly, and other developmental defects of the brain are found. There are intranuclear and cytoplasmic inclusion bodies in the involved organs and also in the epithelium of the salivary and pancreatic ducts and elsewhere. The lesions resemble those caused by salivary gland viruses of various animals. In *benign myalgic encephalomyelopathy,* which usually occurs in isolated epidemics, the early symptoms include headache, stiff neck, muscle soreness, and manifestations of a mild meningoencephalitis as well as of a peripheral neuritis. There may be a pleocytosis with as many as 850 lymphocytes, often with some increase in protein. The disease is self-limited, but convalescence may be prolonged, with profound malaise and asthenia. *Hemorrhagic encephalitis,* which runs an acute course and is characterized pathologically by diffuse hemorrhagic lesions throughout the brain, particularly in the white matter of the cerebral hemispheres, may be a complication of fulminating systemic infections, of toxic etiology (arsphenamine, sulfonamides, carbon monoxide, etc.), an autoallergic or autoimmune disorder, or, occasionally, of viral origin.

The term encephalitis may also be applied to those instances of cerebral involvement that occur in association with systemic infections and inflammatory processes elsewhere in the body, namely brucellosis, malaria, subacute bacterial endocarditis, pulmonary disease, and septicemia. Pathologically there may be either diffuse involvement or multiple miliary lesions. Dementia paralytica, or syphilitic meningoencephalitis, is a widespread, parenchymatous affection caused by the *Treponema pallidum*. Postinfectious and postvaccinial encephalomyelitis is characterized by a diffuse perivascular destruction of nervous tissue, especially the myelinized structures, and pathologically resembles the demyelinating diseases more closely than the encephalitides. Such demyelinating changes may occur after smallpox vaccination or the administration of rabies vaccine, and in association with smallpox, chickenpox, measles, German measles, mumps, and certain types of pneumonia. It is probably the result of an allergic reaction.

A clinical picture suggestive of either meningitis or encephalitis, frequently that of a meningoencephalitis, may occur as a complication or a secondary manifestation of many systemic diseases. Some of these may be listed as follows: virus infections such as herpes zoster, herpes simplex, dengue, psittacosis, yellow fever, mumps, Asian influenza, infectious hepatitis, cat scratch disease, and lymphogranuloma venereum; spirochetal infections such as relapsing fever and Weil's disease; rickettsial infections such as typhus, tsutugamushi disease, tick-bite fever, and Rocky Mountain spotted fever; bacillary infections such as typhoid fever, para-typhoid, anthrax, and tularemia, and secondary invasion by *Myobacterium leprae, Proteus vulgaris, Pasteurella pestis, Escherichia coli,* and *Bacillus pyocyaneus*; infections with fungi, yeasts, and molds such as *Mucor, Candidia, Nocardia, Listeria, Blastomyces Coccidioides, Monilia, Oidium, Aspergillus, Histoplasma, Leptothrix, Sporotrichum, Cryptococcus, Endomyces,* and *Actinomyces*; involvement by protozoa such as *Plasmodium* (malaria), *Endameba histolytica, Trypanosoma* (African sleeping sickness and Chagas' disease), and *Toxoplasma;* invasion by parasites such as *Trichinella, Salmonella, Paragonimus, Toxocara, Echinococcus, Cysticercus,* and *Schistosoma.* Diseases such as rheumatic fever (Sydenham's chorea), infectious mononucleosis, periarteritis nodosa, lupus disseminatus, and sarcoidosis may cause widespread cerebral and meningeal involvement. In *Behçet's syndrome* there is relapsing iritis with recurrent attacks of oral and genital ulceration; encephalomyelitic symptoms may be important manifestations. A syndrome consisting of uveitis, retinal hemorrhage and detachment, alopecia, vitiligo, and deafness, often with associated nervous system signs, has been described by Harada, Vogt, Koyanagi, and others. Involvement of either the meninges and/or the cerebral structures may occur as a complication of middle ear and mastoid disease, sinus infections, petrositis, thrombosis of the venous sinuses, and osteomyelitis and penetrating injuries or compound fractures of the skull.

BRAIN ABSCESS

A brain abscess is a focal area of encephalitis. In the beginning it consists of a localized collection of purulent exudate with softening of the surrounding cerebral tissues. In most instances the abscess becomes encapsulated after a period of two to four or six weeks. The etiology of brain abscesses is variable, and many mechanisms may be responsible. They may develop by either contiguity or continuity from osteomyelitis of the skull, infectious of the pachymeninges or leptomeninges, involvement of the mastoid cells and paranasal sinuses, infections of the face and orbit, and affection of the venous sinuses within the skull. They may originate by metastasis from systemic infections, involvement of the heart or lungs, or focal infectious processes (hematogenous route); they sometimes follow extraction of abscessed teeth. They may be produced by direct implantation from penetrating wounds or compound fractures of the skull. Otogenous abscesses (those which complicate infection of the middle ear, mastoid cells, or petrous pyramid) are usually in either the temporal lobe or the cerebellum; rhinogenous abscesses (those which follow infections of the nose and paranasal sinuses) are usually in the frontal lobes.

The diagnosis of brain abscess is made on the basis of signs of systemic infection (fever, leukocytosis, etc.), manifestations of rapidly increasing intracranial pressure, and signs of focal nervous system involvement. Except for the signs of infection and the frequent rapid increase in symptoms, the clinical picture is quite similar to that encountered with cerebral neoplasms. It must be borne in mind that abscesses near either the surface of the brain or the ventricles may be accompanied by meningeal involvement, and that there may be definite signs of a meningitis. Discrimination must be used, however, in appraising the symptoms, since a spinal puncture done in the presence of a brain abscess may cause either rupture of the abscess or dissemination of the meningeal infection.

Extradural abscess (pachymeningitis externa) is a collection of pus between the dura and the skull; subdural abscess (pachymeningitis interna) is a collection of purulent material between the dura and the arachnoid. Both of these conditions may be produced by the same processes that cause the development of brain abscesses, and the symptoms and diagnostic signs may be similar. It is important, however, to make a correct differential diagnosis, since the prognosis and treatment vary. Often, however, though the diagnosis of either extradural or subdural abscess may be suspected, it can be definitely established only by exploration.

CEREBRAL TRAUMA

In most instances traumatic involvement of the brain may be diagnosed from the history alone. It must be borne in mind, however, that trauma may occur consequent to other types of cerebral involvement, such as acute alcoholic intoxication and epilepsy, and that trauma may precipitate other pathologic changes, such as subarachnoid, extradural, or intracerebral hemorrhage. Furthermore, the late posttraumatic sequelae, especially if they are complicated by the presence of psychoneurotic manifestations, may be exceedingly difficult to appraise.

Acute head injuries are of two main types. *Nonpenetrating,* or *"closed," head injuries* are those in which there has been no exposure of the meninges or brain as a result of the trauma; the scalp alone is wounded, or if the skull has been injured, there is only a small linear fracture without displacement of the fragments, rupture of the dura, or penetration or exposure of the brain substance. *Penetrating,* or *"open," head injuries* are those which occur in association with either compound or depressed fractures or penetrating wounds; there is tearing of the dura with exposure of the brain substance and penetration of the brain by fragments of bone, metal, or other foreign bodies.

The general symptoms of head injury may occur with all forms of trauma, although all of these symptoms need not be present in every case. *Headache* is probably the most common manifestations; it may vary in location, type, severity, and duration. If the headache persists, one must consider the possibility of development of complications or, in some instances, of posttraumatic psychoneurotic reactions. *Vertigo* is probably second to headache in frequency; its persistence has the same implications. *Disturbances of consciousness* are commonly encountered. There may be either brief or prolonged coma after a head injury, or fluctuations in the level of consciousness. There may be no complete loss of consciousness, but a lowering of the patient's awareness of his surroundings, with confusion, disorientation, and delirium. The period of complete coma may be relatively short, but the return to normal consciousness may be prolonged, with disorientation, confusion, irritability, and lethargy. Retrograde amnesia is almost always present if there has been loss of consciousness; it may cover a period which varies from a few seconds to minutes or even hours preceding the time of the injury. Posttraumatic amnesia may cover the period of confusion. *Changes in the temperature, pulse, and respirations* are common after head injuries. There may be a moderate hyperthermia, but occasionally there is hypothermia. The pulse may be rapid and feeble, especially if there is shock; with increased intracranial pressure there is bradycardia. The respirations may be rapid, feeble, and shallow, or they may be depressed and irregular. Cheyne-Stokes' respirations are sometimes observed. The cerebrospinal fluid may be under increased pressure; if there has been a cerebral laceration or subarachnoid bleeding, the fluid is bloody. Cerebrospinal fluid rhinorrhea is a complication of fractures in the frontal region and is caused by a fistula which forms a direct communication between the subarachnoid space and the nasal cavity, either through the cribiform plate or the frontal or ethmoid sinuses; this fistula is a direct pathway by which infections may enter the intracranial cavity, and its presence may lead to the development of meningitis.

The focal symptoms of head injury are dependent, of course, upon the site of the pathologic change. These may consist of sensory, motor, and other manifestations. Anisocoria and cranial nerve palsies may or may not have localizing value. The cranial nerves most frequently affected are those to the muscles of ocular movement and the olfactory, facial, and acoustic nerves. Signs of increasing intracranial pressure (slow pulse and respirations, papilledema, and vomiting) are of grave prognostic import.

The term *concussion* has been applied to those cases of cerebral injury where there is no demonstrable pathologic alteration of tissue. There may be loss of consciousness lasting from a few seconds to hours, probably due to either transient hydrodynamic pressure changes or cerebral anemia; it is usually followed by amnesia for the actual moment of the accident. Courville defines concussion as the direct effect of violence on the nerve cells of the brain resulting in a temporary depression or cessation of cerebral function without immediate detectable evidence of structural changes in these cells. Ward has suggested that the loss of consciousness and other symptoms may be the result of reduction of activity in the reticular formation at the midbrain level. If the loss of consciousness is prolonged, however, and there is retrograde amnesia with headache, vertigo, pupillary inequality, ocular palsies, vomiting and impaired mentation, there probably has been cerebral edema with congestion and petechial hemorrhages, and actual damage to the neurons and nerve fibers which may or may not be reversible. The electroencephalogram taken soon after such injury usually shows a stage of excitation followed by depressed activity. Posttraumatic sequalae with headaches, vertigo, convulsions, emotional lability, irritability, and memory changes indicate that there has been definite cerebral damage. The cerebrospinal fluid in either concussion or edema and congestion may show only a slight increase in pressure without other changes.

If there has been either *contusion* or *laceration* of the brain there are definite structural alterations which may produce focal signs of cerebral dysfunction, often with focal residuals. There may be associated hemorrhage into the subarachnoid space, which may be diagnosed by spinal puncture. With generalized cerebral contusions the brain is often swollen and edematous, and there may be multiple, minute, punctate perivascular hemorrhages. The perivascular spaces are distended and there may be areas of focal necrosis. The predominant damage may be either at the site of the injury or on the opposite side of the brain (contrecoup). With lacerations there are tears of the affected tissues.

Serious complications of compound and depressed skull fractures and of severe contusions and lacerations include cerebral compression, intracerebral hematoma, extradural hemorrhage, subdural hematoma and hydroma, subarachnoid hemorrhage, posttraumatic meningitis and brain abscess, focal cerebral cicatrix, osteomyelitis of the skull, intracerebral aerocele, arteriovenous aneurysm, and posttraumatic epilepsy.

If there are prolonged posttraumatic manifestations, in the absence of definite focal changes such as those which follow contusions and lacerations, it often is difficult to differentiate between organic residuals and superimposed psychoneurotic changes. The most common symptoms, which include headache, vertigo, fatigue, irritability, insomnia, personality changes, intolerance to alcohol, and tremors, may occur in either posttraumatic encephalopathy or posttraumatic psychoneurosis. The presence of focal signs, ocular palsies, organic mental changes, and electroencephalographic and pneumoencephalographic abnormalities, however, is definite evidence that structural alterations persist. Repeated trauma, such as that suffered in boxing injuries, produces multiple petechial hemorrhages, often in the deeper parts of the cerebrum. This may result in traumatic dementia, or the "punch drunk syndrome," with deterioration of memory and intellect and motor changes consisting of ataxia and evidences of both pyramidal and extrapyramidal dysfunction.

TOXIC INVOLVEMENT OF THE CENTRAL NERVOUS SYSTEM

The adjective "toxic" is often used loosely in referring to involvement of both the peripheral and the central nervous systems. Many exogenous toxins, however, have a definite effect on nervous structures, central as well as peripheral, and possibly toxins of endogenous origin may also cause neurologic manifestations. Certain toxic encephalopathies are difficult to differentiate from encephalitides of viral origin. The possibility of either exposure to or ingestion of toxins must always be borne in mind when the clinician is confronted with a bizarre picture of cerebral dysfunction or evidences of diffuse brain damage.

Ethyl alcohol acts upon the nervous system through various mechanisms. Acute intoxication is caused by its depressant action. Disorders of thought and conduct are commonly the first symptoms to appear, with lack of judgment from loss of normal inhibition. Later coordination is affected, with staggering, dysarthria, and diplopia. The state of consciousness is progressively lowered, and coma may result. Abstinence or withdrawal symptoms include tremulousness, hallucinations, and delirium tremens. The so-called alcoholic polyneuropathy, Korsakoff's and Wernicke's syndromes, Marchiafava-Bignami disease, and retrobulbar neuropathy are nutritional disorders, resulting from deficiency of the vitamin B complex, especially thiamin. Chronic ingestion of alcohol in large amounts may lead to progressive cerebellar degeneration and mental deterioration. *Methyl alcohol* has a toxic effect on the optic nerves, and may also cause an encephalopathy, sometimes fatal.

The *bromides* and *barbiturates,* both of which are sedatives and anticonvulsants, in large doses, on prolonged use, and in susceptible individuals cause lethargy, confusion, delirium, and mental symptoms, with a toxic psychosis that resembles organic delirium. Excessive amounts may cause coma and death. Other hypnotics, such as *chloral hydrate, paraldehyde, glutethimide (Doriden), methyprylon (Noludar),* and *sulfonmethane,* may cause similar symptoms. The *phenothiazine preparations,* chlorpromazine (Thorazine), promazine (Sparine), prochlorperazine (Compazine), perphenazine (Trilafon), mepazine (Pactal), triflupromazine (Vesprin), and thioridazine (Mellaril), and other so-called *tranquilizers* such as reserpine, meprobamate (Equanil, Miltown), ethchlorvynol (Placidyl), chlordiazepoxide (Librium), diazepam (Valium), and others, including some of the antihistamines, are also sedatives, especially when used in large doses, and may cause lethargy, depression, and even coma and death. Addiction may develop with the use of all of the above drugs, and on withdrawal there may be insomnia, delirium, and convulsions. The phenothiazines and reserpine may also cause extrapyramidal manifestations, including parkinsonism, dyskinesias, dystonic reactions, and akathisia. Diphenylhydantoin (Dilantin) may also cause lethargy and confusion; in toxic doses it produces vertigo, ataxia, nystagmus, ocular palsies, and cerebellar manifestations.

Alkaloids of *opium* such as morphine, coedine, and heroin, synthetic morphine derivatives such as hydromorphone (Dilaudid), and related analgesics such as meperidine (Demerol) have a narcotic action on the central nervous system as well as a depressant action on vital centers which may lead to death; in certain susceptible individuals they may act as excitants and cause mania and even convulsions. The *general anesthetics* such as ether, chloroform, and nitrous oxide affect the central nervous system principally by their depressant action on the vital centers and the secondary production of anoxia. *Cocaine* and other local anesthetics may, in large doses or in susceptible individuals, cause symptoms of central nervous system stimulation that may lead to convulsions; stimulation is followed by depression and death owing to respiratory failure.

Strychnine, a central nervous system stimulant, may be responsible for fatal convulsions. Other stimulants such as picrotoxin, nikethamide (Coramine), pentamethylentetrazol (Metazol), camphor, caffeine, amphetamine, methylphenidate (Ritalin), pipradol (Meratran), iproniazid (Marsilid), phenelzine (Nardil), isocarboxazid (Marplan), nialamide (Niamid), imipramine (Trofranil), and amitriptyline (Elavil) may also cause insomnia, tremors, excitement, and, on occasion, convulsions. Tranylcypromine (Parnate) is also an antidepressant; it may in some cases, especially if used with some of the above drugs, cause headaches, hypertensive crises, and cerebral hemorrhage.

Among the heavy metals *lead* is best known for its toxic action. In adults the symptoms of lead poisoning are usually manifested by a peripheral neuritis, but in children there may be a lead encephalopathy with headache, tremors, convulsions, hemiplegia, and papilledema; the symptoms may resemble those of brain tumor. Pathologically there is evidence of widespread damage to the brain, with edema and perivascular hemorrhages. *Mercury* also causes a peripheral neuritis and may produce a toxic encephalopathy with irritability, tremors, ataxia, and mental symptoms. Inorganic *arsenical compounds,* especially *arsenic trioxide* (*arsenous acid*) and *potassium arsenite* (Fowler's solution), cause a peripheral neuritis, whereas organic arsenical compounds, such as *arsphenamine, neoarsphenamine,* and *tryparsamide,* may produce an intense hemorrhagic encephalopathy with perivascular hemorrhages and pronounced cerebral damage. Tryparsamide also has a toxic effect on the optic nerves and causes optic atrophy. *Barium* may cause tremors and ascending paralysis. *Thallium* produces not only a peripheral neuritis but also retrobulbar neuritis, cranial nerve palsies, delirium, and convulsions. *Chromium* may cause central nervous system symptoms which resemble those of lead encephalopathy. *Manganese* seems to have a highly selective action on the basal ganglia, and poisoning by it causes a syndrome that closely resembles Parkinson's disease; there may also be disseminated involvement and psychiatric symptoms. Intoxication with gold salts causes either excitement, confusion, and hallucinations, or apathy and withdrawal. The effects of increased or decreased amounts of sodium, postassium, calcium, etc., on the central nervous system will be discussed with disturbances of electrolyte metabolism.

Carbon monoxide, due to its affinity for hemoglobin, causes symptoms of tissue anoxia. Neurologic symptoms of carbon monoxide poisoning consist of headache, weakness, vertigo, dimness of vision, lethargy, confusion, syncope, coma, and convulsions. If a patient survives acute carbon monoxide poisoning, there may be diffuse cerebral changes, often with an extrapyramidal syndrome due to basal ganglion involvement, probably the result of selective destruction of susceptible structures by the anoxia. *Cyanide* preparations also interfere with oxygenation of tissues, not, however, by decreasing the oxygen in the blood, but by rendering the tissues incapable of utilizing oxygen. Cyanide poisoning is usually fatal, and asphyxial convulsions precede death. Recovery from cyanide intoxication is rare, and the existence of chronic manifestations is questionable.

Certain organic solvents and noxious gases and vapors affect the nervous system largely through their effect on the myelin. In acute *carbon tetrachloride* poisoning there is vertigo with lethargy followed by convulsions and coma. *Methyl bromide* and *methyl chloride* cause headache, vertigo, ataxia, pareses, visual symptoms, delirium, convulsions, and coma. Various *benzene derivatives,* including some of the aniline dyes, cause neuritic manifestations, pseudomyasthenic symptoms, retrobulbar neuritis, ataxia, delirium, stupor, and coma. Some of the aniline, or "coal-tar," antipyretics, such as *acetanilid, acetophenetidin, aminopyrine,* and *antipyrine,* cause similar neurologic changes, and the two former drugs also have a secondary effect on the nervous system through the production of methemoglobinemia. *Carbon disulfide* is very toxic to the nervous system; it causes peripheral neuropathy, optic atrophy, headache, vertigo, delirium and dementia, and parkinsonian symptoms.

Trichlorethylene poisoning is characterized by peripheral neuritis, disturbances of consciousness, retrobulbar neuritis, and convulsions. *Triorthcresyl phosphate* is known especially for its effect on the peripheral nerves, but it may cause diffuse central nervous system changes as well. The toxic effects on the nervous system of some of the newer *insecticides* such as chlorophenothane (DDT) have been reported. The organic phosphate inhibitors of cholinesterase may have central as well as peripheral actions and cause respiratory failure, convulsions, coma, and death.

Pharmacologic preparations other than those mentioned above may also have toxic effects in large doses or in susceptible individuals. The *salicylates* in high doses may cause stimulation followed by depression; they also have a specific effect on the eighth nerve, as does *quinine*. The *sulfonamides* may affect the peripheral nerves, or they may cause vertigo, ataxia, confusion, nausea and vomiting, delirium, and convulsions. Other substances which may have a toxic effect on the nervous system include Cannabis indica (marijuana), d-lysergic acid diethylamide (LSD–25), mescaline, and other hallucinogens; atropine and other cholinergic drugs, including those used for the treatment of Parkinson's disease—trihexyphenidyl (Artane), cycrimine (Pagitane), benztropine (Cogentin), and others; the antihistaminic drugs; penicillin, streptomycin, and other antibiotics; cortisone, corticotropin, and allied steroid preparations; heparin, bishydroxycoumarin (Dicumarol), and other anticoagulant agents; and many less common drugs, chemicals, and poisons, including phosphorus, nicotine, formaldehyde, bismuth, nitrites, tetrachlorethane, nitrobenzol, dinitrobenzol, trinitrotoluene (TNT), bulbocapnine, apiol, absinthe, and others.

Organic poisons may have both central and peripheral actions. *Curare* acts principally at the myoneural junction. *Diphtheria toxin* has a predilection for peripheral nerves. *Botulinus toxin* affects the medullary centers, although it may also act on the myoneural junction and peripheral nerves; in botulinus poisoning there are mild gastrointestinal symptoms which are followed by diplopia, blurring of vision, dimness of vision, dysarthria, dysphonia, generalized muscular weakness, lethargy, and paralysis of the muscles supplied by the midbrain and medullary nerves. The convulsive seizures and intense reflex activity of *tetanus* are probably the result of the action of the toxin upon the central nervous system, although there may also be a direct action upon muscles and the end plates of the motor nerve fibers. The toxin of the poisonous *mushrooms, Amanita muscaria* and *phalloides,* produces nausea, vomiting, confusion, irritability, delirium, convulsions, and coma. The toxin of the woodtick, Dermacentor venustus and related species, causes an ascending paralysis. In *ergotism* the peripheral manifestations are most common (gangrenous variety), although there may be psychotic symptoms and convulsions. In *lathyrism* there is nausea with vomiting, and later spastic paralysis and mental symptoms. Poisoning by snake venoms causes paralysis of nerve endings and respiratory centers, with convulsions and respiratory paralysis; that by spider venoms causes pain, restlessness, anxiety, vomiting, cyanosis, and collapse. The encephalopathy with cerebral edema and vascular changes that may develop following stings by bees and other insects is thought to be an allergic response. The term "toxic" is often applied to the cerebral changes that may occur with systemic infections and febrile states; most likely, however, metabolic alterations, inflammation, and other processes are also involved. The postinfectious and postvaccinial encephalitides are sometimes referred to as "toxic" processes; the demyelination that occurs in these, however, is probably the result of an allergic reaction. Endogenous toxins, such as those associated with uremia and eclampsia, also cause nervous system dysfunction; these will be discussed with the metabolic disturbances.

Extensive burns are frequently associated with evidences of severe intoxication. Somnolence, apathy, and delirium are not uncommon; there may be decerebrate rigidity. Pathologically there may be vascular changes, perivascular infiltrations, and edema; there may be thromboses of venous sinuses. Later there is degeneration of the ganglion cells of the brain along with glial infiltrations, scarring, atrophy, and demyelination. *Heat exhaustion, heat stroke,* and *sunstroke* may cause headache, vertigo, lethargy, delirium, convulsions, and coma; impairment of the vital centers causes hyperpyrexia, anhidrosis, disorders of water and electrolyte metabolism, and shock. Pathologically there may be cerebral edema, congestion, and petechial hemorrhages which cause irreversible memory difficulties, loss of ability to concentrate, and irritability. Prolonged *hypothermia* may also cause brain damage characterized by confusion, disorientation, amnesia, and disturbances of consciousness. *Lightning* and *electrical currents* may cause death through paralysis of respiration; if the shock is not immediately fatal, there may be unconsciousness for a variable period of time, with or without convulsions. Pathologically there are petechial hemorrhages, necrosis of the neurons, and degenerative cortical changes. The adult nervous system is relatively resistant to *ionizing radiation,* although excessive amounts of either radium or roentgen-ray therapy to the brain or spinal cord may cause delayed, progressive, irreparable damage to these structures; the peripheral nerves and nerve roots and plexuses may be similarly affected. Relatively small amounts of radiation to the developing brain, especially in the early stages of the development of the fetus, may cause microcephaly, hydrocephalus, and other development anomalies. There may be vascular changes associated with high altitude flying, decompression, and blast injury. The symptoms of caisson disease, namely pains, confusion, disturbances of consciousness, convulsions, and paralyses, are due to multiple small infarcts caused by nitrogen bubbles in the blood stream.

Anoxia, whether due to lack of oxygen in the surrounding air, obstruction of the air way, paralysis of the muscles of respiration, impaired circulation of blood to the brain, impaired utilization or transport of oxygen by the blood, cardiac failure or prolonged circulatory arrest, protracted anesthesia, neonatal asphyxia, carbon monoxide poisoning, high altitude flying, decompression, or blast injury, may cause either transient or irreversible manifestations. The gray matter is most susceptible to oxygen deprivation, and the most pronounced changes are in the cerebral cortex, basal ganglia, hypothalamus, brain stem nuclei, and cerebellum. There may be hemorrhagic changes as well. If the patient survives there may be permanent residuals with paralyses, a clinical state resembling either decerebrate rigidity or parkinsonism, intellectual loss, or blindness. Delayed neurologic deterioration following anoxia has been described.

METABOLIC ALTERATIONS OF THE CENTRAL NERVOUS SYSTEM

The term "metabolic alterations" is used to include a wide variety of systemic disorders—endocrine, deficiency, hepatic, renal, and others—that may affect the nervous system either directly or indirectly. The brain and its functions are extremely sensitive to disturbances in the physiology of the body, and the first clinically apparent symptoms and signs of many systemic diseases may be due to their effect on the nervous system. Certain of these—vascular disease, infections, and toxic involvement—have already been discussed. A survey of the effects of some of the other disturbances of body function follows.

Diabetes mellitus most often causes a neuropathy. This is usually a diffuse polyneuropathy, although there may be a mononeuritis monoplex, cranial nerve involvement (especially the oculomotor and abducens nerves), and visceral changes secondary to the affection of the autonomic nerves. It has been postulated that both metabolic alterations and deficiency factors may be responsible for these. Diabetic myelopathy and amyotrophy have also been described but are rare, as is diabetic encephalopathy. The cerebral changes that are often encountered in patients with long-standing diabetes and in older patients with the disease are usually of vascular origin, either focal or diffuse. It is known that there is a definite predilection for the development of arteriosclerosis in patients with diabetes. *Hypoglycemia* also affects the nervous system through the production of autonomic symptoms, sensory changes, pareses, irritability, hyperkinesias, psychic manifestations, convulsions, and coma, and there may be irreversible cerebral damage due to edema, perivascular infiltrations, extravasation of blood, swelling of the axis cylinders, and degeneration of the ganglion cells. Hypoglycemia may result from excessive doses of insulin (especially regular, or crystalline, insulin) organic or functional hyperinsulinism, or the administration of insulin shock in the treatment of psychoses.

Endocrinopathies may have either primary or secondary effects on the nervous system. Disorders of the *pituitary* gland are discussed in Chapter 43. Deficiency of *thyroid* secretion on a congenital basis causes cretinism with retarded mental and physical development. Acquired deficiency causes myxedema, with lethargy, weakness, slowness of speech, fatigue, and, on occasion, coma. With myxedema there may be an elevation of the cerebrospinal fluid protein, and on examination of the reflexes there is slowness of muscle contraction and relaxation. Hyperthyroidism causes weakness, nervousness, irritability, and tremors; there may be exophthalmos and ocular palsies. Thyrotoxic myopathy is discussed in Chapter 29. A form of periodic paralysis may be associated with hyperthyroidism. Decrease of *parathyroid* function causes hypocalcemia, tetany (Chapter 28), convulsions, and occasional psychotic manifestations. Hyperparathyroidism causes hypercalcemia, bone changes (osteitis fibrosa cystica), nephrolithiasis with resulting renal changes, muscle weakness, and occasional psychotic episodes and organic mental changes. *Adrenal* hypofunction causes Addison's disease, with hypotension and marked weakness, fatigability, and weight loss. There may be psychotic manifestations. Adrenal hyperfunction causes adrenal virilism and the adrenogenital syndrome. A tumor of the adrenal cortex can also cause primary aldosteronism, with hypertension, hypokalemia, hypernatremia, recurring attacks of severe muscular weakness, and occasionally tetany and diabetes mellitus. A chromaffin cell tumor of the adrenal medulla (pheochromocytoma) causes either sustained or intercurrent hypertension. With the latter there are paroxysmal attacks of headache, palpitation, precordial pain, and other symtoms of hyperadrenalism which may give rise to cerebral hemorrhage, pulmonary edema, or cardiac failure. Hypoinsulinism (diabetes mellitus) and hyperinsulinism with resulting hypoglycemia, are discussed above.

Vitamin and nutritional deficiencies may be responsible for a variety of neurologic disorders. *Vitamin A* deficiency in infants may cause mental retardation, hydrocephalus, and signs of increased intracranial pressure. Deficiences of many of the constitutents of the *vitamin B complex* cause serious nervous system alterations. *Thiamin* deficiency affects both the peripheral nerves and the central nervous system. In *beriberi,* the result of prolonged thiamin deficiency, there is a severe polyneuritis; there may be retrobulbar neuropathy and cerebral changes as well. The polyneuropathy, Korsakoff's and Wernicke's syndromes, Marchiafava-Bignami disease, and retrobulbar neuritis of chronic alcoholism are thought to be secondary to thiamin deficiency. Severe and prolonged deificiency of *niacin* (*nicotinic acid*) causes *pellagra,* in which there are both spinal cord involvement and mental symptoms. *Pyridoxine* (B_6) deficiency in infants causes irritability, motor activity, and convulsions. In adults pyridoxine deficiency has been encountered in patients taking isoniazid, with resulting polyneuropathy and, on occasion, convulsions. Deficiency or failure of absorption of *cyanocobalamin* (B_{12}) is responsible for *pernicious anemia,* in which the primary neurologic changes are in the posterior and lateral columns of the spinal cord and the peripheral nerves, but the cerebrum and optic nerves may be affected as well. *Vitamin C* deficiency causes *scurvy* with symptoms of hyperirritability, generalized tenderness, and a tendency toward bleeding; there may be hemorrhagic lesions in the peripheral nerves and central nervous system. A deficiency of *vitamin D* causes a disturbance of calcium metabolism which, in some cases, may lead to the development of tetany.

Hepatic disorders of serious consequence may cause a constellation of neurologic alterations and symptoms. Among the underlying disease processes are cirrhosis, acute and chronic hepatitis, and disturbances of the portal or hepatic circulation, including portacaval anastomoses. There may be motor symptoms, including tremors, asterixis, and rigidity, and mental changes consisting of lethargy, irritability, depression, confusion, disorientation, delirium, and coma. A disturbance of nitrogen metabolism with increase in the concentration of blood ammonia is thought to be responsible for the cerebral changes and resulting symptoms. *Uremia* develops with *renal* failure. An accumulation of toxic substances, principally protein derivatives, in the body fluids may lead to the development of apathy, fatigue, headache, drowsiness, delirium, stupor, convulsions, and coma. Convulsions, encephalopathy, psychotic states, and peripheral neuropathies may also occur in patients undergoing hemodialysis in the treatment of renal disease; with renal transplantation symptoms may appear which are related to either rejection of the organ or the sudden shift of electrolytes as the kidney begins to function. The encephalopathy that may accompany *chronic pulmonary insufficiency* or respiratory failure causes headaches, confusion, tremors, somolence, stupor, and coma; there may be papilledema and other signs of increase in intracranial pressure.

Disturbances of water and electrolytes may cause cerebral changes and neurologic symptoms. *Dehydration* results from either excessive loss of water and electrolytes via the kidneys, gastrointestinal tract, and skin, or decreased fluid intake. There may be fatigue, weakness, and irritability, and in late stages delirium, stupor, and coma. *Water intoxication* may have many etiologies, including excessive or inappropriate secretion of antidiuretic hormone, renal insufficiency, and sodium depletion; it is sometimes either iatrogenic or self-induced. There is reduction of awareness and responsiveness followed by convulsions and signs of increased intracranial pressure. *Disturbances of the electrolytes* consist of alterations of the concentrations of anions (sodium, potassium, calcium, and magnesium) and cations (bicarbonate, chloride, phosphate, sulfate, and proteinate) in both extracellular and intracellular fluids as well as changes in the acid-base balance. There is seldom a simple, one-factor electrolyte change. Dehydration may be accompanied by hypernatremia, overhydration by hyponatremia. With protracted vomiting, hypochloremic alkalosis is accompanied by hypokalemia. Metabolic acidosis may provoke hypokalemia. Hypernatremia may be accompanied by hypokalemia. An extreme variation of any single factor may alter neurologic functions and cause nonspecific symptoms consisting first of lassitude, lethargy, depression, and irritability, and then a confusional mental state progressing to delirium, collapse, and convulsions or coma. Somewhat specific features that accompany altered concentrations of certain electrolytes are the following: With either an excess or deficiency of *potassium* there may be flaccid muscular weakness or paralysis, including the muscles supplied by the cranial nerves, and myocardial and electrocardiographic changes. With either *alkalosis* or *hypocalcemia* there may be tetany. *Magnesium* in high concentrations may cause neuromuscular depression, and a deficiency may cause irritability, confusion, seizures, tremors, and choreiform movements. Hypokalemic, hyperkalemic, and normokalemic varieties of periodic paralysis have been described (Chapter 21). With hypernatremic encephalopathy there may be vascular damage with hemorrhagic lesions within the brain as well as subarachnoid hemorrhages.

Many disturbances of neurologic function occur as a result of multiple underlying metabolic alterations. This is especially apt to be true in certain postoperative syndromes developing in elderly patients. There may be a basic deficiency of blood and oxygen supply to the brain, consequent to anemia, decreased blood concentration, arteriosclerosis, reduced blood flow, and impaired diffusion from capillaries to cells. Secondarily there may be a disturbance of electrolyte, glucose, and protein metabolism, and either lack of enzyme activation, inhibition of enzyme activitiy, or destruction of enzymes. Finally there may be the toxic effects of sedatives and other drugs, as well as the influence of infection. All these, working together, may be responsible for the clinical picture and sometimes for irreversible cellular damage.

Biochemical investigations, chromosome studies, and other avenues of research have shown that there are many neurologic diseases in which the pathologic alterations and clinical manifestations are the result of an inborn error of metabolism. *Wilson's disease* is a genetically determined disorder of copper metabolism; there is a decrease of ceruloplasmin in the blood with accumulations of copper in the brain, liver, and other organs, and the pathologic alterations and symptoms are probably the result of copper toxicity. Disorders of *lipid metabolism* include Gaucher's disease, Niemann-Pick disease, Schüller-Christian disease, Tay-Sachs disease, and the late infantile and juvenile forms of lipidosis; the central nervous system may be affected either primarily or secondarily in these, and different lipid factors may be involved in the various syndromes. *Porphyria* is a biochemical abnormality in which there is an excessive formation and excretion of porphobilinogen and its precursors in the urine and feces. There are several varieties of the disease, but the most important one from a neurologic point of view is acute intermittent porphyria, which is inherited as a mendelian dominant. In this there are recurring symptoms consisting of abdominal pain, hypertension, polyneuritis, mental symptoms, convulsions, and the excretion of burgundy-red urine. Pathologically there are patchy areas of demyelination in the central nervous system and degenerative changes in the dorsal root ganglia and anterior horn cells.

Phenylketonuria is an inherited defect in the hydroxylation of phenylalanine, with secondary alterations in the metabolism of other aromatic amino acids. It causes irreversible changes in the developing brain, and was one of the first-known metabolic causes of mental deficiency. Other biochemical disorders, most of which are inherited, that cause mental deficiency are gargoylism (Hurler's disease), galactosemia, maple syrup urine disease, Hartnup disease, pseudohypoparathyroidism, and glycogen storage disease.

DISTURBANCES OF DEVELOPMENT

The brain, as well as other parts of the body, may fail to develop normally during intrauterine life or may be either injured or deformed at the time of birth. Microcephaly, macrocephaly, cerebral dysplasia and dysgenesis, congenital absence of structures (e.g., the corpus callosum), lissencephaly and other abnormalities of the gyri and convolutions, heterotopias, encephalocele, porencephalic cysts, hydranencephaly, and congenital hydrocephalus may result from abnormalities of brain growth during the embryonic and fetal periods; in most instances these are manifested by mental deficiency, paralytic or dyskinetic phenomena, and convulsive attacks. Congenital spastic paraplegia (Little's disease), cerebral diplegia, infantile hemiplegia, status marmoratus, congenital athetosis, dystonia, and ataxia may be the result of many factors, including abnormalities of development, prolonged or precipitate labor, paranatal anoxia, meningitis or encephalitis preceeding or immediately following birth, injury or hemorrhage during delivery, kernicterus associated with erystoblastosis fetalis, and maternal infections such as toxoplasmosis, cytomegalic inclusion-body disease, and German measles. Malformations or abnormalities of development of the skull and cervical spine, including craniostenosis, craniofacial dysostosis (Crouzon's syndrome), hypertelorism, spina bifida, and cranium bifidum, also affect cerebral development and cause neurologic symptoms.

There are many causes for congenital mental retardation, including the inborn errors of metabolism mentioned above, but in some cases no etiology is found. The following, however, are among the specifically classified syndromes, in some of which the mechanism is known: cretinism, or congenital thyroid deficiency; mongolism (Down's syndrome) and other chromosomal aberrations; tuberous sclerosis (Bourneville's disease), neurofibromatosis (Recklinghausen's disease), and other phakomatoses; Lowe's cerebro-oculorenal syndrome, Heller's syndrome (dementia infantilis), and the Cornelia de Lange syndrome characterized by mental retardation, microcephaly, peculiar facies, and skeletal anomalies, especially of the extremities.

DEGENERATIVE PROCESSES AND MISCELLANEOUS DISORDERS

There are many diseases of the nervous system whose etiology and mode of production are not known. Some of these have been shown to be hereditary conditions, and others may yet be proved to be hereditary. The majority of them, however, have no familial pattern, and their cause is not understood. There are many theories regarding the etiology of this large group of conditions; they may be caused by some unknown infectious process, related to minor vascular change, associated with an inherent disorder of metabolism or a deficiency or dysfunction of certain enzyme systems, of unknown "toxic" etiology, or secondary to abiotrophy, or inadequate vital resistance of certain structures. For lack of better means of classification, the members of this large group of diseases are often called degenerative conditions, and most of them are characterized by progressive impairment of function. There may be endogenous factors (latent weakness in constitution or underlying circulatory or metabolic disorders), exogenous factors, or both. There usually are multiple and cumulative causes, the onset is insidious and asymptomatic, and the course is chronic but increasingly deteriorative. Many degenerative diseases are associated with the aging process.

Disorders which are (under most circumstances) heredofamilial are Huntington's chorea, Wilson's disease, Hallervorden-Spatz disease, dystonia musculorum deformans, essential tremor, the lipidoses, myoclonus epilepsy (Unverricht's disease), the phakomatoses (including tuberous sclerosis and neurofibromatosis) metachromatic leukodystrophy, the diffuse heredofamilial leukodystrophies (Pelizaeus-Merzbacher disease and diffuse cerebral sclerosis of Krabbe), as well as other disorders of the nervous and neuromuscular systems which are not classified as cerebral disorders (the spinocerebellar degenerations, hereditary ataxia with muscular atrophy, parenchymatous cerebellar degeneration, olivopontocerebellar atrophy, the muscular dystrophies, certain hereditary muscular atrophies, Charcot-Marie-Tooth disease, and the hereditary neuropathies).

Cerebral degenerative disease which develops during the presenile and aging periods and which, under most circumstances, are not heredofamilial are Alzheimer's disease, Pick's disease, Creutzfeldt-Jakob disease (spastic pseudosclerosis or corticostriatospinal degeneration), subacute spongiform and/or vascular encephalopathy, the syndrome of occult hydrocephalus with normal cerebrospinal fluid pressure, senile dementia, Parkinson's disease, and amyotrophic lateral sclerosis.

Important among the diseases whose etiologies are still not definitely known are the so-called demyelinating diseases. The commonest is *multiple sclerosis,* which may affect the spinal cord, brain stem, cerebellum, cerebrum, optic nerves, and other portions of the nervous system. Related conditions include disseminated encephalomyelitis, Schilder's disease (encephalitis periaxialis diffusa), diffuse sclerosis, neuromyelitis optica, and others. Many theories of causation have been proposed through the years, although none have been universally accepted. Similar pathologic changes and demyelination of the nervous system occur in the postvaccinial and postinfectious encephalomyelitides, as a reaction to certain toxins, in some deficiency states, and as a result of vascular damage, anoxia, and other nocent mechanisms. Lesions comewhat resembling those of multiple sclerosis can be produced in experimental animals after the injection of homologous brain extracts fortified by a variety of adjuvants. Current opinion favors an autoimmune process or a reaction to some unknown allergin as the causative factor, but other theories, including infection by an as yet unknown virus or similar organism, are still held. There is much that is still to be learned about the above conditions, but their clinical syndromes, with either disseminated or diffuse nervous system involvement, and oftentimes exacerbations and remissions, are fairly well understood.

There are certain miscellaneous disorders that affect the nervous system. The collagen diseases (periarteritis nodosa, disseminated lupus erythematosus, giant cell arteritis, scleroderma, and dermatomyositis) may involve the central or peripheral nervous system or the muscles. *Sarcoidosis* may cause a meningeal reaction, cranial nerve palsies, optic neuritis, and encephalitic symptoms. Primary *amyloidosis* may cause a peripheral neuritis, often with extensive autonomic changes; the spinal cord and brain are usually spared. *Carcinoma* may affect the nervous system through metastasis or direct extension, by pressure on nerves or nerve roots, or as a carcinomatous meningitis; in addition, however, neuromyopathies, cerebellar degeneration, and even myelopathies and encephalopathies have been reported in association with carcinomatosis. The mechanism for these complications is not known, but a metabolic alteration, possibly due to the production of an antimetabolite or antivitamin by the carcinoma, a toxic etiology, and a combination of a viral infection and an autoimmune process have all been suggested. Neurologic manifestations of *allergy, hypersensitivity,* and *anaphylaxis* include angioneurotic edema, the postvaccinial and postinfectious and certain other encephalomyelitides, serum neuritis, and the reactions to some insect bites and drugs. Certain instances of migraine, and possibly even of epilepsy, may be allergic in origin. It has been suggested that some disorders which secondarily involve the nervous system (e.g., the collagen diseases) as well as specific neurologic conditions such as multiple sclerosis, myasthenia gravis, the Guillain-Barré syndrome, and others, may be autoimmune disorders.

REFERENCES

ACHESON, E. D. The clinical syndrome variously called benign myalgic encephalo-myelitis, Iceland disease and epidemic neuromyasthenia. *Am. J. Med.* 26:567, 1959.

ADAMS, R. D., FISHER, C. M., HAKIN, S., OJEMANN, R. G., and SWEET, W. H. Symptomatic occult hydrocephalus with "normal" cerebrospinal-fluid pressure: A treatable syndrome. *New England J. Med.* 273:117, 1965,

AITA, J. Neurologic Manifestations of General Diseases. Springfield, Ill., Charles C Thomas, 1964.

ALLISON, R. S. The Senile Brain: A Clinical Study. London, Edward Arnold (Publishers) Ltd. 1962.

ALVORD, E. C., JR. The relationship of hypersensitivity to infection, inflammation and immunity. *J. Neuropath. & Exper. Neurol.* 25:1, 1966.

BAILEY, P. Intracranial Tumors (ed. 2). Springfield, Ill., Charles C Thomas, 1948.

BAKER, A. B. "Viral encephalitis," in Baker, A. B. (ed.), Clinical Neurology (ed. 2). New York, Hoeber Medical Division, Harper & Row, 1962, vol. 2. pp. 811–858; "Secondary forms of encephalitis," *Ibid.* pp. 859–927.

BASS, M. H., and CAPLAN, J. Vitamin A deficiency in childhood. *J. Pediat.* 74:690, 1955.

BRAIN, R., and NORRIS, F. H., JR. (eds.) Remote Effects of Cancer on the Nervous System. New York, Grune & Stratton, 1965.

BRINKMAN, C. A., WEGST, A. V., and KAHN, E. A. Brain scanning with mercury[203] labeled Neohydrin. *J. Neurosurg.* 19:644, 1962.

BROCK, S. (ed.) Injuries of the Brain and Spinal Cord and Their Coverings (ed. 4). New York, Springer Publishing Co., Inc., 1960.

BRUYN, G. W., STRAATHOF, L. J. A., and RAYMAKERS, G. M. J. Mollaret's meningitis: Differential diagnosis and diagnostic pitfalls. *Neurology* 12:745, 1962.

CHOU, S. N., AUST, J. B., MOORE, G. E., and PEYTON, W. Y. Radioactive iodinated human serum albumin as tracer agent for diagnosing and localizing intracranial lesions. *Proc. Soc. Exper. Biol. & Med.* 77:193, 1951.

COURVILLE, C. B. Contributions to the study of cerebral anoxia. *Bull. Los Angeles Neurol. Soc.* 15:99, 1950; Commotio Cerebri. Los Angeles, San Lucas Press, 1953.

CUMINGS, J. N., and KREMER, M. (eds.) Biochemical Aspects of Neurological Disorders. Springfield, Ill., Charles C Thomas, 1959.

CUSHING, H., and EISENHARDT, LOUISE. Meningiomas. Springfield, Ill., Charles C Thomas, 1938.

DAWSON, J. R. Cellular inclusions in cerebral lesions of epidemic encephalitis. *Arch. Neurol. & Psychiat.* 31:685, 1934.

DEJONG, R. N., and MAGEE, K. R. "Treatment of the metabolic and toxic disorders of the nervous system," in Forster, F. M. (ed.). *Modern Therapy in Neurology.* St. Louis, The C. V. Mosby Company, 1957.

DE VLIEGER, M., and RIDDER, H. J. Use of echoencephalography. *Neurology* 9:216, 1959.

DE VLIEGER, M., DE STERKE, A., MOLIN, C. E., and VAN DER VEN, V. Ultrasound for two-dimensional echo-encephalography. *Ultrasonics* 1:148, 1963.

DODGE, P. R., CRAWFORD, J. D., and PROBST, J. H. Studies in experimental water intoxication. *Arch Neurol.* 3:513, 1960.

DODGE, P. R., and SWARTZ, M. N. Bacterial meningitis—a review of selected aspects. *New England J. Med.* 272:954, 1003, 1965.

DUNBAR, H. S., and RAY, B. S. Localization of brain tumors and other intracranial lesions with radioactive iodinated human serum albumin. *Surg., Gynec. & Obstet.* 98:433, 1954.

EVANS, J. P. Acute Head Injury. Springfield, Ill., Charles C Thomas, 1950.

FIELDS, W. S., and BLATTNER, R. J. (eds.) Viral Encephalitis. Springfield, Ill., Charles C Thomas, 1958.

FINLEY, K. H., *et al.* Western equine and St. Louis encephalitis. *Neurology* 5:223, 1955.

FRIEDMAN, A. P., and MERRITT, H. S. (eds.) Headache: Diagnosis and Treatment. Philadelphia, F. A. Davis Company, 1959.

FUISZ, R. D. Hyponatremia. *Medicine* 42:149, 1963.

GLASER, G. H. Metabolic encephalopathy in hepatic, renal and pulmonary disorders. *Postgrad. Med.* 27:611, 1960.

HENSON, R. A., HOFFMAN, H. L., and URICH, H. Encephalomyelitis with carcinoma. *Brain* 88:449, 1965.

JERVIS, G. A., and STIMSON, C. W. DeLange syndrome. *J. Pediat* 63:634, 1963.

KERNOHAN, J. W., MABON, R. F., SVIEN, H. J., and ADSON, A. W. A simplified classification of the gliomas. *Proc. Staff Meet., Mayo Clin.* 24:71, 1949.

LEKSELL, L. Echo-encephalography: I. Detection of intracranial complications following head injury. *Acta chir. scandiav.* 110:301, 1955.

LUTRELL, C. N., and FINBERG, L. Hemorrhagic encephalopathy induced by hypernatremia: I. Clinical, laboratory, and pathological observations. *Arch. Neurol. & Psychiat.* 81:424, 1959.

McHENRY, L. O., JR. Rheoencephalography: A clinical appraisal. *Neurology* 15:507, 1965.

MENKES, J. H., RICHARDSON, F., and VERPLANCK, S. Program for detection of metabolic diseases. *Arch. Neurol.* 6:462, 1962.

MOORE, G. E. The use of radioactive fluorescein in the diagnosis and localization of brain tumors. *Science* 107:569, 1948.

MUNRO, D. The Treatment of Injuries to the Nervous System. Philadelphia, W. B. Saunders Company, 1952.

OJEMAN, R. G., ARONOW, S. A., and SWEET, W. S. Scanning with positron-emitting isotopes. *Arch. Neurol.* 10:218, 1964.

PLUM, F, POSNER, J. B., and HAIN, R. F. Delayed neurological deterioration after anoxia. *Arch. Int. Med.* 110:18, 1962.

QUINN, J. L., III, CIRIC, I., and HAUSER, W. H. Analysis of 96 abnormal brain scans using technetium 99m (pertechnetate form). *J.A.M.A.* 194:157, 1965.

RICHARDSON, J. C., CHAMBERS, R. A., and HEYWOOD, P. M. Encephalopathies of anoxia. *Arch. Neurol.* 1:178, 1959.

RUSSELL, W. R. Some reactions of the nervous system to trauma. *Br. M. J.* 2:403, 1964.

SAHS, A. L., and JOYNT, R. J. "Meningitis," in Baker, A. B. (ed.), Clinical Neurology (ed. 2). New York, Hoeber Medical Division, Harper & Row., 1962, vol. 2. pp. 717–785.

SHERLOCK, S., SUMMERSKILL, W. H. J., WHITE, L. P., and PHEAR, E. A. Portalsystemtic encephalopathy: Neurological complications of liver disease. *Lancet* 2: 453, 1954.

SMADEL, J. E., BAILEY, P., and BAKER, A. B. (eds.) Sequelae of the anthropod-borne encephalitides. *Neurology* 8:873, 1958.

946 THE NEUROLOGIC EXAMINATION

STANBURY, J. B., WYNGAARDEN, J. B., and FREDRICKSON, D. S. The Metabolic Basis of Inherited Disease (ed. 2). New York, Blakiston Division-McGraw-Hill Book Co., 1966.

SWARTZ, M. N., and DODGE, P. R. Bacterial meningitis—a review of selected aspects. *New England J. Med.* 272:725, 779, 842, 898, 1965.

SYMONDS, C. Concussion and its sequelae. *Lancet* 1:1, 1962.

TANAKA, K., ITO, K., and WAGAI, T. The localization of brain tumors by ultrasonic techniques. *J. Neurosurg.* 23:135, 1965.

TOBIS, J. S., and LOWENTHAL, M. Evaluation and Management of the Brain-Damaged Patient. Springfield, Ill., Charles C Thomas, 1960.

TYLER, H. R. Neurological complications of dialysis, transplantation, and other forms of treatment in chronic uremia. *Neurology* 15:1081, 1965.

VICTOR, M., and ADAMS, R. D. The effect of alcohol on the nervous system. *A. Res. Nerv. & Ment. Dis., Proc.* 32:526, 1952.

WADA, J., and RASMUSSEN, T. Intracarotid injection of Sodium Amytal for the lateralization of cerebral speech dominance: Experimental and clinical observations:. *J. Neurosurg.* 17:266, 1960.

WALTON, J. N. Subarachnoid Haemorrhage. Edinburgh and London, E. & S. Livingstone Ltd., 1956.

WEEKS, D. B., TOOLE, J. F., and ROBINSON, R. Palencephalography. *Neurology* 16:153, 1966.

WARD, A. A.., JR. Physiologic basis of concussion. *J. Neurosurg.* 15:129, 1958.

WOLFF, H. G. Headache and Other Head Pain (ed. 2). New York, Oxford University Press, 1963.

ZIMMERMAN, H. M., NETSKY, M. G., and DAVIDOFF, L. M. Atlas of Tumors of the Nervous System. Philadelphia, Lea & Febiger, 1956.

PART NINE

Special Methods of Examination

THE EXAMINATION IN STATES OF DISORDERED CONSCIOUSNESS: COMA, STUPOR, DELIRIUM, AND CONVULSIONS

THE STATE of consciousness is the level of the individual's awareness and the responsiveness of his mind to himself, his environment, and the impressions made by his senses. This level of awareness may be disturbed in various ways and degrees by alterations in cerebral function as well as by nonorganic factors. In coma, stupor, and hypersomnia there is a lowering of consciousness; in confusion and delirium there is a clouding of consciousness; in amnesia there is a loss of memory that usually affects only either a circumscribed period of time or certain experiences; in the convulsive state there is either paroxysmal loss of consciousness or amnesia, usually accompanied by motor phenomena or disturbances in behavior.

Coma is defined as a state of complete, or almost complete, loss of consciousness from which the patient cannot be aroused by ordinary stimuli, sometimes not by even the most painful or powerful stimulus. It is a state of complete unresponsiveness to the environment. The patient makes no voluntary movements. His reactions are limited to elemental reflexes, and even some of these may be impaired. In profound coma painful stimuli such as pressure on the eyeballs and pinching of the skin fail to arouse the patient. Corneal sensation and reflexes are absent. The pupils may be either dilated or contracted and do not react. The swallowing and cough reflexes are abolished and the patient may be unable to swallow either water or food; he usually

949

is incontinent of urine. The cutaneous reflexes and often the deep reflexes are absent; occasionally in profound degrees of coma the deep reflexes are exaggerated and Babinski responses are obtained.

Stupor, or *semicoma,* is a state of partial or relative loss of response to the environment in which the patient's consciousness may be impaired in varying degrees. There is no significant defect of the elemental reflexes. The patient is difficult to arouse, but it is usually possible to stimulate him briefly, although responses are slow and inadequate. He is otherwise oblivious to what is going on about him, and soon falls back into the stuporous state. In profound stupor the patient may respond only to painful stimulation, but in lighter stages he may react to noises, calls by name, visual threats, and even verbal commands, and he may be able to execute simple acts such as shutting the eyes and protruding the tongue. The corneal and pupillary reflexes are unimpaired, and there are no consistent changes in the superficial and deep reflexes. Pathologic reflexes are not obtained, and swallowing and coughing are normally performed. The patient usually makes no spontaneous movements except when aroused. There is normal control of the sphincters.

Lethargy, or *hypersomnia,* is a morbid drowsiness, or a continued or prolonged sleep; the patient can usually be aroused or awakened and then appears to be in complete possession of his senses, but he may fall back into sleep as soon as the stimulus is removed. *Syncope* is a transient, partial or complete suspension of consciousness which is usually accompanied by temporary respiratory and circulatory impairment, with a rapid, feeble pulse, rapid respirations, pallor, increased perspiration, and coldness of the skin. *Amnesia* is a loss of memory which usually affects either a circumscribed period of time or certain experiences without loss of orientation for the immediate environment.

Confusion is a state in which there is only a mild lowering of the level of consciousness, and the elemental responses, simple mental functions, and reactions to ordinary commands are intact. The impairment of the patient's awareness is manifested by defects in the attention span and memory and loss of normal appreciation for and perception of the environment. The chief symptoms may be in the field of orientation, with a defect in time sense and loss of identification of self and others. There is impaired capacity to think clearly and with customary rapidity, and to perceive, respond to, and remember current stimuli.

Delirium is characterized by confusion with disordered perception and loss of attention, but there are also manifestations of motor and sensory irritability together with abnormal mental phenomena. Disorientation for time is more marked than that for either place or person, and there often are fluctuations in the level of attention, frequently with diurnal or nocturnal variations. Excitement is an outstanding symptom; the patient is restless, and there may be hyperkinesia with marked motor activity and an increased response to all types of stimuli, many of which are interpreted incorrectly. Psychic symptoms include incoherence, illusions, hallucinatory manifestations, and delusional ideas.

The convulsive state is a transient episode of uncontrollable motor activity, either focal or generalized, which usually is accompanied by clouding or loss of consciousness. The motor activity may alternate with either rigidity or atonia. In the postconvulsion period there may be coma, stupor, confusion, or psychic manifestations. Other types of epilepsy include the following: focal seizures in which the motor phenomena are confined to one extremity or one side of the body, with or without sensory manifestations or loss of consciousness; very brief periods of altered or severely obtunded consciousness, usually without motor accompaniments; automatisms with associated amnesia, disturbances of feeling or behavior, hallucinations, and autonomic changes; myoclonic and akinetic seizures and *formes frustes*.

The above-mentioned varieties of disordered consciousness are usually manifestations of organic disease of the central nervous system, although many of them may also be encountered in hysteria and psychotic states. Coma, stupor, and delirium, as well as the convulsive and postconvulsion states, constitute emergency situations which must be evaluated with the least possible delay; treatment must be instituted immediately, and the mode of therapy may vary widely, depending upon the etiology. It is always of utmost importance to determine the causative factors and to discriminate between organic and psychogenic etiologies. This latter differentiation is not always an easy one, however, and a detailed examination with prolonged observation is sometimes necessary. It is the general practitioner of medicine who is usually called upon to diagnose and treat states of disordered consciousness, often under circumstances which render evaluation difficult. Inasmuch, however, as most such disturbances are fundamentally neurologic problems and are associated with altered function of higher nervous centers, the neurologist is often sought as a consultant, especially if the diagnosis is a difficult one to make. Coma, stupor, and allied states must always be distinguished from the following: *mutism,* in which the patient is completely withdrawn from the environment and is unable or refuses to speak; *negativism,* in which, because of mental disease, the patient presents an abnormality of behavior which is characterized by either failure to perform acts which are commanded or suggested (passive negativism), or performance of acts which are the opposite of those suggested (active negativism); *aphasia,* in which, as a result of focal rather than diffuse brain damage, there is a defect in either expression or interpretation of language functions.

The examination of the comatose, stuporous, or delirious patient, or of the individual who is exhibiting either a convulsive paroxysm or a postconvulsion state, may present many difficulties and complications, and often requires special methods of investigation. The general observation of the state of consciousness, including the alertness of the individual, attention span, reaction time, accessibility, and interest in the environment, are mentioned in Chapters 3 and 4. Occasionally however, there is an alteration of consciousness to such a degree that the usual procedure of examination cannot be followed. Special details which must be borne in mind under such circumstances are outlined in the following paragraphs.

THE HISTORY

The examination should be preceded in every instance by a careful history, if it is possible to obtain one. The history must, of course, be taken from a relative or an observer. It should include not only the mode of onset and the manifestations of the present episode, but also a detailed account of the patient's past health and illnesses.

A history, for instance, of convulsive attacks, diabetes mellitus, nephritis or other kidney disease, hypertension, arteriosclerosis, previous cerebrovascular disturbances, cardiac disease, syphilis, recent infections, alcoholism, drug addiction, pregnancy, or past depressions or suicidal attempts may give the necessary clues and aid the physician in starting therapy without delay. Specific details which must be borne in mind in eliciting the history of the manifestations which immediately preceded the period of disordered consciousness are listed separately.

If there is a history of trauma, one should attempt to determine the type, site, and severity of the injury; the time interval between the injury and the loss of consciousness; the degree and character of the loss of consciousness. With concussion, contusion, and laceration of the brain there is usually a history of recent injury with immediate loss of consciousness. With middle meningeal hemorrhage there may have been coma which was followed by a lucid interval and then, in turn, by progressively deepening stupor. With subdural hematoma the trauma may have been less recent. It is important to bear in mind that an epileptic convulsion may cause serious cerebral trauma, but that head injury may also cause immediate convulsions. It is also important to remember that alcoholism and trauma may occur together and that one may be a complication of the other.

Some information should always be obtained relative to the cardiovascular status, and a history of hypertension, arteriosclerosis, or syphilis may aid in the diagnosis of cerebrovascular insufficiency, cerebral thrombosis or hemorrhage, or subarachnoid hemorrhage. A history of cardiac disease such as acute endocarditis, vegetative endocarditis, subacute bacterial endocarditis, or auricular fibrillation may contribute to the diagnosis of cerebral embolism. Pulmonary disease, especially neoplasms or abscesses, and fractures of the long bones may also suggest the presence of cerebral embolism. A history of infections, either generalized or focal, but especially infections around the head and face, may be important in the diagnosis of coma, delirium, and convulsions; meningitis, encephalitis, and brain abscesses may complicate either systemic or localized infectious processes. A history of recurrent or persistent headaches, visual disturbances, convulsions or transient disturbances of consciousness, or personality changes may suggest the presence of brain tumor, brain abscess, subdural hematoma, or encephalitis.

The past mental history is also pertinent in the evaluation of the comatose patient. The previous habits and mental reactions may be informative in the diagnosis of alcoholic intoxication, narcotic or barbiturate intoxication, asphyxiation, and suicidal attempts. Furthermore, one should always bear in mind that hysteria and functional psychoses may cause symptoms which resemble those encountered in states of disordered consciousness of organic etiology.

THE GENERAL EXAMINATION

If the patient is entirely uncommunicative and if no informative history can be obtained from the relatives or observers, one may have to rely entirely upon the examination in the diagnosis of the comatose or delirious state. The investigation must be limited to the objective findings, that is to those signs which can be elicited without the cooperation of the patient. The examination may be far from satisfac-

tory, but every patient, no matter how stuporous, non-cooperative, or even negativistic or actively antagonistic, can be examined to a certain degree, and some
helpful information can be obtained.

In the *general observation* the examiner should note the patient's appearance and
behavior, his apparent age, the neatness and cleanliness of his clothes and person,
signs of acute or chronic illness, and evidences of trauma or blood loss. In attempting to appraise the *depth of impaired consciousness* one should observe vegetative
changes such as stertorous breathing and incontinence as well as responses to noises
and verbal commands, visual stimuli and threats, and tactile and painful stimulation.
Evidences of somatic disease may be made apparent by the presence of fever,
cyanosis, jaundice, pallor, and signs of dehydration and loss of weight; these are discussed more in detail in Chapter 3.

The *posture of the body and its parts* and all spontaneous acts and voluntary and
involuntary movements should be carefully appraised. The positions assumed by
the body as a whole and by the limbs are significant. The patient may appear comfortable, or may lie in an awkward or constrained position. In meningitis there may
be opisthotonos with retraction of the head but with marked flexion of the thighs
and legs. In hysteria there may also be opisthotonos, but the lower extremities are
in extension and the patient assumes the so-called *arc de cercle*. The tonus of the
body and the extremities, the position of the extremities, abnormalities of posture,
and the reaction of the parts of the body to painful and other stimuli and to placing
in awkward or uncomfortable positions may give some clue regarding obvious
paralyses, not only of the limbs, but also of the face and trunk muscles (see below).
The general activity (immobile, underactive, retarded, restless, or hyperkinetic),
tonus (limp, relaxed, rigid, or tense), degree of activity or passivity, and the presence of abnormal movements (tremors, twitches, tics, grimaces, and spasms) should
all be noted. Carphology (floccilation) is an involuntary tugging at the sheets and
picking of imaginary objects from the bedclothes, and jactitation is a tossing to
and fro on the bed; these are seen in acute disease, grave fevers, and great exhaustion. Motor unrest and excessive activity are seen in both organic and psychogenic
states. Stereotypy appears in psychoses, but also in organic delirium. If there are
convulsions, the examiner should note the distribution of the convulsive movements,
the spread of the convulsive phenomena, and associated manifestations such as
degree of impairment of consciousness, frothing at the mouth, tongue-biting, and
incontinence.

The *behavior of the patient* should be observed very closely and at all times. One
should note the patient's reactions to physicians, nurses, and relatives. Do his eyes
follow people and does he show some awareness of what is going on around him?
The conduct may be constant or it may be variable from time to time and influenced by special occurrences. The patient, for instance, may appear to be completely unconscious and fail to respond to any type of stimulation while the observers
are in the room, yet when not aware that he is being watched, he may open his
eyes, make furtive glances, and move around. Both spontaneous acts and defense
movements are important. The former may, on occasion, signify playfulness, mis-
chievousness, or assaultiveness; the latter may indicate depth of coma. One should

note whether the patient, even in coma, appears to be comfortable and natural, or assumes unnatural positions; whether he is drowsy, apathetic, clouded, confused, resistive, evasive, irritable, uncooperative, antagonistic, aggressive, or destructive; whether he can perform any routine acts; whether he can eat voluntarily, must be fed, or refuses food, and how he acts while eating or being fed; whether he can dress and undress himself, or requires assistance; whether he can indicate when he needs to go to the toilet; whether his actions show only initial retardation or consistent slowness throughout. In testing social reactions and responses to stimulation of various types one should note the degree of reaction and whether the movements are slow, abrupt, or natural. The patient may be given simple commands and asked to protrude his tongue, move his extremities, and grasp with his hands, and the type of motor response is noted. There may be compliance and automatic obedience to verbal commands, failure to reply, or negativistic responses. One should notice whether either distraction or commands influence the reaction to various stimuli.

The *facies* may afford valuable clues in diagnosis. The facial expression may be alert, attentive, smiling, placid, mask-like, apathetic, frowning, sulky, scowling, perplexed, bewildered, fearful, distressed, tearful, fixed, tense, angry, changeable, depressed, ecstatic, dramatic, grimacing, or vacant. It may be either constant or variable and, if the latter, the precipitating stimuli should be noted. The facial expression may afford information regarding emotional responsiveness, but one should also note display of emotional responses by acceleration of the pulse and respirations, changes in the color of the face, perspiration, tears, and smiling. One should note the presence of spontaneous emotional display, whether affective responses appear when reference is made to members of the family and certain personal facts or when visitors appear, and whether jokes or sad news elicit any change in facial expression or other responses. One should also observe the effect of unexpected stimuli, such as clapping of the hands and flashes of light, on the emotional reaction.

Evidences of communicativeness and expression by speech, writing, and gesture should be carefully noted. Does the patient take initiative in speech, and does he answer when addressed or stimulated? Even though he may be unable to talk, apparent efforts to speak may be observed by lip movements, whispers, or nodding or shaking of the head. The patient may be consistently mute or may have periods when he speaks, and the speech may be either emotionally precipitated or spontaneous. The exact utterances with the accompanying emotional reactions should be noted. Occasionally a patient who fails to talk may be able to write or to express his feelings by means of gestures or pantomime. Perseveration, loquaciousness, blocking, palilalia, echolalia (imitation of speech of others), and echopraxia (imitation of actions of others) are found in both organic and psychogenic states.

THE PHYSICAL EXAMINATION

The physical examination should be carried out in detail, and usually precedes the neurologic examination. The general appearance of the patient may give evidence of either chronic or acute illness; there may be signs of dehydration, emaciation, cachexia, or fever. The body habitus and general build of the patient may give some clue regarding susceptibility to disease. The color of the skin is significant.

Pallor may indicate recent hemorrhage, anemia, vasomotor syncope, or shock; floridity and ruddiness suggest hypertension or polycythemia; flushing of the skin and erythema may be present in fever; icterus indicates hepatic or gallbladder disease or blood dyscrasia; cyanosis is found in cardiac disease, pneumonia, electric shock, and certain toxic states such as that following exposure to cyanide; a cherry-red color of the skin appears in carbon monoxide poisoning, and vasomotor dilatation in alcoholic intoxication. Increased perspiration is evident in fever and in hypoglycemic shock. Petechiae are seen in blood dyscrasias and subacute bacterial endocarditis. Edema of the ankles may suggest cardiac or renal disease. The odor of the breath should always be noted; an odor of acetone is characteristic of diabetic acidosis, an odor of illuminating gas is sometimes found in carbon monoxide poisoning, and one of alcohol in acute intoxication. In poisoning there may be evidences of the toxic substance about the lips.

The patient should always be examined carefully for signs of injury, especially about the head. Bruises and hematomas, scalp wounds and lacerations, and bleeding from the orifices are all important, as are wounds, lacerations, and fractures of other parts of the body. It is always essential to remember that two conditions may occur together, such as trauma and alcoholic intoxication.

Special attention should be directed toward the blood pressure, temperature, pulse, and respiratory rate and rhythm. The blood pressure may be markedly increased in hypertensive states and renal disease; it may be decreased in shock, and either increased or decreased in increased intracranial pressure. The temperature is elevated in pneumonia, meningitis, encephalitis, and other infections, and is sometimes moderately increased in cerebrovascular disease and subarachnoid hemorrhage; it is decreased in carbon monoxide poisoning, diabetic coma, and many toxic states. The pulse may show variations; it may be rapid in infections, and slow, feeble, and irregular in toxic states and shock. It is full and bounding in hypertension and irregular in cardiac disease. There is profound bradycardia with increased intracranial pressure and also with heart block and Adams-Stokes disease. The respirations may be depressed, stertorous, irregular, or of the Cheyne-Stokes variety with cerebral lesions, and of the Kussmaul variety with evidence of air hunger in diabetic coma.

The association of disorders of consciousness with cardiac and pulmonary disease of various types is always important to bear in mind, and a detailed examination of the heart and lungs should be carried out on every comatose patient. The gastrointestinal and genito-urinary systems are often difficult to examine in states of coma, but vomiting, especially if projectile, and hematemesis should be noted, as well as retention and incontinence of urine and feces, wetting and soiling, priapism, and abdominal distention and rigidity. The examination of the eyes will be stressed under the neurologic appraisal, but it is important to bear in mind that the pupillary and corneal reactions should always be tested and that a fundus examination has utmost importance in the diagnosis of states of disordered consciousness. There may be decreased intraocular tension in diabetic coma. The ears, nose, mouth, and throat should also be investigated; in fact, an otoscopic examination should be considered essential.

THE NEUROLOGIC EXAMINATION

The details of the neurologic examination in the various states of disordered consciousness must vary with the degree of impairment and depth of coma. In semi-stupor, for instance, the patient may respond to certain stimuli with muscular movements and even carry out some commands; the reflexes may be normal, swallowing and vegetative functions unimpaired, and speech present. In deeper coma, however, the patient may show very little response to any type of stimulation, and even a painful stimulus may evoke no muscular movements; the reflexes may be diminished to absent, but occasionally exaggerated; there may be impairment of swallowing, alterations in the pulse and respirations, and failure of the pupils to react; since the palatal muscles are relaxed, respirations may be stertorous.

The *mental examination* is, of course, carried out with difficulty. In confusional states and delirium, however, it may be possible to elicit evidences of failure of attention, loss of perception, illusions, hallucinations, and delusions, and in the amnesias the circumscribed memory defect may be apparent.

The *sensory examination* must vary with the degree of impairment of consciousness. The profoundly comatose patient does not perceive even the most painful stimulus, whereas the stuporous individual may respond to painful irritation by wincing and by withdrawing the part of the body stimulated. If the patient is unable to give any relevant responses, however, it is impossible to evaluate his interpretation of superficial and proprioceptive sensations and his cortical sensory functions. Oftentimes the examination must be limited to observations of the responses to painful stimulation and a comparison of such responses on the two halves of the body. The investigation is carried out by pinching the skin, pricking with a sharp pin, pressing over the supraorbital notches or on the eyeballs, pressing on the knuckles, and squeezing the muscle masses and tendons. If the depth of coma is not too profound, the patient will respond to such testing by wincing, showing an expression of pain on his face, and attempting to withdraw the portion of the body stimulated. If the responses on the two halves of the body are compared, the examiner is able to determine whether painful stimuli are felt equally well on each side. If there is paralysis, of course, the patient will not be able to withdraw the arm or the leg when the skin is pinched, but he may indicate by his general reactions, such as wincing or attempting to withdraw the entire body, that sensation is present on the paretic side. With cerebral lesions there is often hemihypesthesia as well as hemiplegia, but the sensory defects are rarely complete and the patient may show an expression of pain on stimulation of the paretic extremity even though he does not withdraw it.

The *examination of the cranial nerves* can rarely be carried out in detail, and often must be limited to an appraisal of those nerves which are essentially motor in function. It may be possible, however, to test pain sensation on the skin of the face and the cornea and conjunctiva and to elicit certain of the cranial nerve reflexes. The olfactory nerve cannot be examined in stuporous and comatose persons. The optic, oculomotor, trochlear, and abducens nerves are discussed with the examination of the eyes and pupils (see below). The sensory functions of the trigeminal nerve can be examined, both on the face and mucous membranes (especially the cornea and conjunctiva) if coma is not too profound, but motor functions are difficult to test. Certain trigeminal nerve reflexes, however, such as the jaw jerk and the head retraction, corneal, and supraorbital reflexes, should be investigated. There may be trismus in tetanus and allied conditions. The motor supply of the facial nerve to the muscles of facial expression may be evaluated in the examination of motor status (see below); Chvostek's sign is significant in tetany, and a risus sardonicus in tetanus. The sensory functions of the facial nerve are insignificant in comatose states, but the presence of tears and an intact lacrimal reflex may be important. In testing the acoustic nerve one notes the response to loud noises and the presence of the auditory-palpebral, auditory-oculogyric, and general acoustic muscle reflexes. It may be impossible to examine directly the functions of the palatal and pharyngeal muscles, but the examiner should note the patient's ability to swallow, and should test the palatal and pharyngeal reflexes on each side. The carotid sinus reflex may also be investigated. Relaxation of the palatal muscles may cause the respirations to have a stertorous character, and impairment of the laryngeal functions may alter the tone of the voice and interfere with breathing and coughing. The patient may be unable to protrude his tongue, but the position in which it lies in the mouth may be important. The mouth may be either open or closed in stupor, and there may be resistance to passive opening and closing of the mouth in psychotic states. Foaming at the mouth, holding of saliva, and drooling of saliva, especially if unilateral, are all significant.

The *examination of the eyes and pupils* is perhaps the most important part of the cranial nerve evaluation. One should note whether the eyes are open or closed and should compare the width of the palpebral fissures on the two sides. In a facial paresis the fissure is increased in width, and in a third nerve paresis it is decreased. If the eyes are partially or completely closed, the examiner may try to open them by gently raising the upper lids, and then note the speed with which the eyes close again. If there is weakness of one of the orbiculares, there will be less rapid closing on that side. Forceful closing of the eyes may follow painful pressure over the exit of the supraorbital nerve or over the eyeball. In deep coma the eyes may be open with a glassy stare. Often in profound illness the patient lies with his eyes only partially closed, even in sleep, so that a narrow portion of the cornea is visible between the upper and lower lids. In hysterical states the eyes may be kept tightly closed and the patient resists attempts to open them; he may, however, open his eyes and make furtive glances when he is not aware that he is being observed. The examiner should also note whether there is blinking, flickering, or tremor of the eyelids when the patient rests, when light shines in the eyes, and when sudden movements are made toward the eyes, and whether there is blinking or closing of the eyes in response to loud noise (auditory-palpebral reflex). Both the corneal and conjunctival reflexes should be tested, and both the direct and consensual responses noted; in deep coma these reflexes are absent. In lesions of either the fifth or the seventh nerve the reflex may be absent on the involved side. In a seventh nerve lesion, however, there is a retained consensual reflex, but not in a fifth nerve lesion. It is important to recall that in drying of the cornea of an eye which is kept open for a long period of time there is also decreased corneal sensitivity; there may or may not be appearance of tears on touching the cornea.

The position of the eyeballs and function of the extraocular movements should always be noted. Conjugate deviation of the eyes or paralysis of conjugate gaze toward one side may follow either cerebral or brain stem lesions. Paralysis of individual ocular movements may be apparent from the position of the eyes at rest, and nystagmus may also be seen in the resting state. In meningitis and terminal states there may be either loss of coordination or dissociation of ocular movements. In both coma and sleep the eyeballs may be rolled upward, partially under the upper lids. Attempts should always be made to elicit some movement of the eyes. If the stupor is not profound, the patient may attempt voluntary eye movements in response to verbal commands or may follow movements of the examiner or of moving objects within his field of vision. In deeper coma there may be only a fixed, staring gaze, although it may be possible to elicit reflex movements, and rapid turning of the head to one side may be followed by contralateral ocular deviation (the oculocephalic or vestibulo-oculogyric reflex or the doll's head phenomenon). Absence of movement to one side suggests that there is paresis of conjugate gaze to that side, and dissociation of response suggests brain stem involvement. These reflex movements are absent in deep coma. Optokinetic and caloric nystagmus can also be tested in some states of lowered consciousness (Chapter 11). In hysteria and malingering there may be furtive glances and evasion of the use of the eyes. Decreased ocular tension is found in diabetic coma.

The size, shape, position, equality, and reaction of the pupils are all important. In various degrees of stupor and coma the pupils may be either dilated or contracted. In certain toxic states, especially after the ingestion of morphine, they are often pin-point in size. In other varieties of coma, such as those associated with alcoholism, diabetes, uremia, and corbon monoxide poisoning, the pupils are occasionally unequal. The pupillary reflexes may vary, regardless of the degree of coma. In deeper stages there is usually loss of the light reflex and also loss of reflex response to painful stimulation applied to the eyeball (oculosensory reflex) or to the skin of the neck (ciliospinal reflex). The accommodation reflex cannot be tested in coma. In cerebral hemorrhage, subdural hematoma, large expanding neoplasms, and skull fractures with associated middle meningeal bleeding the pupil is usually dilated on the side of the lesion and may not react, either to light or in accommodation. This depends, however, upon the exact localization and extent of the pathologic process, and occasionally the pupil is constricted on the side of the lesion and dilated on the opposite side. Either the dilated or constricted pupil may be fixed to light. In either hemorrhage or thrombosis of the basilar artery the pupils are usually constricted, but there may be anisocoria.

No neurologic appraisal in coma is ever complete without an ophthalmoscopic examination. The presence of either early or fully developed papilledema is, of course, indicative of some type of process which is causing increased intracranial pressure, and is most suggestive of either brain tumor or abscess. The ophthalmoscopic examination is also important, however, in the diagnosis of various systemic diseases which may be responsible for the disorder of consciousness, namely, diabetes (diabetic retinitis), uremia (albuminuric retinitis), hypertension, arteriosclerosis, and blood dyscrasias. It is not possible to test either the visual acuity or the visual fields to any degree if there is significant impairment of consciousness. If there is only partial impairment, however, the examiner should note whether the patient has a fixed gaze, follows objects, makes furtive glances, or evades the use of his eyes. It may be possible to demonstrate a hemianopia in stuporous patients by absence of defense closing of the eyes when objects are brought into the field of vision or sudden threatening movements are made toward the eyes; the response on the two sides must be compared.

The *examination of the motor status* is one of the very essential parts of the neurologic examination in disorders of consciousness. Some reference has already been made to the position assumed by the body as a whole and its parts, the degree of activity and passivity, the presence of tension or relaxation, and the appearance of tremors, twitches, spasms, and convulsions. It is always important to examine the patient very carefully in order to see whether any degree or type of paralysis is present. If a patient is completely comatose and shows no motor activity, no paralysis may be apparent, and it may require skilled observation to elicit the presence of motor dysfunction. The paralysis which follows cerebral lesions is contralateral and may involve either the entire opposite half of the body or the face or upper and lower extremities alone or in combination. The paralysis is usually a flaccid one at the outset, although it later becomes spastic.

If there is paresis of the face on one side, it may be noted that there is increased width of the palpebral fissure, drooping of the angle of the mouth, and a shallow nasolabial fold on the affected side. There may be drooling of saliva out of the angle of the mouth and a pronounced puffing out of the cheek on expiration and retraction of the cheek on inspiration. Respirations may be more difficult if the patient is placed on the paretic side. Firm pressure over the supraorbital notch or the eyeball is followed by retraction of the facial muscles on the normal side, but no movement on the paretic side. If the examiner attempts to open the firmly closed eyes, there may be resistance on the normal side but none on the paretic side; paresis of the orbicularis oculi causes the eye to close slowly.

The position of the arms and legs and the response to passive movement may show evidence of paralysis of the extremities. There is usually flaccidity with marked relaxation and loss of tone of recently paralyzed limbs. If the two arms are lifted and then released by the examiner, or if they are placed with the elbows resting on the bed and the forearms at right angles to the arms, the affected extremity falls in a flail-like manner, whereas the normal extremity drops slowly and may even remain upright for a brief period of time before falling. If the arms are passively rotated before they are released, the affected hand may strike the face in falling; the normal hand rarely, if ever, strikes the face. If the lower extremities are lifted from the bed and then released, the affected extremity falls rapidly, whereas the normal limb gradually drops to the bed. If the lower extremities are passively flexed with the heels resting on the bed and then released, the paretic limb rapidly falls to an extended position with the hip in outward rotation, whereas the unaffected limb maintains the posture for a few moments and then gradually returns to its original position. If the coma is not too deep, there may be some response to painful stimulation; pinching of the skin on the normal side is followed by a withdrawal, whereas a painful stimulus on the paretic side causes no local movement, although grimacing or movements of the opposite side of the body may show that sensation is retained. Other tests of motor function, such as evaluation of coordination and active movement, cannot be carried out in a comatose individual, and electrical tests are rarely indicated. It is always important, however, to appraise the tonus, or resistance to passive movement, and to observe carefully any hyperkinesias, or abnormal movements. Occasionally there is spasticity instead of flaccidity in acute cerebral lesions, and there is especially apt to be hypertonicity of a decerebrate type involving all four extremities in brain stem lesions. It is important to remember that a previous spastic hemiplegia or extrapyramidal syndrome may have caused an alteration in tone which persists even in coma, and that arthropathies and skeletal abnormalities may also interfere with movements of joints. In catatonia there may be a waxy resistance which resembles that of extrapyramidal disease. All hyperkinetic phenomena such as twitches, tremors, muscle spasms, choreiform movements, and focal and generalized convulsive movements should be noted in detail.

The *examination of the reflexes* is the most objective part of the neurologic appraisal and can be carried out without the cooperation of the patient. As a consequence it has special value in the examination of comatose and stuporous individuals. All of the important deep reflexes, certain of the superficial reflexes, and all of the pyramidal tract responses should be tested. In many varieties of disordered consciousness there are insignificant changes in the reflexes. In comatose states which are not associated with focal cerebral lesions both deep and superficial reflexes may be abolished, but in other varieties of alteration there is hyperactivity of the deep reflexes with pyramidal tract responses. In acute cerebral hemiplegia with flaccid paralysis of the extremities the deep and superficial reflexes may be either normal or diminished, but a Babinski response is frequently present. Later the deep reflexes are hyperactive, the superficial reflexes are diminished, and the pyramidal tract responses become more definite. In brain stem lesions one may find either tonic neck reflexes or signs of decerebrate rigidity. In every comatose patient one should attempt to elicit signs of meningeal involvement. The neck should be flexed passively and rotated from side to side in order to determine whether there is nuchal rigidity, and the Kernig and Brudzinski and related signs should always be investigated. In tetany a Chvostek's sign and related phenomena may be found.

LABORATORY EXAMINATIONS

Under many circumstances auxiliary examinations including laboratory tests have inestimable value in the differential diagnosis of the cause of coma. A urinalysis should be carried out in every instance, and if the patient has retention or if he voids without control, it may be necessary to catheterize him in order to obtain a urine specimen, which should be examined for the presence of glucose, acetone, aceto-acetic acid, albumin, leukocytes, erythrocytes, and casts. The blood count is important, especially in the presence of infections, anemia, and hemorrhagic states. Further blood studies include determination of the glucose, nonprotein and urea nitrogens, ammonia, serology, electrolytes, carbon dioxide combining power, and certain enzymes; blood cultures may be indicated. In case of poisoning it may be valuable to examine the blood for determination of the alcohol level, and the blood and urine for bromides, barbiturates, and other drugs. In most cases of suspected poisoning it is advisable to do a gastric lavage and examine the gastric contents for the presence of pills or capsules, opiates, barbiturates, or alcohol. If there is no contraindication to spinal puncture (the presence of papilledema, infections about the head, or infections about the puncture site) and if indications for such an examination are present, a spinal puncture should be done. The pressure should be determined and the cerebrospinal fluid examined (Chapters 58 and 59). Other essential examinations include roentgenograms, especially those of the skull and chest, an electrocardiogram, an electroencephalogram (it is important to bear in mind that this may be influenced by recently ingested drugs), and certain of the ancillary procedures mentioned in Chapter 54.

DIFFERENTIAL DIAGNOSIS OF THE CAUSES OF LOWERED CONSCIOUSNESS

Coma, semicoma, stupor, and related conditions may be the result of any one of a multiplicity of processes including trauma, cerebrovascular disease, intoxications, infections, and metabolic disturbances. Coma and convulsions may constitute the terminal states of serious systemic disease and may be preceded by other signs and symptoms of disordered function, or they may be the first manifestations in a serious illness and appear precipitously before there are other evidences of disease. The relative incidence of the different causes of coma should be borne in mind, since the statistical frequency of the individual conditions may aid in diagnosis. The incidence varies, however, depending upon the circumstances under which the statistics are collected. Figures gathered from the wards and clinics of large city hospitals show that alcoholism is the most common cause of coma and is responsible for about 60 per cent of the cases; trauma is next (13 per cent), then cerebrovascular accidents (10 per cent), and poisoning (3 per cent), and these are followed by epilepsy, diabetes, meningitis, pneumonia, cardiac decompensation, and other less frequent causes. Other statistics, based on autopsy reports, show trauma to be the most common cause for coma which is followed by death, and this, in turn, is succeeded in frequency by vascular diseases, meningitis, pneumonia, uremia, and diabetes. Among the cases seen by the general practitioner of medicine, vascular lesions are the most important; these are followed, in turn, by trauma, postconvulsion states, poisoning, diabetes, and meningitis. It is important in all cases to arrive at a correct diagnosis as rapidly as possible, because immediate treatment may save the life of the patient in conditions such as diabetes, hyperinsulinism, poisoning, trauma, shock, exsanguination, subarachnoid hemorrhage, meningitis, and eclampsia.

Loss of consciousness may occur with either diffuse or focal cerebral lesions, as well as with physiologic alterations in cerebral function associated with metabolic disorders, deficiency in blood or oxygen supply, exposure to toxins, infectious processes, and other disturbances of structure or function. Suggestions have been made, in the past, that there is a specific "center of consciousness," disease of which causes alterations in the state of awareness. It is probable that no such center exists, but the smallest focal lesions that are followed by loss of consciousness are those of the diencephalon and brain stem, and more specifically those of the hypothalamic and midbrain regions. The reticular activating system in the cephalad portion of the brain stem is important in attention and awareness. Stimulation of this area or of the afferents to it causes awakening or arousal; disease of it or impairment of conduction of its afferent or efferent fibers causes loss of awareness and somnolence; destruction of this center or its isolation from other parts of the nervous system may result in complete loss of consciousness.

The degree of impairment of consciousness in many conditions in which there is either stupor or coma may be compared with the stages of surgical and barbiturate anesthesia. In the first stage there is clouding of consciousness, with impairment of contact with the environment, loss of discrimination, and, often, some euphoria; these phenomena are caused by slight to moderate depression of cortical activity. In the next stage there is loss of consciousness due to complete suppression of cortical control, and motor and reflex functions are carried out by subcortical structures. In still deeper stages there is loss of reflex response and of many visceral functions due to depression of midbrain structures. In the final stage, just preceding death, there is a gradual abolition of respiratory and circulatory control due to depression of brain stem activity.

CEREBROVASCULAR DISEASE

Vascular lesions of the brain constitute one of the most important causes for disturbances of consciousness and are responsible for the symptoms in about 10 per cent of comatose patients. The various syndromes of cerebrovascular disease are discussed in Chapter 52.

Acute vascular lesions of the intracerebral arteries usually cause both disturbances of consciousness and hemiplegia. The patient may either be deeply comatose or stuporous with responses to painful stimuli; occasionally there is no disturbance of consciousness. There is paresis of one side of the face and body, with drooping of the angle of the mouth, bulging of the cheek, and flaccidity of the affected extremities. The upper portion of the face is rarely affected, although the corneal reflex is often absent on the side of the paresis. There may be turning of the head and conjugate deviation of the eyes toward the nonparalyzed side, with paralysis of conjugate gaze toward the affected side. The flaccid extremities drop heavily if raised and allowed to fall, whereas the arm and leg drop slowly on the normal side. There is often anisocoria; in the case of a large intracerebral lesion the ipsilateral pupil is dilated owing to the pressure on the third nerve by herniation of the hippocampal gyrus through the incisura of the tentorium cerebelli, although occasionally the ipsilateral pupil is constricted. Both pupils may dilate as coma deepens, the one on the side of the lesion doing so first. The light reflex disappears in profound coma. With intraventricular hemorrhage there may be coma and shock without localizing signs, followed by increasing paralysis of all four extremities, decerebrate rigidity, and signs of meningeal irritation.

In *cerebral hemorrhage* the onset is usually sudden, although there may be a gradual deepening of coma. The ictus is usually the result of sudden increase in blood pressure in an individual whose blood pressure is already elevated, although occasionally it is caused by the rupture of an anomalous cerebral artery. The patient often has the hypertensive or apoplectic habitus; he is moderately obese, with a short, thick neck, broad chest and shoulders, and ruddy, flushed cheeks. There may be history of previously diagnosed hypertension or of former strokes. The onset of symptoms often takes place during violent exercise or emotional stress. Ninety per cent of patients are over 40 years of age. Impending symptoms of cerebral hemorrhage include severe occipital or nuchal headache, vertigo and syncope, drowsiness, confusion, stupor, forgetfulness, hypochondria, tinnitus, nervousness, epistaxis, and retinal hemorrhages. Preceding the hemorrhage there may have been transient focal manifestations which consist of brief attacks of paresis, paresthesia, aphasia, diplopia, or dysarthria, or fleeting localized convulsive seizures. In cerebral hemorrhage the coma may be profound, and often there is some evidence of shock. The blood pressure may be elevated, although it is low in shock. Convulsions are infrequent at the outset. The respirations may be stertorous or of the Cheyne-Stokes type, and the temperature below normal. There may be signs of increased intracranial pressure with a slowing of the pulse. The patient is often incontinent. The pupils may fail to react to light. Examination of the retinal arteries may show evidence of hypertensive changes, often with hemorrhages. There may be increase in cerebrospinal fluid pressure and the protein and cell content of the spinal fluid; there may be frank blood in the fluid.

Cerebral thrombosis, with resulting infarction and encephalomalacia, may have either a precipitous or a gradual onset. The symptoms may appear while the patient is idle or during sleep. There may be a history of previous transient ischemic attacks, arteriosclerosis, hypertension, diabetes, or syphilis, and there may have been premonitory symptoms similar to those described above. Coma is less profound; in fact the patient often fails to lose consciousness. There is rarely evidence of shock. The patient is often younger and there is less apt to be hypertension. The blood pressure is frequently normal, although cerebral thrombosis as well as cerebral hemorrhage may occur in hypertensive individuals. The cerebrospinal fluid is clear and the pressure is normal. With *cerebral embolism* the onset is sudden; the loss of consciousness may be transitory. It is often possible to determine the source of the embolus, and there may be a history of cardiac or pulmonary disease. Cerebral fat and air embolisms occur, but are rare.

Loss or consciousness is uncommon with lesions of the cortical branches of the major cerebral arteries or of the branches of the vertebral or basilar arteries. Either thrombosis or hemorrhage of the basilar artery, however, may cause profound coma. It is also uncommon with the transient ischemic attacks secondary to insufficiency of the extracranial arteries unless such insufficiency in the vertebrobasilar system interferes with the blood supply to the reticular activating system. If this is the case, there may be transient "black-outs" or "drop attacks" which are occasionally brought on by extension of the neck, especially if there is extensive cervical arthritis as well as stenosis of the vertebral arteries.

With *subarachnoid hemorrhage* there is usually the sudden onset of an intense headache in the occipital region or the back of the neck. The patient may state that he felt "something snap" or noted the sensation of a blow in this region. The onset may follow exertion, emotional strain, or coitus. The coma comes on gradually and there may or may not be convulsions. The pulse is often slowed (fifty to sixty per minute) and there may be vertigo, vomiting, and lethargy. Characteristically there are marked signs of meningeal irritation with photophobia, Kernig and Brudzinski manifestations, and nuchal rigidity. The diagnosis is confirmed by spinal puncture; the cerebrospinal fluid contains fresh blood which does not clot, and later there is xanthochromia with crenation of the red blood cells. Bloody fluid and xanthochromia may also be found in intraventricular hemorrhage and in intracerebral hemorrhage accompanied by subarachnoid bleeding. In the latter condition, however, there are signs both of localization and of meningeal irritation.

In *hypertensive encephalopathy,* or *acute hypertensive crisis,* there may be a sudden onset of coma with or without convulsions. There is usually a history of either kidney disease or malignant hypertension, and often of severe headaches, irritability, fatigue, drowsiness, vomiting, and failing vision. There may be an extensive hypertensive retinopathy with papilledema. The cerebrospinal fluid pressure is moderately elevated. Thrombosis of the venous sinuses is not a common cause of coma.

TRAUMA

Trauma is responsible for the symptoms in approximately 13 per cent of the comatose patients who are admitted to large general hospitals and for a much larger percentage of patients who die in coma. It is usually possible to obtain a history of an accident, although the type of injury may not be known. Automobile accidents, gunshot wounds, falls, or blast concussions may be responsible. There is usually evidence of injury on physical examination. There may be bruises and hematomas of the face; lacerations or hemorrhages about the scalp; depressions or other injuries of the skull; bleeding from the ears, nose, or mouth, or cerebrospinal fluid rhinorrhea. In cerebral concussion there may be an immediate brief period of loss of consciousness with no permanent symptoms, prolonged coma, late development of coma, or delirium. On regaining consciousness the patient may be dazed and confused, with retrograde and anterograde amnesia. With more severe injuries there may be petechial hemorrhages and cerebral edema which lead to prolonged stupor. Cerebral contusions and lacerations show focal signs. In middle meningeal hemorrhage there is coma immediately after the accident; this is followed by a lucid interval and then, in turn, by gradually deepening coma. With *subdural hematoma* and *hydroma* the symptoms may become apparent days to weeks after an injury. There is first confusion with slight lowering of the consciousness, which is followed by stupor, gradually increasing coma, and a progressive paralysis. The pupil is usually dilated on the side of the lesion. In all traumatic states the physician should be especially concerned about the blood pressure, pulse, respirations, and temperature, and should watch closely for signs of shock (drop in blood pressure) or increasing intracranial pressure (bradycardia, vomiting, papilledema). The patient should be moved as little as possible and roentgen studies should be deferred until definite information has been obtained regarding the general status of the patient. Spinal puncture may show either increased pressure or subarachnoid bleeding. It is important to bear in mind that cerebral trauma may occur to a patient who is under the influence of alcohol or may complicate epileptic convulsions.

ALCOHOL

Acute alcoholic intoxication is the greatest single cause for loss of consciousness in patients admitted to general hospitals in large cities. It is responsible for the symptoms in 60 per cent of such comatose individuals. It may, of course, be accompanied by trauma. The history of either previous alcoholism or acute alcoholic intoxication may be obtained. On examination the patient shows a flushed face, injected throat and conjunctivae, and diminished to absent reflexes. The pulse may be full and respirations deep, and the patient can usually be aroused slightly. The pupils are dilated and react normally. There are often minor injuries over the body; vomiting is common, and occasionally there are convulsions. There is evidence of alcohol on the breath and in the gastric contents; coma develops when the alcohol blood level is 250 milligrams per 100 milliliters or higher. One should remember that patients in states of alcoholic intoxication may become comatose for other reasons; they may have suffered from cerebral hemorrhage and trauma, and a large percentage of instances of subdural hematoma have been reported in alcoholism.

With *Wernicke's syndrome,* a nutritional disorder usually secondary to chronic alcoholism, there may be alterations in the state of consciousness varying from mild confusion to coma; in addition there are other neurologic changes including ocular palsies, ataxia, and tremors.

POSTCONVULSION COMA

Coma may be a sequel of a recent convulsion in an epileptic or in a patient who has convulsions of other etiology, although it may not be possible to obtain a history of either a recent convulsion or previous attacks. The patient may show evidence of tongue-biting with frothing at the mouth and bloody sputum, and there may be incontinence and lacerations or other injuries to the body. Old scars may be found on the tongue. The stupor is usually brief in duration, but may be followed by either profound sleep or confusion with irrational behavior. In the absence of a history of previous convulsions it may be difficult to differentiate between the postconvulsive state and cerebral trauma. In status epilepticus there are repeated convulsions and the patient fails to regain consciousness between them; in so-called petit mal status there is prolonged lowering or clouding of the consciousness due to rapidly recurring minor seizures.

DIABETES

Diabetic coma is not encountered as frequently as it once was, possibly because of the earlier diagnosis of diabetes. Coma, however, may be the first clinical manifestation of the disease. Most diabetic patients are now requested to carry with them cards which state that they are afflicted with the disease If no history can be obtained regarding the patient who is first observed in coma, diabetes must always be considered as a possible factor. The loss of consciousness may be profound. The tendon reflexes are often absent; there may be a Babinski response. The temperature is subnormal, the blood pressure depressed, and the pulse increased in rate. The respirations are rapid and may be of the Kussmaul type, with air hunger. The eyeballs may be soft due to decreased introcular tension, and the pupils may be constricted and fail to react to light. There may be evidences of dehydration, with dry skin and tongue, and the feet are often cold. The characteristic odor of acetone is often noticed on the breath. The presence of large amounts of glucose together with acetone and aceto-acetic acid in the urine will confirm the diagnosis, as will blood glucose and carbon dioxide combining-power determinations. A nonketotic hyperglycemic coma with associated serum hyperosmolarity and dehydration has also been reported.

POISONING

Various types of poisoning may be responsible for either coma or stupor. The poisons are frequently self-administered in suicidal attempts, although they may have been ingested accidentally, have been given with homicidal intent, or be associated with industrial intoxication. Opium poisoning was at one time the most common cause of coma of toxic origin, although it is now encountered less frequently. It may follow ingestion of opium, morphine, laudanum, or other opium derivatives. The patient is pale and cyanotic; the skin is cold; the temperature is subnormal; the respirations are slow, feeble, and irregular; the pulse is slow and feeble. The face may be livid and the extremities clammy. The pupils are markedly constricted, but may still react to light. The reflexes are diminished; there may be a Babinski response. There may be history of morphine addiction; often needle marks are found on the arms and legs. Intoxication with barbiturates and other sedatives, hypnotics, and tranquilizers (Chapter 54) is now encountered much more frequently than opium poisoning. Large doses of these drugs may be ingested either in a suicidal attempt or accidentally in a patient who is already confused from the use of them. Alcohol may have been ingested simultaneously. It may be possible to obtain a history of excessive use of barbiturates or similarly acting drugs or of depression which might lead to suicidal attempts. The patient may be deeply comatose. The face is pale; the skin is cold and clammy; the respirations are deep, slow, and irregular; the pulse is slow. The pupils are not constricted, but the extraocular movements are often dissociated and there may be nystagmus. The reflexes are abolished and there may be Babinski signs. In profound coma the reflexes may be hyperactive. There may be pills or capsules in the gastric contents. It is not possible to differentiate between short-acting and long-acting barbiturates on the basis of blood examinations, but coma develops with a concentration greater than 1 mg. per 100 ml. of the former and 4 to 5 mg. per 100 ml. of the latter. Laboratory tests are also available for determining the presence of some of the other sedatives and tranquilizers.

Coma due to the inhalation of carbon monoxide may be the result of either suicidal attempts or accidental exposure. It may follow the inhalation of either illuminating gas or exhaust gas from automobiles. The skin is described as cherry-red in color, but it may be pale and cold. The lips and nail beds are also a cherry-red color. The temperature is subnormal; the pulse and respirations may vary and may be irregular, rapid, or shallow. There may be an odor of illuminating gas on the breath. A history of the circumstances under which the patient was found aids in the diagnosis, as do blood studies for carbon monoxide, methemoglobin, and carboxyhemoglobin. Headache, vertigo, nausea, vomiting, and convulsions may precede the loss of consciousness.

Many of the other poisons listed in Chapter 54 cause coma and/or convulsions only when ingested in excessive amounts; confusion and delirium more commonly follow ingestion of or exposure to them. Salicylate intoxication, especially in infants and children, may cause coma, with changes in the respiratory rate, temperature, and reflexes, and with moderate dilatation of the pupils; vomiting frequently precedes loss of consciousness. In cocaine and strychnine intoxication there is usually history of excitement and delirium preceding the coma. Lead poisoning causes convulsions and coma in children more frequently than in adults. Disordered consciousness is an early and important symptom in the hemorrhagic encephalitis associated with the use of organic arsenicals. Methyl bromide and chloride, aniline dyes and benzine derivatives, carbon disulphide, carbon tetrachloride, and many other industrial poisons may also cause disturbances of consciousness. Organic toxins which may cause coma and convulsions include those of botulinus, tetanus, and the poisonous mushrooms, as well as the endogenous toxins associated with anemia, extensive burns, and infections such as pneumonia.

MENINGITIS

Meningitis, especially the acute variety, must always be kept in mind as one of the relatively common causes of coma. The symptoms may come on abruptly with severe headache, and loss of consciousness may follow soon afterwards. This is especially apt to be true in meningococcic meningitis. In streptococcic, pneumococcic, and staphylococcic meningitis there may be a history of infectious processes of some type, especially in the middle ear, about the head, or in the paranasal sinuses. Examination of the patient with meningitis shows evidences of infection (fever, leukocytosis). There may be a characteristic skin rash, especially in meningococcic meningitis. The most important diagnostic signs are those of meningeal irritation (nuchal rigidity and Kernig and Brudzinski phenomena); the patient often is in a position of opisthotonos. Sometimes, however, the signs of meningeal irritation are absent or minimal, especially early in the disease. Other important findings are abnormalities of the pupillary responses, dissociation of ocular movements, convulsive manifestations, and signs of focal neurologic involvement. There may be evidences of increased intracranial pressure. The diagnosis may be confirmed by spinal puncture, which shows increased pressure, pleocytosis, increased protein, and marked decrease in glucose and chlorides. Tuberculous meningitis is less rapid in onset; it is most frequently seen in young children but may occur in any age group, and there need be no history of previous tuberculous infections.

BRAIN TUMORS AND BRAIN ABSCESSES

Brain tumors and brain abscesses may cause coma with or without paralysis. The disturbance of consciousness may be related to the localization of the lesion within the nervous system or may be secondary to increase in intracranial pressure. If a history can be obtained, there is usually a story of gradual onset of symptoms with headaches, vomiting, focal signs, convulsions, apathy, stupor, failing vision, and personality changes, but with certain rapidly growing neoplasms and brain abscesses the symptoms and signs may come on precipitously. A sudden hemorrhage into a tumor or sudden obstruction of the ventricular system may cause abrupt onset or increase in symptoms. With brain abscesses there may be a history of some co-existing infectious process. If there is coma, there often are signs of increased intracranial pressure with vomiting, stupor, papilledema, bradycardia, and changes in the blood pressure and respirations, and there may be evidences of localization of disturbed cerebral function. The symptoms and signs of subdural hematoma and hydroma may be similar to those just described, but there is usually a history of an antecedent injury followed after some time by stupor, increasing coma, and progressive paralysis.

ENCEPHALITIS

Encephalitis causes a lowering of consciousness on many occasions, although there may be hypersomnia rather than stupor or coma, and the patient frequently can be aroused for short periods of time. With the viral encephalitides there often are dissociated eye movements, other abnormalities of the cranial nerves, and hyperkinetic phenomena. Toxic or hemorrhagic encephalitides may follow administration of arsphenamine or exposure to various toxins. Demyelinating encephalitides may be associated with vaccinia, smallpox, measles, and similar conditions. Dementia paralytica, which may be interpreted as a syphilitic encephalitis, usually has a gradual onset, and there is history of intellectual deterioration and delusional manifestations; the symptoms may, however, come on precipitously with convulsive manifestations and apoplectic phenomena which suggest cerebral hemorrhage. Usually, however, the history and the characteristic signs, including Argyll Robertson pupils and hyperactive reflexes as well as the blood and spinal fluid serologic findings, lead to a correct diagnosis. Meningoencephalitic manifestations may accompany many types of infectious disease.

HYPOGLYCEMIA

Hyperglycemia, usually accompanied by acidosis, may cause coma in diabetes, but hypoglycemia may also be responsible for coma. The loss of consciousness is often preceded or accompanied by convulsions. The hypoglycemic state may be the result of any of the following: functional hyperinsulinism associated with either pancreatic or liver disease, organic hyperinsulinism caused by the production of an excessive amount of insulin by an adenoma of the pancreas, or the administration of large doses of insulin in the treatment of either diabetes or psychotic states. The convulsions and loss of consciousness are usually preceded by symptoms which consist of nervousness, weakness, fatigue, hunger, tremulousness, irritability, pallor, increased sweating, and psychic manifestations. Examination of the comatose patient shows dilatation of the pupils, hyperhidrosis, cold skin, and tremors. The tendon reflexes may be retained and are often exaggerated, even in deep coma, and there may be a Babinski response. The coma is often brief in duration. The convulsive manifestations and the bodily responses may call forth additional glucose from storage in the liver, so that by the time the patient has reacted the blood glucose determinations may be within normal range. A diagnosis of either functional or organic hyperinsulinism can usually be made by glucose tolerance studies.

PNEUMONIA AND OTHER INFECTIONS

Pneumonia is said to be responsible for 1.7 per cent of the cases of coma that are admitted to general hospitals. The coma may be caused by either the infectious process itself or endogenous toxic substances produced by the infection. Since pneumonia is diagnosed earlier than it was formerly, and since specific therapeutic measures can be instituted earlier in the course of the disease, coma due to pneumonia is less common than it once was. Other infections such as malaria, typhoid fever, scarlet fever, osteomyelitis, and septicemia may also cause loss of consciousness, and coma may be the terminal stage of any infectious process, as, for instance, the Waterhouse-Friderichsen syndrome in meningitis. Syphilis may cause coma through various mechanisms—dementia paralytica, syphilitic meningitis, or cerebrovascular syphilis.

CARDIAC DECOMPENSATION AND HEART FAILURE

Heart disease of various types, with resulting cardiac decompensation and heart failure, must always be considered in the diagnosis of coma. In Adams-Stokes disease there is profound coma with or without convulsions; the manifestations are accompanied by bradycardia, and may be preceded by vertigo. This syndrome may be caused by heart block with cardiac standstill, ventricular tachycardia and fibrillation, carotid sinus stimulation, and arteriosclerosis of the vertebral and basilar arteries. Either transient or prolonged loss of consciousness may also occur with other types of heart disease, including paroxysmal tachycardia, coronary insufficiency, and aortic stenosis and insufficiency, as well as with pulmonary hypertension.

METABOLIC DISTURBANCES

In addition to the comas of diabetes and hypoglycemia, which have been discussed separately, many other metabolic disturbances may cause disorders of consciousness.

Uremic coma may result from a variety of renal lesions. There are complex metabolic disturbances including the retention of nitrogenous waste products and disorders of acid-base equilibrium and water and electrolyte balance. The coma may be relatively slow in onset and is often preceded by headache, vomiting, dyspnea, muscular twitching, diarrhea, and lethargy. There may have been a period of confusion with gradual lowering of consciousness, followed by delirium and convulsions and then coma. Examination often shows peripheral edema; the breath has a uriniferous odor, and there may be an "uremic frost" about the nose and lips. Urinalysis shows excessive albuminuria along with large numbers of erythrocytes and casts, although there may be anuria. Ophthalmoscopy reveals the presence of an albuminuric retinitis with hemorrhages and exudates. Chemical studies on the blood show a marked increase in nonprotein and urea nitrogens. The cerebrospinal fluid pressure is often increased. Uremic coma may be associated with the manifestations of hypertensive encephalopathy.

Hepatic coma may be a complication of cirrhosis, acute and chronic hepatitis, and disturbances of the portal and hepatic circulation, including portacaval anastomoses. The clinical picture shows fluctuation, and the coma may be preceded by apathy, lethargy, irritability, confusion, delirium, and motor symptoms consisting of coarse, postural, "flapping" tremors of the outstretched extremities. Actual loss of consciousness may come on spontaneously or be precipitated by increased dietary protein, inadequate nutrition, alcohol, drugs, infection, or hemorrhage. Additional motor disturbances include rigidity, dysarthria, grimacing, hyperreflexia, Babinski signs, sucking and grasping reflexes, and convulsions. The presence of large amounts of toxic nitrogenous substances in the systemic circulation may be responsible, and in a majority of patients there are high blood ammonia levels, but other metabolic abnormalities doubtless contribute toward the production of neurologic symptoms.

The *coma of eclampsia* may have features resembling both uremic and hempatic coma, along with manifestations of hypertensive encephalopathy.

Coma may occur with *chronic pulmonary insufficiency* and respiratory failure secondary to emphysema, pulmonary fibrosis, and marked obesity (Pickwickian syndrome). Headache, confusion, somnolence, and stupor may precede the coma, and there may be papilledema and other signs of increased intracranial pressure. The symptoms are believed to be due to carbon dioxide intoxication.

Disturbances in the concentration of the *electrolytes* and of the *acid-base equilibrium* as well as either *dehydration* or *water intoxication* can cause an encephalopathy with lethargy, depression, confusion, delirium, and either convulsions or coma (Chapter 54). Such disturbances may also contribute to the symptomatology in comas of other etiologies.

Comas secondary to disturbances of the endocrine glands are occasionally encountered. *Myxedema coma* occurs with long-standing, greatly depressed thyroid function. It is often precipitated by cold and is accompanied by profound hypothermia. In *Addisonian coma,* from adrenocortical failure, there are associated hypotension, hypoglycemia, and electrolyte disturbances. *Hypopituitary coma* is most commonly seen in women who have suffered ischemic necrosis of the anterior lobe of the pituitary during or after childbirth (Sheehan's syndrome), but also occurs with pituitary cachexia (Simmonds' disease). Adrenocortical deficiency and hypoglycemia contribute to the symptomatology.

ANEMIA, ANOXIA, AND NUTRITIONAL DEFICIENCY

Profound anemia may cause coma, but loss of consciousness associated with deficiency in the blood supply to the brain is usually associated with either exsanguination or some vasomotor disturbance such as vasodepressor syncope or shock. Anoxia may also cause coma; in exposure to high altitudes the loss of consciousness is usually transient, but deficient oxygenation associated with surgical anesthesia, lack of oxygen in the surrounding air, obstruction of the airway, paralysis of the muscles of respiration, impaired transport of oxygen by the blood, smothering, drowning, electric shock, cardiac insufficiency, methemoglobinemia, or cyanide intoxication may constitute the pathologic mechanism underlying coma. In profound nutritional deficiencies such as starvation, beriberi, pellagra, and severe cachexia and dehydration in the aged, there may be coma, as well as in the terminal stages of Wernicke's syndrome and pernicious anemia. Coma associated with ruptured ectopic pregnancy is caused by exsanguination and shock. Profound hypothermia and hyperthermia may also cause coma, as may caisson disease.

Stupor, coma, delirium, and other disorders of consciousness may develop as the result of multiple underlying metabolic alterations and deficiencies. This is often true in postoperative syndromes, especially in elderly persons. There may be a basic deficiency in the blood and oxygen supply to the brain because of anemia, decreased blood concentration, arteriosclerosis, reduced blood flow, and impaired diffusion from capillaries to cells. Secondarily there may be a disturbance of electrolyte, glucose, and protein metabolism, and either lack of enzyme activation, inhibition of enzyme activity, or destruction of essential enzymes. Finally there may be the toxic effects of sedatives and other drugs, as well as the influence of infection. All of these, working together, may play a part in the production of disordered consciousness and sometimes of irreversible cell damage.

SUNSTROKE AND HEAT EXHAUSTION

Sunstroke and heat exhaustion may cause either stupor or convulsions. The coma is usually ushered in by pallor, headache, vertigo, lethargy, and muscular cramps. The patient is restless, often with a high fever; the skin is hot and dry; the pupils are dilated; respirations are shallow and the pulse weak. In lightning and electric shock there may be coma and convulsions associated with either pathologic changes in the brain or anoxia due to paralysis of respiration.

HYPERSOMNIA

In hypersomnia, lethargy, and sopor, which are states of pathologic sleepiness or continued or prolonged sleep, the symptoms resemble closely the manifestations of normal sleep. The patient can usually be aroused to consciousness by shaking, shouting, or other stimuli, and then appears to be in complete possession of his senses, but he may fall back into sleep as soon as the stimulus is removed. In normal sleep, however, unless the result of overpowering fatigue, the patient usually remains awake once he has been aroused, but in states of pathologic sleep the lethargy is continuous or prolonged. Hypersomnia is found in acute encephalitis, posttraumatic states, increased intracranial pressure, Wernicke's syndrome, intoxication by barbiturates and other soporifics, and brain tumors, especially those in the region of the third ventricle with pressure on or involvement of the posterior portion of the hypothalamus or the upper portion of the midbrain. The abnormal sleep may be the result of interruption of connections between the hypothalamus and the reticular activating system and between these structures and other parts of the brain (Chapter 43). Hypnotic trance and hysteria may simulate hypersomnia. In states of pathologic sleep, however, the electroencephalogram resembles that found in sleep, whereas in the hypnotic trance and hysteria the electroencephalogram is no different from that obtained in the normal waking state.

In *narcolepsy* there are brief attacks of uncontrollable sleep which come on precipitously. There may be no warning drowsiness, and the patient suddenly falls asleep while walking, talking, or eating; the symptoms leave as rapidly as they appear. Occasionally there is sustained drowsiness between episodes of sleep. The narcoleptic attacks may alternate with periods of cataplexy in which there is sudden loss of muscular power and tone, especially in the lower extremities, in association with laughter, anger, or other emotional outbursts; the knees may "give way" and the patient suddenly falls to the ground. Less frequent, but occasionally a part of the narcolepsy syndrome, are attacks of paralysis on relaxation or going to sleep and hypnogagic hallucinations. In the *Kleine-Levin syndrome* there are periodic attacks of hypersomnia with associated bulimia, irritability, behavioral changes, and uninhibited sexuality, usually occurring in young males; the basic etiology is unknown.

Recent studies on sleep have shown that it has two phases which differ physiologically. So-called initial, or "fore-brain" sleep is characterized electroencephalographically by slow waves and sleep spindles. During a normal night's sleep, however, most individuals have four or five periods of paradoxic or activated ("hind-brain") sleep which takes up to 20 to 25 per cent of the total sleeping time. This latter variety is accompanied by rapid eye movements (REM) and shows a low voltage, fast pattern on the electroencephalogram. The entire significance of these two phases of sleep is not known, but there is evidence that the latter variety is accompanied by motor inhibition and dreaming.

AKINETIC MUTISM

Akinetic mutism is a variety of disordered consciousness in which the patient lies speechless and motionless in bed and makes very little response to stimuli. He appears to be asleep, but can be aroused. His eyes may follow moving objects and deviate in response to loud noises. There are neither voluntary nor restless movements of the extremities, but there is reflex withdrawal to painful stimuli. The patient has to be fed; he does not chew, but is able to swallow. He is incontinent of urine and feces. This syndrome, which is also referred to as *coma vigil,* has been described with encephalitis, tumors of the third ventricle and midbrain, trauma, thrombosis of the basilar artery, and Wernicke's syndrome, all of which may cause involvement of the reticular activating system at the midbrain or upper pontine levels.

SYNCOPE

Syncope, or fainting, may be difficult to differentiate from episodic coma resulting from other causes, but the loss of consciousness is usually transient and may be incomplete. The commonest type is so-called *vasodepressor syncope,* and it is this variety that is often referred to as simple fainting. It may occur at any age, and often affects young and otherwise healthy individuals. The attacks usually take place while the patient is in the upright position, and may be precipitated by pain, loss of blood, sight of blood, excessive heat, fatigue, hunger, nausea, worry, fear, shock, prolonged standing, sudden change of position, or psychic or emotional upsets. Often there is no warning, although the patient may notice giddiness, vertigo, numbness and tingling of the hands and feet or paresthesias of other parts of the body, tremors, sweating, light-headedness, muscle weakness, yawning or belching, nausea, scotomas, or blurring of vision just before the loss of consciousness. The patient may fall before he becomes unconscious. The attacks are very brief and usually there is a return of consciousness within fifteen seconds, although occasionally the syncope may last longer. Recovery is accelerated by placing the patient in a supine position with the head lower than the body, or, when seated, by placing his head between his knees. The patient usually feels perfectly normal afterwards, and notices no headache or sleepiness. There need be no complete loss of consciousness; the patient may notice only a transient "black-out" or period of giddiness, and may be able to catch himself to avoid falling.

During syncope the bodily musculature is flaccid, and tongue-biting, rigidity, muscular contractions, cyanosis, and incontinence are absent, although the patient may injure himself in falling. Occasionally there are brief muscular twitchings or clonic jerks during the attack or while regaining consciousness. There is usually pallor, with increased perspiration and cold, clammy hands and feet. The temperature, pulse, respirations, and blood pressure may be normal, but often there is a rapid, feeble pulse with rapid respirations and an abrupt fall in blood pressure, all of which soon return to normal. The eyes may be fixed or deviated upwards, and the pupils dilated. The electroencephalogram shows abnormalities only during the period of syncope.

Various causes for syncope have been postulated, and it is believed that both pathophysiologic and psychologic factors may, through vasodepressor action, produce transient cerebral anemia or anoxia, perhaps with alterations in the blood chemistry. There is a fall in mean arterial pressure and a decrease in cerebral blood flow. The manifestations are similar to those which occur with sudden deprivation of oxygen in high altitude flying and with low oxygen tension in experimental studies. It has been stated that when primitive reflex preparation for flight or struggle is initiated, but for some reason appropriate action becomes impossible or must be inhibited, physiologic changes take place in the autonomic nervous system; insufficient blood is delivered to the brain, voluntary tone of muscles is inhibited, and fainting results. In hysterical fainting, without vasodepressor action, there is no preceding weakness or fatigue, and the symptoms are not relieved by change of position; there are no changes in autonomic nervous system function or in brain metabolism.

Syncope may also be a symptom of various circulatory, cardiac, cerebral, and other disturbances. Many of the above-listed causes of coma, if only transitory in action, may cause what might be interpreted as fainting. Among the more important etiologies are the following:

In *orthostatic syncope,* associated with postural hypotension, there is transient loss of consciousness on assuming the upright position. This may occur in "idio-pathic" postural hypotension; after prolonged illness with recumbency, especially in elderly individuals with flabby musculature; after sympathectomy, which abolishes vasopressor reflexes; with adrenal insufficiency; in severe neuropathies and tabes dorsalis; after the ingestion of sympatholytic drugs, catecholamine-depleting agents, and certain tranquilizers; in some individuals with abnormal autonomic nervous system responses (possibly of psychogenic origin) leading to syncope without tachycardia, pallor, sweating, or nausea; and in a specific neurologic syndrome in which there are also anhidrosis, fecal and urinary incontinence, impotence, and other evidences of nervous system involvement.

In *carotid sinus syncope* stimulation of either the carotid sinus or body, in certain susceptible individuals, causes vertigo, pallor, loss of consciousness, and occasionally convulsions; these phenomena are caused by slowing of the heart rate, decrease in cardiac output, fall in blood pressure, and peripheral vasodilatation. Three types of pathologic carotid syndrome responses, have been described: the vagal type, in which the predominant response is slowing of the heart rate; the depressor type, in which fall in blood pressure is the principal manifestation; and the cerebral type, characterized by syncope and sometimes convulsions (Chapter 15). In individuals with atherosclerotic involvement of the carotid and/or vertebrobasilar arterial system the syncope and occasional convulsions and contralateral hemiparesis that may follow pressure in the region of the carotid bifurcation is the result of cerebral ischemia rather than a reflex response.

In *Adams-Stokes disease* there is loss of consciousness, with or without convulsions, associated with heart block and ventricular standstill. Syncope may also occur as a symptom of coronary and myocardial insufficiency, cardiac decompensation, paroxysmal tachycardia, arrhythmias, valvular disease, or other conditions in which there is either reflex cardiac inhibition or decreased cardiac output; the loss of consciousness may be prolonged (see above). With hypertension there may be transient fainting, especially on arising, induced by a sudden increase, not a drop, in blood pressure. Pulmonary hypertension syncope is usually precipitated by exertion.

Among the cerebral causes for syncope are conditions in which there is either impaired cerebral circulation or impaired cerebral metabolism. Decreased blood flow may be secondary to arteriosclerosis, hypertension, vascular insufficiency, trauma, carotid sinus stimulation, or peripheral circulatory failure. Disturbed metabolism may be present in severe anemia, anoxemia secondary to cardiac or pulmonary disease, anoxia of high altitudes, hypoglycemia, acidosis, and drug intoxications. It is often difficult to differentiate between syncope of cerebral or other origin and brief akinetic epileptic seizures. Also, some syncopal attacks are accompanied by brief clonic jerking movements which resemble those occurring in convulsions.

In the *hyperventilation syndrome* rapid breathing produces hypocapnia and respiratory alkalosis, with symptoms of numbness and tingling of the extremities, dizziness, palpitation, stiffness of the muscles, blurring of vision, light-headedness, confusion, and sometimes syncope, which may be accompanied by either convulsions or tetany. The syndrome occurs more frequently in women than in men, and is usually precipitated by anxiety, fear, or other psychic manifestations. It usually occurs in psychoneurotic individuals, and many of the minor symptoms may be related to anxiety rather than to alkalosis. Hyperventilation is also used to activate the electroencephalogram in epileptics and occasionally brings on seizures in such patients.

There are certain varieties of syncope which are related in part to *Valsalva's maneuver* (increase of intrathoracic pressure by forcible exhalation against the closed glottis). *Tussive,* or *cough, syncope* usually follows a paroxysm of coughing in a person with chronic pulmonary or bronchial disease, often with some tracheal or laryngeal obstruction. The fainting comes on suddenly and there is rapid return of consciousness. This usually occurs in robust or obese men. The increased intrathoracic pressure may cause a decrease of venous return to the heart, a diminution of cardiac output, and temporary cerebral anoxia. A transient rise in cerebrospinal fluid pressure and extravascular pressure leading to relative cerebral anoxia may also contribute to the etiology. Similar fainting may occur with straining at stool, vomiting, sneezing, lifting, or excessive laughing. *Micturition syncope* occurs in men (usually healthy young adults) while or following forceful urination immediately after arising from a recumbent position. The mechanisms are similar to those of tussive syncope, but orthostatic hypotension and cardioinhibitory reflexes from the bladder causing cardiac standstill may also contribute to the syndrome. In older men bladder neck obstruction may be an aggravating factor. In the *"fainting lark" or "mess trick"*, brief syncope is brought on by compression of the chest while the subject is forcibly expiring against a closed glottis. In *breath-holding spells,* which usually occur in infants and small children, there is loss of consciousness when the child holds his breath in expiration after a prolonged cry which has often been precipitated by fear, anger, or frustration. There may be associated flushing, cyanosis, upward deviation of the eyeballs, and either tonic muscular spasms or brief convulsive movements. The attack may be difficult to differentiate from a convulsive seizure. Both hyperventilation and the factors that bring about cough syncope may be responsible for the loss of consciousness, but it is probable that anoxia is the principle cause. Among the more rare types of syncope are those occurring when a needle is introduced into the pleural space, after a distended bladder is drained, and following removal of ascitic fluid. The mechanisms of these are poorly understood.

SHOCK

Shock, or, as it is often termed, surgical shock, is closely related to vasodepressor syncope. The onset usually follows trauma, burns, severe pain, or surgical procedures. There is an acute peripheral circulatory failure which results in a sudden drop in the arterial blood pressure due to loss of blood from the exterior of the body and vasodilatation in the splanchnic areas. There is a reduction in the effective circulating volume of blood, and there may also be changes in the electrolytes. The loss of consciousness may be preceded by restlessness, and the coma may be gradual in onset. There is marked pallor, and the skin is cold and moist, with excessive perspiration; the pulse is feeble and rapid; respirations are decreased in amplitude and rapid in rate; the blood pressure is very low. The patient does not respond at once, as he does in syncope, and he must be kept warm and given supportive treatment. The impairment of circulation may continue until there is a state of irreversible circulatory failure with resulting collapse. Transfusions, plasma replacement, fluids, and analgesics may be necessary as emergency measures.

HYSTERIA

In hysteria the loss of consciousness is not deep and is rarely complete. The patient often responds to painful stimuli, unless there is associated hysterical anesthesia, and the reflexes are normal with no pathologic responses. The corneal and pupillary reflexes and the temperature, pulse, respirations, and blood pressure are normal. The eyes may be closed tightly, and the patient may resist attempts to open them; vigorous contractions of the orbiculares oculorum often interfere with both corneal and pupillary reflexes. He may also resist other diagnostic procedures, and be seen to make furtive glances when not aware that he is being watched. If the latter is the case, care must be taken to differentiate between hysteria and malingering (see Chapter 56). Complete loss of consciousness, however, is rare in malingering.

Hysterical loss of consciousness is usually precipitated by emotional stress, and the onset is often dramatic. The patient may appear to be in a trance, or coma may alternate with weeping and thrashing. The performance is appropriately staged, and occurs when observers are in the vicinity. Movements, if present, are not stereotyped, but appear to be coordinated and purposive. The patient may struggle, clutch at objects or parts of the body, or attempt to tear off his clothes. He rarely bites his tongue or injures himself in falling. There is no sleepiness or headache after the attack. Although the patient appears to be unconscious, he may show some response to external stimuli. If there is hypertonicity of the muscles, it is usually of a rigid type, and there may be opisthotonos with the *arc de cercle*. If the patient can be stimulated to talk, his responses may be the type seen in Ganser's syndrome; he evades answers to questions and make approximate but consistently inaccurate replies. The electrical activity of the brain is normal, and the electroencephalogram can be differentiated from that of normal and pathologic sleep, vasodepressor syncope, and organic brain disease. Insight into the condition and return of consciousness can often be obtained by the intravenous administration of drugs such as sodium amobarbital (Amytal) or sodium thiopental (Pentothal).

It is important to bear in mind that vasodepressor syncope and epileptic attacks may also be precipitated by emotional stimuli. Hyperventilation, brought about by either fear or anxiety, may cause loss of consciousness or hasten the onset of convulsions. The electroencephalogram has distinct value in aiding one to differentiate between hysteria, vasodepressor syncope, and epilepsy, but it must not be considered the final criterion in diagnosis.

PSYCHOTIC STATES

There is rarely complete loss of consciousness in psychotic states. In severe depressions, schizophrenia, and organic psychoses there may be mutism in which the patient is either completely withdrawn from the environment or refuses to speak. Negativism, either passive or active, may be a symptom of various psychoses, but especially of schizophrenia. In severe depressions the patient may show both physical and psychomotor retardation which may simulate lowering of consciousness because of organic brain disease. In catatonic stupor there are apathy, mutism, and negativism; there often is a waxy rigidity of the musculature of the extremities, and the patient may hold his limbs or his entire body in bizarre and seemingly uncomfortable positions for long periods of time. He may hold food in his mouth.

AMNESIA

In amnesia there is no loss of consciousness, but there is a memory defect which usually affects only either a circumscribed period of time or certain experiences. Except for the period of time or the experience involved, registration, retention, and recall are normal. There usually is no loss of orientation for the immediate environment. Amnesia may be organic, psychogenic, feigned, or mixed in origin.

Amnesia of organic origin may be secondary to or associated with trauma, epilepsy, toxic states, cerebrovascular disease, fever, hypoglycemia, drug administration, brain tumors, or other causes. It is believed that involvement of the hippocampal-fornical-hypothalamic system is usually responsible, although amnesia may also be caused by lesions of the amygdala and the temporal cortex. It has been stated that memory is dependent upon the intramolecular composition of neuronal proteins, including the continuous replenishment of ribonucleic acid.

Following trauma there may be both retrograde and anterograde (posttraumatic) amnesia. With improvement there is a gradual lessening of the span of the former, but a short period of permanent retrograde amnesia remains. The posttraumatic amnesia is somewhat longer and covers the period of disordered consciousness which follows the injury. In epilepsy there is often amnesia for the convulsions and petit mal attacks, and the patient may fail to recall the aura of the seizures because of retrograde amnesia. In psychomotor epilepsy there is amnesia for the period during which the patient exhibits automatisms and abnormal behavior. Amnesia may be a symptom of either acute alcoholic intoxication or Korsakoff's syndrome; in the latter the patient attempts to compensate for the amnesia by confabulation. Transient attacks of amnesia sometime occur in older persons. In these there is an abrupt onset of disorientation due to loss of recent memory and immediate recall, but there is retention of alertness and responsiveness; either an epileptic or a vascular etiology has been suggested. A memory loss akin to amnesia has followed either unilateral or bilateral temporal lobectomy. Either amnesia or more prolonged loss of memory may follow electroshock therapy. Senescent forgetfulness is usually a memory loss rather than amnesia.

Psychogenic amnesia may occur as a symptom in hysteria; it is usually brought on by specific emotional traumas. Hypnosis, hypnotic hypnosis using sodium amobarbital (Amytal) and similar drugs, dream analysis, free association, word association, or psychoanalysis may bring about a cure. Feigned amnesia occurs in malingering. The electroencephalogram is of value in differentiating between organic and psychogenic amnesia.

DIFFERENTIAL DIAGNOSIS IN CONFUSION AND DELIRIUM

The same processes that cause lowering of the consciousness (coma and stupor) may also be responsible for clouding of the consciousness (confusion and delirium). In addition to disturbances of memory, attention, perception, and orientation, there may be profound excitement with marked motor activity, increased response to all types of stimuli, and mental symptoms in the nature of poverty of ideas, incoherence, emotional lability, illusions, hallucinatory manifestations, and delusional phenomena.

Delirium may be considered a more or less reversible psychotic episode which appears symptomatically in response to brain injury by trauma, after the ingestion of toxins, or during the course of some underlying disease. In this sense it can be termed a symptomatic psychosis. There are fluctuations in the patient's level of awareness, with loss of attention and memory and impairment in the ability to think in the abstract. The memory loss may be caused by failure of registration, retention, or recall, especially the former. Lack of comprehension and insight, loss of personal identification, and flagging of attention are common symptoms. The disorientation for time is often more marked than that for either place or person. (Recognition of time may be a more complex function than that of place or person.) There often are disorders of mood and there may be marked fear and apprehension. Owing to the release of cerebral inhibition and repression there is loss of normal emotional control, with excitement, stereotyped activity, and return of behavior to a primitive order of integration. Overactivity of lower centers causes tremors, excessive motor activity, and increased responsiveness to all stimuli. There is restlessness with overactivity and purposeless body movements. Carphology (floccilation) and jactitation are common; the patient may struggle to get out of bed and have to be restrained. He may refuse food. Overactivity of the autonomic nervous system is shown by the presence of dilated pupils, tachycardia, and marked hyperhidrosis. There are nocturnal and diurnal variations, and the symptoms are often more marked after dark or at night, when there is physiologic lowering of consciousness. Misinterpretation of stimuli leads to illusions. The hallucinations are usually either visual or auditory and are often hypnagogic, becoming manifest in the drowsy state that just precedes sleep; they have a dreamlike character, and the patient is often aware of their hallucinatory nature. The delusions are often brief and unsystematized. The thought content of a delirium has been found to be determined largely by the personality of the patient. Confusion and delirium may precede the development of stupor and coma, and may have the same causes.

Delirium may be psychogenic, but it is usually physiogenic and occurs in toxic, infectious, deficiency, or traumatic states. Impairment of the nutrition and of the circulation of the brain are important factors. It may appear spontaneously in association with drug intoxication, febrile or infectious states, or cardiac or renal disease in patients who have no pre-existing structural cerebral abnormality, or it may follow specific head injuries or convulsions. It is precipitated more readily, however, in patients who already have some type of brain disease, such as cerebral arteriosclerosis. It occurs most frequently as a toxic-exhaustive-infectious state, or psychosis, associated with somatic disease, and usually manifestations of systemic disease are apparent. One must bear in mind that individuals vary widely in their liability or susceptibility to delirium; some persons react with symptoms of delirium with every illness, minor evidences of toxemia or infection, or only slight temperature elevations, whereas others show no signs of delirium in spite of marked evidences of infection or intoxication. Definite electroencephalographic changes are found in most cases of organic delirium.

Delirium occurs with intracranial infections such as meningitis and encephalitis, but febrile delirium may also appear in association with any severe systemic infection, including such diseases as septicemia, pneumonia, typhoid fever, malaria, scarlet fever, and erysipelas. Motor manifestations such as carphology and jactitation may be more apparent than illusions and hallucinations. The diagnosis of the underlying somatic disease can usually be made by physical examination and laboratory procedures.

Toxic delirium may be caused by ingestion of exogenous toxins or dissemination of endogenous poisons. The hallucinations and delusions of the so-called bromide psychosis are evidences of toxic delirium. Symptoms of delirium are found more frequently in chronic than in acute alcoholic intoxication, although acute alcoholic confusion may be considered a delirious state. Alcoholic hallucinosis and delirium tremens are usualy regarded as withdrawal phenomena and Korsakoff's syndrome as a deficiency state. The latter consists of polyneuritis accompanied by confusion and confabulation; the patient often resorts to evasions and generalities and fills in gaps in his memory by the use of fabricated statements. Alkaloids of the belladonna group, including atropine and hyoscine, may cause dilated pupils, dry mouth, rapid pulse, peripheral vasodilatation, and choreiform movements in addition to excitement and hallucinations. In cocaine poisoning excitement and delirium are followed by coma. Administration of or intoxication by the so-called hallucinogenic substances, including *Cannabis indica* (marijuana), mescaline, yohimbine, and lysergic acid diethylamide is characterized by a rapid, incoherent flight of ideas, misinterpretation of time, fantasies, visual and auditory hallucinations, and grandiose excitement. The barbiturates, chloral hydrate, and other hypnotics, sedatives, and tranquilizers produce clouding of the consciousness and occasional delirium (Chapter 54). Amphetamine causes euphoria which leads to delirium. Quinine, the salicylates, the sulfonamides, and many other therapeutic drugs may also be responsible for delirium, either if given in excessive doses or if administered to susceptible persons. In many cases it is essential to make detailed laboratory tests to determine whether any of these substances is responsible for the symptoms. Endogenous toxins which cause delirium include those associated with hepatic, renal, and other systemic diseases as well as the toxins liberated by various infectious processes. Delirium may follow the sudden withdrawal not only of alcohol but also of other sedative and tranquilizing drugs.

Exhaustive or deficiency deliria occur in pellagra, beriberi, inanition, primary or secondary anemia, and in any prolonged illness that may lead to the development of nutritional deficiencies. The delirium of hypoglycemia is secondary to a deficiency of glucose; that of cardiac insufficiency and heart failure is associated with impairment of the blood supply to the brain. Delirium due to dehydration, water intoxication, or disturbances of the electrolytes or of the acid-base equilibrium (Chapter 54) may be precipitated or aggravated by trauma, surgery, vomiting, diarrhea, diuretics or other drugs, or inadequately balanced intravenous fluids. Delirium may develop in hyperthyroidism, Addison's disease, and other endocrine disturbances. In many instances of delirium there are multiple underlying factors, including metabolic alterations, deficiencies in electrolytes or glucose, impairment of cerebral circulation and oxygenation, toxic and infectious processes, and inhibition of enzyme activity. This is especially apt to be the case in postoperative or posttraumatic syndromes in elderly or debilitated persons.

Organic brain diseases of various types, in addition to meningitis and encephalitis, may be accompanied by delirium. Cerebral arteriosclerosis may not only predispose the development of the symptoms, but may also be directly responsible for them. Cerebral edema associated with brain tumors and abscesses and subdural hematomas may also be responsible. Specific cerebrovascular lesions may cause delirium; either the focal process, secondary cerebral edema, temporary cessation of function of the parts of the brain left intact, or influence of pre-existing vascular disease may be responsible. Visual hallucinations may occur in patients with severe visual loss as a result of disease of the eyes or with lesions of any part of the visual pathway, and auditory hallucinations with disease of any part of the auditory pathway. In the syndrome of peduncular hallucinosis there may be either visual or auditory hallucinations with disease at the level of the midbrain. Cataract delirium comes on following surgical therapy in some elderly persons, and is characterized by disorientation, hallucinations, and delusions. Sudden complete loss of vision owing to presence of dressings, drugs and deficiency factors, and underlying organic cerebral disease are all important. The so-called postepileptic confusion is actually a transient delirium. Following cerebral trauma there may be delirium alternating with fluctuations in the level of awareness; there are confusion, disorientation, lowering of the consciousness, and amnesia (especially retrograde), together with headaches and focal neurologic changes. After a subarachnoid hemorrhage there may be symptoms of confusion, confabulation, and fabrication which are similar to those seen in the Korsakoff's psychosis.

Psychogenic delirium is often difficult to diagnose. It may be a symptom of one of the major psychoses (manic-depressive psychosis or schizophrenia), but it is more commonly encountered in hysteria. The nonorganic features can usually be identified. In hysterical delirium there may be evidence of Ganser's syndrome in which the patient gives approximate but incorrect answers to all questions. So-called Bell's mania, or acute delirious mania, may come on precipitously with either the manic or the agitated depressive phase of the manic-depressive psychosis. The motor overactivity and inadequate dietary and fluid intake lead to metabolic alterations and electrolyte imbalance, increased temperature elevation, and accentuation of the symptoms. Delirium may also follow sensory and sleep deprivation.

DIAGNOSIS OF THE CONVULSIVE DISORDER

Although it is usually possible to carry out the various diagnostic procedures and auxiliary examinations which are necessary to determine the etiology of a convulsive disorder during the interval between attacks, under certain circumstances it may be necessary to arrive at the correct diagnosis during a paroxysm. In either case it is essential to determine whether the symptoms are those of so-called idiopathic, or cryptogenic, epilepsy, or whether the convulsions are caused by either focal or generalized cerebral disease or irritation, systemic affections, toxic exposure or ingestion, metabolic disturbances, withdrawal of drugs, or other etiologic factors, or are precipitated by visual, auditory, or other stimuli. It is also important to differentiate between organic convulsions and psychogenic attacks, and to bear in mind that organic attacks may be precipitated by emotional stimuli.

The history is, extremely important in the diagnosis of the convulsive disorder (Chapter 2). This should be obtained not only from the patient but also from relatives and observers. The history should contain not only the details of the present attack, including precipitating factors, development of the attack, exact sequence of events leading up to the seizure, aura, tonic and clonic phases, and postconvulsion manifestations, but also a detailed chronologic account of the entire disease history. Both the aura and the distribution of motor phenomena may be of localizing significance. The examination should include not only a thorough physical survey, in an attempt to demonstrate the presence of underlying somatic disease, but also a detailed neurologic appraisal; one should be especially concerned with looking for signs of increased intracranial pressure and evidences of localized disturbances of cerebral function.

In most convulsions the loss of consciousness does not persist for more than a short period of time, although it may vary from a portion of a minute to hours or even longer. In jacksonian attacks there may be no loss of consciousness. In status epilepticus there are recurring convulsions with no restoration of consciousness between attacks. The patient may be either flaccid or rigid during the period of epileptic coma, but there is usually a tonic stage which is followed by a clonic phase. The distribution of the motor phenomena should be observed closely; in jacksonian, or focal, attacks the movements may be limited to one arm, one leg, one side of the face, or one half of the body. The spread of the movements—e.g., from the thumb to the fingers, wrist, forearm, arm, and then to the forehead and face—may indicate the site of the epileptogenic focus. Generalized attacks may be focal in onset. Turning of the eyes and/or head, either at the outset or during the attack, has localizing significance. The presence of an epileptic cry, cyanosis, stertorous breathing, tongue-biting, foaming at the mouth, bleeding from the mouth, incontinence of urine and feces, or evidences of physical injury during attacks are considered valuable diagnostic criteria, not only in determining the depth of the loss of consciousness, but also in differentiating between organic and hysterical convulsions. These, however, cannot always be relied upon; many epileptics never bite their tongues, injure themselves, or become incontinent, and in hysteria there occasionally is evidence of injury, tongue-biting, or incontinence. During the postconvulsion period one should note the presence of headache, drowsiness, and a tendency to sleep, and should look for manifestations of focal disturbance of function such as residual paralysis, anesthesia, or aphasia, as well as psychic symptoms such as confusion, irritability, and amnesia. It must be borne in mind that trauma and vascular accidents may cause convulsions, but also that an intracranial hemorrhage or a severe head injury, even with a skull fracture, may occur during an epileptic attack. A patient with a convulsive disorder may develop a subdural hematoma or a subarachnoid hemorrhage as a result of injury during a seizure. Furthermore, ingestion of alcohol may precipitate epileptic attacks, and postconvulsion and alcoholic stupor may occur simultaneously.

The term "convulsive disorder" should probably not be used as a synonym for epilepsy, which is not a disease but a symptom-complex characterized by periodic, transient episodes of alteration in the state of consciousness that may be associated with convulsive movements and/or disturbances of feeling or behavior. Epilepsy may be classified variously: clinically, by the seizure type; anatomically, by the site of the lesion responsible; physiologically, by the electrical or biochemical alterations underlying or accompanying the seizure; etiologically, by the primary causal agent; pathologically, by the structural alterations in the brain; therapeutically, by response to drug therapy. Many classifications take into consideration more than one of the above; that is, a clinical description may be given, along with a mention of the probable anatomic lesion and a description of the electroencephalographic changes. The latter are characteristic of many varieties of epilepsy, which often may be differentiated on the basis of wave form, amplitude, frequency, temporal sequence of wave pattern, the localization of the abnormality (Figs. 313–315). The electrical alterations, especially when recorded during an interseizure period, are not specific for all of the clinical types, but when analyzed along with an adequate history and a detailed neurologic examination constitute an important diagnostic aid. Often other ancillary methods of examination as listed in Chapter 54 are also necessary.

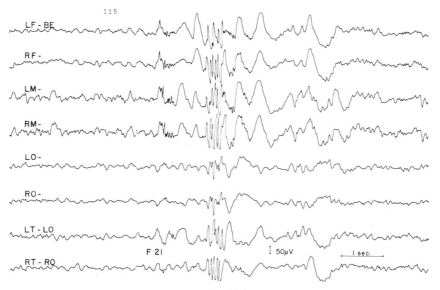

FIG. 313. Electroencephalogram showing bursts of polyspike activity in patient with grand mal epilepsy. (Figs. 313 to 315 courtesy of Dr. Kenneth A. Kooi.)

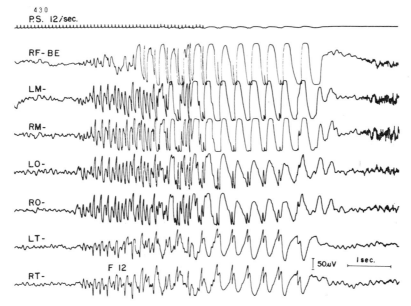

FIG. 314. Electroencephalogram showing activation of three cycles per second spike-wave activity by rhythmic photic stimulation in patient with petit mal and grand mal epilepsy.

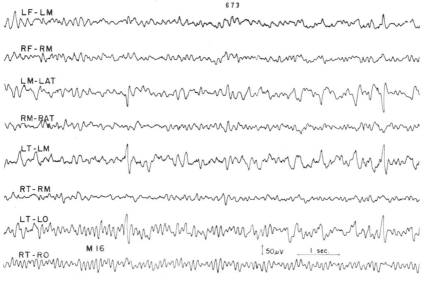

FIG. 315. Electroencephalogram showing left temporal spike and slow wave focus in patient with psychomotor and grand mal epilepsy.

In the clinical classification of the epilepsies the major convulsion, or *grand mal* attack, is the most frequent variety. In this there are generalized convulsive movements, tonic and clonic motor phenomena, loss of consciousness, and often tongue biting or bodily injury during attacks. The electroencephalogram may show evidence of a diffuse dysrhythmia between attacks and high voltage spikelike waves, usually of high frequency but occasionally slow, during attacks. In *petit mal* seizures there is an extremely brief lapse of consciousness, usually without falling. The patient may stop talking, appear to stare for a moment, and drop objects from his hands. He is usually immobile, but there may be brief slow movements of the eyes, eyelids, head, or rarely, the extremities. There is an alternation of fast and slow cortical electrical activity, with a two to three per second high voltage spike and wave pattern that is bilaterally synchronous and probably indicates the presence of a deep-seated disturbance of function that is relayed to the cortex. In *psychomotor* attacks there is a period of automatic or abnormal behavior during which the patient appears to be confused and may carry out some unreasonable, unmotivated, purposeless or seemingly purposeful act. Although there usually is no complete loss of consciousness, the patient may not be aware of what he is doing and have complete amnesia for what transpires during the attack. There usually are no convulsive movements. Accompanying or preceding the automatisms, or in place of them, there may be abnormalities of memory (déjà vu or déjà pensée), auditory or visual hallucinations or misinterpretations, olfactory or gustatory symptoms that may be accompanied by smacking or tasting movements of the lips and tongue, gastric or autonomic nervous system manifestations, or alterations of thinking or affect. These various phenomena, along with the usual electroencephalographic localization, indicate in most instances a disturbance of function in or near one or both temporal regions. In *jacksonian* or focal seizures there are tonic and clonic movements which are confined to one extremity or one side of the body; they may begin in one extremity and spread to involve other parts. Often there is no loss of consciousness. The electroencephalographic picture is similar to that in grand mal attacks, but the abnormal waves originate locally in a specific area of the cortex, and then spread; in the free period there may be a focus of very slow waves.

It is not always possible to classify epileptic attacks into one of the above four types. There may be a variability of manifestations from time to time; there may not be a clear-cut distinction between one type of attack and another; there may be *formes frustes* which cannot be classified; many patients have more than one type of seizure. An attack which starts as a focal, or jacksonian, one with localized movements and turning of the head and eyes to one side at the outset, may terminate as a grand mal seizure; in these the aura and the primary manifestations are important in localization. In akinetic attacks there is sudden loss of postural control with nodding of the head or, if generalized, a sudden fall. In myoclonic epilepsy there are single, quick contractions of the muscles, especially those of the flexor groups, but occasionally of the trunk as well; myoclonic jerkings may precede or accompany grand mal seizures. The term infantile spasm or massive myoclonic epilepsy is used to describe a seizure type that occurs in infants and young children and is characterized by frequent, brief, bilaterally symmetric, jerky flexion movements of the neck, body, and extremities; mental deterioration and a diffuse electroencephalographic abnormality (hypsarhythmia) are usually associated. In cursive epilepsy there are running and other gross bodily movements which persist until the patient falls down and loses consciousness. In autonomic, or diencephalic, epilepsy, the attack consists of flushing of the head and neck, tachycardia, cutis anserina, hyperhidrosis, and other manifestations of autonomic nervous system activity. In so-called brain stem and cerebellar fits there is rigidity of all four extremities, often with opisthotonos.

The diagnosis of epilepsy is made largely on the basis of observation of attacks, adequate history and description, and electroencephalographic criteria. It is often valuable to have an opportunity to observe a convulsive seizure in order to appraise the patient's complaints, differentiate malingered or hysterical attacks from organic ones, and note the characteristics of an organic seizure. Attacks have been precipitated in patients by the use of the pitressin hydration test, but most authorities advise against this procedure. Electroencephalography may aid in the diagnosis, especially in those cases where it is difficult to obtain an adequate description of the seizure, and may be of further value in demonstrating the presence of either focal or generalized cerebral disease that may be responsible for the attacks. On occasion, if abnormality is suspected but not evident on routine recordings, diagnostic changes may be brought out by activation procedures using hyperventilation, sleep, the administration of pentylenetetrazol (Metrazol) or other stimulants, the injection of insulin, visual (photic) or auditory (sonic) stimulation, or combinations of these. Electrical abnormalities, if the investigation is sufficiently complete, are found in 80 to 90 per cent of epileptics, between as well as during attacks. It is important to remember, however, that occasional epileptics have normal recordings and a variable percentage of healthy persons show electroencephalographic changes suggestive of epilepsy. Consequently the diagnosis should not be based on electrical changes alone.

It must always be borne in mind that convulsions may be symptoms not only of epilepsy but also of some somatic disease, and careful physical, neurologic, and laboratory examinations should always be carried out in order to determine their etiology. Convulsions in infancy may be caused by congenital abnormalities of the brain (cerebral aplasia, hereditary defects, or the lipidoses), anoxia, trauma at the time of birth, antenatal or postnatal infections, hemorrhagic disease of the newborn (erythroblastosis fetalis), or infantile tetany; the latter is diagnosed by the presence of the Chvostek and related signs, together with alterations in the blood calcium and phosphorus content. Convulsions in childhood may be caused by tetany, fevers, and acute infections (even in the absence of actual cerebral involvement by the inflammatory process), the ingestion of toxic substances (especially lead), trauma, brain tumors and abscesses, meningitis, encephalitis, vascular disease, tuberous sclerosis, and demyelinating encephalomyelitis. Breathholding spells in children may or may not be related to the convulsive diathesis. Convulsions in adolescents and adults may be caused by brain tumors or abscesses, trauma, meningitis or encephalitis, vascular disease, intoxications, hypoglycemia, uremia, eclampsia, central nervous system syphilis, tetany, tetanus, rabies, cardiac disease, hyperactive carotid sinus syndrome, cerebral degenerations, and other disease processes, as well as by the withdrawal of drugs, or may be precipitated by various sensory stimuli or by reading. Disturbances of consciousness and motor activity which resemble true convulsions may be symptoms of hysteria; the movements, however, are bizarre, and there may be no complete loss of consciousness. It is important to bear in mind that idiopathic epilepsy and psychogenic convulsions may coexist in the same patient. The differentiation between epilepsy (especially if the disturbance of consciousness is more outstanding than the convulsive manifestations), vasodepressor syncope, and hysteria is often a difficult one to make, and emotional stimuli may precipitate organic convulsions and true syncope as well as hysterical attacks; the electroencephalogram may be of aid in the diagnosis.

REFERENCES

AJMONE-MARSON, C., and RALSTON, B. L.   The Epileptic Seizure.   Springfield, Ill., Charles C Thomas, 1957

BAILEY, P.   Concerning the localization of consciousness.   *Tr. Am. Neurol. A.* 80:1, 1955.

BRAIN, W. R.   The cerebral basis of consciousness.   *Brain* 73:465, 1950.

CAIRNS, H.   Disturbances of consciousness with lesions of the brain-stem and diencephalon.   *Brain* 75:109, 1952.

CRAVIOTO, H., SILBERMAN, J., and FEIGIN, I.   A clinical and pathologic study of akinetic mutism. *Neurology* 10:10, 1960.

DEJONG, R. N.   "Psychomotor" or "temporal lobe" epilepsy: A review of the development of our present concepts.   *Neurology* 7:1, 1957.

DEJONG, R. N. (ed.)   Treatment of epilepsy.   *Modern Treatment* 1:1045, 1964.

DELAFRESNAYE, J. F. (ed.).   Brain Mechanisms and Consciousness.   Springfield, Ill., Charles C Thomas, 1954.

DEMENT, W., and KLEITMAN, N.   Cyclic variations of EEG during sleep and their relation to eye movements, body motility, and dreaming.   *Electroencep. & Clin. Neurophysiol.* 9:673, 1957.

DERMKSIAN, G., and LAMB, L. E.   Syncope in a population of healthy young adults. *J.A.M.A.* 168:1200, 1958.

DI BENEDETTO, R. J., CROCCO, J. A., and SOSCIA, J. L.   Hyperglycemic nonketotic coma. *Arch. Int. Med.* 116:74, 1965.

DIXON, K. C.   The amnesia of cerebral concussion. *Lancet* 2:1359, 1962.

ENGEL, G. L.   Fainting (ed. 2).Springfield, Ill., Charles C Thomas, 1962.

FAZEKAS, J. F., and ALMAN, R. W.   Coma: Biochemistry, Physiology and Therapeutic Principles.   Springfield, Ill., Charles C Thomas, 1962.

FISHER, C. M.   Concussion amnesia.   A case report.   *Neurology* 16:826, 1966.

FISHER, C. M., and ADAMS, R. D.   Transient global amnesia. *Acta neurol. scandinav.*, vol. 40, suppl. 9, 1964.

FRENCH, J. D.   Brain lesions associated with prolonged unconsciousness.   *A. M. A. Arch. Neurol. & Psychiat.* 68:727, 1952.

GARLAND, H., SUMNER, D., and FORMAN, R. P.   The Kleine-Levin syndrome. *Neurology* 15:1161, 1965.

GASTAUT, H.   The Epilepsies: Electro-Clinical Correlations.   Springfield, Ill., Charles C Thomas, 1954.

GAUK, E. W., KIDD, L., and PRICHARD, J. S. Mechanism of seizures associated with breath-holding spells. *New England J. Med.* 268:1436, 1963.

GIBBS, F. A., GIBBS, E. L., and LENNOX, W. G. Influence of the blood sugar level on the wave and spike formation in petit mal epilepsy. *Arch. Neurol. & Psychiat.* 41: 1111, 1939; Electroencephalographic classification of epileptic patients and control subjects. *Arch. Neurol. & Psychiat.* 50:111, 1943.

JARVIE, H. F., and HOOD, M. C. Acute delirious mania. *Am. J. Psychiat.* 108:758, 1952.

KARP, H. R., WEISSLER, A. M., and HEYMAN, A. Vasodepressor syncope: EEG and circulatory changes. *Arch. Neurol.* 5:94, 1961.

KENNEDY, A., and NEVILLE, J. Sudden loss of memory. *Brit. M. J.* 2:427, 1957.

KERSHMAN, J. Syncope and seizures. *J. Neurol., Neurosurg. & Psychiat.* 12:25, 1949

KIERSCH, T. A. Amnesia: A clinical study of 98 cases. *Am. J. Psychiat.* 119:57, 1962.

LENNOX, W. G. Amnesia, real and feigned. *Am. J. Psychiat.* 99:732, 1943; The treatment of epilepsy. *M. Clin. North America* 29:1114, 1945.

LENNOX, W. G., and LENNOX, M. A. Epilepsy and Related Convulsive Disorders. Boston, Little, Brown & Company, 1960.

LEON-SOTOMAYOR, L., and BOWERS, C. Y. Myxedema Coma. Springfield, Ill., Charles C Thomas, 1964.

MACLAGAN, N. F. "The biochemistry of coma," in CUMINGS, J. N., and KREMER, M. (eds.). Biochemical Aspects of Neurological Disorders. Springfield, Ill., Charles C Thomas, 1964.

MARTIN, J. P. Consciousness and its disturbances. *Lancet* 1:1 and 48, 1949.

MC HENRY, L. C., JR., FAZEKAS, J. F., and SULLIVAN, J. F. Cerebral hemodynamics of syncope. *Amer. J. M. Sc.* 241:173, 1961.

MCINTOSH, H. D., ESTES, E. H., and WARREN, J. The mechanism of cough syncope. *Am. Heart J.* 52:70, 1956.

MCQUARRIE, I., and PEELER, D. B. The effects of sustained pituitary antidiuresis and forced water drinking in epileptic children: A diagnostic and etiologic study. *J. Clin. Investigation* 10:915, 1931.

MEYERS, R., and MEYERS, M. E. Management of the comatose patient. *Am. Practitioner* 1:1031, 1950.

MOUNT, L. A. The differential diagnosis of coma. *M. Clin. North America* 32:795, 1948.

MUNRO, D. The diagnosis, treatment and immediate prognosis of cerebral trauma. *New England J. Med.* 210:287, 1934.

PENFIELD, W., and JASPER, H. Epilepsy and the Functional Anatomy of the Human Brain. Boston, Little, Brown & Company, 1954.

PLUM, F., and POSNER, J. B. Diagnosis of Stupor and Coma. Philadelphia, F. A. Davis Co., 1966.

PROUDFIT, W. L., and FORTEZA, M. E. Miscturition syncope. *New England J. Med.* 260:328, 1959.

PULLEN, R. L. The differential diagnosis of coma. *South. M. J.* 44:921, 1951.

ROVENSTINE, E. A. The incidence, diagnosis and management of coma. *Anesthesiology* 6:1, 1945.

RUSSELL, W. R. Brain-Memory-Learning: A Neurologist's View. Oxford, The Clarendon Press, 1959.

SALTZMAN, H. A., HEYMAN, A., and SIEKER, H. O.   Correlation of clinical and physiologic manifestations of sustained hyperventilation.   *New England J. Med.* 268:1431,
1963.

SHERLOCK, S.   Hepatic coma.   *Practitioner* 191:18, 1963.

SHY, G. M., and DRAGER, G. A.   A neurological syndrome associated with orthostatic
hypotension: A clinico-pathologic study.   *Arch. Neurol.* 2:511, 1960.

SOLOMON, P., and ARING, C. D.   The causes of coma in patients entering a general
hospital.   *Am. J. M. Sc.* 188:805, 1934; A routine diagnostic procedure for the
patient who enters the hospital in coma.   *Am. J. M. Sc.* 191:357, 1936; The differential diagnosis in patients entering the hospital in coma.   *J.A.M.A.* 105:7, 1935.

THOMAS, J. E., and KLASS, D. W.   Evaluation of the comatose patient.   *Postgrad. Med.*
36:207, 1964.

THOMAS, J. E., and ROOKE, E. D.   Fainting.   *Proc. Staff Meet., Mayo Clinic* 38:397,
1963.

WALKER, A. E.   Posttraumatic Epilepsy.   Springfield, Ill., Charles C Thomas, 1948;
Impairment of memory as a symptom of a focal neurological lesion.   *South. M. J.*
50:1272, 1957.

WAYNE, H. H.   Syncope: Physiological considerations and analysis of characteristics in
510 patients.   *Amer. J. Med.*   30:418, 1961.

WEISS, S., and BAKER, J. P.   The carotid sinus reflex in health and disease: Its rôle in
the causation of fainting and convulsions.   *Medicine* 12:297, 1933.

WHITTY, C. W. M.   "The neurological basis of memory," in WILLIAMS, D. (ed.),
Modern Trends in Neurology, Washington, D.C.: Butterworth's, Vol. 3, pp. 314–335,
1962.

WILLIAMS, M., and ZANGWILL, O. L.   Memory defects after head injury.   *J. Neurol.,
Neurosurg. & Psychiat.* 15:54, 1952.

WILSON, G., RUPP, C., and WILSON, W. W.   Amnesia.   *Am. J. Psychiat.* 106:481,
1950.

WOLFF, H. G., and CURRAN, D.   Nature of delirium and allied states.   *Arch. Neurol.
& Psychiat.* 33:1175, 1935.

CHAPTER 56

EXAMINATION IN CASES OF SUSPECTED HYSTERIA AND MALINGERING

IN THE EVALUATION of every patient who has symptoms of nervous system dysfunction it is essential to differentiate between those manifestations which are organic in origin (i.e., caused by pathoanatomic and pathophysiologic changes) and those which are psychogenic in origin. Furthermore, if nonorganic changes are present, it is essential to distinguish between those which are consciously induced, or feigned (malingered), and those which are unconsciously motivated (hysterical).

Psychogenic manifestations may closely resemble organic ones, and the differentiation between the two may present diagnostic difficulties. It must be borne in mind, however, in the appraisal of every patient, that the presenting symptoms as well as the signs of disease may not be of organic origin. This is especially apt to be the case if the manifestations are somewhat bizarre and do not seem to fit readily into any specific category. Furthermore, organic and nonorganic disease may exist simultaneously; the latter may precipitate manifestations of the former, or organic disease may be accompanied by psychogenic variations and accentuations. An individual with a convulsive disorder, for instance, may on occasion have attacks which are psychogenically precipitated and may, in addition, have occasional pseudoconvulsions (either consciously or unconsciously motivated) which may closely resemble the true organic seizures. If the patient is seen only during the malingered or hysterical attacks, his entire illness may appear to have psychogenic origin, and the organic factors may be overlooked.

The distinction between hysteria and malingering (or between unconscious and conscious motivation) is even more difficult than the differentiation between organic and psychogenic disease, and requires greater diagnostic acumen. Furthermore, hysteria and malingering may occur simultaneously, especially in instances where there is exaggeration of symptoms. By definition, hysteria and malingering are extreme opposites, and for diagnostic purposes one should always attempt to distinguish between them. This differentiation, however, is not always possible, especially in the presence of so-called psychoneurotic malingering.

DEFINITIONS

Hysteria is, by definition, a psychoneurosis, or a disease which has psychogenic origin. There is no underlying organic pathologic basis for the patient's complaints, and the manifestations are produced by conversion mechanisms (i.e., emotions are transformed into physical symptoms). The patient has no control over his acts and emotions; he is unconscious of the genesis of his symptoms, and is not aware of their unreality. The emotional conflict which is responsible has been completely repressed, and the patient believes his symptoms to be the result of organic disease. The manifestations may be either brought on or altered by suggestion.

Malingering is defined as a willful, deliberate, and fraudulent imitation or exaggeration of illness, usually intended to deceive others, and, under most circumstances, conceived for the purpose of gaining a consciously desired end. Simulation (positive malingering) is the feigning or pretense of nonexisting symptoms by word, gesture, action, or behavior; dissimulation (negative malingering) is the concealment of existing symptoms by similar means. Three varieties of malingering have been described. (1) *Pure malingering* is the deliberate and designed feigning of disease or disability, or, if disease exists, its intentional concealment. This may be done by false allegation (untrue attestation that symptoms exist, or spurious denial of existing or previously acquired disease), imitation (feigning or simulation of symptoms of disease), or provocation (intentional production of lesions or symptoms by artificial means). (2) *Partial malingering,* or *exaggeration,* is the magnification or intensification of symptoms which already exist. It is usually conscious and voluntary, and the patient may exaggerate symptoms of real disease and cause an illness which is already present to assume greater severity, superimpose factitious symptoms on a substratum of real disease, or aggravate and protract the course and duration of a disease or injury. Unconscious and involuntary exaggeration may take place through ignorance, fear, or deficient powers of subjective analysis; such exaggeration closely resembles hysteria. (3) *False imputation* is the ascribing of morbid phenomena or symptoms to a definite cause although this cause may be recognized or ascertained to have no relationship to the symptoms. The patient may attempt to blame an innocent episode for manifestations which were present previously or which appeared from some other cause. False imputation may take place through design or through ignorance.

According to the above definitions, hysteria and malingering are widely divergent in both motivation and origin. In hysteria the symptoms are unconsciously determined, and the patient is not aware of their unreality; they develop without apparent design; they are real to him and he deceives himself, but seldom others. The manifestations of disease are often influenced by suggestion, and therefore there may be a variability of signs and symptoms from time to time, contradiction of responses, vagueness of history, and disproportion between the symptoms and general state of well-being of the patient, as well as disproportion between the subjective complaints and the objective manifestations. The symptoms are bizarre and do not fit into any organic pattern which may be explained by a specific anatomic lesion. The patient's attitude varies from complete indifference toward his illness and the examination to which he is subjected to a state of marked apprehension and anxiety. He may appear to be unconcerned in spite of what seems to be incapacitating symptoms, or he may appear to be in great discomfort with marked emotional display. Although the symptoms may fluctuate in severity, there is some involvement at all times; paralyzed extremities can not be used for either work or play.

Hysteria is a disease, in essence an illness of the personality. It represents the unconscious transfer, by the patient, of a psychic difficulty to a somatic one. The hysterical patient often welcomes examinations, and may be eager for repeated examinations, although occasionally he resents and avoids such studies. He is often pleased and reassured at the absence of organic disease. He is usually anxious to follow all recommended treatment procedures; he takes whatever medications are prescribed and is willing to submit to surgical operations. He may accept employment and attempt to work. He is honest and reliable in his contacts with physicians, as far as his unconscious mind permits, and he usually has a good employment record. He frequently shows anxiety concerning his hospitalization and the episode that brought him to the hospital. Because hysteria is a disease, posttraumatic and other psychoneuroses are considered compensable by most workmen's compensation and insurance laws.

In malingering, on the other hand, the patient is conscious of the unreality of his symptoms, and he manufactures them with definite intent; he attempts to deceive others, but does not deceive himself. There is usually but slight variability in symptoms from time to time, they are not influenced by suggestion; the responses are consistent, and the history is specific, especially in regard to the onset of disability following an accident or injury. Usually, however, the disability appears to be much greater than one would suspect from the injury described; the pain is out of proportion to the injury sustained or the disability claimed, and the recovery period has been prolonged beyond clinical expectancy. Malingered symptoms, also fail to fit an organic pattern which may be explained by a specific anatomic lesion, and they may assume bizarre characteristics. The disability is too great for the severity of the trauma or the amount of organic involvement, and the manifestations of disease are unduly prolonged. The malingerer plans to deceive, and his symptoms are fraudulently and deliberately produced. As a result, the patient is defensive, hostile, and suspicious of examinations, which he fears, resents, and attempts to avoid. He may refuse or resist repeated examinations because each new procedure may impose an ordeal which requires great concentration. The patient is aware of the fact that he must be consistent in his symptoms and his disability, so that he will not give himself away. To avoid being enmeshed he is more careful than the normal person in choosing his words. Consequently his answers are evasive, and it frequently is impossible to obtain an exact description of his symptoms. The patient is often sullen, ill at ease, suspicious, uncooperative, and resentful. He may be tense during the examination, yet give himself away during a period of relaxation. He declines to cooperate in recommended therapeutic procedures, insisting on relief of symptoms before starting treatment. He often refuses surgical operations or claims that the investigative tests have aggravated his symptoms. He may state that he is unable to work and refuse employment, yet be able to use his allegedly paralyzed limb at certain times, especially for play. In personality he is greedy and dishonest, and often unpleasant and demanding. He may have a history of previously incapacitating injuries and a poor employment record. The secondary gain from his illness is often readily apparent. Because the malingerer is essentially a deceiver, and the symptoms of which he complains are fraudulent, simulated diseases are not compensable by law.

Too often, especially among the laity and the legal professions, malingering and hysteria are regarded as more or less synonymous terms. In both conditions the symptoms have no organic basis, there is an incongruity of manifestations, many of which may be bizarre in character, and there may be a disproportion between the patient's disability and his general physical status. As a consequence, the symptoms of each are frequently referred to as "imagined." In hysteria, however, the manifestations are unconsciously determined and real to the patient; his arm is paralyzed because he believes it to be, and he has no voluntary power over it. In malingering, on the other hand, the patient alleges, falsifies, and feigns the paralysis; he knows that his arm is not paralyzed, but does not wish to move it and may resist attempts to move it passively. The difficulties are simulated for the patient's own gain. He consciously tries to reproduce symptoms that either he has had before or has seen or heard of in others, or he exaggerates or prolongs a disability.

Either hysterical or simulated symptoms may follow injuries and industrial accidents, but malingering is most apt to follow such accidents if the symptoms are associated with attempts to secure compensation. One must be especially concerned with the possibility of malingering in the following types of individuals; those who have had an injury, especially an industrial accident allegedly suffered in employment, the disability resulting from which is compensable by benefits payable under workmen's compensation laws or by damages based on alleged negligence (the accident and the injury may both be feigned, or the accident real but the injury feigned); those who have suffered either from accidents which are payable by insurance benefits or injuries from which monetary gains may be expected; those who wish to obtain insurance benefits for illness or disability; civilians who wish to evade conscription to military service or members of the Armed Forces who wish to obtain discharge from such service; those who develop symptoms in order to avoid disagreeable duties, evade legal and other responsibilities, gain sympathy or attention, or force others to bow to their will.

Although hysteria and malingering are essentially different, in many instances the distinction between them cannot be made with the ease that the definitions imply. The same tests to distinguish organic from psychogenic disease are used in both, and the results of them are the same in both. The procedures that rule out organic disease do not differentiate between hysteria and malingering. In the tests used to distinguish between true blindness and deafness and either hysterical or malingered loss of vision and hearing, for instance, one may be able to determine that the patient has no organic defect, but may not be able to state whether the difficulty is a conscious or an involuntary one. One must bear in mind, however, that although hysteria and malingering are diametric opposites, the two may occur together in the same patient and they may blend into each other with a gradual transition from the one to the other. In the midposition between the two extremes are the psychoneurotic patient who exaggerates his symptoms and the malingerer who has an unstable nervous system. The two are especially apt to occur together in posttraumatic syndromes where compensation or other medicolegal elements are involved (the so-called compensation or traumatic neurosis). The similarity between the two may be so great that it is not possible to distinguish between and evaluate conscious and unconscious exaggeration of symptoms, and thus appraise the patient's difficulties. Furthermore, it must be borne in mind that either hysteria or malingering or both may occur in association with organic disease, especially if there is an exaggeration of symptoms; under such circumstances the organic and nonorganic features must be appraised individually.

The actual differentiation between hysteria and malingering depends upon the goal sought by the patient. If the goal is an intangible one, such as an escape from the responsibility of life, one should suspect hysteria; if it is tangible, such as an attempt to secure monetary gain, the evidence favors malingering. Perhaps the most important criteria in the distinction between hysteria and malingering are the past history and the personality inventory. Knowledge of the patient's past performances under similar circumstances aids in evaluation. Patterns of behavior and reactions to emotional situations and trauma in early life are important. In the hysterical patient there may have been similar episodes associated with emotional stress and strain, fears, anxieties, shock, and disappointments, and there may be a past history of psychosomatic symptoms starting at an early age which were not specifically related to the nervous system. These include anxiety attacks, tachycardia, respiratory difficulties, cardiospasm, anorexia nervosa, psychogenic vomiting, aerophagia, spastic constipation or emotional diarrhea, urinary disturbances, difficulties in sexual function, pseudocyesis, dermatitis factitia, neurotic excoriations, or other symptoms which may be referred to any of the organs or systems of the body. There is a striking tendency for the manifestations to return from time to time throughout life; they may be brought on by suggestion, and the form they take is determined by suggestion. Furthermore, in hysterical patients there are both past history and present evidence of autonomic nervous system imbalance, with tachycardia, hyperhidrosis, vasomotor instability, pupillary dilatation, and labile blood pressure. In malingerers, on the other hand, if there have been previous episodes, they have all been related to minor traumas and industrial situations; oftentimes there is a history of previous conflict with the law, aggressive and antisocial behavior, prior litigation, and a poor employment record. There may be evidence that the patient has a sociopathic or antisocial personality disturbance (previously called constitutional psychopathic personality), is a "psychopathic liar," or harbors paranoid ideas.

There is some controversy about whether the term hysteria (a mental mechanism operating unconsciously, by which intrapsychic conflicts, which would otherwise give rise to anxiety, are instead given symbolic external expression) should continue to be used. In psychiatric classifications of disease the terms conversion reaction, anxiety state, psychophysiologic disorder, and dissociative process are more widely accepted for the syndromes that are herein described. Slater has recently stated that the diagnosis of hysteria is a disguise for ignorance, and that most patients so diagnosed are later found to have organic disease. Walshe, however, states that hysteria does exist and can be diagnosed if there are no signs of physiologic or morphologic disease, if there are signs which contraindicate the diagnosis of organic disease, and if the patterns of dysfunction suggest a psychogenic origin. Whether or not actual hysteria exists as an entity, there are hysterical (or psychogenic) symptoms, or those of a conversion reaction, and from a neurologic point of view these may include such manifestations as loss of function (paralysis, anesthesia, blindness, deafness), disorders of consciousness (varying from syncope to coma and including convulsive phenomena or "hysteroepilepsy"), simulation of organic disease (hyperkinesias, dizziness, dysphonia, torticollis), syndromes in which pain is the predominant symptom, and combinations with both organic and either conversion or psychophysiologic features.

THE EXAMINATION

There is no special routine for the neurologic examination in the attempt to detect hysteria and malingering. The complete procedures for the neurologic appraisal must be carried out in detail in every case. There is scarcely a symptom or a sign of organic disease which cannot be assumed in either hysteria or malingering; it has been said that hysteria is the most protean disorder in the entire domain of medicine. The examiner must, however, be on the lookout at all times for signs of dysfunction which do not fit into an organic pattern, and if such appear, certain special tests and modifications of the routine procedure have to be carried out. This is often apt to be the case in patients whose symptoms have posttraumatic origin (especially if associated with industrial accidents), have medicolegal complications, or are related to military conscription or service. In all these circumstances psychogenic, predominantly malingered, symptoms are common.

In taking the history one should attempt to differentiate between organic and nonorganic factors; this applies not only to the symptoms which are directly referable to the nervous system, but also to somatic symptoms in general. The history of previous fainting attacks, cardiac or gastrointestinal symptoms of psychic origin, multiple illnesses or complaints, and vague manifestations of disease may help to explain the presence of bizarre neurologic complaints. The history of previous adjustment to the environment, the home situation, employment, and emotional stresses and strains has great significance. Such information should be obtained not only from the patient but also from relatives and friends. In eliciting the history of the present episode one should secure the details of the precipitating experience (trauma, emotional strain, or mental shock) and of the evolution of the symptoms following their first appearance. If there was an accident, the details should be obtained. It is important to know how the injury occurred and whether witnesses were present and the accident was reported. One should inquire whether the patient suffered loss of consciousness, was able to move parts of his body or to walk after the injury, and was given immediate medical treatment. It may help to have the patient re-enact the injury and compare his present muscle power with that before the accident. A naïve malingerer may move the allegedly paralyzed limbs freely to demonstrate his former strength or show the position of his body before or during the accident.

In carrying out the neurologic examination it must be borne in mind that the manifestations that do not fit into the organic pattern may have psychic origin. The patient should be examined in great detail with attempts to distract his attention from the symptoms and break down his guard. It may be important to employ ruses to trick him into making false responses and to carry out repeated examinations to determine whether he is consistent. Apparatus may be employed to confuse and bewilder him. He should be watched carefully but discreetly while he dresses and undresses himself, walks into and out of the examining room, and turns his head to hear or eyes to see. He may be noted to carry out movements and use parts of his body whose functions, during the examination, seem to be impaired. He may, for instance, be unable to stand on one foot without falling while being examined, or even to stand on both feet in the Romberg test, yet be able to perform these acts without difficulty when putting on his trousers or lacing his shoes. The examiner should never allow the patient to gain the impression that either malingering or hysteria is suspected. He should approach the patient in a manner which gives utmost confidence. He should be sympathetic and never use harsh or inquisitional methods, threats, or intimidations, and should not attempt to force admission. He should avoid asking leading questions or making suggestions, and should never give away his feelings about the patient. Friends and relatives should always be excluded from the examining room. Continued observation, often indirect, and re-peated examinations may be necessary.

The patient's facies and general reactions often aid the examiner in his evaluation. Real pain, for instance, affects the eyes, facies, pulse, blood pressure, respirations, and pupillary reactions; there may be grimacing, weeping, tachycardia, pupillary dilatation, vasomotor changes, withdrawal of the part, and defense attitudes and postures to relieve or prevent pain. In both hysteria and malingering these are usually absent. Hysterical patients may show either excessive reactions to painful stimulation, but without physiologic accompaniments, or decreased response to pain. They may appear indifferent and unconcerned while describing excruciating pain. The mode of speech, physiognomy, demeanor, and deportment may also aid in appraisal. In hysteria there may be either bland indifference with no signs of alarm and a cheerful smile in spite of what appears to be severe incapacity, or an excessive emotional reaction. In malingering the patient may betray deceit by blushing con-fusion, or cast-down eyes, there is no open-eyed candor, and there may be either surly reserve or frank ill-temper.

In general, hysteria may be diagnosed if there is absence of objective physical signs to substantiate the patient's subjective symptoms, evidence that the com-plaints had their onset in association with either emotional stress or suggestion, presence of personality features and stigmas (glove and stocking anesthesias or tubular vision) of psychoneurosis, and a therapeutic response to suggestion. In addition, the absence of conjunctival and pharyngeal reflexes and the presence of bizarre tremors, a Rosenbach's sign, hyperhidrosis of the hands and feet, vasomotor instability, and other evidences of autonomic nervous system imbalance aid in the diagnosis. Malingering may be diagnosed if there is absence of objective physical signs to substantiate the patient's complaints, together with the absence of the above criteria of hysteria; the personality pattern and apparent purpose of the illness, however, are essential. Neither should ever be diagnosed merely by the absence of organic features or on the basis of one or two tests. It is necessary to substantiate the impression by the presence of positive features of either hysteria or malingering, and a conclusive diagnosis can be made only after a thorough analysis of the history, the patient's reactions toward his illness, and the findings elicited in a complete neurologic examination. It is important to bear in mind that bizarre symptoms and signs may also occur in organic disease, and that in many somatic disorders there are no objective physical criteria of dysfunction.

Special diagnostic procedures may aid in the final differentiation between organic and nonorganic disease, and sometimes in the distinction between hysteria and malingering. Tests of autonomic nervous system function, such as the determination of skin resistance or reflex erythema, may give essential information (Chapter 42). The electroencephalogram and pneumoencephalogram may be necessary to the diagnosis, especially in posttraumatic cerebral syndromes, and the electromyogram in peripheral nerve and nerve roots lesions. Projective tests and personality inventories may give significant information (Chapter 4). Finally, in certain cases, hypnosis and hypnotic hypnosis or interviews with the use of sodium amobarbital (Amytal) or sodium thiopental (Pentothal) may be of diagnostic value.

NERVOUS SYSTEM SYMPTOMS IN HYSTERIA AND MALINGERING

Either hysteria or malingering may appear to affect any part of the nervous system, and the symptoms may resemble those of any organic neurologic disturbance. By careful examination, however, together with diagnostic acumen, the examiner is able in most instances to make a differentiation and a diagnosis.

THE SENSORY SYSTEM

Either pain, perversion of sensation, or decrease in sensation may be present on a nonorganic basis. Psychogenic pain may be more difficult to evaluate than nonorganic decrease in sensation. Pain is subjective, and the examiner must rely to a great extent upon the patient's account of his symptom. In analyzing the complaint one should obtain an accurate description of its exact location and distribution, areas of radiation, mode of onset, severity, type and character, duration and periodicity, as well as of the factors that accentuate and decrease it. If there are paresthesias, dysesthesias, and phantom sensations, these should be analyzed in the same manner.

The differentiation between genuine, feigned, and exaggerated pain is often difficult. Psychogenic pain may affect any portion of the body and may closely simulate organic pain, although it often is vague, inconstant, and poorly localized, and fails to correspond to any true nerve distribution. Psychogenic headache, for instance, is often band-like in distribution, and it may be the so-called clavus type, which is specifically localized and characterized by a sensation of a nail being driven into the skull. The patient may have pain for which there is no organic basis, or he may exaggerate a minimal discomfort. In general, psychogenic pain is not accompanied by alterations in function and attitude, such as defense movements, withdrawal of the part, spasm of muscles, and suppression of motion; it is not attended by changes in pulse rate, blood pressure, respiratory depth and rate, pupillary diameter, vaso-motor and trophic function, or sweat secretion; it is not reflected in the facial expression; it is not intensified by pressure over the painful area; it is not associated with such phenomena as swelling, redness, and heat. There is often a lack of consistency between the severity of the pain that the patient describes and the intensity of dis-comfort that he seems to be experiencing. There may either be a decreased response or an excessive reaction to the painful stimulus. The patient may complain of intense, unbearable pain, yet he may, at the same time, either smile or exhibit a bland, un-concerned facial expression. On the other hand, there may be such manifestations as dramatizations, theatrical gestures, and facial expressions which are out of propor-tion to the severity of the symptoms described. In spite of what is claimed to be great discomfort, the patient may be able to eat and sleep without difficulty, and is often able to pursue pleasurable activities. Psychogenic pain of long duration may be accompanied by no disturbance in general nutrition or loss of weight. The pain often is influenced by suggestion; it may be diminished by slight physical measures which should not be of therapeutic value, or it may, by the physician's suggestion, travel from one spot to another and change in type during the examination. Psychogenic pain is often relieved by placebos, but on the other hand most individuals are in-fluenced to a certain extent by suggestion, and organic pain may also be diminished by the use of placebos. Furthermore, on occasion psychogenic pain is characterized by the fact that it is relieved by no medication, even the most powerful narcotic.

The determination of the sensory threshold and the patient's reaction to painful stimulation may aid in the evaluation of the severity of pain. The hysterical indi-vidual often over-reacts to all painful stimuli, sometimes with an exaggerated motor response. There is no significant difference between psychoneurotic and normal individuals in the pain *perception* threshold, but there may be a definite lowering of the pain *reaction* threshold in psychoneurotics. This over-reaction may be demon-strated by means of the tests described by Libman, Wolff, Gluzek, and others (Chapter 5). The lowered pain reaction threshold in psychoneurosis is not neces-sarily a manifestation of the conversion process, as such lowering may also occur in anxiety states, neurasthenia, and hypochondriasis. It is important to recall that there is a marked variability of the pain reaction threshold in normal individuals in fatigue and anxiety, and that there may be no lowering in hysteria. The threshold varies, furthermore, with age, race, sex, and state of health.

Hyperesthesia and tenderness are found in both malingering and hysteria. In the former they are usually localized to the involved area, and may be inconstant. The patient may wince and complain of intense tenderness when the affected portion of the body is barely touched, yet if attention is distracted deep pressure on the same area may cause no flinching or other objective change. If the patient is examined while his eyes are closed or his attention distracted, he may be found to contradict himself. *Mannkopf's sign* may be used in differentiating between organic and malingered pain. Pressure over a painful area usually causes a temporary acceleration of the pulse rate of from ten to thirty beats per minute; in the presence of malingered pain there is no change. The hysterical patient often reacts like the normal individual in this test. It has been said that the hysterical patient often has specific areas of hyperesthesia. These are over the breasts, inframammary regions, and "ovarian" area in the female, in the inguinal region in the male, and in the epigastric and vertebral areas of both sexes. These sites are sometimes termed *hysterogenic zones.*

The most significant changes in sensation in both hysteria and malingering are those in which there is a decrease in sensibility. Areas of hypesthesia, hypalgesia, anesthesia, and analgesia are commonly encountered and may have diagnostic significance; these may be complete, partial, or dissociated, and may either affect all modalities or be selective. Anesthesias of various types are actually encountered somewhat more frequently in hysteria than in malingering; in fact, they are almost pathognomonic of the former disorder. Even a normal individual, however, is suggestible, and the examiner must avoid suggesting such sensory changes. Occasionally one may be able to confuse the patient who complains of nonorganic changes in sensation by instructing him to say "Yes" every time he feels the stimulus and "No" when he does not. The malingerer, and less commonly the hysterical patient, will say "No" every time the so-called anesthetic region is stimulated. Variation of the intensity of the stimulus may also aid in evaluating nonorganic sensory changes.

In both consciously and unconsciously motivated anesthesia the distribution of the sensory loss fails to correspond to any organic nerve distribution, either peripheral nerve, nerve root, or segmental. In the extremities the changes frequently have the so-called glove and stocking distribution, with complete loss of all modalities below either the wrist or elbow in the arm and below either the ankle or knee in the leg. There may be loss of tactile, superficial pain, temperature, vibratory, and position sensations, without dissociation, and usually with an abrupt, well-demarcated border, which may, however, vary from examination to examination. This change must be differentiated from the peripheral blunting of sensation in the peripheral neuritides, where there is a suggestive glove and stocking change, but with a gradual transition rather than an abrupt border. In hysteria, furthermore, there is often an inconsistency in responses which cannot be explained by an organic lesion; in spite of complete loss of cutaneous sensibility, the patient may have intact stereognostic sensation and graphesthesia, or in spite of complete loss of position sense, he may be able to use the digits or the distal portions of the extremities without difficulty in the performance of skilled movements and fine acts. In carrying out the finger-to-nose test the hand may wander widely, but the patient is always able to find his nose eventually. The Romberg sign may be negative in spite of claimed absence of position sense. It may be possible to bewilder the patient and confirm the absence of organic changes by examining him while his hands are crossed behind his back. Comparison of sensation on the palmar and dorsal surfaces of the hands also may show an inconsistency in replies. In a test for hysterical hemianalgesia described by Bowlus and Currier the hands are first rotated so that the little fingers are up and the palms are outward. Then the arms are crossed, the palms are placed together, and the fingers interlocked. The hands are then rotated downward, inward, and upward, so that the interlocked fingers are against the chest. At the conclusion of this maneuver the fingertips are on the same side as the respective arm, but the thumbs are not interlocked and are on the side opposite the fingers (Fig. 316). When the fingertips and thumb are stimulated alternately and irregularly, the patient with nonorganic hemianalgesia may make errors, while the one with organic loss of sensation will not. Furthermore, the patient with nonorganic loss may respond slowly, delay his answers, or show sweating or other signs of tension. It must be borne in mind, however, that with practice the patient may learn to identify the stimulus correctly, so the test gives most conclusive results the first time it is done.

Over the face and body the sensory change is usually in the so-called midline distribution; there is complete loss of sensation of one half of the body, and the change takes place either at the midline or beyond it (when stimulating from the anesthetic to the normal area), whereas with organic lesions sensation begins to return slightly before the midline is reached. In psychogenic disorders the midline change may include the penis, vagina, and rectum, a finding which is rare in organic hemianesthesia. Again there often is loss of all types of sensation, with a midline change over the skull and sternum even for vibratory sensation; this latter phenomenon cannot be explained on an organic basis, because vibratory sensation is in part

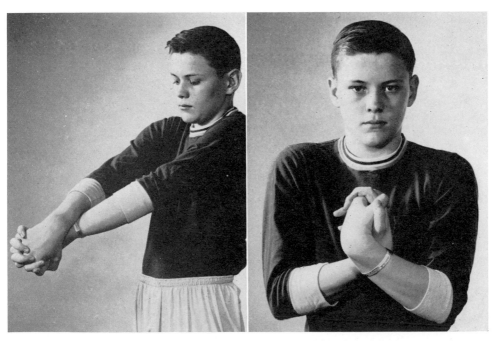

Fig. 316.   Maneuver used in testing for hysterical hemianalgesia. (After Bowlus and Currier).

conducted through bone, and as a consequence a midline change is not possible. If midline sensory changes are found, one should compare the cutaneous reflexes on the two sides; if these reflexes are retained, there can be no anesthesia. In the evaluation of what appears to be psychogenic changes in sensation, it is always essential to recall that there is some variation in nerve supply in normal individuals. Furthermore, hysterical and malingered changes may be superimposed on organic anesthesia in peripheral nerve lesions and other neurologic disorders. Hysterical or malingered hemianesthesia, which almost invariably occurs on the left side, may occasionally be accompanied by ipsilateral decrease or loss of the senses of vision, hearing, smell, and taste.

Auxiliary diagnostic measures are sometimes used to differentiate between organic and psychogenic changes in sensation. If a peripheral nerve, nerve root, or segmental lesion is suspected, sweating tests, the dermometer (electrical skin resistance), the cutaneous histamine reaction, and the psychogalvanic reflex may be used for confirmation. One may also note the galvanic skin response elicited by pinprick and light touch; currents are obtained from a normal portion of the body and recorded on as oscillograph, and the biochemical changes which accompany sweat gland and vasomotor activities of a normally functioning autonomic nervous system are recorded. In organic anesthesia no galvanic skin reflex is obtained when the anesthetic zone is stimulated, whereas in hysterical and malingered anesthesia the reflex is normal. The histamine flare reaction is normal in both hysteria and malingering. In hysteria, however, the reaction is painless, and in malingering it usually is painful. Electrical testing may also aid in the differentiation between genuine and malingered hyperesthesia. Even a mild faradic current over a painful area increases the pain in it; an insufficient current from an apparatus in action may produce a response in malingered hyperesthesia.

THE MOTOR SYSTEM

Abnormalities of the motor system which may be manifestations of both hysteria and malingering include disturbances of muscle strength and power, disorders of tone, dyskinesias, and abnormalities of coordination and of station and gait. There are rarely changes in volume or contour, except for wasting from disuse, and never variations in the electrical reaction. These motor changes of psychic etiology may resemble almost any type of motor disturbance that is brought about by organic disease of the nervous system (Table 2, pp. 382–383).

Psychogenic disturbances of muscle strength and power may cause various types of paresis and paralysis, and often result in contractures and deformities. They may affect any portion of the body that is subject to voluntary control. Although the changes are usually limited to one limb, or part of a limb, there may be a hemiplegia with paralysis of one half of the body, or a paraplegia with involvement of both lower extremities. The paralysis may be flaccid and resemble that of a lower motor neuron disturbance, hypertonic and accompanied by pseudocontractures resembling an upper motor neuron lesion, or characterized by no or variable disturbances in tone. The distribution is usually anomalous and fails to correspond to any organic nerve supply or muscle arrangement; in a psychogenic hemiplegia, for instance, the face, tongue, and platysma and sternocleidomastoid muscles are spared (instead there may be weakness in turning the face toward the hemiparetic side), and in psychogenic paraplegia there is no sphincter paralysis. Although there may be wasting due to disuse together with secondary contractures in psychogenic paralysis, there is never true atrophy. The paralysis never affects isolated muscles; movements, instead, are impaired.

A careful and complete neurologic examination is necessary for the diagnosis of psychogenic disturbances of motor function. Such an examination includes not only tests of muscle strength and power, but also observation of muscle tone, volume, and coordination, and evaluation of abnormal movements; electrical tests may contribute to the diagnosis. Careful testing of the reflexes, including the associated movements, is an important part of the evaluation of the motor defect.

Detailed testing of *muscle power* must always be carried out. In both hysterical and malingered paralyses the patient makes little effort to contract the muscles necessary to execute the desired movement. He may be calm and indifferent while demonstrating his lack of strength; he may show little sign of alarm at the presence of complete paralysis, and smile cheerfully during the examination. Reliable evidence that the patient is not exerting all his power in an attempt to carry out a voluntary movement can be elicited by watching and palpating the contraction of the antagonists as well as the agonists. The patient may, for instance, be contracting the antagonists in order to simulate weakness of the agonists (i.e., he may be observed to be contracting his triceps muscle, the antagonist to flexion of the elbow, when asked to tense the biceps and thus flex the elbow). On passive movement there may be evidence of the contraction of the apparently paretic agonists when the antagonists are moved. Various muscles, muscle groups, and movements should be tested individually. In nonorganic weakness the muscular contractions are poorly sustained and may "give way" abruptly, rather than gradually, as the patient resists the force applied by the examiner; there may be absence of "follow-through" when the examiner withdraws his pressure. The paretic extremities should be raised and then dropped by the examiner. If the paralysis is organic, the extremity drops rapidly (especially if the paralysis is a flaccid one or is the result of a recent cerebral lesion), whereas in psychogenic paralysis the limb may drop slowly "to avoid hurting it." The examiner may suddenly, while distracting the patient's attention, apply a painful stimulus to the paretic limb; if the patient withdraws it, the paresis cannot be organic. On occasion "functional" testing may demonstrate the absence of weakness suspected during the routine test; that is, there may be apparent paresis of either dorsiflexion or plantar flexion of the foot when the patient is examined in the seated or recumbent position, but when upright it may be observed that he is able to stand on either the heel or the toes of that foot, and support his entire body in doing so. Valuable information is obtained by watching the patient's performance while dressing and undressing; he may be found to carry out movements that he fails to perform during the motor examination. Repeated examinations may be used to exhaust and bewilder the patient; complicated tests and apparatus may confuse him.

Certain tests have special value in differentiating organic from nonorganic paresis.

In psychogenic paralysis of the arm the latissimus dorsi may be found to be paretic when tested by downward pressure of the arm, but to contract normally on coughing. In simulated hemiplegia the patient may be unable to adduct either the affected arm or leg against resistance, yet if he is asked to keep both arms against the body or both legs close together, the adductors may be felt to contract strongly on both sides, since it is difficult to adduct one extremity without adducting its apparently paralyzed fellow. In testing paralysis of the finger muscles the patient may be asked to pronate the forearms and interlock the fingers in such a way that the left fingers are on the right and vice versa; the examiner then points to the individual fingers and tells the patient to move them. It is difficult for one to determine immediately whether the indicated finger is on the right or on the left, and if the patient attempts to respond promptly, he makes many mistakes. Similar tests may be carried out by asking the patient to perform individual movements while his hands are behind his back. The dynamometer may be used to test strength of grip; in organic weakness there is progressive fatigue, whereas in simulated paresis the patient may show instead an increase of strength with repeated testing.

The differentiation between hysterical and malingered paralyses may impose a difficult problem. Hysterical paralyses are usually more extensive and more profound; they are rarely limited to isolated muscles or muscle groups, and are usually accompanied by hysterical sensory changes. Simulated paralysis cannot be continuously maintained for any long period of time, but there is usually more resistance to passive movement than in hysterical defects. Hysterical paralyses and contractures may disappear with suggestion, psychotherapy, or hypnosis.

The examination of *muscle tone* gives information in the evaluation of psychogenic motor changes. Tonus may be normal, decreased, or variable, but is often increased, with pseudorigidity or pseudospasticity. Rigidity, if present, resembles voluntary resistance, and voluntary and hysterical rigidity may be difficult to differentiate. The part may be held firmly in a bizarre position. Abnormalities in tone usually vary from time to time, especially under the influence of suggestion.

Muscle volume and contour rarely show significant change in psychogenic disorders; there is no true atrophy, although in long-standing defects there may be wasting because of disuse. Occasionally, with prolonged psychogenic paralyses, there are contractures caused by fibrous alterations and periarticular adhesions about the joints, with secondary wasting of the musculature, and even trophic changes of the skin (cyanosis and edema) and bones (osteoporosis) which closely resemble those of organic dysfunction.

Tests for *coordination* aid in the differentiation between psychogenic and organic motor defects. The patient may exhibit bizarre muscular responses which change from time to time, especially under the influence of suggestion. There may be a "wild" ataxia when he attempts to carry out tests for synergy, but no difficulty in carrying out acts such as buttoning clothes and lacing shoes. The incoordination may be out of proportion with the motor dysfunction. Adiadokokinesis, dysmetria, and dyssynergia may be simulated, but are usually not accompanied by the changes in tone, position, or reflexes that are found in either cerebellar or spinal ataxias.

Dyskinesias and *hyperkinesias* of various types are found in both hysteria and malingering. These may take the form of tremors, choreiform movements, spasms, tics (habit spasms), convulsions, or very bizarre motor anomalies. In hysteria one may find medium-sized arrhythmic tremors, usually accentuated by voluntary movement, or bizarre habit spasms which consist of grimaces, blepharospasms, shrugging movements of the shoulders, twisting motions of the neck, and spasms of the larynx or diaphragm. These latter movements may be in the nature of compulsions, and may closely resemble those seen in organic torticollis, Huntington's chorea, and dystonia musculorum deformans. True fasciculations are considered to be pathognomonic of organic disease, but benign fasciculations, myokymic movements, and muscle tremors resulting from excitement, fright, fatigue, and cold may have to be differentiated from them. It is important to bear in mind that tremors, especially of the hands and fingers, may be symptoms of either tension or fatigue in any normal individual, and that psychogenic tremors may disappear with involuntary movement.

Observation of the *station and gait* may furnish useful information in the detection of hysteria and malingering. The patient should be asked to stand with his feet together, first with his eyes open and then with them closed. He should stand on his heels, his toes, and on one foot at a time. He should walk forward, backward, tandem, and around chairs, both with the eyes open and closed. In the so-called hysterical *astasia-abasia* (or *stasibasiphobia*) the patient is unable to either stand or walk. When tested in the Romberg position, however, he is seen to sway from the hips instead of from the ankles; he may tremble and shake without showing signs of fear or pain. The truly ataxic patient makes every effort to maintain the erect posture and to avoid falling, whereas the simulator or hysteric usually reels from side to side or falls *en masse* without the slightest attempt to maintain his equilibrium. The patient with organic ataxia can usually keep himself in an upright position by very slight support from a wall or table, by lightly touching the examiner's hand, by watching the floor, or by placing his feet a short distance apart; the patient with psychogenic ataxia is not aided by these measures. If a patient with either hysteria or malingering is asked to carry out various commands, such as touching his finger to his nose or alternately pronating and supinating his hands, while standing with his feet together, he may "forget" to sway and fall. Furthermore, in hysterical astasia-abasia, although the patient seems to be unable to stand or walk, he may be able to move his limbs for other purposes, and may skip, jump, run, and walk backward without difficulty. Tests for power, tone, and coordination may be normal if carried out while the patient is lying down. As he attempts to walk, he may show a nondescript type of gait, with swaying far to the side, stumbling, and skipping. Locomotion is accompanied by superfluous movements of other parts of the body. He may appear to be about to fall to the floor, but he either catches himself or, if he falls, does so in a theatrical manner, without injury to himself. In other types of hysterical gaits, and in simulated pareses, there may be various changes from the normal. The patient may be unable to stand or walk because of a psychogenic hemiplegia or paraplegia, apparent foot-drop, pain on movement of the limbs, stiffness of the joints, shortening or anomaly of one leg, or ataxia, and may show bizarre disturbances of both station and gait. Disability due to a simulated sciatic syndrome can usually be differentiated from an organic disorder.

The absence of variations from the normal in the *electrical reactions* affords a valuable objective criterion in the evaluation of hysteria and malingering. In spite of apparent paralysis there is no reaction of degeneration and no change in chronaxie, the strength-duration curve, or the galvanic tetanus ratio. Electrical reactions can be evaluated most satisfactorily if symmetrical portions of the body can be compared. The absence of a myasthenic reaction may aid in the appraisal of a complaint of fatigability, and the electromyogram and nerve conduction studies often afford important information in the differentiation between organic and nonorganic motor dysfunction.

Although the *examination of the reflexes* is not in itself a part of the motor evaluation, careful testing of them is essential to the appraisal of motor function (Table 7, p. 603). Although the deep reflexes are not specifically altered in psychogenic paresis, they may be modified by the tension of the muscles and there may be changes which resemble those seen in organic disease. In hysteria and other nonorganic states there frequently is peculiar hyperactivity of the deep reflexes which is characterized by an increase of range rather than speed of response, with no decrease in the latent period. This change may be present to a marked degree, and a minimal stimulation of the patellar tendon may be followed by an extensive kick of the leg at the knee which resolves slowly and may be accompanied by a generalized bodily response. On the other hand, owing to tension of the muscles, the reflexes may be diminished or appear to be absent; in such circumstances, however, they can usually be obtained with reinforcement,. The responses on the two sides must always be compared. The cutaneous reflexes, too, are not characteristically affected in psychogenic paralyses, although the abdominal reflexes are occasionally increased in hysterical patients. The pyramidal tract responses are exceptionally important in the diagnosis of psychogenic disorders. There is never a Babinski sign or related dorsiflexor and fanning response in nonorganic disease. There may be pseudoclonus at the knee or ankle, but it is irregular and poorly sustained, and can usually be differentiated from organic clonus since it is not stopped by plantar flexion of the foot. The pyramidal tract responses in the upper extremities are more difficult to appraise. Although a Hoffmann sign is usually considered to be evidence of pyramidal tract disease, it may also be present with the generalized reflex hyperactivity of tension states and psychoneurosis and may be found (usually bilaterally and incomplete) in normal persons. As a consequence this sign does not have diagnostic value unless it is unilateral and associated with other signs of paresis and other reflex changes. Absence of the pharyngeal, conjunctival, and sometimes even the corneal reflexes is commonly encountered in hysteria. This finding, should, of course, be bilateral, although occasionally it is unilateral in cases of hemianesthesia.

Changes in the *associated,* or *synkinetic, movements* are valuable signs in the differentiation between organic and psychogenic paralysis. Testing for Hoover's sign, the trunk-thigh sign of Babinski, combined flexion of the thigh and leg (Neri), the various pronation tests, Bechterew's sign, the arm and leg signs of Raimiste, and other procedures to demonstrate the presence or absence of normal or abnormal coordinated associated movements that accompany voluntary contraction of muscles may give essential diagnostic information (Chapter 39).

The differentiation between organic and psychogenic paralysis may be made by the presence of many of the changes which have been mentioned above. In organic hemiparesis there is involvement of the entire half of the body, with sparing only of the upper portion of the face; in psychogenic paralysis there is sparing of the face, tongue, and platysma and sternocleidomastoid muscles. In organic hemiparesis the deep reflexes are exaggerated, the abdominal reflexes are diminished or absent, Babinski and other pyramidal responses are present, and there may be clonus; in psychogenic paresis the deep reflexes are normal or increased in range but not in speed, the abdominal reflexes are normal or increased, there are no pyramidal tract responses, and there is no true clonus. In organic hemiparesis there is spasticity and there are contractures and deformities in the so-called position of predilection (flexion of the upper extremity and extension of the lower extremity); in psychogenic paresis there may be variable changes in tone, and contractures, if present, are irregular and atypical. In organic hemiparesis the gait is the unilateral spastic variety with circumduction of the leg; in psychogenic paralysis the gait is bizarre and there may be dragging of the foot. In organic hemiparesis the Hoover sign and other associated movements show certain changes which are reversed in psychogenic paralysis. Anesthesia on the affected half of the body is rare in organic hemiparesis, and if present, the changes are those seen in cerebral lesions; in psychogenic hemiparesis there is frequently a hemianesthesia which extends to the midline and affects all modalities of sensation, and may occasionally be accompanied by ipsilateral decrease or loss of vision, hearing, taste, and smell.

It must be borne in mind that in psychogenic as well as in organic paralysis there may be secondary contractures and vasomotor changes. Prolonged disuse of either an organically or an hysterically paralyzed limb may lead to wasting of muscles which may resemble true atrophy, and there may be associated joint changes in the digits, periarthritis of the shoulder, and periarticular adhesions elsewhere which may lead to deformities and contractures. There may be trophic changes in the skin and nails, vasomotor changes with cyanosis and edema, abnormalities of sweating, and even osteoporosis of bone. The late sequelae of long-standing psychogenic paralysis may be almost impossible to differentiate from those of organic paralysis. If the immobile extremity is painful such diagnoses as shoulder-arm syndrome, reflex sympathetic dystrophy, and Sudeck's atrophy may have been applied to it.

ARTICULATION

Dysphonia and aphonia are among the most common paralytic phenomena of hysteria; the manifestations usually come on suddenly, in association with shock or fright, and may disappear abruptly. Articulation may be completely absent, the patient may be able to speak by whispering, or speech may be lost while the patient retains his ability to sing, whistle, and cough. There is usually hypesthesia of the pharynx and larynx, with a diminished or absent pharyngeal reflex. Laryngeal examination shows bilateral paresis or paralysis of adduction, and the vocal cords remain in abduction during attempts at phonation, although they meet in the midline on coughing; abduction is unimpaired, and inspiration is normal. There may be associated dysphagia, laryngospasm, and "globus hystericus."

Aphonia and dysphonia of the above type cannot be simulated, but in both hysteria and malingering there may be lalling, imperfect enunciation with so-called "baby talk," mutism, or anarthria. True aphasia is always of organic origin, but may occasionally be confused with hysterical or simulated mutism. An aphasic, however, no matter how speechless, tries to speak; an hysterical mute may appear to make a great effort but to be unable to produce a tone; in simulated mutism the patient makes no effort to speak. One must always bear in mind, however, that mutism may also be encountered in catatonia and severe depressions. Stuttering, stammering, and tremulousness of speech are commonly encountered in tense and nervous individuals, and true stuttering can usually be differentiated from a simulated difficulty.

THE SPECIAL SENSES

SMELL AND TASTE

Hysterical *anosmia* is not commonly encountered, and malingered anosmia is rare. Patients with either condition may retain their ability to distinguish the flavor of foods, an olfactory function, in spite of alleged loss of smell. In hysterical anosmia the patient may be unable to identify acetic acid, formaldehyde, and ammonia, substances which stimulate the trigeminal rather than the olfactory endings in the nose, as well as volatile oils, whereas the patient with organic anosmia retains the ability to identify irritating substances, but not volatile oils. The patient with simulated anosmia may be shown to make grimaces and involuntary withdrawal movements when a disagreeable substance is placed in front of his nose. Hysterical patients may also complain of hyperosmia and parosmia; malingerers rarely describe such phenomena.

Although *ageusia* is an infrequent complaint in both hysteria and malingering, complete absence of taste is usually psychogenic, since such a defect would imply bilateral involvement of the gustatory functions of the seventh, ninth, and tenth cranial nerves. The edges and dorsum of the anterior two-thirds of the tongue are the most sensitive areas; a unilateral facial nerve lesion, causing loss of taste in this distribution on one side of the tongue, causes subjective loss of taste in only the most discriminating individual.

VISION

Both hysterical and malingered defects in the visual apparatus are commonly encountered. These include not only disturbances of vision itself, but also of the sensibility and motility of the eye and of secretion. In hysteria there may be either amaurosis (blindness) or amblyopia (impairment of vision). Amaurosis, if present, is usually bilateral. Amblyopia, however, is more frequent, and is usually associated with tubular or spiral constriction of the visual fields. There may be other disturbances of vision such as blurring, photophobia, ocular fatigue, polyopia, or monocular diplopia. Central angiospastic retinopathy may have psychogenic origin. Many of the above symptoms are also present in malingering, but amaurosis is more common than field constriction, and it is usually unilateral and of sudden onset; it may be intermittent or shifting and accompanied by discrepancies, bizarre exaggerations, and contradictions. Occasionally a self-inflicted or factitious conjunctivitis or keratitis is encountered.

Psychogenic impairment of visual acuity (either amaurosis or ambylopia) may be either hysterical or malingered. Simulated blindness is usually unilateral and hysterical blindness, bilateral. Exaggeration of a pre-existing visual defect resulting from corneal opacity or refractive errors may be either consciously or unconsciously motivated. The detection of simulated and hysterical blindness is not always easy. Many tests have been described; some of these require complicated apparatus, usually employed by the ophthalmologist, and actually differentiate between organic and psychogenic defects and not between voluntary and involuntary changes.

In the detection of psychogenic blindness the eyes themselves should first be carefully inspected, and the routine neurologic procedures, including testing of acuity and fields, together with ophthalmoscopy, should be carried out. The testing of pupillary reflexes makes up an important part of the examination. The pupil of the totally blind eye is usually dilated and does not react to direct light; the maintenance of a moderate amount of vision, however, may be associated with a persistent light reflex. The pupillary reflexes may nevertheless be normal in blindness due to a cortical lesion. Loss of reflexes, especially of the light reflex, as a result of iritis, keratitis, or trauma must be borne in mind; the Argyll Robertson pupil is rarely unilateral. In psychoneurotic individuals the pupils are often dilated, but react normally. In malingered blindness the pupillary reactions are occasionally altered by the use of either miotics or mydriatics. A normal ophthalmoscopic examination does not eliminate the possibility of organic disease, since there is no change in either the optic disk or retina in retrobulbar neuritis and in blindness due to cortical lesions.

If blindness is bilateral and complete, it is usually possible to differentiate that of psychogenic origin from that due to organic disease. When a blind man attempts to look at his hand when it is either in front of his face or placed to one side, he fixes his eyes in a position so that vision would be directed toward it if he could see, since his proprioceptive sensations are intact; a simulator will make no attempt to fix his eyes on his hands and may gaze in any direction (Schmidt-Rimpler test). A blind man is able to touch his forefingers together without difficulty, whereas a malingerer will cause them to wander idly. A simulator may betray himself by lowering his eyelids or wrinkling his forehead in response to a sudden strong light (emergency light reflex), and the presence of normal visual, menace, and fixation reflexes precludes organic blindness. An alleged inability to read anything but the large type of Snellen's chart may be unmasked by the following device: The patient is asked to stand twenty feet from a mirror in front of which is placed a testing chart; after he has read the smallest line which he states he is able to see, the chart is removed from in front of the mirror and the patient is asked to stand ten feet nearer the mirror. Another Snellen's chart with letters the same size as the first chart, but printed backwards, is then placed in front of his chest as he faces the mirror, and he is asked to read the letters which he sees in the mirror. Being half the distance from the mirror, he may be induced to read twice the number of lines he read when he stood twenty feet away if he is ignorant of the laws of reflection.

The detection of unilateral amaurosis of psychogenic origin may be more difficult. It is important to remember, however, that the amaurotic eye usually deviates when the sound eye is fixed. Feigned unilateral blindness may be unmasked by placing a pencil vertically in front of a page of small type while the patient is reading; if he has bilateral vision, he will continue to read, since he can see around the pencil, but if one eye is blind, one or two words on each line will be hidden by the pencil. Testing of visual acuity with the use of a strong convex lens, a prism, or a colored lens may aid in the detection of unilateral simulated blindness. While the patient is reading test type with both eyes open and lenses in front of both, a strong convex lens is placed in front of the good eye, and either a plane lens or a weak minus lens in front of the defective eye; if the patient continues to read distant type, he must be using the allegedly blind eye. While the patient is looking at a light a prism of six degrees with the base outward is placed before the defective eye; if the eye deviates inward and returns to the mid-position when the prism is removed, the eye cannot be completely blind. While the patient is reading aloud a prism with the base outward or upward or downward is placed before the allegedly blind eye; if the vision in that eye is defective, there will be no change in the patient's ability to read, but if vision is retained, the prism will produce double images and inability to continue to read, and at the same time the eye will be seen to deviate. The patient is asked to look at a chart with alternate red and black letters, and a red lens is placed in front of the good eye; the red letters should disappear, and if the patient can read all the letters, he is using the allegedly blind eye. Harman's diaphragm test is another device for determining monocular blindness. It is based on the facts (1) that a person is unable to tell with which of his eyes he is seeing when both eyes are open, and (2) that when objects are viewed through a small aperture properly placed, the right eye sees only those on the left side and the left eye only those on the right. The test is performed as follows: A flat ruler eighteen inches long is constructed so that at one end there is a wooden carrier, set at right angles, on which is placed a small card with letters or numbers on it. Five inches from the carrier there is a small vertical screen, pierced by a hole three-fourths of an inch in diameter. The end of the ruler opposite the carrier is placed on the patient's upper lip, and he is asked to read the letters and numbers on the card through the hole in the screen. If the card has letters ABCDEFG on it, and the patient reads only DEFG, it is obvious that he does not see with the right eye, whereas if he read only ABCD, it is equally clear that he is using only his right eye and that the left is defective. If he reads all the letters, he must be using both eyes. Testing near vision after dilating the pupil of the "good" eye and instilling saline in the affected one may also reveal the presence of simulated blindness.

There are many other tests and devices whereby hysterical and simulated blindness may be detected, but most of them involve complicated ophthalmologic instruments and procedures, and the above tests usually give adequate information. The presence of opticokinetic nystagmus in cases of alleged blindness is evidence that there is not complete loss of vision. A final criterion of complete bilateral amaurosis may rest upon the use of the electroencephalogram, which aids in the differentiation between the real and false blindness. Normal alpha waves are present only when the eyes are closed, and they disappear when the patient opens his eyes and looks around. An electroencephalographic reading is taken while the eyes are closed, and then after they are open; if alpha waves disappear when the eyes are open, the patient must have a certain amount of vision. If alpha waves persist when the patient attempts to look at objects, one may conclude that there is true organic blindness. The response to photic stimulation and the presence of evoked potentials in the occipital regions also give information about vision.

Changes in visual fields are encountered more frequently in hysteria than in malingering. The so-called tubular fields are considered pathognomonic of hysteria, and spiral and star-shaped fields may also be found (Figs. 33 and 34). The latter two types, however, may also be obtained in fatigue states, and the examiner must always bear in mind that concentric contraction, suggestively tubular in type, may occur in organic defects and in states of fatigue and poor concentration. Hemianopia, either homonymous or heteronymous, is never found in psychogenic disorders.

Psychogenic diplopia may be difficult to differentiate from organic diplopia, but can usually be distinguished by the use of the Lancaster chart. Monocular diplopia and polyopia are encountered more commonly than true diplopia in both hysteria and malingering; these symptoms occasionally have no organic etiology. Blurring of vision may be difficult to appraise. Erythropsia, micropsia, macropsia, scotomas, flashes of light, and hallucinations may be psychogenic or may occur in association with migraine or temporal or occipital lobe irritations. Myopia secondary to spasm of accommodation is said to occur on a psychogenic basis, but is probably infrequent. Color blindness may be simulated, but such change is rarely significant.

Disturbances of sensibility, such as anesthesia or hyperesthesia of the skin and conjunctiva, or pain, burning, or itching of the eyes, can be diagnosed only by a complete history and examination. Photophobia may be either hysterical or simulated in origin. The patient with psychogenic photophobia may be able to keep his eyes open in the presence of intense illumination and may show no blinking, blepharospasm, or lacrimation when a strong light is flashed into the eyes. Disturbances of secretion (excessive or decreased lacrimation) are usually diagnosed without too much difficulty.

Spasm of the extraocular and associated muscles is common in psychogenic disturbances, but paralytic phenomena are rare, and their presence throws doubt upon the diagnosis. Blepharospasm is commonly a compulsive manifestation, although it may be a reflex response to photophobia and irritation of the eyes. Real ptosis of psychogenic origin is rare, and impairment of raising the eyelids is usually a quasiptosis brought about by spasm of the orbiculares oculorum; it is most commonly bilateral. When the patient who has a psychogenic ptosis attempts to raise his eyelids, there is no compensatory overactivity of the frontalis (an invariable accompaniment of true ptosis). When the patient who has a psychogenic quasiptosis attempts to look upward, he may contract the levators and raise his eyelids as he raises his head. In unilateral hysterical and simulated ptosis the affected eyebrow is lower than the unaffected one; in true ptosis it is higher. Spasm of the individual ocular muscles may occur in psychogenic disorders. Spasm of convergence is most frequently encountered; this is usually bilateral and disappears on looking quickly either to one side or in an upward direction. Spasmodic conjugate deviation of psychogenic origin is rare. Spasm of accommodation occasionally causes myopia. Both voluntary and hysterical varieties of nystagmus have been described, but such instances are rare, and their existence is doubtful.

HEARING

Both hysterical and malingered deafness may be either partial or total and either unilateral or bilateral; there may be an exaggeration of a previously existing defect. Hysterical deafness is usually bilateral and total; the patient makes no attempt to hear what is said to him or to read the speaker's lips. In most instances it is a transitory symptom which appears suddenly after mental excitement or emotional stress, and it is not infrequently associated with hysterical mutism and blindness. If hysterical deafness is unilateral, it is usually incomplete and is on the same side as hysterical motor and sensory disturbances. Simulated deafness is usually unilateral and has its onset following trauma. It is rare, however, to have unilateral deafness of posttraumatic origin without impairment of vestibular function. As a consequence, marked depression of the vestibular responses, especially the caloric, supports the assumption that the cochlear division of the acoustic nerve is also impaired. Conversely, normal labyrinthine responses suggest that the claimed loss of hearing is either simulated or exaggerated.

In cases of suspected hysterical and malingered deafness it is very important to obtain a detailed past history; this should include reference of any type of deafness, otitis and ear pain, vertigo and tinnitus, past infections such as measles and scarlet fever, specific illnesses such as meningitis and syphilis, and occupation, as well as a history of the mode of onset of the deafness. The external auditory canals and tympanic membranes should be carefully examined, and all hearing tests, for both air and bone conduction, should be carried out while the patient is blindfolded. The Rinné, Schwabach, and Weber tests should be carefully performed. Inconsistent responses afford a good criterion that the deafness is not organic. Repeated audiometric examinations are also essential; discrepancies and inconsistencies in the tests are common with hysterical and simulated deafness, and it may be difficult to obtain two or three successive audiograms which are comparable.

Simulated bilateral deafness, if the person under examination persistently refuses to give evidence of any hearing power, is naturally difficult to detect. Individuals who have been deaf for long periods of time usually raise their voices during conversation and keep their eyes fixed on the speaker's face and lips, watching for every gesture of the speaker which may aid in their interpretation of what he is saying. A deaf man who is eager to hear automatically turns his best ear toward the speaker. A clearly enunciated whisper is sometimes more audible than a loud, indistinct shout. Even an experienced lip-reader has difficulty with certain letters, especially the consonants, and may not be able to differentiate "mutton" from "button," "no" from "toe," "die" from "tie," and "most" from "post"; a person who is simulating partial deafness may be able to differentiate these words by appearing to read lips. Sometimes the patient with bilateral simulated deafness can be caught off his guard, and the making of disparaging remarks about him may cause changes in his facial expression.

Many tests have been devised for the detection of unilateral simulated deafness. The good ear may be partially occluded with a cotton or perforated plug. Words and numbers are then repeated, starting with a low voice and progressively raising it. The voice should be heard by the sound ear, and if the patient states that he cannot hear he is probably malingering. The good ear may then be completely occluded with a closed speculum, and the test be repeated; if the patient hears, the so-called affected ear cannot be completely deaf. The stethoscope test is sometimes employed in detecting feigned unilateral deafness. An ordinary stethoscope, one earpiece of which is occluded, is used. First the occluded earpiece is put into the "deaf" ear, and the examiner says a few words into the funnel; the patient should be able to repeat these words because the sounds are coming into the normal ear. The stethoscope is then removed and placed with the occluded earpiece in the sound ear, and the process is repeated. If the patient is able to hear as well as before, it means that he must be hearing with the so-called deaf ear. It may be of value to reverse the procedure and first adjust the closed earpiece to the sound ear and the open earpiece to the affected ear. If the patient comprehends what is said, he must have hearing in the "deaf" ear. The reliability of the stethoscope test, however, is doubtful.

Lombard's test is carried out by first asking the patient to read aloud a selected passage. As long as he hears his own voice, there is no change in pitch. Then a Bárány noise apparatus is inserted into the sound ear, and he is asked to read again; if he is actually deaf, he will raise the pitch and intensity of his voice while reading, and the voice will return to normal when the noise stops. If he continues to read in a normal voice, he probably hears with the allegedly deaf ear.

The Stenger test is based upon the fact that the preponderance of a sound of a certain pitch in one ear eliminates the perception of a sound of the same pitch in the opposite ear. For instance, if two equally vibrating tuning forks of an identical pitch are placed at different distances from the two normal ears, the fork nearer one ear will mask out the hearing for the fork at a greater distance from the other ear. The examiner should first determine at what distance from the good ear a tuning fork of a certain pitch is heard. He then holds the vibrating tuning fork one inch from the affected ear (the patient will deny hearing it). The second fork is then struck and brought slowly to the good ear. If the patient has normal hearing on the affected side, he will not hear the fork until it is the same distance (one inch) from the good ear, but if he is really deaf on the affected side, the fork will be heard at a greater distance with the good ear. The Block-Stenger modification is based upon the fact that when two vibrating tuning forks of different pitches are held simultaneously and equally distant from both ears, only the one of the higher pitch is audible. A low-pitched tuning fork may be placed just in front of the good ear, and then a higher-pitched fork near the affected ear. If the patient is deaf in that ear he perceives no change, but if he hears with the so-called affected ear, the sound of the low-pitched fork on the good side will be masked, and he will hear the higher-pitched instrument.

Teal's test is performed in the following manner: If the patient claims to hear by neither air conduction nor bone conduction, he is blindfolded and a nonvibrating tuning fork is placed over the mastoid area on the affected side. Then a vibrating tuning fork is placed a short distance from the same ear. If the patient is deaf, he will not hear, and if he is able to hear it, he must have air conduction. In the Doerfler-Stewart test speech is introduced through binaural headphones from a sound-proof control room to the patient in an adjacent sound-proof room. The patient is asked to repeat what he hears. The patient's auditory thresholds for speech and for static noise are determined. Then speech is introduced at a constant level of intensity of five decibels louder than the established threshold and the patient is asked to continue to repeat what he hears while noise at increasing intensities is superimposed as a background. The normal person continues to perceive speech until the noise is from ten to twenty-five decibels more intense than speech. In either hysteria or malingering the patient loses perception of speech before the voice reaches the intensity level of speech. The auditory-palpebral, or cochleo-orbicularis, reflex may also be used as a criterion in unilateral deafness. The sound ear is closed tightly and a loud noise is made near the supposedly deaf ear. A slight winking movement or contraction of the lid on the corresponding side means that the sound was heard. The cocheopapillary reflex, in which there is dilatation, or constriction followed by dilatation, of the pupils in response to a loud noise, has the same significance. Other more detailed tests for psychogenic deafness may require complex otologic equipment and testing.

VESTIBULAR FUNCTION

It may be difficult to differentiate between simulated and true vertigo. True vertigo, however, is usually rotatory in type and is accompanied by nausea, vomiting, pallor, hyperhidrosis, difficulty with equilibrium, and nystagmus. The absence of the latter manifestations, however, does not rule out true vertigo. The various examinations of vestibular function, which include the rotating chair, caloric, and galvanic tests, are evaluated entirely by objective criteria, and it is not possible to alter the responses to these tests in either hysteria or malingering. A history of ataxia, staggering, or syncope with change of position is helpful in evaluation of vestibular function. Tests for coordination, including the Romberg test, are also important.

DISORDERS OF CONSCIOUSNESS

States of disordered consciousness, with or without convulsive motor manifestations, may occur in either hysteria or malingering. In hysteria the loss of consciousness is not deep and is rarely complete. Unless there is hysterical anesthesia in association, the patient usually responds to painful and unpleasant stimulation. The reflexes are normal, and there are no pathologic reflex responses. The temperature, pulse, respirations, and blood pressure are normal. The eyes may be tightly closed, and the patient often resists attempts on the part of the examiner to open them. There may be vigorous contractions of the orbiculares oculorum which makes it difficult to test the corneal and pupillary reflexes. Careful observation may show the patient to be aware of what is going on in his environment in spite of apparent complete loss of consciousness. In malingering there is rarely complete loss of consciousness, and the patient may be seen to be making furtive glances when he is not aware that he is being watched.

Hysterical loss of consciousness is usually precipitated by emotional stress, and the onset is frequently dramatic. The patient may appear to be in a trance, or coma may alternate with weeping and laughing. The performance is appropriately staged and occurs when the observers are present. The movements are coordinated and purposive. The patient may struggle, clutch at objects or parts of his body, or attempt to tear off his clothes. Insight into the condition and return of consciousness may frequently be brought about by the intravenous injection of sodium amobarbital (Amytal) or sodium thiopental (Pentothal). Simulated loss of consciousness may often be terminated by painful stimulation, cold water, or apparent neglect. It is important to bear in mind that vasodepressor syncope may also follow emotional shock. This syndrome, however, is usually preceded by a transient period of giddiness, weakness, fatigue, nausea, or vomiting. The attack is usually brief, with return to consciousness in a very few minutes. Recovery may be accelerated by placing the head lower than the body.

Hysterical and malingered convulsions may resemble organic convulsions. They are usually, however, more bizarre, and are unpredictable in their course. There is no manifestation of epilepsy which cannot be duplicated in either hysteria or malingering, but in both the attacks resemble more closely grand mal than petit mal or jacksonian seizures. The attack is not preceded by an aura, and may follow immediately after emotional stress or mental shock. As in the case with psychogenic loss of consciousness, the performance is appropriately staged, and the onset is usually dramatic. A significant time and place are chosen for the attack, usually when spectators are present. The patient may fall to the floor, but he is usually careful to avoid injury to himself. He rarely bites his tongue or loses sphincter control. There is no cyanosis or frothing at the mouth. There are no pupillary changes, loss of reflexes, or Babinski sign. Loss of consciousness is rarely complete. There may be generalized muscular rigidity, sometimes with retraction of the head and true opisthotonos, and the patient may be in the position of the *arc de cercle* of major hysteria (hysteroepilepsy). The patient may laugh or weep throughout the attack, or laughter and crying may alternate. Muscular movements are much more purposive than in true epilepsy. Sleepiness, headache, and confusion are absent after the attack and there are no other postconvulsion manifestations. Psychomotor seizures are sometimes quite difficult to differentiate from psychogenic ones with a similar clinical picture or from similar syndromes precipitated by rage or frustration. Often the automatisms and bizarre movements of psychomotor epilepsy are thought to be of psychogenic rather than organic origin.

Repeated observations, a detailed history, and a thorough neurologic investigation may, on occasion, be necessary in order to differentiate psychogenic from organic seizures, and, if psychogenic, those of hysterical from those of malingered origin. It is important to bear in mind that emotional stimuli may also precipitate organic attacks and, in addition, that epilepsy and hysteria may coexist. Response to medication may give helpful but not conclusive information, since anticonvulsants, which are also sedatives, may favorably influence psychogenic as well as organic seizures, or may have a placebo effect, and furthermore not all epilepsies respond satisfactorily to the usual anticonvulsants. The objective information obtained from the electroencephalogram may be essential to the differential diagnosis.

ABNORMAL MENTAL STATES

The mental symptoms of hysteria vary widely, but usually follow a fairly definite pattern. Both mental and somatic symptoms may be associated with anxiety, conversion manifestations, and depression. The somatic symptoms may be referable to any organ or system of organs of the body. The mental symptoms may vary from moderate anxiety to severe depression and suggestive schizoid manifestations. In addition to disturbances of consciousness and convulsions, there may be amnesia, fugues, trance states, emotional instability, insomnia, and fatigue states. The diagnosis can usually be made by a review of the past history, the total personality, and the positive findings of hysteria in the neurologic examination. The so-called Ganser syndrome of approximate answers is said to occur in hysteria. If the mental symptoms are posttraumatic in origin, it is extremely important to differentiate between the organic and psychogenic factors.

Simulation of mental disease is less common than the presence of abnormal mental states in hysteria, but it may occur. It may be practiced in order to void or nullify civil contracts, escape conviction for crime, or evade military duty. Dissimulation of mental disease is occasionally practiced by chronic alcoholics and paranoics in order to obtain release from mental hospitals or to remove previously adjudicated incompetence. Insanity as such is a legal term, and in most instances the diagnosis of either simulated or dissimulated insanity must be made by a competent medicolegal expert and psychiatrist. Psychologic tests, projective technics, and the use of intravenous barbiturates may aid in the diagnosis. Simulation, however, is usually found only in individuals with personality disturbances, and malingering in general, as well as simulation of mental disease, implies the need for psychiatric management.

REFERENCES

ARNOLD, F. O.   The detection of malingering.   *Medicolegal & Criminolog. Rev.* 8:199, 1940.

BENTON, A. L.   Rorschach performances of suspected malingers.   *J. Abnorm. & Social Psychol.* 40:94, 1945.

BRILL, N. Q., and FARRELL, M. J.   Neurotic reactions in psychopaths (hysteromalingering).   *A. Res. Nerv. & Ment. Dis. Proc.* (1944) 25:11, 1946.

BOWLUS, W. E., and CURRIER, R. D.   A test for hysterical heminalagesia.   *New England J. Med.* 269:1253, 1963.

DAVIDSON, H. A.   Neurosis and malingering.   *Am. J. M. Jurisprudence* 2:94, 1939.

DOERFLER, L., and STEWART, K.   Malingering and psychogenic deafness.   *J. Speech Disorders* 11:181, 1946.

GARNER, J. R.   Malingering.   *Am. J. M. Jurisprudence* 2:173, 1939.

GIFFORD, E. S.   Psychogenic ocular symptoms.   *A. M. A. Arch. Ophth.* 53:318, 1955.

GOOD, R.   Malingering.   *Brit. M. J.* 2:359, 1942.

HARDY, W. G.   Special techniques for the diagnosis and treatment of psychogenic deafness.   *Ann. Otol., Rhin. & Laryng.* 57:65, 1948.

HOFLING, C. K.   Some psychological aspects of malingering.   *GP* 31:115, 1965.

KESCHNER, M.   "Simulation (malingering) in relation to injuries of the brain and spinal cord and their coverings," in BROCK, S. (ed.), Injuries of the Brain and Spinal Cord and Their Coverings (ed. 4).   New York, Springer Publishing Company, Inc., 1960, pp. 410–439.

KLECKNER, J. F.   Malingering in relation to visual acuity.   *Am. J. Ophth.* 35:47, 1952.

LEMERE, F.   Electroencephalography as a method of distinguishing true from false blindness.   *J.A.M.A.* 118:884, 1942.

LINCOFF, H. A., and ENNIS, J.   Differential diagnosis of hysteria and malingering in functional amblyopia.   *Am. J. Ophth.* 42:415, 1956.

LIVINGOOD, W. C.   Psychogenic deafness: Evaluation and management.   *Arch. Environ. Health* 7:413, 1963.

MACLEAN, A. R.   The paradox of psychoneurotic malingering.   *J. Indiana M. A.* 40: 1223, 1947.

MAGEE, K. R.   Hysterical hemiplegia and hemianesthesia.   *Postgrad. Med.* 31:339, 1962.

MOERSCH, F. B.   Malingering, with reference to its neuropsychiatric aspects in civil and military practice.   *M. Clin. North America* 28:928, 1944.

RASKIN, M., TALBOTT, J. A., and MEYERSON, A. T.   Diagnosis of conversion reactions.   *J.A.M.A.* 197:530, 1966.

SCHWARTZ, L. H.   A device for the detection of malingerers.   *Arch. Ophth.* 15:520, 1936.

SEARS, R. R., and COHEN, L. H.   Hysterical anesthesia, analgesia and astereognosis: Experimental study.   *Arch. Neurol. & Psychiat.* 29:260, 1933.

SHAW, R. S.   Pathologic malingering: The painful disabled extremity.   *New England J. Med.* 271:22, 1964.

SLATER, E.   Diagnosis of "hysteria."   *Brit. M. J.* 1:1395, 1965.

SONIAT, T. L. L.   The problem of "compensation" neurosis.   *South. M. J.* 53:365, 1960.

SPAETH, E. B.   The differentiation of the ocular manifestations of hysteria and of ocular malingering.   *Arch. Ophth.* 4:911, 1930.

STEPHENS, J. H., and KAMP, M.   On some aspects of hysteria: A clinical study. *J. Nerv. & Ment. Dis.* 134:305, 1962.

TYRER, J. H.   The differentiation of hysteria from organic neurological disease.   *M. J. Australia* 1:566, 1957.

WALSHE, F.   Diagnosis of hysteria.   *Brit. M. J.* 2:1451, 1965.

WETZEL, J. O.   Malingering tests.   *Am. J. Ophth.* 26:577, 1943.

YASUNA, E. R.   Hysterical amblyopia: Its differentiation from malingering.   *Am. J. Ophth.* 29:570, 1946.

ZIEGLER, F. J., IMBODEN, J. B., and MEYER, E.   Contemporary conversion reactions.   *Am. J. Psychiat.* 116:901, 1960.

PART TEN

Spinal Puncture and the Examination of the Cerebrospinal Fluid

CHAPTER 57

THE CEREBROSPINAL FLUID

THE EXISTENCE of the cerebrospinal fluid has been known since antiquity, but recognition of the functions and clinical significance of the fluid is of fairly recent date. It is common knowledge that craniotomies and trephines were performed by the ancients, probably in cases of trauma, hydrocephalus, and undiagnosed intracranial disease. Herophilus (280 B.C.) was aware of the presence of the cerebral ventricles and the choroid plexus. Galen (150 A.D.) considered the cerebrospinal fluid a watery excretion going from the brain to the nasal cavity. Vesalius (1552) recognized that the content of the ventricles was a watery humor.

Cotugno (1764) described the cerebrospinal fluid and subarachnoid spaces. Haller (1766) first postulated the circulation of the fluid. Magendie (1825–42) expressed the modern conception of the protective nature of the fluid and brought its existence and functions to the attention of the medical profession. Faivre (1853–1854) and Luschka (1855) studied the formation and circulation of the fluid. In 1875 and 1876 Key and Retzius published their researches on the physiology of the formation, circulation, and absorption of the fluid. The first monograph on the subject was that of Mestrezat (1912) who described the chemical composition of the fluid in health and disease; his quantitative determinations gave definite results which allowed certain syndromes to be described. Further knowledge on the physiology of the fluid was contributed by the researches of Weed and his associates (1914–1927) and Dandy (1919).

Corning, in 1885, was the first to puncture the subarachnoid space of a living person; this was done for the purpose of introducing cocaine. Wynter and Morton, in 1891, drained the spinal fluid in the treatment of cases of tuberculous meningitis; this was done with a trocar and cannula, through an incision in the skin. Quincke, also in 1891, simplified the procedure, using a plain needle which he introduced through the skin and into the subarachnoid space. He was the first to remove spinal fluid for diagnostic purposes. Since that time modifications have been made in the examination and technic, namely, the Wassermann reaction (1908); Lange colloidal gold test (1912); Queckenstedt procedure (1916); encephalography (Dandy,

1919); puncture of the cisterna magna (Ayer, 1920); myelography (Sicard and Forstier, 1921).

FORMATION, CIRCULATION, ABSORPTION, AND FUNCTIONS OF THE CEREBROSPINAL FLUID

The concepts of the formation, circulation, and absorption of the spinal fluid are still controversial. It has been generally believed, however, that under normal circumstances the major portion of the fluid originates in the choroid plexus of the ventricles of the brain, although there is also some production of cerebrospinal fluid through the ependymal lining of the ventricles and in the subarachnoid and perivascular spaces. It is discharged into and fills the ventricles, basal cisterns, and subarachnoid spaces (Fig. 317). The most important source is the choroid plexus of the lateral ventricles, although the plexuses in the roof of the third and fourth

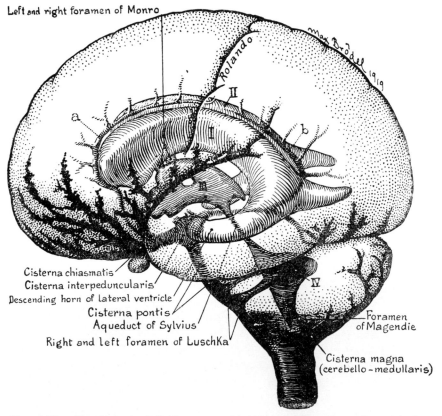

Fig. 317.   Cerebrospinal fluid spaces, showing a lateral view of ventricular system, foraminal connections with subarachnoid spaces, and some of the major subarachnoid cisterns. *I* and *II,* lateral ventricles; *III,* third ventricle; *IV,* the fourth ventricle. (Dandy, W. E.: *Bull. Johns Hopkins Hosp.* 32:67, 1921.)

ventricles, that in the latter extending into the lateral recesses and protruding slightly through the foramina of Luschka into the subarachnoid space, also contribute to the formation. There is movement of the fluid from the lateral ventricles through the foramina of Monro and into the third ventricle, and thence through the aqueduct of Sylvius into the fourth ventricle. The latter structure communicates with the subarachnoid space through the two foramina of Luschka, one of which is situated in each of its lateral recesses, and the mid-line foramen of Magendie. From the fourth ventricle the fluid also goes into the central canal of the spinal cord.

In the subarachnoid space the fluid lies between the arachnoid and the pia mater. This space, however, is only a potential one, inasmuch as web-like strands of arachnoid extend between the arachnoid and pia. The pia closely invests the surface of the brain and spinal cord, dipping into the fissures and sulci. The arachnoid, however, bridges the fissures and sulci. As a consequence, the subarachnoid space varies greatly in depth, especially between the gyri and convolutions. At the base of the brain the pia and the arachnoid are widely separated to form enlargements or cisterns. The largest of these are the following: *cisterna pontis,* situated ventral to the pons; *cisterna interpeduncularis* (*basalis*), which is cephaled to cisterna pontis and between the cerebral peduncles and the tips of the temporal lobes; *cisterna chiasmatis,* between the optic chiasm and the rostrum of the corpus callosum and above the pituitary body; and *cisterna magna* (*cerebellomedullaris*), which lies in the angle between the cerebellum and the posterior surface of the medulla.

The blood vessels which penetrate the nervous tissue go through the subarachnoid space and become invested with two layers of arachnoid; these subarachnoid cuffs which accompany the vessels for varying distances into the nervous tissue are known as the *perivascular spaces of Virchow-Robin* (Fig. 318). The spinal fluid flows into these, and thus it is carried for a certain distance into the substance of the brain and spinal cord. It is also carried outward from the subarachnoid cavity for varying distances in the periradicular, perineural, and perivascular spaces. In the spinal canal there is a large subarachnoid sac which extends from the termination of the spinal cord at the lower limits of the first lumbar vertebra to about the second sacral vertebra. This sac, which contains the cauda equina, is the usual site for performing the spinal puncture. Sometimes the ventricles and central canal are spoken of as the *internal cerebrospinal fluid system,* and the subarachnoid spaces including the cisterns and the perivascular and perineural spaces, as the *external system.* They communicate by means of the foramina of Luschka and Magendie.

The choroid plexus is a rich network of pial vessels within the ventricles of the brain. It is, in reality, a vascular invagination of the pia into the ventricles, and is covered by a layer of ependymal cells continuous with the lining of the ventricles. The choroid plexus of the lateral ventricles is present only in the body and inferior horn and not in the anterior and posterior horns. The arterial supply of the choroid plexus is provided by the anterior choroidal artery, a branch of the internal carotid, and the posterior choroidal branches of the posterior cerebral artery. The innervation of the choroid plexus is largely from the superior cervical ganglion and the network around the internal carotid artery. Stimulation of the cervical portion of the

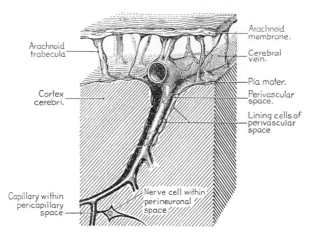

FIG. 318. Schematic diagram of leptomeninges and nervous tissue, showing relationship of subarachnoid space, perivascular channels, and nerve cells. (From original by Weed, L. H.: *Am. J. Anat.* 31:191, 1923.)

sympathetic division of the autonomic nervous system causes constriction of the vessels of the choroid plexus, whereas stimulation of the vagus is said to cause a dilatation of these vessels.

The mechanism of the formation of the cerebrospinal fluid is still a matter of controversy. Faivre (1854), and Luschka (1855), believed it to be secreted by the cells of the choroid plexus, but Metrezat (1912), on the basis of chemical studies, suggested that it is a dialysate (or filtrate) in equilibrium with the blood plasma, and stated that the ependyma of the choroid plexus acts as the dialyzing membrane. Arguments in favor of the theory of dialysis are as follows (Merritt and Fremont-Smith): The cerebrospinal fluid is isotonic with the blood plasma and tends to remain in osmotic equilibrium with the blood when the latter is changed experimentally or in disease. Variations in the plasma levels of glucose, urea, chlorides, lactic acid, and alcohol are followed by parallel changes in the cerebrospinal fluid. The distribution of the chloride and sodium ions is qualitatively in accordance with the Donnan theory of membrane equilibrium. The pressure and volume of the cerebrospinal fluid can be changed by varying the osmotic or hydrostatic pressure of the blood; there is increased flow when blood is made hypotonic, and a reversal of the direction of flow when the blood is made hypertonic. There is no known substance in the cerebrospinal fluid which is not a normal constituent of the blood. The balance between the osmotic and hydrostatic pressures of the capillary blood in the choroid plexus and the venous blood in the dural sinuses can account for known facts regarding the formation, absorption, and pressure of the cerebrospinal fluid. The cells of the choroid plexus are not glandular in type. The composition of the cerebrospinal fluid resembles that of other protein-free or protein-poor dialysates, such as the aqueous humor of the eye, edema, and other intracellular and extracellular fluids, and the glomerular filtrate of the kidneys, although differences may depend upon the degree of permeability and selectivity of action of the membranes involved. Arguments against the dialysate theory are as follows: There is an unequal distribution of calcium, potassium, phosphates, uric acid, creatinine, amino acids, and magnesium between the blood plasma and the cerebrospinal fluid which is not readily explainable by the dialysate theory. The distribution of the sodium and chloride ions is not quantitatively in accordance with the Donnan theory. The composition of the cerebrospinal fluid is not quantitatively identical with that of artificially produced filtrates and dialysates. Colloidal substances and certain inorganic salts do not enter the cerebrospinal fluid, even when the concentration in the blood is high.

It is probable that both dialysis and secretion enter into the formation of the cerebrospinal fluid. A large portion may be formed by filtration across the membranes which line the spaces containing the fluid (the ependyma of both the choroid plexuses and the ventricles, as well as the arachnoid), with the rate of entry determined largely by particle size. In addition, certain substances such as protein and sodium may be actively secreted, presumably by the choroid plexuses.

Although the cerebrospinal fluid does not circulate in the manner that the blood does, with an organ such as the heart to provide energy for motion of the fluid, there is a definite movement of the fluid from the lateral ventricles downward and into the subarachnoid spaces (Fig. 317). It is constantly circulating in the sense that it is being continuously secreted and absorbed, and is in continuous movement in a definite direction through a highly specialized pathway. There is a flow from the lateral ventricles through the foramina of Monro into the third ventricle, and thence through the aqueduct of Sylvius into the fourth ventricle. The fluid goes through the foramina of Luschka and Magendie into the subarachnoid space about the medulla, and thence some of it flows into the spinal subarachnoid space. The major portion, however, passes forward beneath the incisura tentorii and along the base of the brain through the pontine, interpeduncular, and chiasmatic cisterns to reach the sylvian fissure, and thence ascends in the subarachnoid spaces over the convexity of the brain to spread over the hemispheres. It has been demonstrated, for instance, that obstruction of one foramen of Monro will cause a unilateral hydrocephalus and that occlusion of the aqueduct of Sylvius will cause a bilateral hydrocephalus involving the third as well as both lateral ventricles. This so-called circulation of the spinal fluid and its rate of flow are influenced or brought about by arterial pulsations within the choroid plexuses, respiration, increase in the venous pressure by thoracic and abdominal movements, changes in position and movements of the head and body, filtration and secretion pressures, and other factors.

The spinal fluid is absorbed into the venous system. It was originally stated that the major portion was absorbed through the arachnoid villi or pacchionian granulations and discharged into the dural sinuses and thence into the peripheral venous circulation. The arachnoid villi are small convolutions which penetrate the venous lacunae in the dura mater adjoining the sinuses. They lie directly beneath the vascular endothelium of the dural sinuses. There is no subdural space here, and the cerebrospinal fluid in the villi is separated from the venous blood by only a layer of mesothelial arachnoid cells and a layer of vascular endothelium (Fig. 319). When enlarged, these villi are known as the pacchionian granulations. They are most

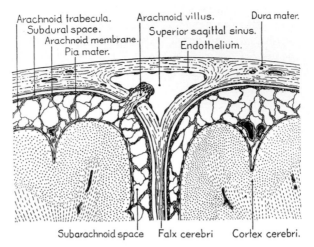

Arachnoid trabecula.   Arachnoid villus.   Dura mater.
Subdural space.   Superior sagittal sinus.
Arachnoid membrane.   Endothelium.
Pia mater.

Subarachnoid space   Falx cerebri   Cortex cerebri.

FIG. 319.   Schematic diagram of a coronal section of meninges and cerebral cortex, showing relationship of an arachnoid villus to subarachnoid space and dural venous sinus. (From original by Weed, L. H.: *Am. J. Anat.* 31:191, 1923.)

numerous in the superior sagittal sinus but are also found in the other sinuses and along the spinal cord. Welch and Friedman have suggested that they act as valves for the unidirectional flow of cerebrospinal fluid into venous blood. It is probable, however, that a large part of the spinal fluid is absorbed into the venous system from the periradicular and perineural spaces along the spinal roots and cranial nerves and from the perivenous spaces. There may also be some absorption through the ventricular ependyma and in a reverse direction through the choroid plexus, and some fluid may be absorbed by osmosis directly into the pial veins on the surface of the brain or by the capillaries of the pia-arachnoid.

The concept of the blood-brain, or hematoencephalic, barrier (including also the blood-cerebrospinal fluid and cerebrospinal fluid-brain barriers) has been introduced to explain the mechanism for the regulation of passage of various substances from the blood to the fluid or into the brain. The permeability of the barrier to substances normally in the blood or introduced experimentally or therapeutically may be altered by various disease states. The site of this so-called barrier may be in the choroid plexus, pia mater, arachnoid, ependyma, vascular endothelium, perivascular glia, or parenchyma, and may be at different sites for different substances. The increase or decrease in permeability found in certain disease states may be caused by chemical or physical alterations in the blood, changes in the meninges or nervous tissues, or variations in the permeability of the vascular structures. Knowledge about this barrier and the effect of disease upon it is important to the understanding of the action of drugs and other substances on the meninges and central nervous system.

Recent investigations on the secretion, flow, and absorption of the spinal fluid by the use of multiple simultaneous isotope tracers (Sweet and others) have materially altered many of the above concepts. These studies show that water, electrolytes, and protein both enter and leave the cerebrospinal fluid in both the ventricles and the subarachnoid space at rates that vary both with the site of formation or absorption and the nature of the substance concerned. The rate of exchange varies inversely with the molecular size, with that for water being most rapid, then electrolytes, and finally protein. Water exchange is more rapid in the region of the cisterna magna than through the walls of the ventricles, suggesting that water molecules are more retarded in their motion by the ependyma and choroidal epithelium than by the pia and pial-glial membranes. The electrolytes enter the fluid more rapidly in the ventricles than in the cortical, cisternal, or lumbar subarachnoid areas, suggesting specific secretory activity of the choroidal epithelium. Protein appears to enter the ventricles more rapidly than the subarachnoid space, and leaves the cisternal region more rapidly than it leaves the ventricles. The primary function of the intracranial arachnoid villi may be the absorption of protein, which leaves the spinal subarachnoid space at an extremely slow rate. Minor injuries in the region of the ventricles cause a more rapid and erratic entry and departure of substances. These studies suggest that the cerebrospinal fluid is both a secretion and an ultrafiltrate. It is secreted in the choroid plexus and also enters through the ependyma and the walls of the subarachnoid space as an ultrafiltrate, dependent upon the balance between the hydrostatic and osmotic pressures of the blood and fluid as well as the permeability of the membrane between them. The amount formed within the ventricles is normally much smaller than the volume exchanged within the subarachnoid space.

The functions of the cerebrospinal fluid are many but are chiefly mechanical. It bathes and protects and serves as a water-jacket for the brain and spinal cord. It helps to support the weight of the brain and acts as a cushion for it. It serves as a lubricant between the brain and spinal cord on the one side and the skull and spinal column on the other. It acts as a buffer to distribute the force of a blow on the head. It serves as a space-compensating mechanism in regulating the contents of the cranium and aids in keeping the intracranial pressure relatively constant; if there is an increase in arterial pulsations, blood content, or brain volume, there is a decrease in amount of cerebrospinal fluid, and if there is degeneration or atrophy of brain tissue, there is an increase in amount of fluid. It is a medium for the transfer of substances from the tissues of the brain and spinal cord to the blood stream; it receives metabolic waste products and aids in eliminating them, and is important in the removal of pathologic products in disease and in the circulation of drugs in therapy. It does not, however, contain sufficient nutritive material to have much value in the role of metabolism of nervous tissue, and it does not actually penetrate the brain tissue.

The amount of cerebrospinal fluid is said to be from about 100 to 150 cc. in the normal adult. The rate of formation is related to factors such as the osmotic and hydrostatic pressures of the blood and variations in venous pressure. The volume of fluid is increased by either excessive formation or deficient absorption. Excessive formation can be caused by various factors. There may be a decrease in the osmotic pressure of the serum; this may be brought about by intravenous injections of hypotonic solutions or it may occur at the onset of febrile illnesses, especially in children; increased formation in the latter circumstance leads to development of the syndrome of meningismus. There may also be increased formation in meningitis and other infections, and also in association with increase of the venous pressure within the skull. Decreased absorption may be brought about by block to the flow of the spinal fluid by obstruction caused by processes such as tumors or stenosis of the aqueduct, with resulting non-communicating hydrocephalus, or by obstruction of the arachnoid villi and perivenous spaces by the presence of blood, serum, or inflammatory processes, resulting in a communicating hydrocephalus. Increased formation and decreased absorption may occur simultaneously. Figures on the rate of formation of cerebrospinal fluid vary from 50 cc. to as much as 500 cc. within a period of twenty-four hours. Thus the normal amout of fluid is reformed three to four times in a period of one day, or the total volume is changed every six to eight hours.

REFERENCES

BAKAY, L.   The Blood-Brain Barrier with Special Regard to the Use of Radioactive Isotopes.   Springfield, Ill., Charles C Thomas, 1956.

BERING, E. A., JR.   Circulation of the cerebrospinal fluid: Demonstration of the choroid plexuses as the generator of the force for flow of fluid and ventricular enlargement. *J. Neurosurg.* 19:405, 1962.

BOWSHER, D.   Cerebrospinal Fluid Dynamics in Health and Disease.   Springfield, Ill., Charles C Thomas. 1960.

CORNING, J. L.   Spinal anesthesia and local medication of the cord.   *New York M. J.* 42:483, 1885.

DANDY, W. E.   The cause of so-called idiopathic hydrocephalus.   *Bull. Johns Hopkins Hosp.* 32:67, 1921.

DAVSON, H.   Physiology of the Ocular and Cerebrospinal Fluids.   Boston, Little, Brown & Company, 1956.

FISHMAN, R. A.   "Cerebrospinal fluid," in BAKER, A. B. (ed.), Clinical Neurology (ed. 2).   New York, Hoeber Medical Division, Harper & Row, 1962, vol. 1, pp. 350–388.

FLEXNER, L. B.   Some problems of origin, circulation and absorption of cerebrospinal fluid.   *Quart. Rev. Biol.* 8:397, 1933.

HASSIN, G. B.   Cerebrospinal fluid; its origin, nature and function.   *J. Neuropath. & Exper. Neurol.* 7:172, 1948.

KATZENELBOGEN, S.   The Cerebrospinal Fluid and Its Relation to the Blood: A Physiological and Clinical Study.   Baltimore, The Johns Hopkins Press, 1935.

LEVINSON, A.   Cerebrospinal Fluid in Health and in Disease (ed. 3).   St. Louis, The C. V. Mosby Company, 1929.

LUPS, S., and HAAN, A. M. F. H.   The Cerebrospinal Fluid.   Amsterdam, Elsevier Publishing Company, 1956.

MERRITT, H. H., and FREMONT-SMITH, F.   The Cerebrospinal Fluid.   Philadelphia, W. B. Saunders Company, 1937.

MESTREZAT, W.   Le liquide céphalo-rachidien normal et pathologique: Valeur clinique de l'examen chimique; Syndromes humoraux dans les diverses affections.   Paris, A. Maloine, 1912.

MILLEN, J. W., and WOOLLAM, D. H. M. The Anatomy of the Cerebrospinal Fluid. London, Oxford University Press, 1962.

MORTON, C. A. The pathology of tuberculous meningitis, with reference to its treatment by tapping the subarachnoid space of the spinal cord. *Brit. M. J.* 2:840, 1891.

QUINCKE, H. Die Lumbalpunction des Hydrocephalus. *Berl. klin. Wchnschr.* 28:929 and 965, 1891.

RUSSELL, D. S. Observations on the Pathology of Hydrocephalus. London, His Majesty's Stationery Office, 1949.

SCHALTENBRAND, G. Normal and pathological physiology of cerebrospinal fluid circulation. *Lancet* 1:805, 1953.

SWEET, W. H., *et al.* The formation, flow and absorption of the cerebrospinal fluid; newer concepts based on studies wilth isotopes. *A. Res. Nerv. & Ment. Dis., Proc.* (1954) 34:101, 1956.

TIMME, W. Historical résumé of the knowledge of the human cerebrospinal fluid. *A. Res. Nerv. & Ment. Dis., Proc.* (1924) 4:3, 1926.

WEED, L. H. The cerebrospinal fluid. *Physiol. Rev.* 2:171, 1922.

WELCH, K., and FRIEDMAN, V. The cerebrospinal fluid valves. *Brain* 83:454, 1960.

WOLSTENHOLME, G. E. W., and O'CONNOR, C. M. Ciba Foundation Symposium on the Cerebrospinal Fluid: Production, Circulation and Absorption. Boston, Little, Brown & Company, 1958.

WOOLAM, D. H. M. The historical significance of the cerebrospinal fluid. *Medical History* 1:91, 1957.

WYNTER, W. E. Four cases of tubercular meningitis in which paracentesis of the theca vertebralis was performed for the relief of fluid pressure. *Lancet* 1:981, 1891.

CHAPTER 58

SPINAL PUNCTURE

INDICATIONS FOR AND CONTRAINDICATIONS TO SPINAL PUNCTURE

Although the technic of spinal puncture is a relatively simple one, and the procedure has come to be almost a routine measure in neurologic diagnosis, it must be borne in mind that withdrawal of the cerebrospinal fluid is not without danger under certain circumstances, and should not be done unless necessary for either diagnosis or treatment.

The *indications for spinal puncture* are either diagnostic or therapeutic, but principally the former. *Diagnostic punctures* are performed for the purpose of examining either the fluid itself or the hydrodynamics of the fluid. Under most circumstances the test is carried out to withdraw cerebrospinal fluid for examination, in order to observe the physical, chemical, cytologic, serologic, or bacteriologic composition of the fluid in the diagnosis of nervous system or somatic disease. It is often an indispensable part of the neurologic investigation of diseases of the meninges and of many organic diseases of the nervous system. Changes in the composition of the fluid may aid in making a diagnosis, confirm a suspected diagnosis, assist in estimating the prognosis, and give information essential to deciding on the correct mode of treatment. Alterations in the cerebrospinal fluid may also be of help in the diagnosis of obscure nervous system diseases and of conditions where the diagnosis is not apparent on clinical grounds alone. Spinal puncture may also be done to determine the cerebrospinal fluid pressure and investigate abnormalities in pressure, such as spinal subarachnoid block, and as a part of special procedures and methods of investigation such as pneumoencephalography and myelography.

Therapeutic spinal punctures are done for various reasons, although therapeutic punctures are not indicated as frequently as diagnostic ones. Occasionally removal of fluid is carried out to relieve increased intracranial pressure in meningismus, posttraumatic states, acute alcoholic intoxication, uremia, eclampsia, meningitis, and nonobstructive hydrocephalus, but under most circumstances it is better to relieve increased intracranial pressure by means other than spinal puncture, such as by the intravenous administration of hypertonic solutions, urea, or mannitol, or by the administration of magnesium sulphate by mouth or rectum. If punctures are done to relieve increased intracranial pressure, the pressure should never be decreased by more than half of its original amount. Spinal puncture may also be performed to remove inflammatory, toxic, irritating, or noxious substances and products of disease in conditions such as meningitis and subarachnoid hemorrhage. It has been found, however, that such substances are usually absorbed rapidly, and consequently the removal of them is unnecessary under most circumstances. Spinal puncture has been performed as part of the forced drainage of the subarachnoid space in meningitis.

Spinal puncture is also used to introduce substances into the subarachnoid space in the diagnosis and treatment of disease: namely, novocaine and related drugs in spinal anesthesia, alcohol and phenol in the relief of intractable pain or spasticity, sera in the treatment of meningitis and tetanus, antibiotics in meningeal disease, and air (pneumoencephalography) and other radiopaque substances (myelography) in neurologic diagnosis. The intrathecal adminstration of drugs and sera in therapy, however, is now generally considered to be inadvisable. These substances, given intraspinally, may produce an aseptic meningitis or an arachnoiditis with spinal subarachnoid block, and furthermore most of them are just as effective, or more so, when administered by intravenous and other routes.

The *contraindications to the spinal puncture* are even more important to bear in mind than the indications. The principal ones are as follows: Spinal puncture is contraindicated if there are infections in the skin or subcutaneous tissues, such as erysipelas, boils, carbuncles, or infected decubiti in the region of puncture site. Under most circumstances spinal puncture is contraindicated in cases of septicemia or general systemic infection (scarlet fever, pneumonia, etc.). The procedure is a dangerous one in Pott's disease (tuberculous osteitis of the vertebrae), and in cases where there is suppuration or infection near the cranial cavity (osteomyelitis of the skull, lateral or cavernous sinus thrombosis, or suppuration of the mastoid air cells or paranasal sinuses). Under all of the above circumstances, introduction of a needle into the subarachnoid space or change in the pressure relationships of the spinal fluid may cause transmission or spread of the infection to the meninges and subarachnoid space. Spinal puncture is also contraindicated, or should be done with extreme caution, in all instances where there is increase in intracranial pressure. This is especially true if the increase in pressure is caused by an expanding lesion of the posterior cranial fossa, such as a cerebellar tumor, or if there is a possibility that the increase in pressure is caused by a brain abscess. Sudden change of pressure in posterior fossa lesions may force the tonsils of the cerebellum and the medulla into the foramen magnum with pressure on the respiratory and circulatory centers, causing respiratory failure, stupor, and sudden death. Sudden decrease in subtentorial pressure in supratentorial lesions may cause herniation of the hippocampal gyrus through the incisura of the tentorium cerebelli producing pressure on the midbrain, also with fatal results. Changes in pressure in brain abscess may cause rupture of the abscess and dissemination of the infection. It should be stated that spinal puncture is contraindicated whenever the diagnosis is evident from the history and examination and no additional information can be obtained from the procedure.

Under all circumstances the indications and contraindications must be weighed and evaluated before the procedure is carried out. It may be necessary, in certain cases, to perform punctures in spite of contraindications. The procedure may be essential in the presence of septicemia, especially if the diagnosis of meningitis is suspected, or in cases of suspected posterior fossa neoplasm or brain abscess. The puncture under such circumstances should be done, however, only if absolutely necessary. If the indications, either diagnostic or therapeutic, outweigh the contraindications, it may be carried out, but must be done with extreme caution. If the spinal fluid pressure is found to be elevated, only a small amount of fluid (two or three drops) should be removed, or if more fluid is necessary for examination, it should be removed very slowly. If increased intracranial pressure is suspected, a small needle should be used, and every precaution taken to avoid loss of fluid. A spinal puncture should never be performed before the patient has had a complete examination, especially a neurologic appraisal. An ophthalmoscopic examination of the optic disks, for evidence of papilledema, is a prerequisite in every case, and under most circumstances, except in acute meningitis or subarachnoid hemorrhage, reontgenograms of the skull for signs of increased intracranial pressure should also precede the puncture.

TECHNIC

Spinal puncture is performed by introducing a needle into the subarachnoid space, usually below the level of the termination of the spinal cord. In the adult the spinal cord ends at the lower level of the first lumbar vertebral body, or between the first and second bodies (although in women it may extend to the second lumbar body), but the subarachnoid and subdural spaces extend to about the second sacral body. Within the lumbosacral sac are the roots of the cauda equina, but no spinal cord. It must be borne in mind, however, that in infants and children the spinal cord may extend to about the third lumbar vertebral body. The puncture is usually done in the interspace between the second and third, third and fourth, or fourth and fifth lumbar spinous processes. The site of preference is usually between the third and fourth vertebrae (Fig. 320), or, alternatively, at the level where the separation between the spinous processes is the widest. In infants and children the interspace between the fourth and fifth lumbar spinous processes is the one of choice. The procedure may be carried out with the patient either seated or in the lateral recumbent position, but if accurate pressure studies are to be made, the latter position is essential. The patient lies on his side on a relatively hard and firm table or stretcher, or, if in bed, he is brought to the edge of the bed. He should be comfortable, warm, and relaxed. It is well to reassure the patient before the test is carried out, and if he is tense or nervous, he may be given some preliminary sedation by mouth about one-

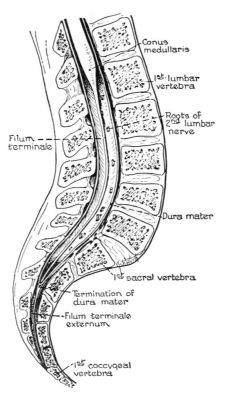

Conus medullaris

1st lumbar vertebra

Roots of 2nd lumbar nerve

Filum terminale

Dura mater

1st sacral vertebra

Termination of dura mater

Filum terminale externum

1st coccygeal vertebra

FIG. 320. Sagittal section of vertebral canal, showing lower end of spinal cord, filum terminale, and subarachnoid space. (Larsell, O.: Anatomy of the Nervous System. New York, D. Appleton-Century, 1939.)

half hour before the puncture is to be done. It is desirable that the bowels and bladder be empty.

The position of the patient is very important. The back should be parallel with the edge of the bed. If the neck and trunk are acutely flexed and the hips and knees are flexed, the spinous processes are separated as widely as possible. It is often desirable to have the neck flexed so that the chin is on the chest, and the knees drawn up to the abdomen and clasped by the hands, which are in the popliteal fossae. The head may approximate the knees. The shoulders and pelvis should be vertical. A small pillow should be placed under the head so that the entire spine is horizontal. Most difficulties in performing spinal punctures are due to inadequate position of the body.

Spinal puncture should always be carried out with aseptic precautions. The skin in the region of the puncture site and for some distance beyond should be washed with soap and water, and if necessary should be shaved. This same area is then sterilized with tincture of iodine and cleaned off with 70 per cent alcohol; other antiseptic preparations such as Merthiolate (thiomerosal) may be used if desired. Sterile towels or surgical drapes are placed around the puncture site; sterile instruments are used (Fig. 321), and the examiner should wear sterile rubber gloves. In most instances it is valuable to use local anesthesia, such as procaine hydrochloride or some similar preparation. If procaine is used, a few cubic centimeters of a 0.5 to 2 per cent solution are infiltrated in the skin and subcutaneous tissues with a very small hypodermic needle, and then a slightly larger amount may be injected with a somewhat larger needle into the deeper structures, namely the muscles and fasciae, the interspinal ligament in the interspinous space, and the vicinity of the periosteum and the outer meninges. If the patient is very tense or nervous, it may be necessary to have an assistant hold him firmly. Occasionally, if he is excited or delirious, it may be essential to use general anesthesia for the test; since inhalation anesthesia increases the venous congestion of the brain, intravenous barbiturates are usually preferable. Such measures are rarely necessary, however, and under most circumstances the puncture can be performed without difficulty by first reassuring the patient, using oral sedation if necessary, employing a trained aide, and carrying out the test rapidly and skillfully.

The spinal puncture needle should be well-sharpened, and have a short bevel with a well-fitting stylet. The needle used should be as small as possible in every instance; it should be of flexible steel, nickel, or nickeloid construction. If the determination of the hydrodynamics is an important part of the puncture, an 18 to 20 gauge needle

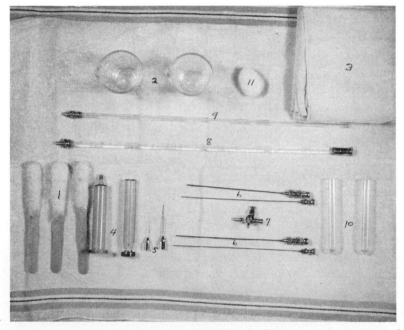

Fig. 321.   Instruments and supplies used in spinal puncture; *1*, cotton swabs; *2*, medicine glasses for tincture of iodine and alcohol; *3*, sterile drape; *4*, hypodermic syringe; *5*, hypodermic needles for infiltration of local anesthetic; *6*, spinal puncture needles with stylets; *7*, three-way stopcock; *8* and *9*, Ayer water manometer; *10*, specimen tubes; *11*, cotton sponge.

should be used, but if the Queckenstedt test is not so important, and especially if increased intracranial pressure is suspected, a 21 or 22 gauge or even smaller needle may be employed. In the adult a needle from three to four inches or from eight to twelve centimeters in length is preferable; in infants and children the needle may be much smaller and shorter. Either the Quincke type to which a stopcock may be attached or the Fleischer type with an attached stopcock is suitable.

The site for the puncture is determined by drawing a line or placing the fingers between the iliac crests. This line crosses the vertebral column at the level of the interspace between the third and fourth lumbar spines, or at that of the fourth lumbar spinous process. By palpating the spinal processes, the correct site may be determined. Careful positioning and time taken to select the correct interspace are important. After waiting a few minutes for the local anesthesia to take effect, the needle is inserted in the midline and directed at right angles to the plane of the back and parallel to the plane of the floor; on some occasions it is tilted slightly cephalad. Some authorities introduce the needle a centimeter or two lateral to the midline and insert it at a slight angle. The needle should be grasped firmly by the hilt with the right hand, and the point guided by holding the shaft with the left hand. After the skin has been punctured the needle should be realigned and pushed deeper slowly and carefully by pressure with both hands. The bevel of the needle is kept parallel to the dural fibers (which are parallel to the long axis of the body), to separate the fibers and avoid cutting through them. The needle penetrates the skin, subcutaneous tissues, supraspinal ligament, interspinal ligament, ligamentum flavum, epidural fat, dura, and arachnoid, and enters the subarachnoid space. In adults it usually must be introduced five to six centimeters to reach the subarachnoid space, the depth depending on the thickness of the lumbar muscles and the amount of subcutaneous tissue. One should not change the course of the needle during the puncture, and if obstruction is met or bone is encountered, it should be withdrawn to the subcutaneous tissues and reintroduced at another and slightly different angle.

Usually the examiner can feel a slight "give" or a sharp "click" when the resistance of the deep tissues is suddenly released as the needle goes through the ligamentum flavum. The stylet is then withdrawn to see whether the needle is in the subarachnoid space. If no fluid is obtained, the stylet is reintroduced and the needle is inserted for a few more millimeters. Usually another "give" is felt as the needle penetrates the dura. The stylet is then withdrawn again, and if no fluid is obtained the position of the needle is readjusted slightly, or it is rotated about ninety degrees, since its point may be obstructed by a nerve root or a film of arachnoid tissue. If there is still failure to obtain fluid, the point of the needle is withdrawn almost to the skin and redirected. A change in the direction of the needle cannot be made by shifting the hilt while the point is deep in the tissue. The needle should not be introduced too far, since it may damage the intervertebral disks or traumatize the extradural venous plexus. If blood is obtained before the arachnoid has been penetrated, it is well to use a clean needle and introduce it at a slightly different site.

If fluid is obtained, the stylet is reintroduced or the stopcock is turned to a neutral position. The patient is now reassured, and to assist him in relaxing he may be told that the puncture has been successful and that he will suffer no more discomfort. The manometer is attached without losing fluid; it is placed in a vertical position and the pressure is determined (Fig. 322). Air bubbles should be removed from the manometer, since they alter the pressure readings and the determination of the hydrodynamics. If the patient is tense, the examiner should wait a few moments before determining the pressure; sometimes the patient relaxes better after taking a few deep breaths. It is sometimes necessary to wait five or ten minutes to secure adequate relaxation. Not infrequently a pressure of over 200 mm. will fall to a normal range with adequate relaxation. It is important to be certain that the needle is in the subarachnoid space and that there is free communication between this space and the manometer; this is ascertained by the presence of normal oscillations and normal response to coughing and straining (see below). Then the hydrodynamics are determined as described below, and, following this, the fluid is removed for examination. The fluid is collected in two clean, dry, sterile test tubes, with 1 to 2 cc. in the first tube, to be used for the cell count, Pandy test, and qualitative glucose determination, and 6 to 8 cc. in the second for the serologic tests for syphilis, total protein determination, and colloidal gold test. If other tests, such as quantitative glucose, chlorides, or cultures are indicated, additional fluid is obtained in other tubes. Pressure readings are again taken, the stylet is reintroduced, and the needle is withdrawn slowly. The puncture site is then resterilized with iodine and alcohol; pressure is applied for a minute or two to prevent oozing, the wound is covered with a bit of liquid collodion which is allowed to dry and adhere, and a sterile dressing is applied. The patient should lie on his back for at least one hour, and many authorities advise remaining in this position for twenty-four hours. A record should always be made of the initial and final pressures and the amount of fluid removed.

Pain is usually experienced by the patient only when the skin and the dura are penetrated. If local anesthesia is used, this pain may be eliminated. If the periosteum of the spinous processes or the vertebral bodies is traumatized, there may be pain,

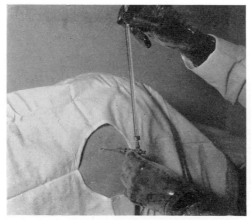

Fig. 322.   Manometer in place for determination of spinal fluid pressure readings.

and in certain instances where there is arthritis of the spinal column, the puncture may be quite painful. Occasionally there is a brief lancinating pain shooting down one leg; this indicates that one of the roots of the cauda equina was traumatized. This pain usually disappears immediately. It is best not to change the position of the needle during puncture. If the puncture is performed with difficulty, or if blood is obtained, the puncture should be attempted at another level, preferably a higher one. If the fluid is slightly blood-tinged, a few cubic centimeters should be allowed to escape before collecting the fluid for examination; if two or three specimens are obtained, the last one should be examined. If the fluid is grossly bloody, unless bloody because of subarachnoid hemorrhage, the examination of the fluid is unreliable, and the puncture should be repeated in from one to five days. If there is a rapid fall of pressure or a deterioration of the patient's condition during drainage of the fluid, the procedure should be stopped immediately; some authorities advise the intraspinal injection of ten cubic centimeters of normal saline if there is a change of respirations during the test.

Theoretically, it should be possible to perform a spinal puncture and to obtain spinal fluid in every patient, but occasionally the procedure is difficult or almost impossible to perform. If the subarachnoid space cannot be entered, one of the following may be the cause: The needle is incorrectly placed; it may be lateral to the canal or introduced obliquely and not directed straight toward the canal. The needle has been introduced too far or not far enough, or is at the wrong level. The needle is too blunt, and the dural sac is pushed forward or to one side. A root of the cauda equina or a fold of arachnoid may be obstructing the point. (Under most of the above circumstances, slight adjustment of the position of the needle will lead to a free flow of spinal fluid.) The needle is plugged with foreign material such as pus or coagulated spinal fluid which will not flow freely. There is an anomaly of the lumbar spine (scoliosis) or severe spondylitis. There is an obstructing tumor in the region of the conus medullaris or cauda equina. There is a complete block of the subarachnoid space above the puncture site. The intracranial pressure is too low to allow free flow of fluid. (If the latter is the case, the use of gentle suction with a syringe may be followed by some flow of fluid.)

PRESSURE DETERMINATIONS AND THE HYDRODYNAMICS OF THE SPINAL FLUID

No spinal puncture is complete without determination of spinal fluid pressure. The Ayer water manometer is preferable for this, since it is a delicate instrument and will show slight variations in hydrodynamics It is a vertical glass tube with a 1 mm. bore which is attached to the needle by means of a three-way stopcock; the level of the fluid in the tube indicates the cerebrospinal fluid pressure in millimeters of water. The normal spinal fluid pressure with the patient in the lateral recumbent position is from 50 to 80 to 150 to 180 mm., and it is identical, or nearly so, in the lumbar sac, cisterna magna, and ventricles. If the head and body are raised, however, the ventricular and cisternal pressures drop and the lumbar pressure rises. Pressures of from 180 to 200 mm. are considered borderline or at the upper limits of normal, and those of over 200, as definitely elevated. The pressure is lower in children than in adults. If the needle is in the subarachnoid space, minor oscillations of the pressure of the fluid are seen. There are relatively small oscillations (4 to 10 mm.) which are synchronous with the respiratory rate (Fig. 323), and even finer oscillations (2 to 5 mm.) which are synchronous with the pulse. In addition to these, it is not unusual to observe spontaneous fluctuations of from 5 to 15 mm. with slight movement of the body and increase or decrease of tension and relaxation, and even more marked and irregular fluctuations in some patients with increased intracranial pressure, especially after trauma or cerebral hemorrhage. It is also seen, if the needle is in the subarachnoid space, that the pressure increases with coughing and straining and decreases with deep respirations. Since it takes a slight interval for the pressure to adjust to a change in position from the upright to the horizontal, it is best to have the patient recumbent for a short period before doing the puncture or determining the pressure. Manometry is not reliable if the patient is tense or excited, and it is important to wait for adequate relaxation. Instructing the patient to take a few deep breaths or engaging him in conversation may aid in this. On the other hand, if the pressure is found to be high, sudden changes in intracranial tension and loss of fluid may be prevented by placing one finger over the open end of the manometer to prevent the fluid from rising too rapidly; under such circumstances only a few drops of fluid should be removed for examination. If a mercury manometer is used, the pressure is multiplied by 13.546 to obtain a reading in millimeters of water, and the normal variation is from 4 to 6 to from 11 to 13 mm. of mercury. The mercury manometer, however, is not very delicate and fails to show slight abnormalities of pressure or incomplete blockage of the subarachnoid channels. Electromanometry will be discussed below.

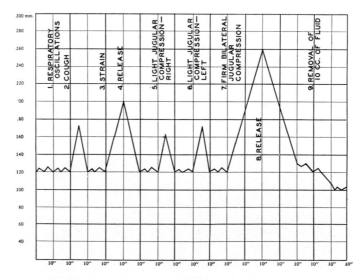

FIG. 323.   Manometric chart showing respiratory and pulse oscillations and normal response of pressure to coughing, straining, and light and firm jugular compression.

One should not attempt to estimate the spinal fluid pressure by noting the rate or force of flow, size of drops, or number of drops per minute; these are dependent largely upon the size of the needle, but also upon the position and relaxation of the patient, surface tension of the spinal fluid, and pulse and respiratory fluctuations. There is no accurate method of pressure determination without the use of a manometer. It has been stated that if the pressure is obtained with the patient seated, the reading is equal to that of the pressure in the lateral recumbent position together with the pressure of the column of spinal fluid above the level of the puncture site. Experimental investigations have shown, however, that there is no mathematical relationship between the lumbar spinal fluid pressures in the erect and recumbent positions; neither can be computed from the other, even though the pressure in the erect or seated position has been found to be approximately equivalent to the vertical distance from the needle to the cisterna magna. Von Storch and his co-workers found the normal lumbar spinal fluid pressure in the erect position to be a reflection of the intradural venous pressure at the point of measurement together with the volume of blood in the lumbar subarachnoid veins. This is dependent upon the right auricular cardiac pressure and the vertical distance from the needle to the auricle; the sum of these approximates the lumbocisternal distance.

The spinal fluid pressure is influenced by many factors. It is said to reflect the intracranial venous pressure and to be about equal to the venous pressure in the torcular Herophili. It is not definitely related to either the diastolic or systolic arterial pressures, although rapid rise in arterial pressure causes a transitory elevation of spinal fluid pressure. Arterial hypertension, on the other hand, sometimes occurs with increased intracranial pressure if the cerebrospinal fluid pressure is elevated to a level approaching that of the diastolic blood pressure. The rate of production, rate of absorption, osmotic pressure, hydrostatic pressure, rate of dialysis, "secretion pressure," elasticity of the vertebral and cerebral dura, size of the subarachnoid reservoir, osmotic equilibrium with the blood, blocking of the crculation of the fluid, disease states, and drugs also affect spinal fluid pressure. The cranial cavity is relatively fixed in volume. It is completely filled by the brain, cerebrospinal fluid, and blood vessels and blood. Increase in the volume or pressure of one of these is carried out at the expense of the volume or pressure of the others. Increase in intracranial pressure may result from increase in volume or pressure of either the blood and blood vessels, the brain or its coverings, or the cerebrospinal fluid. The spinal fluid pressure, consequently, is increased under a variety of circumstances.

THE BLOOD AND BLOOD VESSELS

The venous pressure and the volume of blood within the skull are the most important factors in determining the spinal fluid pressure. Changes in the intracranial venous pressure are transmitted through the entire ventriculosubarachnoid space and are quickly followed by changes in spinal fluid pressure, although the latter may not be maintained. The systemic venous pressure is influenced by the position of the heart, volume of blood in the great veins, weight of the viscera, and tension of the abdominal and thoracic muscles. It may be increased with cardiac decompensation, obstruction of the venous trunks in the thorax and neck by tumors and anomalies, emphysema and other pulmonary disorders, or elevation of the intrathoracic and abdominal pressures by coughing, straining, or compression. The elevation of systemic venous pressure is accompanied by increase of intracranial venous pressure and thence of spinal fluid pressure. Manual compression of the jugular veins (Queckenstedt maneuver) interferes with venous drainage from the head and causes an increase in intracranial pressure. Venous pressure within the skull may be increased by interference with venous drainage by neoplasms or other expanding masses or by obstruction of venous circulation by thrombosis of major venous channels or dural sinuses, especially the lateral or superior sagittal sinuses. So-called otitic hydrocephalus, one of the causes of "benign intracranial hypertension," may follow thrombosis of one of the lateral sinuses. Alterations in the relationship between lumbar and ventricular pressures secondary to changes in posture may be on the basis of changes of the intracranial venous pressure.

Variations in the cerebral blood supply also influence the intracranial pressure, which may be raised with increased blood flow and blood volume within the skull. Drugs and other substances which dilate the cerebral blood vessels (amyl nitrite, histamine, carbon monoxide) as well as those which cause a sudden elevation of the arterial and sometimes venous pressures (epinephrine) increase the volume of the intracranial contents and thus the intracranial pressure. The pressure is decreased by caffeine and other substances which constrict cerebral blood vessels, increase the cerebrovascular resistance, and lessen the blood flow. Intracranial pressure is also elevated by the presence of free or clotted blood within the skull, as in intracerebral, subarachnoid, or extradural hemorrhage or subdural hematoma. With polycythemia there may be both increased blood volume and venous thromboses.

THE BRAIN AND ITS COVERINGS

Increase in volume of the brain or its coverings also increases the intracranial pressure. The presence of a foreign body or an expanding lesion such as a neoplasm, abscess, granuloma, cyst, or hematoma may increase the pressure by increase in bulk alone as well as by obstructing the circulation of the blood and the cerebrospinal fluid. Slow increase in brain volume, however, is compensated for by a decrease in the amount of cerebrospinal fluid, and it is often possible to have normal intracranial pressure with slowly growing brain tumors. Normal pressure, however, is rare with posterior fossa (cerebellar) tumors. Cerebral edema is probably intracellular, rather than extracellular, because of an increase in the volume of the oligodendroglial cytoplasm. Contributing to or associated with this there may be increased permeability of the capillaries, venous congestion, and petechial hemorrhages. Such edema occurs in the immediate posttraumatic state, acute alcoholic intoxication, other drug intoxications, lead encephalopathy, meningitis and encephalitis, uremia, eclampsia, respiratory acidosis, anoxia, severe anemia and deficiency states, vitamin A intoxication, certain allergic and metabolic disorders, water intoxication, and alterations in electrolyte balance. It causes tissue hydration, increase in brain volume, and elevation of intracranial pressure. Some cases of "benign intracranial hypertension" may be on the basis of such allergic or metabolic alterations. Suppuration of the meninges and the presence of inflammatory exudate also increase the intracranial pressure.

THE CEREBROSPINAL FLUID

Spinal fluid pressure is elevated with increase in the amount of cerebrospinal fluid, owing to either increased formation or decreased absorption. There is increased formation of the fluid under the following circumstances: decrease in osmotic pressure of the blood serum by the intravenous injection of hypotonic solutions; decrease in osmotic pressure of the serum at the onset of febrile illnesses, especially in children, leading to the syndrome of meningismus; alterations of the vascular endothelium in encephalitis, meningitis, and other infections; hypertrophy or increased activity of the choroid plexus (some types of hydrocephalus); increase in venous pressure within the skull causing greater filtration. Obstruction of the arachnoid villi and perivenous spaces by inflammatory reaction or blood serum causes decreased absorption and subsequent rise in pressure. Similar decrease in absorption and rise in pressure may occur with a significant elevation of the protein content of the cerebrospinal fluid; this has been observed in the Guillain-Barré syndrome and late poliomyelitis and with some brain and spinal cord tumors. There is also increased fluid if its circulation is interfered with by neoplasms or adhesions, narrowing of the foramina of Monro, Luschka, or Magendie, or stenosis of the aqueduct. Internal or noncommunicating hydrocephalus is caused by either oversecretion of fluid or obstruction of the foramina or aqueduct, and external or communicating hydrocephalus by impaired absorption by the arachnoid villi or within the perivenous spaces. The presence of pus or blood in the spinal fluid may also increase the amount of the fluid. Increased formation and decreased absorption may occur simultaneously, as they do in meningitis and encephalitis; the increase in the volume of the cerebrospinal fluid may be accompanied, furthermore, by edema of the brain and venous congestion, all of which lead to great elevation of spinal fluid pressure.

Spinal fluid pressure is decreased in shock, fainting, dehydration, degenerative diseases of the brain, wasting and cachectic diseases, asthenia, depression, and decrease in the systemic arterial and venous pressures. The pressure may be low due to decreased formation of fluid following spinal puncture, trauma, or intracranial surgery, and occasionally in the presence of a subdural hematoma. Schaltenbrand has described the syndrome of spontaneous aliquorrhea characterized by decreased fluid formation and very low pressure; the etiology of this is not known. The pressure may be decreased, either because of diminished formation or withdrawal of fluid, under circumstances where there is increased viscosity of the blood. The pressure may also be low with a complete spinal subarachnoid block and with continued leakage of fluid following a spinal puncture; it may appear to be low if there is inadequate communication between the lumen of the needle and the subarachnoid space. Under most circumstances, however, low spinal fluid pressure has little significance.

Drugs and other substances which raise the osmotic pressure of the blood serum lower the intracranial pressure by decreasing the formation and pressure of the cerebrospinal fluid as well as by counteracting the cerebral edema. This reduction is temporary, however, and is most apt to occur when the fluid pressure is already elevated. Hypertonic solutions of dextrose, sucrose, or sodium chloride, administered intravenously, have long been used, but their efficacy is hampered by the "rebound" of pressure which may occur after a few hours. The intravenous administration of either a 30 per cent solution of urea in 10 per cent invert sugar or a 25 per cent solution of mannitol brings about a more prolonged decrease in pressure, with a less abrupt secondary rise. The glucocorticoids have also been shown to be of value in decreasing cerebral edema, and acetazolamide (Diamox) slows the secretion of cerebrospinal fluid in some types of hydrocephalus through inhibition of the carbonic anhydrase in the choroid plexus.

In 1923 Ayala suggested the *rachidian quotient* as a means of ready differential diagnosis between an expanding intracranial lesion and other causes of increased intracranial pressure. A rapid drop in pressure after the removal of a small amount of cerebrospinal fluid indicates that there is a small fluid reservoir and, accordingly, suggests the presence of an expanding intracranial lesion. A slow fall in pressure indicates that the spinal fluid reservoir is large. The quotient, or Ayala index, is computed as the final pressure divided by the initial pressure and multiplied by the amout of fluid removed. The normal quotient is from 5.5 to 6.5. A value below 5 indicates that there is a small reservoir and suggests the presence of a brain tumor or abscess, obstructive hydrocephalus, or a spinal subarachnoid block. A value above 7 indicates a large reservoir and the presumed presence of nonobstructive hydrocephalus, serous meningitis (meningismus), or cerebral atrophy. At least 10 cc. of fluid must be removed if the test is to be reliable.

DETERMINATION OF SPINAL SUBARACHNOID BLOCK

Once the spinal fluid pressure has assumed a constant level, it is important under many circumstances to examine the hydrodynamics further in order to determine whether there is any interference with the flow of the fluid. The patient is first asked to cough; the pressure is seen to increase from 40 to 50 mm. of water (depending upon the normal pressure and the intensity of the cough) and it descends about as rapidly as it ascended (Fig. 323). The patient is then asked to strain, as in moving his bowels; the pressure goes up from 50 to 100 mm., and again descends after straining. Both coughing and straining cause compression of the thorax and abdomen, and by retarding the venous return to the thorax, they produce an increase in intracranial pressure which is transmitted to the fluid in the ventricles and the subarachnoid space. The increase of the intra-abdominal and intrathoracic pressures also interferes with the return of blood through the spinal veins and thus elevates the intraspinal venous pressure. If there is no rise on abdominal pressure, coughing, and straining, it is probable that the lumen of the needle is obstructed or that there is lack of free communication between the subarachnoid space and the manometer, and further adjustment of the needle is necessary.

Next the jugular veins are constricted by an assistant (Queckenstedt maneuver); this increases the intracranial venous pressure by obstructing the venous return from the head, and causes a rise in intracranial pressure. They may be compressed either manually or with an inflatable cuff, such as used on a sphygmomanometer. In performing manual compression, the veins on each side are first constricted lightly, one at a time, then firmly, one at a time, and then the two are constricted simultaneously, lightly, then firmly. There should be a prompt rise in the spinal fluid followed by a fall to about the original pressure. With firm jugular compression for about ten seconds there is a rise of from 100 to 300 mm. of water of cerebrospinal fluid pressure, depending on the degree of constriction, and within ten seconds after release the pressure falls to the original pressure, or to within a few millimeters of the original pressure. In doing the Queckenstedt test the neck is constricted near the trachea (to include the internal jugular veins) with sufficient pressure to collapse the veins, but not enough to compress the carotid arteries, interfere with respirations, cause pain, or stimulate the carotid sinus reflex. If pressure is applied to the larynx, the patient may cough and there may be elevation of the spinal fluid pressure, even with presence of a complete block. If the jugular veins are constricted by means of a sphygmomanometer cuff, the examiner first inflates the cuff to 20 mm. of mercury, notes the height of the cerebrospinal fluid pressure in ten seconds, and then releases the pressure and takes readings for every ten seconds or longer. Then, after an interval of from ten to fifteen seconds, the test can be repeated with the cuff inflated to 40 mm., and again with the cuff inflated to 60 mm. (Fig. 324). Occasionally, instead of jugular compression, the patient may be given an amyl nitrite "pearl" (2.0 cc.) to inhale; there is usually a definite rise of cerebrospinal fluid pressure within ten seconds, and a fall in one minute. It is important to stress that the Queckenstedt test should never be carried out if the cerebrospinal fluid pressure is abnormally elevated (over 200 mm.), if a brain tumor is suspected, or if there is grave intracranial disease such as a subarachnoid hemorrhage. It is an important

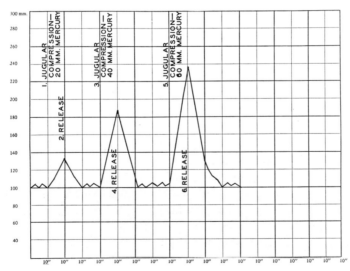

FIG. 324.   Manometric chart showing normal response to jugular compression by means of a sphygmomanometer cuff.

diagnostic test, but one that should be performed only when indicated and not routinely with every spinal puncture.

Spinal subarachnoid block may be either partial or complete. It is caused by some interruption of the continuity of the spinal fluid along the spinal subarachnoid space. This may be the result of meningeal arachnoiditis with adhesions; hypertrophic pachymeningitis; compression of the spinal subarachnoid space by neoplasm, granuloma, or abscess of the spinal cord, spinal epidural abscess, or herniated nucleus pulposus; deformity of the vertebrae by fracture or dislocation, Paget's disease, Pott's disease, or nontuberculous kyphoscoliosis; or other causes.

If there is a *complete spinal subarachnoid block,* the pulse and respiratory oscillations are usually somewhat decreased, and the pressure is often low. There will, under most circumstances, be a normal rise in pressure on coughing and straining. since the intraspinal pressure is still increased by these maneuvers. Occasionally there is an exaggerated response on coughing and straining in a high block, at least exaggerated in comparison to the response to jugular compression, although if the block is in the lower thoracic or upper lumbar region there may be very little change in pressure on coughing and straining, or a slow rise and a delayed fall. With a complete block, however, there is no change in the spinal manometric pressure following either jugular compression or inhalation of amyl nitrite (Figs. 325 and 326). With a *partial spinal subarachnoid block* there will be normal response to coughing and straining, or very slight modifications, depending upon the level of the partial obstruction. In partial block, however, while there is a definite rise and fall on firm jugular compression, there is very little or a delayed rise followed by a slow, delayed fall on light jugular compression or inhalation of amyl nitrite (Fig. 327). The pressure may fail to fall to its original level, and a new, higher level may be maintained. Occasionally, especially in a partial block, the reponse to jugular compression may falsely appear to be normal if the patient strains, coughs, or holds his breath during the test. In cervical lesions the response to the Queckenstedt test may sometimes be modified by either flexion or extension of the neck during the study of the pressure relationships. Under certain circumstances the dynamics may be normal if they are tested with the head in the neutral position, but there may be either a partial or a complete block when they are tested with the neck in either full flexion or full extension. Such maneuvers are especially important in the diagnosis of lesions in the cervical region. With both partial and complete block there is a rapid fall in pressure on removal of spinal fluid. If a complete, or even a partially complete, block is found, very little fluid should be removed, usually not more than 1 or 2 cc., and it is usually advisable in such cases to inject contrast medium for myelography at once. With spinal cord tumors and similar obstructions of the spinal subarachnoid space, the removal of fluid from the lumbar region may increase the relative pressure above the tumor and force it downward in the spinal canal; this may be followed by an increase in symptoms and even by the sudden development of total paralysis below the level of the tumor.

The Ayer or Tobey-Ayer modification of the Queckenstedt test has been said to be of value in the diagnosis of thrombosis of the lateral sinus. There is a normal response on compression of the jugular vein on the normal side, but no rise on com-

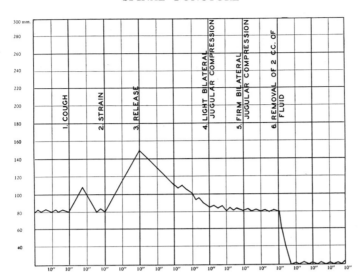

FIG. 325. Manometric chart in a case of complete spinal subarachnoid block.

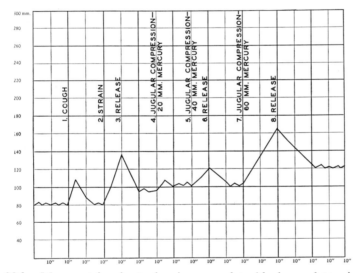

FIG. 326. Manometric chart showing complete block as determined by means of a sphygmomanometer cuff.

pression of the jugular vein on the affected side. This procedure is not always reliable, however, due to individual variations in the amount of drainage from the two sides of the skull. It is said that a neoplasm in the region of the cerebellopontine angle may also cause a positive Tobey-Ayer response.

Occasionally combined lumbar and cisternal puncture readings are carried out in the determination of block. With a complete block, the pressure is normal in the

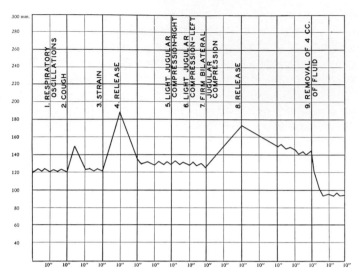

FIG. 327. Manometric chart in a case of partial spinal subarachnoid block.

cisterna magna but is usually low in the lumbar region; respiratory and pulse oscillations are normal at the cistern, but may be decreased or absent at the lumbar region; jugular compression and inhalation of amyl nitrite are followed by normal response at the cistern, but no response at the lumbar region; abdominal compression, coughing, and straining cause a normal response at the cistern, but sometimes an exaggerated response at the lumbar level; removal of cisternal fluid is followed by a slow fall in pressure at the cisternal level, but no change in pressure at the lumbar level; removal of lumbar fluid is followed by a rapid fall in pressure at the lumbar level, but no change at the cistern; the fluid is normal in appearance at the cistern, but may be xanthochromic at the lumbar level.

The technic of electromanometry for the recording of spinal fluid pressure and the determination of spinal subarachnoid block has recently been described by Gilland. A pressure transducer of a strain gauge type is used, with an ink writer for recording the results. The electromanometer is said to be much more sensitive than the water manometer, even when a needle with a very fine caliber is used. It is able to record very low pressures and slight differences in pressure on combined lumbar-cisternal punctures or in response to jugular compression.

COMPLICATIONS OF SPINAL PUNCTURE

Complications of spinal puncture are infrequent in occurrence and rarely have serious prognostic import if clinical judgment is used in the performance of the test and if the various contraindications mentioned above are not present. The development of a purulent meningitis or of herniation of the medulla and/or cerebellar tonsils into the foramen magnum or the hippocampal gyrus through the incisura, with respiratory and circulatory distress, usually indicates that the puncture was ill-advised or was performed without the usual precautions. It is usually possible, however, to carry out a spinal puncture without dire effects even in the presence of papilledema and other signs of increased intracranial pressure, but one should use caution, employ a fine gauged needle, and remove only a very small amount of fluid.

Pain in the nerve roots which may occur during the puncture is usually brief in duration and rarely causes persisting symptoms. The same is true of back pain which follows a puncture done with difficulty in the presence of arthritis or skeletal anomalies. Patients in whom back or leg pain persists are usually (but not always) suggestible or hypochondriacal individuals. Rare cases of injury to the inter-vertebral disks, vertebrae, interarticular facets, or venous sinusoids of the vertebrae have been reported with spinal puncture. It is said that in the exaggerated flexion of the torso the pressure is increased within the intervertebral disks; puncture of the disks with a needle may cause rupture of the nucleus pulposus into the canal. Osteomyelitis of the vertebrae has been reported on a few occasions following spinal puncture, as have extradural hemorrhage and extradural abscess.

Temporary meningitic signs are occasionally encountered following spinal puncture. There may be either a slight pleocytosis or a moderate increase in cerebrospinal fluid pressure, usually with fever but no organisms; this may be taken to indicate either a slight inflammatory reaction (aseptic meningitis) or toxic sequelae due to the presence in the needle of foreign matter from disinfectants or detergents (chemical meningitis). Either temporary or permanent paralysis of the oculomotor, abducens, or other cranial nerves has been reported following either spinal puncture or spinal anesthesia. The removal of spinal fluid in the presence of either a complete or partially complete subarachnoid block may force the obstructing lesion downward in the spinal canal, change a partial to a complete block, or cause the development of a complete paralysis below the level of the lesion. The dangers of punctures in the presence of brain tumor and other causes in increased intracranial pressure are referred to above. It has often been stated that spinal puncture may cause an increase in the symptoms of multiple sclerosis and myelitis, but there is no definite scientific evidence for this. Breaking of the spinal puncture needle is rare if the equipment is good and the technic is adequate. Intraspinal treatment, not spinal puncture, sometimes leads to the development of an aseptic meningitils, sensory and paralytic manifestations, and arachnoid adhesions with a consequent complete subarachnoid block.

The most frequent and most annoying sequel of spinal puncture, distressing both the patient and physician, is the postpuncture headache which occurs in some form in a certain percentage of patients. Statistics vary widely regarding the frequency; it has been stated that a residual headache occurs in anywhere from 10 to 50 per cent of patients on whom spinal punctures are performed. Possibly it occurs in a very mild form in a fairly large number of patients, but it appears as a definite complication in from 15 to 30 per cent of cases. It is present slightly more frequently in males than females, and in younger rather than older persons. The headache is usually occipital in site and may be accompanied by pain and stiffness in the back of the neck and back. It is usually present only when the patient is upright and is relieved by recumbency. It may throb with the pulse and be increased by coughing, shaking of the head, sudden movement, and jugular compression. If severe, it may be accompanied by vertigo, nausea, vomiting, blurred vision, tinnitus, temporary deafness, backache, and stiff neck. If the complication is transitory, it lasts for only an hour or two; if moderate, it generally lasts but one or two days; in severe cases the patient may be incapacitated for a week, ten days, or even two weeks. Sometimes there is a latent period of one to three days before the development of the headache. The symptom has been known to occur in patients in whom the dura was punctured but no fluid withdrawn.

Various etiologic factors have been hypothesized as responsible for the postpuncture headache. Continued escape of the fluid at the puncture site, mainly into the subdural space and subcutaneous tissues, is generally said to be the cause, although other theories include decrease in the intracranial pressure consequent to rapid removal of fluid, increase in intracranial pressure brought on by stimulation to formation of the fluid, and psychogenic factors including suggestibility and emotional instability. Multiple causes may be responsible. Some patients who have had more than one puncture have developed headaches on some occasions and not on others. The headache does not seem to be dependent upon the amount of fluid withdrawn. It is rare after puncture of the cisterna magna. The reported frequency of postpuncture headache in patients with certain neurologic diseases such as multiple sclerosis has never been statistically demonstrated. Some patients with postpuncture headaches have been found to have a slight pleocytosis, others not; some have a decrease in cerebrospinal fluid pressure, some an increase, and others normal pressure.

Experimental studies have shown that the complication occurs much more frequently if the puncture is done with a large, 16 gauge needle, than with a 22 gauge needle, so that physiologic factors such as drainage are probably more important than the psychologic ones (anxiety and hypochondriasis). It is generally believed also, that postpuncture headaches occur less often if the patient is kept recumbent for at least one hour after the puncture, and possibly if he is kept at bed rest for twenty-four hours. Rest in the prone position for several hours after the puncture has also been recommended. The effect of position during and immediately after the puncture, as well as the influence of bed rest are controversial points. Bed rest, however, is probably a prophylactic measure, at least in many cases. Withdrawal of fluid through a small needle, such as one of the 24 or 25 gauge size, is very infrequently followed by headache, but objections to its use are the time required for the removal of the fluid and the lack of reliability of the Queckenstedt test. Most authorities recommend that a 22 gauge needle be used if the puncture is done only to record the resting pressure and to withdraw cerebrospinal fluid, and an 18 gauge needle be employed if the Queckenstedt test is to be performed. Also, a needle with a pencil point is less apt to cut the dural fibers than one with a bevel. It is now generally believed that continued seepage of fluid is the most important factor in postpuncture headaches. This leads to traction on and caudal displacement of the base and posterior parts of the brain and the vascular structures about the base of the brain, with tension on and irritation of the pain-sensitive structures, the veins and larger arteries at the base of the brain. Furthermore, with loss of the water-cushion the weight of the brain is transmitted to the veins at its base, with consequent congestion and further increase in venous pressure. Under certain circumstances there may also be edema of the brain secondary to venous congestion, rapid loss of fluid, and disturbance of the normal arterio-venous dynamics.

The best mode of treatment of postpuncture headaches is complete bed rest with the head as low or lower than the rest of the body, together with the use of analgesics and sedatives as necessary. A generous fluid intake is said to be advisable. Various drugs and procedures have been suggested, namely pituitrin to increase the cerebrospinal fluid pressure, vasodilators such as amyl nitrite and glyceryl trinitrate to cause intracranial hyperemia, cerebral vasoconstrictors such as caffeine with sodium benzoate and ergotamine tartrate, cortisone or desoxycotricosterone acetate, and abdominal compression; none of these measures has been uniformly successful, however. Some authorities have advised the intravenous use of hypotonic fluids or distilled water, intravenous administration of hypertonic fluids, intrathecal injection of saline or glucose to restore the intraspinal pressure to normal, epidural injection of saline solution, or even repair of the dural defect; the efficacy of none of these procedures is definite. Rest and time are the most important factors in therapy; perhaps sedation before and immediately after the puncture may be additional prophylactic measures.

REFERENCES

AYALA, G.   Ueber den diagnostischen Wert des Liquordruckes und einen Apparat zu seiner Messung.   *Ztschr. f. d. ges. Neurol. u. Psychiat.* 84:42, 1923.

AYER, J. B.   Spinal subarachnoid block as determined by combined cistern and lumbar puncture with special reference to the early diagnosis of cord tumors.   *Arch. Neurol. & Psychiat.* 7:38, 1922.

ECKER, A.   Irregular fluctuation of elevated cerebrospinal fluid pressure.   *A. M. A. Arch. Neurol. & Psychiat.* 74:641, 1955.

ELSBERG, C. A., and HARE, C. C.   A new and simplified manometric test for the determination of spinal subarachnoid block by means of the inhalation of nitrite of amyl.   *Bull. Neurol. Inst. New York* 2:347, 1932.

FISHER, R. G., and COPENHAVER, J. H.   The metabolic activity of the choroid plexus.   *J. Neurosurg.* 16:167, 1959.

FOLEY, J.   Benign forms of intracranial hypertension—"toxic" and "otitic" hydrocephalus.   *Brain* 78:1, 1955.

FREMONT-SMITH, F., and KUBIE, L. S.   The relation of vascular hydrostatic pressure and osmotic pressure to the cerebrospinal fluid pressure.   *A. Res. Nerv. & Ment. Dis., Proc.* (1927) 8:104, 1929.

GILLAND, O.   Cerebrospinal fluid dynamics in spinal subarachnoid block.   *Acta neurol. scandinav.* 38:285, 1962.

GRANT, W. T., and CONE, W. V.   Graduated jugular compression in the lumbar manometric test for spinal subarachnoid block.   *Arch. Neurol. & Psychiat.* 32:1194, 1934.

HODGSON, J. S.   The relation between increased intracranial pressure and increased intraspinal pressure; Changes in the cerebrospinal fluid in increased intracranial pressure.   *A. Res. Nerv. & Ment. Dis., Proc.* (1927) 8:182, 1929.

JAVID, M., and SETTLAGE, P.   Effect of urea on cerebrospinal fluid pressure in human subjects.   *J.A.M.A.* 160:943, 1956.

KAPLAN, L., and KENNEDY, F.   The effect of head posture on the manometrics of the cerebrospinal fluid in cervical lesions: A new diagnostic test.   *Brain* 73:337, 1950.

KUNKLE, E. C., RAY, B. S., and WOLFF, H. G.   Experimental studies on headache: Analysis of the headache associated with changes in intracranial pressure.   *Arch. Neurol. & Psychiat.* 49:323, 1943.

LA FIA, D. J.   Abuse of the Queckenstedt test.   *New England J. Med.* 251:348, 1956.

LUSE, S. A., and HARRIS, B.   Brain ultrastructure in hydration and dehydration.   *Arch. Neurol.* 4:139, 1961.

MAREN, T. H., and ROBINSON, B.   The pharmacology of acetazolimide as related to cerebrospinal fluid and the treatment of hydrocephalus.   *Bull. Johns Hopkins Hosp.* 106:1, 1960.

MYERSON, A., and LOMAN, J.   Internal jugular venous pressure in man: Its relationship to cerebrospinal fluid and carotid arterial pressure.   *Arch. Neurol. & Psychiat.* 27:836, 1932.

O'CONNELL, J. E. A.   The vascular factor in intracranial pressure and the maintenance of the cerebrospinal fluid circulation.   *Brain* 66:204, 1943; The cerebrospinal fluid pressure as an aetiological factor in the development of lesions affecting the central nervous system.   *Brain* 76:279, 1953.

QUECKENSTEDT, M. E.   Zur Diagnose der Rückenmarkskompression.   *Deutsch Ztschr. f. Nervenh.* 55:325, 1916.

RICH, M., SCHEINBERG, P., and BELLE, M. S.   Relationship between cerebrospinal fluid pressure changes and cerebral blood flow.   *Circulation Research* 1:389, 1953.

RYDER, H. W. *et. al.* Influence of changes in cerebral blood flow on the cerebrospinal fluid pressure.   *A. M. A. Arch. Neurol. & Psychiat.* 68:165, 1952; Effect of changes in systemic venous pressure on cerebrospinal fluid pressure.   *A. M. A. Arch. Neurol. & Psychiat.* 68:175, 1952.

SAHS, A. L., and JOYNT, R. J.   Brain swelling of unknown cause.   *Neurology* 6:791, 1956.

SCHALTENBRAND, G.   Die akute Aliquorrhoe.   *Verhandl. deutsch. Gesellsch. inn. Med.* 52:473, 1940.

SHENKIN, H. A., and FINNESON, B. E.   Clinical significance of low cerebral spinal fluid pressure.   *Neurology* 8:157, 1958.

STOOKEY, B., and KLENKE, D.   A study of the spinal fluid pressure in differential diagnosis of diseases of the spinal cord.   *Arch. Neurol. & Psychiat.* 20:84, 1928.

SYMONDS, C.   Otitic hydrocephalus.   *Neurology* 6:681, 1956.

TOBEY, G. L., and AYER, J. B.   Dynamic studies on the cerebrospinal fluid in the differential diagnosis of lateral sinus thrombosis.   *Arch. Otolaryng.* 2:50, 1925.

TOURTELLOTTE, W. W., HAERER, A. F., HELLER, G. L. and SOMERS, J. E.   Post-Lumbar Puncture Headaches.   Springfield, Ill., Charles C Thomas 1964.

TURNER, O., and BYRNE, V. C.   The Queckenstedt test: A consideration of the method of application and the nursing problems related to it.   *Yale J. Biol. & Med.* 12:737, 1940.

VON STORCH, T. J. C., CARMICHAEL, E. A., and BANKS, T. E.   Factors producing lumbar cerebrospinal fluid pressure in man in the erect posture.   *Arch. Neurol. & Psychiat.* 38:1158, 1937.

WHITE, D. N., and FYLES, S.   Cerebrospinal fluid manometry.   *Canad. M. A. J.* 62:384, 1950.

WISE, B. L., and CHATER, N.   Effect of mannitol on cerebrospinal fluid pressure.   *Arch. Neurol.* 4:200, 1961.

EXAMINATION OF THE CEREBROSPINAL FLUID

UNDER MOST CIRCUMSTANCES spinal puncture is carried out for the purpose of examining the cerebrospinal fluid; the physical, cytologic, chemical, serologic, and bacteriologic compositions of the fluid are observed as a part of the diagnosis of nervous system and somatic disease. As was stated above, two specimens are usually obtained. One tube, with 1 to 2 cc. of fluid, is used for the cell count, Pandy test, and qualitative glucose determination. Another, containing 6 to 8 cc., is used for the total protein determination, the serologic tests for syphilis, and the colloidal gold reaction. If other examinations, such as electrophoresis, quantitative glucose or chloride determinations, cultures, or special diagnostic procedures are indicated, additional fluid is obtained in other tubes.

Normal spinal fluid is a clear, colorless liquid. Its specific gravity is low, from 1.006 to 1.009, and that of ventricular fluid is even lower (1.002–1.004); the specific gravity is increased with elevation of the protein content and presence of abnormal constituents. It is slightly alkaline in reaction, with a pH of from 7.3 to 7.4 (about the same as that of the blood). Its total solids constitute about 1 per cent, and the water content is about 99 per cent. The freezing point is from 0.53° to 0.58° C., with an average of 0.57° C. There are about three to five mononuclear cells per cu. mm. The various chemical tests are listed below. The serologic tests for syphilis, colloidal gold reaction, and related procedures give normal results. No organisms are present.

PHYSICAL EXAMINATION OF THE CEREBROSPINAL FLUID

The appearance of the fluid is noted with the naked eye. This is done most satisfactorily if the fluid is held up to the light against a dark background. If there is slight discoloration, this is sometimes more apparent against a white background. Moderate changes in color and turbidity may often be evaluated by comparing the spinal fluid with a like amount of clear water in a similar tube, or by observing the fluid by looking through the depth of the tube. The presence of foam on shaking may indicate the presence of pathologic fluid.

As was stated above, the normal cerebrospinal fluid is clear and colorless. Physical alterations may be present in the form of either color change or turbidity. The most common physical change in a *pinkish to red discoloration*. This usually indicates the presence of blood or blood pigments in the fluid, and in every case in which such discoloration is found it is essential to determine whether such blood was present before the puncture was carried out (subarachnoid or intracerebral hemorrhage) or whether the blood entered the fluid at the time of the puncture ("traumatic tap" or venipuncture). Even the most skilled technician, performing a puncture under the most favorable circumstances, may occasionally traumatize some of the small vertebral, meningeal, or other veins and obtain fluid which is contaminated by the presence of blood. The following criteria may be used to differentiate between a "bloody tap" and subarachnoid and related bleeding: *Three to four specimens of fluid are obtained.* If the blood is present as a result of trauma during the puncture, each consecutive tube will be progressively more clear than the preceding one, and the last one may be colorless, and there will be a progressive fall in the erythrocyte and hemoglobin content of the serial tubes. Spinal fluid appears colorless to the naked eye if it contains fewer than 360 erythrocytes per cu. mm. On the other hand, if there had been a subarachnoid hemorrhage, each tube will be equally discolored. *The fluid is centrifuged.* If the blood is fresh and traumatic, it will not be mixed with the fluid; the supernatant fluid will be clear and colorless (unless the amount of blood is excessive) and the benzidine test done on it will be negative. If there had been subarachnoid bleeding, the supernatant fluid will be xanthochromic (see below). *The fluid is allowed to stand.* Blood present as a result of trauma may clot (if the erythrocyte count exceeds 200,000), whereas that from a subarachnoid hemorrhage will not. *The erythrocytes are examined under a microscope.* The cells present as a result of recent trauma will appear as normal, biconcave disks (if examined immediately); the cells present from subarachnoid hemorrhage will be seen to be crenated. *The puncture is repeated at a higher level or on the following day.* The fluid should be clear if blood was present only as a contaminant. It is important to bear in mind the following: traumatic and subarachnoid bleeding may both be present; the lumbar fluid may be clear for a period of up to two hours after a spontaneous subarachnoid hemorrhage, but will be uniformly bloody thereafter; if normal fluid in the subarachnoid space is grossly contaminated by a traumatic venipuncture, some blood may be apparent for as long as two to five days after the original puncture.

The next most common type of discoloration of the spinal fluid is *xanthochromia,* or the appearance of a yellow color. This occurs with subarachnoid hemorrhage, and is seen in the supernatant fluid both soon after such a hemorrhage and also during convalescence, long after the gross and microscopic blood have disappeared. It is not present immediately, but develops within three or four hours; it assumes its greatest intensity in about a week (the erythrocytes begin to disappear within two or three days), and may last for three to four weeks. Xanthochromia is also seen in association with the excessive protein content of fluid removed below a spinal subarachnoid block. In *Froin's syndrome* there is xanthochromia with increased protein, often to such a degree that the fluid clots spontaneously, and with or without pleocytosis. This is usually found in complete spinal subarachnoid block due to the presence of spinal cord tumor, arachnoiditis with adhesions, hypertrophic pachymeningitis, Pott's disease, or traumatic compression of the spinal cord. Xanthochromia is also present, on occasion, in polyradiculoneuritis, acute and chronic meningitis, subdural hematoma, brain tumor, recent infarcts, progressive brain and spinal cord lesions, and other conditions in which there is excessive protein without block. It has been stated that the fluid always has a faint yellowish discoloration when compared with water if the protein content is more than 100 to 150 mg. per cu. mm.

A slight xanthochromia has been reported in the spinal fluids of a large percentage of premature and newborn infants; this gradually disappears within one month. In jaundice, whether associated with liver disease of various types, biliary obstruction, or hemolytic anemia, the spinal fluid is discolored along with other body fluids; both the direct and indirect van den Bergh tests may give positive results. Other conditions in which the color of body fluids is altered (carotenemia) may show similar changes in the cerebrospinal fluid. With meningeal melanosarcomatosis the fluid may be deeply colored. The supernatant fluid following a traumatic puncture will be xanthochromic if the fluid contains more than 150,000 to 200,000 erythrocytes per cu. mm., if the protein content had been excessive prior to contamination, or if the tube had been washed with a markedly hemolytic substance such as a detergent. Xanthochromia and traumatic bleeding may be present simultaneously.

Spectrophotometric examinations of xanthochromic cerebrospinal fluids have shown that the discoloration is due to the presence of both protein and products of red blood cell disintegration, namely oxyhemoglobin, bilirubin, and, more rarely, methemoglobin. *Oxyhemoglobin,* which is red but with dilution varies from orange to orange-yellow, is the first pigment to appear after subarachnoid hemorrhage; it is a product of hemolysis and may be found within two hours of onset. It increases rapidly, becoming maximal in the first few days, and gradually diminishes over a week or ten days if no further bleeding occurs. Its presence may be ascertained by a positive benzidine test. *Bilirubin,* the iron-free derivative of hemoglobin, is yellow in color. It also appears in hemorrhagic fluids following hemolysis of erythrocytes; it is first apparent in two or three days and increases as the amount of oxyhemoglobin decreases. It may persist for two or three weeks. Bilirubin is also the predominant pigment present in the spinal fluid in cases of subarachnoid (and ventricular) block, the result of transudation from blood plasma, and is the only pigment detected in the fluid in jaundice and liver disease. With subarachnoid block, however, it is accompanied by excessive protein, whereas with jaundice the protein content is normal. The presence of bilirubin may be confirmed by a positive van den Bergh reaction. *Methemoglobin,* which is brown but yellow with dilution, is found most commonly in fluids from subdural and intracerebral hematomas and in fluids near encapsulated blood; its presence can be confirmed by a postassium cyanide test. Although the supernatant fluid is usually clear in traumatic punctures, it has been shown that oxyhemoglobin may be found by spectrophotometry if there are more than 12,000 erythrocytes per cubic millimeter. It has been reported that xanthochromia may also be caused by the presence of lipidlike substances resulting from the breakdown of nervous tissue, but this has not been confirmed.

The cerebrospinal fluid may vary from *opalescent to turbid* in appearance owing to the presence of foreign or pathologic matter; this is usually the result of an increase in cellular content (more than 500 cells per cubic millimeter), the presence of organisms or fibrin, an increase in globulin or protein, or contamination by blood. Degenerated cells are especially apt to cause the fluid to be turbid in appearance. A slightly bloody fluid may be turbid as well as discolored, and a grossly bloody fluid is opaque. In tuberculous meningitis, with a moderate increase in cells (mainly lymphocytes), the fluid may vary from a ground-glass appearance to opalescence. In suppurative meningitis, with a marked increase in cells along with organisms and protein, the fluid may be cloudy or purulent, and may have a yellow or green discoloration. If the fluid is opalescent or cloudy, meningitis should be suspected and additional specimens should always be obtained for direct bacteriologic examination, cultures, and quantitative glucose tests, and some should be set aside for observation of a pellicle formation. Fat globules have been demonstrated in the cerebrospinal fluid in cases of traumatic fat embolism.

In certain conditions, such as tuberculous meningitis and other diseases in which there is an increase in protein, a *pellicle* or *fibrin web* appears if the fluid is allowed to stand. The fluid should be set aside for this purpose immediately after it has been drawn; it may be either left at room temperature or placed in a refrigerator. The formation of a pellicle or web indicates the presence of fibrinogen or fibrin ferment. A fine cobweb-like pellicle appears in tuberculous and other subacute meningitides, and occasionally in poliomyelitis and brain tumor; a coarse fibrin clot is seen in the acute meningitides. Cells and organisms, if present, may be studied more advantageously by examination of this web.

If the protein content is sufficiently increased, the entire specimen may solidify. This occurs in xanthochromic fluid, the Guillain-Barré syndrome, Froin's syndrome, and meningitis. The clot may be jelly-like in appearance. It may be possible to precipitate the clotting by adding a single drop of blood to the spinal fluid.

CYTOLOGIC EXAMINATION OF THE CEREBROSPINAL FLUID

The spinal fluid normally contains no erythrocytes and fewer than five cells of the leukocyte group (mononuclear cells or possibly lymphocytes) per cubic millimeter. The count is slightly lower in cisternal and ventricular fluid. The determination of the presence, number, and kind of cells is an essential part of every spinal fluid examination. The cell count should be done at once, or within one hour after the fluid has been drawn, since with longer standing the cells may adhere to the walls of the specimen tube or become disintegrated, making the estimation inaccurate. The cell count is usually carried out in the improved Neubauer or Thoma-Zeiss blood counting chamber; if available, a Fuchs-Rosenthal chamber may be used. If the fluid appears to be clear, it is not diluted and the number of cells in the entire chamber is noted. Since the ruled surface of the Neubauer or Thoma-Zeiss chamber (the nine large squares) has an area of nine square millimeters and a depth of $1/10$ millimeter, to obtain the number of cells in one cubic millimeter of fluid, the number of cells counted is multiplied by $10/9$. If the number of cells is too great to count satisfactorily without dilution, the fluid is diluted with the usual acetic acid solution that is used for leukocyte counts on the blood, and the cell content determined proportionately. If red blood cells are present, their number should also be noted, diluting the fluid if necessary. Then the erythrocytes are eliminated by rinsing the pipette in glacial acetic acid several times before drawing spinal fluid into it. This dissolves the erythrocytes, and a cell count repeated after this should show only white blood cells. The fluid is allowed to stand in the pipette for two or three minutes, the first few drops are discarded, and the count is made on the next drop. The fluid is undiluted (except for the volatile acetic acid) and the red cells are either hemolyzed or badly crenated. This procedure should also be carried out whenever a count of more than six cells is made.

Many alternative methods of performing the cell count on the spinal fluid are in use. Many clinicians add a drop of some stain such as thionin, methylene blue, gentian violet, or Unna's polychrome methylene blue to the fluid. These aid in the differentiation between the leukocytes and the erythrocytes inasmuch as they stain the nuclei of the former but do not affect the latter; they also aid in the differentiation between mononuclear and polymorphonuclear cells. If stain is used in making the routine cell count, it may be possible to do an approximate differential estimation in the counting chamber. Others use both acetic acid, to dissolve the red cells, and stain. The dilute acetic acid solution used for white blood counts usually contains a small amount of stain. An ordinary pipette, such as is employed for blood leukocyte counts, is filled to the 1.0 mark with acetic acid, and then to the 11 mark with spinal fluid. The fluid and the diluent are shaken in the pipette for one minute, they are allowed to stand for two minutes, the first few drops are discarded, and then a drop is applied to the counting chamber. At least two counts are made, and an average is taken. The total is multiplied by $10/9$, since $9/10$ of a cubic millimeter were counted, and again by $11/10$ to compensate for the dilution. If the Fuchs-Rosenthal chamber is used, the total count of cells from undiluted fluid is divided by 3.2 to obtain the number per cubic millimeter.

The cells normally found in the spinal fluid are mononuclear in type. Some of these may be lymphocytes, but the majority are probably mesothelial cells derived from the meninges, the ependymal lining of the ventricles, and the perivascular spaces of Virchow-Robin. In disease states other cells are present, including lymphocytes, neutrophils, eosinophils, plasma cells, and fibroblasts. They may be hematogenous in origin, or may be derived from the meninges or perivascular spaces. A count of from five to ten cells is considered borderline, and one of over ten, definitely elevated. An increased number of cells in the cerebrospinal fluid is known as a *pleocytosis;* this may be lymphocytic, polymorphonuclear, or mixed. The presence of 5 to 10 cells is known as a slight pleocytosis; 25 to 50 cells indicate a moderate pleocytosis; 50 to 250, a severe pleocytosis; more than 250, an extreme pleocytosis.

If there is an increase in the number of cells present (six or more), a smear should be made and stained with gentian violet, methylene blue, Wright's, or some related stain, and a differential count made. If the fluid is purulent or the pleocytosis is marked, the smear is made directly from the fluid; if a pellicle is present, it is stained; if there is no opalesence and the cell count is not excessive, one should centrifuge the fluid, decant the supernatant, and place some sediment on a slide and allow it to dry. The preparation may be fixed by drying, but better fixation is obtained by adding either egg albumen or commercial albumin. If meningitis is suspected, a Gram or Ziehl-Neelsen stain may be made at the same time. A careful study of the stained smear may be essential to the diagnosis of the disease process. It is possible to differentiate lymphocytes, neutrophils, eosinophils, monocytes, and phagocytes. In addition it is sometimes possible to identify tumor cells, Cryptococci, actinomycotic granules, and fragments of Echinococci and Cysticerci. In estimating the number of cells present, one should always be aware of the fact that tumor or yeast cells may resemble leukocytes under the low-power objective of the microscope. Special technics, such as staining with India ink, may aid in identifying Cryptococci. If the presence of tumor cells is suspected, the fluid should be centrifuged and the sediment fixed and stained. In every case of suspected meningitis the fluid should be cultured.

Red blood cells may be present in the cerebrospinal fluid as the result either of *disease* or of *trauma* to the vertebral or meningeal vessels at the time the puncture was performed. With the latter the cells may appear normal if examined immediately, but crenation occurs promptly. Blood may be present in substantial amount in the case of subarachnoid and intraventricular hemorrhages, as well as in a large percentage of intracerebral hemorrhages, and occasionally in association with subdural hematomas and extradural hemorrhages. Blood is also found in the spinal fluid in posttraumatic states (cerebral contusions and lacerations), brain tumor (especially a vascular or degerating neoplasm), subarachnoid or meningeal angiomatosis or hemangiomatosis, meningeal inflammations with congestion of the meningeal vessels and diapedesis of cells through their walls, congestion of the meningeal vessels in association with spinal cord tumor or subarachnoid block, blood dyscrasias, and hemorrhagic encephalopathy or myelopathy. In general, if the cerebrospinal fluid is contaminated by large amounts of blood as a result of trauma at the time of the puncture, it is best to centrifuge the fluid, and to decant the supernatant fluid and use only that for the various diagnostic tests. A cell count can never be considered accurate if the fluid is contaminated by the presence of blood. On occasion, however, an approximate correction for the blood cells may be made as follows:

$$\frac{Leukocytes \text{ (blood)} \times Erythrocytes \text{ (fluid)}}{Erythrocytes \text{ (blood)}} = Leukocytes \text{ (fluid)}$$

It has been stated that about one white cell per cubic millimeter is added to the fluid by enough blood to add 600 to 700 red cells to such a unit.

A *pleocytosis,* or an increase in the number of the leukocytes in the cerebrospinal fluid, usually indicates the presence of meningeal irritation, but not necessarily meningeal infection. Whether these cells are polymorphonuclear, lymphocytic, or mixed depends upon the type of irritation, the nature and site of the pathologic process, and the nature of the infecting organism. The presence of polymorphonuclear cells is indicative of an acute process or an exacerbation of a chronic inflammation caused by a pyogenic organism. The process is usually close to or involves the meninges and ependyma, but polymorphonuclear cells may be present in association with a pyogenic infection in the neighborhood of the meninges (in the mastoid cells, or within the brain tissue), with no actual contamination of the meninges. The presence of lymphocytes usually indicates either a chronic or low grade inflammatory process (not necessarily due to infection) of the meninges or ependyma, a more extensive process at some distance from the meninges and ependyma, or an inflammation caused by a neurotropic virus. A mixed pleocytosis suggests that the process is a subacute one. The presence of eosinophils is usually considered pathognomonic of an infection by parasites, yeast, or fungi, or of an allergic or a foreign body reaction.

A *slight to moderate lymphocytic pleocytosis* (5 to 50 cells) is found in a variety of diseases, some of the more important of which are as follows: syphilitic involvement of the central nervous system and/or meninges; multiple sclerosis; viral infections of the central nervous system and/or meninges (viral encephalitis and meningitis, poliomyelitis, rabies, herpes zoster); brain or spinal cord tumors near the meninges or ependyma; sterile or toxic meningitis following the intraspinal injection of serum, air, novocaine, iodized oil, penicillin, or streptomycin, or in association with the presence of blood in the subarachnoid spaces; aseptic meningitis associated with some focus of infection within the cranium, such as sinus thrombosis, mastoid disease, brain abscess, subdural and epidural abscesses, or osteomyelitis; trauma to the central nervous system; cerebrovascular disease (cerebral infarction secondary to thrombosis or embolism, arteriosclerosis); subdural hematoma toxic processes or degenerative diseases of obscure etiology; tetanus; some varieties of polyneuritis; central nervous system complications of systematic diseases such as malaria, mumps, measles, whooping cough, vaccinia, varicella, lymphogranuloma venereum, infectious mononucleosis, Weil's disease, undulant fever, sarcoidosis, or the collagen disorders; reactions to yeasts, fungi, and parasites; meningeal carcinomatosis and leukemic infiltrations. There is often a slight pleocytosis in premature and newborn infants, which disappears by three months.

A *severe to extreme lymphocytic pleocytosis* (50 to 500 or more cells) is observed in chronic to subacute inflammations of the meninges. The more important conditions in which such a cell change occurs include tuberculous, syphilitic and cryptococcal meningitis, lymphocytic choriomeningitis, and trypamosomiasis. Occasionally with brain tumors which are near the meninges or ependyma, aseptic meningitis, viral encephalitis, herpes zoster, carcinomatous meningitis, infections by fungi and parasites, and the meningoencephalitides and encephalomyelitides associated with the systemic diseases listed above the pleocytosis may be severe rather than moderate. In none, or almost none, of these conditions with a moderate to severe pleocytosis is the increase in cells entirely an elevation in the number of lymphocytes, and the percentage of polymorphonuclear cells present may give some clue in regard to the activity or the chronicity of the process.

A *polymorphonuclear pleocytosis* of mild degree is rarely seen except in the preparalytic stage of poliomyelitis, where there may be from 50 to 100 or even more polymorphonuclear cells. Occasionally there is a slight increase in neutrophils in cases of vascular disease or trauma without bloody spinal fluid, and in status epilepticus and insulin coma. If there is an increase in polymorphonuclear cells, however, it is usually to a marked degree, varying from 500 to 5000 or more. This is indicative of a suppurative meningitis, usually of a coccus origin, namely the meningococcic, streptococcic, pneumococcic, or staphylococcic varieties, but it is occasionally seen in influenzal meningitis. If a large number of cells is found, with a high percentage of neutrophils, a tentative diagnosis of acute meningitis must be made. In such cases additional tests such as stained smears, cultures, and glucose determinations are essential. If organisms are found or the sugar is low, the case must be treated as one of purulent meningitis. If no organisms are found and the glucose is normal, it is probable that the patient has an aseptic meningitis in association with some process such as brain abscess or sinus thrombosis.

A *mixed pleocytosis,* with increase in both lymphocytes and polymorphonuclear cells, usually indicates a subacute meningeal inflammation, and is found in influenzal meningitis, the more malignant varieties of tuberculous meningitis, and in aseptic meningitis associated with brain abscess or some other intracranial infection. The relative percentage of polymorphonuclear cells and lymphocytes is indicative of the activity of the infection. In late tuberculous meningitis the proportion of neutrophils may be increased to one third or more. In early poliomyelitis the pleocytosis may be a mixed one.

Carcinomatous meningitis may be difficult to differentiate from the infectious meningitis; the cellular response may be similar in the two conditions, and the glucose content is low in both. If the diagnosis is suspected, special stains of the concentrated sediment (Wright, Leishman, or Papanicolaou) and occasionally paraffin fixation with tissue-staining technics are indicated. Some of the cells first thought to have been lymphocytes or monocytes may be found to be neoplastic instead, but more characteristic are larger cells with multiple nuclei and mitotic figures (Fig. 328). Such cells are occasionally found with primary tumors of the nervous system, but more commonly with metastatic involvement. Large, vacuolated foam cells have been observed in the spinal fluid of patients with Tay-Sachs disease and following myelography.

CHEMICAL EXAMINATION OF THE CEREBROSPINAL FLUID

The chemical examination of the cerebrospinal fluid includes many different determinations, but the most important from a clinical point of view are the estimation of the protein, glucose, and chloride contents.

THE PROTEIN CONTENT

The total protein of the spinal fluid normally ranges from 15 to 40 mg. per 100 cc. (in contrast to the blood serum protein of from 6.3 to 8 gm. per 100 cc.). This varies, however, with the site from which the fluid is obtained, and the above figure applies to the lumbar fluid; that obtained from the cisterna magna has from 10

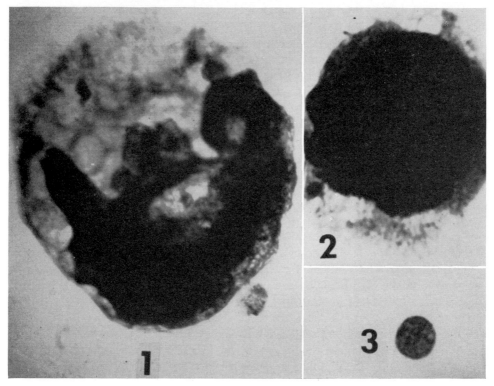

FIG. 328.   Cells found in cerebrospinal fluid of patient with metastatic malignant melanoma: 1, and 2, neoplastic cells; 3, normal mononuclear cell; Wright's stain. (Courtesy of Dr. W. W. Tourtellotte.)

to 25 mg. of protein, that from the ventricles, 5 to 15 mg. The protein content of the fluid is normally lower in children and slightly higher in elderly persons. It is said to be slightly higher in males than in females. Some clinicians consider a protein content of up to 35 mg. as normal, 35 to 50 mg. as borderline, and over 50 mg. as abnormal. The cerebrospinal fluid protein consists mainly of albumin and globulin, with the former somewhat in excess in the normal state. These can be partitioned into fractions, such as the alpha, beta, and gamma globulins, and further into subfractions. A significant change in the ratio of these constituents can occur without an increase in the total protein content.

Many tests for protein in the spinal fluid have been described. They may be classed as qualitative, to indicate merely an excess of either globulin or albumin, and quantitative, to indicate the total protein but not the relative amount of the two factors.

The *qualitative protein tests* should be carried out by the clinician immediately after the puncture is completed. Although they do not give numerical results regarding the amount of protein present, they are of help in neurologic diagnosis, and at least one of them should be performed as a screening test.

The Pandy Test: The Pandy test is used most commonly. It is carried out by placing one or two drops of cerebrospinal fluid in 1 cc. of a saturated solution of phenol (carbolic acid). Normally there is no change in the appearance of the solution, or only a very faint opalescence. If there is an increase in the protein content of the fluid (especially globulin), a white or smoke-like cloud will be seen descending in the phenol solution as the spinal fluid drops through it. If there is a marked increase in protein, the entire solution will take on a bluish opalescence. It is important that the solution be crystal clear and thoroughly saturated. If it has deteriorated or taken on water, it may appear cloudy and give a falsely positive reaction. The Pandy solution should be replaced if test results do not correlate with quantitative protein determinations.

The Ross-Jones and Nonne-Apelt Tests: These tests, which consist of the addition of cerebrospinal fluid to a saturated solution of ammonium sulphate, are used less frequently today. The formation of an opaque ring when the fluid is superimposed on the solution, or of a cloudy white precipitate when the two are mixed, indicates the presence of increased globulin. The presence of a white precipitate after boiling the two together for three minutes indicates the presence of an excessive amount of albumin.

Other qualitative tests include the Heller's ring test (using nitric acid), Noguchi's test (precipitation of protein by use of butyric acid), and Weichbrodt's reaction (precipitation of protein by use of mercuric chloride).

The *quantitative protein tests* are usually carried out in clinical laboratories. The clinician does not perform them, but should be able to interpret them. The reliability depends upon the laboratory in which the test is carried out. For most accurate quantitative examination the protein is precipitated by various agents, and then the nitrogen content of the precipitate is determined by some modification of the Kjeldahl method. Such testing is complicated and tedious, however, and in the past the accuracy has been questionable if the amount of protein is small. Recently developed microtechnics give accurate results but are not as yet practicable for routine clinical testing. Other technics include colorimetric (Matz and Novick), nephelometric or turbimetric (Denis and Ayer, Exton and Rose), biuret and ninhydrin reactions, gravimetric and volumetric determinations, and ultraviolet photometry. Among the most widely used methods are modifications of the Denis-Ayer sulphosalcylic acid technic and of the Lowry colorimetric method in which the Folin phenol reagent is used after alkaline copper treatment of the protein. Spectrophotometry is also used for quantitative protein determinations.

It is often important to determine not only the total protein content of the spinal fluid, but also the quantitative albumin and globulin fractions, the albumin-globulin ratio, and the individual globulin components. These have been differentiated and analyzed by photometric technics, paper chromatography, electrophoresis on various supporting media (paper, starch, agar gel, polyacrylamide gel), and immunoassays and immunochemical procedures whereby the albumin and globulins are precipitated by specific antisera and then separated by immunoelectrophoresis and microelectrophoresis and by double diffusion (Ouchterlony) technics. Most of these procedures are too complex to be practicable for routine diagnostic studies, but are important research methods by which the more detailed chemistry of the cerebrospinal fluid is being investigated. By some of these same technics additional information has been brought forth about the presence and quantity of paraproteins, free amino acids, glycoproteins, and lipoproteins in the spinal fluid.

The protein content of the cerebrospinal fluid is increased in many diseases of the meninges and nervous system. In fact, an elevation of the proteins or an alteration of the protein quotient under most circumstances indicates the presence of an organic disease of the central nervous system or its membranes. Many factors are responsible. With either gross or microscopic blood in the spinal fluid there is direct invasion of the subarachnoid channels by blood proteins. With inflammatory processes and associated congestion of the meningeal and other vessels there is an increased permeability of the blood vessel walls allowing transudation of blood proteins into the spinal fluid. With edema of the nervous tissues and meninges there may be transudation of serum from the perineural spaces. With damage to or destruction of nervous tissue in encephalomalacia, trauma, or degenerative or neoplastic processes there may be either actual formation of protein or release of it to the spinal fluid pathways, although edema, congestion, and hemorrhage may instead be the responsible mechanisms. With stagnation or blockage of the spinal fluid there may be both increased permeability and decreased absorption of proteins. There is always an elevation of the protein content of the fluid in association with an increase in the cellular constituents, and especially with cellular disintegration and the presence of organisms. Except when associated with blood, cells, or organisms, increased protein comes mainly from the blood vessels and perineural spaces. With a marked elevation of protein there may be spontaneous clotting and xanthochromia (Froin's syndrome).

Among those conditions (mainly meningeal and neurologic, but including some systemic disorders) in which an elevation of the cerebrospinal fluid protein is a significant and more or less consistent finding are the following: acute and chronic meningeal inflammations, carcinomatous meningitis, reactive and aseptic meningitides, arachnoiditis, acute and chronic encephalitides, poliomyelitis (especially in the postparalytic phase), central nervous system syphilis (tabes dorsalis, dementia paralytica, meningovascular syphilis, and asymptomatic central nervous system syphilis), brain neoplasms and abscesses (especially if near the meninges or ventricles, or if they obstruct the flow of blood or cerebrospinal fluid), vascular malformations and neoplasms (angiomas, arteriovenous anomalies, aneurysms), subarachnoid and cerebral hemorrhage, posttraumatic states, subdural hematoma, multiple sclerosis, certain of the leukodystrophies and degenerative diseases of the brain and/or spinal cord, leprosy, diphtheritic and diabetic polyneuropathies (and occasionally in diabetes without neurologic involvement), some chronic progressive neuropathies, myxedema, hyperparathyroidism, multiple myeloma, spondylitis, and rheumatoid arthritis. There is a marked increase in the protein content in the lumbar fluid below a spinal cord tumor or other causes for spinal subarachnoid block, probably due to stagnation as well as transudation, but there may be an increase in the protein content above the level of the block as well, probably due to congestion of the meninges. This same factor may be responsible for the increase in protein in the spinal fluid in many cases of herniation of a nucleus polposus in the lumbosacral region, even though the fluid is obtained from above the level of the herniation. In certain types of polyneuritis or polyradiculoneuritis, especially in the Guillain-Barré syndrome, there may be an outstanding elevation in protein without a parallel pleocytosis (albuminocytologic dissociation). Similar dissociations, however, may also be observed with spinal cord tumors, some brain tumors, and postparalytic poliomyelitis. There may be a moderate elevation of the protein with nonhemorrhagic vascular disease (either diffuse cerebrospinal arteriosclerosis or focal involvement such as cerebral thrombosis), certain of the slowly progressive cerebral degenerations, and some of the toxic and metabolic encephalopathies, as well as after convulsive seizures. The protein is also moderately elevated in premature and newborn infants, but assumes normal values at the age of two or three months. It has been said that a certain percentage of patients with so-called functional psychoses (schizophrenia, manic-depressive psychosis, and involutional melancholia) show an increase in the protein content of the spinal fluid, but there is no actual confirmation for this. Occasionally no cause is found for elevated protein. The spinal fluid protein is diminished in children in the early stages of acute infections, in meningismus, and in some types of communicating hydrocephalus. If a large amount of fluid is removed, the protein content of the last specimens is lower than that of the first (i.e., the fluid is obtained from higher levels, and probably from the ventricles).

The statement has been made that a moderate increase in the protein content of the cerebrospinal fluid in the presence of nonorganic diseases of the nervous system may indicate poor technic in performing the puncture. If the needle is inserted too far and the venous plexus along the anterior wall of the spinal canal is irritated, there may be a slight oozing of plasma which will cause a false increase in the protein content of the fluid. If gross blood is present in the fluid as a result of actual trauma to the venous plexus while performing the puncture, a correction can be made for the protein content contributed by the blood by subtracting 1 mg. of protein per 100 cc. for every 750 erythrocytes per cubic millimeter of fluid.

The differential quantitative determination of the albumin and globulin fractions of the spinal fluid and often the specific globulin components, as well as an appraisal of the albumin-globulin ratio, is important in the study of certain diseases of the nervous system. In dementia paralytica, tabes dorsalis, and multiple sclerosis there may be a marked increase in the spinal fluid globulin without an associated elevation of albumin (which may even be decreased) or a distinct change in the total protein; the albumin-globulin ratio is accordingly decreased. In these diseases the globulin component that is most characteristically elevated is the gamma globulin, which is considered to present in excessive amounts if it constitutes over 15 per cent of the spinal fluid protein, and such an elevation has been reported in 73 per cent of the patients with multiple sclerosis. This is thought to be significant in the colloidal reactions (see below). The gamma globulin may also be increased in tuberculous meningitis and polyradiculoneuritis, whereas the beta globulin is elevated in the acute meningitides, with neoplasms, and occasionally with vascular disease. Further fractionation of the various globulin constituents may give important information about diseases of the nervous system. Fibrinogen is occasionally found in the spinal fluid, but its presence is usually associated with an elevation of the total protein.

Glycoproteins and lipoproteins have been found to be elevated with some neoplastic, vascular, and inflammatory diseases of the nervous system, but such changes have not been found to be specific for any of these disorders.

THE GLUCOSE CONTENT

The glucose content of the cerebrospinal fluid is said to be from one half to two thirds of the glucose content of the blood plasma (80 to 120 mg. per 100 cc.). The normal values are usually considered to be from 50 to 65 mg. per 100 cc., although some authorities believe values as high as 80 mg. to be within the physiologic range. The glucose content is higher in ventricular fluid, although not as high as in the blood. A rapid qualitative test for glucose can be carried out by adding 16 to 20 drops of spinal fluid (twice the amount used for determination of glucose in the urine) to 4 cc. of the Benedict's qualitative glucose solution and boiling for five minutes. A normal reduction of the solution is seen by the presence of a small amount of reddish precipitate at the bottom of the tube. If there is decreased sugar, there is a faint yellowish green color, or no change whatever. With increased glucose there is an increase in precipitation and color change. The determination should be made as soon as possible after withdrawing the spinal fluid, as the glucose may break down with standing. Colorimetric paper strips used for qualitative testing of the urine for glucose may also be employed. If there is any change from the normal in these qualitative tests, or if there is any reason for more accurate determinations, a quantitative determination should be made, using a modification of the Folin-Wu or Benedict tests on the blood for examining the spinal fluid. If a quantitative test is to be made, however, it is desirable under most circumstances to obtain a fasting specimen (i.e., before breakfast in the morning), and it is usually advisable to obtain simultaneous glucose determinations of the blood and spinal fluid. A normal value for the spinal fluid sugar, for instance, in association with an elevation of the blood sugar, may indicate a pathologic decrease in the glucose content of the spinal fluid.

The glucose content of the spinal fluid is most important, from a diagnostic point of view, if it is decreased. It may be decreased slightly in tabes dorsalis and dementia paralytica, but it is decreased to a major degree principally with inflammations and infiltrations of the meninges. Hypoglycorrhachia is an early and important diagnostic sign of meningitis. In tuerculous meningitis the spinal fluid sugar is often between 20 and 40 mg. and even lower in the terminal stages of the disease, and in the acute pyogenic meningitides it is often below 20 mg. The spinal fluid glucose is also decreased in some 60 per cent of cases of cryptococcal meningitis; it may be slightly decreased in syphilitic meningitis and sarcoidosis, but is usually normal in the viral, aseptic, and reactive meningitides. It is markedly decreased also in carcinomatous meningitis and in the meningitides associated with sarcomatosis and leukemia. It has been stated generally that the decrease of glucose in the spinal fluid in the bacterial, cryptococcal, and carcinomatous meningitides was the result of the glycolytic action of the organisms, yeasts, and tumor cells, and possibly, also, of the leukocytes. Fishman and others have demonstrated, however, that in carcinomatous meningitis, and probably in the inflammatory types as well, there is an interference with glucose transport across the infiltrated meningeal membranes and a decreased entry into the cerebrospinal fluid. Possibly both lack of transport and glycolosis play a part. The glucose content of the cerebrospinal fluid is also low in insulin shock and hyperinsulinism.

Increase in the glucose content of the spinal fluid is known as hyperglycorrhachia. An elevation of the glucose content of the spinal fluid usually occurs in association with elevation of the blood glucose. Consequently the spinal fluid glucose is increased in diabetes. It is sometimes elevated in nephritis and uremia, and it may be increased on occasion in association with increased intracranial pressure, brain tumor, hypothalamic lesions, hydrocephalus, senile psychoses, and epilepsy, and after cerebral trauma. The spinal fluid sugar is also elevated in certain of the acute encephalitides, namely Japanese type B encephalitis and the eastern and western varieties of equine encephalomyelitis, and elevations have been reported with von Economo's encephalitis and poliomyelitis. Some observers have questioned whether there is an actual increase in these virus infections, or whether the fact that there is no decrease in the glucose content in association with a pleocytosis aids in differentiating them from certain of the meningitides, but the evidence seems to indicate the presence of a definite hyperglycorrhachia in these disorders.

Although the statement has been made that the glucose content of the spinal fluid is from one half to two thirds that of the blood, and the two should always be examined simulaneously and compared, it has been found experimentally that there is a definite delay in the elevation of the cerebrospinal fluid glucose after a rise in the blood glucose content, and the proportional increase in the spinal fluid is much less than that in the blood. Alimentary hyperglycemia causes only a slight to moderate rise in the spinal fluid glucose, probably through a selective action of the choroid plexus in regulating the glucose content of the fluid, although there is a more pronounced elevation of the spinal fluid glucose accompanying the hyperglycemia produced by an injection of epinephrine. Simultaneous examinations of the glucose levels in the spinal fluid and blood are valuable, however, and these are best done in the fasting state because at this time the equilibrium between the blood and spinal fluid glucose contents are at physiologic levels. Recently there has also been some interest in the polysaccharides and glycoproteins in the spinal fluid, but mainly from a research point of view.

THE CHLORIDE CONTENT

The chloride content of the cerebrospinal fluid varies from 700 to 750 mg. per 100 cc., with an average of 726 mg., determined as sodium chloride, or 120 to 130 with an average of 124 expressed as milli-equivalents per liter. The chloride content is the only factor examined clinically that is significantly higher in the spinal fluid than in the blood (the blood plasma chlorides vary from 570 to 620 mg., with an average of 594 mg. per 100 cc., determined as sodium chloride, or 95 to 105 with an average of 101 milli-equivalents per liter). As is the case with the glucose determination, the chloride content should always be compared with that of the blood. The chlorides are also decreased in infections, especially infections of the meninges. They are slightly diminished in acute poliomyelitis, and definitely in many forms of meningitis, where they may vary from 630 to 680 mg. In tuberculous meningitis they frequently are decreased to from 520 to 610 mg., and may even be as low as 420 to 500 mg. This decrease in the chloride content of the spinal fluid is not necessarily characteristic of meningitis, however, since it occurs in all acute and chronic infections, including fevers and systemic infections without meningeal involvement, and it accompanies the decrease in blood chlorides which occurs in such conditions. There is also decrease in the blood and spinal fluid chlorides in severe vomiting and in Addison's disease. The chlorides are low in the spinal fluid in nephrosis, in association with low blood chlorides, but they are elevated in nephritis and uremia, due to impaired renal function and chloride retention in the blood. They may also be increased in dehydration and in cardiac insufficiency. In general the spinal fluid chloride content is a reflection of the blood chlorides, except in conditions where there is an elevation of the protein content of the spinal fluid; when the protein content of the fluid is increased, the chloride content decreases and the difference between the blood and cerebrospinal fluid chlorides is diminished.

OTHER CHEMICAL CONSTITUENTS

The above-mentioned are the major chemical constituents of the cerebrospinal fluid which are examined routinely, but there are other substances which may be investigated experimentally or in individual cases. On occasion determinations of the cerebrospinal fluid electrolytes and acid-base balance may give important information.

The *calcium* content of the spinal fluid varies from 4.5 to 5.5 mg. per 100 cc., with an average of 5 mg. (or values of 2.2 to 3.4 with an average of 2.7 expressed as milli-equivalents per liter). This is approximately one half of the blood serum content of 9 to 11 mg. per 100 cc. (4.5 to 6.0 milli-equivalents per liter). The calcium of the spinal fluid is decreased in conditions such as tetany in which the blood calcium is low, and is also said to be decreased on occasion in tetanus and tumors of the diencephalon. It is increased with elevation of the blood calcium (hyperparathyroidism), and is sometimes slightly increased in meningitis and other conditions in which there is an elevation of the spinal fluid proteins.

The *inorganic phosphorus* content of the spinal fluid is also about one half of the blood serum content, varying from 1.25 to 2.1 mg. per 100 cc., with an average of 1.53 mg. (The blood serum inorganic phosphorus varies between 2.5 and 4.5 mg. per 100 cc.). It is increased with increase in the blood phosphorus (tetany), in encephalitis, poliomyelitis, and other viral diseases of the nervous system, and in meningitis and other conditions in which there is an elevation of the protein content of the spinal fluid.

The *sodium* content of the cerebrospinal fluid varies from 301 to 343 mg. per 100 cc., with an average of 324 mg. (or values of from 130 to 152 with an average of 143 expressed as milli-equivalents per liter). This is slightly in excess of the normal blood serum sodium content, which averages about 316 mg. (138 milli-equivalents). The sodium content of the spinal fluid may be elevated in hypertension.

The *potassium* content of the spinal fluid varies from 9 to 14.5 mg. per 100 cc., with an average of 12 mg. (or values of 2.5 to 3.5 with an average of 3 milli-equivalents per liter). This is slightly lower than the blood serum potassium, which averages from 20 to 24 mg. per 100 cc. or 4.0 to 5.5 milli-equivalents per liter.

The *magnesium* content of the spinal fluid varies from 1 to 3.5 mg. per 100 cc., with an average of 2.5 mg. This is slightly higher than the blood plasma content which averages 2 mg. The magnesium content of the spinal fluid is said to be slightly elevated in purulent meningitis and slightly decreased in tuberculous meningitis.

There have been various statements about the *iron* content of the cerebrospinal fluid, but the usual range is from 23 to 52 micrograms per 100 cc., with an average of 35 micrograms. The iron values are lowered in tuberculous meningitis and also in the presence of increased cerebral metabolism. High values, said to indicate reduced cellular activity of brain tissue, have been reported in patients with organic psychoses.

The *bicarbonate* content of the cerebrospinal fluid averages 21 milli-equivalents per liter, about equal to the blood plasma content (23 milli-equivalents). The *total base* of the spinal fluid averages 157 milli-equivalents per liter, again about equal to the blood plasma content (155 milli-equivalents); it is increased in tuberculous meningitis and uremia, and is said occasionally to be elevated in schizophrenia and epilepsy. On occasion the acid-base balance, oxygen tension, carbon dioxide tension, and hydrogen ion concentration are also determined.

The *lactic acid* content of the cerebrospinal fluid averages from 9 to 25 mg. per 100 cc., about the same as that of the blood plasma.

The *nonprotein nitrogen* of the cerebrospinal fluid varies from 10 to 25 with an average of 19 mg. per 100 cc., or about two thirds that of the blood plasma (25 to 35 mg.). The *urea nitrogen* ranges from 8 to 17 mg. per 100 cc., or about the same as that of the blood plasma. The *creatinine* in the spinal fluid ranges from 0.5 to 2 with an average of 1.2 mg. per 100 cc., or about the same as that of the blood plasma. The *uric acid* of the spinal fluid ranges from 0.3 to 1.3 with an average of 0.7 mg. per 100 cc., in contrast to the blood serum uric acid of 3 to 5 with an average of 4 mg. The *ammonia* content of the spinal fluid averages 6.0 micrograms per 100 cc., whereas the blood ammonia is from 40 to 70 micrograms per 100 cc. All of the above increase, but not always proportionately, in uremia and other conditions in which the blood content is elevated. The parallel between the blood and spinal fluid urea content, however, is not as great as that of the others. In addition, the ammonia content is elevated in hepatic disease, and the uric acid content has been said to be elevated in association with cerebral atrophy.

There are certain special chemical tests which have been considered valuable in the diagnosis of specific diseases. Among these are the Levinson and tryptophan tests, both of which, when positive, are said to be pathognomonic of tuberculous meningitis. In the *Levinson test* the precipitation of proteins as albuminates when the cerebrospinal fluid is treated with certain metallic salts is compared with their precipitation as insoluble salts when it is treated with weak organic acids. It is said to be positive when the amount of precipitate with mercuric chloride is at least twice as great as that with sulphosalicylic acid. The test is positive in from 78 to 100 per cent of all cases of tuberculous meningitis, but also in certain cases of purulent meningitis and in other central nervous system affections. In the *tryptophan test* concentrated hydrochloric acid and formaldehyde are added to spinal fluid, following which sodium nitrite is layered over the solution. If the test is positive, a delicate violet ring appears at the junction of the fluids. This test, too, is positive in nearly 100 per cent of cases of tuberculous meningitis, but similar results may occur in the presence of blood, pus, or xanthochromia. It must be concluded that neither test positively confirms nor excludes the diagnosis of tuberculosis meningitis.

Many other chemical determinations may be performed under special circumstances. Benzidine and guaiac tests may be carried out for the presence of blood in the fluid. In certain toxic states determinations may be made for the presence of lead, alcohol, bromides, or barbiturates in the cerebrospinal fluid. Studies of the content and distribution of the various lipid constituents of the cerebrospinal fluid show promise of giving important information in the understanding and diagnosis of certain of the so-called degenerative diseases of the nervous system characterized by breakdown of myelin, as well as the lipidoses. Among the substances investigated are the total lipids, fatty acids, neutral fat, free and esterified cholesterol, phospholipids (cephalin, lecithin, and sphingomyelin), nonphosphorus sphingolipids (cerebrosides, sulfatides, and gangliosides), and the lipoproteins. By means of ultramicrochemical technics it is possible to differentiate and quantitate each of these.

Investigation of enzymes and enzyme activity in the cerebrospinal fluid, furthermore, may be important in both study and diagnosis of certain diseases of the nervous system. It is known that there is a high level of glutamic oxalacetic transaminase activity in the blood serum following liver damage, myocardial infarction, and other conditions characterized by tissue breakdown. Some observers have reported an elevation of transaminase activity in the cerebrospinal fluid following cerebral infarction and subarchnoid hemorrhage and in association with infections, tumors, multiple sclerosis, and cerebral atrophy, but the significance of this is not known since other investigators report that there is no apparent correlation between the transaminase level and the severity of the pathologic process, duration of illness, or the chemical and cytologic findings in the spinal fluid in degenerative, neoplastic, inflammatory, or vascular diseases of the nervous system. Levels of lactic dehydrogenase in the cerebrospinal fluid may also be elevated with some of the above-mentioned conditions, as well as with leukemia and carcinomatosis. An increased level of certain nucleases (ribonuclease and desoxyribonuclease) has been noted in the spinal fluid of patients with various diseases of the nervous system, but principally in acute meningitis and poliomyelitis. Increased levels of alkaline and acid phosphatases in the cerebrospinal fluid seem to be correlated with the concentration of protein and leukocytes in the fluid; these enzymes are often elevated in meningitis. Tests for other enzymes such as beta-glucuronidase, phosphohexase, isomerase, isocitric acid dehydrogenase, leucine aminopeptidase, cholinesterase, cerruloplasmin, amylase, catalase, diastase, lipase, oxidase, aldolase, and protease may sometimes be carried out, but the importance of changes in their levels of activity is not known. They may be related to alterations in the permeability of the blood-brain barrier, the presence of either blood or inflammatory cells in the spinal fluid, elevation of the protein level, anoxia, or hypoxia, or other pathologic abnormalities. At the time of this writing, changes in the levels of these enzymes have no specific diagnostic or prognostic significance.

Other chemicals that have been investigated in the cerebrospinal fluid include acetylcholine, serotonin, histamine, glutamine, indoles, polypeptides, and hexosamine. The spinal fluid alcohol content is elevated in cryptococcal meningitis, due to fermentation of glucose to alcohol, and the spinal fluid vitamin B_{12} content is decreased in pernicious anemia with neurologic manifestations. Some investigators have reported decreased levels of neuranimic acid in schizophrenia. On occasion it is valuable to perform special examinations for miningeal permeability and for the estimation of the blood-cerebrospinal fluid barrier. Most of the above-mentioned chemical determinations are still in experimental stages and not yet generally applicable clinically. At the present time they have little diagnostic or prognostic significance, but they are important from a research point of view and may in the future lead to important clinical advances.

Of late there has been an increasing interest in special physicochemical examinations, with electrophoretic methods, ultraspectrophotometric measurements, ultraviolet absorption studies, and electron microscopic observations of the chemical and cellular constituents of the spinal fluid. Many of these will doubtless reveal important information, but they are still in experimental stages and are not yet applicable clinically.

BACTERIOLOGIC EXAMINATION OF THE CEREBROSPINAL FLUID

In every case in which a smear of the spinal fluid is made and stained for the study of the cellular constituents, a careful search should be made for the presence of organisms. Under many circumstances an ordinary gentian violet or methylene blue stain will suffice, but if the spinal fluid picture is suggestive of a purulent meningitis, a Gram stain should always be made to differentiate meningococci (Gram negative, intracellular organisms) from streptococci, staphylococci, and pneumococci. If the latter are found, it may be important to type them. If there is a pleocytosis that is predominantly lymphocytic, a Ziehl-Neelsen stain should be made in the search for tubercle bacilli. In suspected cryptococcal meningitis the fluid is stained with India ink or fluorescein. Sometimes the examination for organisms is carried out more successfully if the fluid is first centrifuged, and the sediment examined, or, in the case of tuberculous meningitis, if a pellicle is allowed to form, and that is examined. The tubercle bacilli are very difficult to demonstrate in a large percentage of cases of tuberculous meningitis, although a few instances have been reported in which the organisms were found in the absence of significant chemical or cytologic changes in the fluid (serous tuberculous meningitis). Not only should the examiner search the smear closely for evidences of bacteria, especially cocci and bacilli, but also for evidences of yeasts, fungi, and parasites.

If no organisms are found on the examination of the direct smear, cultures and other studies are indicated in all cases that show evidence of meningeal infection. An ordinary pyogenic culture is sufficient in most cases of purulent meningitis, but special culture media are necessary in suspected tuberculous and other less common varieties of meningitis. Sabouraud's medium is used if cryptococcosis is suspected. After observing the growth in the culture, further smears and studies may be made to determine the identity of the infecting organism and its sensitivity to antibiotics. In brucellosis meningo-encephalitis, especially if caused by *Brucella melitensis,* var. *abortus,* the culture may have to be grown under anaerobic conditions. In every case of suspected tuberculous meningitis in which the diagnosis is not established on the basis of the direct smear, guinea pig inoculations should be made. In must always be borne in mind, in view of the present-day advances in the treatment of meningitis, that cultures should be started before the administration of sulfonamides, penicillin, or streptomycin, or other antibiotics has been instituted. Further bacteriologic examinations include agglutination, precipitation, complement-fixation, neutralization, and flocculation tests for investigation of special organisms. In suspected invasion by neurotropic ultramicroscopic viruses, such as those of the St. Louis and Japanese B types of encephalitis, lymphocytic choriomeningitis, and the eastern and western varieties of equine encephalomyelitis, complement-fixation and neutralization tests should be carried out on the blood during the acute and convalescent stages of the disease. In these, as well as in poliomyelitis, the virus can on occasion be isolated from the cerebrospinal fluid by special cultures and intercerebral inoculations of experimental animals.

SEROLOGIC AND COLLOIDAL EXAMINATIONS OF THE CEREBROSPINAL FLUID

SEROLOGIC TESTS FOR SYPHILIS

Too often, in the analysis of the spinal fluid made in commercial and public health laboratories, the principal if not only examination made is one of the specific tests for syphilis, either the Wassermann or the Kahn reaction. Although each of these is an exceedingly important diagnostic procedure, it is but one part of the examination of the cerebrospinal fluid. Even in the diagnosis of syphilis alone, the cell count, qualitative and quantitative protein determinations, and colloidal reactions have equal importance and may give essential information regarding the activity of the disease process. It so happens, however, that in fluid which must be shipped elsewhere for examination the cell count is unreliable, and some of the other chemical studies may also lose their value.

Most of the serologic tests for syphilis done with blood serum have been modified for use on the cerebrospinal fluid. These include the complement-fixation reactions (Wassermann and Kolmer) and the flocculation or precipitation tests (Kahn, Kline, and Hinton). Because of greater specificity as well as simplicity, the latter have been more widely used. Currently the VDRL (Venereal Disease Research Laboratory) test has been the one of choice in most laboratories. This is a rapidly performed, slide-technic flocculation test employing cardiolipin antigen, and is highly sensitive and specific. A positive spinal fluid reaction with one of these tests (if laboratory errors can be excluded) may be considered as diagnostic of some type of central nervous system syphilis. Titration of some of the tests (especially the Wassermann and Kahn) may also give important information. Although the strength of the reaction cannot be used as an absolute indicator of the severity of the disease, a strongly positive quantitative reaction (measured in Kahn units) using a small amount of spinal fluid, usually indicates serious involvement of the nervous system. On occasion presumptive, verification, and provocative tests may be used.

If there is a large amount of blood in the spinal fluid, from cerebral or subarachnoid hemorrhage or a traumatic spinal puncture, a falsely positive reaction may be obtained. In such cases it is necessary to repeat the test when the blood has disappeared from the fluid. Falsely positive reactions are also sometimes found in the spinal fluid, as well as in the blood, in cases of infectious mononucleosis, yaws, trypanosomiasis, cerebral malaria, lymphosarcoma, the collagen disorders, and some other systemic disorders. It must be borne in mind that a negative serologic test for syphilis does not eliminate the possibility of diagnosing some type of central nervous system syphilis, since in a certain percentage of cases of tabes dorsalis and meningovascular syphilis, especially those that have undergone some treatment, the serologic reactions may be normal; the spinal fluid Kahn and Wassermann reactions are rarely normal, however, in dementia paralytica. Furthermore, it is possible to have positive tests for syphilis in patients with brain tumor, multiple sclerosis, and other diseases if they also have syphilis; a positive test does not mean that the clinically significant disease is necessarily syphilis.

Serologic tests for the detection of antibody to treponemata have made it possible, in many cases, to differentiate between positive and falsely positive reagin reactions. Furthermore, certain of these tests are more highly specific than the above-mentioned ones. These include the Treponema pallidum immobilization (TPI), agglutination, and complement-fixation tests, the fluorescent treponemal antibody determination, and the Reiter complement-fixation test. The Treponema pallidum immobilization test can be performed with cerebrospinal fluid and is of value in the diagnosis of neurosyphilis..

THE COLLOIDAL REACTIONS

The Colloidal Gold Test: The precipitation of a colloidal suspension of gold (derived from gold chloride) with varying concentrations of cerebrospinal fluid occurs in certain diseases of the nervous system. In a series of ten tubes are placed increasing dilutions (from 1:10 to 1:5120) of cerebrospinal fluid in normal saline. A colloidal gold solution having a deep red-orange color is added to each. After standing over night, the color in the tubes is read as follows: *0:* Deep orange-red (no change in color); *1:* Very slight change to a deeper red, or red-blue; *2:* Lilac or violet; *3:* Blue; *4:* Pale Blue, with some precipitation of the colloidal gold; *5:* Colorless; complete precipitation of the gold with a clear supernatant fluid (Fig. 329).

In normal spinal fluid there is no precipitation of the gold, and as a result, a "flat" or 0000000000 curve. In certain disease processes, however, there is precipitation in various dilutions. The exact mechanism for this was not known when the test was first described, but further studies have shown it to be related to the quantitative and qualitative protein pattern of the cerebrospinal fluid—the total protein concentration, the albumin and globulin contents, the albumin-globulin ratio, the quality of the globulins, and the electrical charge of the contained

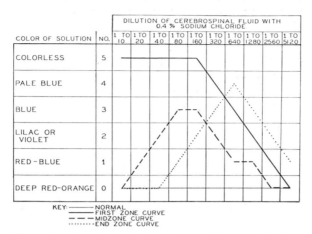

Fig. 329.   Chart showing characteristic types of Lange colloidal gold curves.

proteins. In general, most precipitation occurs in fluids having a reversal of the normal albumin-globulin ratio, even though there is no increase in the total protein content. The gamma globulin fraction is especially important in the precipitation, and is usually found to be elevated in those spinal fluids showing an abnormal curve. It has been demonstrated that gamma globulin facilitates or causes precipitation of the colloidal gold, whereas albumin and the alpha and beta globulins inhibit such precipitation or maintain the colloidal gold in suspension. The colloidal gold test is not reliable if large amounts of blood are present in the spinal fluid, but a content of less than 20,000 erythrocytes per cubic millimeter is said to have no appreciable influence on the curve.

In general four types of abnormal colloidal gold curves are observed. The most significant and outstanding is the *first zone curve*. In this the major amount of precipitation is in the tubes with the stronger concentrations of spinal fluid. A typical first zone curve reads 5555443210. It is frequently found in dementia paralytica, and consequently is often, but incorrectly, referred to as a "paretic" curve. It may also be found, however, in secondary syphilis, meningovascular syphilis, tabes dorsalis, in some 25 per cent of cases of multiple sclerosis, and in subacute inclusion-body encephalitis. A similar curve may also be found, on occasion, in conditions in which there are excessive amounts of protein in the spinal fluid, namely the Guillain-Barré syndrome, diabetic neuropathy, acute meningitis, tuberculous meningitis, brain tumor and abscess, and in fluids from cases of spinal subarachnoid block. The paraproteins that are found in the spinal fluid of patients with myeloma may also cause a first zone precipitation of the colloidal gold curve.

The *midzone curve* shows the maximum change in the middle tubes. A typical curve of this type reads 0123321100. It is frequently found in tabes dorsalis, and consequently has been called a "tabetic" or "luetic" curve. It is also found in meningovascular syphilis and poliomyelitis. The *end zone curve* shows the most marked change in the greater dilutions. A typical curve may read 0001234321. Inasmuch as it is occasionally found in acute meningitis, it has been known as a "meningitic" curve.

None of the above curves is in itself diagnostic of any special form of disease, although each may aid in the diagnosis. As important as any one of these "typical" curves is the so-called *nonspecific curve* which may show a minor change or a few evidences of minimal color alteration in certain dilutions. Such a curve might be 0001210000. This change may occur in association with almost any parenchymatous disease of the central nervous system, inflammation of the nervous tissues or of the meninges, or degenerative alterations of nervous structures; it is commonly found in multiple sclerosis. It is not diagnostic of any disease process, but does indicate that organic changes are present. Abnormalities in the colloidal gold reaction are also reported in leprosy.

Lange has recently modified the colloidal gold reaction and has shown that its sensitivity is increased by controlling the size of the colloidal particles and the pH at which the test is performed. The results of this quantitative test are listed as follows: Type A, normal curve; Type B, midzone curve; Type C, end zone curve; Type D, first zone curve (color changes in lower dilutions). The latter curve is found in fluids in which there is an increase in gamma globulin without a corresponding increase in albumin, and appears most characteristically in association with central nervous system syphilis and multiple sclerosis.

The Mastic Test: Instead of a precipitation of a colloidal suspension of gold, a precipitation of an emulsion of an alcoholic solution of gum mastic is brought about by varying dilutions of spinal fluid. Complete precipitation of the emulsion compares to complete decolorization in the colloidal gold test. Usually six tubes are employed. In most varieties of central nervous system syphilis the major precipitation takes place in the first three or four tubes, and in the various forms of meningitis, in the last three or four tubes. This test is simple and less complicated than the collodial gold test, but is not as definite or accurate, and is used infrequently.

The Benzoin Test: In this test a colloidal emulsion of benzoin is precipitated by various dilutions of spinal fluid. Usually four to six dilutions are employed. It is less sensitive even than the mastic test, and is rarely used at the present time.

REFERENCES

AYER, J. B., DAILEY, M. E., and FREMONT-SMITH, F.   Denis-Ayer method for the quantitative estimation of protein in the cerebrospinal fluid.   *Arch. Neurol. & Psychiat.* 26: 1038, 1931.

BARROWS, L. J., HUNTER, F. T., and BANKER, B. Q.   The nature and clinical significance of pigments in the cerebrospinal fluid.   *Brain* 78:59, 1955.

BAUER, C. H., NEW, M. I., and MILLER, J. M.   Cerebrospinal fluid protein values of premature infants.   *J. Pediat.* 66:1017, 1965.

BERMAN, L. B., LAPHAM, L. W., and PASTORE, E.   Jaundice and xanthochromia of the spinal fluid.   *J. Lab. & Clin. Med.* 44:273, 1954.

BOGOCH, S.   Cerebrospinal fluid neuranimic acid deficiency in schizophrenia.   *Arch. Neurol. & Psychiat.* 80:221, 1958.

BULGER, R. J., SCHRIER, R. W., AREND, W. P., and SWANSON, A. G.   Spinal fluid acidosis and the diagnosis of pulmonary encephalopathy. *New England J. Med.* 274:433, 1966.

CLAUSEN, J., DENCKER, S. J., and SVENNERHOLM, L. Proposed standardization of analysis of cerebrospinal fluid proteins. *Acta neurol. scandinav. Sup.* 10, 1964, pp. 89–94.

COLLING, K. G., and ROSSITER, R. J. Alkaline and acid phosphatase in cerebrospinal fluid. *Canad. J. Research* 28:56, 1950.

CROSBY, R. M. N., and WEILAND, G. L. Xanthochromia of the cerebrospinal fluid: II. Preliminary description of several new colored substances. *A. M. A. Arch. Neurol. & Psychiat.* 69:732, 1953.

CROSS, H. E. Examination of CSF in fat embloism. *Arch. Int. Med.* 115:470, 1965.

DAWSON, D. M., and TAGHAVY, A. A test for spinal-fluid alcohol in Torula meningitis. *New England J. Med.* 269:1424, 1963.

DENCKER, S. J., and ZETHRAEUS, S. Sex differences in total protein content of cerebrospinal fluid. *Acta psychiat. et neurol.* 36:76, 1961.

EVANS, J. H., and QUICK, D. T. Polyacrylamide gel electrophoresis of spinal fluid proteins. *Arch. Neurol.* 14:64, 1966.

FISHMAN, R. A. Carrier transport and the concentration of glucose in cerebrospinal fluid in meningeal disease. *Ann. Int. Med.* 63:153, 1965.

FROIN, G. Inflammations méningées avec réactions chromatique, fibrineuse et cytologique du liquid céphalorachidien. *Gaz. d. hôp.* 76:1005, 1903.

GEAR, J. Virus diseases of the central nervous system: A review. *J. Neurol., Neurosurg. & Psychiat.* 12:66, 1949.

GOLDSTEIN, N. P., HILL, N. C., McKENZIE, B. F., McGUCKIN, W. F., and SVIEN, H. J. Identification and quantification of proteins, glycoproteins and lipoproteins of cerebrospinal fluid. *M. Clin. North America* 44:1053, 1960.

GREEN, J. B., OLDEWURTEL, H. A., O'DOHERTY, D. S., and FORSTER, F. M. Cerebrospinal fluid transaminase and lactic dehydrogenase activities in neurologic disease. *Arch. Neurol & Psychiat* 80:148, 1958.

GREEN, J. B., and PERRY, M. Leucine aminopeptidase activity in cerebrospinal fluid. *Neurology* 13:924, 1963.

HELMSWORTH, J. A. Potassium content of normal cerebrospinal fluid. *J. Lab. & Clin. Med.* 32:1486, 1947.

JACKSON, I. J., and ROSE, B. Observations on the histamine content of the cerebrospinal fluid in man. *J. Lab. & Clin. Med.* 34:250, 1949.

KABAT, E. A., GLUSMAN, M., and KNAUB, V. Quantitative estimation of the albumin and gamma globulin in normal and pathologic cerebrospinal fluid by immunochemical methods. *Am. J. Med.* 4:653, 1948.

KATZMAN, R., FISHMAN, R. A., and GOLDENSOHN, E. S. Glutamic-oxalacetic transaminase activity in spinal fluid. *Neurology* 7:853, 1957.

KOENIGSTEIN, R. P., and CHANG, S. T. Colloidal gold reaction in the spinal fluid in leprosy. *Internat. J. Leprosy* 19:323, 1951.

KOVACS, E. Nucleases in the cerebrospinal fluid. *J. Pediat.* 46:691, 1955.

KRIETE, F. A., EPSTEIN, H. C., and TOOMEY, J. A. The Levinson ratio and the tryptophan test: Comparative value in the diagnosis of tuberculous meningitis. *Am. J. Dis. Child.* 67:469, 1944.

LANGE, C. Über die Ausflockung von Goldsol durch Liquor cerebrospinalis. *Berl. klin. Wchnschr.* 49:897, 1912; Theory of the colloidal gold reaction: Reactions between gold sol and isolated protein fractions. *J. Lab. & Clin. Med.* 30:1006, 1945.

LARSON, C. P., ROBSON, J. T., and REBERGER, C. C. Cytologic diagnosis of tumor cells in cerebrospinal fluid. *J. Neurosurg.* 10:337, 1953.

LEHMANN, H. E., and KRAL, V. A. Studies on the iron content of cerebrospinal fluid in different psychotic conditions. *A. M. A. Arch. Neurol. & Psychiat.* 65:326, 1951.

LEMMEN, L. J., NEWMAN, N. A., and DeJONG, R. N. Study of cerebrospinal fluid proteins with paper electrophoresis: I. A review of the literature. *Univ. Michigan Med. Bull.* 23:3, 1957.

LICHTENBERG, H. H. The tryptophan test in tuberculous meningitis. *Am. J. Dis. Child.* 43:32, 1932.

LOGOTHETIS, J. Cerebrospinal fluid free amino acids in neurologic diseases. *Neurology* 8:374, 1958.

LUDEWIG, S. Glutamine, glutamic acid, and γ-aminobutyric acid in cerebrospinal fluids. *A. M. A. Arch. Neurol. & Psychiat.* 70:268, 1953.

LUDWIG, A. O., SHORT, C. L., and BAUER, W. Rheumatoid arthritis as a cause of increased cerebrospinal fluid protein. *New England J. Med.* 228:306, 1943.

MADONICK, M. J., and MARGOLIS, J. Protein content of spinal fluid in diabetes mellitus. *A. M. A. Arch. Neurol. & Psychiat.* 68:641, 1952.

MARKS, V., and MARRACK, D. Tumour cells in the cerebrospinal fluid. *J. Neurol., Neurosurg. & Psychiat.* 23:194, 1960.

MATZ, P. B., and NOVICK, N. Improved colorimetric procedures for the quantitative estimation of the proteins of the cerebrospinal fluid. *J. Lab. & Clin. Med.* 15:370, 1930.

McMENEMY, W. H. The significance of subarachnoid bleeding. *Proc. Roy. Soc. Med.* 47:701, 1954.

MILLER, J. L., SLATKIN, M. H., and HILL, J. H. Significance of the Treponema pallidum immobilization test on spinal fluid. *J.A.M.A.* 160:1394, 1956.

MUNCH-PETERSON, C. J., and WINTHER, K. Recherches sur la glycorachie expérimentale. *Acta psychiat. et neurol.* 1:209, 1926.

MYERSON, R. M., HURWITZ, J. K., and SALL, T. Serum and cerebrospinal-fluid transaminase concentrations in various neurologic disorders. *New England J. Med.* 257:273, 1957.

NAYLOR, B. An exfoliative cytologic study of intracranial fluids. *Neurology* 11:560, 1961.

NEEL, A. V. The Content of Cells and Proteins in the Normal Cerebro-spinal Fluid: The Diagnostic Importance of Demonstrating Small Pathological Changes in the Cells and Proteins; The Technique of the Investigation. London, Oxford University Press, 1939.

ODESSKY, L., ROSENBLATT, P., BEDO, A. V., and LANDAU, L. Cerebrospinal fluid inorganic phosphorus in normal individuals and in those with viral involvement of the central nervous system. *J. Lab. & Clin. Med.* 41:745, 1953.

PANDY, K. Über eine neue Eiweissprobe für die cerebrospinal Flüssigkeit. *Neurol. Centralbl.* 29:915, 1910.

PLUM, C. M. Electrolyte variations in the cerebrospinal fluid in various pathological conditions. *Acta psychiat. et neurol.* 33:477, 1958.

POSER, S. M., and CURRAN, G. L. Cerebrospinal fluid free cholesterol as an index of activity of multiple sclerosis and allied diseases. *Arch. Neurol. & Psychiat.* 80:304, 1958.

POSNER, J. B., SWANSON, A. G., and PLUM, F. Acid-base balance in cerebrospinal fluid. *Arch. Neurol.* 12:479, 1965.

RHODES, A. J. Virus infections of the central nervous system. *Canad. M. A. J.* 59:32, 1948.

RICHTER, D., and REES, L.   A note on the ammonia and glutamine content of the cerebrospinal fluid.   *J. Ment. Sc.* 95:148, 1949.

RIVERS, T. M.   Virus diseases of the nervous system.   *J.A.M.A.* 132:427, 1946.

SACHS, E., JR.   Acetylcholine and serotinin in the spinal fluid.   *J. Neurosurg.* 14:22, 1957.

SHAW, C. W., and HOLLEY, H. L.   Sodium and potassium concentration in the human cerebrospinal fluid: I. Normal values.   *J. Lab. & Clin. Med.* 38:574, 1951.

SIBLEY, W. A., and WURZ, L.   Immunoassay of cerebrospinal fluid gamma-globulin.   *Arch. Neurol.* 9:386, 1963.

SPIEGEL-ADOLF, M.   Physicochemical studies of the cerebrospinal fluid.   *Arch. Neurol. & Psychiat.* 59:836, 1948.

SPOLTER, H., and THOMPSON, H. G., JR.   Factors affecting lactic dehydrogenase and glutamic oxalacetic transaminase activities in cerebrospinal fluid.   *Neurology* 12:53, 1962.

SVENNILSON, E., DENCKER, S. J., and SWAHN, B.   Immunoelectrophoretic studies of cerebrospinal fluid.   *Neurology* 11:989, 1961.

TASHIRO, S., and LEVINSON, A.   Alkaloidal and metallic precipitation of cerebrospinal fluid in the diagnosis of meningitis.   *J. Infect. Dis.* 21: 571, 1917.

THOMPSON, H. G., JR., HIRSCHBERG, E., OSNOS, M. and GELLHORN, H.   Evaluation of phosphohexase isomerase activity in cerebrospinal fluid in neoplastic disease of the central nervous system.   *Neurology* 9:545, 1959.

THOMPSON, W. O., THOMPSON, P. K., SILVEUS, E., and DAILEY, M. E.   The cerebrospinal fluid in myxedema.   *Arch. Int. Med.* 44:368, 1929.

TOURETLLOTTE, W. W.   Study of lipides in the cerebrospinal fluid: VI. The normal lipid profile.   *Neurology* 9:375, 1959.

TOURTELLOTTE, W. W., DEJONG, R. N., and VAN HOUTEN, W. H.   A study of the lipids in the cerebrospinal fluid: I. The historical aspects.   *Univ. Michigan Med. Bull.* 24: 81, 1958.

TOURTELLOTTE, W. W., QUAN, K.-C., HAERER, A. F., and BRYAN, E. R.   Neoplastic cells in the cerebrospinal fluid.   *Neurology* 13:866, 1963.

TOURTELLOTTE, W. W., SOMERS, J. F., PARKER, J. A., ITABASHI, H. H., and DEJONG, R. N.   A study on traumatic lumbar punctures.   *Neurology* 8:129, 1958.

TYLER, R.   Spinal fluid alcohol in yeast meningitis.   *Am. J. M. Sc.* 232:560, 1956.

VAN DER MEULEN, J. P.   Cerebrospinal fluid xanthochromia: An objective index.   *Neurology* 16:170, 1966.

VAN RYMENANT, M., ROBERT, J., and OTTEN, J.   Isocitric dehydrogenase in the cerebrospinal fluid: Clinical usefulness of its determination.   *Neurology* 16:351, 1966.

VON STORCH, T. J. C., LAWYER, T., JR., and HARRIS, A. H.   Colloidal gold reaction in multiple sclerosis.   *Arch. Neurol. & Psychiat.* 64:668, 1950.

WALKER, B. S., TELLES, N. C., and PASTORE, E. J.   Amino acids of the cerebrospinal fluid: Normal paper chromatographic pattern and its duplication in multiple sclerosis.   *A. M. A. Arch. Neurol. & Psychiat.* 73:149, 1955.

WEISS, A. H., and CHRISTOFF, N.   The effect of CSF paraproteins on the colloidal gold test.   *Arch. Neurol.* 14:100, 1966.

WORM-PETERSEN, J.   Vitamin B_{12} in the serum and cerebrospinal fluid in neurological diseases.   *Acta neurol. scandinav.* 38:241, 1962.

WORTIS, S. B., and MARSH, F.   The lactic acid content of the blood and of the cerebrospinal fluid.   *Arch. Neurol. & Psychiat.* 35:717, 1936.

CHAPTER 60

RELATED EXAMINATIONS AND PROCEDURES

PUNCTURE OF THE CISTERNA MAGNA

In 1919 Wegeforth, Ayer, and Essick first described the approach to the cisterna magna for the removal of cerebrospinal fluid based on preliminary studies on the cadaver, and in 1920 Ayer described the puncture of the cisterna magna as a clinical diagnostic procedure. The cisterna magna (cerebellomedullaris) is the largest of the subarachnoid cisterns. It is situated at the base of the brain and is below the inferior surface of the cerebellum, behind the posterior surface of the medulla and upper cervical spinal cord, and above and in front of the dura covering the posterior atlanto-occipital membrane. A needle can be introduced into this space without contact with nervous tissues.

In performing a cisternal puncture the patient is placed on an examining table in the lateral recumbent position with his shoulders perpendicular to the table and his neck slightly flexed. A firm pillow or small sand bag is placed under the head to make certain that the plane of the cervical spine is horizontal. The position of the patient is very important. The skin is prepared by shaving the hair over the area from the occipital protuberance to the midcervical level. As in doing a spinal puncture, rubber gloves are worn, aseptic technics and sterile instruments are used, and the skin around the area of the puncture is sterilized and infiltrated with a local anesthetic preparation. Either an ordinary Quincke lumbar puncture needle or a Fleischer needle with an incorporated three-way stopcock may be used. An 18 to 20 gauge caliber is best. Many technicians prefer to use a needle that is marked in centimeters, or to have a guard on the needle to indicate when a depth of 6.5 or 7 centimeters has been reached.

The needle is inserted in the suboccipital depression, at a point just below the external occipital protuberance and just above the spine of the axis or second cervical vertebra (the highest palpable spinous process), exactly in the midline. It is then directed inward and slightly upward in a plane which passes through the external auditory meatus and continues to the glabella (Fig. 330). It penetrates the skin, subcutaneous tissues, superficial muscles of the neck, ligamentum nuchae, posterior atlanto-occipital membrane, dura mater (to which this ligament is intimately adherent), and arachnoid, and enters the subarachnoid cistern between the medulla and the cerebellum. After the needle has been introduced about three centimeters, the stylet is withdrawn to note whether fluid has been obtained. If not, the stylet is replaced, the needle is introduced another half centimeter, and the stylet is again withdrawn. This procedure is repeated every one-half centimeter until fluid is obtained. Usually a "give" is felt when the needle goes through the atlanto-occipital membrane and dura. If the base of the occiput is encountered, the needle should be withdrawn slightly and then depressed enough to pass through the dura at the upper limits and posterior margin of the foramen magnum. If blood is encountered, the needle should be withdrawn and a clean one used. The distance from the skin to

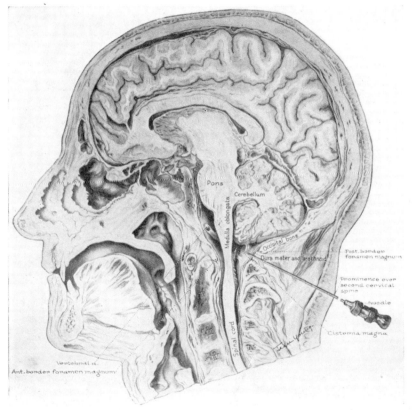

FIG. 330. Sagittal section of skull and its contents, showing relative positions of structures involved in doing a cisternal puncture, with needle in place. (Waggoner, R.W., in Piersol, G.W (ed.) The Cyclopedia of Medicine, Surgery and Specialties. Philadelphia, F.A. Davis Company, 1941.)

the cisterna averages between four and six centimeters, although occasionally in extremely muscular individuals the needle may have to be introduced as much as 7.5 centimeters. Under most circumstances it is unwise to insert the neeedle more than 7.5 centimeters. The testing of the dynamics, removal of the fluid, and the later withdrawal of the needle and care of the puncture site are the same as with a puncture in the lumbar region.

A cisternal puncture can be done with ease and with minimum discomfort to the patient in most cases. It is less likely to be followed by a headache than lumbar puncture, and there is less danger of continued leakage of cerebrospinal fluid or herniation of the medulla into the foramen magnum. In some clinics the procedure is done routinely for the withdrawal of spinal fluid for examination. It is certainly more hazardous than spinal puncture, however, because of the approximation of the needle to the medulla and the possibility of hemorrhage resulting from trauma to abnormally placed blood vessels. It should always be carried out by an experienced technician. Many authorities recommend practice on a cadaver before performing the examination of the living subject. If the puncture is done with care and judgment, however, it is quite safe. Cisternal puncture may be performed under the following circumstances: for routine examination of the spinal fluid in those cases in which puncture at the lumbar area is either inadvisable or contraindicated by local conditions such as infections, or in cases where lumbar puncture is unsuccessful because of deformities or anomalies of the spine or spinal subarachnoid block; for the introduction of contrast medium in myelography when it is necessary to determine the upper level of the tumor or obstruction, and occasionally for the introduction of air in performing pneumoencephalography; for the introduction of serum and drugs in the treatment of meningitis; for the diagnosis of spinal subarachnoid block by combined cisternal and lumbar punctures. Cisternal puncture is contraindicated if there is either subcutaneous infection at the puncture site or septicemia, if there is increased intracranial pressure (especially if caused by a posterior fossa tumor), or if the presence of a brain abscess is suspected.

VENTRICULAR PUNCTURE

Ventricular puncture (i.e., of one of the lateral ventricles) is sometimes carried out to obtain cerebrospinal fluid when it cannot be obtained by the lumbar or cisternal routes, to diagnose conditions such as obstructive hydrocephalus, to inject air or oxygen in ventriculography, or in combination with either cisternal or lumbar puncture. Ventricular puncture in adults is a surgical procedure necessitating trephination of the skull, and must be carried out by a neurosurgeon. In infants, however, before the closing of the fontanelles, ventricular puncture is a fairly simple procedure, and may be preferred to cisternal puncture. The patient is wrapped in a sheet and placed on his back on a firm table, and the head is held firmly by a nurse or assistant. The region of the anterior fontanelle is shaved, sterilized with tincture of iodine, and cleaned with 70 per cent alcohol. A short spinal puncture needle or a needle used for intravenous injections is used. The needle is introduced about one-half to one centimeter to one side of the midline to avoid the superior sagittal sinus. It is then directed forward, downward, and slightly outward for a distance of from two to four centimeters. If no fluid is obtained, the needle should be withdrawn to the skin and the direction slightly altered. In internal hydrocephalus the ventricle may be encountered at a distance of only one centimeter. Ventricular puncture is occasionally done, in either adults or children, to decrease intracranial pressure before operations for brain tumor, to inject dyes in the diagnosis of hydrocephalus, to inject serum in the treatment of meningitis, or to compare the pressure in the two lateral ventricles. Subdural punctures may be done in infants to diagnose and treat subdural hemorrhages and fluid collections.

Pneumoencephalography, or the withdrawal of the cerebrospinal fluid and its replacement with air, was first described by Dandy in 1919 as an ancillary neurologic diagnostic procedure. The gas (oxygen, nitrogen, and helium have also been used) enters the ventricles of the brain and the subarachnoid channels and cisterns, and may be visualized in these sites by roentgenography. Changes in the size, shape, and position of the ventricles as well as of the subarachnoid pathways may provide essential information in the diagnosis of cerebral neoplasms, hydrocephalus, atrophy, and congenital anomalies. Originally large amounts of cerebrospinal fluid were removed and similar amounts of air injected. Later observations, however, have shown that with taking multiple films in various positions, only small amounts of air need be injected and very little or even no fluid need be removed. The air is injected fractionally, and films are taken after each injection. With this modification of the procedure the risk, discomfort, and morbidity associated with it are markedly decreased.

The same contraindications that have been listed for spinal puncture should be borne in mind when considering pneumoencephalography, and the same complications may result. In addition, many authorities warn against the procedure in elderly patients and those with evidences of arteriosclerosis. Papilledema and other signs of increased intracranial pressure and suspected posterior fossa neoplasms were formerly cited as contraindications to the procedure, but it is now considered safe under such circumstances if carried out with controlled, fractional injections of only small amounts of air. It is generally contraindicated, however, if the presence of a brain abscess is suspected. The operation should always be preceded by a spinal puncture for the determination of pressure and for cytologic, chemical, and serologic examinations of the cerebrospinal fluid. Cisternal pneumoencephalography is occasionally performed.

Ventriculography (described by Dandy in 1918) is the withdrawal of cerebrospinal fluid and injection of air directly into the ventricles. It is a neurosurgical procedure. Although more hazardous than pneumoencephalography, it is the safer of the two if the intracranial pressure is markedly elevated or if the presence of a posterior fossa neoplasm is suspected. Also, ventriculography provides a better view of the ventricular system, but usually does not give much information about the subarachnoid channels. Direct injection into the ventricles may be the only means of introducing air in some types of hydrocephalus, such as those associated with stenosis of the aqueduct. Contrast ventriculography, in which Pantopaque or some other contrast medium is injected into the ventricles during the procedure, is of special aid in the delineation of the posterior portion of the third ventricle, the aqueduct, and the fourth ventricle. With all of the above procedures the interpretation of the roentgenograms may be enhanced by the use of autotomography and subtraction technics.

MYELOGRAPHY

Myelography is carried out by introducing some radiopaque contrast medium into the spinal canal for the purpose of roentgen evaluation of the cause of a spinal subarachnoid block and for the diagnosis of other space-occupying lesions within the spinal canal, including ruptured intervertebral disks. It may also provide pertinent information in the interpretation of cervical spondylosis and lesions at the level of the foramen magnum. Air, or gas, myelography has been used, but the radiologic contrast is difficult to interpret. Lipiodol (iodized poppy-seed oil) was once used extensively, but has been generally replaced by Pantopaque (ethyl iodopheylundecylate or iophendylate), which is felt to be safer and which can usually be removed following the procedure. Some water-soluble contrast substances have also been tried, but their use has not been widely adopted. The contrast medium is injected into the spinal canal at the usual site for spinal puncture, and the patient is placed on a tilting table under a fluoroscope. If the lower portion of the canal is to be examined, as in cases of suspected lumbosacral herniations of the nucleus pulposus, the table is tilted so that the lower portions of the body are downward, the course of the radiopaque substance is followed, and roentgenograms are taken. If an obstruction is suspected above the level of the puncture site, the table is tilted so that the upper portions of the body are downward, and the same procedure is carried out. Sometimes, if lumbar myelography is impossible or unsuccessful or if it is important to determine the upper limits of the lesion, the contrast medium is introduced into the cisterna magna, and the body is tilted so that the lower portions are downward. Myelography is indicated in cases of either partial or complete subarachnoid block in which the exact extent or location of the lesion is not known, and in the diagnosis of conditions affecting the cauda equina, conus medullaris, or lumbosacral nerve roots. It is contraindicated if there is evidence of infection of the nervous tissues or meninges, if there is roentgen evidence of a destructive lesion or compression of the vertebral bodies, or if Pott's disease is suspected. Complications and sequelae of myelography occur infrequently, but include meningeal irritation, headache, meningitis, intravasation into the vascular system, pulmonary emboli, and residual arachnoiditis.

Myeloscopy, a technic in which a small endoscope is introduced into the lumbar subarachnoid space for direct visualization of the structures in that region, has had little application in clinical diagnosis. *Diskography,* or the diagnostic puncture of and direct injection of radiopaque substances into the intervertebral disk, has been used on occasion as a diagnostic procedure, and has been performed at both cervical and lumbar levels. However, it has never been widely accepted, and some of its early proponents have abandoned the procedure.

SPINAL AND CAUDAL ANESTHESIA

Spinal anesthesia has become a routine part of surgical anesthesia, and is indicated in many cases where either general or local anesthesia is either contraindicated or unsatisfactory. The anesthetic agent (procaine or related preparations, usually with epinephrine) is introduced into the subarachnoid space at the usual site for spinal puncture, and the level of anesthesia is regulated by altering the position of the body. Neurologic complications, including aseptic or septic meningitis, myelopathy, cranial nerve palsies, and later developing arachnoiditis, have been reported, but are rare. These may be the result of the toxic action of or sensitivity to the anesthetic drug or the nonanesthetic drugs or chemicals injected with it, or may be caused by contamination, trauma, or the spinal puncture itself. *Sacral,* or *caudal, anesthesia* is carried out by injecting the anesthetic agent through the sacrococcygeal ligament and the sacral hiatus into the sacral canal, which is continuous with the spinal epidural space. The third and fourth and occasionally the first and second sacral nerves are blocked, and there is anesthesia in the region of the anus, perineum, and genitalia. This procedure is used in obstetrics and in providing anesthesia for sacral or perineal operations. *Epidural injections* of procaine through the sacral hiatus into the spinal epidural space have been used in the relief of pain of lumbosacral radiation and also for the treatment of painful affections of the rectum and perineum. In performing the *reverse Queckenstedt* test, saline solution is injected into the epidural space and changes are noted in the spinal fluid pressure as determined by means of a manometer attached to a needle which is introduced into the subarachnoid space at the level of the second or third lumbar intervertebral space. The injection of either *absolute alcohol* or *phenol* into the subarachniod space has been used in the treatment of intractable pain, usually if pelvic or sacral in distribution, and also in the relief of spacticity in transverse myelitis and related conditions.

REFERENCES

AYER, J. B. Puncture of the cisterna magna. *Arch. Neurol. & Psychiat.* 4:529, 1920.

BULL, J. W. D. Positive contrast ventriculography. *Acta radiol.* 34:253, 1950.

DANDY, W. E. Ventriculography following the injection of air into the cerebral ventricles. *Ann. Surg.* 68:5, 1918; Roentgenography of the brain after the injection of air into the spinal canal. *Ann. Surg.* 70:397, 1919.

DAVIDOFF, L. M., and DYKE, C. G. The Normal Encephalogram (ed. 3). Philadelphia, Lea & Febiger, 1951.

DAVIDOFF, L. M., and EPSTEIN, B. S. The Abnormal Encephalogram (ed. 2). Philadelphia, Lea & Febiger, 1955.

DI CHIRO, G. An Atlas of Detailed Normal Pneumoencephalographic Anatomy, Springfield, Ill. Charles C Thomas, 1961.

LINDBLOM, K. Technique and results of diagnostic disc puncture and injection (discography) in the lumbar region. *Acta orthop. scandinav.* 20:315, 1951.

LINDGREN, E. Some aspects of the technique of encephalography. *Acta radiol.* 31:160, 1949.

MULLAN, S., and PINEDA, A.   Cisternal pneumoencephalography.   *Am. J. Roentgenol.* 81:992, 1959.

NELSON, D. A., JEFFREYS, W. H., LEAMING, R. H., and MCDOWELL, F.   Encephalography by displacement technique.   *Arch. Neurol. & Psychiat.* 79:498, 1958.

POOL, J. L.   Direct visualization of dorsal nerve roots of the cauda equina by means of a myeloscope.   *Arch. Neurol. & Psychiat.* 39:1308, 1938.

RAMSEY, G. H., FRENCH, J. D., and STRAIN, W. H.   Iodinated organic compounds as contrast media for radiographic diagnosis: IV. Pantopaque myelography.   *Radiology* 45:236, 1944.

ROBERTSON, E. G.   Pneumoencephalography.   Springfield, Ill., Charles C Thomas, 1957.

SCHECTER, M. M., and JING, B. -S.   Improved visualization of the ventricular system with the technic of autotomography.   *Radiology* 74:593, 1960.

SCOTT, W. G., and FURLOW, L. T.   Myelography with pantopaque and a new technique for its removal.   *Radiology* 44:241, 1944.

SHEALY, C. N., and NEW, P. F. J.   Cerebrospinal fluid pressure changes in fractional pneumoencephalography without removal of cerebrospinal fluid.   *Radiology.* 43:236, 1944.

SICARD, J. A., and FORESTIER, J.   Méthode radiographique d'exploration de la cavite épidural par le lipiodol.   *Rev. neurol.* 27:1264, 1921.

TAVERAS, J. M., and WOOD, E. H.   Diagnostic Neuroradiology. Baltimore, The Williams & Wilkins Company, 1964.

WAGGONER, R. W.   "Cisterna puncture," in PIERSOL, G. W. (ed.).   *The Cyclopedia of Medicine, Surgery and Specialties.*   Philadelphia, F. A. Davis Company, 1941, vol. 4, pp. 277–279.

WEGEFORTH, P., AYER, J. B., and ESSICK, C. R.   The method of obtaining cerebrospinal fluid by puncture of the cisterna magna (cistern puncture).   *Am. J. M. Sc.* 157:789, 1919.

WOOD, E. H., JR.   An Atlas of Myelography.   Washington, D. C., Registry Press, 1948.

CHAPTER 61

CEREBROSPINAL FLUID SYNDROMES

IN THE SPINAL PUNCTURE in the normal individual, as has been stated above, the pressure may vary from 50 to 180 mm. of water, and there is normal response to coughing, straining, and jugular compression. *The normal cerebrospinal fluid* is clear and colorless, with no clot or web. There are fewer than five mononuclear cells per cu. mm. The Pandy test is negative, the protein varies from 15 to 40 mg. per 100 cc., and the glucose from 50 to 65 mg. No bacteria or organisms are present. The serologic tests for syphilis are negative, and the gold and mastic curves show no variations from the normal. The cell count and protein content are slightly less in cisternal and ventricular fluid, whereas the glucose content is slightly higher in ventricular fluid.

If blood is present in the normal fluid, owing to trauma to the spinal venous plexus or the meningeal or vertebral veins, the pressure relationships will be normal but the fluid will be blood-tinged, varying from a pink to a deep red color; the presence of blood may also give a turbid appearance to the fluid. If successive specimens of fluid are taken, the later ones will be more clear than the first ones. If much blood is present, a clot will form spontaneously. When the fluid is centrifuged, the super-natant fluid is clear and colorless unless the amount of blood is excessive. The erythrocytes appear normal microscopically. No organisms are present. Contamination of the spinal fluid by blood will influence the leukocyte count and the Pandy and total protein determinations, but not the glucose content to any appreciable extent. The serologic tests for syphilis are not affected, unless the blood serology (but not the spinal fluid) is positive for syphilis. The protein content of the blood may cause nonspecific changes in the colloidal gold curve.

Specific cerebrospinal fluid syndromes have been described in association with certain disease processes. Some of the more important of these are listed.

1081

MENINGITIS

Acute Purulent, or Suppurative, Meningitis: In acute meningitis there is a marked elevation of spinal fluid pressure which may reach as high as 500 to 1000 mm. of water. There is no block early in the course of the disease, but block may develop later due to the formation of arachnoid adhesions; adhesions may also form as a result of intrathecal administration of serum and drugs. The fluid may vary in appearance from one that is faintly cloudy to a turbid, purulent, or opaque appearance, due to the presence of leukocytes and organisms. It may be slightly xanthochromic due to elevated protein, or even greenish due to the presence of pus; it sometimes is blood-tinged. The fluid may be viscid and may clot on standing. There is a marked pleocytosis, sometimes reaching from 1000 to 5000 or even 50,000 cells per cubic millimeter; nearly 100 per cent of the cells are polymorphonuclears. As a reaction to the presence of debris in the fluid, the cell count may remain elevated even after the fluid is sterile. There is a distinct increase in the total protein, which may reach 1000 mg. per cc.; both albumin and globulin may be increased. The glucose is diminished, often below 20 or even 10 mg. per 100 cc. The chlorides are also diminished, and may range from 630 to 680 mg. Organisms are usually found on the direct smear; these may be either meningococci (Gram negative, intracellular cocci), pneumococci, streptococci, staphylococci, or influenzal bacilli; rare instances of purulent meningitis may be caused by other agents, including typhoid and colon bacilli. Occasionally multiple organisms are found. Often the organisms may be isolated from cultures even if not found on direct smear. The serologic tests for syphilis are normal, but the colloidal reactions are pathologic, often with an end zone but occasionally a first zone or midzone rise.

Tuberculous Meningitis: In tuberculous meningitis the pressure is also elevated, although rarely beyond 300 to 500 mm. of water. There may be a spinal subarachnoid block late in the course of the disease or after intrathecal streptomycin therapy. The fluid may be clear and colorless early in the course of the disease, but it is often opalescent or ground-glass in appearance. Occasionally it is blood-tinged or faintly xanthochromic. A fine, cob-web like fibrin web or pellicle appears after the fluid has stood for twenty-four hours. There is a pleocytosis, often ranging between 100 and 500 cells per cubic millimeter, but sometimes going as high as 1000. The cells are predominantly lymphocytes (usually 85 to 95 per cent, with the other 15 to 5 per cent polymorphonuclears). In terminal stages the percentage of polymorphonuclear cells increases; neutrophils also appear early in infants. The protein content is increased, often to 500 mg. or higher, and is both albumin and globulin. The glucose is decreased, and is usually between 20 and 40 mg., although in terminal stages it may go lower. The chlorides are lower even than in pyogenic meningitis, and may be below 550 or 600 mg. Acid-fast organisms may be found, especially if the pellicle is examined; they frequently are difficult to demonstrate on the direct smear, but cultures and guinea pig inoculations are positive. A *serous tuberculous meningitis* has been described (in contrast to the caseous variety presented above), in which there may be an increase in spinal fluid pressure without alterations in cells or chemistry; organisms, however, are occasionally found, possibly derived from a minimal meningeal lesion which has resolved. The serologic tests for syphilis are negative in tuberculous meningitis, but the colloidal gold and mastic reactions show either a midzone or an end zone, or occasionally a first zone, curve. It is said that the presence of organisms in the smear, culture, or guinea pig inoculation is necessary for the diagnosis of tuberculous meningitis, but one can usually be relatively certain of the diagnosis on the basis of the clinical findings together with the cytologic picture and the alteration in the content of the proteins, glucose, and chlorides. Some authorities rely on the Levinson and tryptophan tests for the diagnosis.

Cryptococcus (Torula) Meningitis: In the meningitis caused by *Cryptococcus neoformans (Torula histolytica)* the spinal fluid picture closely resembles that of tuberculous meningitis, with moderately elevated pressure, no block, faintly cloudy fluid, a pleocytosis that is predominantly lymphocytic, and a moderate increase in protein. The glucose is significantly decreased in 60 per cent of cases. Tubercle bacilli are never found, however, and in most cases budding forms of the yeasts may be seen on direct smear or obtained by cultures, using either ordinary culture media or Sabouraud's medium (Fig. 331). They may also be demonstrated by mouse inoculation. Occasionally the yeast cells are mistaken for lymphocytes when seen in the counting chamber, but when stained with India ink their refractive capsules may be observed. They may also be identified by fluorescent technics. Eosinophils are sometimes demonstrated in the differential count. The yeasts contain the enzyme alcohol dehydrogenase which ferments glucose to alcohol, and assays may show the spinal fluid alcohol content to be elevated. A similar spinal fluid picture may be found in meningitides caused by other yeasts, fungi and molds.

Acute Syphilitic Meningitis: Rarely seen at the present time, acute syphilitic meningitis most characteristically develops during the secondary stage of syphilis. There is a moderate to severe lymphocytic pleocytosis, and moderate elevation of the pressure and protein. The glucose and chlorides are normal or slightly decreased. The serologic tests for syphilis are positive in over 95 per cent of the cases, and the colloidal gold curve is usually the first zone or midzone type.

Lymphocytic Meningitides: There are many meningitides in which the cerebrospinal fluid response is predominantly a lymphocytic one, with from 25 to 50 cells to 200 or sometimes more. There are few other changes in the fluid, and the course is usually benign. These are often called instances of aseptic meningitis because no organism is found in the fluid on direct examination or by the usual culture methods. Many of them, however, are of viral origin, and in some of them the virus has been isolated from the fluid by special technics; in others it has been found in the feces or in the nasal and pharyngeal washings, or the diagnosis has been confirmed by neutralization or complement-fixation tests done on blood serum. Among the most common viral etiologies are the virus of lymphocytic meningitis, the Coxsackie, ECHO and Giles viruses, and those of mumps, herpes zoster, or herpes simplex. Poliomyelitis virus and those responsible for the arthropod-borne encephalitides may cause a similar meningeal response. A benign recurrent meningitis for which no etiology has been found is known as *Mollaret's meningitis.*

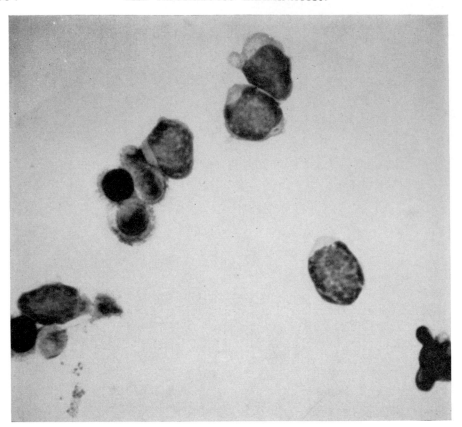

FIG. 331.   Cells found in cerebrospinal fluid of patient with Cryptococcus meningitis; budding forms of Cryptococci as well as mononuclear cells may be seen; Wright's stain. (Courtesy of Dr. W. W. Tourtellotte.)

Meningismus: Meningismus occurs in association with febrile illnesses, often in children. There is an increase in the spinal fluid pressure with an excessive amount of clear spinal fluid. The cell count, glucose, bacteriologic examination, serologic tests, and colloidal gold curve are normal. The protein and chloride constituents of the fluid may be decreased, especially if the blood chlorides are decreased.

Aseptic Meningitis: An aseptic (sympathetic) meningeal reaction occurs when there is a pyogenic infection near the meninges which has not yet invaded them, namely in mastoid suppuration, paranasal sinus infections, cavernous or lateral sinus thrombosis, osteomyelitis of the skull, brain abscess, and subdural or extradural abscesses. A similar process (chemical or irritative meningitis) may occur as a meningeal reaction to the intraspinal injection of air, drugs, sera, or other foreign substances. There is an increase in the spinal fluid pressure and often a marked pleocytosis (lymphocytic, mixed, or polymorphonuclear). The protein content of the fluid is usually elevated, sometimes markedly so, but the glucose content is not reduced, the smears show no organisms, and the cultures are sterile.

sociation which resembles that of the Guillain-Barré syndrome. The glucose and chlorides are usually normal. The serologic tests for syphilis are normal, but there may be a midzone or mild nonspecific change in the colloidal gold curve. It is important to bear in mind that there may be significant cerebrospinal fluid changes in the nonparalytic and subclinical varieties of poliomyelitis, and also increased protein during convalescence from these varieties, but it is also possible to have entirely normal spinal fluid in acute poliomyelitis. Some of the viral infections mentioned above (Coxsackie and ECHO) may cause clinical and spinal fluid pictures which closely simulate those seen in poliomyelitis.

Transverse Myelitis: If an acute inflammatory transverse myelitis is suppurative in type and is secondary to meningitis, adjacent infections, or infections elsewhere in the body, there may be a marked increase in cells and protein in the cerebrospinal fluid. Transverse myelitis, however, may come on acutely without evidence of coexisting infection. In such cases the spinal fluid may be normal or there may be only a slight to moderate increase in cells (lymphocytes) and protein, with normal pressure and no block. This last criterion is important in differentiating between inflammatory myelitis and spinal cord tumor and other conditions in which there is a sudden development of paraplegia due to cord compression.

Ascending Paralysis: Acute ascending paralysis, or Landry's paralysis, is a syndrome rather than a disease entity. Consequently there are no characteristic spinal fluid changes. In some cases the spinal fluid examination is entirely normal. In others, in which the ascending paralysis is probably related to a polyradiculoneuritis (see below), there may be a pronounced elevation of protein, without increase in cells.

INTRACRANIAL LESIONS

Brain Tumor: The most characteristic finding in brain tumor is an increase in the spinal fluid pressure, which varies, of course, with the amount of elevation of the intracranial pressure. This is most marked in association with neoplasms of the posterior fossa, principally of the cerebellum, or with rapidly expanding neoplasms such as glioblastoma multiforme. Paradoxically, posterior fossa neoplasms such as spongioblastoma polare which involve the medulla, pons, and midbrain frequently cause no elevation of intracranial pressure. The spinal fluid pressure need not be proportional to the amount of papilledema, and the pressure at spinal puncture may be markedly elevated in cases with no papilledema, or, on the other hand, nearly normal in cases with advanced papilledema. The fluid is usually normal in appearance, although occasionally it is slightly yellow or blood-tinged. There may be a pleocytosis, sometimes relatively high, if the tumor is near to or encroaches on either the meninges or the ventricles; the cells are predominantly lymphocytes. Occasionally tumor cells may be found in the centrifuged sediment (Fig. 328). There may be erythrocytes in the fluid in association with vascular tumors (angiomas and hemangioblastomas) or degenerating neoplasms. The protein is often moderately elevated, especially with neoplasms near the meninges or ventricles, those that obstruct the flow of blood or cerebrospinal fluid, and vascular tumors. It is characteristically high with cerebellopontine angle tumors, and often with those of the parasellar region. Occasionally the glucose content of the spinal fluid is elevated with brain tumors. The bacteriologic and serologic examinations are normal; there may be a nonspecific change in the colloidal gold curve, especially if there is increase in protein in the fluid. The spinal fluid findings in meningeal carcinomatosis are discussed above. While spinal puncture and examination of the fluid may occasionally be of some aid in the diagnosis of brain tumor, it should be stressed that often the spinal fluid shows little or no abnormality and the puncture gives no information that may not be obtained by other means. Furthermore, if there is increase in intracranial pressure, the procedure may be harmful. A spinal puncture should never be carried out in a patient suspected of having an intracranial tumor unless the procedure is necessary in order to establish the diagnosis; the Queckenstedt test should never be done if a brain tumor is suspected.

"Benign Intracranial Hypertension":   In the syndrome known variously as benign intracranial hypertension, otitic hydrocephalus, pseudotumor cerebri, and brain swelling of unknown etiology there is increased intracranial pressure with headache and papilledema. There may be blurring or loss of vision, but usually no other significant neurologic abnormalities. Spinal puncture shows increased pressure but usually normal protein and cells and no other definite changes. The ventricles are not enlarged and the pneumoencephalogram is normal. There are probably multiple etiolgies for this syndrome. Sometimes it is associated with middle ear disease and lateral sinus thrombosis (otitic hydrocephalus), on other occasions thrombosis of the superior sagittal sinus, infections elsewhere in the body, trauma, or vitamin A intoxication may be responsible. In many instances the etiology is not determined, but since the syndrome often occurs in obese young or middle-aged women and may be associated with menstrual dysfunction, pregnancy, or steroid administration, various endocrine, hormonal, metabolic, toxic, and allergic factors have been suggested. It is important to differentiate this syndrome from some of the more malignant causes of increased intracranial pressure.

Brain Abscess: In brain abscess the spinal fluid findings are those of an expanding intracranial lesion together with those of an aseptic meningeal reaction. The pressure is usually elevated, especially with posterior fossa abscesses, as it is in brain tumor. In addition, there is often evidence of meningeal irritation, with a pleocytosis. There may be 100 to 200 cells per cu. mm. and occasionally as many as 1000 cells. The differential count varies, depending on the location of the abscess and the meningeal reaction to it. If the lesion is near the meninges or the ventricles, the cells may be predominantly polymorphonuclears, whereas if it is deeper in the brain tissue, they are mainly lymphocytes. Oftentimes there are nearly 50 per cent of each. The cell count and the percentage of neutrophils are both higher in acute than chronic abscesses. The number and nature of the cells may indicate the progress of encapsulation; the percentage of polymorphonuclear cells is high in acute abscesses that are not yet walled off, and it decreases after encapsulation has taken place. The persistence of neutrophils may indicate failure of encapsulation. If the pleocytosis is marked, the fluid may be cloudy or turbid. The protein is increased, sometimes markedly, but the glucose is usually normal. The collodial gold curve is usually the nonspecific type, but occasionally a first zone curve is found, depending on the protein content. The smears show no organisms and cultures are sterile. Increased spinal fluid pressure with an outstanding meningeal reaction, but with no decrease in glucose and no organisms, is considered pathognomonic of brain abscess. If the abscess ruptures into the ventricles or subarachnoid space, the spinal fluid picture is that of a pyogenic meningitis.

Epidural Abscess: The spinal fluid picture in an epidural or extradural abscess is identical with that of intracerebral abscess, and the two cannot be differentiated by spinal fluid study. The same is true of *subdural abscess.*

Lateral Sinus and Cavernous Sinus Thrombosis: The spinal fluid findings in lateral sinus and cavernous sinus thrombosis may be either those of an aseptic meningitis, if there is a pronounced meningeal reaction to the disease, or those of "benign intracranial hypertension." They often closely resemble the changes seen in brain abscess, with a mixed pleocytosis, increased protein, and normal glucose, but the pressure is usually not elevated to the same degree. The Tobey-Ayer modification of the Queckenstedt test may be positive on the side of a lateral sinus thrombosis. Occasionally with thrombosis of the lateral sinus, and more often with that of the cavernous sinus, there is an associated meningitis with its characteristic spinal fluid picture.

Cerebral Trauma: The spinal fluid findings in cerebral trauma are dependent upon the amount of damage to the cerebral tissues and to the meninges and meningeal vessels. In cases of concussion there is often a significant elevation of spinal fluid pressure, secondary to cerebral edema, and there may be a moderate lymphocytic pleocytosis and a slight increase in protein. If there have been contusions or lacerations of the brain or of one or more of the meningeal vessels, there may be a more marked elevation of spinal fluid pressure, and the fluid may contain erythrocytes or be xanthochromic; there is also a more marked increase in cells (mainly lymphocytes) and protein. More significant changes in the spinal fluid are noted if there is an associated subarachnoid hemorrhage or subdural hematoma.

Subdural Hematoma: In subdural hematoma the spinal fluid picture varies with the age of the hematoma. Early in the development of the clot the fluid often contains gross blood and increased protein, owing to associated subarachnoid bleeding and concomitant cerebral contusion; there is usually increased pressure as well. Later, after the disappearance of the blood cells, there is xanthochromia with increased protein, and a continued elevation of pressure. Still later the fluid is normal in appearance, without blood cells or xanthochromia, but there is evidence of gradually increasing intracranial pressure; there may be increased protein and a moderate pleocytosis, owing to transudation of serum and an associated meningeal reaction. The bacteriologic examination and the serologic tests are normal, and the colloidal gold curve is nonspecific in type. It is said that slightly xanthochromic fluid under increased pressure but with only moderately increased protein is pathognomonic of a developing subdural hematoma. In *extradural hemorrhage* there may be increase in spinal fluid pressure; if there is associated damage to the brain or the meninges, there may be erythrocytes, leukocytes, and increased protein in the spinal fluid.

Lead Encephalopathy: Lead encephalopathy is encountered primarily in children. The pressure is usually elevated, sometimes to 1000 mm. of water, and there is often a pleocytosis, predominantly lymphocytic. The protein and glucose are normal or slightly elevated. The colloidal gold curve is variable. Lead may be present in the cerebrospinal fluid.

"Epilepsy": In so-called idiopathic, or cryptogenic, epilepsy the spinal fluid is normal in all respects, although occasionally there is a slight increase in pressure and protein during and immediately after convulsions. The statement has often been made that abnormalities in the spinal fluid are sometimes encountered in epilepsy. These include a slight increase in pressure (from 180 to 250 mg.) in 5 to 10 per cent, a slight increase in protein (45 to 75 mg.) in 5 to 10 per cent, a mild pleocytosis, and a slight increase in sugar. If, however, a patient with a convulsive disorder is found to have definite abnormalities in the nature of increased pressure, pleocytosis, and elevated protein, one should consider seriously the probability that the attacks are symptomatic, or secondary to some intracranial abnormality such as brain tumor or abscess or encephalitis. The diagnosis of epilepsy should be made with caution if there are any abnormalities in the cerebrospinal fluid.

Miscellaneous Conditions: The low spinal fluid pressure syndromes and spontaneous aliquorrhea are discussed in Chapter 58. Usually there are no changes in the fluid itself, but occasionally there is a slight xanthochromia with a moderate elevation in protein. In the syndrome of symptomatic occult hydrocephalus with "normal" cerebrospinal fluid pressure there are no changes in the fluid. In cerebrospinal fluid rhinorrhea and otorrhea, which are usually posttraumatic, the escaping fluid is normal except for an occasional slight increase in lymphocytes, unless infection supervenes. Spontaneous spinal fluid rhinorrhea has been reported with neoplasms in the vicinity of the sella turcica.

LESIONS OF THE SPINAL CORD, NERVE ROOTS, AND PERIPHERAL NERVES

Spinal Cord Tumor: With spinal cord tumor the spinal fluid pressure may be normal or decreased. If there is encroachment on the spinal subarachnoid space, interfering with the flow of the fluid, there may be either a partial or a complete block, which appears earlier and is more marked with extradural and extramedullary intradural tumors than with intramedullary ones. The characteristics of the fluid depend upon the presence, location, and degree of block. Its appearance may be normal, or it may be markedly xanthochromic and may clot spontaneously (Froin's syndrome). The cells may be normal or moderately elevated. The protein varies from normal to marked increase, and the colloidal gold curve depends upon the amount and type of protein present; occasionally there is a first zone curve. The glucose and the bacteriologic and serologic examinations are normal. The comparison of the cerebrospinal fluid findings on combined lumbar and cisternal puncture is discussed in Chapter 58. If block is found, myelography should be performed unless contraindications are present. There may also be pleocytosis and increased protein with spinal cord and cauda equina tumors which are below the level of the puncture, but block, of course, cannot be demonstrated. It is important to bear in mind that a partial block may be changed to a complete block by removal of spinal fluid, and that complete paralysis sometimes follows spinal puncture in spinal cord tumors. The reservoir is small, and if the pressure drops rapidly, the needle should be withdrawn.

Pott's Disease, Vertebral Compression, and Adhesive Arachnoiditis: In Pott's disease, vertebral compression from trauma or neoplasm, adhesive arachnoiditis, and hypertrophic cervical pachymeningitis, any of which may cause spinal subarachnoid block, the spinal fluid findings are identical with those in spinal cord tumor and depend, of course, on the degree and location of the block. The increased protein that has been reported with rheumatoid arthritis may be secondary to spondylitis and due to either interference with the circulation of the spinal fluid or increased permeability of the blood vessels walls or meninges.

Spinal Epidural Abscess: If a spinal puncture is performed below the level of the abscess in a patient with a spinal epidural abscess, the findings will be similar to those in spinal cord tumor, depending upon the degree of block. There may, however, be a pleocytosis, largely polymorphonuclear. If the puncture is attempted at the level of the abscess, the examiner may encounter pus when the epidural space is reached. It is important to use care to avoid puncturing the dura.

Syringomyelia: The spinal fluid findings are essentially normal in syringomyelia unless swelling of the cord causes a partial spinal subarachnoid block. In a few cases there is a slight increase in protein and cells.

Herniated Nucleus Pulposus: With rupture of the intervertebral disk and herniation of the nucleus pulposus, the spinal fluid picture may vary. If the herniation is in the cervical region (or, as is much less frequent, in the thoracic spine) the findings depend upon the degree of protrusion and the amount of interruption of the continuity of flow of the spinal fluid. There may be no change in the fluid, or a moderate increase in the protein content, or there may be a partial to complete block, with increase in protein (and occasionally of cells), and sometimes with xanthochromia and changes in the colloidal gold curve. The picture under such circumstances is similar to that found in spinal cord tumors and vertebral compression.

If the herniation is in the lower lumbar or lumbosacral area, where it most frequently occurs, the findings at spinal puncture and on examination of the fluid may be normal, since the lesion is below the site of puncture. In a fairly large percentage of cases (at least 50 per cent), however, there is a moderate increase in protein. If the elevation of protein is marked, some diagnosis other than herniated nucleus pulposus must be considered.

Polyneuritis and Polyradiculoneuritis: In most cases of toxic polyneuritis (i.e., those due to lead, mercury, arsenic, thallium, etc.) no spinal fluid abnormalities are found. In so-called alcoholic polyneuritis and the other vitamin deficiency neuritides there is a pleocytosis (5 to 25 cells) in 10 per cent and a slight increase in protein (to 75 or 100 mg.) in 15 per cent. In diphtheritic polyneuritis, however, there is often an increase in the protein content of the fluid, sometimes to 250 mg. per 100 cc., without an associated pleocytosis; there may be a midzone colloidal gold curve. In so-called diabetic polyneuritis, also, there may be a marked elevation of the protein content, sometimes with a first zone colloidal gold curve. Other peripheral nerve disorders in which the spinal fluid protein may be increased are leprosy, some of the chronic progressive neuropathies, hereditary sensory neuropathy, hereditary ataxic polyneuropathy (Refsum's syndrome), the neuropathy associated with primary familial amyloidosis, and neurofibromatosis.

In the so-called polyradiculoneuritis (the Guillain-Barré syndrome, infectious neuronitis, polyneuritis with facial diplegia) there is usually a significant elevation of the total protein, which in most cases is over 100 to 150 mg. per 100 cc., and may reach as high as 1000 mg. Sometimes the protein content continues to rise during the course of the disease, often for four to eight weeks, and even after convalescence has started. It may rise to a plateau and then gradually decline. Those rare cases in which the clinical syndrome is characteristic of the disorder but there is no elevation of the spinal fluid protein are difficult to classify; it may be that in some of these cases a puncture done at the correct stage of the illness would have shown an increase of protein. There are usually nonspecific or midzone changes in the colloidal gold curve, and sometimes a characteristic first zone alteration. The fluid may be xanthochromic. Of extreme importance in the diagnosis is the fact that the increase in protein is not accompanied by a proportionate increase in cells, and in most cases, even though the protein is elevated to a marked degree, the cell count is entirely normal. This co-called albuminocytologic dissociation (although the globulin may also be elevated) is said to be characteristic of this condition, and is very important in differentiating it from poliomyelitis, which it may resemble closely from a clinical point of view. It is important to bear in mind, however, that there may also be an albuminocytologic dissociation in the convalescent stage of poliomyelitis, but elevation of the portion does not last so long (usually two to four weeks) and is usually not so high. Albuminocytologic dissociation is also encountered in spinal cord tumors and brain tumors. Consequently the diagnosis of the Guillain-Barré syndrome should not be made on the spinal fluid findings alone—the clinical manifestations of the illness are exceedingly important.

VASCULAR DISEASES

Subarachnoid and Intraventricular Hemorrhage: In subarachnoid and intraventricular hemorrhage the spinal fluid examination may be essential to the diagnosis. There is often a marked increase in pressure, without evidence of block. The fluid is grossly bloody (within two hours after the onset of the hemorrhage) and it is uniformly bloody throughout; i.e., there is no clearing of the fluid as additional samples are obtained. There may be 1000 to 3,500,000 erythrocytes per cubic millimeter. The blood does not clot. On microscopic examination the cells are crenated. The erythrocytes begin to hemolyze within twelve to twenty-four hours, and have usually completely disappeared by seven to nine days. Within a few hours after the hemorrhage slight xanthochromia may be noted in the supernatant fluid on centrifuging (oxyhemoglobin may be detected by spectrophotometry within two hours), and the color change is grossly visible by twelve to twenty-four hours. The color deepens during the first few days, as bilirubin appears in the fluid, and assumes its greatest intensity at the end of a week. The xanthochromia may leave by the sixteenth day but may last for twenty-eight days or longer. Soon after the hemorrhage the benzidine test on the supernatant fluid is positive, and later the van den Bergh reaction. There may be an increase in both mononuclear and polymorphonuclear cells, out of proportion to those contained in the blood, as a result of the reaction of the meninges to the presence of blood. The protein is markedly elevated, both the albumin and globulin, but the glucose and chlorides are usually normal. (Occasionally the glucose is slightly decreased owing to the glycolytic action of ferments in the blood.) There are no organisms; the serologic tests for syphilis are usually negative, and there are no specific changes in the colloidal gold curve. During the period of recovery from an acute subarachnoid hemorrhage there is a progressive decrease in the number of erythrocytes (which may be absorbed directly into the blood stream, phagocytized by mesothelial cells lining the subarachnoid space, or enmeshed and fixed in the arachnoid) and also a progressive disappearance of pigments and lowering of the protein.

Intracerebral Hemorrhage: The spinal fluid is grossly bloody in about 75 per cent of cases of intracerebral hemorrhage, and it may be turbid or xanthochromic in another 10 per cent. Occasionally red cells may be observed microscopically in certain of the remaining cases. The spinal fluid pressure is elevated (over 200 mm.) in more than half the cases, and is over 300 mm. in about a third; this elevation may remain after repeated punctures. A moderate to significant increase in the protein content is common, and is usually proportional to the amount of blood present. As with subarachnoid hemorrhage, there may be an irritative meningitis, with a leukocyte elevation out of proportion to the amount of blood.

Cerebral Infarction: With cerebral infarction secondary to either thrombosis or embolism there are no characteristic changes in the cerebrospinal fluid. Pressure is normal, and there is no alteration in the appearance, cytology, chemistry, or serology. Occasionally, however, one finds microscopic blood, slight xanthochromia, or a moderate elevation in the cell count and/or protein. This occurs more frequently with embolism, in which the infaract may be hemorrhagic than with thrombosis, and there may even be gross blood in the fluid with cerebral embolism. If the thrombosis is of syphilitic origin, the spinal fluid changes of meningovascular syphilis may be present. With *septic embolism* the fluid may be turbid, with pleocytosis and elevated protein, and occasionally organisms are found.

Extracranial Vascular Disease, Cerebral Arteriosclerosis, and Arterial Hypertension: With transient cerebral ischemic attacks secondary to extracranial vascular insufficiency and atherosclerosis, generalized cerebral arteriosclerosis, and arterial hypertension, there are no characteristic changes in the spinal fluid unless these conditions are complicated by cerebral hemorrhage or infarction, congestive heart failure, or uremia. The pressure is usually normal, even with extremes of hypertension. With cardiac decompensation and elevation of the systemic venous pressure, however, the cerebrospinal fluid pressure is also elevated, and there may be a high intracranial pressure with papilledema. In hypertensive encephalopathy also there may be papilledema; the spinal fluid pressure is increased, and there may be a moderate pleocytosis and a protein elevation. These conditions must be differentiated from brain tumor.

DEGENERATIVE DISEASES OF THE NERVOUS SYSTEM

Multiple Sclerosis: There is a wide variation in the spinal fluid findings in multiple sclerosis. In about 25 per cent of the cases the fluid is normal or nearly normal in all respects. In 50 per cent there are nonspecific changes characterized by a slight increase in lymphocytes (10 to 25, rarely as high as 50), a moderate increase in protein (from 50 to 75 mg.), or a mild, nonspecific or midzone change in the colloidal gold curve. In another 25 per cent there are outstanding changes, with a pleocytosis (25 to 100 lymphocytes), increase in protein (up to 100 mg. per 100 cc.), or a first zone colloidal gold curve. In no case, however, is there characteristically any change in pressure, block, abnormality in appearance of the fluid, alteration in the glucose or chloride content, or positive serologic reaction for syphilis. It is said that the presence of a strongly positive first zone gold curve in the presence of a negative Kahn or Wassermann test in a patient who was not previously treated for syphilis is presumptive evidence for a diagnosis of multiple sclerosis. It is often important, in the diagnosis of multiple sclerosis, to observe each of the individual constituents of the spinal fluid as well as the spinal fluid picture as a whole. In 30 per cent there is a moderate elevation of protein. In 70 per cent there is a change in the gold curve (nonspecific in 25 per cent, midzone in 20 per cent, and first zone in 25 per cent). Slight changes in any one of these may not be significant from a diagnostic point of view, but when considered together they may be of importance.

Electrophoretic and other quantitative studies of the protein fractions in the spinal fluid show that it is the globulin which is most apt to be elevated in multiple sclerosis, and especially the gamma globulin, which is abnormally high in 73 to 80 per cent of cases. It is this latter fraction that facilitates or causes precipitation of the colloidal gold and thus is responsible for the first zone gold curve. In Lange's modification of the colloidal gold reaction the D curve, which parallels the increase in gamma globulin over albumin, is obtained in 70 per cent of cases. On the other hand, the beta globulins, which inhibit precipitation of the collodial curve, have been shown to be decreased in 93 per cent of multiple sclerosis patients. Occasionally there is some degree of correlation between the severity of the clinical picture in multiple sclerosis and the presence of abnormal cerebrospinal fluid findings, and an elevated cell count may be present with an acute exacerbation. Most often, however, there is no definite relationship between the abnormalities in the fluid and the clinical course, duration, or severity of the disease. The spinal fluid findings in Schilder's disease and retrobulbar neuritis are similar to those in multiple sclerosis. There may be significant alterations in the lipid constituents of the spinal fluid in the various demyelinating disorders.

Neuromyelitis Optica: In neuromyelitis optica and acute encephalomyelitis the spinal fluid changes may resemble those of multiple sclerosis, but in almost every instance they are more marked. A pleocytosis of from 25 to 50 mononuclear cells, and even up to 200 cells, is almost characteristic. The protein is elevated in 60 per cent of cases. Although changes are found in the colloidal gold curve in about 60 per cent of cases, they are usually of the midzone or nonspecific type rather than the first zone change that is sometimes encountered in multiple sclerosis.

Amyotrophic Lateral Sclerosis: Characteristically there are no spinal fluid changes in amyotrophic lateral sclerosis, *primary lateral sclerosis, progressive bulbar palsy,* or *progressive spinal muscular atrophy,* although on occasion there may be a slight increase in the protein and/or cells. The protein may be increased in one third of the cases, but it usually is not over 75 mg. per 100 cc. The presence of pronounced alterations in the cerebrospinal fluid should lead one to consider some diagnosis other than amyotrophic lateral sclerosis.

Posterolateral Sclerosis: There are no significant or characteristic changes in the cerebrospinal fluid in posterolateral sclerosis, although there may be a slight pleocytosis (as many as 10 cells in 20 per cent of patients) or a protein varying from 45 to 95 mg. per 100 cc.

Other Diseases: In some of the leukodystrophies and other progressive cerebral deteriorations of infancy and childhood, as well as in some of the toxic and metabolic encephalopathies, there may be nonspecific changes in the spinal fluid, with

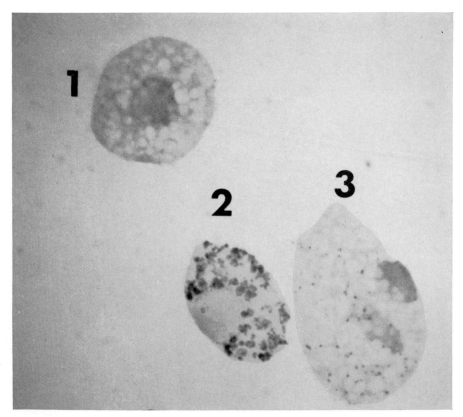

FIG. 332. Vacuolated foam cells in cerebrospinal fluid of patient with Tay-Sachs disease; Wright's stain. (Courtesy of Dr. W. W. Tourtellotte.)

borderline to marked elevations of the pressure, protein, and cells. In the lipidoses there is often a change in the lipid profile of the cerebrospinal fluid, as well as some increase in protein, and large, vacuolated foam cells have been observed in the fluid of patients with *Tay-Sachs disease* (Fig. 332). In the presenile deteriorations such as *Pick's* and *Alzheimer's diseases,* on the other hand, the spinal fluid is essentially normal, although in far advanced cases there may be a slight increase in protein. There are no characteristic spinal fluid changes in *Huntington's chorea, Parkinson's disease, Friedreich's ataxia, myasthenia gravis, migraine, narcolepsy,* or the *myopathies.*

SYPHILIS

Primary Syphilis: There may be occasional changes in the spinal fluid in the primary stage of syphilis. In from 15 to 35 per cent of patients there is a slight lymphocytic pleocytosis (5 to 10 cells) or a slight increase in the protein content. These changes usually disappear either spontaneously or as a result of treatment. The Kahn and Wassermann reactions are rarely positive.

Secondary Syphilis: Spinal fluid changes are somewhat more common in secondary syphilis. In 35 to 45 per cent of patients there is a moderate pleocytosis (10 to 50 cells), with increased protein and an abnormal colloidal gold curve of either the midzone or first zone type. The Kahn and Wassermann reactions may be positive. These changes usually leave with treatment.

Dementia Paralytica: The spinal fluid changes in dementia paralytica are important. The pressure is normal or very slightly increased, without block, and the fluid is normal in appearance. There usually is a meningeal reaction with a mononuclear pleocytosis of from 10 to 50 cells, sometimes as high as 150 or 200. The protein is definitely elevated, and may range from 50 to 150 mg. per 100 cc. It occasionally is elevated as high as 300 to 400 mg. The globulin is increased more than the albumin. The glucose content is normal or slightly decreased. The serologic tests for syphilis are strongly positive in from 95 to 100 per cent of cases, and the blood serologic reactions are positive in from 85 to 95 per cent. There is a marked alteration in the colloidal gold reaction, frequently with a first zone curve, but it must be borne in mind that the presence of a "paretic" curve does not necessitate the diagnosis of paresis, and that dementia paralytica may be present with a midzone or nonspecific curve. The diagnosis of dementia paralytica must always be made on the basis of clinical findings, not laboratory results.

Tabes Dorsalis: The spinal fluid findings in tabes dorsalis depend upon the activity of the process. In early cases they are very similar to those in dementia paralytica. In late cases the abnormalities are less marked as regards pressure, appearance, cytology, protein (including globulin), and glucose. The serologic tests are not positive so frequently in tabes dorsalis as in dementia paralytica. The spinal fluid is positive in from 70 to 90 per cent, and large amounts of fluid may be necessary for a positive reaction. The blood serology is positive in from 60 to 80 per cent. The spinal fluid and/or blood serology are more apt to be negative in treated, old, or "burnt-out" cases. The colloidal gold reaction often gives a midzone curve, but a first zone curve is sometimes found, and the diagnosis must be made on clinical grounds, and not on the type of colloidal gold reaction.

Acute Syphilitic Meningitis: See above.

Meningovascular Syphilis: The spinal fluid findings vary in meningovascular syphilis. If the *meningeal reaction* is pronounced, there may be increased pressure, pleocytosis, elevated protein, and first zone or midzone changes in the colloidal gold test. On occasion the fluid is turbid and the cell count reaches 500 lymphocytes per cubic millimeter. The serologic reactions on the spinal fluid are positive in about 90 per cent of cases, and on the blood in 70 to 80 per cent. In predominantly *vascular involvement* the pressure and cytology are more apt to be normal, but there may be an increase in the protein and a nonspecific change in the colloidal gold test. The serologic reactions are positive in the spinal fluid in about 60 per cent of cases, and in the blood in about 80 per cent.

Asymptomatic Central Nervous System Syphilis: In asymptomatic central nervous system syphilis there are alterations in the cerebrospinal fluid without apparent clinical symptoms or signs of disease. This condition is generally considered to be a forerunner of symptomatic central nervous system syphilis, and the severity of the alterations in the spinal fluid may parallel the patient's probability of developing clinical neurosyphilis. In the mild variety the changes are minimal. The cells and protein may be slightly increased, but the serologic tests are negative and the colloidal gold curve, if abnormal, is the nonspecific type. In the moderate variety the cells may be increased to 20 per cubic millimeter (all lymphocytes), the protein may be elevated to 60 mg. per 100 cc., the serologic reactions may be positive, and the colloidal gold curve is the midzone or nonspecific type. In the severe variety the cell count is more markedly elevated, the protein content is over 100 mg., the colloidal gold curve is the first zone type, and the serologic reactions are always positive. The more marked spinal fluid changes generally indicate a stronger and more prolonged infection, and consequently a poorer prognosis.

Gumma: In general the spinal fluid findings in patients with gummata involving the central nervous system are those of brain tumor (if the gumma involves the cerebrum) or of spinal cord tumor (if the gumma is within the spinal canal). Changes in the pressure (including block), protein, cells, and gold curve may be dependent on the site of the gumma and its proximity to the spinal fluid pathways. In a large percentage of cases, however, the serologic reactions are positive.

It must be stressed that in all varieties of neurosyphilis the activity of the process is reflected in the cell count, protein content, and colloidal gold curve as well as in the serologic reactions. Often the protein and cells give the most important information.

The protein may be the last to return to normal after treatment. In occasional "Wassermann fast" cases the serologic reaction remains positive after adequate therapy and disappearance of other evidences of activity. Occasionally the Treponema pallidum immobilization test on the spinal fluid, as well as on the blood, is of value in the diagnosis of neurosyphilis.

MISCELLANEOUS CONDITIONS

Uremia and Eclampsia: There are no changes in the spinal fluid in chronic nephritis. In acute nephritis and in uremia and eclampsia, however, there are definite abnormalities. The intracranial pressure is often increased, owing to cerebral edema, and as a result the spinal fluid pressure is elevated; this is the case in about 80 per cent of patients, and the pressure may be as high as 400 or 500 mm. of water. The fluid is normal in appearance, although on rare occasions it may be slightly xanthochromic. There is a slight pleocytosis in 20 per cent of cases, and a slight increase in protein (50 to 75 mg.) in 40 per cent. The chlorides are increased (750 to 900 mg.) in 50 per cent, and sometimes the glucose also is slightly increased. On occasion there is a change in the colloidal gold test, with a midzone or sometimes a first zone type of curve. The nonprotein and urea nitrogens may be increased in proportion to the changes in the blood. In *nephrosis* the spinal fluid is usually normal, although there may be some decrease in chlorides.

Diabetes: The most characteristic alteration of the cerebrospinal fluid in diabetes mellitus is an increase in the glucose content, which usually parallels the hyperglycemia. With ketosis, acetone bodies may be found in the fluid. In diabetic neuropathy and myelopathy, as well as in association with the cerebrovascular complications of diabetes, there is often an increase in the spinal fluid protein, which is sometimes present in significant amounts, and there may be first zone changes in the colloidal gold test. These same changes are sometimes found in diabetes without neurologic or vascular involvement.

Hepatic Disease: In jaundice, whether associated with liver disease or bile duct obstruction, the spinal fluid may be discolored along with other body fluids, and may be grossly xanthochromic. The van den Bergh test is usually positive, but there often is no definite correlation between the amount of bilirubin in the spinal fluid and the amount in the blood. The spinal fluid protein is not usually elevated unless there is associated hepatic coma. In Weil's disease the fluid is icteric, but there may also be a pleocytosis and a slight increase in protein. In Wilson's disease the usual spinal fluid tests are normal, but the ammonia content may be elevated, as it may be in other hepatic diseases.

Cardiac Disease: In congestive heart failure, pericarditis with effusion, occlusion of the vena cava, and related conditions there is elevation of the systemic venous pressure, and consequently of the cerebrospinal fluid pressure. Usually there are no associated changes in the spinal fluid, but the intracranial venous congestion may cause an increase in the protein content of the fluid, and sometimes a pleocytosis.

Myeloma: Multiple myeloma may cause spinal cord compression, with the spinal fluid changes of spinal subarachnoid block. In addition, however, the paraproteins associated with the disorder may also be found in the spinal fluid and may cause a first zone precipitation of the colloidal gold curve. Spinal fluid abnormalities may also be found with some of the other serum protein disturbances such as macroglobulinemia and cryoglobulinemia.

Leukemia: Leukemic infiltrations may affect the meninges and the nervous tissues, and in the various types of leukemia, as well as in lymphosarcoma and Hodgkin's disease, there may be an increase in leukocytes in the spinal fluid, sometimes with associated rise in the protein content and the pressure. The type of cell found (lymphocytic, neutrophilic, etc.) depends upon the variety of leukemia.

Polycythemia: In polycythemia there may be spinal fluid changes if there are cerebral or meningeal hemorrhages or thromboses.

Myxedema: In myxedema the spinal fluid pressure is normal or slightly elevated. The protein content of the fluid is often increased, sometimes to 200 mg. per 100 cc. or more, and the tests for globulin are positive. There often is a minimal pleocytosis (5 to 10 cells), and there is a midzone colloidal gold curve in 25 per cent of cases. These changes disappear with the administration of thyroid extract. The spinal fluid protein is also said to be elevated in hyperparathyroidism.

Collagen Disorders: Central nervous system manifestations may occur with the various collagen disorders, especially with disseminated lupus erythematosus and periarteritis nodosa. With such involvement there may be spinal fluid changes consisting of protein elevation (especially gamma globulin), a lymphocytic pleocytosis, and colloidal gold test abnormalities, usually with a first zone curve. The serologic test for syphilis done on the blood serum may be falsely positive. The spinal fluid protein may also be elevated with rheumatoid arthritis and spondylitis.

Alcoholic Intoxication: The spinal fluid pressure is often markedly increased in acute alcoholic intoxication with cerebral edema. There may also be some increase in the cells and protein, and there is often a positive test for alcohol in the fluid. It has been said that in about 20 per cent of cases of chronic alcoholism there is an increase in the spinal fluid protein.

The Psychoses: Many studies have been made of the cerebrospinal fluid findings in the functional psychoses—schizophrenia, manic-depressive psychosis, and involutional melancholia (Breutsch and others). It has been stated that the protein may be increased in from 3 to 5 per cent of cases of schizophrenia, 3 to 5 per cent of cases of manic-depressive psychosis, and 5 per cent of cases of involutional melancholia. Other minor changes that have been reported are elevation in the pressure, cell count, glucose content (especially in senile psychoses), and potassium, calcium, lactic acid, and cholesterol content, as well as alterations in the colloidal gold reaction. Some observers have reported low neuranimic acid levels in the spinal fluid in schizophrenia, but others have failed to confirm this. The above changes are all too minor and too near the range of experimental error to be considered diagnostic criteria. In general it may be said that the spinal fluid should be normal in the functional psychoses, and that the presence of any significant deviation from the normal casts serious doubt on the validity of the diagnosis.

REFERENCES

BELL, W. E., JOYNT, R. J., and SAHS, A. L. Low spinal fluid pressure syndromes. *Neurology* 10:512, 1960.

BRONSKY, D., KAPLITZ, S. E., ADE, R. D., and DUBIN, A. Spinal fluid proteins in cerebrovascular disease. *Am. J. M. Sc.* 244:54, 1962.

BRUETSCH, W. L., BAHR, M. A., DIETER, W. J., and SKOBBA, J. S. The cerebrospinal fluid protein in the psychoses. *Dis. Nerv. System,* 2:319, 1941.

CAMPBELL, W. G. Diagnosis of poliomyelitis. *Arizona Med.* 8:25, 1951.

CARGILL, W. H., JR., and BEESON, P. B. The value of spinal fluid examination as a diagnostic procedure in Weil's disease. *Ann. Int. Med.* 27:36, 1947.

CHISTONI, G, and ZAPPOLI, R. Neuranimic acids in the cerebrospinal fluid of schizophrenic and oligophrenic patients. *Am. J. Psychiat.* 117:246, 1960.

CHOREMIS, K., and VRACHNOS, G. Primary tuberculosis with meningism and bacilli in the spinal fluid: Significance in streptomycin treatment of tuberculous meningitis. *Lancet* 2:408, 1948.

COSGROVE, J. B. R., and AGIUS, P. Studies in multiple sclerosis: II. Comparison of the beta-globulin ratio, gamma globulin elevation, and first-zone colloidal gold curve in the cerebrospinal fluid. *Neurology* 16:197, 1966.

CURNEN, E. C., SHAW, E. W., and MELNICK, J. L. Disease resembling nonparalytic poliomyelitis associated with a virus pathogenic for infant mice. *J.A.M.A.* 141:894, 1949.

DATTNER, B. Significance of the spinal fluid findings in neurosyphilis. *Am. J. Med.* 5: 709, 1948.

DAWSON, D. M., and TAGHAVY, A. A test for spinal-fluid alcohol in Torula meningitis. *New England J. Med.* 269:1424, 1963.

DENCKER, S. J. (ed.) Vessel-plaque and cerebrospinal fluid and brain tissue changes in multiple sclerosis. *Acta neurol. scand.* vol. 40, suppl. 10, 1964.

FORD, G. D., ELDRIDGE, F. L., and GRULEE, C. G., JR. Spinal fluid in acute poliomyelitis. *Am. J. Dis. Child.* 79:633, 1950.

FREEDMAN, D. A., and MERRITT, H. H. The cerebrospinal fluid in multiple sclerosis. *A. Res. Nerv. & Ment. Dis., Proc.* (1949) 28:428, 1950.

FREMONT-SMITH, F. Cerebrospinal fluid in differential diagnosis of brain tumor. *Arch. Neurol. & Psychiat.* 27:691, 1932.

GIERSON, H. W., and MARX, J. I. Tuberculous meningitis: The diagnostic and prognostic significance of spinal fluid sugar and chloride. *Ann. Int. Med.* 42:902, 1955.

GREENFIELD, J. G., and CARMICHAEL, E. A. The Cerebro-spinal Fluid in Clinical Diagnosis. London, Macmillan and Co., Ltd., 1925.

GUILLAIN, G., BARRE, J. A., and STROHL, A. Sur un syndrome de radiculo-névrite avec hyperalbuminose du liquide céphalo-rachidien sans réaction cellulaire. *Bull. et mém. Soc. méd. d. hôp. de Paris* 40:1462, 1916.

HAGBERG, B., SOURANDER, P., and SVENNERHOLM. L. Diagnosis of Krabbe's infantile leucodystrophy. *J. Neurol., Neurosurg. & Psychiat.* 26:195, 1963.

IVERS, R. R., MCKENZIE, B. F., MCGUCKIN, W. F., and GOLDSTEIN, N. P. Spinal-fluid gamma globulin in multiple sclerosis and other neurologic diseases. *J.A.M.A.* 176:515, 1961.

JAWORSKI, A. A., and WEST, E. J. Aseptic meningitis of new virus origin. *J.A.M.A.* 141:902, 1949.

JOHNSON, C. E., and JOHNSON, G. L. A. Cerebrospinal fluid studies in advanced dementia praecox. *Am. J. Psychiat.* 104:778, 1948.

KATZENELBOGEN, S. Studies in schizophrenia: Chemical analyses of blood and cerebrospinal fluid. *Arch. Neurol. & Psychiat.* 37:881, 1937.

KILHAM, L., LEVENS, J., and ENDERS, J. F. Nonparalytic poliomyelitis and mumps meningo-encephalitis: Differential diagnosis. *J.A.M.A.* 140:934, 1949.

KUTT, H., HURWITZ, L. J., GINSBURG, S. M., and MCDOWELL, F. Cerebrospinal fluid protein in diabetes mellitus. *Arch. Neurol.* 4:31, 1961.

LEVINSON, S. O. Early acute anterior poliomyelitis without an increase in cells in the spinal fluid. *J. Pediat.* 1:337, 1932.

LINCOLN, E. M. Tuberculous meningitis in children with special reference to serous meningitis: I. Tuberculous meningitis. *Am. Rev. Tuberc.* 56:75, 1947; II. Serous tuberculosis meningitis. *Am. Rev. Tuberc.* 56:95, 1947.

Locoge, M., and Cumings, J. N.   Cerebrospinal fluid in various diseases.   *Brit. M. J.* 1:618, 1958.

McFarland, H. R., and Heller, G. L.   Guillaïn-Barré disease complex.   *Arch. Neurol.* 14:196, 1966.

Mc Menemy, W. H., and Cumings, J. N.   The value of the examination of the cerebrospinal fluid in the diagnosis of intracranial tumours.   *J. Clin. Path.* 12:400, 1959.

Melnick, J. L., Shaw, E. W., and Curnen, E. C.   A virus isolated from patients diagnosed as non-paralytic poliomyelitis or aseptic meningitis.   *Proc. Soc. Exper. Biol. & Med.* 71:344, 1949.

Spiegel-Adolf, M., Wycis, H. T., and Spiegel, E. A.   Cerebrospinal fluid studies in cerebral concussion.   *J. Nerv. & Ment. Dis.* 106:359, 1947.

Tourtellotte, W. W., Metz, L. N., Bryan, E. R., and De Jong, R. N.   Spontaneous subarachnoid hemorrhage: Factors affecting rate of clearing of the cerebrospinal fluid.   *Neurology* 14:301, 1964.

Tourtellotte, W. W.   Multiple sclerosis and spinal fluid.   *M. Clin. North America* 74:1619, 1963; "A Selected Review of Reactions of the Cerebrospinal Fluid to Disease," in Fields, W. S. (ed.), Neurological Diagnostic Techniques.   Springfield, Ill., Charles C Thomas, 1966, pp. 25-50.

Townsend, S. R., Craig, R. L., and Braunstein, A. L.   Neutrophilic leucocytosis in spinal fluid associated with cerebral vascular accidents.   *Arch. Int. Med.* 63:848, 1939.

Trowbridge, E. H., Jr., and Secunda, L.   The protein of the cerebrospinal fluid in patients with chronic alcoholism.   *New England J. Med.* 226, 195, 1942.

Walton, J. N.   Subarachnoid Haemorrhage.   Edinburgh, E. & S. Livingstone, Ltd., 1956.

Watkins, A. L.   The cerebrospinal fluid in optic neuritis, "toxic amblyopia" and tumors producing central scotomas.   *New England J. Med.* 220:227, 1939.

Wiederholt, W. C., and Mulder, D. W.   Cerebrospinal fluid findings in the Landry-Guillain-Barré-Strohl syndrome.   *Neurology* 15:184, 1965.

GENERAL REFERENCES

CLINICAL NEUROLOGY

ALPERS, B. J.   Clinical Neurology (ed. 5).   Philadelphia, F. A. Davis Company, 1963.

BAKER, A. B. (ed.)   Clinical Neurology (ed. 2).   New York, Hoeber Medical Division, Harper & Row, 1962.

BICKERSTAFF, E. R.   Neurological Examination in Clinical Practice. Philadelphia, F. A. Davis Company, 1963.

BRAIN, W. R.   Clinical Neurology (ed. 2). London, Oxford University Press, 1964.

BRAIN, W. R.   Diseases of the Nervous System (ed. 6).   London, Oxford University Press, 1962.

BROCK, S., and KRIEGER, H. P.   The Basis of Clinical Neurology (ed. 4).   Baltimore, The Williams & Wilkins Company, 1963.

COLLINS, R. D.   Illustrated Manual of Neurologic Diagnosis.   Philadelphia, J. B. Lippincott Company, 1962.

DAVIS, L., and DAVIS, R. A.   Principles of Neurological Surgery.   Philadelphia, W. B. Saunders Company, 1963.

DENNY-BROWN, D.   Handbook of Neurological Examination and Case Recording (ed. 2).   Cambridge, Mass., Harvard University Press, 1957.

ELLIOTT, F. A.   Clinical Neurology.   Philadelphia, W. B. Saunders Company, 1964.

FARMER, T. W. (ed.)   Pediatric Neurology.   New York, Hoeber Medical Division, Harper & Row, 1964.

FIELDS, W. S. (ed.)   Neurological Diagnosic Techniques.   Springfield, Ill., Charles C Thomas, 1966.

FORD, F. R.   Diseases of the Nervous System in Infancy, Childhood and Adolescence (ed. 4).   Springfield, Ill., Charles C Thomas, 1960.

FORSTER, F. M.   Synopsis of Neurology (ed. 2).   St. Louis, The C. V. Mosby Company, 1966.

GRINKER, R. R., BUCY, P. C., and SAHS, A. L.   Neurology (ed. 5).   Springfield, Ill., Charles C Thomas, 1960.

GURDJIAN, E. S., and WEBSTER, J. E.   Operative Neurosurgery (ed. 2).   Baltimore, The Williams & Wilkins Company, 1964.

HAYMAKER, W.   Bing's Local Diagnosis in Neurological Diseases.   St. Louis, The C. V. Mosby Company, 1956.

KAHN, E. A., BASSETT, R. C., SCHNEIDER, R. C., and CROSBY, E. C.   Correlative Neurosurgery.   Springfield, Ill., Charles C Thomas, 1955.

KLEIN, R., and MAYER-GROSS, W.   The Clinical Examination of Patients with Organic Cerebral Disease.   Springfield, Ill., Charles C Thomas, 1957.

MATTHEWS, W. B.   Practical Neurology.   Oxford, Blackwell Scientific Publications, Ltd., 1963.

MC DOWELL, F., and WOLFF, H. G.   Handbook of Neurological Diagnostic Methods.   Baltimore, The Williams & Wilkins Company, 1960.

Members of the Sections of Neurology and Section of Physiology, Mayo Clinic.   Clinical Examinations in Neurology (ed. 2).   Philadelphia, W. B. Saunders Company, 1963.

MERRITT, H. H.   A Textbook of Neurology (ed. 3).   Philadelphia, Lea & Febiger, 1963.

MONRAD-KROHN, G. H., and REFSUM, S.   The Clinical Examination of the Nervous System (ed. 12).   New York, Hoeber Medical Division, Harper & Row, 1964.

NIELSEN, J. M.   A Textbook of Clinical Neurology (ed. 3).   New York, Paul B. Hoeber, Inc., 1951.

PAINE, R. S., and OPPÉ, T. E.   The Neurological Examination of Children.   London, Heinemann Medical Books, Ltd., 1966.

PRITCHARD, E. A. B.   Aids to Neurology (ed. 2).   London, Baillière, Tindall & Cox, 1959.

PURVES-STEWART, J.   The Diagnosis of Nervous Disease (ed. 10).   Baltimore, The Williams & Wilkins Company, 1952.

RENFREW, S.   An Introduction to Diagnostic Neurology.   Edinburgh, E. & S. Livingstone, Ltd., 1962.

SMITH, B. H.   Principles of Clinical Neurology.   Chicago, The Year Book Publishers, Inc., 1965.

SPURLING, R. G.   Practical Neurological Diagnosis (ed. 5).   Springfield, Ill., Charles C Thomas, 1953.

STEEGMANN, A. T.   Examination of the Nervous System: A Student's Guide (ed. 2).   Chicago, The Year Book Publishers, Inc., 1962.

THOMAS, A., CHESNI, Y., and SAINT-ANNE DARGASSIES, S.   The Neurological Examination of the Infant.   London, National Spastics Society, 1960.

WALTON, J. N.   Essentials of Neurology.   Philadelphia, J. B. Lippincott Company, 1961.

WALSHE, F. M. R.   Diseases of the Nervous System (Described for Practitioners and Students) (ed. 10).   Baltimore, The Williams & Wilkins Company, 1963.

WARTENBERG, R.   Diagnostic Tests in Neurology.   Chicago, The Year Book Publishers, Inc., 1953.

WECHSLER, I. S.   A Textbook of Clinical Neurology (ed. 9).   Philadelphia, W. B. Saunders Company, 1963.

WILIAMS, D. (ed.)   Modern Trends in Neurology—3.   Washington, D. C., Butterworth's, 1962.

WILSON, S. A. K., and BRUCE, A. N.   Neurology (ed. 2).   Baltimore, The Williams & Wilkins Company, 1955.

ANATOMY, PHYSIOLOGY, AND PATHOLOGY

BEST, C. H., and TAYLOR, N. B.   Physiological Basis of Medical Practice (ed. 7).   Baltimore, The Williams & Wilkins Company, 1961.

BIGGART, J. H.   Pathology of the Nervous System (ed. 3).   Baltimore, The Williams & Wilkins Company, 1961.

BLACKWOOD, W., DODDS, T. C., and SOMMERVILLE, J. C. Atlas of Neuropathology (ed. 2). Edinburgh, E. & S. Livingstone, Ltd., 1964.

BLACKWOOD, W., MC MENEMEY, W. H., MEYER, A., NORMAN, R. M. and RUSSELL, D. S. Greenfield's Neuropathology (ed. 2). Baltimore, The Williams & Wilkins Company, 1963.

BRODAL, A. Neurological Anatomy in Relation to Clinical Medicine. New York, Oxford University Press, 1948.

CHATFIELD, P. O. Fundamentals of Clinical Neurophysiology. Springfield, Ill., Charles C Thomas, 1957.

CROSBY, E. C., HUMPHERY, T., and LAUER, E. W. Correlative Anatomy of the Nervous System. New York, The Macmillan Company, 1962.

CUMINGS, J. N., and KREMER, M. (eds.) Biochemical Aspects of Neurological Disorders. Springfield, Ill., Charles C Thomas, 1959.

ELLIOTT, H. C. Textbook of the Nervous System (ed. 2). Philadelphia, J. B. Lippincott Co., 1954.

EVERETT, N. B., BADEMER, C. W., and RIEKE, W. O. Functional Neuroanatomy (ed. 5). Philadelphia. Lea & Febiger, 1965.

FIELD, J., MAGOUN, H. W., and HALL, V. E. (eds.) Handbook of Physiology. Section 1: Neurophysiology. Washington, D. C., American Physiological Society, 1959 and 1960.

FULTON, J. F. Physiology of the Nervous System (ed. 3). New York, Oxford University Press, 1949.

GARLAND, H. (ed.) Scientific Aspects of Neurology. Baltimore, The Williams & Wilkins Company, 1961.

GOODMAN, L., and GILMAN, A. The Pharmacological Basis of Therapeutics (ed. 3). New York, The Macmillan Company, 1965.

HAUSMAN, L. Clinical Neuroanatomy, Neurophysiology and Neurology. Springfield, Ill., Charles C Thomas, 1958.

HOUSE, E. L., and PANSKY, B. A Functional Approach to Neuroanatomy. New York, The Blakiston Division, McGraw-Hill Book Company, Inc., 1960.

KAPPERS, C. U. A., HUBER, G. C., and CROSBY, E. C. The Comparative Anatomy of the Nervous System of Vertebrates, Including Man. New York, The Macmillan Company, 1936.

KREIG, W. J. S. Functional Neuroanatomy (ed. 2). New York, The Blakiston Division, McGraw-Hill Book Company, 1953.

MALAMUD, N. Atlas of Neuropathology. Berkeley, University of California Press, 1957.

PEELE, T. L. The Neuroanatomical Basis for Clinical Neurology (ed. 2). New York, The Blakiston Division, McGraw-Hill Book Company, Inc., 1961.

RANSON, S. W., and CLARK, S. M. The Anatomy of the Nervous System (ed. 9). Philadelphia, W. B. Saunders Company, 1953.

RUCH, T. C., PATTON, H. D., WOODBURY, J. W., and TOWE, H. L. Neurophysiology (ed. 2). Philadelphia, W. B. Saunders Company, 1965

RUSSELL, D S., and RUBINSTEIN, L. J. Pathology of Tumours of the Nervous System (ed. 2). Baltimore, The Williams & Wilkins Company, 1963.

SCHADÉ, J. P., and FORD, D. H. Basic Neurology, Amsterdam, Elsevier Publishing Company. 1965.

SHERRINGTON, C. S. The Integrative Action of the Nervous System. New York, Charles Scribner's Sons, 1906.

SINGER, M., and YAKOVLEV, P. I. The Human Brain in Sagittal Section. Springfield, Ill., Charles C Thomas, 1954.

TILNEY, F. The Brain from Ape to Man. New York, Paul B. Hoeber, Inc., 1928.

TILNEY, F., and RILEY, H. A. The Form and Functions of the Central Nervous System (ed. 3). New York, Paul B. Hoeber, Inc., 1938.

TRUEX, R. C., and CARPENTER, M. B. Strong and Elwyn's Human Neuroanatomy (ed. 5). Baltimore, The Williams & Wilkins Company, 1964.

WALSH, E. G. Physiology of the Nervous System (ed. 2). London, Longmans, Green & Co., Ltd., 1964.

WYBURN, G. M. The Nervous System. London, Academic Press, 1960.

ZIMMERMAN, H. M., NETSKY, M. G., and DAVIDOFF, L. M. Atlas of Tumors of the Nervous System. Philadelphia, Lea & Febiger, 1956.

ZULCH, K. J. Brain Tumors, Their Biology and Pathology (ed. 2). New York, Springer Publishing Company, Inc., 1965.

INDEX

low back pain in, 813
motor weakness in, 448
muscle biopsy in, 35
ocular nerves in, 206
Myospasm, localized, 551
Myotatic irritability, 509, 587
Myotonia, 507
congenita, 388, 576
deep reflexes in, 604
dystrophica, electrical reactions in, 576
electromyography in, 578
hypertrophy in, 520
of lids, 180
speech in, 366
tongue in, 338
Myotonic reaction, 507
Myxedema, 721, 938
cerebrospinal fluid in, 1099
coma in, 970
deep reflexes in, 604
facies in, 23
hypertrophy in, 520
muscle tone in, 507
speech in, 366

Naffziger test, 811
Nails, examination of, 25, 699
Naming of objects, 892, 893
Narcolepsy, 739, 972
cerebrospinal fluid in, 1096
hypotonicity in, 502
Narcosis, deep reflexes in, 604, 606
Narcotics, effects of, 934
Nasal muscle, 239
paralysis of, 249
Nasal reflex, 227, 317
Nasolacrimal reflex, 247
Nasomental reflex, 245
Nasopalpebral reflex, 244
Near vision, 124
Neck
Brudzinski sign. See Brudzinski neck sign
examination of, 27, 30
movements of, 453-455
nuchal rigidity, 657
righting reflexes, 640
tonic reflexes, 189, 283, 642-643
traction test, 784
tumor of, tongue in, 341
whiplash injury, 798
wryneck. See Torticollis
Negativism, 951, 977
Negro's sign, 250
Neologisms, 367
Neopallium, 823
Neoplasms
accessory nerve in, 330
biopsies in, 34-35

blood vessel, 922
of cerebellopontine angle, 295-296
cerebral, 918-923
cerebrospinal fluid in, 1087-1088
coma in, 968
papilledema in, 147
of cervical portion of spinal cord, 782
congenital, 923
of corpus callosum, 863
dystonic movements in, 549
facial nerve in, 256
of frontal lobe, 42, 52, 845
of glomus jugulare, 296, 352
of glossopharyngeal nerve, 304
hippus in, 171
hypersomnia in, 971
intracranial, 918-923
ocular nerves in, 209
olfactory function in, 115
low back pain in, 813
of medulla, 344
metastatic, 923
orbital, papilledema in, 147
percussion note in, 30
pineal, pupils in, 173
pituitary, 922
optic atrophy in, 145
polyneuritis in, 771
of skull bones, 923
of spinal cord, 30, 798-801
cerebrospinal fluid in, 1090
of temporal lobe, 853
of third ventricle, 173, 201
trigeminal nerve in, 230
vagus nerve in, 321
Neostigmine, 683, 684, 712
affecting pupil, 176
for distention, 96
in myasthenia gravis, 178, 385, 448
Neostriatum, 392
Nephritis, 153, 1097
See also Kidney
Neri's sign, 649, 808
in hysteria, 1004
pronation sign, 653
Nerve deafness, 273, 277
Nerve plexus diseases, 777-785
Nerve root diseases, 103, 774-776
Nerves
abducens, 164-165, 170, 212
accessory, spinal, 79, 300, 309, 324-332, 364, 454, 456, 457
acoustic, 267-296, 922, 957
adrenergic, 682
of Arnold, 309

auditory. See Acoustic nerve
auricular, great, 220
autonomic, 665-743
See also Autonomic nervous system
axillary, 456, 461, 763-764
calcaneal, 769
cardiac, superior, 670
carotid, internal, 669
cervical sympathetic, 166-168, 170-205, 669
cholinergic, 682
chorda tympani, 220, 222, 229, 242, 263, 264
ciliary, 166, 221
cochlear, 267-278
common peroneal, 484, 489, 767-768
compression of, 754-755
conduction velocity tests, 579-580
contusion of, 755
cranial, 109-368
See also Cranial nerves
cutaneous, 765
femoral, 766-767, 771
sural, 767, 769
deep peroneal, 484, 491, 492, 767
dorsal
of clitoris, 771
of penis, 771
scapular, 456
eighth cranial. See Acoustic nerve
electrical stimulation of, 569-572
eleventh cranial. See Accessory nerve
facial, 164, 233, 237-264, 341, 363, 667
femoral, 483, 484, 488, 489, 765
cutaneous, 766-767, 771
fifth cranial. See Trigeminal nerve
first cranial. See Olfactory nerve
fourth cranial. See Trochlear nerve
genitofemoral, 770
glossopharyngeal, 299-305, 325, 667
gluteal, 483, 486, 770
greater
splanchnic, 671
superficial petrosal, 242-243
hemorrhoidal, inferior, 771
hypoglossal, 240, 334-341, 346, 363
iliohypogastric, 478, 480, 770

with electrical stimulation, 99
face-hand, 101
finger-to-finger, 528
finger-to-nose, 527
foraminal compression, 784
galvanic tests, 289-290
for graphesthesia, 98
grip sign, 653
head dropping, 500
of hearing, 269-273, 1011
heel-to-knee-to-toe, 531
hyperabduction test, arm, 784
for hysteria and malingering, 994-1014
laboratory procedures, 32-35, 960-961
leg sign of Barré, 489
levator sign of Dutemps and Cestan, 250
for memory, 44-46
of mental functions, 43-52
of motion, 87-88
neck traction test, 784
nerve stretching tests, 810
nose-finger-nose, 528
for nystagmus, 194-203
of ocular movements, 180
for pain, superficial, 66
past pointing test, 285-286, 529
pendulousness of legs, 500
peroneal sign, 661
pinhole test of vision, 128
platysma sign of Babinski, 251
pointing tests, 529
of position, 87-88
for pressure sense, 90
pronation of hands, 500-501
pronation signs of Strümpell and Babinski, 501
psychological, 48-50
psychometric, 48-50
rebound test of Holmes, 437, 527, 529
rotation tests, 286-288
for sensory extinction, 99
shoulder bracing test, 784
shoulder shaking, 500
of smell, 113-114
stepping test, 526
for stereognosis, 97-98
straight-leg-raising test, 809
sweating tests, 701-704, 754
in syphilis, 33, 1067-1068
for texture recognition, 98
of touch, 69-70
for two-point discrimination, 98
vestibular function tests, 284-290

for vibration, 88-90
for visual acuity, 124-128
for visual fields, 129-142
See also Examination; Reflexes and specific tests and signs
Tetanus
convulsive seizures in, 936
deep reflexes in, 606
galvanic, 571, 574
Hoffmann sign in, 618
lingual spasm in, 338
medullary syndromes in, 355
rigidity in, 508
risus sardonicus of, 261
speech in, 366
trismus in, 228
Tetany
Chvostek's sign in, 550
deep reflexes in, 606
electrical reactions in, 577
Hoffmann sign in, 618
laryngeal spasm in, 320
myokymia in, 543
rigidity in, 508
signs of, 659-661
spasms in, 230, 320
Tetraethylammonium salts, 683
Tetraplegia, 449
Texture, recognition of, 98
Thalamic radiations, 864, 865
Thalamic syndrome of Dejerine and Roussy, 101, 861
Thalamofrontal fibers, 864
Thalamogeniculate arteries, 871
Thalamopallidum, 390-398
Thalamotomy, 406, 538, 846
Thalamus, 392, 823, 857-862
blood supply to, 881
functions of, 861
lesions of, 101, 861-862
pain with, 82
sensory changes in, 104
nuclei of, 217, 857-860
pain impulses in, 64, 82
peduncles of, 860
proprioceptive terminations in, 86
pulvinar of, 121
and smell and taste sensations, 242
tactile centers in, 68
trigeminothalamic tract, 218
Thallium, toxic effects of, 935
Thematic apperception test, 50, 51
Thermal tests of vestibular function, 288-289
Thermanesthesia, 67
Thermhyperesthesia, 67
Thermhypesthesia, 67

Thermic sign of Kashida, 661
Thiamin deficiency, 939
ocular palsies in, 208
skin changes in, 25
tongue in, 27, 340
Thigh
extension of, 649
flexion of, 649
movements of, 486-488
Thigmanesthesia, 70
Thigmesthesia, 68
Third ventricle neoplasms, 186, 187, 278
Thomsen's disease, 576
Thoracic nerves, 456, 459, 462
long, 764
Thoracodorsal nerve, 456, 463
Thorax
examination of, 27
muscles of, 479-480
Thorborn's sign, 793
Thought processes, evaluation of, 40-41, 42
Threshold
pain perception, 79
pain reaction, 79
sensory reaction, 78
vibration, 88
Throat, examination of, 27
Throckmorton sign, 626
Thromboangiitis obliterans, 24, 152, 699, 724
Thrombosis
of auditory artery, internal, 295, 351
of basilar artery, 350-351
of cavernous sinus, 209, 885, 1089
of central vein of retina, 151
of cerebellar arteries, 101, 240, 347, 349, 423, 863, 880, 924, 963, 1094
of cerebral veins, 884, 1089
of dural sinuses, 147, 884, 1089
of internal carotid artery, 31, 883, 1094
of jugular vein, 304, 1089
of spinal artery, anterior, 321, 345-347, 801
of vertebral artery, 349
Thumb
movements of, 473-478
reflex, 593
adductor, of Marie-Foix, 618
Thyroarytenoid muscles, 307
paralysis of, 312
Thyrohyoid branch of hypoglossal nerve, 335
Thyrohyoid muscle, 337